Molecular Structures and Dimensions
Vol. A1
Interatomic Distances 1960–1965
Solid State Classes 1–86

Molecular Structures and Dimensions

Vol. A1

Interatomic Distances 1960-65 Organic and Organometallic Crystal Structures

Edited by Olga Kennard D. G. Watson
F. H. Allen N. W. Isaacs W. D. S. Motherwell
R. C. Pettersen W. G. Town
University Chemical Laboratory
Cambridge England

Published for the
Crystallographic Data Centre Cambridge
and the
International Union of Crystallography
by N.V. A.Oosthoek's Uitgevers Mij Utrecht

iii

Printed in the United Kingdom by Unwin Brothers Ltd.

Library of Congress catalogue card number 76-133989

ISBN 90 6046 088 X

Distributors:

A. Oosthoek, Domstraat 5-13, Utrecht, Netherlands.
Crystallographic Data Centre, University Chemical Laboratory, Cambridge CB2 1EW, England.
Polycrystal Book Service, P.O. Box 11567, Pittsburgh, Pa 15238, U.S.A.

Contents

Preface

This volume in the *Molecular Structures and Dimensions* series is a continuation of the *Tables of Interatomic Distances and Configurations in Molecules and Ions* (Chemical Society Special Publications; No. 11 London 1958, No. 18 London 1965) edited by L. E. Sutton. The two Chemical Society publications covered the literature till the end of 1959 and gave information on interatomic distances, and, where relevant, bond angles, obtained by spectroscopy, electron, neutron and X-ray diffraction for organic and inorganic molecules and ions and for metals.

In the present volume the editors have attempted to continue the tradition established by Sutton and his colleagues of providing a definitive compilation in a form readily usable by specialist and non-specialist alike. Because of the spectacular increase in the number of studies since the early 1960s the scope of this volume had to be restricted to cover only organic and organometallic compounds, investigated by X-ray and neutron diffraction methods and published during 1960–1965. Computer methods have been used both for the evaluation of numeric data and the presentation of the results. These methods have enabled us to extend the information contained in the original paper by preparing stereo illustrations of individual molecular structures and, where appropriate, computing the torsion angles from the original data. We have tried to trace and correct errors resulting in differences between our computed values and those published in the original paper. For the sake of completeness we have also included bibliographic references and chemical formulae for publications where, for reasons listed in the introduction, numeric tables could not be given. With these changes the original aim of the *Interatomic Distances Tables* has been preserved and we would like to acknowledge our indebtedness to Dr L. E. Sutton and his co-editors for their pioneering work on which the present volume is based.

Companion volumes in the series give classified bibliographic information for papers published from 1935 onwards. Three volumes have appeared to date, covering the literature till mid-1971 and annual volumes will appear regularly. Future plans include numeric volumes for the post-1965 period. The bibliographic and numeric data are also available on magnetic tapes and further details can be obtained from the editors.

We would be grateful to our readers if they would inform us of any errors or omissions in these tables and suggestions for improvements in the contents of future volumes.

Olga Kennard
University Chemical Laboratory
Cambridge, England
August 1972

Acknowledgments

The production of this volume was made possible by the generous sponsorship of the Office for Scientific and Technical Information (OSTI), Department of Education and Science, who have been providing financial support for the Crystallographic Data Centre at the University of Cambridge since 1965.

The planning of this volume was guided by members of the OSTI Scientific Advisory Committee; the late Professor J. D. Bernal, Professor J. W. Linnett, the late Dame Kathleen Lonsdale, Dr M. F. Lynch, Dr F. W. Matthews, Professor D. C. Phillips, Professor H. W. Rooksby, Dr E. Stern, Professor M. R. Truter, and Professor A. J. C. Wilson.

Past and present members of the Crystallographic Data Centre have all contributed to various aspects of the work and we have received considerable help from individuals and organisations both in England and abroad. The following individual contributions are acknowledged:

Mrs S. Weeds was responsible for literature searches, primary abstracting and problems relating to chemical nomenclature.

Dr K. Loening of the Nomenclature Division of the Chemical Abstracts Service, and Dr R. S. Cahn have helped with questions of nomenclature.

Mrs A. O'Brien, Mrs E. Doyle and Mrs A. Town have encoded the numeric data for input to the computer file. Mrs. K. Watson assisted with the editing.

Dr A. Boskey, Dr M. Ciechanowicz and Mr D. Sales have checked the output from the data evaluation program and corrected errors in the data.

The evaluation program was developed in collaboration with Mr T. Scott of the MRC Computer Services Centre.

We are grateful to the University of California Los Alamos Scientific Laboratory for allowing a member of their staff, Dr A. C. Larson, to collaborate with us and use their computer facilities to produce, from our magnetic tapes, the film negatives of all the stereo-illustrations in this book.

The majority of the chemical diagrams were adapted from *Numeric Data and Functional Relationships in Science and Technology, III Vol. 5 a, b* Ed. K.-H. and A. M. Hellwege, Berlin: Springer, 1971 and we are grateful to the Editors and Publishers for permission to reproduce this material.

We have used the IBM 360/44 computer at the Institute of Theoretical Astronomy, Cambridge, and were greatly helped by both the technical staff and operators.

Computer typesetting of the text and data were carried out in collaboration with INSPEC, (Information Service in Physics, Electrotechnology, Computers and Control) and we are especially indebted to Mr P. Simmons, who modified and developed the computer typesetting programs.

We were greatly aided in the production of this volume by individual staff members of the printers, Unwin Brothers Ltd., particularly Mr P. Crew and Mr F. T. Lovett. The book was designed and the page make-up carried out by Mr J. van de Watering. Additional chemical diagrams were prepared by Mr D. Halls and the stereo-prints by Mr R. S. Hammons.

We are grateful to the Medical Research Council for allowing a member of their external scientific staff (O. Kennard) to participate in the work on this volume. We have, in the early stages of the preparation of this volume, used interactive display facilities at the National Institute of Medical Research and received much help from Mr W. J. Perkins and Mr E. A. Piper of the Engineering Division.

We thank the University of Cambridge for the administration of the OSTI grant and Professor Lord Todd and members of the staff of the University Chemical Laboratory for their interest and advice on chemical matters.

Introduction

Criteria for Inclusion

A crystallographic study, by X-ray or neutron diffraction methods, of a single crystal of a carbon-containing substance is included if it meets the following requirements:

(i) the study has been published during 1960–1965 and has not been superseded by a later study by the same author(s)

(ii) three positional coordinates for each non-hydrogen atom in the molecule have been determined, even if not specifically recorded in the publication or

(iii) the determination of two coordinates for each non-hydrogen atom has proved sufficient to resolve an ambiguity in the chemical structure.

It should be noted that this compilation deals only with organic and organometallic compounds. Purely inorganic substances such as inorganic carbides, carbonyls, carbonates, cyanides, thiocyanates, etc., are excluded even though they contain carbon. Polymers and high molecular weight compounds such as proteins are excluded.

Ordering of Entries

Entries are grouped in 86 chemical classes and, within each class, are listed in order of increasing CH content with other elements in alphabetic sequence (see the section on the use of the indexes). The chemical classification is identical with the system used in the bibliographic volumes in this series.

Entries are numbered serially within each class.

Standard Entries

A standard entry has the following categories of information:

    compound name
    molecular formula
    bibliographic reference
    chemical diagram
    crystallographic diagram
    text
    numeric data

(a) The *compound name* is generally the name assigned to the compound by the author. For certain susbstances a synonym is also provided. Unless indicated to the contrary by a parenthetical phrase following the compound name, each entry refers to an X-ray study at room temperature.

(b) The *molecular formula* is expressed in terms of residues, i.e. discrete, covalently-bonded groupings of molecules or ions. Further details are given in the section on indexes.

(c) The *bibliographic reference* is the reference to the original publication from which the numeric data were derived.

(d) The *chemical diagram* gives the conventional two-dimensional or linear formulation of the compound. The majority of the diagrams are taken from a recent publication of crystallographic data (*Numerical Data and Functional Relationships in Science and Technology, III Vol. 5a, b;* Ed. K.-H. and A. M. Hellwege, Berlin: Springer, 1971).

(e) The *crystallographic diagram* consists of a stereoscopic pair which has been computer-generated from the published atomic coordinates (for further details see the section on evaluation procedures). The stereo pair can be studied with the aid of the viewer provided in the inside cover of this book. The following points should be noted:

(i) All diagrams are plotted with respect to a right-handed system of axes and, as a result, some structures may appear with the incorrect absolute configuration. In these cases the author may have given the correct absolute configuration but with respect to a non-standard left-handed axial system.

(ii) The labelling of atoms is consistent with the labelling in the tables of numeric data but it is not necessarily the same as in the original publication.

(iii) When a residue (molecule or ion) contains symmetry, then labels are provided for the basic unit and those atoms bonded to the basic unit.

(iv) Bond types are not indicated and must be identified by comparison with the chemical diagram.

(v) When the hydrogen atom positions have been established they are often included in the stereo diagram, even though numeric data involving hydrogen atoms are omitted from the tables.

(vi) Small residues (e.g. solvent molecules, ionic species, etc.) have usually been omitted for the sake of clarity.

(vii) The diagrams for some multi-residue structures (e.g. molecular complexes or structures having more than one molecule per asymmetric unit) have been 'composed' to give a reasonable overall view of the structure. As a result the mutual orientation of the residues is arbitrary and not that found in the crystal structure.

(viii) For polymeric structures, diagrams showing the linking of several monomer units are given.

(f) The *text* can contain seven categories of information:

    editorial comments
    space group symbol
    Z value
    R-factor
    supplementary references
    reference code
    Landolt-Börnstein number

(i) The *editorial comments* provide additional information on the structure, e.g. details of disorder, notes regarding errors in the original published data, etc. These are discussed further in the section on evaluation procedures. Some of these comments were computer-generated.

(ii) The *space-group symbol* is recorded using the Hermann-Mauguin notation (*International Tables for X-Ray Crystallography, Vol. 1.* Birmingham: Kynoch Press,1962).

(iii) The *Z value* is the number of formula units per unit cell. One formula unit is equivalent to the atomic assembly expressed in the molecular formula – see (b) above.

If the value of Z is less than the number of general positions of the space group and if the structure is not disordered, then the molecule has the symmetry of one of the special positions of the space group. Certain space groups are very common for organic structures and the number of general positions for these are listed below:

Space Group	No. of General Positions	Value of Z	Symmetry of Special Position
$P\bar{1}$	2	1	$\bar{1}(C_i)$
C2	4	2	$2(C_2)$
$P2_1/m$	4	2	$m(C_s)$ or $\bar{1}(C_i)$
$P2_1/c$ $P2_1/a$ $P2_1/n$	4	2	$\bar{1}(C_i)$
C2/c	8	4	$2(C_2)$ or $\bar{1}(C_i)$

(iv) The *R-factor* provides an indication of the reliability of the structure determination. R is usually defined as $\Sigma|(|F_o|-|F_c|)|/ \Sigma|F_o|$, where $|F_o|$ is the observed structure amplitude, $|F_c|$ the calculated structure amplitude. Thus R represents the discrepancy, expressed as a fraction, between the experimental and calculated model structures. R(h0l), R(hk0), R(0kl), etc. refer to projection data and R to three-dimensional data. No distinction is made between R-factors which include or exclude 'unobserved' reflections. In general the lowest value of R in the paper is recorded.

Non-crystallographers may wish to note that an R-factor less than 0.05–0.06 denotes a high precision analysis. If the R-factor is greater than ca. 0.15 then the overall molecular configuration is probably correct but the structure could possibly be refined further. In structures containing one or more heavy atoms the bond lengths involving heavy atoms will be more precisely determined than those involving only light atoms.

The distribution of the 791 three-dimensional R-factors for which numeric tables are presented is indicated by the histogram.

(v) The *supplementary references* indicate additional studies of the same compound published before 1960 or after 1965.

(vi) The *reference code* is a code used by the Crystallographic Data Centre to identify entries. It is composed of six letters and a possible two numerals. This code can be used in communications between the Centre and outside users.

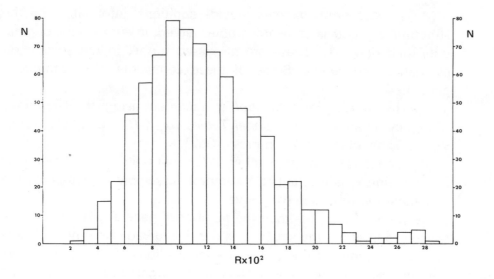

Rx10²

(vii) The *Landolt-Börnstein number* provides a cross-reference to the corresponding entry in *Numerical Data and Functional Relationships in Science and Technology, III Vol.5a,b:* Ed. K.-H. and A. M. Hellwege, Berlin: Springer, 1971.

This publication contains unit cell data and chemical diagrams for organic crystals studied in the period 1922–68.

(g) The *numeric data* are of three types:

> bond lengths (in Å, to two decimal places)
> bond angles (to the nearest degree)
> torsion angles (to the nearest degree)

Bond lengths

In general complete bond length lists are presented but very exceptionally may be omitted for structures of low precision where a more precise study is available or where errors in the published data result in the wrong connectivity.

Bond lengths involving hydrogen and deuterium atoms are included for all neutron studies and, at the discretion of the editors, for a few X-ray studies.

Bond lengths for small residues such as solvent molecules, inorganic ions, etc. will, in general, have been omitted from the tables.

Bond lengths are grouped by residue and within each residue the list is sorted as follows (M = transition metal):

M-M	X-X	N-O	M-H	N-D
M-X	X-N	C-N	M-D	O-H
M-N	X-O	O-O	X-H	O-D
M-O	X-C	C-O	X-D	C-H
M-C	N-N	C-C	N-H	C-D

All bond lengths were recomputed from the published coordinates and compared with the published values (see section on evaluation procedures). If the difference between the two values is greater than 0.05Å then the published value is also recorded, in parentheses.

Bond angles

Complete bond angle tables are presented for classes 1–70. The same criteria were applied for H,D and small residues as for the bond length lists. In classes 71–86 some angles have been omitted, e.g. C-C-C angles in triphenylphosphine groups, angles about the metal atom in ferrocene-like compounds, etc.

Within each residue the bond angles are sorted by the apex atom in the following order: M,X,N,O,C,H,D (M=transition metal). Bond angles have not been directly compared with the published values on the assumption that the comparison of calculated and published bond lengths has provided a sufficient check.

Torsion angles

Torsion angles provide a sensitive indication of molecular conformation but were only rarely listed in papers published between 1960 and 1965. We have computed torsion angles for all classes and have included them in the tables wherever they seemed appropriate. Thus a selection of torsion angles is presented which, in the editors' view, are of the greatest conformational interest, i.e. they define the conformation of a ring system or indicate fairly accurately the dihedral angle between two planar groupings.

We have used the torsion angle definition of Klyne and Prelog (Experientia, *16*, 521, 1960): for a set of four atoms i,j,k,l the torsion angle about the bond jk is the angle between the projections of the bonds ij and kl on to a plane perpendicular to the bond jk when viewed in the direction from j to k. Its value is positive if a clockwise rotation causes the projection of bond ij to overlie the projection of bond kl.

Partial Entries

A partial entry has the following categories of information:

      compound name
      molecular formula
      bibliographic reference
      chemical diagram
      text

Partial entries generally correspond to publications in which numeric data were not reported or where certain data problems were present. A full list of the situations resulting in partial entries is given below:

(i) Studies in which the atomic coordinates were not reported in the publication.

(ii) Two-dimensional studies in which only two coordinates were established for each atom.

(iii) Clathrate structures.

(iv) Structures in which all (or a substantial proportion) of the atoms were disordered.

(v) Structures where our evaluation procedures indicated incomplete or wrong connectivity or other serious errors which could not be resolved.

(vi) In the case where several entries have been amalgamated into a composite entry, then the 'component' entries are partial in their make-up. In these situations the partial entries will generally not carry chemical diagrams. For further details see the section on amalgamated entries.

Multiple Entries

Multiple entries are independent studies of the same chemical compound and occur for a variety of reasons:

> independent studies by different authors
> studies of different crystal forms
> studies at different temperatures
> studies by both X-ray and neutron diffraction
> refinements of different data sets
> refinements of different space group models.

If these multiple entries have not been amalgamated (see next section), then each entry has the form of a standard or partial entry.

Amalgamated Entries

For certain sets of multiple entries the information has been amalgamated into a composite entry which allows for easy comparison of the results of different studies.

For a given set of multiple entries one entry is taken as the basic entry and the information from additional entries merged with it. The composite entry will have all the information types of a standard entry and the additional entries will be represented by partial entries, without chemical diagrams.

Evaluation Procedures

The data base from which this volume has been prepared is a subset of the structural data file of the Crystallographic Data Centre. Input to the file, relevant to this volume, consists of:

> crystal data, e.g. unit cell parameters, space group, Z etc.
> atomic coordinates of the asymmetric unit.
> published bond lengths.

The internal consistency of the data is checked by a computer program which performs the following main functions:

(i) Bonded atom-pairs are found using a set of atomic covalent radii and the space-group symmetry. All input atoms are then placed in the same asymmetric unit.

(ii) This process is extended until all bonded networks are established. These may contain additional atoms which are symmetry-related to the asymmetric unit. For example, a benzene ring located on a centre of symmetry would have three atoms in the asymmetric unit but six in the full network – the crystal chemical unit. This unit may contain several residues, i.e. molecular or ionic species. The coordinates of the crystal chemical unit replace the input coordinates in the file.

(iii) The connectivity of the entire system is logged and added to the file in compact notation, in terms of chains and ring closures for each residue. The 'molecular' formula of each residue is also calculated.

(iv) The crystallographically unique bond lengths are recalculated. Any interatomic distance found to be shorter, by more than 0.4Å, than the sum of the covalent radii is flagged as 'short'.

(v) Each calculated bond length is compared with the corresponding published value and the difference, Δ, is flagged

* if $0·02\text{Å} \leqslant \Delta < 0·05\text{Å}$
** if $\Delta \geqslant 0·05\text{Å}$

(vi) Checks are made that the normal valence requirements are not violated for certain common elements.

(vii) A record is added to the file indicating whether the data set is error-free or an error set.

Error sets were checked for clerical and transcription errors followed by a thorough scientific check. Of the 1305 entries in this volume, 148 had to be checked in this way. The chief sources of error have been typographic errors in the original publication and space-group origin problems. The latter has arisen in those cases where the author used an origin different from the conventional origin (*International Tables for X-Ray Crystallography, Vol. 1*).

The above problems were often resolved by a close inspection of published diagrams, which gave an indication of missing negative signs in coordinates or transposed digits. If we were unable to trace the errors, individual authors were contacted and we are grateful for all replies received before the pre-publication deadline.

An indication of the non-clerical errors contained in each entry was added to the data base and these comments are reproduced in this volume. Entries containing unresolved errors are of two types:

(a) One or more atoms are slightly misplaced or the reported bond lengths are in error, resulting in correct connectivity but giving bond length comparisons of the ** type ($\Delta \geqslant 0·05\text{Å}$). The numeric data for these entries are reported in this volume, but for the 'poor-agreement' bond lengths the published values are also recorded in parentheses.

(b) Errors are present which destroy the chemical connectivity. Numeric data for these entries have been suppressed but remarks on the nature of the errors are included.

List of Classes

1.1   Oxalyl bromide

$C_2Br_2O_2$

P.Groth, O.Hassel, Acta Chem. Scand., 16, 2311, 1962

$P2_1/c$ $Z = 2$ $R_{hk0} = 0.051,$
$R_{h0l} = 0.141$

OXALYB

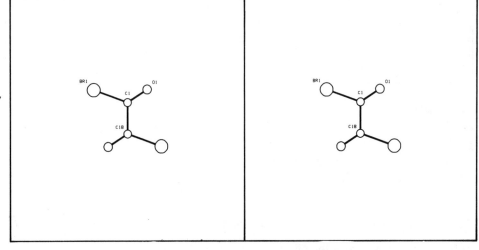

Bond Lengths			Bond Angles				Torsion Angles				
Br1	C1	1.84	Br1	C1	O1	128	Br1	C1	C1B	O1B	8
C1	O1	1.18	Br1	C1	C1B	109					
C1	C1B	1.56	O1	C1	C1B	122					

1.2   Oxalyl chloride

$C_2Cl_2O_2$

P.Groth, O.Hassel, Acta Chem. Scand., 16, 2311, 1962

No comparison of bond lengths is
possible since they are not reported
in the paper.
Pbca $Z = 4$ $R_{h0l} = 0.102,$
$R_{0kl} = 0.126$

OXALYC

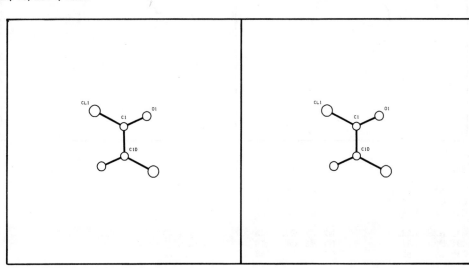

Bond Lengths			Bond Angles				Torsion Angles				
Cl1	C1	1.70	Cl1	C1	O1	128	Cl1	C1	C1D	O1D	25
C1	O1	1.30	Cl1	C1	C1D	116					
C1	C1D	1.47	O1	C1	C1D	110					

1.3   Monofluoroacetamide

C_2H_4FNO

D.O.Hughes, R.W.H.Small, Acta Cryst., 15, 933, 1962

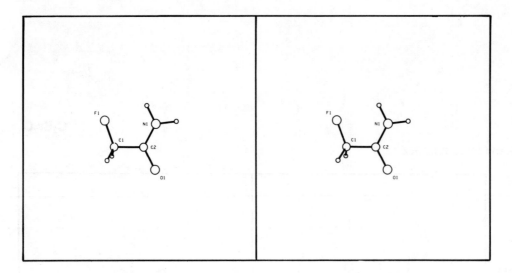

FCH_2—$CONH_2$

P-1   Z = 2   R = 0.093

FACETA   LB 2-4-22

Bond Lengths			Bond Angles				Torsion Angles				
F1	C1	1.39	F1	C1	C2	110	F1	C1	C2	N1	0
C2	N1	1.31	N1	C2	O1	124	F1	C1	C2	O1	179
C2	O1	1.24	N1	C2	C1	119					
C1	C2	1.52	O1	C2	C1	117					

1.4   Acetamide (orthorhombic form)

C_2H_5NO

W.C.Hamilton, Acta Cryst., 18, 866, 1965

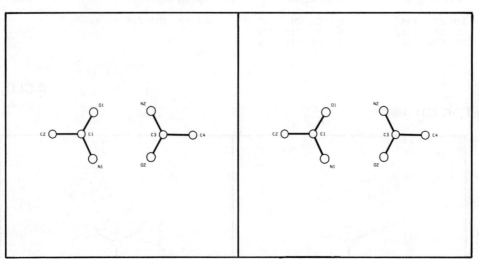

CH_3—C with O and NH_2

See also Denne & Small, Acta Cryst. (B), 27, 1094, 1971.
Pccn   Z = 16   R = 0.101

ACEMID   LB 2-5-11

Bond Lengths			Bond Angles			
C1	N1	1.35	N1	C1	O1	123
C1	O1	1.25	N1	C1	C2	116
C1	C2	1.49	O1	C1	C2	121
C3	N2	1.32	N2	C3	O2	123
C3	O2	1.27	N2	C3	C4	119
C3	C4	1.52	O2	C3	C4	118

1.5   Acrylic acid

$C_3H_4O_2$

(i)   M.A.Higgs, R.L.Sass, Acta Cryst., 16, 657, 1963   (at −150°C)

(ii)   Y.Chatani, Y.Sakata, I.Nitta, J. Polym. Sci., B, 1, 419, 1963   (at −95°C)

$CH_2{=}CH{-}COOH$

(i)

Ibam   Z = 8   R = 0.102

ACRLAC   LB 3-4-14

(ii)

Ibam   Z = 8
No R factor was given.

ACRLAC01   LB 3-4-14

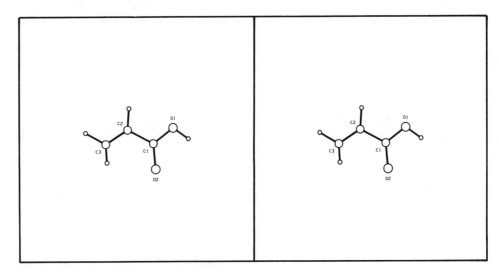

Bond Lengths

		(i)	(ii)
C1	O1	1.28	1.32
C1	O2	1.26	1.24
C1	C2	1.47	1.46
C2	C3	1.30	1.33

Bond Angles

			(i)	(ii)
O1	C1	O2	122	123
O1	C1	C2	116	113
O2	C1	C2	122	124
C1	C2	C3	121	121

1.6   Acrylic acid (at −95 °C)

$C_3H_4O_2$

For complete entry see 1.5

1.7   α - Hydroxymalonic acid

$C_3H_4O_5$

Tartronic acid
B.P.van Eijck, J.A.Kanters, J.Kroon, Acta Cryst., 19, 435, 1965

```
      COOH
       |
HO—CH
       |
      COOH
```

P2₁2₁2₁   Z = 4   R = 0.037

HMALAC   LB 3-4-21

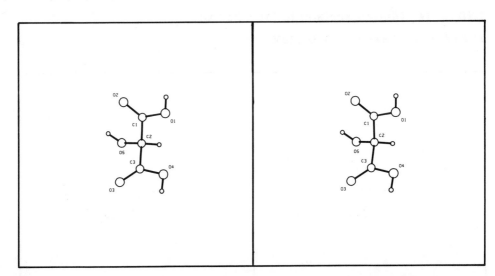

Bond Lengths

C1	O1	1.30
C1	O2	1.21
C3	O3	1.21
C3	O4	1.30
C2	O5	1.40
C1	C2	1.53
C2	C3	1.54

Bond Angles

O1	C1	O2	126
O1	C1	C2	113
O2	C1	C2	120
O5	C2	C1	111
O5	C2	C3	112
C1	C2	C3	109
O3	C3	O4	126
O3	C3	C2	122
O4	C3	C2	112

Torsion Angles

O1	C1	C2	O5	−165
O1	C1	C2	C3	71
O2	C1	C2	O5	15
O2	C1	C2	C3	−109
O5	C2	C3	O3	−18
O5	C2	C3	O4	161
C1	C2	C3	O3	106
C1	C2	C3	O4	−75

1.8   Propionic acid

$C_3H_6O_2$

(i)   F.J.Strieter, D.H.Templeton, R.F.Scheurman, R.L.Sass, Acta Cryst., 15, 1233, 1962 (at −95°C)

(ii)   F.J.Strieter, D.H.Templeton, R.F.Scheurman, R.L.Sass, Acta Cryst., 15, 1233, 1962 (at −135°C)

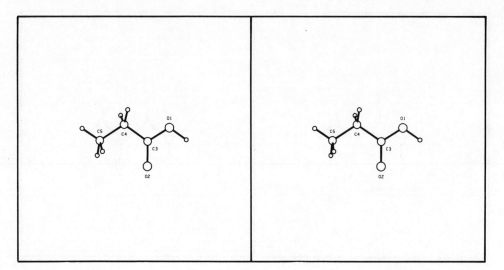

$CH_3—CH_2—COOH$

(i)
$P2_1/c$ Z = 4   R = 0.116

PRONAC   LB 3-6-38

(ii)
$P2_1/c$ Z = 4   R = 0.148

PRONAC01   LB 3-6-38

Bond Lengths

		(i)	(ii)
C3	O1	1.31	1.34
C3	O2	1.23	1.22
C3	C4	1.50	1.50
C4	C5	1.52	1.55

Bond Angles

			(i)	(ii)
O1	C3	O2	122	122
O1	C3	C4	114	113
O2	C3	C4	124	125
C3	C4	C5	114	112

Torsion Angles

				(i)	(ii)
O1	C3	C4	C5	−168	−167
O2	C3	C4	C5	13	15

1.9   Propionic acid (at −135 °C)

$C_3H_6O_2$

For complete entry see 1.8

1.10   N - Methyl acetamide (at −35 °C)

C_3H_7NO

J.L.Katz, B.Post, Acta Cryst., 13, 624, 1960

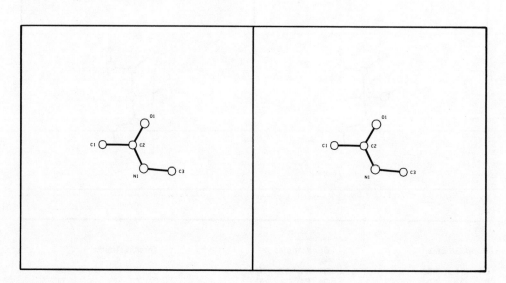

$H_3C—CO—NH—CH_3$

Pnma   Z = 4   R = 0.169

METACM   LB 3-7-10

Bond Lengths

C2	N1	1.29
C3	N1	1.46
C2	O1	1.23
C1	C2	1.55

Bond Angles

C2	N1	C3	121
N1	C2	O1	123
N1	C2	C1	117
O1	C2	C1	120

1.11   Maleic anhydride

$C_4H_2O_3$

R.E.Marsh, E.Ubell, H.E.Wilcox, Acta Cryst., 15, 35, 1962

$P2_12_12_1$ $Z = 4$ $R = 0.055$

MLEICA   LB 4-2-12

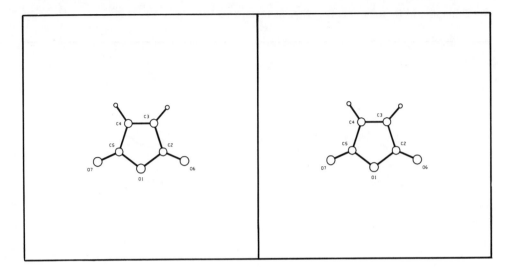

Bond Lengths

C2	O1	1.39
C5	O1	1.38
C2	O6	1.18
C5	O7	1.19
C2	C3	1.47
C3	C4	1.30
C4	C5	1.47

Bond Angles

C2	O1	C5	107
O1	C2	O6	121
O1	C2	C3	108
O6	C2	C3	131
C2	C3	C4	108
C3	C4	C5	109
O1	C5	O7	120
O1	C5	C4	108
O7	C5	C4	132

1.12   N - Chlorosuccinimide

$C_4H_4ClNO_2$

R.N.Brown, Acta Cryst., 14, 711, 1961

No comparison of bond lengths is possible since they are not reported in the paper.
$P2_12_12_1$ $Z = 4$ $R_{0kl} = 0.109$, $R_{h0l} = 0.106$

CSUCIM   LB 4-4-9

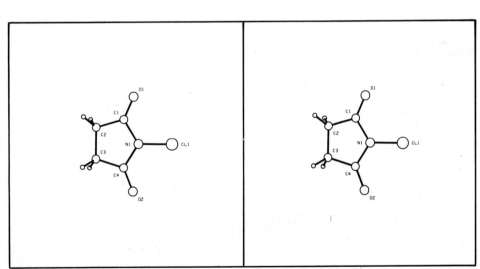

Bond Lengths

Cl1	N1	1.69
C1	N1	1.41
C4	N1	1.38
C1	O1	1.20
C4	O2	1.23
C1	C2	1.49
C2	C3	1.55
C3	C4	1.48

Bond Angles

Cl1	N1	C1	122
Cl1	N1	C4	122
C1	N1	C4	115
N1	C1	O1	124
N1	C1	C2	107
O1	C1	C2	129
C1	C2	C3	104
C2	C3	C4	107
N1	C4	O2	124
N1	C4	C3	106
O2	C4	C3	130

Torsion Angles

C4	N1	C1	C2	−9
C1	N1	C4	C3	3
N1	C1	C2	C3	10
C1	C2	C3	C4	−8
C2	C3	C4	N1	3

1.13 Succinic anhydride

C₄H₄O₃ → $C_4H_4O_3$

(i) M.Ehrenberg, Acta Cryst., 19, 698, 1965

(ii) S.Biagini, M.Cannas, Ric. Sci., 2, A, 8, 1518, 1965

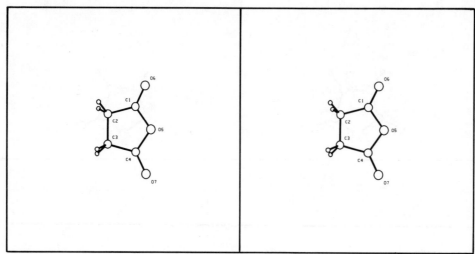

The structure is isomorphous with maleic anhydride.

(i)
The structure is isomorphous with maleic anhydride.
$P2_12_12_1$ Z = 4   R = 0.076

SUCANH   LB 4-4-57

(ii)
$P2_12_12_1$ Z = 4 $R_{hk0} = 0.18$, $R_{0kl} = 0.19$

SUCANH11   LB 4-4-57

Bond Lengths

		(i)	(ii)
C1	O5	1.38	1.38
C4	O5	1.37	1.37
C1	O6	1.19	1.20
C4	O7	1.19	1.20
C1	C2	1.47	1.50
C2	C3	1.51	1.55
C3	C4	1.48	1.48

Bond Angles

			(i)	(ii)				(i)	(ii)
C1	O5	C4	110	110	C2	C3	C4	104	104
O5	C1	O6	120	120	O5	C4	O7	119	120
O5	C1	C2	110	111	O5	C4	C3	110	112
O6	C1	C2	130	129	O7	C4	C3	130	128
C1	C2	C3	105	103					

1.14 Succinic anhydride

C₄H₄O₃ → $C_4H_4O_3$

For complete entry see 1.13

1.15 Succinimide

C₄H₅NO₂ → $C_4H_5NO_2$

R.Mason, Acta Cryst., 14, 720, 1961

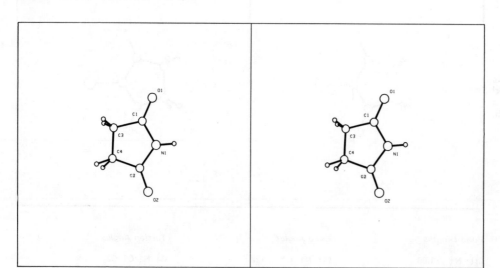

Pbca   Z = 8   R = 0.091

SUCCIN   LB 4-5-18

Bond Lengths

C1	N1	1.37	C1	C3	1.51
C2	N1	1.40	C2	C4	1.50
C1	O1	1.24	C3	C4	1.50
C2	O2	1.21			

Bond Angles

C1	N1	C2	113	N1	C2	C4	108
N1	C1	O1	124	O2	C2	C4	128
N1	C1	C3	109	C1	C3	C4	104
O1	C1	C3	127	C2	C4	C3	106
N1	C2	O2	124				

1.16   n - Butyric acid (at −43 °C)

$C_4H_8O_2$

F.J.Strieter, D.H.Templeton, Acta Cryst., 15, 1240, 1962

$CH_3—CH_2—CH_2—COOH$

C2/m   Z = 4   R = 0.127

BUTRAC   LB 4-8-92

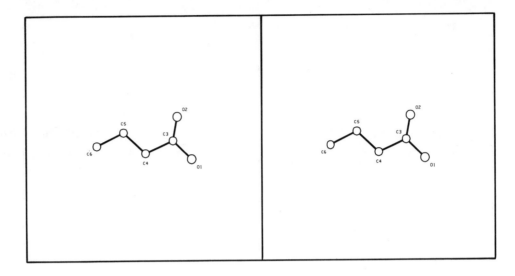

Bond Lengths

C3	O1	1.32
C3	O2	1.20
C3	C4	1.52
C4	C5	1.51
C5	C6	1.51

Bond Angles

O1	C3	O2	123
O1	C3	C4	113
O2	C3	C4	124
C3	C4	C5	114
C4	C5	C6	111

1.17   Valeric acid (at −135 °C)

$C_5H_{10}O_2$

R.F.Scheuerman, R.L.Sass, Acta Cryst., 15, 1244, 1962

$H_3C—CH_2—CH_2—CH_2—COOH$

P2₁/c   Z = 4   R = 0.11

VALRAC   LB 5-10-19

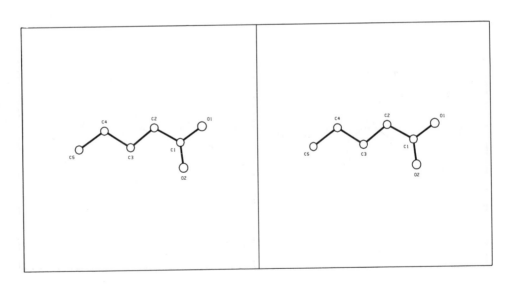

Bond Lengths

C1	O1	1.35
C1	O2	1.26
C1	C2	1.53
C2	C3	1.53
C3	C4	1.57
C4	C5	1.58

Bond Angles

O1	C1	O2	119
O1	C1	C2	117
O2	C1	C2	125
C1	C2	C3	113
C2	C3	C4	109
C3	C4	C5	112

1.18   Adipic acid

$C_6H_{10}O_4$

J.Housty, M.Hospital, Acta Cryst., 18, 693, 1965

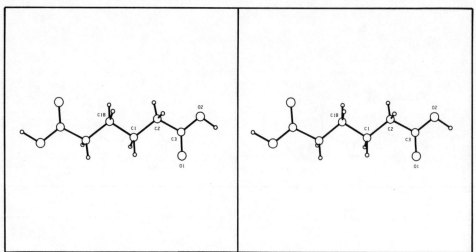

HOOC—(CH$_2$)$_4$—COOH

See also MacGillavry, Rec. Trav. Chim. Pays - Bas, 60, 605, 1941; Morrison & Robertson, J. Chem. Soc., 987, 1949; Kirokawa, Bull. Chem. Soc. Jap., 23, 91, 1950.
P2$_1$/c   Z = 2   R = 0.08

ADIPAC   LB 6-10-38

Bond Lengths			Bond Angles				Torsion Angles				
C3	O1	1.23	C2	C1	C1B	110	C1B	C1	C2	C3	−174
C3	O2	1.29	C1	C2	C3	115	C2	C1	C1B	C2B	180
C1	C2	1.52	O1	C3	O2	122	C1	C2	C3	O1	−8
C1	C1B	1.51	O1	C3	C2	122	C1	C2	C3	O2	173
C2	C3	1.50	O2	C3	C2	116					

1.19   Pimelamide

$C_7H_{14}N_2O_2$

M.Hospital, J.Housty, C. R. Acad. Sci., Fr., 261, 3820, 1965

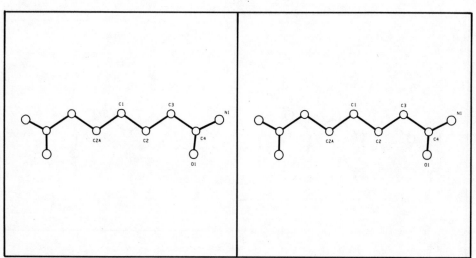

H$_2$NOC—(CH$_2$)$_5$—CONH$_2$

No comparison of bond lengths is possible since they are not reported in the paper.
C2/c   Z = 4   R = 0.17

PIMAMI   LB 7-14-8

Bond Lengths			Bond Angles				Torsion Angles				
C4	N1	1.33	C2	C1	C2A	112	C2A	C1	C2	C3	−179
C4	O1	1.24	C1	C2	C3	113	C1	C2	C3	C4	−175
C1	C2	1.53	C2	C3	C4	114	C2	C3	C4	N1	−159
C2	C3	1.53	N1	C4	O1	123	C2	C3	C4	O1	20
C3	C4	1.53	N1	C4	C3	117					
			O1	C4	C3	120					

1.20 Suberic acid   C₈H₁₄O₄

J.Housty, M.Hospital, Acta Cryst., 18, 753, 1965

HOOC—(CH₂)₆—COOH

The bond lengths given for C - H in
Table 2 are rounded to nearest 0.5A.

P2₁/c   Z = 2   R = 0.10

SUBRAC   LB 8-14-27

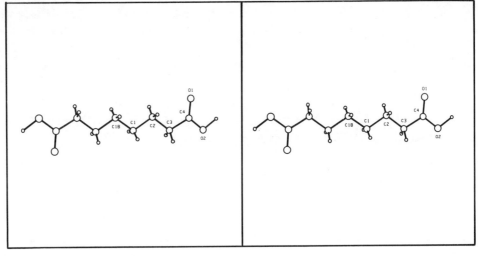

Bond Lengths

C4	O1	1.23
C4	O2	1.31
C1	C2	1.53
C1	C1B	1.50
C2	C3	1.51
C3	C4	1.50

Bond Angles

C2	C1	C1B	115
C1	C2	C3	113
C2	C3	C4	115
O1	C4	O2	122
O1	C4	C3	123
O2	C4	C3	115

Torsion Angles

C1B	C1	C2	C3	178
C2	C1	C1B	C2B	180
C1	C2	C3	C4	−176
C2	C3	C4	O1	−5
C2	C3	C4	O2	177

1.21 Peroxypelargonic acid (at −30 ° C)   C₉H₁₈O₃

D.Belitskus, G.A.Jeffrey, Acta Cryst., 18, 458, 1965

H₃C—(CH₂)₇—C(=O)—O—OH

P2₁/c   Z = 4   R = 0.18

OPELAC   LB 9-18-15

Bond Lengths

O1	O2	1.45
C1	O2	1.35
C1	O3	1.23
C1	C2	1.50
C2	C3	1.53
C3	C4	1.55
C4	C5	1.54
C5	C6	1.56
C6	C7	1.57
C7	C8	1.56
C8	C9	1.55

Bond Angles

O1	O2	C1	112
O2	C1	O3	122
O2	C1	C2	110
O3	C1	C2	128
C1	C2	C3	112
C2	C3	C4	110
C3	C4	C5	112
C4	C5	C6	112
C5	C6	C7	112
C6	C7	C8	110
C7	C8	C9	111

Torsion Angles

O1	O2	C1	O3	3
O1	O2	C1	C2	−179
O2	C1	C2	C3	−154
O3	C1	C2	C3	25
C1	C2	C3	C4	−171
C2	C3	C4	C5	−175
C3	C4	C5	C6	−178
C4	C5	C6	C7	179
C5	C6	C7	C8	179
C6	C7	C8	C9	−178

1.22 N - p - Bromophenylsuccinimide

C₁₀H₈BrNO₂

J.Barassin, Ann. Chim., 8, 637, 1963

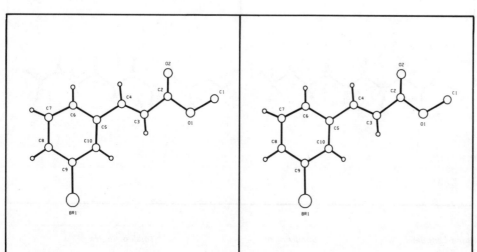

No comparison of bond lengths is possible since they are not reported in the paper. The bond distances in the publication are the mean values of supposed identical bonds.

$P2_12_12_1$ Z = 4   R = 0.27

BPSUCA   LB 10-8-3

Bond Lengths

Br1	C4	1.95	C2	C3	1.38
C1	N1	1.52	C3	C4	1.29
C7	N1	1.40	C4	C5	1.46
C10	N1	1.46	C5	C6	1.36
C7	O1	1.20	C7	C8	1.62
C10	O2	1.16	C8	C9	1.42
C1	C2	1.29	C9	C10	1.52
C1	C6	1.38			

Bond Angles

C1	N1	C7	122	C2	C3	C4	114	N1	C7	C8	106
C1	N1	C10	123	Br1	C4	C3	122	O1	C7	C8	130
C7	N1	C10	114	Br1	C4	C5	115	C7	C8	C9	103
N1	C1	C2	119	C3	C4	C5	122	C8	C9	C10	113
N1	C1	C6	114	C4	C5	C6	122	N1	C10	O2	120
C2	C1	C6	127	C1	C6	C5	110	N1	C10	C9	103
C1	C2	C3	123	N1	C7	O1	124	O2	C10	C9	137

Torsion Angles

C7	N1	C1	C6	62

1.23 Methyl m - bromocinnamate

C₁₀H₉BrO₂

L.Leiserowitz, G.M.J.Schmidt, Acta Cryst., 18, 1058, 1965

Published value of C5 - C6 = 1.44A. The correct value is 1.41A.

$P2_1/a$ Z = 4   R = 0.066

MBRCIN   LB 10-9-3

Bond Lengths

Br1	C9	1.86	C5	C6	1.41
C1	O1	1.43	C5	C10	1.37
C2	O1	1.40	C6	C7	1.38
C2	O2	1.18	C7	C8	1.47
C2	C3	1.50	C8	C9	1.42
C3	C4	1.28	C9	C10	1.41
C4	C5	1.49			

Bond Angles

C1	O1	C2	115	C6	C5	C10	119
O1	C2	O2	124	C5	C6	C7	124
O1	C2	C3	108	C6	C7	C8	116
O2	C2	C3	127	C7	C8	C9	120
C2	C3	C4	120	Br1	C9	C8	121
C3	C4	C5	124	Br1	C9	C10	120
C4	C5	C6	118	C8	C9	C10	119
C4	C5	C10	123	C5	C10	C9	122

Torsion Angles

C1	O1	C2	O2	0
C1	O1	C2	C3	175
O1	C2	C3	C4	179
O2	C2	C3	C4	−5
C2	C3	C4	C5	−179
C3	C4	C5	C6	168
C3	C4	C5	C10	−10

1.24   Methyl p - bromocinnamate

$C_{10}H_9BrO_2$

L.Leiserowitz, G.M.J.Schmidt, Acta Cryst., 18, 1058, 1965

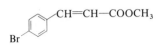

P2$_1$/n   Z = 4   R = 0.101

MEBCIN   LB 10-9-4

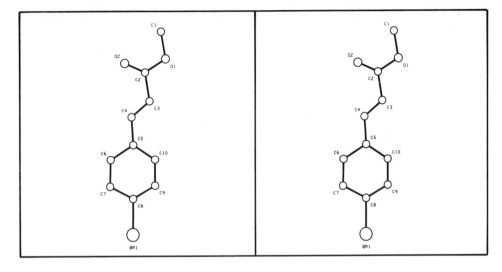

Bond Lengths

Br1	C8	1.88
C1	O1	1.45
C2	O1	1.31
C2	O2	1.19
C2	C3	1.52
C3	C4	1.27
C4	C5	1.43
C5	C6	1.44
C5	C10	1.39
C6	C7	1.38
C7	C8	1.39
C8	C9	1.36
C9	C10	1.36

Bond Angles

C1	O1	C2	113
O1	C2	O2	123
O1	C2	C3	113
O2	C2	C3	123
C2	C3	C4	121
C3	C4	C5	127
C4	C5	C6	119
C4	C5	C10	126
C6	C5	C10	115
C5	C6	C7	124
C6	C7	C8	116
Br1	C8	C7	117
Br1	C8	C9	121
C7	C8	C9	122
C8	C9	C10	120
C5	C10	C9	123

Torsion Angles

C1	O1	C2	O2	1
C1	O1	C2	C3	179
O1	C2	C3	C4	−174
O2	C2	C3	C4	5
C2	C3	C4	C5	177
C3	C4	C5	C6	175
C3	C4	C5	C10	−3

1.25   Ethylenediamine tetra - acetic acid

$C_{10}H_{16}N_2O_8$

L.Y.Tsein, S.M.Chen, Sci. Sinica, 11, 496, 1962

The published coordinates cannot be connected to form a molecule. The structure has been redetermined by Cotrait, Acta Cryst. (B), 28, 781, 1972.
C2/c   Z = 4   No R factor was given.

EDTAXX   LB 10-16-33

$$HOOC-CH_2 \diagdown \qquad \diagup CH_2-COOH$$
$$N-CH_2-CH_2-N$$
$$HOOC-CH_2 \diagup \qquad \diagdown CH_2-COOH$$

1.26   11 - Bromoundecanoic acid (form D)

$C_{11}H_{21}BrO_2$

K.Larsson, Acta Chem. Scand., 17, 199, 1963

$$Br-CH_2-(CH_2)_9-COOH$$

P2$_1$/c   Z = 4   R$_{h0l}$ = 0.17,
R$_{0kl}$ = 0.12

BUNDAC   LB 11-21-1

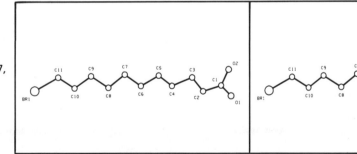

Bond Lengths

Br1	C11	2.02
C1	O1	1.23
C1	O2	1.40
C1	C2	1.45
C2	C3	1.48
C3	C4	1.71
C4	C5	1.48
C5	C6	1.68
C6	C7	1.58
C7	C8	1.59
C8	C9	1.64
C9	C10	1.66
C10	C11	1.57

Bond Angles

O1	C1	O2	116
O1	C1	C2	116
O2	C1	C2	127
C1	C2	C3	106
C2	C3	C4	98
C3	C4	C5	105
C4	C5	C6	98
C5	C6	C7	104
C6	C7	C8	103
C7	C8	C9	104
C8	C9	C10	103
C9	C10	C11	100
Br1	C11	C10	112

Torsion Angles

O1	C1	C2	C3	112
O2	C1	C2	C3	−63
C1	C2	C3	C4	174
C2	C3	C4	C5	169
C3	C4	C5	C6	−179
C4	C5	C6	C7	−173
C5	C6	C7	C8	−164
C6	C7	C8	C9	179
C7	C8	C9	C10	171
C8	C9	C10	C11	176
C9	C10	C11	Br1	−171

1.27   3 - Thiadodecanoic acid

$C_{11}H_{22}O_2S$

S.Abrahamsson, A.Westerdahl, Acta Cryst., 16, 404, 1963

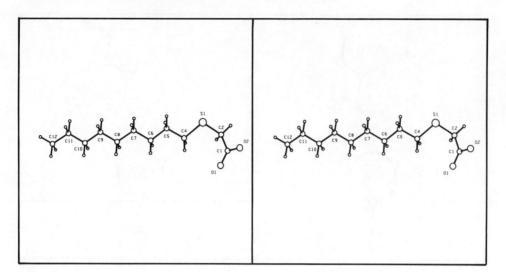

$$H_3C—(CH_2)_8—S—CH_2—COOH$$

P-1   Z = 2   R = 0.11

SDODAC   LB 11-22-2

Bond Lengths

S1	C2	1.73	C6	C7	1.48
S1	C4	1.84	C7	C8	1.57
C1	O1	1.19	C8	C9	1.48
C1	O2	1.37	C9	C10	1.53
C1	C2	1.58	C10	C11	1.47
C4	C5	1.50	C11	C12	1.56
C5	C6	1.57			

Bond Angles

C2	S1	C4	104	C5	C6	C7	111
O1	C1	O2	123	C6	C7	C8	114
O1	C1	C2	114	C7	C8	C9	116
O2	C1	C2	122	C8	C9	C10	116
S1	C2	C1	112	C9	C10	C11	117
S1	C4	C5	110	C10	C11	C12	119
C4	C5	C6	113				

Torsion Angles

C4	S1	C2	C1	−77	C5	C6	C7	C8	−179
C2	S1	C4	C5	−169	C6	C7	C8	C9	−179
O1	C1	C2	S1	91	C7	C8	C9	C10	178
O2	C1	C2	S1	−86	C8	C9	C10	C11	180
S1	C4	C5	C6	180	C9	C10	C11	C12	−179
C4	C5	C6	C7	−180					

1.28   N,N' - Hexamethylenebispropionamide

$C_{12}H_{24}N_2O_2$

(i)   L.H.Jensen, Acta Cryst., 15, 433, 1962

(ii)   M.Sundaralingam, L.H.Jensen, Acta Cryst., 16, A61, 1963 (refinement)

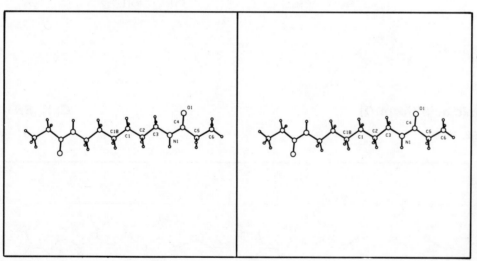

$$C_2H_5—\overset{\displaystyle O}{\overset{\|}{C}}—NH—(CH_2)_6—NH—\overset{\displaystyle O}{\overset{\|}{C}}—C_2H_5$$

(i)
Published value of y(C6) = 0.5420.
The correct value is 0.4520.
P2₁/a   Z = 2   R = 0.073

HEXMPR   LB 12-24-19

(ii)
Atomic coordinates were not reported in the paper.
P2₁/a   Z was not reported.
R = 0.049

HEXMPR01   LB 12-24-19

Bond Lengths

C3	N1	1.46	C1	C1B	1.53
C4	N1	1.33	C2	C3	1.53
C4	O1	1.23	C4	C5	1.53
C1	C2	1.53	C5	C6	1.50

Bond Angles

C3	N1	C4	121	N1	C4	O1	123
C2	C1	C1B	113	N1	C4	C5	115
C1	C2	C3	112	O1	C4	C5	122
N1	C3	C2	111	C4	C5	C6	114

Torsion Angles

C4	N1	C3	C2	−169	C2	C1	C1B	C2B	−180
C3	N1	C4	O1	−1	C1	C2	C3	N1	−178
C3	N1	C4	C5	177	N1	C4	C5	C6	169
C1B	C1	C2	C3	180	O1	C4	C5	C6	−13

1.29   N,N' - Hexamethylenebispropionamide (refinement)

$C_{12}H_{24}N_2O_2$

For complete entry see 1.28

1.30   Lauric acid (form A₁) $C_{12}H_{24}O_2$

T.R.Lomer, Acta Cryst., 16, 984, 1963

$H_3C—(CH_2)_{10}—COOH$

No comparison of bond lengths is possible since they are not reported in the paper.

P-1   Z = 2 R_{h0l} = 0.138, R_{0kl} = 0.141

LAURAC   LB 12-24-22

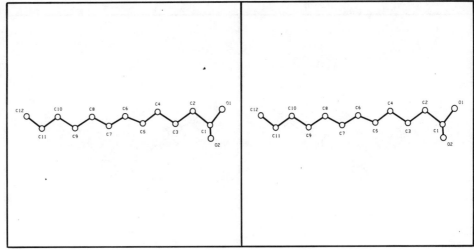

Bond Lengths

C1	O1	1.47		C6	C7	1.41
C1	O2	0.99		C7	C8	1.45
C1	C2	1.68		C8	C9	1.50
C2	C3	1.60		C9	C10	1.57
C3	C4	1.59		C10	C11	1.45
C4	C5	1.42		C11	C12	1.50
C5	C6	1.43				

Bond Angles

O1	C1	O2	138		C5	C6	C7	128
O1	C1	C2	91		C6	C7	C8	124
O2	C1	C2	131		C7	C8	C9	121
C1	C2	C3	107		C8	C9	C10	116
C2	C3	C4	112		C9	C10	C11	114
C3	C4	C5	111		C10	C11	C12	107
C4	C5	C6	122					

Torsion Angles

O1	C1	C2	C3	−168		C5	C6	C7	C8	−175
O2	C1	C2	C3	15		C6	C7	C8	C9	−173
C1	C2	C3	C4	177		C7	C8	C9	C10	−175
C2	C3	C4	C5	179		C8	C9	C10	C11	180
C3	C4	C5	C6	172		C9	C10	C11	C12	−176
C4	C5	C6	C7	175						

1.31   cis - D,L - 8,9 - Methyleneheptadecanoic acid $C_{18}H_{34}O_2$

G.A.Jeffrey, M.Sax, Acta Cryst., 16, 1196, 1963

$$CH_2$$
$$H_3C—(CH_2)_7—CH—CH—(CH_2)_6—COOH$$

A2/a   Z = 8   R = 0.148

MEHPDA   LB 18-34-1

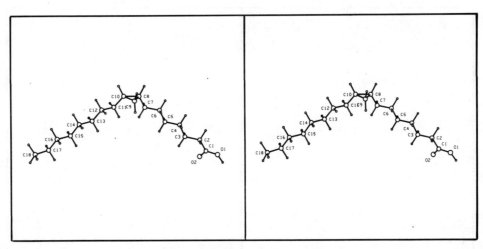

Bond Lengths

C1	O1	1.30		C8	C10	1.51
C1	O2	1.24		C9	C10	1.50
C1	C2	1.49		C10	C11	1.50
C2	C3	1.53		C11	C12	1.52
C3	C4	1.52		C12	C13	1.51
C4	C5	1.52		C13	C14	1.52
C5	C6	1.52		C14	C15	1.52
C6	C7	1.54		C15	C16	1.52
C7	C8	1.51		C16	C17	1.48
C8	C9	1.51		C17	C18	1.49

Bond Angles

O1	C1	O2	123		C8	C9	C10	60
O1	C1	C2	115		C8	C10	C9	60
O2	C1	C2	122		C8	C10	C11	124
C1	C2	C3	116		C9	C10	C11	119
C2	C3	C4	111		C10	C11	C12	114
C3	C4	C5	114		C11	C12	C13	114
C4	C5	C6	113		C12	C13	C14	116
C5	C6	C7	113		C13	C14	C15	114
C6	C7	C8	112		C14	C15	C16	114
C7	C8	C9	119		C15	C16	C17	115
C7	C8	C10	122		C16	C17	C18	119
C9	C8	C10	60					

Torsion Angles

C6	C7	C8	C9	−80
C6	C7	C8	C10	−150
C7	C8	C9	C10	−112
C7	C8	C10	C9	107
C7	C8	C10	C11	0
C9	C8	C10	C11	−107
C8	C9	C10	C11	115
C8	C10	C11	C12	151
C9	C10	C11	C12	79

1.32 Oleic acid (low melting form)

C₁₈H₃₄O₂

S.Abrahamsson, I.Ryderstedt-Nahringbauer, Acta Cryst., 15, 1261, 1962

$$CH_3-(CH_2)_7-CH=CH-(CH_2)_7-COOH$$

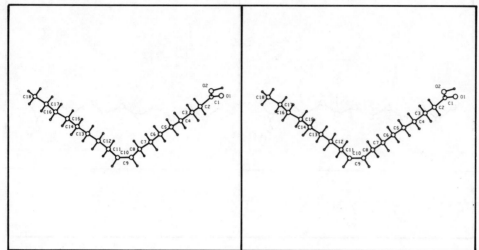

Published value of y(H34) = 0.699.
The correct value is −0.699.
P2₁/a   Z = 4   R = 0.11

OLECAC

Bond Lengths

C1	O1	1.25		C9	C10	1.39
C1	O2	1.33		C10	C11	1.51
C1	C2	1.50		C11	C12	1.55
C2	C3	1.50		C12	C13	1.56
C3	C4	1.55		C13	C14	1.50
C4	C5	1.54		C14	C15	1.55
C5	C6	1.49		C15	C16	1.55
C6	C7	1.54		C16	C17	1.50
C7	C8	1.56		C17	C18	1.51
C8	C9	1.50				

Bond Angles

O1	C1	O2	119	C8	C9	C10	126
O1	C1	C2	121	C9	C10	C11	126
O2	C1	C2	119	C10	C11	C12	107
C1	C2	C3	116	C11	C12	C13	111
C2	C3	C4	107	C12	C13	C14	113
C3	C4	C5	111	C13	C14	C15	112
C4	C5	C6	110	C14	C15	C16	112
C5	C6	C7	112	C15	C16	C17	114
C6	C7	C8	111	C16	C17	C18	116
C7	C8	C9	106				

Torsion Angles

O1	C1	C2	C3	151
O2	C1	C2	C3	−18
C7	C8	C9	C10	132
C8	C9	C10	C11	−2
C9	C10	C11	C12	−128

1.33 Methyl stearate

C₁₉H₃₈O₂

S.Aleby, E.von Sydow, Acta Cryst., 13, 487, 1960

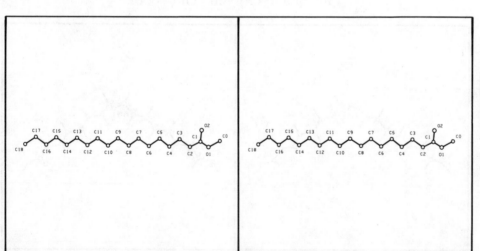

$$H_3C-(CH_2)_{16}-COO-CH_3$$

No comparison of bond lengths is possible since they are not reported in the paper.
See also MacGillavry & Wolthius - Spuy, Acta Cryst. (B), 26, 645, 1970.
A2/a   Z = 8   R = 0.18

MSTEAR   LB 19-38-7

Bond Lengths

C0	O1	1.55		C8	C9	1.55
C1	O1	1.25		C9	C10	1.51
C1	O2	1.31		C10	C11	1.52
C1	C2	1.41		C11	C12	1.48
C2	C3	1.56		C12	C13	1.56
C3	C4	1.54		C13	C14	1.49
C4	C5	1.52		C14	C15	1.59
C5	C6	1.57		C15	C16	1.51
C6	C7	1.53		C16	C17	1.58
C7	C8	1.48		C17	C18	1.56

Bond Angles

C0	O1	C1	118	C7	C8	C9	113
O1	C1	O2	117	C8	C9	C10	112
O1	C1	C2	120	C9	C10	C11	112
O2	C1	C2	123	C10	C11	C12	113
C1	C2	C3	118	C11	C12	C13	113
C2	C3	C4	110	C12	C13	C14	112
C3	C4	C5	109	C13	C14	C15	111
C4	C5	C6	109	C14	C15	C16	110
C5	C6	C7	112	C15	C16	C17	108
C6	C7	C8	112	C16	C17	C18	110

Torsion Angles

C0	O1	C1	O2	14
C0	O1	C1	C2	−177
O1	C1	C2	C3	−164
O2	C1	C2	C3	5
C1	C2	C3	C4	−172

1.34 Ethyl stearate

A.McL.Mathieson, H.K.Welsh, Acta Cryst., 18, 953, 1965

Atomic coordinates were not reported in the paper. This is a reinterpretation of the structure reported by Aleby, Acta Cryst., 13, 1248, 1962. The correct structure is fully reported later by Aleby, Acta Chem. Scand., 22, 811, 1968.
Ia   Z = 4   No R factor was given.

ESTEAR01   LB 20-40-7

$$C_{20}H_{40}O_2$$

$$H_3C—(CH_2)_{16}—COO—C_2H_5$$

1.35 3 - Thiadodecanoic acid - 1,3 - diglyceride

K.Larsson, Acta Cryst., 16, 741, 1963

Published value of x(C18) = 0.7669. The correct value is 0.7969. In Table 4 bond O5 - C25 should read O5 - C24 (private communication).
Pca2₁   Z = 4   R = 0.16

SDODGL   LB 25-48-1

$$C_{25}H_{48}O_5S_2$$

$$H_3C—(CH_2)_8—S—CH_2—C \overset{O}{\underset{O—CH_2—CH—CH_2—O}{\diagup\diagdown}} C—CH_2—S—(CH_2)_8—CH_3$$
$$\underset{OH}{|}$$

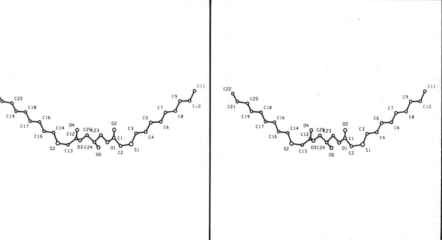

Bond Lengths

S1	C2	1.82
S1	C3	1.78
S2	C13	1.76
S2	C14	1.83
C1	O1	1.47
C23	O1	1.51
C1	O2	1.17
C12	O3	1.40
C25	O3	1.50
C12	O4	1.23
C24	O5	1.47
C1	C2	1.55
C3	C4	1.50
C4	C5	1.49
C5	C6	1.52
C6	C7	1.44
C7	C8	1.55
C8	C9	1.50
C9	C10	1.48
C10	C11	1.52
C12	C13	1.55
C14	C15	1.52
C15	C16	1.56
C16	C17	1.48
C17	C18	1.57
C18	C19	1.47
C19	C20	1.46
C20	C21	1.52
C21	C22	1.47
C23	C24	1.49
C24	C25	1.58

Bond Angles

C2	S1	C3	105	C5	C6	C7	115	C15	C16	C17	114
C13	S2	C14	105	C6	C7	C8	119	C16	C17	C18	115
C1	O1	C23	112	C7	C8	C9	118	C17	C18	C19	115
C12	O3	C25	130	C8	C9	C10	114	C18	C19	C20	114
O1	C1	O2	128	C9	C10	C11	113	C19	C20	C21	116
O1	C1	C2	105	O3	C12	O4	100	C20	C21	C22	122
O2	C1	C2	126	O3	C12	C13	106	O1	C23	C24	96
S1	C2	C1	107	O4	C12	C13	133	O5	C24	C23	111
S1	C3	C4	110	S2	C13	C12	126	O5	C24	C25	111
C3	C4	C5	117	S2	C14	C15	106	C23	C24	C25	100
C4	C5	C6	115	C14	C15	C16	114	O3	C25	C24	112

Torsion Angles

C3	S1	C2	C1	69	C12	O3	C25	C24	−136
C2	S1	C3	C4	172	O1	C1	C2	S1	101
C14	S2	C13	C12	63	O2	C1	C2	S1	−73
C1	S2	C14	C15	174	O3	C12	C13	S2	76
C23	O1	C1	O2	−1	O4	C12	C13	S2	−45
C23	O1	C1	C2	−175	O1	C23	C24	O5	−66
C1	O1	C23	C24	−163	O1	C23	C24	C25	176
C25	O3	C12	O4	−26	O5	C24	C25	O3	57
C25	O3	C12	C13	−166	C23	C24	C25	O3	174

1.36 11 - Bromoundecanoic acid triglyceride (β form)

K.Larsson, Ark. Kemi, 23, 1, 1965

The structure was determined in two dimensions only. Atomic coordinates were not reported in the paper. The structure is isomorphous with β - trilaurin. The bromine atom position was used to determine the structure of β - trilaurin.
P-1   Z = 2   No R factor was given.

BUNTGL   LB 39-71-1

$$C_{36}H_{65}Br_3O_6$$

$$CH_2—OOC—(CH_2)_9—CH_2Br$$
$$CH—OOC—(CH_2)_9—CH_2Br$$
$$CH_2—OOC—(CH_2)_9—CH_2Br$$

1.37 Trilaurin (β form)

C₃₉H₇₄O₆

K.Larsson, Ark. Kemi, 23, 1, 1965

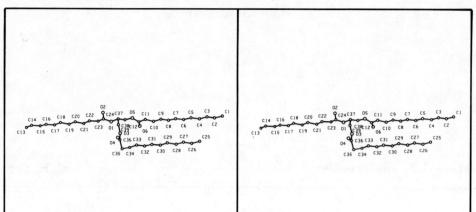

$$CH_2-OOC-(CH_2)_{10}-CH_3$$
$$CH-OOC-(CH_2)_{10}-CH_3$$
$$CH_2-OOC-(CH_2)_{10}-CH_3$$

In Table 4 bond C38 - O2 should read C38 - O5.
P-1   Z = 2   R = 0.20

BTRILA   LB 39-74-1

Bond Lengths

C24	O1	1.40	C15	C16	1.51
C37	O1	1.44	C16	C17	1.54
C24	O2	1.22	C17	C18	1.50
C36	O3	1.31	C18	C19	1.56
C39	O3	1.45	C19	C20	1.52
C36	O4	1.23	C20	C21	1.60
C12	O5	1.33	C21	C22	1.52
C38	O5	1.44	C22	C23	1.59
C12	O6	1.22	C23	C24	1.57
C1	C2	1.61	C25	C26	1.58
C2	C3	1.45	C26	C27	1.52
C3	C4	1.56	C27	C28	1.51
C4	C5	1.60	C28	C29	1.60
C5	C6	1.53	C29	C30	1.47
C6	C7	1.57	C30	C31	1.53
C7	C8	1.58	C31	C32	1.51
C8	C9	1.51	C32	C33	1.50
C9	C10	1.60	C33	C34	1.56
C10	C11	1.57	C34	C35	1.59
C11	C12	1.46	C35	C36	1.57
C13	C14	1.55	C37	C38	1.50
C14	C15	1.57	C37	C39	1.54

Bond Angles

C24	O1	C37	124	C13	C14	C15	106	C28	C29	C30	115
C36	O3	C39	126	C14	C15	C16	112	C29	C30	C31	117
C12	O5	C38	121	C15	C16	C17	114	C30	C31	C32	121
C1	C2	C3	110	C16	C17	C18	112	C31	C32	C33	119
C2	C3	C4	110	C17	C18	C19	114	C32	C33	C34	113
C3	C4	C5	113	C18	C19	C20	113	C33	C34	C35	104
C4	C5	C6	116	C19	C20	C21	112	C34	C35	C36	104
C5	C6	C7	110	C20	C21	C22	107	O3	C36	O4	111
C6	C7	C8	109	C21	C22	C23	111	O3	C36	C35	123
C7	C8	C9	106	C22	C23	C24	107	O4	C36	C35	126
C8	C9	C10	108	O1	C24	O2	117	O1	C37	C38	109
C9	C10	C11	112	O1	C24	C23	109	O1	C37	C39	104
C10	C11	C12	109	O2	C24	C23	124	C38	C37	C39	116
O5	C12	O6	126	C25	C26	C27	118	O5	C38	C37	110
O5	C12	C11	108	C26	C27	C28	117	O3	C39	C37	111
O6	C12	C11	125	C27	C28	C29	117			

Torsion Angles

C37	O1	C24	C23	164
C24	O1	C37	C38	−153
C24	O1	C37	C39	83
C39	O3	C36	C35	−179
C36	O3	C39	C37	−170
C38	O5	C12	C11	−176
C12	O5	C38	C37	145
C34	C35	C36	O3	42
O1	C37	C38	O5	−173
C39	C37	C38	O5	−57
O1	C37	C39	O3	70
C38	C37	C39	O3	−50

2.1 Magnesium formate dihydrate

$2CHO_2^-$, Mg^{2+} , $2H_2O$

K.Osaki, Y.Nakai, T.Watanabe, J. Phys. Soc. Jap., 19, 717, 1964

$Mg^{2+}(HCOO^-)_2 \cdot 2H_2O$

$P2_1/c$ Z = 4 R_{0kl} = 0.095,
R_{h0l} = 0.115

MGFORD   LB 2-2-24

Bond Lengths

Mg1	O1	2.08	Mg2	O6	2.07			
Mg1	O2	2.05	C1	O1	1.28			
Mg1	O4	2.10	C1A	O2	1.26			
Mg2	O3	2.13	C2	O3	1.26			
Mg2	O5	2.08	C2	O4	1.25			

Bond Angles

Mg1	O1	C1	127
Mg1	O2	C1A	122
Mg2	O3	C2	139
Mg1	O4	C2	129
O1	C1	O2A	124
O3	C2	O4	124

2.2 Strontium formate dihydrate

$2CHO_2^-$, Sr^{2+} , $2H_2O$

J.-L.Galigne, J.Falgueirettes, C. R. Acad. Sci., Fr., 253, 994, 1961

Atomic coordinates were not reported in the paper. The authors have informed us of errors in this analysis. The structure has been determined previously by Osaki, Ann. Rep. Scient. Works Fac. Sci. Osaka, 6, 13, 1958. See also discussion by Clark, Acta Cryst., 17, 459, 1964.
The space group and Z were not reported. R_{0kl} = 0.15,
R_{hk0} = 0.19

SRFORM   LB 2-2-38

$Sr^{2+}(HCOO^-)_2 \cdot 2H_2O$

2.3 Ammonium trifluoroacetate

$C_2F_3O_2^-$, H_4N^+

D.W.J.Cruickshank, D.W.Jones, G.Walker, J. Chem. Soc., 1303, 1964

F_3C-COO^- NH_4^+

$P2_1/a$ Z = 4   R = 0.113

AMTFAC   LB 2-4-23

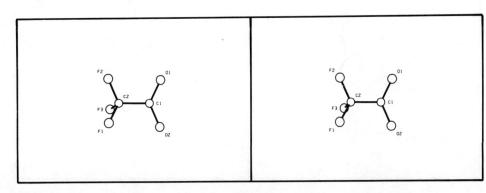

Bond Lengths

F1	C2	1.34
F2	C2	1.35
F3	C2	1.35
C1	O1	1.27
C1	O2	1.26
C1	C2	1.54

Bond Angles

O1	C1	O2	128	F1	C2	C1	111
O1	C1	C2	116	F2	C2	F3	108
O2	C1	C2	115	F2	C2	C1	113
F1	C2	F2	108	F3	C2	C1	110
F1	C2	F3	106				

Torsion Angles

O1	C1	C2	F1	−141
O1	C1	C2	F2	−20
O1	C1	C2	F3	102
O2	C1	C2	F1	42
O2	C1	C2	F2	163
O2	C1	C2	F3	−75

2.4 Cesium hydrogen di - trifluoroacetate

$C_2F_3O_2{}^-$, $C_2HF_3O_2$, Cs^+

L.Golic, J.C.Speakman, J. Chem. Soc., 2530, 1965

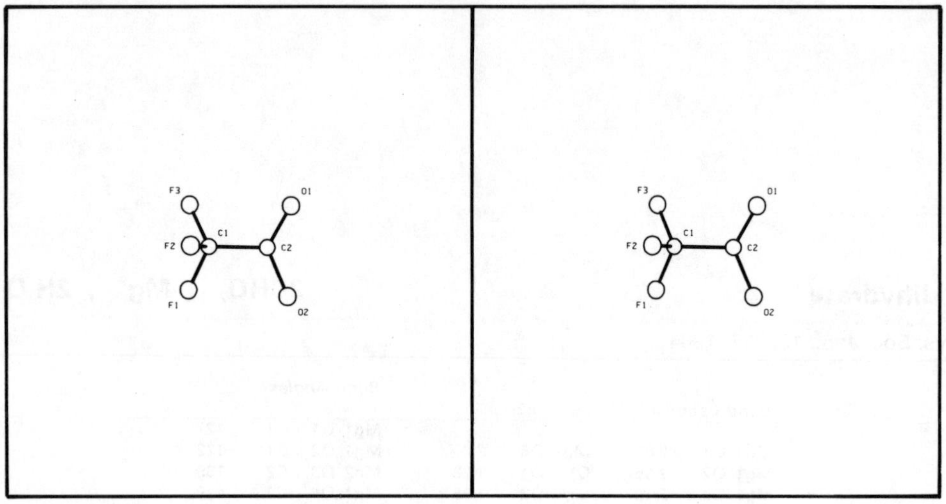

$$CF_3—COO^-$$
$$CF_3—COOH$$ Cs^+

A2/a   Z = 4   R = 0.103

CHFLAC   LB 4-1-1

Bond Lengths

F1	C1	1.34
F2	C1	1.35
F3	C1	1.30
C2	O1	1.20
C2	O2	1.32
C1	C2	1.52

Bond Angles

F1	C1	F2	105
F1	C1	F3	109
F1	C1	C2	112
F2	C1	F3	107
F2	C1	C2	110
F3	C1	C2	113
O1	C2	O2	127
O1	C2	C1	119
O2	C2	C1	114

Torsion Angles

F1	C1	C2	O1	153
F1	C1	C2	O2	−26
F2	C1	C2	O1	−90
F2	C1	C2	O2	91
F3	C1	C2	O1	29
F3	C1	C2	O2	−150

2.5 Potassium hydrogen di - trifluoroacetate

$C_2F_3O_2{}^-$, $C_2HF_3O_2$, K^+

L.Golic, J.C.Speakman, J. Chem. Soc., 2530, 1965

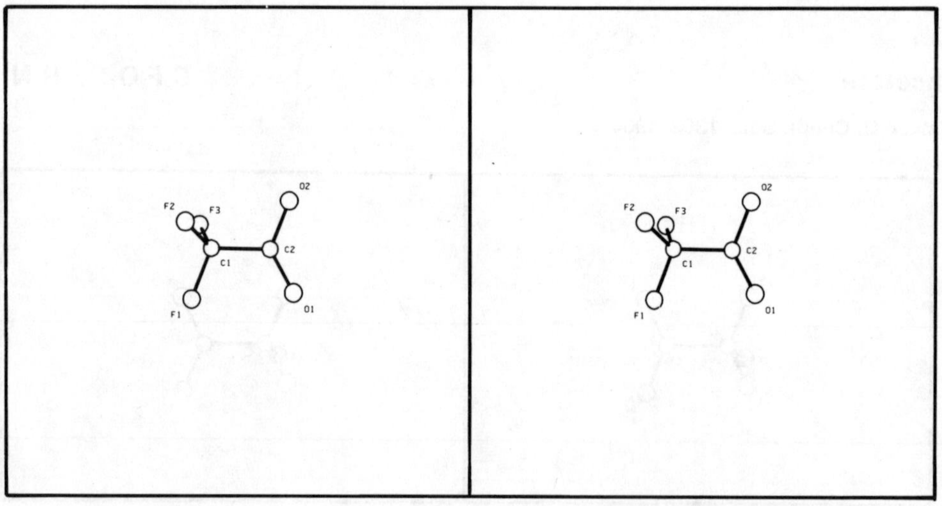

$$CF_3—COO^-   K^+$$
$$CF_3—COOH$$

The rubidium salt is reported to be isomorphous but the structure is not given.
I2/a   Z = 4   R = 0.0679

KHFLAC   LB 4-1-2

Bond Lengths

F1	C1	1.34
F2	C1	1.31
F3	C1	1.35
C2	O1	1.21
C2	O2	1.27
C1	C2	1.51

Bond Angles

F1	C1	F2	108
F1	C1	F3	106
F1	C1	C2	112
F2	C1	F3	107
F2	C1	C2	113
F3	C1	C2	111
O1	C2	O2	128
O1	C2	C1	120
O2	C2	C1	112

Torsion Angles

F1	C1	C2	O1	1
F1	C1	C2	O2	180
F2	C1	C2	O1	123
F2	C1	C2	O2	−59
F3	C1	C2	O1	−117
F3	C1	C2	O2	62

2.6   Calcium oxalate monohydrate

$C_2O_4{}^{2-}$, Ca^{2+} , H_2O

G.Cocco, Atti Accad. Nazion. Lincei, R. C., Cl. Sci. Fis. Mat. Nat., 31, 292, 1961

$$\begin{array}{c} COO^- \\ | \\ COO^- \end{array} \quad Ca^{++} \quad H_2O$$

No comparison of bond lengths is possible since they are not reported in the paper.

$P2_1/c$ $Z = 8$ $R = 0.20$

CALOXM   LB 2-0-13

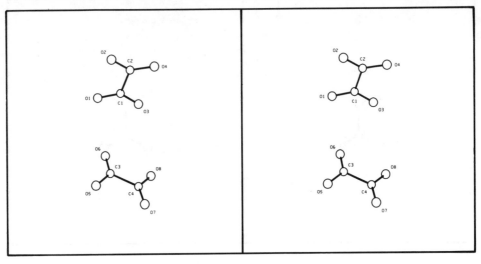

Bond Lengths

C1	O1	1.22
C2	O2	1.13
C1	O3	1.18
C2	O4	1.24
C1	C2	1.52
C3	O5	1.30
C3	O6	1.24
C4	O7	1.24
C4	O8	1.30
C3	C4	1.57

Bond Angles

O1	C1	O3	133
O1	C1	C2	119
O3	C1	C2	108
O2	C2	O4	138
O2	C2	C1	106
O4	C2	C1	116
O5	C3	O6	133
O5	C3	C4	107
O6	C3	C4	120
O7	C4	O8	133
O7	C4	C3	120
O8	C4	C3	107

2.7   Calcium oxalate dihydrate

$C_2O_4{}^{2-}$, Ca^{2+} , $2H_2O$

Weddellite
C.Sterling, Acta Cryst., 18, 917, 1965

$$\begin{array}{c} COO^- \\ | \\ COO^- \end{array} \quad Ca^{++} \quad 2H_2O$$

I4/m $Z = 8$ $R = 0.130$

CAOXAL   LB 2-0-14

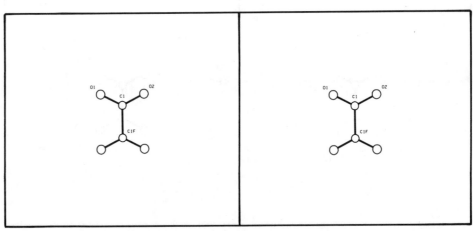

Bond Lengths

C1	O1	1.23
C1	O2	1.26
C1	C1I	1.54

Bond Angles

O1	C1	O2	127
O1	C1	C1I	117
O2	C1	C1I	116

2.8   Potassium oxalate monohydrate

$C_2O_4{}^{2-}$, $2K^+$, H_2O

B.F.Pedersen, Acta Chem. Scand., 18, 1635, 1964

$$\begin{array}{c} COO^- \\ | \\ COO^- \end{array} \quad 2K^+ \quad H_2O$$

See also Hodgson, Acta Cryst. (B), 25, 469, 1969; Sequeira et al., Acta Cryst. (B), 26, 77, 1970.

C2/c $Z = 4$ $R = 0.101$

KOXALM01   LB 2-0-39

Bond Lengths

C1	O1	1.24
C1	O2	1.25
C1	C1F	1.59

Bond Angles

O1	C1	O2	126
O1	C1	C1F	116
O2	C1	C1F	117

2.9   Lithium oxalate

$C_2O_4^{2-}$, $2Li^+$

B.Beagley, R.W.H.Small, Acta Cryst., 17, 783, 1964

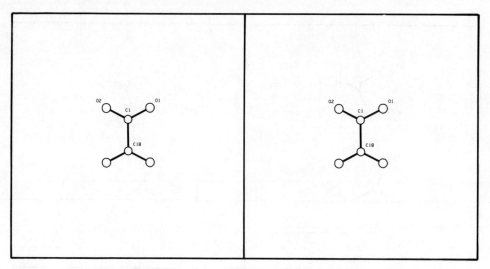

$$\begin{array}{c} COO^- \\ | \\ COO^- \end{array} \quad 2\,Li^+$$

$P2_1/n$ $Z = 2$ $R = 0.060$

LIOXAT   LB 2-0-42

Bond Lengths			Bond Angles			
C1	O1	1.26	O1	C1	O2	127
C1	O2	1.25	O1	C1	C1B	116
C1	C1B	1.56	O2	C1	C1B	117

2.10   Sodium oxalate perhydrate

$C_2O_4^{2-}$, $2Na^+$, H_2O_2

B.F.Pedersen, B.Pedersen, Acta Chem. Scand., 18, 1454, 1964

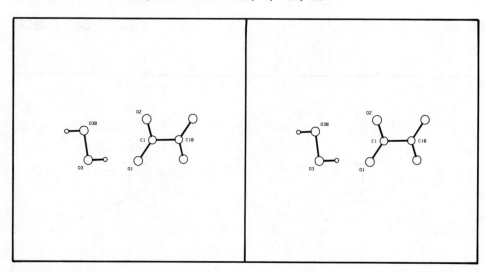

$$\begin{array}{c} COO^- \\ | \\ COO^- \end{array} \quad 2Na^+ . H_2O_2$$

$P2_1/c$ $Z = 2$ $R = 0.066$

NAOXAP   LB 2-0-49

Bond Lengths			Bond Angles			
C1	O1	1.27	O1	C1	O2	127
C1	O2	1.26	O1	C1	C1B	115
C1	C1B	1.57	O2	C1	C1B	118
O3	O3B	1.47				

2.11   Rubidium oxalate monohydrate

$C_2O_4^{2-}$, $2Rb^+$, H_2O

B.F.Pedersen, Acta Chem. Scand., 19, 1815, 1965

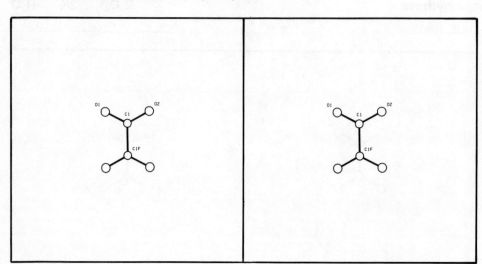

$$\begin{array}{c} COO^- \\ | \\ COO^- \end{array} \quad 2Rb^+ . H_2O$$

The structure is isomorphous with the potassium salt.
C2/c   Z = 4   R = 0.102

RBOXAL   LB 2-0-51

Bond Lengths			Bond Angles			
C1	O1	1.27	O1	C1	O2	125
C1	O2	1.27	O1	C1	C1F	117
C1	C1F	1.58	O2	C1	C1F	118

2.12   Strontium oxalate hydrate

$C_2O_4^{2-}$, Sr^{2+} , $2.17H_2O$

C.Sterling, Nature, 205, 588, 1965

$$\begin{array}{c} COO^- \\ | \\ COO^- \end{array} \quad Sr^{++}.2·17\ H_2O$$

I4/m   Z = 8   R = 0.11

SROXAL   LB 2-0-56

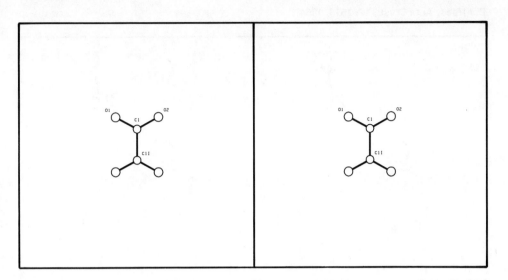

Bond Lengths			Bond Angles			
C1	O1	1.25	O1	C1	O2	123
C1	O2	1.23	O1	C1	C1I	118
C1	C1I	1.51	O2	C1	C1I	119

2.13   Ammonium oxalate monohydrate (at 30 °K)

$C_2O_4^{2-}$, $2H_4N^+$, H_2O

J.H.Robertson, Acta Cryst., 18, 410, 1965

$$\begin{array}{c} COO^- \\ | \\ COO^- \end{array} \quad 2(NH_4{}^+).H_2O$$

P2$_1$2$_1$2   Z = 2   R = 0.080

AMOXAL   LB 2-8-38

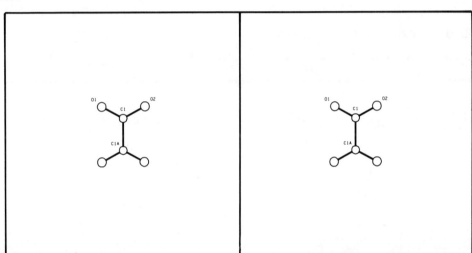

Bond Lengths			Bond Angles			
C1	O1	1.25	O1	C1	O2	126
C1	O2	1.26	O1	C1	C1A	117
C1	C1A	1.58	O2	C1	C1A	117

Torsion Angles

O1   C1   C1A   O2A   −27

2.14   Ammonium oxalate monohydrate (neutron study)

$C_2O_4^{2-}$, $2H_4N^+$, H_2O

V.M.Padmanabhan, S.Srikantha, S.M.Ali, Acta Cryst., 18, 567, 1965

$$\begin{array}{c} COO^- \\ | \\ COO^- \end{array} \quad 2(NH_4{}^+).H_2O$$

P2$_1$2$_1$2   Z = 2   R = 0.082

AMOXAL01   LB 2-8-38

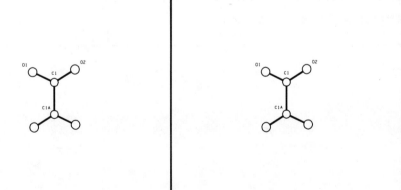

Bond Lengths			Bond Angles			
C1	O1	1.25	O1	C1	O2	126
C1	O2	1.23	O1	C1	C1A	114
C1	C1A	1.58	O2	C1	C1A	120
N1	H1	1.02	H1	N1	H2	109
N1	H2	1.03	H1	N1	H3	117
N1	H3	1.01	H1	N1	H4	103
N1	H4	1.04	H2	N1	H3	105
			H2	N1	H4	114
O3	H5	0.97	H3	N1	H4	109
			H5	O3	H5A	110

Torsion Angles

O1   C1   C1A   O2A   −28

2.15 Potassium tetraoxalate dihydrate

D.J.Haas, Acta Cryst., 17, 1511, 1964

$C_2HO_4^-$, $C_2H_2O_4$, K^+ , $2H_2O$

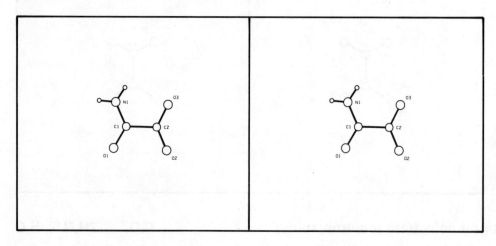

$$\begin{array}{ccc} COOH & COOH & \\ | & | & K^+ . 2H_2O \\ COO^- & COOH & \end{array}$$

P-1   Z = 2   R = 0.05

KTOXAL   LB 4-3-6

Bond Lengths			Bond Angles			
C1	O1	1.21	O1	C1	O3	126
C1	O3	1.29	O1	C1	C1A	121
C1	C1A	1.55	O3	C1	C1A	112
C2	O2	1.29	O2	C2	O4	127
C2	O4	1.21	O2	C2	C2A	112
C2	C2A	1.54	O4	C2	C2A	121
C3	O5	1.30	O5	C3	O6	124
C3	O6	1.21	O5	C3	C4	113
C4	O7	1.27	O6	C3	C4	122
C4	O8	1.22	O7	C4	O8	127
C3	C4	1.55	O7	C4	C3	114
			O8	C4	C3	118

Torsion Angles

O5 C3 C4 O8   −6

2.16 Ammonium oxamate

B.Beagley, R.W.H.Small, Proc. R. Soc., A, 275, 469, 1963

$C_2H_2NO_3^-$, H_4N^+

NH_4^+ $(NH_2—CO—COO)^-$

$P2_1/n$ Z = 4   R = 0.043

AMOXAM   LB 2-6-37

Bond Lengths			Bond Angles			
C1	N1	1.31	N1	C1	O1	124
C1	O1	1.24	N1	C1	C2	116
C2	O2	1.25	O1	C1	C2	120
C2	O3	1.25	O2	C2	O3	128
C1	C2	1.56	O2	C2	C1	116
			O3	C2	C1	117

2.17 Lithium acetate dihydrate (discussion)

J.R.Clark, Acta Cryst., 17, 459, 1964

$C_2H_3O_2^-$, Li^+ , $2H_2O$

$CH_3 COO^- Li^+ . 2H_2O$

This is a discussion of the structure reported by Amirthalingham & Padmanabhan, Acta Cryst., 11, 896, 1958.
See also Galigne et al., Acta Cryst. (B), 26, 368, 1970.
Cmm2   Z = 2   R = 0.18

LIACET   LB 2-3-22

Bond Lengths			Bond Angles			
C2	O1	1.22	O1	C2	O2	115
C2	O2	1.35	O1	C2	C1	121
C1	C2	1.55	O2	C2	C1	124

2.18   Sodium hydrogen diacetate

$C_2H_3O_2^-$, $C_2H_4O_2$, Na^+

J.C.Speakman, H.H.Mills, J. Chem. Soc., 1164, 1961

CH_3COOH

CH_3COO^- Na^+

Ia3   Z = 24   R = 0.092

NAHACE   LB 4-7-20

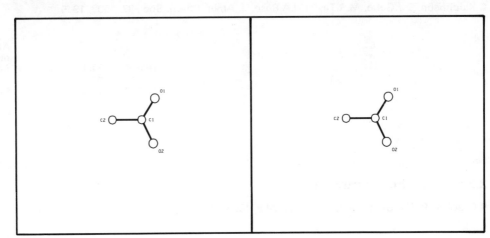

Bond Lengths			Bond Angles			
C1	O1	1.24	O1	C1	O2	122
C1	O2	1.30	O1	C1	C2	122
C1	C2	1.49	O2	C1	C2	116

2.19   Lithium glycollate monohydrate

$C_2H_3O_3^-$, Li^+ , H_2O

R.H.Colton, D.E.Henn, Acta Cryst., 18, 820, 1965

$HO—CH_2—COO^- Li^+ . H_2O$

C2/m   Z = 4   R = 0.11

LIGOLM   LB 2-3-23

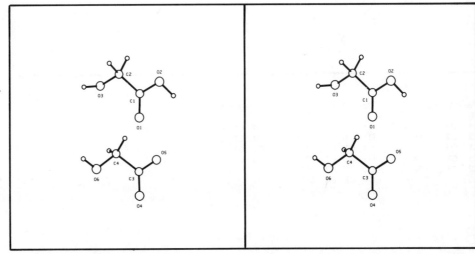

Bond Lengths			Bond Angles			
C1	O1	1.22	O1	C1	O2	124
C1	O2	1.29	O1	C1	C2	119
C2	O3	1.42	O2	C1	C2	117
C1	C2	1.57	O3	C2	C1	110

2.20   Rubidium hydrogen glycollate

$C_2H_3O_3^-$, $C_2H_4O_3$, Rb^+

L.Golic, J.C.Speakman, J. Chem. Soc., 2521, 1965

$HO—CH_2—COOH$
$HO—CH_2—COO^-$ Rb^+

The potassium salt is isomorphous.

$P2_1/n$ Z = 4   R = 0.093

RHGLYL   LB 4-7-21

Bond Lengths						Bond Angles							Torsion Angles							
C1	O1	1.21	C3	O4	1.24	O1	C1	O2	123	O4	C3	O5	123	O1	C1	C2	O3	−8	O4	C3	C4	O6	−4
C1	O2	1.31	C3	O5	1.26	O1	C1	C2	125	O4	C3	C4	120	O2	C1	C2	O3	173	O5	C3	C4	O6	−180
C2	O3	1.43	C4	O6	1.43	O2	C1	C2	112	O5	C3	C4	116								
C1	C2	1.47	C3	C4	1.52	O3	C2	C1	114	O6	C4	C3	112								

2.21 Lithium α - monodeuterioglycollate (neutron study, absolute configuration)

$C_2H_2DO_3^-$, Li^+

C.K.Johnson, E.J.Gabe, M.R.Taylor, I.A.Rose, J. Amer. Chem. Soc., 87, 1802, 1965

$$\text{HO}-\overset{\overset{\text{H}}{|}}{\underset{\underset{\text{D}}{|}}{\text{C}}}-\text{COO}^- \quad Li^+$$

Atomic coordinates were not reported in the paper.
See also Gabe & Taylor, Acta Cryst., 21, 418, 1966.
$P2_1$ $Z = 4$ $R = 0.039$

LIDEGL01   LB 2-2-17

2.22 Lithium pyruvate

$C_3H_3O_3^-$, Li^+

B.Beagley, R.W.H.Small, Acta Cryst., 16, A59, 1963

$$CH_3-CO-COO^- \ Li^+$$

Atomic coordinates were not reported in the paper.
The space group and Z were not reported.   No R factor was given.

LIPYRU

2.23 Sodium pyruvate

$C_3H_3O_3^-$, Na^+

S.S.Tavale, L.M.Pant, A.B.Biswas, Acta Cryst., 14, 1281, 1961

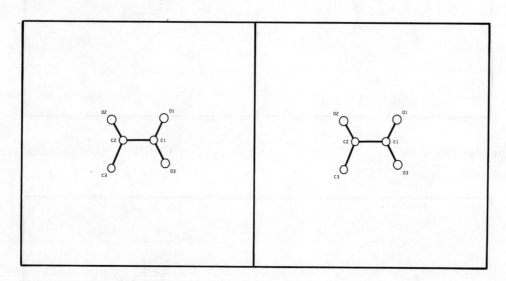

$$CH_3-CO-COO^- \ Na^+$$

$P2_1/a$ $Z = 4$ $R = 0.192$

NAPYRU   LB 3-3-20

Bond Lengths			Bond Angles				Torsion Angles				
C1	O1	1.24	O1	C1	O3	126	O1	C1	C2	O2	−30
C2	O2	1.18	O1	C1	C2	115	O1	C1	C2	C3	164
C1	O3	1.28	O3	C1	C2	118	O3	C1	C2	O2	158
C1	C2	1.58	O2	C2	C1	119	O3	C1	C2	C3	−8
C2	C3	1.52	O2	C2	C3	126					
			C1	C2	C3	114					

2.24   Potassium hydrogen chloromaleate (neutron study) $C_4H_2ClO_4^-$, K^+

R.D.Ellison, H.A.Levy, Acta Cryst., 19, 260, 1965

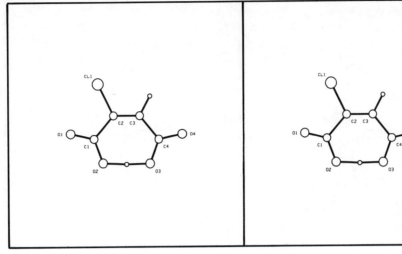

An intramolecular hydrogen bond has H1 midway between O2 and O3.

Pbcn   Z = 8   R = 0.079

KHCMAL   LB 4-2-4

Bond Lengths					Bond Angles						Torsion Angles				
Cl1	C2	1.74	C2	C3	1.34	C1	O2	H1	114	C2	C3	C4	130	O1	C1	C2	Cl1	−7
C1	O1	1.23	C3	C4	1.50	C4	O3	H1	111	C2	C3	H2	118	O1	C1	C2	C3	172
C1	O2	1.28	O2	H1	1.21	O1	C1	O2	123	C4	C3	H2	113	O2	C1	C2	Cl1	172
C4	O3	1.28	O3	H1	1.20	O1	C1	C2	119	O3	C4	O4	123	O2	C1	C2	C3	−9
C4	O4	1.24	C3	H2	1.09	O2	C1	C2	118	O3	C4	C3	120	Cl1	C2	C3	C4	−179
C1	C2	1.52				Cl1	C2	C1	112	O4	C4	C3	117	C1	C2	C3	C4	2
						Cl1	C2	C3	117	O2	H1	O3	175	C2	C3	C4	O3	9
						C1	C2	C3	131					C2	C3	C4	O4	−173

2.25   Potassium hydrogen maleate $C_4H_3O_4^-$, K^+

(i)   S.F.Darlow, W.Cochran, Acta Cryst., 14, 1250, 1961

(ii)   S.F.Darlow, Acta Cryst., 14, 1257, 1961 (discussion)

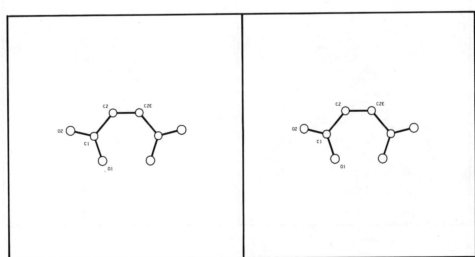

(i)
No comparison of bond lengths is possible since they are not reported in the paper.
See also Peterson & Levy, J. Chem. Phys., 29, 948, 1958.
Pbcm   Z = 4   R = 0.049

KHMALA   LB 4-3-5

(ii)

Pbcm   Z = 4   No R factor was given.

KHMALA01   LB 4-3-5

Bond Lengths			Bond Angles				Torsion Angles				
C1	O1	1.28	O1	C1	O2	123	O1	C1	C2	C2E	2
C1	O2	1.23	O1	C1	C2	120	O2	C1	C2	C2E	−180
C1	C2	1.50	O2	C1	C2	117	C1	C2	C2E	C1E	0
C2	C2E	1.35	C1	C2	C2E	130					

2.26   Potassium hydrogen maleate (discussion) $C_4H_3O_4^-$, K^+

For complete entry see 2.25

2.27   Potassium sodium DL - tartrate tetrahydrate (discussion) $C_4H_4O_6^{2-}$, K^+ , Na^+ , $4H_2O$

J.R.Clark, Acta Cryst., 17, 459, 1964

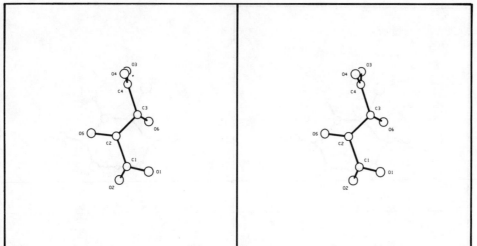

$$COO^-$$
$$|$$
$$CHOH$$
$$|$$
$$CHOH$$
$$|$$
$$COO^-$$

K^+. Na^+.$4H_2O$

A discussion of the structure reported by Sadanaga, Acta Cryst., 3, 416, 1950.
P-1   Z = 2   No R factor was given.

KNATAR   LB 4-4-22

Bond Lengths

C1	O1	1.19	C3	O6	1.40
C1	O2	1.29	C1	C2	1.58
C4	O3	1.28	C2	C3	1.53
C4	O4	1.27	C3	C4	1.58
C2	O5	1.42			

Bond Angles

O1	C1	O2	117	O6	C3	C2	106
O1	C1	C2	119	O6	C3	C4	112
O2	C1	C2	115	C2	C3	C4	115
O5	C2	C1	114	O3	C4	O4	126
O5	C2	C3	123	O3	C4	C3	123
C1	C2	C3	114	O4	C4	C3	111

Torsion Angles

O1	C1	C2	O5	178	C1	C2	C3	O6	57
O1	C1	C2	C3	32	C1	C2	C3	C4	−180
O2	C1	C2	O5	32	O6	C3	C4	O3	12
O2	C1	C2	C3	−114	O6	C3	C4	O4	−159
O5	C2	C3	O6	−86	C2	C3	C4	O3	−109
O5	C2	C3	C4	38	C2	C3	C4	O4	80

2.28   Potassium mesotartrate dihydrate $C_4H_4O_6^{2-}$, $2K^+$, $2H_2O$

J.Kroon, A.F.Peerdeman, J.M.Bijvoet, Acta Cryst., 19, 293, 1965

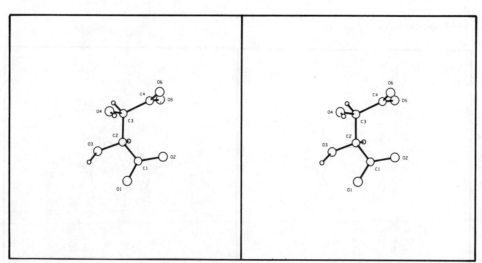

$$COO^-$$
$$|$$
$$CHOH$$
$$|$$
$$CHOH$$
$$|$$
$$COO^-$$

$2K^+$.$2H_2O$

The structure is isomorphous with the rubidium salt. Published values of   x(O1) = 0.8852   and x(O4) = 0.8534 are incorrect. The correct values are 0.8552 and 0.8354 respectively (private communication).
P-1   Z = 2   R = 0.080

KMTART   LB 4-4-29

Bond Lengths

C1	O1	1.30	C4	O6	1.26
C1	O2	1.30	C1	C2	1.50
C2	O3	1.40	C2	C3	1.51
C3	O4	1.42	C3	C4	1.51
C4	O5	1.28			

Bond Angles

O1	C1	O2	120	O4	C3	C2	110
O1	C1	C2	123	O4	C3	C4	114
O2	C1	C2	117	C2	C3	C4	114
O3	C2	C1	112	O5	C4	O6	125
O3	C2	C3	112	O5	C4	C3	117
C1	C2	C3	111	O6	C4	C3	118

Torsion Angles

O1	C1	C2	O3	−14	C1	C2	C3	O4	−66
O1	C1	C2	C3	113	C1	C2	C3	C4	63
O2	C1	C2	O3	170	O4	C3	C4	O5	−173
O2	C1	C2	C3	−63	O4	C3	C4	O6	7
O3	C2	C3	O4	61	C2	C3	C4	O5	61
O3	C2	C3	C4	−170	C2	C3	C4	O6	−120

2.29 Rubidium mesotartrate dihydrate

$C_4H_4O_6^{2-}$, $2Rb^+$, $2H_2O$

J.Kroon, A.F.Peerdeman, J.M.Bijvoet, Acta Cryst., 19, 293, 1965

COO⁻
|
CHOH
| $2Rb^+.2H_2O$
CHOH
|
COO⁻

No comparison of bond lengths is possible since they are not reported in the paper.
P-1   Z = 2   R = 0.074

RMTART   LB 4-4-64

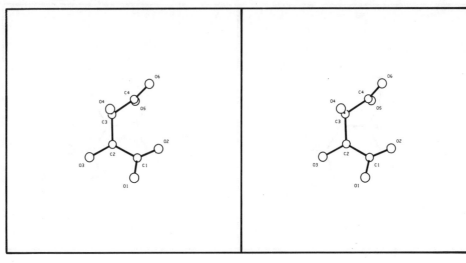

Bond Lengths

C1	O1	1.24	C4	O6	1.25
C1	O2	1.25	C1	C2	1.51
C2	O3	1.38	C2	C3	1.49
C3	O4	1.40	C3	C4	1.52
C4	O5	1.28			

Bond Angles

O1	C1	O2	127	O4	C3	C2	110
O1	C1	C2	118	O4	C3	C4	113
O2	C1	C2	115	C2	C3	C4	114
O3	C2	C1	112	O5	C4	O6	123
O3	C2	C3	111	O5	C4	C3	119
C1	C2	C3	111	O6	C4	C3	118

Torsion Angles

O1	C1	C2	O3	−4	C1	C2	C3	O4	−62
O1	C1	C2	C3	121	C1	C2	C3	C4	66
O2	C1	C2	O3	173	O4	C3	C4	O5	−174
O2	C1	C2	C3	−62	O4	C3	C4	O6	1
O3	C2	C3	O4	63	C2	C3	C4	O5	60
O3	C2	C3	C4	−169	C2	C3	C4	O6	−125

2.30 Sodium - α - ketobutyrate

$C_4H_5O_3^-$, Na^+

S.S.Tavale, L.M.Pant, A.B.Biswas, Acta Cryst., 16, 566, 1963

CH_3—CH_2—CO—COO^-Na^+

Pbcn   Z = 8 R_{hk0} = 0.159,
R_{h0l} = 0.140

NKETBY   LB 4-5-23

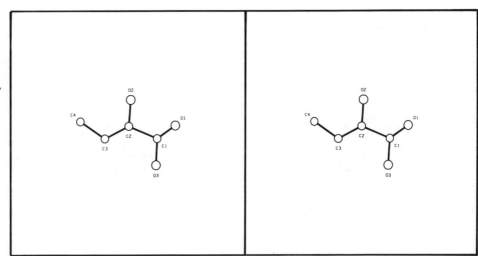

Bond Lengths

C1	O1	1.15
C2	O2	1.29
C1	O3	1.33
C1	C2	1.59
C2	C3	1.38
C3	C4	1.51

Bond Angles

O1	C1	O3	128
O1	C1	C2	123
O3	C1	C2	107
O2	C2	C1	109
O2	C2	C3	121
C1	C2	C3	127
C2	C3	C4	119

Torsion Angles

O1	C1	C2	O2	0
O1	C1	C2	C3	160
O3	C1	C2	O2	165
O3	C1	C2	C3	−35
O2	C2	C3	C4	−9
C1	C2	C3	C4	−167

2.31 Dipotassium ethylenetetracarboxylate

$C_6H_2O_8^{2-}$, $2K^+$

S.K.Kumra, S.F.Darlow, Acta Cryst., 18, 98, 1965

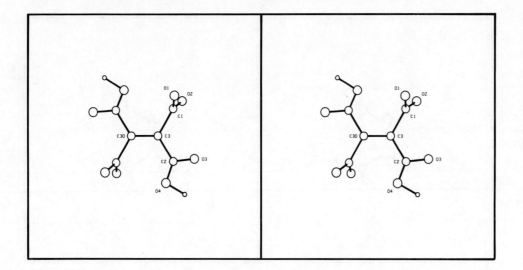

HOOC，COO⁻ ... C=C ... ⁻OOC，COOH $2K^+$

Pbca   Z = 4   R = 0.104

KETCOX   LB 6-2-36

Bond Lengths			Bond Angles				Torsion Angles			
C1	O1	1.25	O1	C1	O2	126	O1	C1	C3	C2	−103
C1	O2	1.21	O1	C1	C3	116	O2	C1	C3	C2	77
C2	O3	1.28	O2	C1	C3	119	O3	C2	C3	C1	−33
C2	O4	1.23	O3	C2	O4	124	O4	C2	C3	C1	145
C1	C3	1.54	O3	C2	C3	114	C2	C3	C3D	C1D	1
C2	C3	1.48	O4	C2	C3	122					
C3	C3D	1.37	C1	C3	C2	118					
			C1	C3	C3D	121					
			C2	C3	C3D	122					

2.32 (+) - iso - Citric acid lactone monopotassium salt

$C_6H_5O_6^-$, K^+

J.P.Glusker, A.L.Patterson, W.E.Love, M.L.Dornberg, Acta Cryst., 16, 1102, 1963

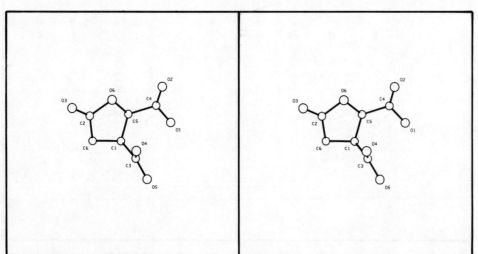

K^+ O, O, COO⁻ ... COOH

The structure is isomorphous with the rubidium salt.
$P2_12_12_1$ Z = 4 $R_{hk0} = 0.07$, $R_{0kl} = 0.12$, $R_{h0l} = 0.13$

KISCIT   LB 6-5-31

Bond Lengths			Bond Angles								Torsion Angles			
C4	O1	1.32	C2	O6	C5	105	O5	C3	C1	117	C5	O6	C2	O3	−174
C4	O2	1.17	C3	C1	C5	111	O1	C4	O2	128	C5	O6	C2	C6	4
C2	O3	1.16	C3	C1	C6	109	O1	C4	C5	108	C2	O6	C5	C1	−23
C3	O4	1.19	C5	C1	C6	105	O2	C4	C5	124	C6	C1	C5	O6	31
C3	O5	1.28	O3	C2	O6	119	O6	C5	C1	108	C5	C1	C6	C2	−27
C2	O6	1.38	O3	C2	C6	130	O6	C5	C4	106	O3	C2	C6	C1	−168
C5	O6	1.49	O6	C2	C6	111	C1	C5	C4	122	O6	C2	C6	C1	14
C1	C3	1.54	O4	C3	O5	125	C1	C6	C2	101	C1	C5	C4	O1	40
C1	C5	1.41	O4	C3	C1	119					C5	C1	C3	O4	50
C1	C6	1.51													
C2	C6	1.51													
C4	C5	1.55													

2.33 Magnesium citrate decahydrate

$2C_6H_5O_7^{3-}$, $3Mg^{2+}$, $10H_2O$

C.K.Johnson, Acta Cryst., 18, 1004, 1965

$$2 \begin{bmatrix} COO^- \\ | \\ CH_2 \\ | \\ HO-C-COO^- \\ | \\ CH_2 \\ | \\ COO^- \end{bmatrix} 3Mg^{++}.10H_2O$$

$P2_1/n$ $Z = 2$ $R = 0.031$

MGCITD   LB 12-10-47

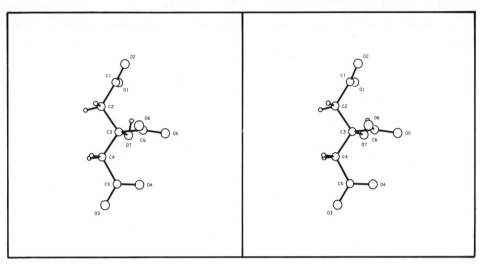

Bond Lengths

C1	O1	1.27	C3	O7	1.44
C1	O2	1.25	C1	C2	1.51
C5	O3	1.25	C2	C3	1.54
C5	O4	1.26	C3	C4	1.53
C6	O5	1.26	C3	C6	1.55
C6	O6	1.25	C4	C5	1.52

Bond Angles

O1	C1	O2	123	C4	C3	C6	110
O1	C1	C2	116	C3	C4	C5	115
O2	C1	C2	121	O3	C5	O4	123
C1	C2	C3	111	O3	C5	C4	117
O7	C3	C2	112	O4	C5	C4	120
O7	C3	C4	107	O5	C6	O6	124
O7	C3	C6	108	O5	C6	C3	117
C2	C3	C4	109	O6	C6	C3	119
C2	C3	C6	111				

Torsion Angles

O1	C1	C2	C3	72	O7	C3	C6	O5	−4
O2	C1	C2	C3	−104	O7	C3	C6	O6	177
C1	C2	C3	O7	−52	C2	C3	C6	O5	−127
C1	C2	C3	C4	−170	C2	C3	C6	O6.	54
C1	C2	C3	C6	69	C4	C3	C6	O5	113
O7	C3	C4	C5	64	C4	C3	C6	O6	−66
C2	C3	C4	C5	−176	C3	C4	C5	O3	166
C6	C3	C4	C5	−54	C3	C4	C5	O4	−14

2.34 Lithium dihydrogen citrate

$C_6H_7O_7^-$, Li^+

J.P.Glusker, D.van der Helm, W.E.Love, M.L.Dornberg, J.A.Minkin, C.K.Johnson, A.L.Patterson, Acta Cryst., 19, 561, 1965

$$\begin{array}{c} COOH \\ | \\ CH_2 \\ | \\ HO-C-COO^- \quad Li^+ \\ | \\ CH_2 \\ | \\ COOH \end{array}$$

No comparison of bond lengths is possible since they are not reported in the paper. The structure is isomorphous with the sodium salt.
$P2_1/a$ $Z = 4$ $R = 0.084$

LIHCIT   LB 6-7-9

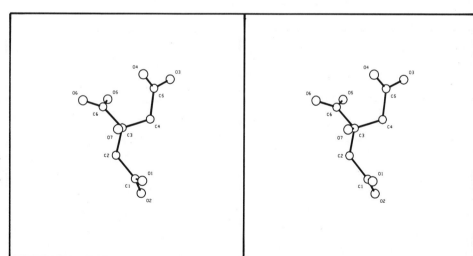

Bond Lengths

C1	O1	1.31	C3	O7	1.45
C1	O2	1.19	C1	C2	1.55
C5	O3	1.32	C2	C3	1.55
C5	O4	1.18	C3	C4	1.52
C6	O5	1.27	C3	C6	1.55
C6	O6	1.25	C4	C5	1.52

Bond Angles

O1	C1	O2	127	C4	C3	C6	110
O1	C1	C2	113	C3	C4	C5	112
O2	C1	C2	120	O3	C5	O4	126
C1	C2	C3	114	O3	C5	C4	112
O7	C3	C2	112	O4	C5	C4	123
O7	C3	C4	110	O5	C6	O6	126
O7	C3	C6	106	O5	C6	C3	115
C2	C3	C4	111	O6	C6	C3	118
C2	C3	C6	108				

Torsion Angles

O1	C1	C2	C3	41	O7	C3	C6	O5	165
O2	C1	C2	C3	−142	O7	C3	C6	O6	−19
C1	C2	C3	O7	−67	C2	C3	C6	O5	−75
C1	C2	C3	C4	56	C2	C3	C6	O6	101
C1	C2	C3	C6	176	C4	C3	C6	O5	46
O7	C3	C4	C5	−78	C4	C3	C6	O6	−138
C2	C3	C4	C5	158	C3	C4	C5	O3	−147
C6	C3	C4	C5	39	C3	C4	C5	O4	35

2.35 Sodium dihydrogen citrate

$C_6H_7O_7^-$, Na^+

J.P.Glusker, D.van der Helm, W.E.Love, M.L.Dornberg, J.A.Minkin, C.K.Johnson,
A.L.Patterson, Acta Cryst., 19, 561, 1965

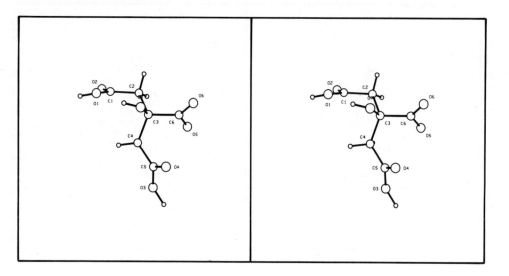

$P2_1/a$ Z = 4   R = 0.066

NAHCIT   LB 6-7-28

Bond Lengths

C1	O1	1.32	C3	O7	1.43
C1	O2	1.20	C1	C2	1.52
C5	O3	1.31	C2	C3	1.54
C5	O4	1.22	C3	C4	1.53
C6	O5	1.25	C3	C6	1.56
C6	O6	1.25	C4	C5	1.51

Bond Angles

O1	C1	O2	124	C4	C3	C6	109
O1	C1	C2	113	C3	C4	C5	113
O2	C1	C2	122	O3	C5	O4	124
C1	C2	C3	115	O3	C5	C4	113
O7	C3	C2	111	O4	C5	C4	124
O7	C3	C4	111	O5	C6	O6	126
O7	C3	C6	108	O5	C6	C3	115
C2	C3	C4	110	O6	C6	C3	118
C2	C3	C6	107				

Torsion Angles

O1	C1	C2	C3	42	O7	C3	C6	O5	164
O2	C1	C2	C3	−140	O7	C3	C6	O6	−17
C1	C2	C3	O7	−68	C2	C3	C6	O5	−77
C1	C2	C3	C4	56	C2	C3	C6	O6	102
C1	C2	C3	C6	174	C4	C3	C6	O5	42
O7	C3	C4	C5	−77	C4	C3	C6	O6	−138
C2	C3	C4	C5	159	C3	C4	C5	O3	−151
C6	C3	C4	C5	43	C3	C4	C5	O4	28

2.36 Rubidium dihydrogen citrate

$C_6H_7O_7^-$, Rb^+

C.E.Nordman, A.S.Weldon, A.L.Patterson, Acta Cryst., 13, 414, 1960

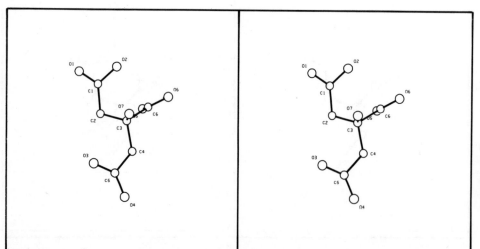

The analysis used a subcell with $c' = c/3$.
$P2_1/a$ Z = 12 $R_{h0l} = 0.13$, $R_{hk0} = 0.10$

RBHCIT   LB 6-7-29

Bond Lengths

C1	O1	1.29	C3	O7	1.39
C1	O2	1.31	C1	C2	1.49
C5	O3	1.28	C2	C3	1.50
C5	O4	1.23	C3	C4	1.52
C6	O5	1.28	C3	C6	1.58
C6	O6	1.28	C4	C5	1.59

Bond Angles

O1	C1	O2	110	C4	C3	C6	106
O1	C1	C2	125	C3	C4	C5	119
O2	C1	C2	124	O3	C5	O4	128
C1	C2	C3	108	O3	C5	C4	117
O7	C3	C2	111	O4	C5	C4	115
O7	C3	C4	105	O5	C6	O6	131
O7	C3	C6	112	O5	C6	C3	112
C2	C3	C4	113	O6	C6	C3	117
C2	C3	C6	110				

Torsion Angles

O1	C1	C2	C3	177	O7	C3	C6	O5	−167
O2	C1	C2	C3	5	O7	C3	C6	O6	15
C1	C2	C3	O7	68	C2	C3	C6	O5	−43
C1	C2	C3	C4	−174	C2	C3	C6	O6	139
C1	C2	C3	C6	−56	C4	C3	C6	O5	79
O7	C3	C4	C5	57	C4	C3	C6	O6	−98
C2	C3	C4	C5	−64	C3	C4	C5	O3	9
C6	C3	C4	C5	176	C3	C4	C5	O4	−162

2.37   Potassium hydrogen bis(phenylacetate) $C_8H_7O_2^-$, $C_8H_8O_2$, K^+

(i)   G.E.Bacon, N.A.Curry, Acta Cryst., 13, 717, 1960 (neutron study)

(ii)   G.E.Bacon, N.A.Curry, Acta Cryst., 13, 717, 1960 (neutron study at 120°K)

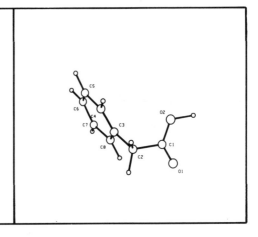

CH₂—COOH

CH₂—COO⁻   K⁺

(i)

The acidic hydrogen takes part in a centred hydrogen bond.
See also Manojlovic & Speakman, Acta Cryst. (B), 24, 323, 1968.
C2/c   Z = 4   R = 0.07

KHDPAC ·   LB 16-15-8

(ii)

The y coordinates are not given in the paper. We have used those given by Bacon and Curry in Acta Cryst., 10, 524, 1957.
C2/c   Z = 4   R = 0.08

KHDPAC01   LB 16-15-8

Bond Lengths

		(i)	(ii)				(i)	(ii)
C1	O1	1.21	1.24	C7	C8		1.46	1.41
C1	O2	1.30	1.29	O2	H10		1.27	1.26
C1	C2	1.53	1.52	C2	H2		1.11	1.13
C2	C3	1.52	1.53	C2	H20		1.10	1.06
C3	C4	1.35	1.35	C4	H4		1.12	1.09
C3	C8	1.39	1.40	C5	H5		1.14	1.11
C4	C5	1.41	1.44	C6	H6		1.16	1.07
C5	C6	1.32	1.41	C7	H7		1.18	1.13
C6	C7	1.42	1.39					(1.03)
				C8	H8		1.06	1.12

Bond Angles

			(i)	(ii)				(i)	(ii)
C1	O2	H10	110	112	C5	C4	H4	117	118
O1	C1	O2	131	127	C4	C5	C6	117	118
O1	C1	C2	119	120	C4	C5	H5	118	120
O2	C1	C2	110	113	C6	C5	H5	125	122
C1	C2	C3	110	109	C5	C6	C7	124	119
C1	C2	H2	107	107	C5	C6	H6	121	119
C1	C2	H20	109	107	C7	C6	H6	115	121
C3	C2	H2	112	113	C6	C7	C8	116	122
C3	C2	H20	109	112	C6	C7	H7	124	121
H2	C2	H20	110	108	C8	C7	H7	120	118
C2	C3	C4	124	122	C3	C8	C7	121	119
C2	C3	C8	119	118	C3	C8	H8	114	117
C4	C3	C8	117	120	C7	C8	H8	125	124
C3	C4	C5	125	122	O2	H10	O2D	180	180
C3	C4	H4	118	120					

Torsion Angles

				(i)	(ii)
O1	C1	C2	C3	−111	−114
O2	C1	C2	C3	72	73
C1	C2	C3	C4	−109	−107
C1	C2	C3	C8	72	74

2.38   Potassium hydrogen bis(phenylacetate) (neutron study, at 120 ° K) $C_8H_7O_2^-$, $C_8H_8O_2$, K^+

For complete entry see 2.37

2.39   Sodium 2 - oxocaprylate $C_8H_{13}O_3^-$, Na^+

S.S.Tavale, L.M.Pant, A.B.Biswas, Acta Cryst., 17, 215, 1964

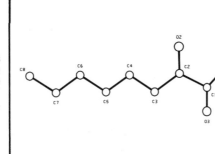
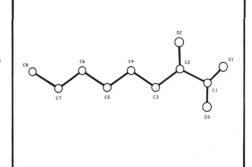

CH₃—(CH₂)₅—CO—COO⁻ Na⁺

This analysis used sharp reflexions only. For a discussion of diffuse reflexions in terms of disorder, see Pant, Acta Cryst., 17, 219, 1964.
Pbcn   Z = 8 R_{h0l} = 0.119, R_{hkl} = 0.237

NOXCAP   LB 8-13-5

Bond Lengths

C1	O1	1.18	C3	C4	1.53
C2	O2	1.32	C4	C5	1.47
C1	O3	1.18	C5	C6	1.58
C1	C2	1.61	C6	C7	1.52
C2	C3	1.54	C7	C8	1.58

Bond Angles

O1	C1	O3	137	C2	C3	C4	111
O1	C1	C2	111	C3	C4	C5	111
O3	C1	C2	111	C4	C5	C6	112
O2	C2	C1	119	C5	C6	C7	112
O2	C2	C3	123	C6	C7	C8	113
C1	C2	C3	118				

Torsion Angles

O1	C1	C2	O2	−15	C1	C2	C3	C4	−165
O1	C1	C2	C3	165	C2	C3	C4	C5	−173
O3	C1	C2	O2	161	C3	C4	C5	C6	−179
O3	C1	C2	C3	−20	C4	C5	C6	C7	175
O2	C2	C3	C4	14	C5	C6	C7	C8	170

2.40 Strontium caprylate hydrate

$2C_8H_{15}O_2^-$, Sr^{2+} , xH_2O

E.Stanley, Nature, 204, 1375, 1964

$$2(CH_3—(CH_2)_6—COO^-)\ Sr^{++} . xH_2O$$

Atomic coordinates were not given but bond lengths were reported. The author states that low accuracy is due to poor photographic data.
P-1   Z = 4   R = 0.16

SRCAPH   LB 16-30-8

2.41 Ammonium hydrogen dicinnamate

$C_9H_7O_2^-$, $C_9H_8O_2$, H_4N^+

R.F.Bryan, H.H.Mills, J.C.Speakman, J. Chem. Soc., 4350, 1963

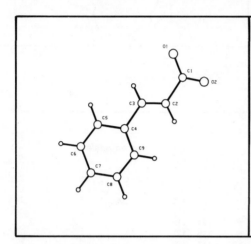

CH=CH—COOH

NH_4^+

CH=CH—COO$^-$

This compound is isomorphous with potassium hydrogen dicinnamate.
I2/a   Z = 4   R = 0.134

AMHCIN   LB 18-19-10

Bond Lengths					Bond Angles								Torsion Angles				
C1	O1	1.28	C4	C9	1.39	O1	C1	O2	125	C5	C4	C9	119	O1	C1	C2	C3	1
C1	O2	1.21	C5	C6	1.39	O1	C1	C2	122	C4	C5	C6	121	O2	C1	C2	C3	−175
C1	C2	1.55	C6	C7	1.40	O2	C1	C2	113	C5	C6	C7	119	C1	C2	C3	C4	180
C2	C3	1.26	C7	C8	1.36	C1	C2	C3	123	C6	C7	C8	120	C2	C3	C4	C5	−163
C3	C4	1.52	C8	C9	1.39	C2	C3	C4	124	C7	C8	C9	122	C2	C3	C4	C9	18
C4	C5	1.38				C3	C4	C5	118	C4	C9	C8	119					
						C3	C4	C9	123									

2.42 Potassium palmitate (form B)

$C_{16}H_{31}O_2^-$, K^+

J.H.Dumbleton, T.R.Lomer, Acta Cryst., 19, 301, 1965

$H_3C—(CH_2)_{14}—COO^-$ K^+

P-1   Z = 2   R = 0.116

KPALMA   LB 16-31-2

Bond Lengths						Bond Angles								Torsion Angles				
C1	O1	1.27	C8	C9	1.50	O1	C1	O2	123	C7	C8	C9	115	O1	C1	C2	C3	−15
C1	O2	1.21	C9	C10	1.52	O1	C1	C2	117	C8	C9	C10	116	O2	C1	C2	C3	163
C1	C2	1.54	C10	C11	1.51	O2	C1	C2	120	C9	C10	C11	116	C2	C3	C4	C5	178
C2	C3	1.51	C11	C12	1.52	C1	C2	C3	118	C10	C11	C12	115					
C3	C4	1.50	C12	C13	1.53	C2	C3	C4	114	C11	C12	C13	113					
C4	C5	1.53	C13	C14	1.54	C3	C4	C5	113	C12	C13	C14	113					
C5	C6	1.52	C14	C15	1.51	C4	C5	C6	115	C13	C14	C15	112					
C6	C7	1.51	C15	C16	1.55	C5	C6	C7	115	C14	C15	C16	114					
C7	C8	1.52				C6	C7	C8	115									

3.1   Methylammonium bromide

CH_6N^+ , Br^-

E.J.Gabe, Acta Cryst., 14, 1296, 1961

$$CH_3 — NH_3^+ \quad Br^-$$

Bond Lengths

C1   N1   1.48

P4/nmm   Z = 2   R = 0.089

MAMMBR   LB 1-6-3

3.2   Methylammonium alum (at 113 ° K)

CH_6N^+ , $H_{12}AlO_6^{3+}$, $2O_4S^{2-}$, $6H_2O$

R.O.W.Fletcher, H.Steeple, Acta Cryst., 17, 290, 1964

$$CH_3 — NH_3^+ . 2SO_4^{--} Al^{+++} . 12H_2O$$

No comparison of bond lengths is possible since they are not reported in the paper.

$Pca2_1$ Z = 4 $R_{hk0} = 0.116$,
$R_{h0l} = 0.099$

MAMALM   LB 1-6-1

Bond Lengths

Al1	O9	1.86	S1	O1	1.46
Al1	O10	1.90	S1	O2	1.49
Al1	O11	1.90	S1	O3	1.46
Al1	O12	1.80	S1	O4	1.48
Al1	O13	1.76			
Al1	O14	1.96	S2	O5	1.46
			S2	O6	1.44
C1	N1	1.51	S2	O7	1.51
			S2	O8	1.48

Bond Angles

O1	S1	O2	113	O5	S2	O6	108
O1	S1	O3	107	O5	S2	O7	112
O1	S1	O4	112	O5	S2	O8	108
O2	S1	O3	109	O6	S2	O7	112
O2	S1	O4	112	O6	S2	O8	110
O3	S1	O4	104	O7	S2	O8	107

3.3   Ethylenediammonium chloride

$C_2H_{10}N_2^{2+}$, $2Cl^-$

T.Ashida, S.Hirokawa, Bull. Chem. Soc. Jap., 36, 704, 1963

$$H_3N^+ — CH_2 — CH_2 — NH_3^+ . 2Cl^-$$

$P2_1/a$ Z = 2 $R_{h0l} = 0.065$,
$R_{hk0} = 0.081$

EDAMCL   LB 2-10-7

Bond Lengths

C1   N1   1.49
C1   C1B   1.53

Bond Angles

N1   C1   C1B   108

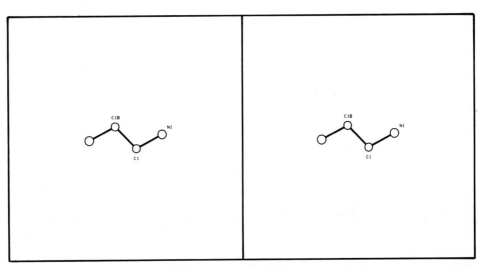

3.4 Ethylenediammonium sulfate

$C_2H_{10}N_2{}^{2+}$, O_4S^{2-}

K.Sakurai, J. Phys. Soc. Jap., 16, 1205, 1961

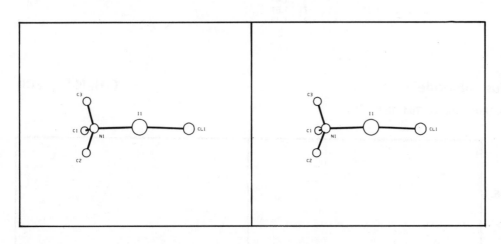

H_3N^+—CH_2—CH_2—NH_3^+ SO_4^{--}

$C4_122_1$ $Z = 8$ $R_{hk0} = 0.12,$
$R_{0kl} = 0.16$

ETDAMS   LB 2-10-12

Bond Lengths

S1	O1	1.49
S1	O2	1.48
C1	N1	1.49
C1	C1H	1.55

Bond Angles

O1	S1	O2	80
O1	S1	O1H	106
O1	S1	O2H	150
O2	S1	O1H	150
O2	S1	O2H	110
N1	C1	C1H	107

Torsion Angles

N1	C1	C1H	N1H	−76

3.5 Trimethylamine iodomonochloride

C_3H_9ClIN

O.Hassel, H.Hope, Acta Chem. Scand., 14, 391, 1960

$(CH_3)_3\,N \cdot ICl$

Pbca $Z = 8$ $R = 0.09$

TMEICL   LB 3-9-9

Bond Lengths

Cl1	I1	2.52
I1	N1	2.30
C1	N1	1.55
C2	N1	1.42
C3	N1	1.45

Bond Angles

Cl1	I1	N1	177
I1	N1	C1	109
I1	N1	C2	108
I1	N1	C3	104
C1	N1	C2	109
C1	N1	C3	108
C2	N1	C3	119

Torsion Angles

Cl1	I1	N1	C1	−90
Cl1	I1	N1	C2	28
Cl1	I1	N1	C3	155

3.6 Tetramethylammonium disilver iodide

$C_4H_{12}N^+$, $Ag_2I_3^-$

H.-J.Meyer, Acta Cryst., 16, 788, 1963

$[N(CH_3)_4]^+ [Ag_2I_3]^-$

The tetramethylammonium ion is disordered.
Pnam $Z = 4$ $R = 0.160$

TMAAGI   LB 4-12-1

3.7 Tetramethylammonium mercury tribromide   C₄H₁₂N⁺ , Br₃Hg⁻

$C_4H_{12}N^+$, Br_3Hg^-

J.G.White, Acta Cryst., 16, 397, 1963

$[N(CH_3)_4]^+ [HgBr_3]^-$

P2₁   Z = 4   R = 0.12

TMAHGB   LB 4-12-13

Bond Lengths

Hg1	Br1	2.48
Hg1	Br2	2.54
Hg1	Br3	2.57
Hg2	Br4	2.55
Hg2	Br5	2.48
Hg2	Br6	2.51
C1	N1	1.30
C2	N1	1.32
C3	N1	1.42
C4	N1	1.25
C5	N2	1.33
C6	N2	1.34
C7	N2	1.37
C8	N2	1.44

Bond Angles

Br1	Hg1	Br2	122
Br1	Hg1	Br3	114
Br2	Hg1	Br3	119
Br4	Hg2	Br5	125
Br4	Hg2	Br6	117
Br5	Hg2	Br6	113
C1	N1	C2	102
C1	N1	C3	112
C1	N1	C4	112
C2	N1	C3	108
C2	N1	C4	116
C3	N1	C4	107
C5	N2	C6	115
C5	N2	C7	106
C5	N2	C8	108
C6	N2	C7	111
C6	N2	C8	108
C7	N2	C8	109

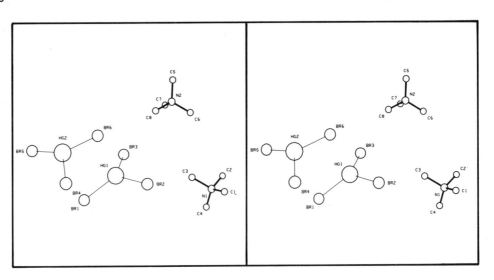

3.8 Tetramethylammonium perchlorate   C₄H₁₂N⁺ , ClO₄⁻

$C_4H_{12}N^+$, ClO_4^-

J.D.McCullough, Acta Cryst., 17, 1067, 1964

$[(CH_3)_4N]^+ ClO_4^-$

The perchlorate oxygens are disordered.
P4/nmm   Z = 2   R = 0.127

TMAPCL   LB 4-12-20

Bond Lengths

C1	N1	1.47		
			C1 N1 C1B	109
			C1 N1 C1L	109

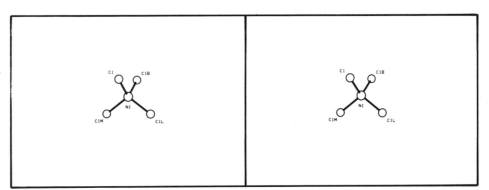

3.9 Tetramethylammonium dichloroiodide   C₄H₁₂N⁺ , Cl₂I⁻

$C_4H_{12}N^+$, Cl_2I^-

G.J.Visser, A.Vos, Acta Cryst., 17, 1336, 1964

$[(CH_3)_4N]^+ (ICl_2)^-$

P-42₁m   Z = 2   R = 0.041

METAMM   LB 4-12-21

Bond Lengths   *Bond Angles*

Cl1	I1	2.55	Cl1	I1	Cl1A	179
C1	N1	1.47	C1	N1	C1A	105
			C1	N1	C1B	112

3.10   Tetramethylammonium tetrachlorocuprate

$2C_4H_{12}N^+$, Cl_4Cu^{2-}

B.Morosin, E.C.Lingafelter, J. Phys. Chem., 65, 50, 1961

$$[(CH_3)_4N^+]_2[CuCl_4]^{2-}$$

The structure was determined in two dimensions only. Atomic coordinates were not reported in the paper. An approximate structure was deduced from h0l and hk0 data. The averaged x coordinates are given in Table 3. There are faint reflexions indicating a triple cell with a = 36A.
Pnma   Z = 4 R_{h0l} = 0.119, R_{hk0} = 0.181

TMECUC   LB 8-24-15

3.11   Tetramethylammonium hexahydrohexaborate

$2C_4H_{12}N^+$, $H_6B_6^{2-}$

R.Schaeffer, Q.Johnson, G.S.Smith, Inorg. Chem., 4, 917, 1965

$$[(CH_3)_4N^+]_2[B_6H_6]^{2-}$$

Fm3m   Z = 4   R = 0.053

TMAMHB   LB 8-30-1

Bond Lengths		Bond Angles		
B1	B1P	1.69	C1 N1 C1E	109
C1	N1	1.47		

3.12   Tetramethylene diammonium chloride

$C_4H_{14}N_2^{2+}$, $2Cl^-$

T.Ashida, S.Hirokawa, Bull. Chem. Soc. Jap., 36, 1086, 1963

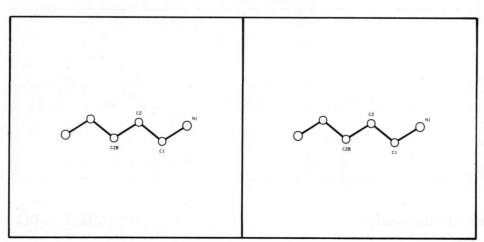

$$H_3N^+—(CH_2)_4—NH_3^+.2Cl^-$$

$P2_1/a$ Z = 2 R_{h0l} = 0.058, R_{hk0} = 0.075

TMEAMC   LB 4-14-4

Bond Lengths			Bond Angles		
C1	N1	1.50	N1 C1 C2	111	
C1	C2	1.52	C1 C2 C2B	111	
C2	C2B	1.49			

3.13   Triethylammonium chloride

$C_6H_{16}N^+$, Cl^-

F.Genet, Bull. Soc. Fr. Mineral. Cristallogr., 88, 463, 1965

$$(C_2H_5)_3NH^+.Cl^-$$

The structure is totally disordered.
$P6_3mc$ Z = 2   R = 0.10

ETAMCL   LB 6-16-9

3.14   Triethylammonium iron carbonyl hydride

$C_6H_{16}N^+$, $C_{11}HFe_3O_{11}^-$

L.F.Dahl, J.F.Blount, Inorg. Chem., 4, 1373, 1965

$$((C_2H_5)_3NH)^+[HFe_3(CO)_{11}]^-$$

Atomic coordinates were not reported in the paper.
P-1   Z = 2   R = 0.080

TEMFCH   LB 17-17-2

3.15 Hexamethylenediamine dihydroiodide $C_6H_{18}N_2^{2+}$, $2I^-$

K.Han, J. Korean Chem. Soc., 7, 74, 1963

$$H_3N^+—(CH_2)_6—NH_3^+.2I^-$$

Published value of C1-C2 = 1.59A. The correct value is 1.65A. The bond lengths reported for C2 - C3 and C3 - N1 have been interchanged.
P2$_1$/c   Z = 2 R_{0kl} = 0.24, R_{h0l} = 0.23

HXMAMI   LB 6-18-20

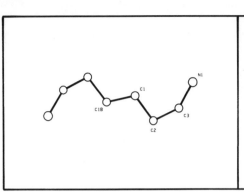 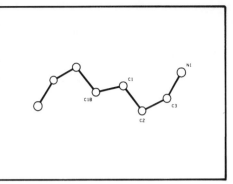

Bond Lengths			Bond Angles				Torsion Angles			
C3	N1	1.56	C2	C1	C1B	105	C1B	C1	C2	C3	171
C1	C2	1.65	C1	C2	C3	94	C2	C1	C1B	C2B	−180
C1	C1B	1.59	N1	C3	C2	132	C1	C2	C3	N1	−67
C2	C3	1.49								

3.16 2, 2′, 2″ - Triamino - triethylamine trihydrochloride platinate $C_6H_{21}N_4^{3+}$, $3Cl^-$

S.E.Rasmussen, R.Gronbaek, Acta Chem. Scand., 17, 832, 1963

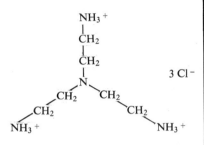

3 Cl$^-$

See also Hazell & Rasmussen, Acta Chem. Scand., 22, 348, 1968.
P2$_1$3   Z = 4   R = 0.142

TRIAEH   LB 6-21-3

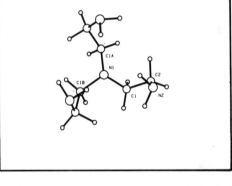

Bond Lengths			Bond Angles				Torsion Angles			
C1	N1	1.52	C1	N1	C1A	108	C1A	N1	C1	C2	87
C2	N2	1.47	N1	C1	C2	112	C1B	N1	C1	C2	−156
C1	C2	1.46	N2	C2	C1	113	N1	C1	C2	N2	61

3.17 N - t - Butylpropylamine hydrochloride $C_7H_{18}N^+$, Cl^-

L.M.Trefonas, J.Couvillion, Acta Cryst., 16, 576, 1963

$$H_3C—CH_2—CH_2—\overset{+}{N}H_2—C(CH_3)(CH_3)—CH_3 \quad Cl^-$$

Pna2$_1$ Z = 4   R = 0.15

BPRACL   LB 7-18-1

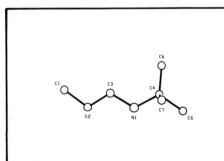 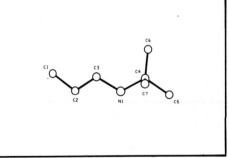

Bond Lengths						Bond Angles											Torsion Angles			
C3	N1	1.51	C4	C5	1.60	C3	N1	C4	114	N1	C4	C5	112	C5	C4	C6	111	C4	N1	C3	C2	171
C4	N1	1.51	C4	C6	1.50	C1	C2	C3	110	N1	C4	C6	116	C5	C4	C7	102	C3	N1	C4	C5	180
C1	C2	1.52	C4	C7	1.56	N1	C3	C2	106	N1	C4	C7	103	C6	C4	C7	112	C3	N1	C4	C6	−51
C2	C3	1.56																C3	N1	C4	C7	72
																		C1	C2	C3	N1	−165

3.18 β - Phenylethylamine hydrochloride

$C_8H_{12}N^+$, Cl^-

G.Tsoucaris, Acta Cryst., 14, 909, 1961

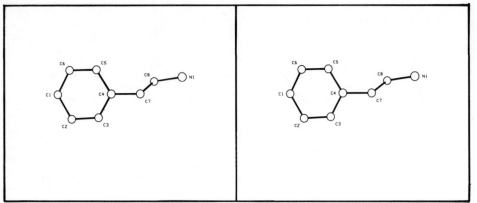

⬡—CH_2—CH_2—NH_3^+ Cl^-

$P2_12_12_1$ Z = 4   R = 0.14

PEAHCL   LB 8-12-10

Bond Lengths

C8	N1	1.49	C4	C5	1.40
C1	C2	1.42	C4	C7	1.49
C1	C6	1.38	C5	C6	1.43
C2	C3	1.43	C7	C8	1.54
C3	C4	1.35			

Bond Angles

C2	C1	C6	121	C5	C4	C7	121
C1	C2	C3	117	C4	C5	C6	121
C2	C3	C4	123	C1	C6	C5	119
C3	C4	C5	119	C4	C7	C8	111
C3	C4	C7	120	N1	C8	C7	112

Torsion Angles

C3	C4	C7	C8	112
C5	C4	C7	C8	−72
C4	C7	C8	N1	171

3.19 Tetraethylammonium oxotetrabromoaquorhenate(v)

$C_8H_{20}N^+$, $H_2Br_4O_2Re^-$

F.A.Cotton, S.J.Lippard, Inorg. Chem., 4, 1621, 1965

$[(C_2H_5)_4N]^+ [ReOBr_4(OH_2)]^-$

The tetraethylammonium cation is disordered.
Pnam   Z = 4   R = 0.135

EAOBRE   LB 8-22-1

3.20 Tetraethylammonium tetrabromo - μ,μ' - dibromo - platinate

$2C_8H_{20}N^+$, $Br_6Pt_2^{2-}$

N.C.Stephenson, Acta Cryst., 17, 587, 1964

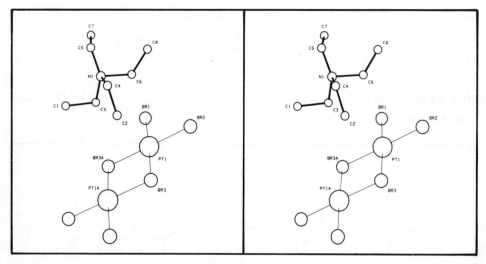

$[(C_2H_5)_4N^+]_2 \begin{bmatrix} Br & & Br & & Br \\ & Pt & & Pt & \\ Br & & Br & & Br \end{bmatrix}^{2-}$

P-1   Z = 1   R = 0.14

ETABPT   LB 16-40-4

Bond Lengths

Pt1	Br1	2.42	C3	N1	1.57
Pt1	Br2	2.45	C4	N1	1.78
Pt1	Br3	2.41	C5	N1	1.46
Pt1	Br3A	2.45	C6	N1	1.62
			C1	C3	1.59
			C2	C4	1.44
			C5	C7	1.73
			C6	C8	1.58

Bond Angles

Br1	Pt1	Br2	94	C3	N1	C4	112
Br1	Pt1	Br3	176	C3	N1	C5	134
Br1	Pt1	Br3A	90	C3	N1	C6	93
Br2	Pt1	Br3	90	C4	N1	C5	107
Br2	Pt1	Br3A	175	C4	N1	C6	96
Br3	Pt1	Br3A	86	C5	N1	C6	106
Pt1	Br3	Pt1A	94	N1	C3	C1	97
				N1	C4	C2	109
				N1	C5	C7	113
				N1	C6	C8	111

Torsion Angles

C4	N1	C3	C1	84	C3	N1	C5	C7	−47
C5	N1	C3	C1	−62	C4	N1	C5	C7	167
C6	N1	C3	C1	−178	C6	N1	C5	C7	65
C3	N1	C4	C2	23	C3	N1	C6	C8	−177
C5	N1	C4	C2	178	C4	N1	C6	C8	−65
C6	N1	C4	C2	−73	C5	N1	C6	C8	45

3.21 Pentamethylene di(trimethylammonium) iodide hydrate $C_{11}H_{28}N_2^{2+}$, $2I^-$, $0.25H_2O$

Pentamethonium iodide hydrate
F.G.Canepa, Acta Cryst., 16, 145, 1963

$(CH_3)_3N^+—(CH_2)_5—N^+(CH_3)_3.2I^-$

No comparison of bond lengths is possible since they are not reported in the paper. The iodine atoms are disordered.
Pnam Z = 8 R = 0.084

PMEAIO LB 11-28-1

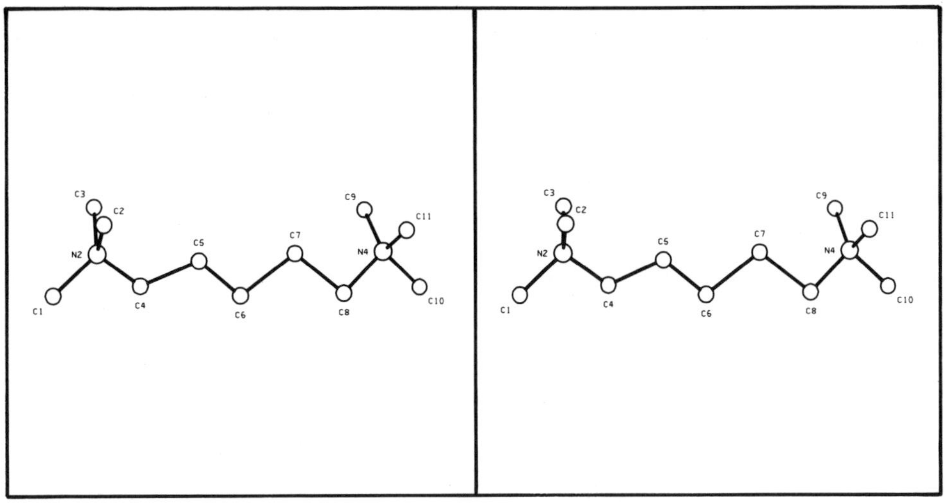

Bond Lengths

C1	N2	1.53
C2	N2	1.44
C3	N2	1.58
C4	N2	1.47
C8	N4	1.46
C9	N4	1.65
C10	N4	1.51
C11	N4	1.32
C4	C5	1.71
C5	C6	1.55
C6	C7	1.74
C7	C8	1.74

Bond Angles

C1	N2	C2	121	C9	N4	C10	106
C1	N2	C3	112	C9	N4	C11	115
C1	N2	C4	98	C10	N4	C11	109
C2	N2	C3	104	N2	C4	C5	107
C2	N2	C4	120	C4	C5	C6	104
C3	N2	C4	101	C5	C6	C7	99
C8	N4	C9	114	C6	C7	C8	104
C8	N4	C10	95	N4	C8	C7	99
C8	N4	C11	116				

Torsion Angles

C1	N2	C4	C5	−158
C2	N2	C4	C5	−25
C3	N2	C4	C5	88
C9	N4	C8	C7	−66
C10	N4	C8	C7	−175
C11	N4	C8	C7	71
N2	C4	C5	C6	−179
C4	C5	C6	C7	161
C5	C6	C7	C8	170
C6	C7	C8	N4	168

3.22 Hexamethylene di(trimethylammonium) dibromide dihydrate $C_{12}H_{30}N_2^{2+}$, $2Br^-$, $2H_2O$

Hexamethonium bromide dihydrate
K.Lonsdale, H.J.Milledge, L.M.Pant, Acta Cryst., 19, 827, 1965

$(CH_3)_3N^+—(CH_2)_6—N^+(CH_3)_3.2Br^-.2H_2O$

No comparison of bond lengths is possible since they are not reported in the paper.
$P2_1/c$ Z = 2 R = 0.097

HMENAM LB 12-30-11

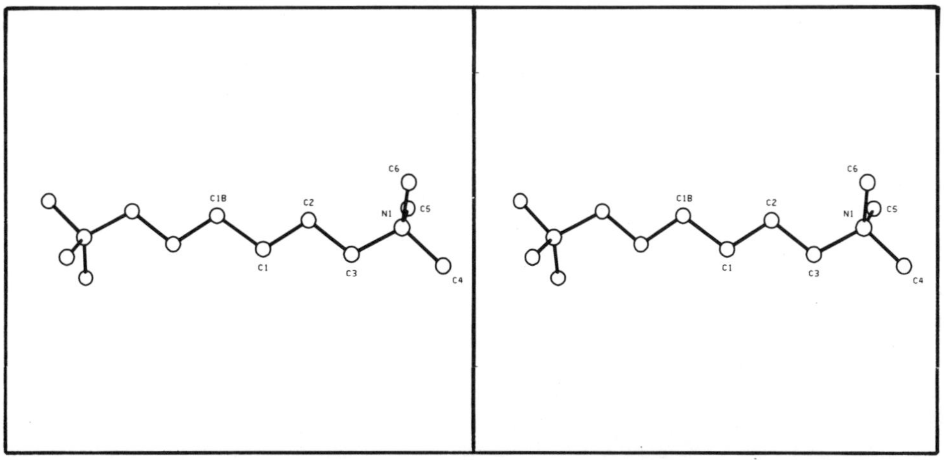

Bond Lengths

C3	N1	1.52
C4	N1	1.53
C5	N1	1.47
C6	N1	1.51
C1	C2	1.48
C1	C1B	1.56
C2	C3	1.48

Bond Angles

C3	N1	C4	108
C3	N1	C5	114
C3	N1	C6	110
C4	N1	C5	110
C4	N1	C6	105
C5	N1	C6	108
C2	C1	C1B	114
C1	C2	C3	111
N1	C3	C2	115

Torsion Angles

C4	N1	C3	C2	168
C5	N1	C3	C2	−69
C6	N1	C3	C2	54
C1B	C1	C2	C3	−177
C2	C1	C1B	C2B	−180
C1	C2	C3	N1	161

3.23 Decamethylene di(trimethylammonium) dibromide dihydrate $C_{16}H_{38}N_2^{2+}$, $2Br^-$, $2H_2O$

Decamethonium bromide dihydrate
K.Lonsdale, H.J.Milledge, L.M.Pant, Acta Cryst., 19, 827, 1965

$$(CH_3)_3\,N^+—(CH_2)_{10}—N^+(CH_3)_3 . 2Br^- . 2H_2O$$

No comparison of bond lengths is possible since they are not reported in the paper.
P2$_1$/a   Z = 2   R = 0.10

DMENAM   LB 16-38-2

Bond Lengths		
C5	N1	1.49
C6	N1	1.51
C7	N1	1.51
C8	N1	1.51
C1	C2	1.47
C1	C1B	1.61
C2	C3	1.59
C3	C4	1.58
C4	C5	1.53

Bond Angles			
C5	N1	C6	110
C5	N1	C7	115
C5	N1	C8	114
C6	N1	C7	104
C6	N1	C8	107
C7	N1	C8	107
C2	C1	C1B	110
C1	C2	C3	113
C2	C3	C4	114
C3	C4	C5	107
N1	C5	C4	112

Torsion Angles				
C6	N1	C5	C4	−180
C7	N1	C5	C4	−64
C8	N1	C5	C4	60
C1B	C1	C2	C3	−174
C2	C1	C1B	C2B	180
C1	C2	C3	C4	171
C2	C3	C4	C5	176
C3	C4	C5	N1	170

4.1　Dithio - oxamide

$C_2H_4N_2S_2$

Rubeanic acid
P.J.Wheatley, J. Chem. Soc., 396, 1965

P-1　　Z = 2　　R = 0.071

SSOXAM　　　LB 2-4-33

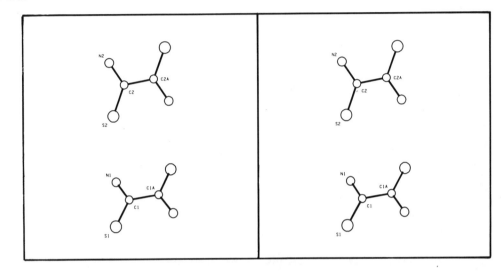

Bond Lengths

S1	C1	1.67	S2	C2	1.63
C1	N1	1.34	C2	N2	1.31
C1	C1A	1.54	C2	C2A	1.54

Bond Angles

S1	C1	N1	125	S2	C2	N2	125
S1	C1	C1A	120	S2	C2	C2A	121
N1	C1	C1A	115	N2	C2	C2A	115

4.2　Thioacetamide

C_2H_5NS

M.R.Truter, J. Chem. Soc., 997, 1960

P2$_1$/a　　Z = 8　　R = 0.117

THACEM　　　LB 2-5-17

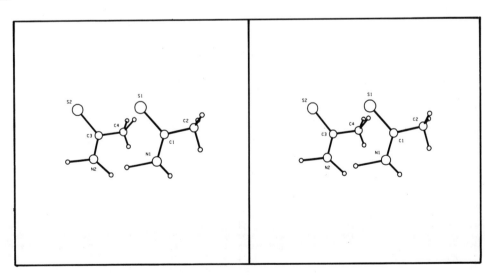

Bond Lengths

S1	C1	1.69	S2	C3	1.69
C1	N1	1.31	C3	N2	1.31
C1	C2	1.48	C3	C4	1.48

Bond Angles

S1	C1	N1	122	S2	C3	N2	122
S1	C1	C2	120	S2	C3	C4	122
N1	C1	C2	119	N2	C3	C4	117

4.3   bis - Dimethylamine sulfone

$C_4H_{12}N_2O_2S$

T.H.Jordan, H.W.Smith, L.L.Lohr, W.N.Lipscomb, J. Amer. Chem. Soc., 85, 846, 1963

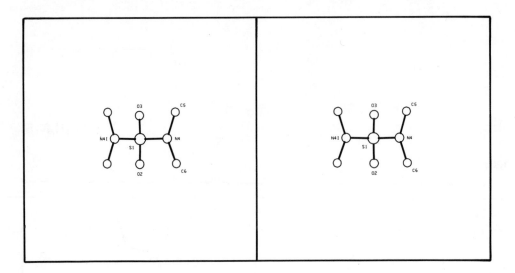

$(CH_3)_2N{-}\overset{\displaystyle O}{\underset{\displaystyle O}{S}}{-}N(CH_3)_2$

Cmca   Z = 8   R = 0.085

DMAMSO   LB 4-12-45

Bond Lengths

S1	N4	1.61
S1	O2	1.44
S1	O3	1.42
C5	N4	1.47
C6	N4	1.46

Bond Angles

N4	S1	N4I	113
N4	S1	O2	105
N4	S1	O3	107
O2	S1	O3	120
S1	N4	C5	118
S1	N4	C6	120
C5	N4	C6	113

Torsion Angles

N4I	S1	N4	C5	−72
N4I	S1	N4	C6	72
O2	S1	N4	C5	173
O2	S1	N4	C6	−43
O3	S1	N4	C5	45
O3	S1	N4	C6	−171

4.4   N - Ethyl - 2,2′ - dimethylsulfonylvinylideneamine

$C_6H_{11}NO_4S_2$

J.J.Daly, J. Chem. Soc., 2801, 1961

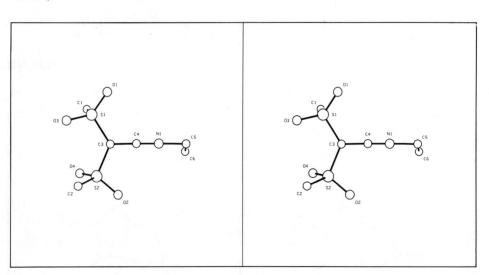

$\begin{array}{c}H_3C{-}O_2S \\ \\ H_3C{-}O_2S\end{array}\!\!\!\Big\rangle C{=}C{=}N{-}C_2H_5$

P2₁2₁2₁   Z = 4   R = 0.10

EMSVIN   LB 6-11-16

Bond Lengths

S1	O1	1.44
S1	O3	1.43
S1	C1	1.77
S1	C3	1.74
S2	O2	1.44
S2	O4	1.43
S2	C2	1.77
S2	C3	1.74
C4	N1	1.17
C5	N1	1.47
C3	C4	1.36
C5	C6	1.53

Bond Angles

O1	S1	O3	119
O1	S1	C1	109
O1	S1	C3	108
O3	S1	C1	108
O3	S1	C3	107
C1	S1	C3	106
O2	S2	O4	119
O2	S2	C2	108
O2	S2	C3	106
O4	S2	C2	109
O4	S2	C3	108
C2	S2	C3	107
C4	N1	C5	145
S1	C3	S2	122
S1	C3	C4	122
S2	C3	C4	117
N1	C4	C3	173
N1	C5	C6	111

Torsion Angles

O1	S1	C3	S2	167
O1	S1	C3	C4	−10
O2	S2	C3	S1	171
O2	S2	C3	C4	−12
C5	N1	C4	C3	167
C4	N1	C5	C6	−15
S1	C3	C4	N1	96
S2	C3	C4	N1	−81

4.5 Tetramethylthiuram disulfide

$C_6H_{12}N_2S_4$

K.Maroy, Acta Chem. Scand., 19, 1509, 1965

No comparison of bond lengths is possible since they are not reported in the paper.
C2/c   Z = 4   R = 0.10

METHUS   LB 6-12-39

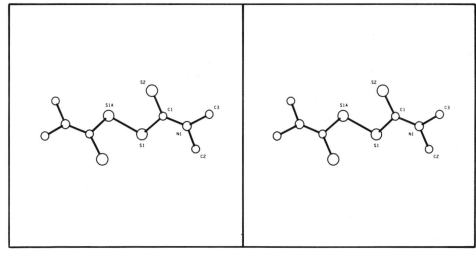

Bond Lengths

S1	S1A	2.00
S1	C1	1.86
S2	C1	1.61
C1	N1	1.31
C2	N1	1.51
C3	N1	1.52

Bond Angles

C1	N1	C2	127
C1	N1	C3	119
C2	N1	C3	114
S1	C1	S2	122
S1	C1	N1	110
S2	C1	N1	128

Torsion Angles

C1	S1	S1A	C1A	−88
S1A	S1	C1	S2	1
S1A	S1	C1	N1	−176
C2	N1	C1	S1	−4
C2	N1	C1	S2	178
C3	N1	C1	S1	−178
C3	N1	C1	S2	4

4.6 trans - N - Methyl - N - benzyl - thioformamide

$C_9H_{11}NS$

A.M.Piazzesi, R.Bardi, M.Mammi, W.Walter, Ric. Sci., 2, A, 6, 173, 1964

Atomic coordinates were not given but bond lengths were reported.
P2$_1$/c   Z = 4   R$_{hk0}$ = 0.08,
R$_{0kl}$ = 0.13, R$_{h0l}$ = 0.14

MBSFAM   LB 9-11-28

5.1 Chloral hydrate

$C_2H_3Cl_3O_2$

K.Ogawa, Bull. Chem. Soc. Jap., 36, 610, 1963

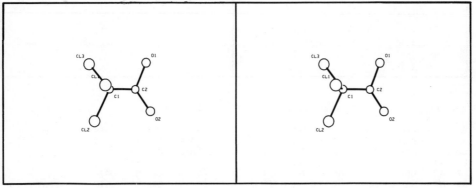

$$Cl \quad OH$$
$$Cl-C-C-H$$
$$Cl \quad OH$$

$P2_1/c \qquad Z = 4 \qquad R_{h0l} = 0.183,$
$R_{0kl} = 0.177, R_{hk0} = 0.255$

CHORLH   LB 2-3-13

Bond Lengths			Bond Angles							Torsion Angles				
Cl1	C1	1.72	Cl1	C1	Cl2	108	Cl3	C1	C2	110	Cl1	C1	C2	O1	−55
Cl2	C1	1.87	Cl1	C1	Cl3	107	O1	C2	O2	110	Cl1	C1	C2	O2	60
Cl3	C1	1.86	Cl1	C1	C2	122	O1	C2	C1	99	Cl2	C1	C2	O1	−178
C2	O1	1.52	Cl2	C1	Cl3	103	O2	C2	C1	108	Cl2	C1	C2	O2	−63
C2	O2	1.44	Cl2	C1	C2	105					Cl3	C1	C2	O1	72
C1	C2	1.51									Cl3	C1	C2	O2	−173

5.2 Bromomalonic dialdehyde

$C_3H_3BrO_2$

G.Lundgren, B.Aurivillius, Acta Chem. Scand., 18, 1642, 1964

$$CHO$$
$$|$$
$$CHBr$$
$$|$$
$$CHO$$

The molecule generated from the published coordinates has wrong connectivity. O2 is too close to C3 and is also connected to C2.
$Cmc2_1 \quad Z = 2 \quad R = 0.155$

BMALAL   LB 3-3-3

5.3 n - Hexane (at −115 °C)

C_6H_{14}

N.Norman, H.Mathisen, Acta Chem. Scand., 15, 1755, 1961

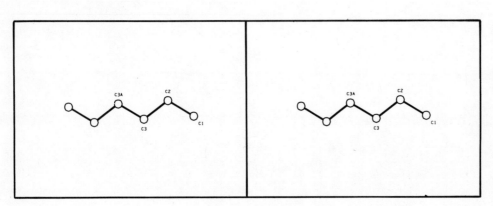

$$CH_3-(CH_2)_4-CH_3$$

$P-1 \quad Z = 1 \quad R_{0kl} = 0.064$

HEXANE   LB 6-14-1

Bond Lengths			Bond Angles			
C1	C2	1.53	C1	C2	C3	114
C2	C3	1.53	C2	C3	C3A	114
C3	C3A	1.52				

5.4   n - Heptane

C_7H_{16}

N.Norman, H.Mathisen, Acta Cryst., 13, 1043, 1960

Atomic coordinates were not reported in the paper.
P1   Z = 2   No R factor was given.

$$H_3C-(CH_2)_5-CH_3$$

HEPTAN   LB 7-16-1

5.5   2,3,3 - Trimethyl butan - 2 - ol hemihydrate (at $-15\,^\circ$C)

$C_7H_{16}O$, $0.5H_2O$

K.Pachler, M.v. Stackelberg, Z. Kristallogr., 119, 15, 1963

$$H_3C-\underset{\underset{CH_3}{|}}{\overset{\overset{CH_3}{|}}{C}}-\underset{\underset{CH_3}{|}}{\overset{\overset{CH_3}{|}}{C}}-OH.0\cdot5\ H_2O$$

No comparison of bond lengths is possible since they are not reported in the paper.
Iba2   Z = 8   R = 0.12

TMBUOL   LB 7-16-11

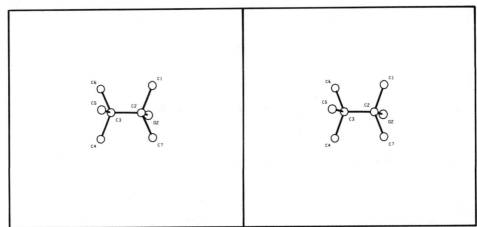

Bond Lengths			Bond Angles								Torsion Angles				
C2	O2	1.45	O2	C2	C1	110	C2	C3	C4	109	O2	C2	C3	C4	60
C1	C2	1.54	O2	C2	C3	109	C2	C3	C5	109	O2	C2	C3	C5	179
C2	C3	1.53	O2	C2	C7	109	C2	C3	C6	110	O2	C2	C3	C6	−60
C2	C7	1.53	C1	C2	C3	109	C4	C3	C5	109	C1	C2	C3	C4	−180
C3	C4	1.55	C1	C2	C7	110	C4	C3	C6	110	C1	C2	C3	C5	−61
C3	C5	1.55	C3	C2	C7	109	C5	C3	C6	110	C1	C2	C3	C6	60
C3	C6	1.52									C7	C2	C3	C4	−59
											C7	C2	C3	C5	60
											C7	C2	C3	C6	180

5.6   n - Hexadecanol (monoclinic form)

$C_{16}H_{34}O$

S.Abrahamsson, G.Larsson, E.von Sydow, Acta Cryst., 13, 770, 1960

$$H_3C-(CH_2)_{14}-CH_2OH$$

A2/a   Z = 8 $R_{h0l} = 0.13$,
$R_{0kl} = 0.13$

HEXDEC   LB 16-34-3

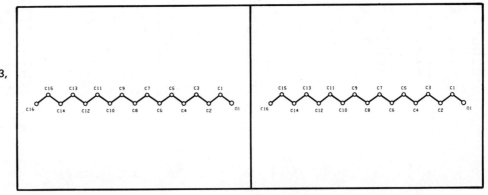

Bond Lengths						Bond Angles						
C1	O1	1.44	C8	C9	1.57	O1	C1	C2	109	C8	C9	C10	112
C1	C2	1.52	C9	C10	1.52	C1	C2	C3	110	C9	C10	C11	111
C2	C3	1.57	C10	C11	1.57	C2	C3	C4	110	C10	C11	C12	111
C3	C4	1.56	C11	C12	1.54	C3	C4	C5	110	C11	C12	C13	110
C4	C5	1.54	C12	C13	1.59	C4	C5	C6	110	C12	C13	C14	111
C5	C6	1.52	C13	C14	1.55	C5	C6	C7	111	C13	C14	C15	110
C6	C7	1.55	C14	C15	1.55	C6	C7	C8	112	C14	C15	C16	109
C7	C8	1.54	C15	C16	1.53	C7	C8	C9	113				

5.7 α,ω - Diphenyl - octatetra - yne (α form, at 30 °C and −110 °C)

C$_{20}$H$_{10}$

I.Nitta, Acta Cryst., 13, 1035, 1960

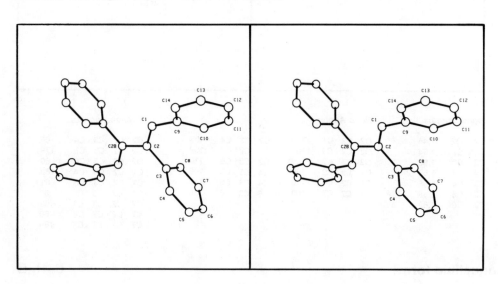

Atomic coordinates were not given but bond lengths were reported.
P2$_1$/a   Z = 2   No R factor was given.

DPOCTT   LB 20-10-1

5.8 α,ω - Diphenyl - decapenta - yne (at 30 °C and −110 °C)

C$_{22}$H$_{10}$

I.Nitta, Acta Cryst., 13, 1035, 1960

Atomic coordinates were not reported in the paper.
P2$_1$/a   Z = 2   No R factor was given.

DPDECP   LB 22-10-1

5.9   1,2,3,4 - Tetraphenyl - cis,cis - butadiene

C$_{28}$H$_{22}$

I.L.Karle, K.S.Dragonette, Acta Cryst., 19, 500, 1965

P2$_1$/c   Z = 2   R = 0.121

TEPBUT   LB 28-22-1

Bond Lengths

C1	C2	1.36	C6	C7	1.37
C1	C9	1.48	C7	C8	1.43
C2	C3	1.52	C9	C10	1.42
C2	C2B	1.49	C9	C14	1.40
C3	C4	1.40	C10	C11	1.40
C3	C8	1.40	C11	C12	1.40
C4	C5	1.44	C12	C13	1.40
C5	C6	1.38	C13	C14	1.41

Bond Angles

C2	C1	C9	129	C6	C7	C8	120
C1	C2	C3	122	C3	C8	C7	118
C1	C2	C2B	121	C1	C9	C10	123
C3	C2	C2B	117	C1	C9	C14	118
C2	C3	C4	118	C10	C9	C14	118
C2	C3	C8	120	C9	C10	C11	119
C4	C3	C8	122	C10	C11	C12	122
C3	C4	C5	118	C11	C12	C13	119
C4	C5	C6	120	C12	C13	C14	119
C5	C6	C7	121	C9	C14	C13	122

Torsion Angles

C9	C1	C2	C3	4
C9	C1	C2	C2B	−178
C2	C1	C9	C10	33
C2	C1	C9	C14	−151
C1	C2	C3	C4	72
C1	C2	C3	C8	−105
C2B	C2	C3	C4	−107
C2B	C2	C3	C8	76
C1	C2	C2B	C3B	1

6.1   Potassium diketocyclobutenediolate monohydrate $C_4O_4^{2-}$, $2K^+$, H_2O

W.M.Macintyre, M.S.Werkema, J. Chem. Phys., 40, 3563, 1964

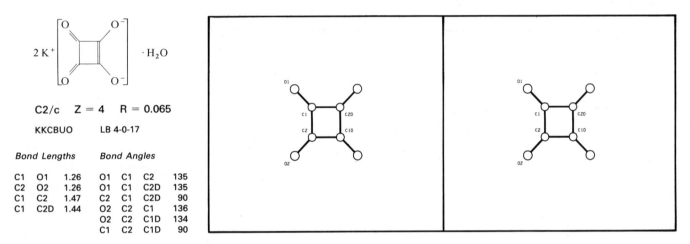

C2/c   Z = 4   R = 0.065

KKCBUO   LB 4-0-17

Bond Lengths			Bond Angles			
C1	O1	1.26	O1	C1	C2	135
C2	O2	1.26	O1	C1	C2D	135
C1	C2	1.47	C2	C1	C2D	90
C1	C2D	1.44	O2	C2	C1	136
			O2	C2	C1D	134
			C1	C2	C1D	90

6.2   Diammonium croconate $C_5O_5^{2-}$, $2H_4N^+$

N.C.Baenziger, J.J.Hegenbarth, D.G.Williams, J. Amer. Chem. Soc., 85, 1539, 1963

Atomic coordinates were not given
but bond lengths were reported.
Cm   Z = 4   R = 0.106

DACROC

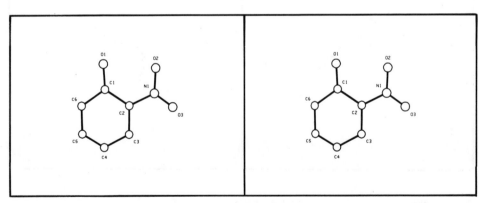

6.3   Potassium o - nitrophenol hemihydrate $C_6H_4NO_3^-$, K^+ , $0.5H_2O$

J.P.G.Richards, Z. Kristallogr., 116, 468, 1961

C2/c   Z = 8   R = 0.12

KNPHEH   LB 6-4-47

Bond Lengths						Bond Angles											Torsion Angles				
N1	O2	1.25	C1	C6	1.43	O2	N1	O3	122	C2	C1	C6	113	C3	C4	C5	122	O2	N1	C2	C1	5
N1	O3	1.18	C2	C3	1.41	O2	N1	C2	118	N1	C2	C1	123	C4	C5	C6	122	O2	N1	C2	C3	−178
C2	N1	1.40	C3	C4	1.41	O3	N1	C2	120	N1	C2	C3	116	C1	C6	C5	123	O3	N1	C2	C1	−170
C1	O1	1.26	C4	C5	1.30	O1	C1	C2	126	C1	C2	C3	122					O3	N1	C2	C3	7
C1	C2	1.47	C5	C6	1.38	O1	C1	C6	121	C2	C3	C4	118									

7.1 Cyanogen (at −95 °C)

C₂N₂

A.S.Parkes, R.E.Hughes, Acta Cryst., 16, 734, 1963

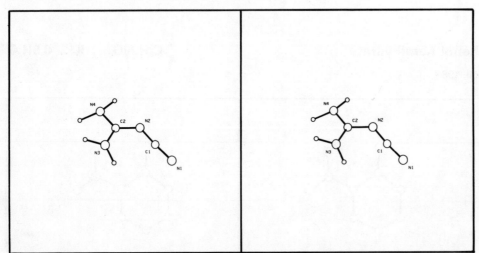

$$N \equiv C - C \equiv N$$

Pcab   Z = 4   R = 0.0865

CYNGEN   LB 2-0-43

Bond Lengths			*Bond Angles*			
C1	N1	1.13	N1	C1	C1D	180
C1	C1D	1.37				

7.2 Dicyanodiamide (neutron study)

C₂H₄N₄

N.V.Rannev, R.P.Ozerov, Dokl. Akad. Nauk S. S. S. R., 155, 1415, 1964

$$(H_2N)_2C = N - C \equiv N$$

No comparison of bond lengths is possible since they are not reported in the paper.
See also Hope & Kim, Amer. Cryst. Assoc., Abstr. Papers (Winter Meeting), 22, 1971; Rannev et al., Kristallografija, 11, 175, 1966.
C2/c   Z = 8   R = 0.16

CYAMPD01   LB 2-4-34

Bond Lengths						*Bond Angles*					
C1	N1	1.20	N3	H1	1.05	C1	N2	C2	117	H3 N4 H4	157
C1	N2	1.27	N3	H2	1.05	C2	N3	H1	105	N1 C1 N2	172
C2	N2	1.33	N4	H3	1.16	C2	N3	H2	127	N2 C2 N3	125
C2	N3	1.34	N4	H4	0.96	H1	N3	H2	127	N2 C2 N4	118
C2	N4	1.30				C2	N4	H3	107	N3 C2 N4	117
						C2	N4	H4	75		

7.3 Dicyanodiamide

C$_2$H$_4$N$_4$

Z.V.Zvonkova, V.Ya.Krivnov, A.N.Khvatkina, Dokl. Akad. Nauk S. S. S. R., 155, 398, 1964

(H$_2$N)$_2$C=N—C≡N

C2/c   Z = 8   R = 0.13

CYAMPD02   LB 2-4-34

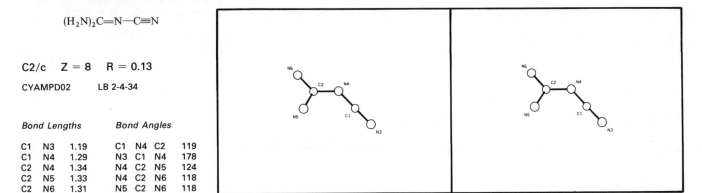

Bond Lengths			Bond Angles			
C1	N3	1.19	C1	N4	C2	119
C1	N4	1.29	N3	C1	N4	178
C2	N4	1.34	N4	C2	N5	124
C2	N5	1.33	N4	C2	N6	118
C2	N6	1.31	N5	C2	N6	118

7.4 Iodo - cyano - acetylene

C$_3$IN

B.Borgen, O.Hassel, C.Romming, Acta Chem. Scand., 16, 2469, 1962

I—C≡C—C≡N

P2$_1$/m   Z = 2   R$_{h0l}$ = 0.05,
R$_{hk0}$ = 0.05, R$_{0kl}$ = 0.08

ICACEN   LB 3-0-5

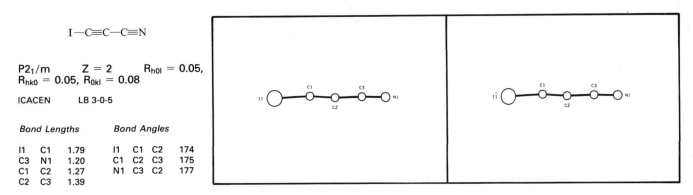

Bond Lengths			Bond Angles			
I1	C1	1.79	I1	C1	C2	174
C3	N1	1.20	C1	C2	C3	175
C1	C2	1.27	N1	C3	C2	177
C2	C3	1.39				

7.5 Potassium tricyanomethanide

C$_4$N$_3^-$, K$^+$

P.Andersen, B.Klewe, Nature, 200, 464, 1963

Atomic coordinates were not reported in the paper.
See also Witt & Britton, Acta Cryst. (B), 27, 1835, 1971.
P-1   Z = 2   R$_{0kl}$ = 0.07

KTCYME   LB 4-0-14

$$K^+ \left(NC-C \begin{matrix} CN \\ CN \end{matrix} \right)^-$$

7.6 Ammonium tricyanomethanide

C$_4$N$_3^-$, H$_4$N$^+$

R.Desiderato, R.L.Sass, Acta Cryst., 18, 1, 1965

$$NH_4^+ \left(NC-C \begin{matrix} CN \\ CN \end{matrix} \right)^-$$

P2$_1$/c   Z = 4   R = 0.104

AMCYME   LB 4-4-48

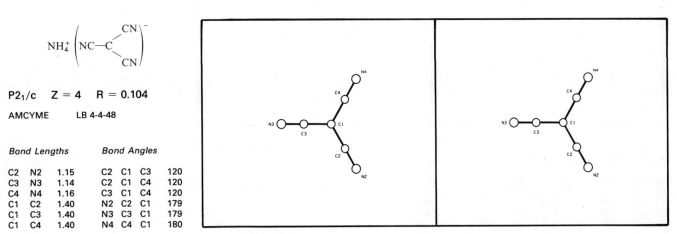

Bond Lengths			Bond Angles			
C2	N2	1.15	C2	C1	C3	120
C3	N3	1.14	C2	C1	C4	120
C4	N4	1.16	C3	C1	C4	120
C1	C2	1.40	N2	C2	C1	179
C1	C3	1.40	N3	C3	C1	179
C1	C4	1.40	N4	C4	C1	180

7.7   Copper(ii) tricyanomethanide

C.Biondi, Chem. Communic., 191, 1965

$2C_4N_3^-$, Cu^{2+}

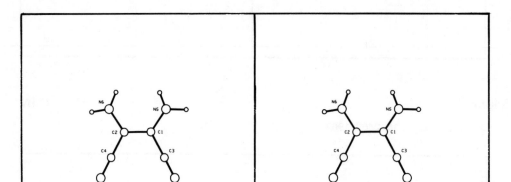

Atomic coordinates were not given but bond lengths were reported.
Pmna   Z = 2   R = 0.099

CUTCYM   LB 8-0-4

7.8   Diaminomaleonitrile

B.R.Penfold, W.N.Lipscomb, Acta Cryst., 14, 589, 1961

$C_4H_4N_4$

$P2_1/c$ Z = 4   R = 0.057

DAMALN   LB 4-4-50

Bond Lengths

C1	N5	1.37		C1	C2	1.36
C2	N6	1.39		C1	C3	1.43
C3	N7	1.14		C2	C4	1.42
C4	N8	1.14				

Bond Angles

N5	C1	C2	125		N6	C2	C4	117
N5	C1	C3	117		C1	C2	C4	119
C2	C1	C3	118		N7	C3	C1	179
N6	C2	C1	124		N8	C4	C2	180

7.9   Tetracyanoethylene

D.A.Bekoe, K.N.Trueblood, Z. Kristallogr., 113, 1, 1960

C_6N_4

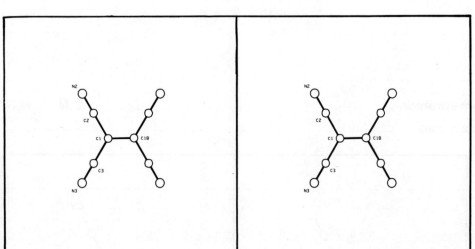

See also Little et al., Acta Cryst. (B), 27, 1493, 1971.
$P2_1/n$ Z = 2   R = 0.083

TCYETY   LB 6-0-34

Bond Lengths

C2	N2	1.13
C3	N3	1.13
C1	C2	1.45
C1	C3	1.44
C1	C1B	1.31

Bond Angles

C2	C1	C3	117
C2	C1	C1B	120
C3	C1	C1B	122
N2	C2	C1	180
N3	C3	C1	180

7.10   p - Iodobenzonitrile

C₇H₄IN

E.O.Schlemper, D.Britton, Acta Cryst., 18, 419, 1965

C2/c   Z = 4   R = 0.117

IOBNIT   LB 7-4-9

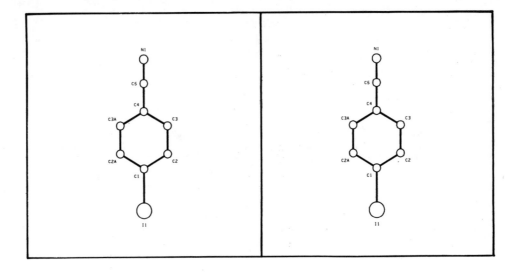

Bond Lengths

I1	C1	2.06
C5	N1	1.20
C1	C2	1.41
C2	C3	1.39
C3	C4	1.40
C4	C5	1.37

Bond Angles

I1	C1	C2	121
C2	C1	C2A	118
C1	C2	C3	121
C2	C3	C4	120
C3	C4	C5	120
C3	C4	C3A	120
N1	C5	C4	180

7.11   7,7,8,8 - Tetracyanoquinodimethane

C₁₂H₄N₄

R.E.Long, R.A.Sparks, K.N.Trueblood, Acta Cryst., 18, 932, 1965

C2/c   Z = 4   R = 0.071

TCYQME   LB 12-4-8

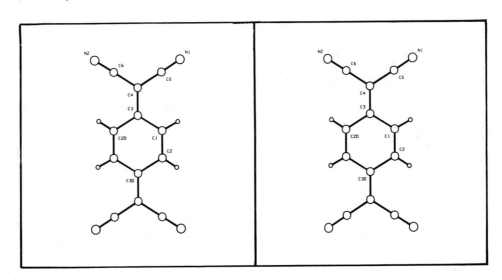

Bond Lengths

C5	N1	1.14
C6	N2	1.14
C1	C2	1.35
C1	C3	1.45
C2	C3D	1.45
C3	C4	1.37
C4	C5	1.44
C4	C6	1.44

Bond Angles

C2	C1	C3	121
C1	C2	C3D	121
C1	C3	C4	121
C1	C3	C2D	118
C4	C3	C2D	121
C3	C4	C5	122
C3	C4	C6	122
C5	C4	C6	116
N1	C5	C4	179
N2	C6	C4	180

7.12 2,6 - Dibromo - α - cyanostilbene

$C_{15}H_9Br_2N$

H.Bois d'Enghien, M.van Meerssche, Bull. Soc. Chim. Belges, 71, 503, 1962

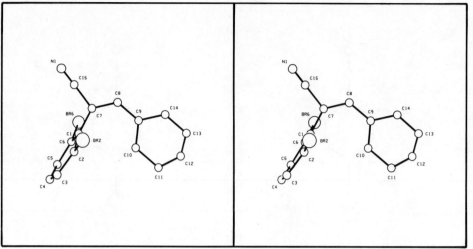

P-1   Z = 2 R_{hk0} = 0.128, R_{hkl} = 0.171, R_{hhl} = 0.136

BCYSTI

Bond Lengths

Br2	C2	2.05 (1.88)	C5	C6	1.37
Br6	C6	1.89	C7	C8	1.36
C15	N1	1.04 (1.13)	C7	C15	1.49
C1	C2	1.31 (1.43)	C8	C9	1.39
C1	C6	1.34 (1.39)	C9	C10	1.41
C1	C7	1.43	C9	C14	1.39 (1.34)
C2	C3	1.39	C10	C11	1.59 (1.45)
C3	C4	1.23 (1.33)	C11	C12	1.39
C4	C5	1.43 (1.36)	C12	C13	1.22 (1.40)
			C13	C14	1.46 (1.38)

Bond Angles

C2	C1	C6	113	C1	C7	C15	113
C2	C1	C7	126	C8	C7	C15	115
C6	C1	C7	122	C7	C8	C9	128
Br2	C2	C1	117	C8	C9	C10	123
Br2	C2	C3	102	C8	C9	C14	128
C1	C2	C3	137	C10	C9	C14	107
C2	C3	C4	105	C9	C10	C11	125
C3	C4	C5	126	C10	C11	C12	103
C4	C5	C6	122	C11	C12	C13	119
Br6	C6	C1	119	C12	C13	C14	109
Br6	C6	C5	126	C9	C14	C13	128
C1	C6	C5	115	N1	C15	C7	165
C1	C7	C8	131				

Torsion Angles

C2	C1	C7	C8	76
C2	C1	C7	C15	−93
C6	C1	C7	C8	−101
C6	C1	C7	C15	90
C1	C7	C8	C9	5
C15	C7	C8	C9	174
C7	C8	C9	C10	6
C7	C8	C9	C14	171

7.13 trans - α,β - Dicyanostilbene

$C_{16}H_{10}N_2$

S.C.Wallwork, Acta Cryst., 14, 375, 1961

C2/c   Z = 4 R_{hk0} = 0.19, R_{0kl} = 0.16

DCNSTI   LB 16-10-13

Bond Lengths

C2	N1	1.25	C3	C8	1.41
C1	C2	1.48	C4	C5	1.39
C1	C3	1.51	C5	C6	1.35
C1	C1D	1.46	C6	C7	1.38
C3	C4	1.39	C7	C8	1.39

Bond Angles

C2	C1	C3	116	C4	C3	C8	121
C2	C1	C1D	115	C3	C4	C5	117
C3	C1	C1D	124	C4	C5	C6	122
N1	C2	C1	178	C5	C6	C7	123
C1	C3	C4	115	C6	C7	C8	117
C1	C3	C8	123	C3	C8	C7	120

Torsion Angles

C2	C1	C3	C4	−52	C2	C1	C1D	C2D	−180
C2	C1	C3	C8	128	C2	C1	C1D	C3D	26
C1D	C1	C3	C4	154	C3	C1	C1D	C2D	−26
C1D	C1	C3	C8	−25	C3	C1	C1D	C3D	−180

7.14   2 - Bromo - 4' - dimethylamino - α - cyanostilbene

M.van Meerssche, G.Leroy, Bull. Soc. Chim. Belges, 69, 204, 1960

C₁₇H₁₅BrN₂

$C_{17}H_{15}BrN_2$

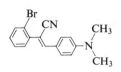

Published y coordinate for 41(relabelled C10) = 0.171. The correct value is 0.071.
P2₁2₁2₁   Z = 4   R = 0.25,
R$_{hk0}$ = 0.137

BCSTIL   LB 17-15-1

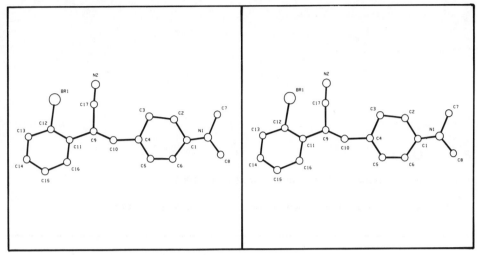

Bond Lengths

Br1	C12	1.88	C9	C10	1.38
C1	N1	1.33	C9	C11	1.45
C7	N1	1.39	C9	C17	1.52
C8	N1	1.44	C11	C12	1.36
C17	N2	1.13	C11	C16	1.36
C1	C2	1.43	C12	C13	1.37
C1	C6	1.37	C13	C14	1.35
C2	C3	1.44	C14	C15	1.43
C3	C4	1.40	C15	C16	1.34
C4	C5	1.41			(1.41)
C4	C10	1.45			
C5	C6	1.32			
		(1.38)			

Bond Angles

C1	N1	C7	113		C5	C4	C10	122
C1	N1	C8	127		C4	C5	C6	125
C7	N1	C8	120		C1	C6	C5	118
N1	C1	C2	120		C10	C9	C11	129
N1	C1	C6	121		C10	C9	C17	102
C2	C1	C6	115		C11	C9	C17	109
C1	C2	C3	130		C4	C10	C9	139
C2	C3	C4	106		C9	C11	C12	128
C3	C4	C5	124		C9	C11	C16	113
C3	C4	C10	114		C12	C11	C16	119

Br1	C12	C11	118
Br1	C12	C13	112
C11	C12	C13	130
C12	C13	C14	109
C13	C14	C15	124
C14	C15	C16	122
C11	C16	C15	116
N2	C17	C9	176

Torsion Angles

C7	N1	C1	C2	11
C7	N1	C1	C6	167
C8	N1	C1	C2	−172
C8	N1	C1	C6	−16
C3	C4	C10	C9	72
C5	C4	C10	C9	−101
C11	C9	C10	C4	157
C17	C9	C10	C4	−76
C10	C9	C11	C12	172
C10	C9	C11	C16	−9
C17	C9	C11	C12	49
C17	C9	C11	C16	−133

7.15   Hexacrylonitrile

M.J.Kornblau, R.E.Hughes, Acta Cryst., 17, 1033, 1964

C₁₈H₁₈N₆

$C_{18}H_{18}N_6$

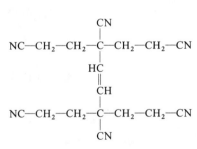

P2₁/a   Z = 2   R = 0.110

HACRYN   LB 18-18-23

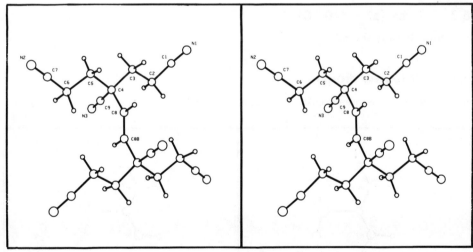

Bond Lengths

C1	N1	1.10	C4	C5	1.56
C7	N2	1.12	C4	C8	1.56
C9	N3	1.14	C4	C9	1.46
C1	C2	1.50	C5	C6	1.54
C2	C3	1.51	C6	C7	1.48
C3	C4	1.56	C8	C8B	1.34

Bond Angles

N1	C1	C2	178		C5	C4	C9	110
C1	C2	C3	110		C8	C4	C9	111
C2	C3	C4	111		C4	C5	C6	112
C3	C4	C5	106		C5	C6	C7	111
C3	C4	C8	110		N2	C7	C6	179
C3	C4	C9	109		C4	C8	C8B	124
C5	C4	C8	110		N3	C9	C4	179

Torsion Angles

C1	C2	C3	C4	−176		C9	C4	C5	C6	59
C2	C3	C4	C5	−177		C3	C4	C5	C8B	−120
C2	C3	C4	C8	64		C5	C4	C8	C8B	123
C2	C3	C4	C9	−59		C9	C4	C8	C8B	1
C3	C4	C5	C6	177		C4	C5	C6	C7	172
C8	C4	C5	C6	−64						

8.1 Urea

CH$_4$N$_2$O

(i) N.Sklar, M.E.Senko, B.Post, Acta Cryst., 14, 716, 1961

(ii) N.Sklar, M.E.Senko, B.Post, Acta Cryst., 14, 716, 1961 (at −140°C)

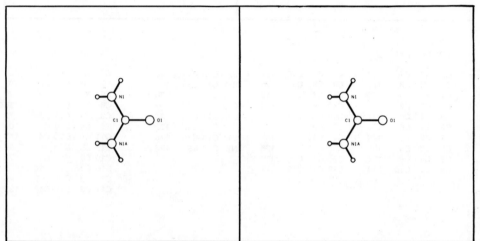

(i)

See also Worsham Junior & Levy, Acta Cryst., 10, 319, 1957; Caron & Donohue, Acta Cryst. (B), 25, 404, 1969.

P-42$_1$m   Z = 2   R$_{hk0}$ = 0.070, R$_{h0l}$ = 0.058

UREAXX   LB 1-4-15

(ii)

P-42$_1$m   Z = 2   R$_{hk0}$ = 0.070, R$_{h0l}$ = 0.059

UREAXX01   LB 1-4-15

Bond Lengths				Bond Angles				
		(i)	*(ii)*				*(i)*	*(ii)*
C1	N1	1.34	1.34	N1	C1	N1A	118	118
C1	O1	1.26	1.26	N1	C1	O1	121	121

8.2 Urea (at −140 °C)

CH$_4$N$_2$O

For complete entry see 8.1

8.3 Thiourea dioxide

CH$_4$N$_2$O$_2$S

R.A.L.Sullivan, A.Hargreaves, Acta Cryst., 15, 675, 1962

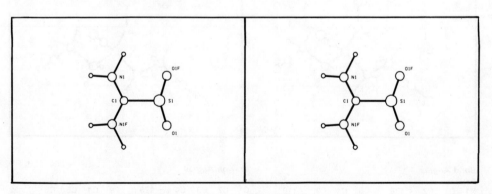

Pmnb   Z = 4   R = 0.090

SURDOX   LB 1-4-20

Bond Lengths			Bond Angles				Torsion Angles				
S1	O1	1.49	O1	S1	O1F	112	O1	S1	C1	N1	−150
S1	C1	1.85	O1	S1	C1	100	O1	S1	C1	N1F	36
C1	N1	1.31	S1	C1	N1	118					
			N1	C1	N1F	125					

8.4   Uronium chlorocadmiate

$CH_5N_2O^+$, $CdCl_3^-$

M.Nardelli, P.Boldrini, Acta Cryst., 16, A68, 1963

Atomic coordinates were not reported in the paper.
P2$_1$/c   Z = 4   R = 0.22

URNCCD

$$\begin{array}{c} NH_2 \\ | \\ C=O \quad Cd\,Cl_3^- \\ | \\ NH_3^+ \end{array}$$

8.5   Guanidinium chloride

$CH_6N_3^+$, Cl^-

D.J.Haas, D.R.Harris, H.H.Mills, Acta Cryst., 19, 676, 1965

$$\left[NH_2=C \underset{NH_2}{\overset{NH_2}{<}} \right]^+ Cl^-$$

Pbca   Z = 8   R = 0.062

GANIDC   LB 1-6-10

Bond Lengths			Bond Angles			
C1	N1	1.32	N1	C1	N2	121
C1	N2	1.33	N1	C1	N3	120
C1	N3	1.32	N2	C1	N3	119

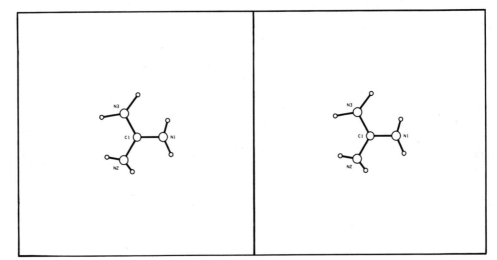

8.6   Biuret hydrate

$C_2H_5N_3O_2$, $0.6H_2O$

E.W.Hughes, H.L.Yakel, H.C.Freeman, Acta Cryst., 14, 345, 1961

P2$_1$/c   Z = 4   R = 0.157

BIUHYD   LB 2-5-19

$$\begin{array}{ccc} O & & O \\ \| & & \| \\ NH_2-C-NH-C-NH_2 & & .0{\cdot}6\,H_2O \end{array}$$

Bond Lengths			Bond Angles			
C1	N1	1.33	C1	N2	C2	128
C1	N2	1.39	N1	C1	N2	114
C2	N2	1.40	N1	C1	O1	121
C2	N3	1.36	N2	C1	O1	125
C1	O1	1.26	N2	C2	N3	118
C2	O2	1.25	N2	C2	O2	117
			N3	C2	O2	125

Torsion Angles

C2	N2	C1	N1	−173
C2	N2	C1	O1	12
C1	N2	C2	N3	−6
C1	N2	C2	O2	177

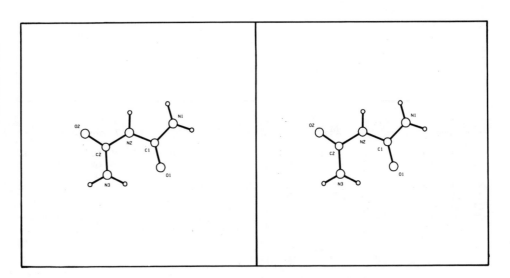

8.7 S - Methylthiouronium p - chlorobenzoate

$C_2H_6N_2S^+$, $C_7H_5ClO_2^-$

O.Kennard, J.Walker, J. Chem. Soc., 5513, 1963

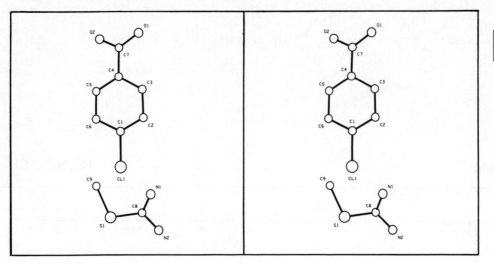

$P2_1/c$ Z = 4   R = 0.101

MSCBZO   LB 9-11-6

Bond Lengths

Cl1	C1	1.75
C7	O1	1.26
C7	O2	1.26
C1	C2	1.33
C1	C6	1.40
C2	C3	1.40
C3	C4	1.40
C4	C5	1.35
C4	C7	1.49
C5	C6	1.40

S1	C8	1.73
S1	C9	1.81
C8	N1	1.31
C8	N2	1.34

Bond Angles

Cl1	C1	C2	118
Cl1	C1	C6	118
C2	C1	C6	124
C1	C2	C3	117
C2	C3	C4	121
C3	C4	C5	119
C3	C4	C7	120
C5	C4	C7	122
C4	C5	C6	121

C1	C6	C5	117
O1	C7	O2	123
O1	C7	C4	119
O2	C7	C4	118
C8	S1	C9	101
S1	C8	N1	125
S1	C8	N2	115
N1	C8	N2	120

Torsion Angles

C3	C4	C7	O1	−18
C3	C4	C7	O2	164
C5	C4	C7	O1	163
C5	C4	C7	O2	−16
C9	S1	C8	N1	17
C9	S1	C8	N2	−167

8.8 S - Methylisothiourea sulfate

$2C_2H_7N_2S^+$, O_4S^{2-}

C.H.Stam, Acta Cryst., 15, 317, 1962

$[H_3C—S—C(NH_2)_2^+]_2 (SO_4)^{2-}$

Pcan   Z = 4   R = 0.152

MISURS   LB 4-14-10

Bond Lengths

S1	O1	1.47
S1	O2	1.46
S2	C1	1.80
S2	C2	1.74
C2	N1	1.31
C2	N2	1.33

Bond Angles

O1	S1	O2	110
O1	S1	O1C	110
O1	S1	O2C	109
O2	S1	O1C	109
O2	S1	O2C	109

C1	S2	C2	104
S2	C2	N1	114
S2	C2	N2	123
N1	C2	N2	123

Torsion Angles

C1	S2	C2	N1	−161
C1	S2	C2	N2	16

8.9 Triuret (monoclinic form)

$C_3H_6N_4O_3$

D.Carlstrom, H.Ringertz, Acta Cryst., 18, 307, 1965

O=C
/NH—CO—NH₂
\NH—CO—NH₂

See also Ringertz, Acta Cryst., 20, 932, 1966.

C2/c   Z = 8   R = 0.126

TRURET   LB 3-6-25

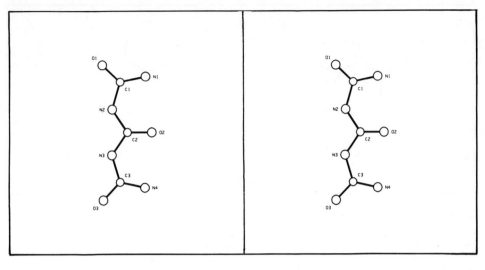

Bond Lengths		
C1	N1	1.32
C1	N2	1.41
C2	N2	1.37
C2	N3	1.37
C3	N3	1.39
C3	N4	1.33
C1	O1	1.23
C2	O2	1.22
C3	O3	1.24

Bond Angles			
C1	N2	C2	129
C2	N3	C3	128
N1	C1	N2	118
N1	C1	O1	125
N2	C1	O1	116
N2	C2	N3	111
N2	C2	O2	124
N3	C2	O2	125
N3	C3	N4	120
N3	C3	O3	117
N4	C3	O3	123

Torsion Angles				
C2	N2	C1	N1	3
C2	N2	C1	O1	−177
C1	N2	C2	N3	171
C1	N2	C2	O2	−9
C3	N3	C2	N2	174
C3	N3	C2	O2	−5
C2	N3	C3	N4	−12
C2	N3	C3	O3	169

8.10 Allylthiourea

$C_4H_8N_2S$

K.S.Dragonette, I.L.Karle, Acta Cryst., 19, 978, 1965

S=C
/NH—CH₂—CH=CH₂
\NH₂

In Table 8 the bonds to H(6) and H(6′) have been interchanged.

P2₁/c   Z = 4   R = 0.101

ALYTUR   LB 4-8-73

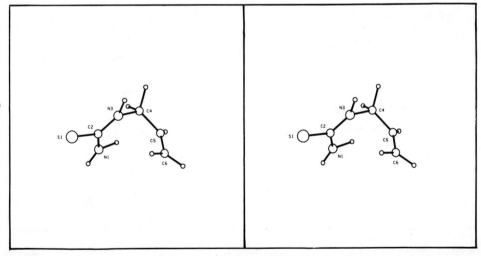

Bond Lengths		
S1	C2	1.66
C2	N1	1.36
C2	N3	1.35
C4	N3	1.48
C4	C5	1.53
C5	C6	1.27

Bond Angles			
C2	N3	C4	123
S1	C2	N1	120
S1	C2	N3	121
N1	C2	N3	120
N3	C4	C5	113
C4	C5	C6	128

Torsion Angles				
C4	N3	C2	S1	−174
C4	N3	C2	N1	7
C2	N3	C4	C5	−79
N3	C4	C5	C6	−11

8.11 Trimethylenethiourea

C₄H₈N₂S

H.W.Dias, M.R.Truter, Acta Cryst., 17, 937, 1964

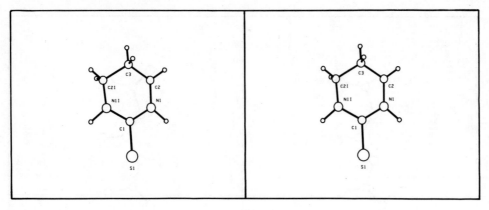

Abam   Z = 4   R = 0.108
TMETHU   LB 4-8-74

Bond Lengths

S1	C1	1.72
C1	N1	1.33
C2	N1	1.45
C2	C3	1.51

Bond Angles

C1	N1	C2	123
S1	C1	N1	120
N1	C1	N1I	120
N1	C2	C3	109
C2	C3	C2I	110

Torsion Angles

C2	N1	C1	S1	175
C2	N1	C1	N1I	−6
C1	N1	C2	C3	30
N1	C2	C3	C2I	−53

8.12 N - (1 - Phenylethyl) - N' - (3 - n - propyl methylsulfoxide) - thiourea (absolute configuration)

C₁₃H₂₀N₂OS₂

K.K.Cheung, A.Kjaer, G.A.Sim, J. Chem. Soc. (D), 100, 1965

Atomic coordinates were not reported in the paper.
P2₁2₁2₁   Z = 4   R = 0.118

BZSOTU   LB 13-20-2

$$H_3C-S-(CH_2)_3-NH-C-NH-CH-\text{(phenyl)}$$

with O double-bonded to S (left) and S double-bonded to C (centre), CH₃ on the CH.

8.13 N - Phenyl - N' - benzoylselenourea

C₁₄H₁₂N₂OSe

H.Hope, Acta Cryst., 18, 259, 1965

P2₁/c   Z = 4   R = 0.071

PBOSEU   LB 14-12-18

Bond Lengths

Se1	C2	1.82		C7	C8	1.40
C2	N3	1.32		C8	C9	1.38
C4	N3	1.43		C11	C12	1.48
C2	N10	1.40		C12	C13	1.40
C11	N10	1.39		C12	C17	1.37
C11	O18	1.22		C13	C14	1.37
C4	C5	1.38		C14	C15	1.39
C4	C9	1.37		C15	C16	1.39
C5	C6	1.40		C16	C17	1.39
C6	C7	1.35				

Bond Angles

C2	N3	C4	133		C4	C9	C8	121
C2	N10	C11	127		N10	C11	O18	122
Se1	C2	N3	129		N10	C11	C12	116
Se1	C2	N10	116		O18	C11	C12	122
N3	C2	N10	115		C11	C12	C13	116
N3	C4	C5	126		C11	C12	C17	124
N3	C4	C9	114		C13	C12	C17	120
C5	C4	C9	120		C12	C13	C14	120
C4	C5	C6	118		C13	C14	C15	120
C5	C6	C7	121		C14	C15	C16	119
C6	C7	C8	120		C15	C16	C17	120
C7	C8	C9	119		C12	C17	C16	120

Torsion Angles

C4	N3	C2	Se1	2
C4	N3	C2	N10	−176
C2	N3	C4	C5	1
C2	N3	C4	C9	179
C11	N10	C2	Se1	−172
C11	N10	C2	N3	6
C2	N10	C11	O18	−4
C2	N10	C11	C12	174
N10	C11	C12	C13	−150
N10	C11	C12	C17	31
O18	C11	C12	C13	28
O18	C11	C12	C17	−151

9.1   syn - Potassium methyldiazotate

$CH_3N_2O^-$, K^+

R.Huber, R.Langer, W.Hoppe, Acta Cryst., 18, 467, 1965

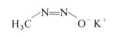

C2/c   Z = 8   R = 0.084

KMEDIZ   LB 1-3-9

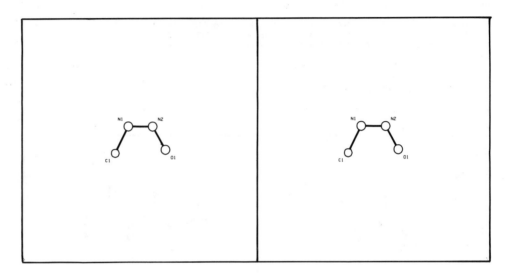

Bond Lengths			Bond Angles				Torsion Angles				
N1	N2	1.25	N2	N1	C1	116	C1	N1	N2	O1	1
N2	O1	1.31	N1	N2	O1	120					
C1	N1	1.48									

9.2   Semicarbazide hydrochloride

$CH_6N_3O^+$, Cl^-

M.Nardelli, G.Fava, G.Giraldi, Acta Cryst., 19, 1038, 1965

H_3N^+ —NH—CO—NH_2 Cl^-

$P2_12_12_1$ Z = 4   R = 0.128

SECAZC   LB 1-6-11

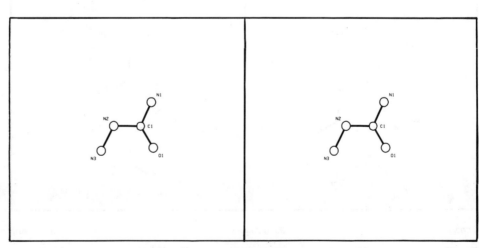

Bond Lengths			Bond Angles				Torsion Angles				
N2	N3	1.41	N3	N2	C1	114	N3	N2	C1	N1	161
C1	N1	1.31	N1	C1	N2	115	N3	N2	C1	O1	−22
C1	N2	1.38	N1	C1	O1	124					
C1	O1	1.24	N2	C1	O1	121					

9.3 Azodicarbonamide

C$_2$H$_4$N$_4$O$_2$

J.H.Bryden, Acta Cryst., 14, 61, 1961

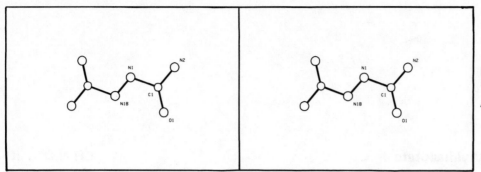

H$_2$N—CO—N=N—CO—NH$_2$

P2$_1$/n   Z = 2   R$_{0kl}$ = 0.132,
R$_{1kl}$ = 0.202

AZDCAR   LB 2-4-36

Bond Lengths

N1	N1B	1.24
C1	N1	1.48
C1	N2	1.30
C1	O1	1.26

Bond Angles

N1	C1	N2	111
N1	C1	O1	123
N2	C1	O1	126

Torsion Angles

C1	N1	N1B	C1B	−180
N1B	N1	C1	N2	−166
N1B	N1	C1	O1	15

9.4 Diacetylhydrazine

C$_4$H$_8$N$_2$O$_2$

R.Shintani, Acta Cryst., 13, 609, 1960

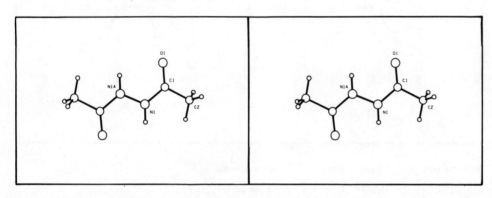

H$_3$C—CO—NH—NH—CO—CH$_3$

Ccma   Z = 4   R = 0.073

DIACHZ   LB 4-8-62

Bond Lengths

N1	N1A	1.40
C1	N1	1.34
C1	O1	1.22
C1	C2	1.50

Bond Angles

N1	C1	O1	122
N1	C1	C2	114
O1	C1	C2	123

9.5 p - Nitrophenylazide (at 100 °K)

C$_6$H$_4$N$_4$O$_2$

A.Mugnoli, C.Mariani, M.Simonetta, Acta Cryst., 19, 367, 1965

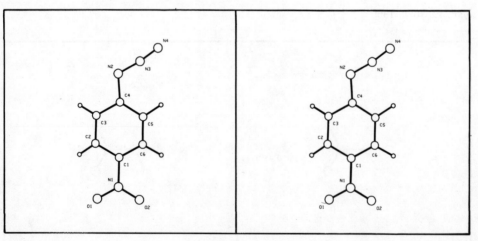

N$^-$—N$^+$≡N

NO$_2$

P2$_1$2$_1$2$_1$ Z = 4   R = 0.087

NIPHAZ   LB 6-4-63

Bond Lengths

N2	N3	1.27	C1	C2	1.39
N3	N4	1.13	C1	C6	1.37
N1	O1	1.23	C2	C3	1.39
N1	O2	1.25	C3	C4	1.37
C1	N1	1.45	C4	C5	1.39
C4	N2	1.42	C5	C6	1.38

Bond Angles

O1	N1	O2	121	C1	C2	C3	117
O1	N1	C1	120	C2	C3	C4	121
O2	N1	C1	119	N2	C4	C3	115
N3	N2	C4	115	N2	C4	C5	124
N2	N3	N4	173	C3	C4	C5	121
N1	C1	C2	118	C4	C5	C6	120
N1	C1	C6	119	C1	C6	C5	119
C2	C1	C6	123				

Torsion Angles

O1	N1	C1	C2	−3
O1	N1	C1	C6	−179
O2	N1	C1	C2	174
O2	N1	C1	C6	−2
N3	N2	C4	C3	174
N3	N2	C4	C5	−6

9.6   Benzenediazonium tribromide (at −20 °C) $C_6H_5N_2^+$, Br_3^-

O.Andresen, C.Romming, Acta Chem. Scand., 16, 1882, 1962

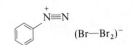

C2/c   Z = 4 R_{0kl} = 0.080,
R_{hk0} = 0.073, R_{h0l} = 0.073

BZDZTB   LB 6-5-9

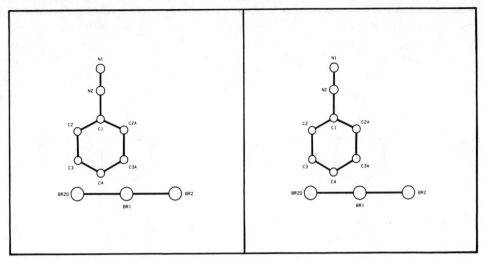

Bond Lengths

Br1	Br2	2.54	C1	C2	1.37
			C2	C3	1.45
N1	N2	1.11	C3	C4	1.38
C1	N2	1.41			

Bond Angles

Br2	Br1	Br2D	180	C2	C1	C2A	131
				C1	C2	C3	114
N1	N2	C1	180	C2	C3	C4	118
N2	C1	C2	114	C3	C4	C3A	125

9.7   Benzenediazonium copper(i) bromide complex (at −25 °C) $C_6H_5N_2^+$, $Br_3Cu_2^-$

C.Romming, K.Waerstad, Chem. Communic., 299, 1965

Atomic   coordinates   were   not
reported in the paper.
Pnma   Z = 4 R_{h0l} = 0.09,
R_{hk0} = 0.11

BDCUBR   LB 6-5-8

$[Cu_2Br_3]^-$.

9.8   Benzenediazonium chloride $C_6H_5N_2^+$, Cl^-

C.Romming, Acta Chem. Scand., 17, 1444, 1963

Cl^-

$C222_1$ Z = 4   R = 0.06

BZDIZC   LB 6-5-12

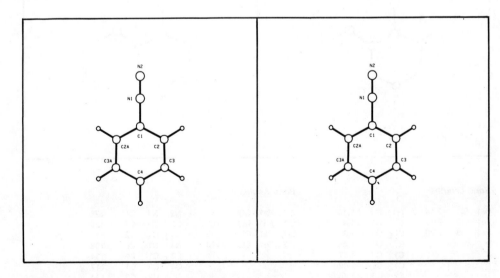

Bond Lengths

N1	N2	1.10	C2	C3	1.38
C1	N1	1.38	C3	C4	1.41
C1	C2	1.37			

Bond Angles

N2	N1	C1	180	C1	C2	C3	118
N1	C1	C2	118	C2	C3	C4	118
C2	C1	C2A	125	C3	C4	C3A	123

9.9 Phenylhydrazine hydrochloride

$C_6H_9N_2{}^+$, Cl^-

C.H.Koo, Bull. Chem. Soc. Jap., 38, 286, 1965

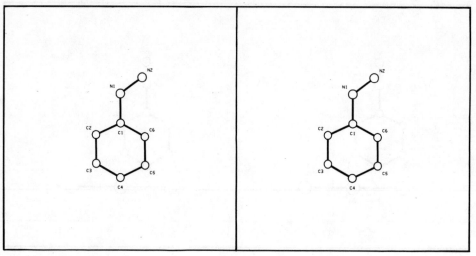

$P2_1/a$ $Z = 4$ $R_{hk0} = 0.10$, $R_{0kl} = 0.12$

PHYDZC   LB 6-9-7

Bond Lengths			Bond Angles				Torsion Angles				
N1	N2	1.43	N2	N1	C1	120	N2	N1	C1	C2	151
C1	N1	1.46	N1	C1	C2	114	N2	N1	C1	C6	−30
C1	C2	1.40	N1	C1	C6	119					
C1	C6	1.42	C2	C1	C6	128					
C2	C3	1.42	C1	C2	C3	114					
C3	C4	1.42	C2	C3	C4	119					
C4	C5	1.41	C3	C4	C5	127					
C5	C6	1.41	C4	C5	C6	114					
			C1	C6	C5	119					

9.10 o - Methoxybenzenediazonium chloride - ferric chloride

$C_7H_7N_2O^+$, Cl_4Fe^-

T.N.Polynova, N.G.Bokii, M.A.Porai-Koshits, Zh. Strukt. Khim., 6, 841, 1965

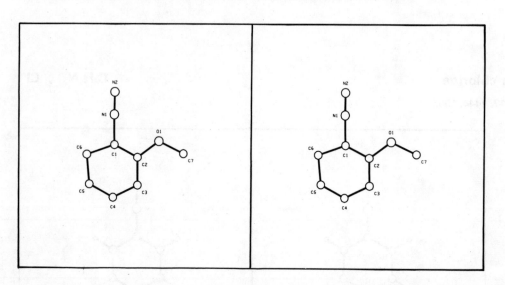

Pbmm $Z = 4$ $R = 0.133$

BEDNFE   LB 7-7-11

Bond Lengths						Bond Angles							
Fe1	Cl1	2.18	N1	N2	1.10	Cl1	Fe1	Cl2	110	N2	N1	C1	179
Fe1	Cl2	2.17	C1	N1	1.47	Cl1	Fe1	Cl3	108	C2	O1	C7	120
Fe1	Cl3	2.23	C2	O1	1.37	Cl1	Fe1	Cl1F	108	N1	C1	C2	118
			C7	O1	1.45	Cl2	Fe1	Cl3	114	N1	C1	C6	108
			C1	C2	1.37					C2	C1	C6	134
			C1	C6	1.49					O1	C2	C1	117
			C2	C3	1.40					O1	C2	C3	124
			C3	C4	1.41					C1	C2	C3	119
			C4	C5	1.41					C2	C3	C4	114
			C5	C6	1.49					C3	C4	C5	126
										C4	C5	C6	124
										C1	C6	C5	103

9.11 n - Nonanoic acid hydrazide

$C_9H_{20}N_2O$

L.H.Jensen, E.C.Lingafelter, Acta Cryst., 14, 507, 1961

$H_3C-(CH_2)_7-CO-NH-NH_2$

A2/a   Z = 2   R = 0.075

NONACH   LB 9-20-10

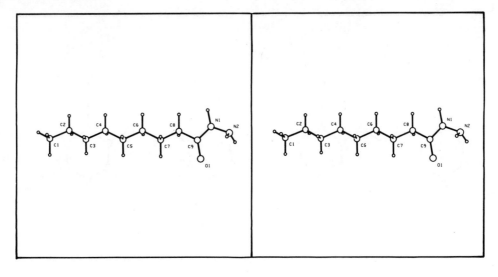

Bond Lengths

N1	N2	1.42
C9	N1	1.33
C9	O1	1.25
C1	C2	1.52
C2	C3	1.53
C3	C4	1.52
C4	C5	1.52
C5	C6	1.52
C6	C7	1.52
C7	C8	1.53
C8	C9	1.49

Bond Angles

N2	N1	C9	123
C1	C2	C3	113
C2	C3	C4	113
C3	C4	C5	114
C4	C5	C6	114
C5	C6	C7	113
C6	C7	C8	112
C7	C8	C9	111
N1	C9	O1	121
N1	C9	C8	117
O1	C9	C8	123

Torsion Angles

N2	N1	C9	O1	−2
N2	N1	C9	C8	178
C7	C8	C9	N1	−123
C7	C8	C9	O1	56

9.12 p - Dibromodiazoaminobenzene

$C_{12}H_9Br_2N_3$

Yu.D.Kondrashev, Kristallografija, 6, 515, 1961

Br—〈 〉—N=N—N—〈 〉—Br
                    |
                    H

$P2_1/n$ Z = 4 R_{hol} = 0.17

DBAABZ   LB 12-9-7

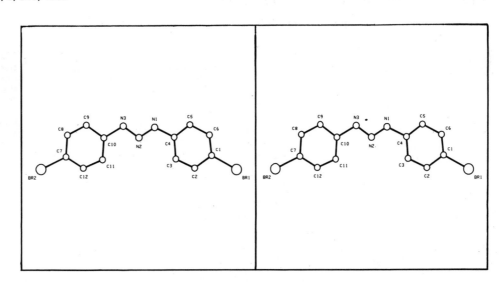

Bond Lengths

Br1	C1	1.89	C3	C4	1.41
Br2	C7	1.86	C4	C5	1.33
N1	N2	1.23	C5	C6	1.42
N2	N3	1.27	C7	C8	1.41
C4	N1	1.44	C7	C12	1.36
C10	N3	1.46	C8	C9	1.40
C1	C2	1.36	C9	C10	1.42
C1	C6	1.33	C10	C11	1.41
C2	C3	1.38	C11	C12	1.39

Bond Angles

N2	N1	C4	123	C1	C6	C5	123
N1	N2	N3	112	Br2	C7	C8	119
N2	N3	C10	115	Br2	C7	C12	123
Br1	C1	C2	116	C8	C7	C12	118
Br1	C1	C6	124	C7	C8	C9	120
C2	C1	C6	120	C8	C9	C10	120
C1	C2	C3	119	N3	C10	C9	116
C2	C3	C4	120	N3	C10	C11	124
N1	C4	C3	120	C9	C10	C11	120
N1	C4	C5	119	C10	C11	C12	117
C3	C4	C5	122	C7	C12	C11	125
C4	C5	C6	116				

9.13   2,4 - Dibromodiazoaminobenzene $C_{12}H_9Br_2N_3$

Yu.A.Omel'Chenko, Yu.D.Kondrashev, Kristallografija, 10, 822, 1965

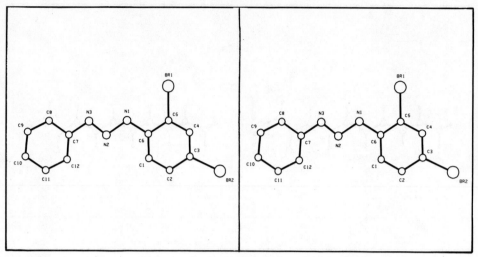

Published value of z(Br1) = 0.781.
The correct value is 0.219.
$P2_1/n$ Z = 4 R_{hk0} = 0.109,
R_{hk3} = 0.136

DBDAAB   LB 12-9-8

Bond Lengths

Br1	C5	1.90	C3	C4	1.36
Br2	C3	1.91	C4	C5	1.39
N1	N2	1.44	C5	C6	1.38
N2	N3	1.25	C7	C8	1.39
C6	N1	1.44	C7	C12	1.36
C7	N3	1.41	C8	C9	1.38
C1	C2	1.38	C9	C10	1.39
C1	C6	1.37	C10	C11	1.40
C2	C3	1.40	C11	C12	1.37

Bond Angles

N2	N1	C6	115	N1	C6	C1	123
N1	N2	N3	109	N1	C6	C5	116
N2	N3	C7	110	C1	C6	C5	121
C2	C1	C6	119	N3	C7	C8	113
C1	C2	C3	119	N3	C7	C12	126
Br2	C3	C2	123	C8	C7	C12	121
Br2	C3	C4	115	C7	C8	C9	120
C2	C3	C4	121	C8	C9	C10	121
C3	C4	C5	119	C9	C10	C11	118
Br1	C5	C4	118	C10	C11	C12	122
Br1	C5	C6	121	C7	C12	C11	120
C4	C5	C6	120				

9.14   p - Dimethyldiazoaminobenzene $C_{14}H_{15}N_3$

Yu.D.Kondrashev, Kristallografija, 9, 403, 1964

$$H_3C-\bigcirc-N=N-NH-\bigcirc-CH_3$$

The structure was determined in two dimensions only. Atomic coordinates were not reported in the paper.
$P2_1/n$ Z = 4 R_{h0l} = 0.19

DMDAZB   LB 14-15-8

10.1   Formamidoxime (refinement of data of Hall and Llewellyn, Acta Cryst., 9,108,1956)

CH_4N_2O

D.Hall, Acta Cryst., 18, 955, 1965

$$NH_2—CH=N—OH$$

P2$_1$2$_1$2$_1$ Z = 4   R = 0.079

FORAMO   LB 1-4-14

Bond Lengths			Bond Angles				Torsion Angles			
N2	O1	1.42	O1	N2	C1	110	O1	N2	C1	N1	1
C1	N1	1.33	N1	C1	N2	127				
C1	N2	1.29								

10.2   O - Methyl hydroxylamine hydrochloride

CH_6NO^+ , Cl^-

A.Laurent, C.Rerat, Acta Cryst., 17, 277, 1964

$$H_3C—O—NH_3^+ Cl^-$$

Bbam   Z = 8   R = 0.276

MOXAMC   LB 1-6-8

Bond Lengths			Bond Angles			
N1	O1	1.42	N1	O1	C1	109
C1	O1	1.46				

10.3   cis - bis(Nitrosomethane)

$C_2H_6N_2O_2$

G.Germain, P.Piret, M.van Meerssche, Acta Cryst., 16, 109, 1963

CH$_3$ CH$_3$
   \   /
    N=N
   /   \
  O   O

P2$_1$2$_1$2$_1$ Z = 4   R = 0.156

NSOMET   LB 2-6-35

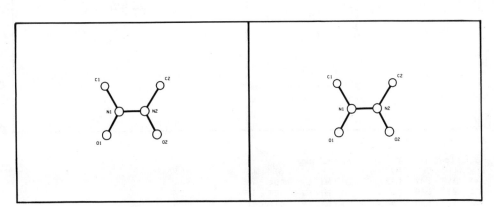

Bond Lengths			Bond Angles				Torsion Angles				
N1	N2	1.31	N2	N1	O1	120	O1	N1	N2	O2	3
N1	O1	1.32	N2	N1	C1	120	O1	N1	N2	C2	176
N2	O2	1.30	O1	N1	C1	120	C1	N1	N2	O2	−179
C1	N1	1.45	N1	N2	O2	118	C1	N1	N2	C2	−6
C2	N2	1.48	N1	N2	C2	123					
			O2	N2	C2	119					

10.4   Trimethylamine oxide

C_3H_9NO

A.Caron, G.J.Palenik, E.Goldish, J.Donohue, Acta Cryst., 17, 102, 1964

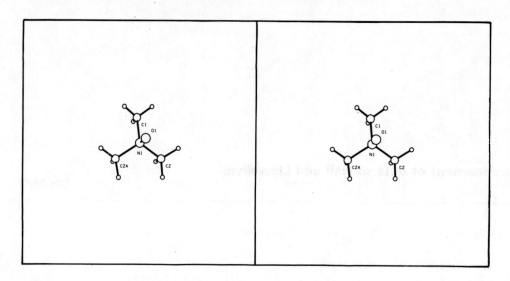

$(CH_3)_3 N{\rightarrow}O$

C2/m   Z = 4   R = 0.079

TMEAMO   LB 3-9-31

Bond Lengths

N1	O1	1.39
C1	N1	1.47
C2	N1	1.48

Bond Angles

O1	N1	C1	110
O1	N1	C2	110
C1	N1	C2	109
C2	N1	C2A	109

10.5   Trimethylamine oxide hydrochloride

$C_3H_{10}NO^+$, Cl^-

(i)   A.Caron, J.Donohue, Acta Cryst., 15, 1052, 1962 (refinement)

(ii)   C.Rerat, Acta Cryst., 13, 63, 1960

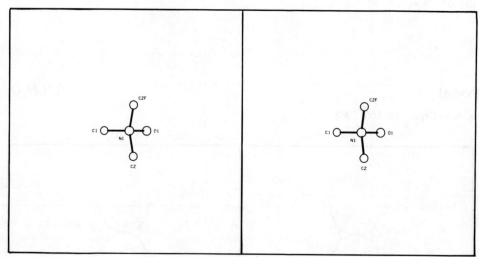

$(CH_3)_3 N^+{-}OH.Cl^-$

(i)

Pnam   Z = 4   R = 0.140

TMOHCL   LB 3-10-7

(ii)

Pnam   Z = 4   R = 0.22

TMOHCL01   LB 3-10-7

Caron and Donohue (ref. i) refined the structure reported by Rerat (ref. ii) making full allowance for thermal anisotropy and the effect of hydrogen atoms.

Bond Lengths

		(i)	(ii)
N1	O1	1.42	1.42
C1	N1	1.48	1.50
C2	N1	1.48	1.50

Bond Angles

			(i)	(ii)
O1	N1	C1	104	105
O1	N1	C2	109	109
C1	N1	C2	111	111
C2	N1	C2F	112	112

10.6   Trimethylamine oxide hydrochloride

$C_3H_{10}NO^+$, Cl^-

For complete entry see 10.5

10.7   Dimethylglyoxime

$C_4H_8N_2O_2$

W.C.Hamilton, Acta Cryst., 14, 95, 1961

P-1   Z = 1 R_{hk0} = 0.090,
R_{0kl} = 0.123

DMEGLY   LB 4-8-63

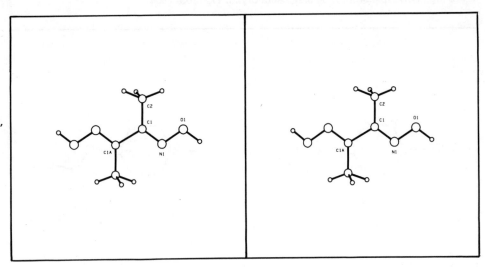

Bond Lengths			Bond Angles				Torsion Angles				
N1	O1	1.32	O1	N1	C1	111	O1	N1	C1	C2	1
C1	N1	1.25	N1	C1	C2	126	O1	N1	C1	C1A	176
C1	C2	1.48	N1	C1	C1A	114	N1	C1	C1A	N1A	−180
C1	C1A	1.56	C2	C1	C1A	120	N1	C1	C1A	C2A	5
							C2	C1	C1A	N1A	−5
							C2	C1	C1A	C2A	−180

10.8   anti - p - Chlorobenzaldoxime (refinement of data of Jerslev, Nature, 180,1410,1957)

C_7H_6ClNO

K.Folting, W.N.Lipscomb, B.Jerslev, Acta Cryst., 17, 1263, 1964

No comparison of bond lengths is
possible since they are not reported
in the paper.
See also Jensen, Acta Chem.
Scand., 24, 3293, 1970.
$P2_12_12_1$ Z = 4   R = 0.182

CBALOA   LB 7-6-8

Bond Lengths			Bond Angles				Torsion Angles			
Cl1	C2	1.80	O10	N9	C8	122	O10	N9	C8	C5	−1
N9	O10	1.44	Cl1	C2	C3	115	C4	C5	C8	N9	161
C8	N9	1.22	Cl1	C2	C7	115	C6	C5	C8	N9	−10
C2	C3	1.34	C3	C2	C7	130					
C2	C7	1.39	C2	C3	C4	116					
C3	C4	1.44	C3	C4	C5	118					
C4	C5	1.43	C4	C5	C6	122					
C5	C6	1.34	C4	C5	C8	114					
C5	C8	1.60	C6	C5	C8	123					
C6	C7	1.49	C5	C6	C7	121					
			C2	C7	C6	112					
			N9	C8	C5	128					

10.9 syn - p - Chlorobenzaldoxime (refinement of data of Jerslev, Nature, 180,1410,1957)

C_7H_6ClNO

K.Folting, W.N.Lipscomb, B.Jerslev, Acta Cryst., 17, 1263, 1964

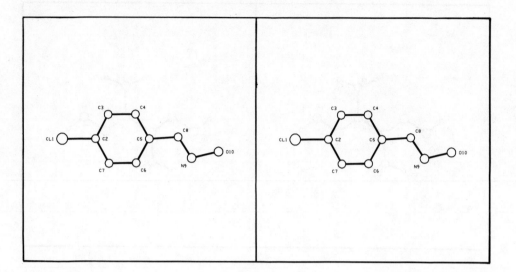

$P2_1/c$ Z = 4   R = 0.116

CBALOS   LB 7-6-9

Bond Lengths

Cl1	C2	1.73	C3	C4	1.40
N9	O10	1.41	C4	C5	1.40
C8	N9	1.26	C5	C6	1.37
C2	C3	1.37	C5	C8	1.49
C2	C7	1.40	C6	C7	1.38

Bond Angles

O10	N9	C8	111	C4	C5	C6	121
Cl1	C2	C3	119	C4	C5	C8	117
Cl1	C2	C7	120	C6	C5	C8	122
C3	C2	C7	122	C5	C6	C7	120
C2	C3	C4	119	C2	C7	C6	119
C3	C4	C5	119	N9	C8	C5	121

Torsion Angles

O10	N9	C8	C5	180
C4	C5	C8	N9	−171
C6	C5	C8	N9	9

10.10 5 - Chlorosalicylaldoxime

$C_7H_6ClNO_2$

S.H.Simonsen, C.E.Pfluger, C.M.Thompson, Acta Cryst., 14, 269, 1961

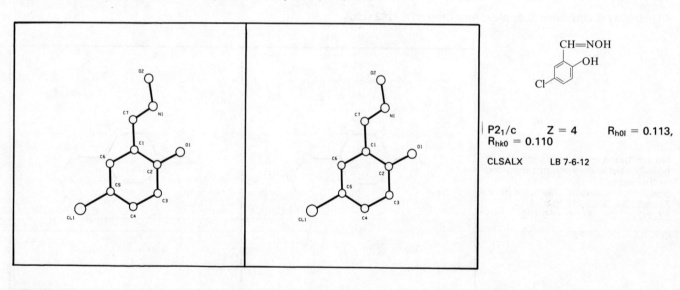

$P2_1/c$ Z = 4 R_{h0l} = 0.113, R_{hk0} = 0.110

CLSALX   LB 7-6-12

Bond Lengths

Cl1	C5	1.78	C1	C7	1.47
N1	O2	1.38	C2	C3	1.41
C7	N1	1.24	C3	C4	1.43
C2	O1	1.34	C4	C5	1.37
C1	C2	1.38	C5	C6	1.39
C1	C6	1.42			

Bond Angles

O2	N1	C7	114	C2	C3	C4	116
C2	C1	C6	120	C3	C4	C5	120
C2	C1	C7	125	Cl1	C5	C4	119
C6	C1	C7	116	Cl1	C5	C6	118
O1	C2	C1	120	C4	C5	C6	123
O1	C2	C3	116	C1	C6	C5	117
C1	C2	C3	123	N1	C7	C1	120

Torsion Angles

O2	N1	C7	C1	177
C2	C1	C7	N1	6
C6	C1	C7	N1	−176

10.11   N - Methyl - p - chlorobenzaldoxime   C₈H₈ClNO

K.Folting, W.N.Lipscomb, B.Jerslev, Acta Cryst., 17, 1263, 1964

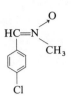

P2₁/a   Z = 4   R = 0.085

MCBZOX   LB 8-8-15

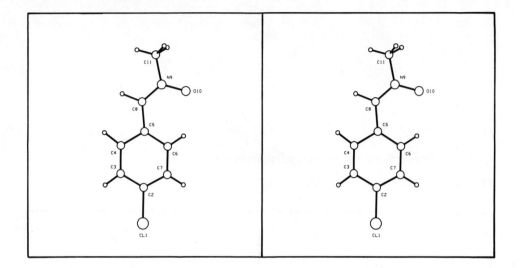

Bond Lengths

Cl1	C2	1.77	C3	C4	1.39
N9	O10	1.28	C4	C5	1.41
C8	N9	1.31	C5	C6	1.40
C11	N9	1.50	C5	C8	1.46
C2	C3	1.36	C6	C7	1.39
C2	C7	1.36			

Bond Angles

O10	N9	C8	125	C3	C4	C5	120
O10	N9	C11	116	C4	C5	C6	118
C8	N9	C11	119	C4	C5	C8	114
Cl1	C2	C3	119	C6	C5	C8	128
Cl1	C2	C7	118	C5	C6	C7	121
C3	C2	C7	122	C2	C7	C6	119
C2	C3	C4	120	N9	C8	C5	125

Torsion Angles

O10	N9	C8	C5	4
C11	N9	C8	C5	−177
C4	C5	C8	N9	174
C6	C5	C8	N9	−6

10.12   Nitrosoisobutane trans - dimer   C₈H₁₈N₂O₂

H.Dietrich, D.C.Hodgkin, J. Chem. Soc., 3686, 1961

P2₁/c   Z = 2   R$_{h0l}$ = 0.111,
R$_{hk0}$ = 0.198

NOSBUD   LB 8-18-16

Bond Lengths

N1	N1B	1.27
N1	O1	1.30
C1	N1	1.50
C1	C2	1.53
C2	C3	1.55
C2	C4	1.55

Bond Angles

O1	N1	C1	120
N1	C1	C2	111
C1	C2	C3	107
C1	C2	C4	105
C3	C2	C4	108

Torsion Angles

N1B	N1	C1	C2	76
O1	N1	C1	C2	−105
N1	C1	C2	C3	62
N1	C1	C2	C4	177

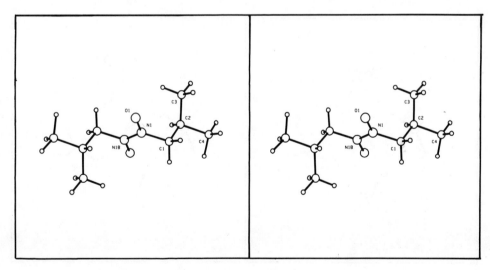

11.1   Potassium methylenedisulfonate

$CH_2O_6S_2^{2-}$, $2K^+$

M.R.Truter, J. Chem. Soc., 3393, 1962

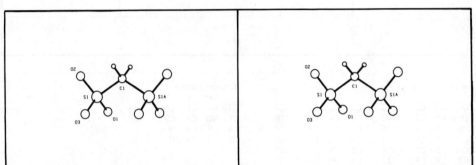

$[CH_2(SO_3)_2]^{2-} 2K^+$

No comparison of bond lengths is possible since they are not reported in the paper.
C2/c   Z = 4   R = 0.10

POTMES   LB 1-2-2

Bond Lengths

S1	O1	1.46
S1	O2	1.45
S1	O3	1.45
S1	C1	1.76

Bond Angles

O1	S1	O2	114	O2	S1	C1	102
O1	S1	O3	113	O3	S1	C1	106
O1	S1	C1	107	S1	C1	S1A	120
O2	S1	O3	113				

Torsion Angles

O1	S1	C1	S1A	−62
O2	S1	C1	S1A	178
O3	S1	C1	S1A	59

11.2   Trithiocarbonic acid (at − 100 ° C)

CH_2S_3

B.Krebs, G.Gattow, Z. Anorg. Allg. Chem., 340, 294, 1965

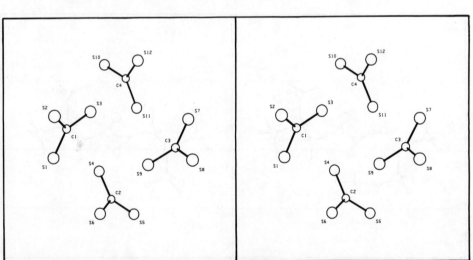

$P2_1/a$ Z = 16 $R_{hk0} = 0.088$, $R_{0kl} = 0.090$

TSCARB   LB 1-2-11

Bond Lengths

S1	C1	1.71	S7	C3	1.73
S2	C1	1.76	S8	C3	1.77
S3	C1	1.70	S9	C3	1.71
S4	C2	1.69	S10	C4	1.71
S5	C2	1.71	S11	C4	1.70
S6	C2	1.75	S12	C4	1.77

Bond Angles

S1	C1	S2	119	S7	C3	S8	119
S1	C1	S3	120	S7	C3	S9	121
S2	C1	S3	121	S8	C3	S9	120
S4	C2	S5	121	S10	C4	S11	121
S4	C2	S6	120	S10	C4	S12	119
S5	C2	S6	119	S11	C4	S12	120

11.3   Sodium methanethiosulfonate monohydrate

$CH_3O_2S_2^-$, Na^+ , H_2O

O.Foss, A.Hordvik, Acta Chem. Scand., 18, 619, 1964

$Na^+(CH_3S_2O_2)^- \cdot H_2O$

Pnma   Z = 4 R_{hol} = 0.10,
R_{0kl} = 0.087

NAMESM   LB 1-3-19

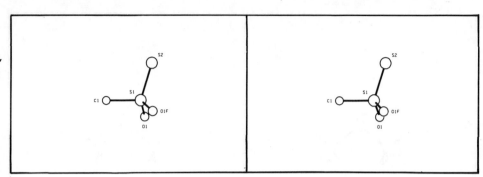

Bond Lengths			Bond Angles			
S1	S2	1.98	S2	S1	O1	111
S1	O1	1.45	S2	S1	C1	108
S1	C1	1.77	O1	S1	O1F	115
			O1	S1	C1	106

11.4   Sodium hydroxymethane sulfinate dihydrate (refinement of structure of Truter, J.Chem.Soc., 3064,1955)

$CH_3O_3S^-$, Na^+ , $2H_2O$

M.R.Truter, J. Chem. Soc., 3400, 1962

$\cdot Na^+(HO-CH_2-SO_2^-) \cdot 2H_2O$

No comparison of bond lengths is possible since they are not reported in the paper.
Pbca   Z = 8   R = 0.128

NAHMSD   LB 1-3-20

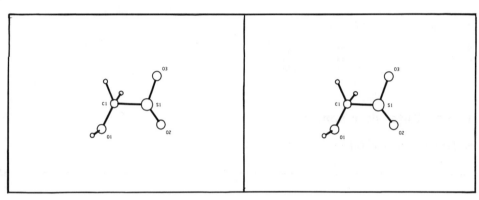

Bond Lengths			Bond Angles			
S1	O2	1.51	O2	S1	O3	109
S1	O3	1.51	O2	S1	C1	102
S1	C1	1.82	O3	S1	C1	101
C1	O1	1.40	S1	C1	O1	111

Torsion Angles

O2	S1	C1	O1	64
O3	S1	C1	O1	176

11.5   Perchlorodimethyl trisulfide

$C_2Cl_6S_3$

H.J.Berthold, Z. Kristallogr., 116, 290, 1961

$Cl_3C-S_3-CCl_3$

P2$_1$/c   Z = 4   R = 0.124

TCLMES   LB 2-0-23

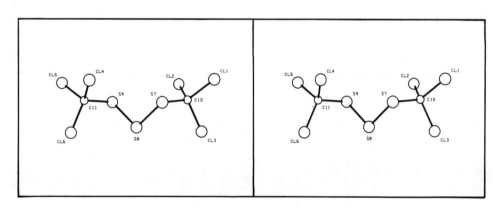

Bond Lengths						Bond Angles							Torsion Angles				
Cl1	C10	1.81	Cl6	C11	1.73	S8	S7	C10	102	Cl3	C10	S7	113	C10	S7	S8	S9	−92
Cl2	C10	1.74	S7	S8	2.03	S7	S8	S9	106	Cl4	C11	Cl5	108	S8	S7	C10	Cl1	−176
Cl3	C10	1.79	S7	C10	1.77	S8	S9	C11	101	Cl4	C11	Cl6	111	S8	S7	C10	Cl2	65
Cl4	C11	1.77	S8	S9	2.04	Cl1	C10	Cl2	108	Cl4	C11	S9	112	S8	S7	C10	Cl3	−61
Cl5	C11	1.82	S9	C11	1.81	Cl1	C10	Cl3	107	Cl5	C11	Cl6	109	S7	S8	S9	C11	−96
						Cl1	C10	S7	104	Cl5	C11	S9	102	S8	S9	C11	Cl4	72
						Cl2	C10	Cl3	108	Cl6	C11	S9	114	S8	S9	C11	Cl5	−172
						Cl2	C10	S7	116					S8	S9	C11	Cl6	−55

11.6   Dimethyl sulfone

D.E.Sands, Z. Kristallogr., 119, 245, 1963

$C_2H_6O_2S$

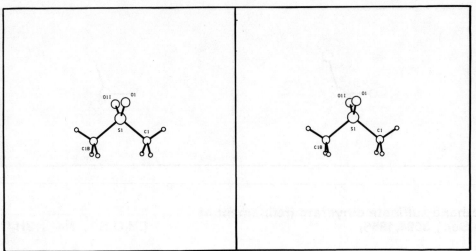

$(CH_3)_2SO_2$

See also Langs et al., J. Chem. Soc.
(D), 1653, 1970.
Cmcm   Z = 4 $R_{h0l} = 0.074$,
$R_{hk0} = 0.140$, $R_{0kl} = 0.151$

DMSULO   LB 2-6-45

Bond Lengths

S1	O1	1.45
S1	C1	1.78

Bond Angles

O1	S1	O1l	117
O1	S1	C1	109
C1	S1	C1B	103

11.7   Potassium xanthate

F.Mazzi, C.Tadini, Z. Kristallogr., 118, 378, 1963

$C_3H_5OS_2^-$, K^+

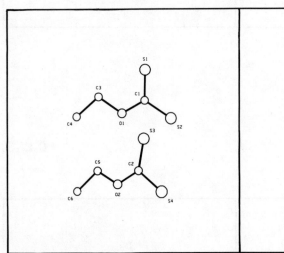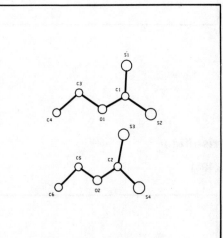

$C_2H_5-O-C\overset{\displaystyle S}{\underset{\displaystyle S^-}{}}$ K^+

$P2_1/c$ Z = 8 $R_{0kl} = 0.135$,
$R_{3kl} = 0.146$, $R_{h0l} = 0.134$,
$R_{hk0} = 0.124$

KXANTH   LB 3 - 5 - 6

Bond Lengths

S1	C1	1.69
S2	C1	1.66
C1	O1	1.36
C3	O1	1.48
C3	C4	1.55
S3	C2	1.67
S4	C2	1.71
C2	O2	1.34
C5	O2	1.45
C5	C6	1.53

Bond Angles

C1	O1	C3	116
S1	C1	S2	124
S1	C1	O1	121
S2	C1	O1	115
O1	C3	C4	103
C2	O2	C5	122
S3	C2	S4	125
S3	C2	O2	121
S4	C2	O2	113
O2	C5	C6	108

Torsion Angles

C3	O1	C1	S1	−10
C3	O1	C1	S2	172
C1	O1	C3	C4	−178
C5	O2	C2	S3	−7
C5	O2	C2	S4	−179
C2	O2	C5	C6	−177

11.8 Trimethyloxosulfonium fluoroborate

$C_3H_9OS^+$, BF_4^-

I.C.Zimmerman, M.Barlow, J.D.McCullough, Acta Cryst., 16, 883, 1963

$[(CH_3)_3SO]^+ BF_4^-$

The fluoroborate ions are disordered.
Pbcn   Z = 8   R = 0.101

TMOSFB   LB 3-9-6

Bond Lengths

S1	O1	1.44
S1	C1	1.75
S1	C2	1.76
S1	C3	1.76

Bond Angles

O1	S1	C1	113
O1	S1	C2	112
O1	S1	C3	113
C1	S1	C2	107
C1	S1	C3	107
C2	S1	C3	105

11.9 Trimethyloxosulfonium perchlorate

$C_3H_9OS^+$, ClO_4^-

C.L.Coulter, P.K.Gantzel, J.D.McCullough, Acta Cryst., 16, 676, 1963

$[(CH_3)_3SO]^+ ClO_4^-$

There are two structural types of perchlorate ions of which the second is disordered (CL2, O3, O4, O5).
P-42₁m   Z = 4   R = 0.067

TMOSPC   LB 3-9-10

Bond Lengths

S1	O1	1.42
S1	C1	1.75
S1	C2	1.73
Cl1	O2	1.41

Bond Angles

O1	S1	C1	112
O1	S1	C2	115
C1	S1	C2	106
C1	S1	C1G	106
O2	Cl1	O2A	112
O2	Cl1	O2B	108

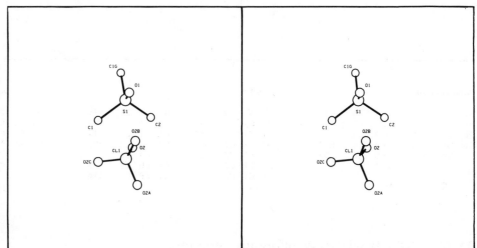

11.10 Tri (methylsulfonyl) methane

$C_4H_{10}O_6S_3$

J.V.Silverton, D.T.Gibson, S.C.Abrahams, Acta Cryst., 19, 651, 1965

H₃C—SO₂—CH with SO₂—CH₃ groups

Diffuse scattering is interpreted as disordered packing of stacks of ordered molecules.
R3c   Z = 6   R = 0.091

MESMET   LB 4-1-41

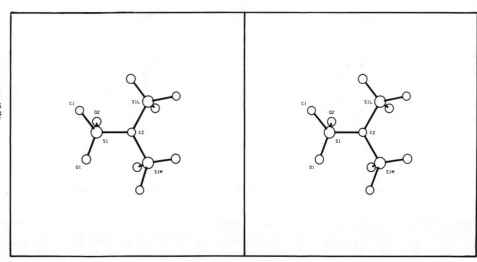

Bond Lengths

S1	O1	1.43
S1	O2	1.44
S1	C1	1.73
S1	C2	1.83

Bond Angles

O1	S1	O2	119
O1	S1	C1	107
O1	S1	C2	107
O2	S1	C1	111
O2	S1	C2	106
C1	S1	C2	105
S1	C2	S1L	111

Torsion Angles

O1	S1	C2	S1L	167
O1	S1	C2	S1M	44
O2	S1	C2	S1L	38
O2	S1	C2	S1M	−85
C1	S1	C2	S1L	−80
C1	S1	C2	S1M	157

11.11   Methyl phenyl sulfone

$C_7H_8O_2S$

L.G.Vorontsova, Kristallografija, 10, 187, 1965

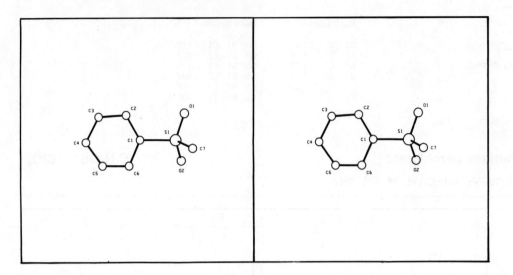

$P2_1/c$ Z = 4   R = 0.19

MPSUFO   LB 7-8-17

Bond Lengths

S1	O1	1.45	C1	C6	1.41
S1	O2	1.47	C2	C3	1.43
S1	C1	1.83	C3	C4	1.42
S1	C7	1.76	C4	C5	1.44
C1	C2	1.42	C5	C6	1.37

Bond Angles

O1	S1	O2	117	S1	C1	C6	114
O1	S1	C1	110	C2	C1	C6	123
O1	S1	C7	104	C1	C2	C3	117
O2	S1	C1	106	C2	C3	C4	120
O2	S1	C7	108	C3	C4	C5	117
C1	S1	C7	113	C4	C5	C6	126
S1	C1	C2	121	C1	C6	C5	114

Torsion Angles

O1	S1	C1	C2	−19
O1	S1	C1	C6	176
O2	S1	C1	C2	−146
O2	S1	C1	C6	49
C7	S1	C1	C2	97
C7	S1	C1	C6	−69

11.12   Dimethylphenylsulfonium perchlorate

$C_8H_{11}S^+$, ClO_4^-

A.Lopez-Castro, M.R.Truter, Acta Cryst., 17, 465, 1964

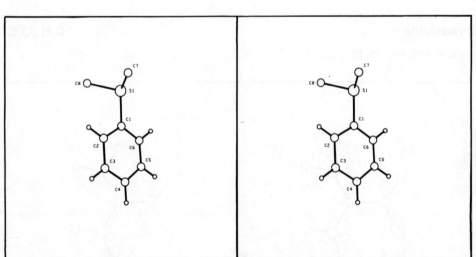

No comparison of bond lengths is possible since they are not reported in the paper.

$P2_1/c$ Z = 4   R = 0.14

MEPSOP   LB 8-11-4

Bond Lengths

Cl1	O1	1.47	S1	C1	1.82
Cl1	O2	1.46	S1	C7	1.79
Cl1	O3	1.54	S1	C8	1.82
Cl1	O4	1.34	C1	C2	1.39
			C1	C6	1.34
			C2	C3	1.46
			C3	C4	1.35
			C4	C5	1.41
			C5	C6	1.35

Bond Angles

O1	Cl1	O2	110	C1	S1	C7	103
O1	Cl1	O3	100	C1	S1	C8	105
O1	Cl1	O4	120	C7	S1	C8	102
O2	Cl1	O3	108	S1	C1	C2	122
O2	Cl1	O4	113	S1	C1	C6	115
O3	Cl1	O4	105	C2	C1	C6	123
				C1	C2	C3	118
				C2	C3	C4	119
				C3	C4	C5	118
				C4	C5	C6	125
				C1	C6	C5	117

Torsion Angles

C7	S1	C1	C2	63
C7	S1	C1	C6	−117
C8	S1	C1	C2	−44
C8	S1	C1	C6	136

11.13   4,4′ - Dichlorodiphenyl sulfone

$C_{12}H_8Cl_2O_2S$

J.G.Sime, S.C.Abrahams, Acta Cryst., 13, 1, 1960

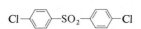

I2/a   Z = 4   R = 0.108

CLPSUL   LB 12-8-25

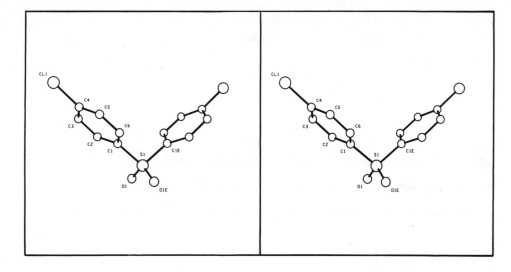

Bond Lengths			Bond Angles								Torsion Angles				
Cl1	C4	1.74	O1	S1	O1E	120	C1	C2	C3	119	O1	S1	C1	C2	−20
S1	O1	1.43	O1	S1	C1	107	C2	C3	C4	119	O1	S1	C1	C6	162
S1	C1	1.77	O1	S1	C1E	108	Cl1	C4	C3	120	O1E	S1	C1	C2	−151
C1	C2	1.38	C1	S1	C1E	105	Cl1	C4	C5	119	O1E	S1	C1	C6	31
C1	C6	1.39	S1	C1	C2	120	C3	C4	C5	122	C1E	S1	C1	C2	95
C2	C3	1.37	S1	C1	C6	119	C4	C5	C6	119	C1E	S1	C1	C6	−83
C3	C4	1.40	C2	C1	C6	121	C1	C6	C5	120					
C4	C5	1.38													
C5	C6	1.37													

11.14   4,4′ - Dichlorodiphenyl sulfone (neutron study)

$C_{12}H_8Cl_2O_2S$

G.E.Bacon, N.A.Curry, Acta Cryst., 13, 10, 1960

The y coordinates of non - hydrogen atoms are from Sime and Abrahams, Acta Cryst., 13, 1, 1960.

I2/a   Z = 4   R = 0.08

CLPSUL01   LB 12-8-25

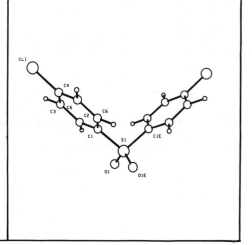

Bond Lengths			Bond Angles								Torsion Angles				
Cl1	C4	1.74	O1	S1	O1E	120	C2	C3	H3	120	O1	S1	C1	C2	−20
S1	O1	1.43	O1	S1	C1	107	C4	C3	H3	120	O1	S1	C1	C6	162
S1	C1	1.77	O1	S1	C1E	108	Cl1	C4	C3	120	O1E	S1	C1	C2	−151
C1	C2	1.38	C1	S1	O1E	108	Cl1	C4	C5	119	O1E	S1	C1	C6	31
C1	C6	1.39	C1	S1	C1E	105	C3	C4	C5	121	C1E	S1	C1	C2	95
C2	C3	1.37	S1	C1	C2	120	C4	C5	C6	119	C1E	S1	C1	C6	−83
C3	C4	1.39	S1	C1	C6	119	C4	C5	H5	121					
C4	C5	1.38	C2	C1	C6	121	C6	C5	H5	120					
C5	C6	1.37	C1	C2	C3	119	C1	C6	C5	120					
C2	H2	1.04	C1	C2	H2	117	C1	C6	H6	120					
C3	H3	1.09	C3	C2	H2	124	C5	C6	H6	120					
C5	H5	1.08	C2	C3	C4	119									
C6	H6	1.05													

12.1　Triphenylmethyl perchlorate (high temp. form)

A.H.Gomes de Mesquita, C.H.MacGillavry, K.Eriks, Acta Cryst., 18, 437, 1965

$C_{19}H_{15}^{+}$, ClO_4^{-}

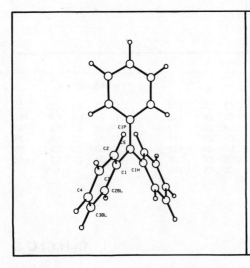
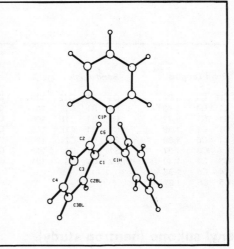

One perchlorate group, $ClO_4(a)$, is disordered.
$F4_132$　$Z = 16$　$R = 0.084$

TIPMEP　　　LB 19-15-3

Bond Lengths			Bond Angles				Torsion Angles				
C1	C2	1.40	C2	C1	C5	122	C2	C1	C5	C1H	148
C1	C5	1.45	C2	C1	C2BL	115	C2	C1	C5	C1P	-32
C2	C3	1.36	C1	C2	C3	124	C2BL	C1	C5	C1H	-32
C3	C4	1.37	C2	C3	C4	116	C2BL	C1	C5	C1P	148
			C3	C4	C3BL	125					
Cl2	O2	1.37	C1	C5	C1H	120					
			O2	Cl2	O2D	109					

12.2　Tri - (p - aminophenyl)carbonium perchlorate

L.L.Koh, Dissert. Abstr., 25, 3860, 1965

$C_{19}H_{18}N_3^{+}$, ClO_4^{-}

Atomic coordinates were not reported in the paper.
See also Koh & Eriks, Acta Cryst. (B), 27, 1405, 1971.
$P2_1/c$　$Z = 4$　$R = 0.097$

APCRBP　　　LB 19-18-1

12.3　3 - Chloro - 1,2,3,4 - tetraphenylcyclobutenium pentachlorostannate

R.F.Bryan, J. Amer. Chem. Soc., 86, 733, 1964

$C_{28}H_{20}Cl^{+}$, Cl_5Sn^{-}

Atomic coordinates were not given but bond lengths were reported.
Pbca　$Z = 8$　$R = 0.202$

CPBCSN　　　LB 28-20-4

13.1   2 - Chloro - 5 - nitrobenzoic acid

$C_7H_4ClNO_4$

G.Ferguson, G.A.Sim, J. Chem. Soc., 1767, 1962

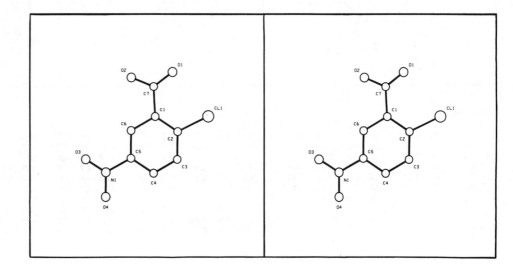

$P2_1/c$ Z = 4   R = 0.090

CLNBZA   LB 7-4-5

Bond Lengths

Cl1	C2	1.75	C1	C6	1.39
N1	O3	1.21	C1	C7	1.49
N1	O4	1.22	C2	C3	1.37
C5	N1	1.45	C3	C4	1.39
C7	O1	1.22	C4	C5	1.37
C7	O2	1.29	C5	C6	1.36
C1	C2	1.37			

Bond Angles

O3	N1	O4	122	Cl1	C2	C1	122	N1	C5	C6	119
O3	N1	C5	119	Cl1	C2	C3	116	C4	C5	C6	121
O4	N1	C5	118	C1	C2	C3	122	C1	C6	C5	121
C2	C1	C6	118	C2	C3	C4	120	O1	C7	O2	125
C2	C1	C7	125	C3	C4	C5	118	O1	C7	C1	121
C6	C1	C7	117	N1	C5	C4	119	O2	C7	C1	114

Torsion Angles

C2	C1	C7	O1	−23
C6	C5	N1	O3	−8

13.2   o - Bromobenzoic acid

$C_7H_5BrO_2$

G.Ferguson, G.A.Sim, Acta Cryst., 15, 346, 1962

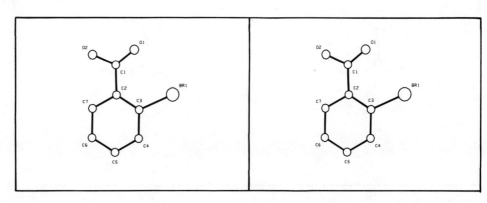

C2/c   Z = 8   R = 0.132

BRBZAC   LB 7-5-2

Bond Lengths

Br1	C3	1.89	C2	C7	1.38
C1	O1	1.20	C3	C4	1.43
C1	O2	1.35	C4	C5	1.38
C1	C2	1.49	C5	C6	1.36
C2	C3	1.36	C6	C7	1.44

Bond Angles

O1	C1	O2	120	C3	C2	C7	120	C4	C5	C6	119
O1	C1	C2	126	Br1	C3	C2	125	C5	C6	C7	121
O2	C1	C2	114	Br1	C3	C4	114	C2	C7	C6	119
C1	C2	C3	123	C2	C3	C4	121				
C1	C2	C7	117	C3	C4	C5	120				

Torsion Angles

O2	C1	C2	C7	−19

13.3   3,5 - Dibromo - p - aminobenzoic acid $C_7H_5Br_2NO_2$

(i)   A.K.Pant, Acta Cryst., 19, 440, 1965   (at −250°C)

(ii)   A.K.Pant, Acta Cryst., 19, 440, 1965   (at −150°C)

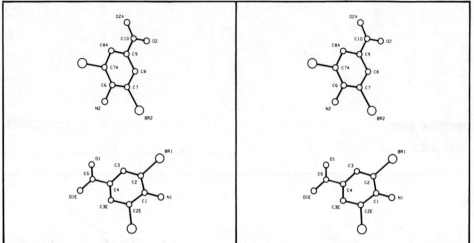

(i)

Pman   Z = 8 R_{hk0} = 0.094,
R_{0kl} = 0.102, R_{h0l} = 0.118

BRABZA   LB 7-5-7

(ii)

Pman   Z = 8 R_{hk0} = 0.088,
R_{0kl} = 0.098, R_{h0l} = 0.086

BRABZA01   LB 7-5-7

Bond Lengths

		(i)	(ii)			(i)	(ii)
Br1	C2	1.90	1.89	Br2	C7	1.91	1.85
C1	N1	1.31	1.40	C6	N2	1.44	1.37
C5	O1	1.27	1.27	C10	O2	1.27	1.30
C1	C2	1.40	1.40	C6	C7	1.35	1.43
C2	C3	1.48	1.42	C7	C8	1.44	1.40
C3	C4	1.39	1.41	C8	C9	1.39	1.43
C4	C5	1.47	1.43	C9	C10	1.45	1.42

Bond Angles

			(i)	(ii)				(i)	(ii)
N1	C1	C2	122	121	N2	C6	C7	120	120
C2	C1	C2E	116	118	C7	C6	C7A	120	119
Br1	C2	C1	120	120	Br2	C7	C6	122	121
Br1	C2	C3	116	118	Br2	C7	C8	115	119
C1	C2	C3	124	122	C6	C7	C8	122	120
C2	C3	C4	115	119	C7	C8	C9	115	121
C3	C4	C5	117	120	C8	C9	C10	118	121
C3	C4	C3E	126	120	C8	C9	C8A	124	119
O1	C5	O1E	124	121	O2	C10	O2A	118	119
O1	C5	C4	118	120	O2	C10	C9	121	120

Torsion Angles

				(i)	(ii)
C3	C4	C5	O1	4	1
C8	C9	C10	O2	2	0

13.4   3,5 - Dibromo - p - aminobenzoic acid (at − 150 ° C) $C_7H_5Br_2NO_2$

For complete entry see 13.3

13.5   o - Chlorobenzoic acid $C_7H_5ClO_2$

G.Ferguson, G.A.Sim, Acta Cryst., 14, 1262, 1961

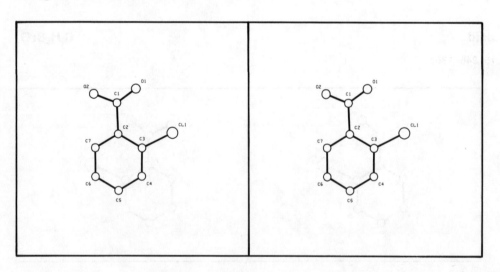

C2/c   Z = 8   R = 0.105

CLBZAC   LB 7-5-9

Bond Lengths

Cl1	C3	1.74	C2	C7	1.37
C1	O1	1.21	C3	C4	1.39
C1	O2	1.29	C4	C5	1.39
C1	C2	1.52	C5	C6	1.36
C2	C3	1.41	C6	C7	1.41

Bond Angles

O1	C1	O2	125	C3	C2	C7	120	C4	C5	C6	120
O1	C1	C2	122	Cl1	C3	C2	125	C5	C6	C7	121
O2	C1	C2	113	Cl1	C3	C4	116	C2	C7	C6	119
C1	C2	C3	123	C2	C3	C4	119				
C1	C2	C7	117	C3	C4	C5	121				

Torsion Angles

O2	C1	C2	C7	−14

13.6   o - Nitroperoxybenzoic acid   C₇H₅NO₅

M.Sax, P.Beurskens, S.Chu, Acta Cryst., 18, 252, 1965

P2₁/c   Z = 4   R = 0.119

NOXBZA   LB 7-5-29

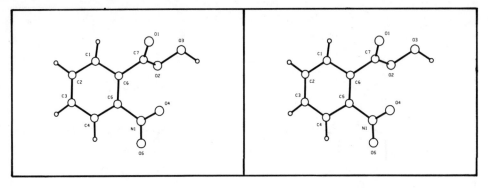

Bond Lengths

N1	O4	1.24	C1	C6	1.40
N1	O5	1.22	C2	C3	1.38
O2	O3	1.48	C3	C4	1.40
C5	N1	1.48	C4	C5	1.40
C7	O1	1.21	C5	C6	1.39
C7	O2	1.34	C6	C7	1.50
C1	C2	1.40			

Bond Angles

O4	N1	O5	125	C2	C3	C4	121	C1	C6	C7	117
O4	N1	C5	117	C3	C4	C5	118	C5	C6	C7	124
O5	N1	C5	118	N1	C5	C4	117	O1	C7	O2	125
O3	O2	C7	109	N1	C5	C6	121	O1	C7	C6	125
C2	C1	C6	120	C4	C5	C6	122	O2	C7	C6	110
C1	C2	C3	121	C1	C6	C5	119				

Torsion Angles

O3	O2	C7	O1	5
O3	O2	C7	C6	−180
C1	C6	C7	O1	56
C1	C6	C7	O2	−119
C5	C6	C7	O1	−126
C5	C6	C7	O2	59
C4	C5	N1	O5	26

13.7   m - Fluorobenzamide   C₇H₆FNO

T.Taniguchi, Y.Kato, Y.Takaki, K.Sakata, Mem. Osaka Gakugei Univ., B14, 56, 1965

The fluorine atoms are statistically distributed between the meta positions. The published bond lengths are incorrect (private communication).
P2₁/a   Z = 4 $R_{hk0} = 0.16$,
$R_{h0l} = 0.16$

BENAFM

Bond Lengths

C7	N1	1.34
C7	O1	1.22
C1	C2	1.37
C1	C6	1.39
C1	C7	1.48
C2	C3	1.40
C3	C4	1.38
C4	C5	1.37
C5	C6	1.37

Bond Angles

C2	C1	C6	120
C2	C1	C7	118
C6	C1	C7	121
C1	C2	C3	119
C2	C3	C4	120
C3	C4	C5	120
C4	C5	C6	120
C1	C6	C5	120
N1	C7	O1	122
N1	C7	C1	115
O1	C7	C1	123

Torsion Angles

C6	C1	C7	O1	154

13.8   p - Fluorobenzamide   C₇H₆FNO

Y.Takaki, T.Taniguchi, K.Sakurai, Mem. Osaka Gakugei Univ., B14, 48, 1965

The published bond lengths are incorrect (private communication).
P2₁/a   Z = 4 $R_{hk0} = 0.12$,
$R_{h0l} = 0.14$, $R_{0kl} = 0.18$

BENAFP

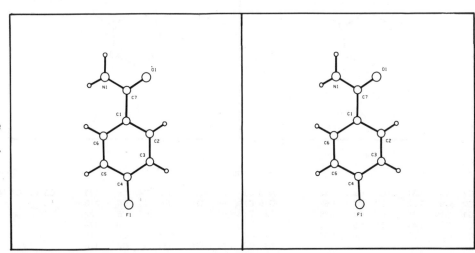

Bond Lengths

F1	C4	1.36	C1	C7	1.51
C7	N1	1.36	C2	C3	1.37
C7	O1	1.24	C3	C4	1.39
C1	C2	1.38	C4	C5	1.37
C1	C6	1.39	C5	C6	1.37

Bond Angles

C2	C1	C6	121	F1	C4	C3	119	N1	C7	O1	121
C2	C1	C7	117	F1	C4	C5	121	N1	C7	C1	118
C6	C1	C7	122	C3	C4	C5	120	O1	C7	C1	121
C1	C2	C3	118	C4	C5	C6	119				
C2	C3	C4	121	C1	C6	C5	121				

Torsion Angles

C6	C1	C7	O1	147

13.9 Salicylic acid

C₇H₆O₃

M.Sundaralingam, L.H.Jensen, Acta Cryst., 18, 1053, 1965

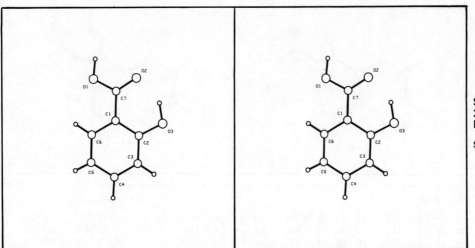

See also Cochran, Acta Cryst., 6, 260, 1953.
P2₁/a   Z = 4   R = 0.059

SALIAC   LB 7-6-25

Bond Lengths

C7	O1	1.31	C1	C7	1.46
C7	O2	1.23	C2	C3	1.38
C2	O3	1.36	C3	C4	1.38
C1	C2	1.40	C4	C5	1.38
C1	C6	1.40	C5	C6	1.37

Bond Angles

C2	C1	C6	119	C3	C4	C5	120
C2	C1	C7	120	C4	C5	C6	120
C6	C1	C7	121	C1	C6	C5	121
O3	C2	C1	123	O1	C7	O2	121
O3	C2	C3	118	O1	C7	C1	116
C1	C2	C3	120	O2	C7	C1	123
C2	C3	C4	121				

Torsion Angles

C2	C1	C7	O2	1

13.10 Salicylamide

C₇H₇NO₂

Y.Sasada, T.Takano, M.Kakudo, Bull. Chem. Soc. Jap., 37, 940, 1964

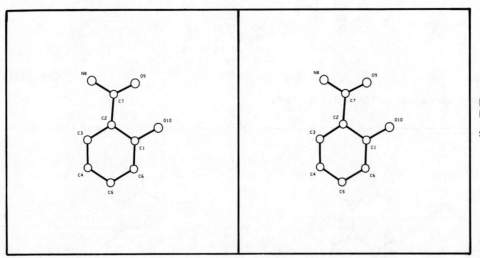

I2/a   Z = 8   R_hol = 0.087,
R_hk0 = 0.12, R_0kl = 0.12, R_h1l = 0.18

SALMID   LB 7-7-26

Bond Lengths

C7	N8	1.31	C2	C3	1.42
C7	O9	1.22	C2	C7	1.52
C1	O10	1.36	C3	C4	1.38
C1	C2	1.43	C4	C5	1.38
C1	C6	1.39	C5	C6	1.37

Bond Angles

O10	C1	C2	119	C3	C4	C5	123
O10	C1	C6	120	C4	C5	C6	118
C2	C1	C6	121	C1	C6	C5	122
C1	C2	C3	116	N8	C7	O9	124
C1	C2	C7	119	N8	C7	C2	116
C3	C2	C7	125	O9	C7	C2	120
C2	C3	C4	120				

Torsion Angles

C3	C2	C7	N8	5

13.11   m - Methylbenzamide

C_8H_9NO

S.Orii, T.Nakamura, Y.Takaki, Y.Sasada, M.Kakudo, Bull. Chem. Soc. Jap., 36, 788, 1963

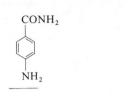

$P2_1/a$ $Z = 4$ $R_{hk0} = 0.11$,
$R_{h0l} = 0.20$, $R_{0kl} = 0.11$

MEBENA   LB 8-9-4

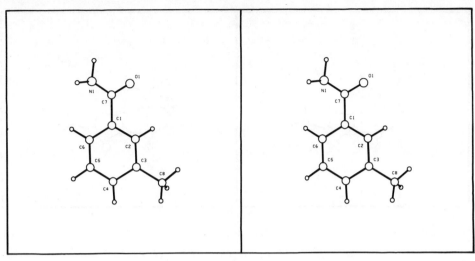

Bond Lengths

C7	N1	1.29	C2	C3	1.38
C7	O1	1.25	C3	C4	1.39
C1	C2	1.38	C3	C8	1.53
C1	C6	1.36	C4	C5	1.37
C1	C7	1.50	C5	C6	1.37

Bond Angles

C2	C1	C6	118	C3	C4	C5	119
C2	C1	C7	121	C4	C5	C6	121
C6	C1	C7	121	C1	C6	C5	120
C1	C2	C3	122	N1	C7	O1	121
C2	C3	C4	119	N1	C7	C1	119
C2	C3	C8	122	O1	C7	C1	119
C4	C3	C8	119				

Torsion Angles

C2	C1	C7	O1	27

13.12   2 - Amino - 3 - methylbenzoic acid

$C_8H_9NO_2$

(i)   G.M.Brown, R.E.Marsh, Acta Cryst., 16, 191, 1963   (visual intensities A)

(ii) G.M.Brown, R.E.Marsh, Acta Cryst., 16, 191, 1963   (visual intensities B)

(i)

$P2_1/c$ $Z = 4$ $R = 0.056$

AMEBAC   LB 8-9-6

(ii)

$P2_1/c$ $Z = 4$ $R = 0.074$

AMEBAC01   LB 8-9-6

The values in tables (i) and (ii) refer to two sets of intensity measurements independently determined.

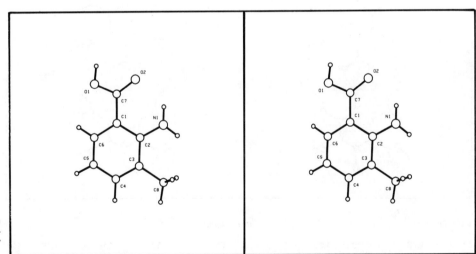

Bond Lengths

		(i)	(ii)			(i)	(ii)
C2	N1	1.37	1.37	C2	C3	1.42	1.42
C7	O1	1.32	1.32	C3	C4	1.38	1.38
C7	O2	1.23	1.23	C3	C8	1.50	1.50
C1	C2	1.41	1.42	C4	C5	1.39	1.39
C1	C6	1.41	1.41	C5	C6	1.37	1.38
C1	C7	1.46	1.46				

Bond Angles

			(i)	(ii)				(i)	(ii)
C2	C1	C6	120	120	C4	C3	C8	121	121
C2	C1	C7	122	121	C3	C4	C5	122	122
C6	C1	C7	119	119	C4	C5	C6	119	119
N1	C2	C1	122	122	C1	C6	C5	121	121
N1	C2	C3	119	119	O1	C7	O2	121	121
C1	C2	C3	119	119	O1	C7	C1	115	115
C2	C3	C4	119	119	O2	C7	C1	124	125
C2	C3	C8	120	120					

Torsion Angles

				(i)	(ii)
C6	C1	C7	O1	−3	−3

13.13   2 - Amino - 3 - methylbenzoic acid (visual intensities B)

$C_8H_9NO_2$

For complete entry see 13.12

13.14 Acetylsalicylic acid

P.J.Wheatley, J. Chem. Soc., 6036, 1964

$C_9H_8O_4$

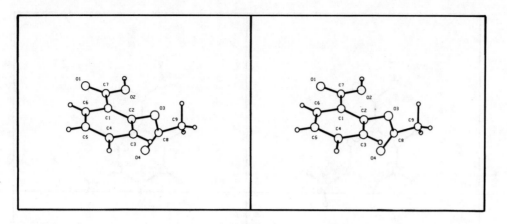

P2$_1$/c   Z = 4   R = 0.108

ACSALA   LB 9-8-18

Bond Lengths

C7	O1	1.24	C1	C7	1.50
C7	O2	1.29	C2	C3	1.39
C2	O3	1.40	C3	C4	1.39
C8	O3	1.36	C4	C5	1.38
C8	O4	1.18	C5	C6	1.38
C1	C2	1.40	C8	C9	1.50
C1	C6	1.39			

Bond Angles

C2	O3	C8	116	C4	C5	C6	120
C2	C1	C6	118	C1	C6	C5	121
C2	C1	C7	125	O1	C7	O2	123
C6	C1	C7	118	O1	C7	C1	119
O3	C2	C1	122	O2	C7	C1	118
O3	C2	C3	117	O3	C8	O4	123
C1	C2	C3	121	O3	C8	C9	111
C2	C3	C4	120	O4	C8	C9	126
C3	C4	C5	120				

Torsion Angles

C8	O3	C2	C1	−86
C8	O3	C2	C3	98
C2	O3	C8	O4	−2
C2	O3	C8	C9	178
C2	C1	C7	O2	−2

13.15 Mellitic acid

S.F.Darlow, Acta Cryst., 14, 159, 1961

$C_{12}H_6O_{12}$

Pccn   Z = 8   R = 0.117

MELLIT   LB 12-6-8

Bond Lengths

C7	O1	1.23	C15	O11	1.23
C8	O2	1.21	C16	O12	1.23
C9	O3	1.34	C17	O13	1.19
C8	O8	1.30	C16	O14	1.29
C9	O9	1.26	C17	O15	1.29
C10	O10	1.27	C18	O16	1.25
C1	C2	1.38	C11	C12	1.39
C1	C7	1.55	C11	C15	1.50
C2	C3	1.38	C12	C13	1.37
C2	C8	1.52	C12	C16	1.51
C3	C4	1.42	C13	C14	1.38
C3	C9	1.52	C13	C17	1.53
C4	C10	1.51	C14	C18	1.51

Bond Angles

C2	C1	C7	120	C12	C11	C15	121
C2	C1	C2A	120	C12	C11	C12A	119
C1	C2	C3	121	C11	C12	C13	121
C1	C2	C8	120	C11	C12	C16	120
C3	C2	C8	119	C13	C12	C16	119
C2	C3	C4	120	C12	C13	C14	119
C2	C3	C9	122	C12	C13	C17	122
C4	C3	C9	119	C14	C13	C17	118
C3	C4	C10	121	C13	C14	C18	119
C3	C4	C3A	119	C13	C14	C13A	121
O1	C7	O1A	128	O11	C15	O11A	129
O1	C7	C1	116	O11	C15	C11	115
O2	C8	O8	125	O12	C16	O14	126
O2	C8	C2	119	O12	C16	C12	119
O8	C8	C2	115	O14	C16	C12	115
O3	C9	O9	129	O13	C17	O15	127
O3	C9	C3	113	O13	C17	C13	119
O9	C9	C3	118	O15	C17	C13	114
O10	C10	O10A	128	O16	C18	O16A	127
O10	C10	C4	116	O16	C18	C14	116

Torsion Angles

C2	C1	C7	O1	−67
C1	C2	C8	O8	−31
C2	C3	C9	O9	−80
C3	C4	C10	O10	−25
C12	C11	C15	O11	−55
C11	C12	C16	O14	−44
C12	C13	C17	O15	−67
C13	C14	C18	O16	−51

13.16   p - Bromobenzoic anhydride

$C_{14}H_8Br_2O_3$

C.S.McCammon, J.Trotter, Acta Cryst., 17, 1333, 1964

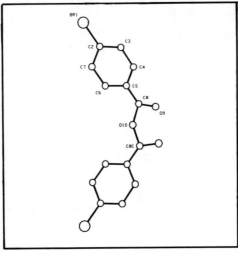

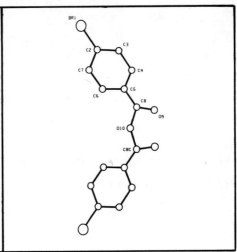

No comparison of bond lengths is possible since they are not reported in the paper. Published value of $x(C7) = 0.166$. The correct value is 0.116.

C2   Z = 2 $R_{h0l} = 0.25$,
$R_{hk0} = 0.23$

BBENAN   LB 14-8-7

Bond Lengths

Br1	C2	1.78
C8	O9	1.31
C8	O10	1.40
C2	C3	1.44
C2	C7	1.38
C3	C4	1.46
C4	C5	1.32
C5	C6	1.43
C5	C8	1.37
C6	C7	1.43

Bond Angles

C8	O10	C8C	146
Br1	C2	C3	126
Br1	C2	C7	120
C3	C2	C7	114
C2	C3	C4	125
C3	C4	C5	120
C4	C5	C6	115
C4	C5	C8	119
C6	C5	C8	126
C5	C6	C7	127
C2	C7	C6	119
O9	C8	O10	107
O9	C8	C5	131
O10	C8	C5	122

Torsion Angles

C4	C5	C8	O10	174
C5	C8	O10	C8C	−154

14.1 Potassium hydrogen di - p - chlorobenzoate

$C_7H_4ClO_2^-$, $C_7H_5ClO_2$, K^+

H.H.Mills, J.C.Speakman, J. Chem. Soc., 4355, 1963

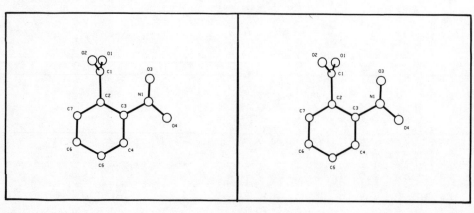

C2/c   Z = 4   R = 0.118

KHCBZO   LB 14-9-4

Bond Lengths

Cl1	C5	1.74	C2	C7	1.37				
C1	O1	1.32	C3	C4	1.39				
C1	O2	1.22	C4	C5	1.37				
C1	C2	1.49	C5	C6	1.38				
C2	C3	1.40	C6	C7	1.39				

Bond Angles

O1	C1	O2	122	C3	C2	C7	121	C4	C5	C6	122
O1	C1	C2	115	C2	C3	C4	119	C5	C6	C7	119
O2	C1	C2	123	C3	C4	C5	120	C2	C7	C6	120
C1	C2	C3	118	Cl1	C5	C4	120				
C1	C2	C7	121	Cl1	C5	C6	118				

Torsion Angles

O1	C1	C2	C7	−10

14.2 Rubidium hydrogen di - o - nitrobenzoate

$C_7H_4NO_4^-$, $C_7H_5NO_4$, Rb^+

H.N.Shrivastava, J.C.Speakman, J. Chem. Soc., 1151, 1961

No comparison of bond lengths is possible since they are not reported in the paper.

P-1   Z = 2 R_{h0l} = 0.188,
R_{hk0} = 0.178

RHNBZA   LB 14-9-15

Bond Lengths

N1	O3	1.15	C2	C3	1.35
N1	O4	1.24	C2	C7	1.37
C3	N1	1.43	C3	C4	1.36
C1	O1	1.21	C4	C5	1.31
C1	O2	1.26	C5	C6	1.43
C1	C2	1.53	C6	C7	1.30

Bond Angles

O3	N1	O4	127	C1	C2	C3	119	C3	C4	C5	119
O3	N1	C3	120	C1	C2	C7	118	C4	C5	C6	124
O4	N1	C3	113	C3	C2	C7	124	C5	C6	C7	116
O1	C1	O2	126	N1	C3	C2	125	C2	C7	C6	120
O1	C1	C2	120	N1	C3	C4	118				
O2	C1	C2	112	C2	C3	C4	117				

Torsion Angles

O2	C1	C2	C3	−106
O3	N1	C3	C2	12

14.3 Potassium hydrogen di - p - nitrobenzoate

$C_7H_4O_4^-$, $C_7H_5NO_4$, K^+

H.N.Shrivastava, J.C.Speakman, J. Chem. Soc., 1151, 1961

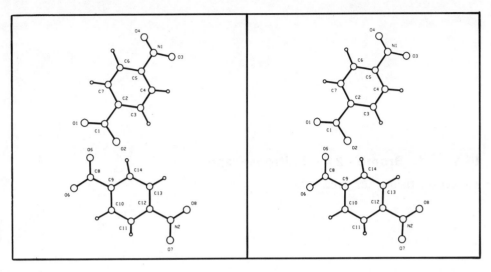

$K^+ H^+ \left(\begin{array}{c} COO^- \\ \\ NO_2 \end{array} \right)_2$

P-1   Z = 2   R = 0.104

KHNIBO   LB 14-9-11

Bond Lengths

N1	O3	1.23	N2	O7	1.23				
N1	O4	1.19	N2	O8	1.19				
C5	N1	1.49	C12	N2	1.46				
C1	O1	1.22	C8	O5	1.26				
C1	O2	1.32	C8	O6	1.24				
C1	C2	1.49	C8	C9	1.50				
C2	C3	1.41	C9	C10	1.40				
C2	C7	1.39	C9	C14	1.39				
C3	C4	1.36	C10	C11	1.41				
C4	C5	1.36	C11	C12	1.38				
C5	C6	1.38	C12	C13	1.39				
C6	C7	1.37	C13	C14	1.40				

Bond Angles

O3	N1	O4	125	N1	C5	C4	120	O6	C8	C9	118
O3	N1	C5	115	N1	C5	C6	118	C8	C9	C10	118
O4	N1	C5	119	C4	C5	C6	122	C8	C9	C14	123
O1	C1	O2	123	C5	C6	C7	119	C10	C9	C14	119
O1	C1	C2	123	C2	C7	C6	118	C9	C10	C11	121
O2	C1	C2	113					C10	C11	C12	118
C1	C2	C3	121	O7	N2	O8	124	N2	C12	C11	119
C1	C2	C7	117	O7	N2	C12	116	N2	C12	C13	118
C3	C2	C7	121	O8	N2	C12	120	C11	C12	C13	123
C2	C3	C4	118	O5	C8	O6	123	C12	C13	C14	118
C3	C4	C5	120	O5	C8	C9	120	C9	C14	C13	122

Torsion Angles

O4	N1	C5	C6	−7
O2	C1	C2	C3	12
O8	N2	C12	C13	−8
O6	C8	C9	C10	6

14.4 Potassium acid phthalate

$C_8H_5O_4^-$, K^+

Y.Okaya, Acta Cryst., 19, 879, 1965

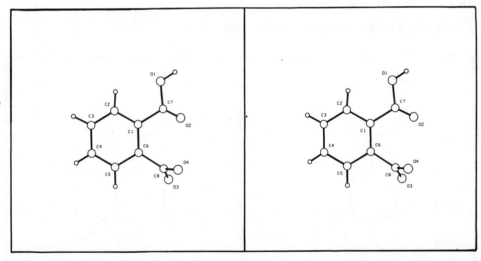

K^+ [benzene ring with] COOH / COO⁻

Published value of c = 13.857A. The correct value is 13.257A.
P2₁ab   Z = 4   R = 0.044

KHPHAL   LB 8-5-8

Bond Lengths

C7	O1	1.39	C1	C7	1.50	
		(1.30)	C2	C3	1.39	
C7	O2	1.21	C3	C4	1.38	
C8	O3	1.23	C4	C5	1.38	
C8	O4	1.27	C5	C6	1.40	
C1	C2	1.39	C6	C8	1.50	
C1	C6	1.40				

Bond Angles

C2	C1	C6	120	C4	C5	C6	120	O2	C7	C1	122
C2	C1	C7	120	C1	C6	C5	119	O3	C8	O4	125
C6	C1	C7	120	C1	C6	C8	123	O3	C8	C6	118
C1	C2	C3	120	C5	C6	C8	118	O4	C8	C6	117
C2	C3	C4	120	O1	C7	O2	121				
C3	C4	C5	120	O1	C7	C1	114				

Torsion Angles

O2	C7	C1	C6	31
O4	C8	C6	C1	75

15.1   1 - Bromo - 2,4 - dinitrobenzene

K.J.Watson, Nature, 188, 1102, 1960

$C_6H_3BrN_2O_4$

Atomic coordinates were not reported in the paper. The structure is isomorphous with the chloro compound.
See also Gopalakrishna, Acta Cryst. (A), 25, S150, 1969.
Pccn   Z = 8 R_{0kl} = 0.097, R_{hol} = 0.087

BENBRN   LB 6-3-2

15.2   1 - Chloro - 2,4 - dinitrobenzene

K.J.Watson, Nature, 188, 1102, 1960

$C_6H_3ClN_2O_4$

Atomic coordinates were not reported in the paper. The structure is isomorphous with the bromo compound.
See also Gopalakrishna, Acta Cryst. (A), 25, S150, 1969.
Pccn   Z = 8 R_{0kl} = 0.137, R_{hol} = 0.118

BENCLN   LB 6-3-8

15.3   m - Bromonitrobenzene

T.L.Charlton, J.Trotter, Acta Cryst., 16, 313, 1963

$C_6H_4BrNO_2$

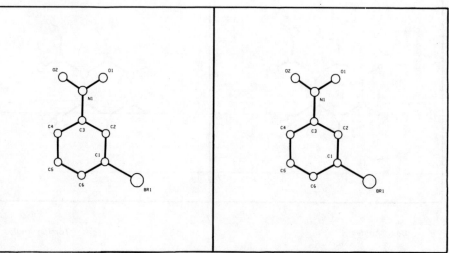

No comparison of bond lengths is possible since they are not reported in the paper.
Pbn2$_1$ Z = 4 R_{0kl} = 0.14, R_{hk0} = 0.14

BRNIBZ   LB 6-4-9

Bond Lengths

Br1	C1	1.88	C1 C6	1.37
N1	O1	1.23	C2 C3	1.38
N1	O2	1.21	C3 C4	1.40
C3	N1	1.46	C4 C5	1.41
C1	C2	1.39	C5 C6	1.36

Bond Angles

O1	N1	O2	115	C2 C1 C6	119	C3 C4 C5	117
O1	N1	C3	123	C1 C2 C3	116	C4 C5 C6	118
O2	N1	C3	123	N1 C3 C2	117	C1 C6 C5	124
Br1	C1	C2	117	N1 C3 C4	118		
Br1	C1	C6	123	C2 C3 C4	125		

Torsion Angles

C2	C3	N1	O1	2

15.4   m - Chloronitrobenzene $C_6H_4ClNO_2$

E.M.Gopalakrishna, Z. Kristallogr., 121, 378, 1965

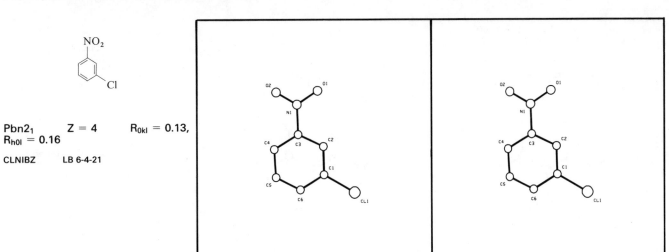

Pbn2₁   Z = 4 R_{0kl} = 0.13,
R_{h0l} = 0.16

CLNIBZ   LB 6-4-21

Bond Lengths

Cl1	C1	1.79	C1	C6	1.40
N1	O1	1.25	C2	C3	1.41
N1	O2	1.22	C3	C4	1.42
C3	N1	1.48	C4	C5	1.38
C1	C2	1.39	C5	C6	1.38

Bond Angles

O1	N1	O2	117	C2	C1	C6	120	C3	C4	C5	117
O1	N1	C3	121	C1	C2	C3	116	C4	C5	C6	119
O2	N1	C3	122	N1	C3	C2	117	C1	C6	C5	123
Cl1	C1	C2	120	N1	C3	C4	118				
Cl1	C1	C6	119	C2	C3	C4	125				

Torsion Angles

C2	C3	N1	O1	1

15.5   p - Chloronitrobenzene $C_6H_4ClNO_2$

T.C.W.Mak, J.Trotter, Acta Cryst., 15, 1078, 1962

No comparison of bond lengths is possible since they are not reported in the paper. There is a random interchange in the positions of the chloro and nitro groups.
P2₁/c   Z = 2 R_{0kl} = 0.23,
R_{h0l} = 0.26

CNITBZ   LB 6-4-22

Bond Lengths

C1	C2	1.35
C1	C3	1.34
C2	C3B	1.45

Bond Angles

C2	C1	C3	116
C1	C2	C3B	122
C1	C3	C2B	122

15.6   p - Dinitrobenzene $C_6H_4N_2O_4$

J.Trotter, Canad. J. Chem., 39, 1638, 1961

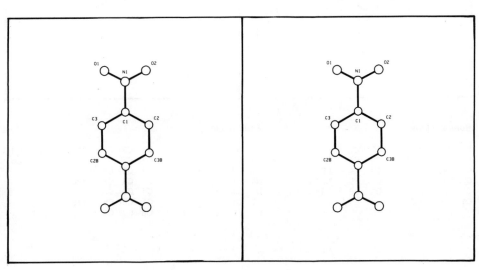

P2₁/n   Z = 2   R = 0.190

DNITBZ   LB 6-4-56

Bond Lengths

N1	O1	1.19
N1	O2	1.20
C1	N1	1.49
C1	C2	1.36
C1	C3	1.36
C2	C3B	1.36

Bond Angles

O1	N1	O2	126
O1	N1	C1	116
O2	N1	C1	117
N1	C1	C2	118
N1	C1	C3	119
C2	C1	C3	123
C1	C2	C3B	118
C1	C3	C2B	119

Torsion Angles

C2	C1	N1	O2	12

15.7   1,3,5 - Triamino - 2,4,6 - trinitrobenzene

$C_6H_6N_6O_6$

H.H.Cady, A.C.Larson, Acta Cryst., 18, 485, 1965

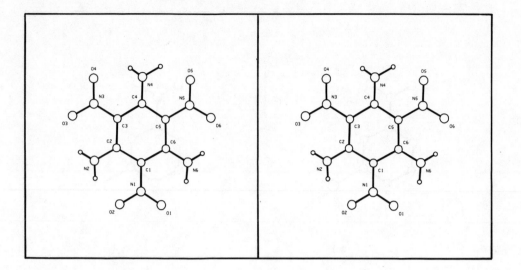

P-1   Z = 2   R = 0.056

TATNBZ   LB 6-6-55

Bond Lengths

N1	O1	1.24	C4	N4	1.32
N1	O2	1.24	C5	N5	1.42
N3	O3	1.25	C6	N6	1.31
N3	O4	1.24	C1	C2	1.44
N5	O5	1.24	C1	C6	1.45
N5	O6	1.26	C2	C3	1.45
C1	N1	1.42	C3	C4	1.44
C2	N2	1.31	C4	C5	1.45
C3	N3	1.42	C5	C6	1.44

Bond Angles

O1	N1	O2	118	N1	C1	C2	119	N4	C4	C3	121
O1	N1	C1	121	N1	C1	C6	119	N4	C4	C5	121
O2	N1	C1	121	C2	C1	C6	122	C3	C4	C5	118
O3	N3	O4	118	N2	C2	C1	121	N5	C5	C4	119
O3	N3	C3	121	N2	C2	C3	121	N5	C5	C6	119
O4	N3	C3	121	C1	C2	C3	118	C4	C5	C6	122
O5	N5	O6	117	N3	C3	C2	119	N6	C6	C1	121
O5	N5	C5	121	N3	C3	C4	119	N6	C6	C5	121
O6	N5	C5	121	C2	C3	C4	122	C1	C6	C5	118

Torsion Angles

C2	C1	N1	O2	3
C2	C3	N3	O3	−2
C4	C5	N5	O5	−1

15.8   o - Nitrobenzaldehyde (stable form)

$C_7H_5NO_3$

P.Coppens, G.M.J.Schmidt, Acta Cryst., 17, 222, 1964

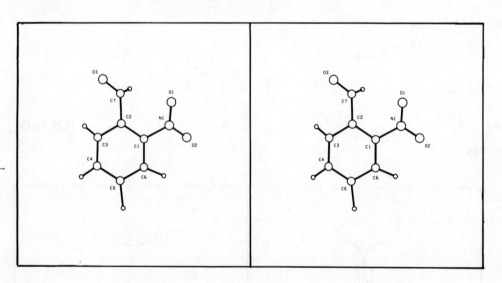

P2$_1$ Z = 2   R = 0.096

NIBZAL   LB 7-5-23

Bond Lengths

N1	O1	1.23	C2	C3	1.38
N1	O2	1.23	C2	C7	1.49
C1	N1	1.47	C3	C4	1.39
C7	O3	1.20	C4	C5	1.37
C1	C2	1.38	C5	C6	1.39
C1	C6	1.38			

Bond Angles

O1	N1	O2	125	C1	C2	C7	125
O1	N1	C1	118	C3	C2	C7	117
O2	N1	C1	117	C2	C3	C4	121
N1	C1	C2	120	C3	C4	C5	120
N1	C1	C6	117	C4	C5	C6	120
C2	C1	C6	123	C1	C6	C5	118
C1	C2	C3	117	O3	C7	C2	122

Torsion Angles

C3	C2	C7	O3	34
C6	C1	N1	O2	30

15.9   o - Nitrobenzaldehyde (stable form, neutron diffraction)   C₇H₅NO₃

P.Coppens, Acta Cryst., 17, 573, 1964

P2₁   Z = 2   R = 0.140

NIBZAL01   LB 7-5-23

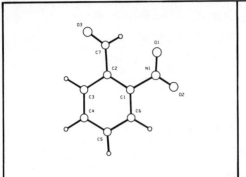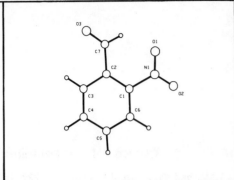

Bond Lengths

N1	O1	1.23	C3	C4	1.39
N1	O2	1.23	C4	C5	1.37
C1	N1	1.47	C5	C6	1.39
C7	O3	1.20	C3	H3	1.07
C1	C2	1.38	C4	H4	1.09
C1	C6	1.38	C5	H5	1.07
C2	C3	1.38	C6	H6	1.09
C2	C7	1.49	C7	H7	1.12

Bond Angles

O1	N1	O2	125	C3	C2	C7	117	C4	C5	H5	124
O1	N1	C1	118	C2	C3	C4	121	C6	C5	H5	116
O2	N1	C1	117	C2	C3	H3	118	C1	C6	C5	118
N1	C1	C2	120	C4	C3	H3	120	C1	C6	H6	121
N1	C1	C6	117	C3	C4	C5	120	C5	C6	H6	121
C2	C1	C6	123	C3	C4	H4	121	O3	C7	C2	122
C1	C2	C3	117	C5	C4	H4	119	O3	C7	H7	122
C1	C2	C7	125	C4	C5	C6	120	C2	C7	H7	115

Torsion Angles

C3	C2	C7	O3	34
C6	C1	N1	O2	30

15.10   Methyl o - nitrobenzenesulfenate   C₇H₇NO₃S

W.C.Hamilton, S.J.La Placa, J. Amer. Chem. Soc., 86, 2289, 1964

Atomic coordinates were not given
but bond lengths were reported.
P2₁/n   Z = 4   No R factor was
given.

MENBZS   LB 7-7-29

15.11   4,4' - Dinitrodiphenyl   C₁₂H₈N₂O₄

E.G.Boonstra, Acta Cryst., 16, 816, 1963

Pc   Z = 2   R = 0.150

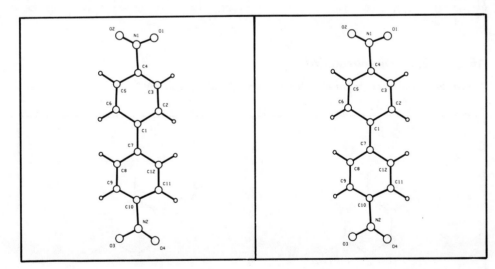

Bond Lengths

N1	O1	1.24	C3	C4	1.32
N1	O2	1.13	C4	C5	1.41
N2	O3	1.25	C5	C6	1.40
N2	O4	1.17	C7	C8	1.39
C4	N1	1.52	C7	C12	1.40
C10	N2	1.54	C8	C9	1.37
C1	C2	1.44	C9	C10	1.31
C1	C6	1.48	C10	C11	1.40
C1	C7	1.50	C11	C12	1.36
C2	C3	1.44			

Bond Angles

O1	N1	O2	137	C1	C2	C3	117	C8	C7	C12	120
O1	N1	C4	107	C2	C3	C4	122	C7	C8	C9	121
O2	N1	C4	117	N1	C4	C3	123	C8	C9	C10	115
O3	N2	O4	120	N1	C4	C5	112	N2	C10	C9	120
O3	N2	C10	114	C3	C4	C5	124	N2	C10	C11	110
O4	N2	C10	126	C4	C5	C6	119	C9	C10	C11	130
C2	C1	C6	120	C1	C6	C5	118	C10	C11	C12	114
C2	C1	C7	120	C1	C7	C8	118	C7	C12	C11	120
C6	C1	C7	119	C1	C7	C12	121				

Torsion Angles

C2	C1	C7	C8	−146
C3	C4	N1	O1	13
C9	C10	N2	O3	5

16.1   2 - Chloro - 4 - nitroaniline

A.T.McPhail, G.A.Sim, J. Chem. Soc., 227, 1965

$C_6H_5ClN_2O_2$

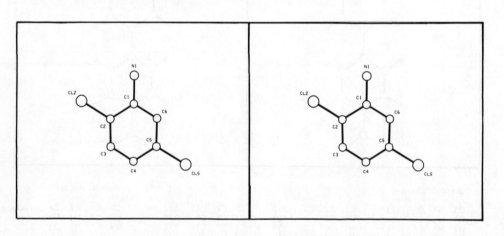

Pna2$_1$ Z = 4   R = 0.103

CLONAN   LB 6-5-13

Bond Lengths

Cl1	C2	1.76	C1	C6	1.42
N2	O1	1.23	C2	C3	1.40
N2	O2	1.23	C3	C4	1.40
C1	N1	1.38	C4	C5	1.39
C4	N2	1.47	C5	C6	1.39
C1	C2	1.39			

Bond Angles

O1	N2	O2	123	C2	C1	C6	117	N2	C4	C3	118
O1	N2	C4	118	Cl1	C2	C1	118	N2	C4	C5	119
O2	N2	C4	119	Cl1	C2	C3	118	C3	C4	C5	123
N1	C1	C2	124	C1	C2	C3	123	C4	C5	C6	118
N1	C1	C6	119	C2	C3	C4	117	C1	C6	C5	122

Torsion Angles

C5	C4	N2	O2	7

16.2   2,5 - Dichloraniline

T.Sakurai, M.Sundaralingam, G.A.Jeffrey, Acta Cryst., 16, 354, 1963

$C_6H_5Cl_2N$

P2$_1$/c   Z = 4   R = 0.126

DCHLAN   LB 6-5-18

Bond Lengths

Cl2	C2	1.74	C1	C2	1.42	C3	C4	1.37
Cl5	C5	1.73	C1	C6	1.39	C4	C5	1.39
C1	N1	1.40	C2	C3	1.36	C5	C6	1.38

Bond Angles

N1	C1	C2	122	Cl2	C2	C1	118	C2	C3	C4	123	Cl5	C5	C6	119
N1	C1	C6	120	Cl2	C2	C3	122	C3	C4	C5	117	C4	C5	C6	123
C2	C1	C6	118	C1	C2	C3	121	Cl5	C5	C4	118	C1	C6	C5	120

16.3   4 - Nitroaniline

K.N.Trueblood, E.Goldish, J.Donohue, Acta Cryst., 14, 1009, 1961

$C_6H_6N_2O_2$

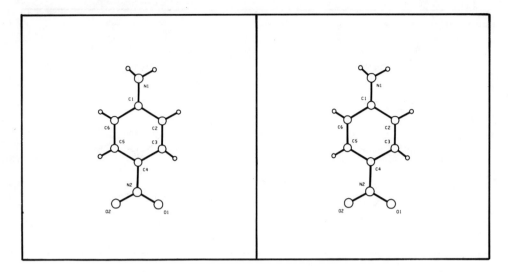

P2$_1$/n   Z = 4   R = 0.095

NANILI   LB 6-6-49

Bond Lengths

N2	O1	1.23
N2	O2	1.23
C1	N1	1.35
C4	N2	1.45
C1	C2	1.41
C1	C6	1.41
C2	C3	1.37
C3	C4	1.39
C4	C5	1.39
C5	C6	1.37

Bond Angles

O1	N2	O2	123		C2	C3	C4	119
O1	N2	C4	118		N2	C4	C3	120
O2	N2	C4	119		N2	C4	C5	118
N1	C1	C2	121		C3	C4	C5	121
N1	C1	C6	120		C4	C5	C6	120
C2	C1	C6	119		C1	C6	C5	120
C1	C2	C3	121					

Torsion Angles

C5	C4	N2	O2	−3

16.4   Aniline - m - sulfonic acid

S.R.Hall, E.N.Maslen, Acta Cryst., 18, 301, 1965

$C_6H_7NO_3S$

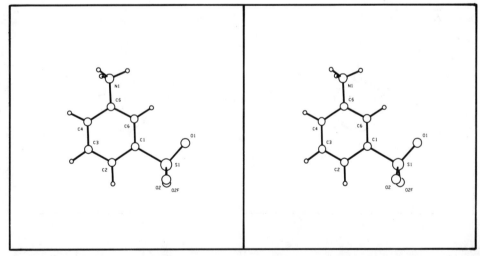

Pnam   Z = 4   R$_{hk0}$ = 0.059,
R$_{0kl}$ = 0.065

ANISAC   LB 6-7-20

Bond Lengths

S1	O1	1.44
S1	O2	1.44
S1	C1	1.80
C5	N1	1.44
C1	C2	1.41
C1	C6	1.37
C2	C3	1.37
C3	C4	1.38
C4	C5	1.41
C5	C6	1.36

Bond Angles

O1	S1	O2	113		C1	C2	C3	119
O1	S1	C1	104		C2	C3	C4	121
O2	S1	O2F	112		C3	C4	C5	120
O2	S1	C1	107		N1	C5	C4	119
S1	C1	C2	117		N1	C5	C6	121
S1	C1	C6	121		C4	C5	C6	121
C2	C1	C6	121		C1	C6	C5	119

Torsion Angles

O1	S1	C1	C6	0

16.5 Sulfanilic acid monohydrate

$C_6H_7NO_3S$, H_2O

A.I.M.Rae, E.N.Maslen, Acta Cryst., 15, 1285, 1962

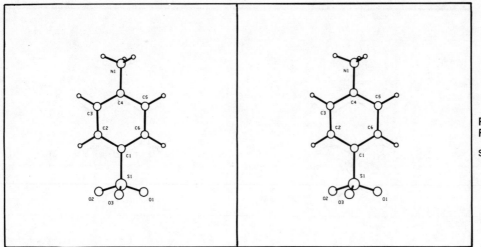

$P2_1/c$ $\quad$ Z = 4 $\quad$ $R_{hk0} = 0.123$, $R_{0kl} = 0.146$

SANACM $\quad$ LB 6-7-21

Bond Lengths

S1	O1	1.42
S1	O2	1.46
S1	O3	1.44
S1	C1	1.77
C4	N1	1.49
C1	C2	1.37

C1	C6	1.40
C2	C3	1.41
C3	C4	1.36
C4	C5	1.42
C5	C6	1.40

Bond Angles

O1	S1	O2	110
O1	S1	O3	116
O1	S1	C1	107
O2	S1	O3	112
O2	S1	C1	106
O3	S1	C1	105
S1	C1	C2	119
S1	C1	C6	120

C2	C1	C6	120
C1	C2	C3	122
C2	C3	C4	117
N1	C4	C3	120
N1	C4	C5	116
C3	C4	C5	125
C4	C5	C6	116
C1	C6	C5	120

Torsion Angles

C6	C1	S1	O1	−28
C6	C1	S1	O2	−145
C6	C1	S1	O3	96

16.6 Aniline hydrobromide (high temp. form)

$C_6H_8N^+$, Br^-

I.Nitta, T.Watanabe, I.Taguchi, Bull. Chem. Soc. Jap., 34, 1405, 1961

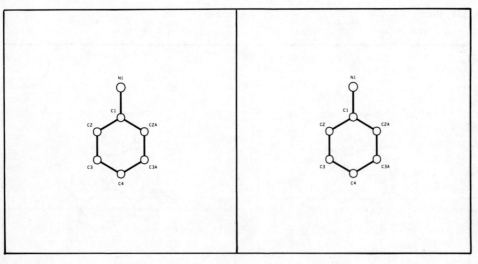

Pnaa $\quad$ Z = 4 $\quad$ $R_{hk0} = 0.065$, $R_{h0l} = 0.079$

ANLINB $\quad$ LB 6-8-5

Bond Lengths

C1	N1	1.47
C1	C2	1.39
C2	C3	1.39
C3	C4	1.39

Bond Angles

N1	C1	C2	120
C2	C1	C2A	121
C1	C2	C3	120
C2	C3	C4	120
C3	C4	C3A	121

16.7 Sulfanilamide $C_6H_8N_2O_2S$

(i) B.H.O'Connor, E.N.Maslen, Acta Cryst., 18, 363, 1965 (α form)

(ii) M.Alleaume, J.Decap, Acta Cryst., 18, 731, 1965 (β form)

(iii) M.Alleaume, J.Decap, Acta Cryst., 19, 934, 1965 (γ form)

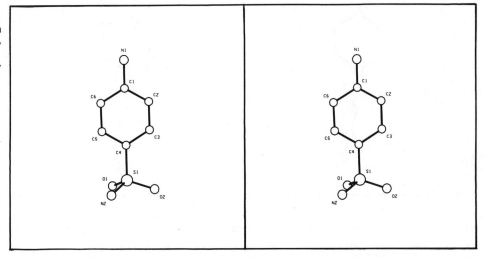

(i)

See also O'Connell & Maslen, Acta Cryst., 22, 134, 1967; Alleaume, Thesis, Bordeaux, 16, 1967.
Pbca   Z = 8 R_{0kl} = 0.148, R_{1kl} = 0.135, R_{4kl} = 0.195

SULAMD   LB 6-8-46

(ii)

$P2_1/c$ Z = 4 R_{0kl} = 0.110, R_{hk0} = 0.150

SULAMD01   LB 6-8-47

(iii)

$P2_1/c$ Z = 4   R = 0.092

SULAMD02   LB 6-8-48

Bond Lengths

		(i)	(ii)	(iii)
S1	N2	1.61	1.63	1.67
S1	O1	1.41	1.44	1.45
S1	O2	1.47	1.44	1.44
S1	C4	1.74	1.75	1.74
C1	N1	1.40	1.38	1.38
C1	C2	1.38	1.41	1.37
C1	C6	1.44	1.40	1.39
C2	C3	1.39	1.38	1.38
C3	C4	1.41	1.41	1.38
C4	C5	1.40	1.41	1.38
C5	C6	1.38	1.38	1.39

Bond Angles

			(i)	(ii)	(iii)
N2	S1	O1	106	106	107
N2	S1	O2	106	107	107
N2	S1	C4	109	111	108
O1	S1	O2	119	118	118
O1	S1	C4	107	107	108
O2	S1	C4	108	107	109
N1	C1	C2	119	119	121
N1	C1	C6	120	121	120
C2	C1	C6	120	120	119
C1	C2	C3	120	119	121
C2	C3	C4	120	121	121
S1	C4	C3	120	120	122
S1	C4	C5	120	121	119
C3	C4	C5	119	119	119
C4	C5	C6	121	120	120
C1	C6	C5	118	120	120

Torsion Angles

				(i)	(ii)	(iii)
C3	C4	S1	N2	124	−110	88
C3	C4	S1	O1	−121	135	−157
C3	C4	S1	O2	9	7	−29

16.8 Sulfanilamide (β form) $C_6H_8N_2O_2S$

For complete entry see 16.7

16.9 Sulfanilamide (γ form) $C_6H_8N_2O_2S$

For complete entry see 16.7

16.10   Aniline p - thiocyanate

$C_7H_6N_2S$

I.V.Isakov, Z.V.Zvonkova, Kristallografija, 10, 194, 1965

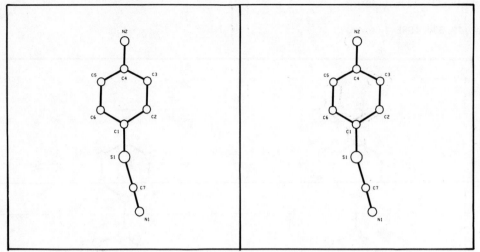

NH$_2$

SCN

No comparison of bond lengths is possible since they are not reported in the paper.
$P2_1/c$ $Z = 4$ $R_{hol} = 0.26$

ANLINT   LB 7-6-18

Bond Lengths

S1	C1	1.60	C1	C6	1.40
S1	C7	1.57	C2	C3	1.39
C7	N1	1.24	C3	C4	1.34
C4	N2	1.37	C4	C5	1.35
C1	C2	1.39	C5	C6	1.38

Bond Angles

C1	S1	C7	164	N2	C4	C3	116
S1	C1	C2	121	N2	C4	C5	120
S1	C1	C6	120	C3	C4	C5	125
C2	C1	C6	118	C4	C5	C6	120
C1	C2	C3	123	C1	C6	C5	118
C2	C3	C4	115	S1	C7	N1	179

Torsion Angles

C2	C1	S1	C7	−8

16.11   p - Toluidine

C_7H_9N

A.Bertinotti, C. R. Acad. Sci., Fr., 257, 4174, 1963

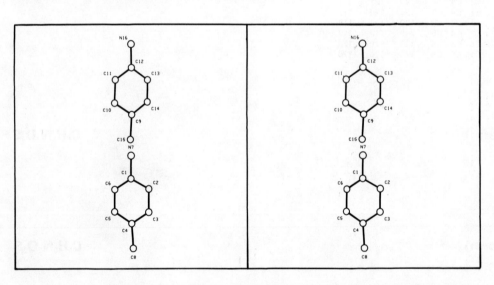

NH$_2$

CH$_3$

$Pna2_1$ $Z = 8$ $R = 0.124$

TOLDIN   LB 7-9-16

Bond Lengths

C1	N7	1.43	C12	N16	1.46
C1	C2	1.38	C9	C10	1.41
C1	C6	1.37	C9	C14	1.41
C2	C3	1.39	C9	C15	1.53
C3	C4	1.38	C10	C11	1.42
C4	C5	1.41	C11	C12	1.36
C4	C8	1.51	C12	C13	1.40
C5	C6	1.39	C13	C14	1.38

Bond Angles

N7	C1	C2	118	C10	C9	C14	116
N7	C1	C6	117	C10	C9	C15	118
C2	C1	C6	124	C14	C9	C15	126
C1	C2	C3	118	C9	C10	C11	119
C2	C3	C4	120	C10	C11	C12	125
C3	C4	C5	119	N16	C12	C11	124
C3	C4	C8	118	N16	C12	C13	120
C5	C4	C8	123	C11	C12	C13	116
C4	C5	C6	122	C12	C13	C14	121
C1	C6	C5	116	C9	C14	C13	123

16.12   2,6 - Dichloro - 4 - nitro - N,N - dimethylaniline $C_8H_8Cl_2N_2O_2$

Yu.T.Struchkov, T.L.Hotsyanova, Izvest. Akad. Nauk S. S. S. R., Ser. Khim., 1369, 1960

Pbcn   Z = 4   R = 0.160

DCNDMA

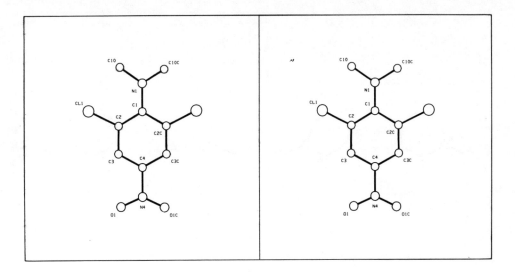

Bond Lengths			Bond Angles									Torsion Angles				
Cl1	C2	1.72	C1	N1	C10	120	Cl1	C2	C1	124		C2	C1	N1	C10	26
N4	O1	1.23	C10	N1	C10C	119	Cl1	C2	C3	115		C3	C4	N4	O1	7
C1	N1	1.40	O1	N4	O1C	131	C1	C2	C3	121						
C10	N1	1.46	O1	N4	C4	114	C2	C3	C4	118						
C4	N4	1.44	N1	C1	C2	120	N4	C4	C3	118						
C1	C2	1.39	C2	C1	C2C	120	C3	C4	C3C	123						
C2	C3	1.38														
C3	C4	1.39														

16.13   N,N - Dimethyl - p - nitroaniline $C_8H_{10}N_2O_2$

T.C.W.Mak, J.Trotter, Acta Cryst., 18, 68, 1965

P2₁   Z = 2   R = 0.116

DIMNAN   LB 8-10-13

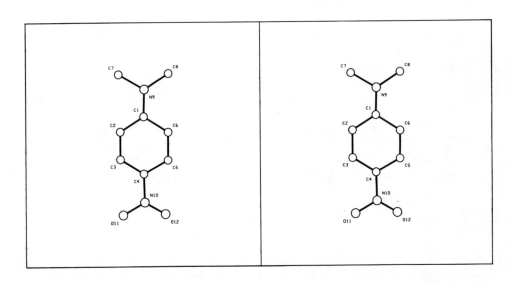

Bond Lengths			Bond Angles									Torsion Angles				
N10	O11	1.26	C1	N9	C7	119	C2	C1	C6	117		C6	C1	N9	C8	−6
N10	O12	1.20	C1	N9	C8	123	C1	C2	C3	121		C3	C4	N10	O11	6
C1	N9	1.35	C7	N9	C8	118	C2	C3	C4	121						
C7	N9	1.52	O11	N10	O12	121	N10	C4	C3	122						
C8	N9	1.45	O11	N10	C4	118	N10	C4	C5	117						
C4	N10	1.40	O12	N10	C4	120	C3	C4	C5	121						
C1	C2	1.41	N9	C1	C2	123	C4	C5	C6	119						
C1	C6	1.46	N9	C1	C6	120	C1	C6	C5	121						
C2	C3	1.37														
C3	C4	1.39														
C4	C5	1.41														
C5	C6	1.38														

16.14   p,p′ - Dichlorodiphenylamine

K.Plieth, G.Ruban, Z. Kristallogr., 116, 161, 1961

$C_{12}H_9Cl_2N$

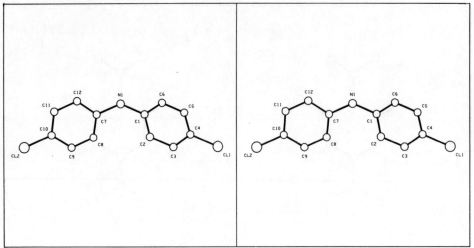

No comparison of bond lengths is possible since they are not reported in the paper.
P2₁/a   Z = 4   No R factor was given.

CDPHAM   LB 12-9-11

Bond Lengths

Cl1	C4	1.68	C4	C5	1.39
Cl2	C10	1.68	C5	C6	1.39
C1	N1	1.45	C7	C8	1.37
C7	N1	1.44	C7	C12	1.38
C1	C2	1.40	C8	C9	1.38
C1	C6	1.41	C9	C10	1.39
C2	C3	1.39	C10	C11	1.38
C3	C4	1.41	C11	C12	1.39

Bond Angles

C1	N1	C7	134	Cl1	C4	C5	118	C7	C8	C9	119
N1	C1	C2	119	C3	C4	C5	121	C8	C9	C10	121
N1	C1	C6	121	C4	C5	C6	118	Cl2	C10	C9	121
C2	C1	C6	120	C1	C6	C5	121	Cl2	C10	C11	120
C1	C2	C3	119	N1	C7	C8	119	C9	C10	C11	119
C2	C3	C4	121	N1	C7	C12	121	C10	C11	C12	120
Cl1	C4	C3	121	C8	C7	C12	120	C7	C12	C11	120

Torsion Angles

C2	C1	N1	C7	−39
C1	N1	C7	C8	−23

16.15   2 - Chloro - N - (salicylidene)aniline

J.Bregman, L.Leiserowitz, K.Osaki, J. Chem. Soc., 2086, 1964

$C_{13}H_{10}ClNO$

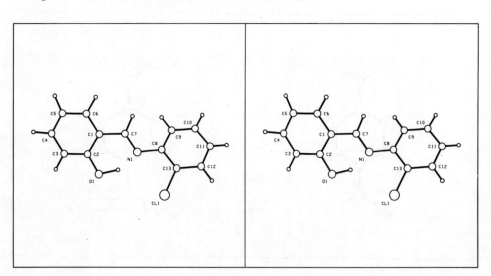

P2₁2₁2₁   Z = 4   R = 0.046

CHLSAN   LB 13-10-13

Bond Lengths

Cl1	C13	1.74	C4	C5	1.37
C7	N1	1.28	C5	C6	1.39
C8	N1	1.43	C8	C9	1.38
C2	O1	1.37	C8	C13	1.38
C1	C2	1.40	C9	C10	1.38
C1	C6	1.40	C10	C11	1.38
C1	C7	1.46	C11	C12	1.37
C2	C3	1.39	C12	C13	1.40
C3	C4	1.38			

Bond Angles

C7	N1	C8	119	C3	C4	C5	122	C9	C10	C11	120
C2	C1	C6	118	C4	C5	C6	119	C10	C11	C12	120
C2	C1	C7	122	C1	C6	C5	121	C11	C12	C13	119
C6	C1	C7	120	N1	C7	C1	121	Cl1	C13	C8	120
O1	C2	C1	121	N1	C8	C9	121	Cl1	C13	C12	119
O1	C2	C3	118	N1	C8	C13	120	C8	C13	C12	121
C1	C2	C3	121	C9	C8	C13	118				
C2	C3	C4	119	C8	C9	C10	121				

Torsion Angles

C2	C1	C7	N1	−4
C1	C7	N1	C8	175
C9	C8	N1	C7	−47

16.16   N - (5 - Chlorosalicylidene)aniline   C₁₃H₁₀ClNO

$C_{13}H_{10}ClNO$

(i)   J.Bregman, L.Leiserowitz, G.M.J.Schmidt, J. Chem. Soc., 2068, 1964

(ii)   J.Bregman, L.Leiserowitz, G.M.J.Schmidt, J. Chem. Soc., 2068, 1964   (at 90°K)

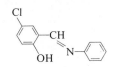

(i)

Pca2₁   Z = 4   R = 0.057

CSALAN   LB 13-10-17

(ii)

Pca2₁   Z = 4   R = 0.062

CSA1AN01   LB 13-10-17

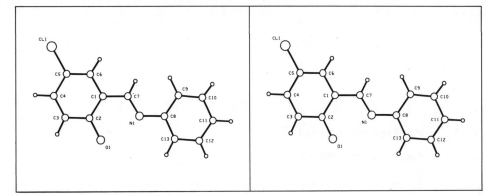

Bond Lengths

		(i)	(ii)			(i)	(ii)
Cl1	C5	1.75	1.76	C4	C5	1.40	1.40
C7	N1	1.27	1.29	C5	C6	1.36	1.38
C8	N1	1.41	1.40	C8	C9	1.40	1.41
C2	O1	1.35	1.36	C8	C13	1.38	1.41
C1	C2	1.41	1.42	C9	C10	1.37	1.36
C1	C6	1.41	1.42	C10	C11	1.39	1.41
C1	C7	1.43	1.44	C11	C12	1.37	1.41
C2	C3	1.39	1.38	C12	C13	1.41	1.39
C3	C4	1.36	1.38				

Bond Angles

			(i)	(ii)				(i)	(ii)
C7	N1	C8	122	122	C4	C5	C6	121	122
C2	C1	C6	117	118	C1	C6	C5	121	120
C2	C1	C7	122	123	N1	C7	C1	122	122
C6	C1	C7	120	120	N1	C8	C9	124	126
O1	C2	C1	120	119	N1	C8	C13	116	116
O1	C2	C3	119	119	C9	C8	C13	120	118
C1	C2	C3	121	121	C8	C9	C10	120	121
C2	C3	C4	120	120	C9	C10	C11	121	122
C3	C4	C5	120	119	C10	C11	C12	119	118
Cl1	C5	C4	119	119	C11	C12	C13	121	120
Cl1	C5	C6	120	119	C8	C13	C12	119	121

Torsion Angles

				(i)	(ii)
C2	C1	C7	N1	2	5
C1	C7	N1	C8	179	179
C9	C8	N1	C7	−4	−3

16.17   N - (5 - Chlorosalicylidene)aniline (at 90 ° K)   C₁₃H₁₀ClNO

$C_{13}H_{10}ClNO$

For complete entry see 16.16

16.18   N - (4 - Bromo - 2,5 - dimethylphenyl) - benzenesulfonamide   C₁₄H₁₄BrNO₂S

$C_{14}H_{14}BrNO_2S$

B.Rerat, G.Dauphin, A.Kergomard, C.Rerat, C. R. Acad. Sci., Fr., 261, 139, 1965

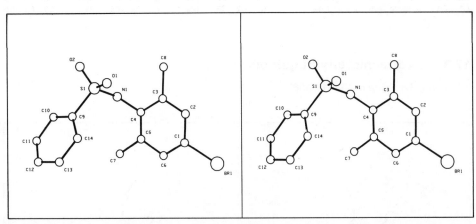

No comparison of bond lengths is possible since they are not reported in the paper.

P2₁/n   Z = 4   R = 0.20

BPHBZS   LB 14-14-9

Bond Lengths

Br1	C1	1.95	C3	C8	1.57
S1	N1	1.64	C4	C5	1.39
S1	O1	1.42	C5	C6	1.46
S1	O2	1.47	C5	C7	1.55
S1	C9	1.78	C9	C10	1.34
C4	N1	1.49	C9	C14	1.50
C1	C2	1.46	C10	C11	1.47
C1	C6	1.35	C11	C12	1.45
C2	C3	1.39	C12	C13	1.36
C3	C4	1.41	C13	C14	1.44

Bond Angles

N1	S1	O1	106	C1	C2	C3	116
N1	S1	O2	107	C2	C3	C4	120
N1	S1	C9	108	C2	C3	C8	117
O1	S1	O2	120	C4	C3	C8	123
O1	S1	C9	109	N1	C4	C3	120
O2	S1	C9	107	N1	C4	C5	117
S1	N1	C4	123	C3	C4	C5	122
Br1	C1	C2	114	C4	C5	C6	120
Br1	C1	C6	119	C4	C5	C7	126
C2	C1	C6	127	C6	C5	C7	114

C1	C6	C5	115
S1	C9	C10	117
S1	C9	C14	116
C10	C9	C14	127
C9	C10	C11	114
C10	C11	C12	122
C11	C12	C13	120
C12	C13	C14	121
C9	C14	C13	115

Torsion Angles

O1	S1	N1	C4	33
O2	S1	N1	C4	161
C9	S1	N1	C4	−84
C10	C9	S1	N1	−90
C10	C9	S1	O1	155
C10	C9	S1	O2	24
C3	C4	N1	S1	−80

17.1 Pentachlorophenol

C$_6$HCl$_5$O

T.Sakurai, Acta Cryst., 15, 1164, 1962

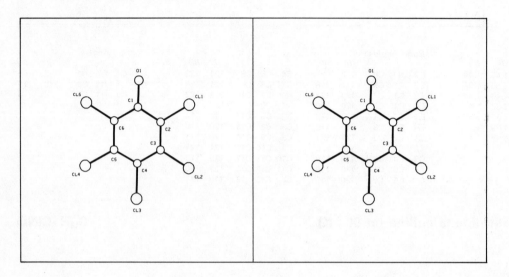

C2/c   Z = 8   R = 0.140

PCPHOL   LB 6-1-2

Bond Lengths

Cl1	C2	1.70	C1	C2	1.37
Cl2	C3	1.71	C1	C6	1.38
Cl3	C4	1.73	C2	C3	1.37
Cl4	C5	1.67	C3	C4	1.36
Cl5	C6	1.69	C4	C5	1.36
C1	O1	1.33	C5	C6	1.42

Bond Angles

O1	C1	C2	120	Cl2	C3	C2	121	Cl4	C5	C4	123
O1	C1	C6	121	Cl2	C3	C4	120	Cl4	C5	C6	119
C2	C1	C6	119	C2	C3	C4	119	C4	C5	C6	119
Cl1	C2	C1	118	Cl3	C4	C3	120	Cl5	C6	C1	119
Cl1	C2	C3	120	Cl3	C4	C5	118	Cl5	C6	C5	121
C1	C2	C3	122	C3	C4	C5	122	C1	C6	C5	119

17.2 Tetrachlorohydroquinone

C$_6$H$_2$Cl$_4$O$_2$

T.Sakurai, Acta Cryst., 15, 443, 1962

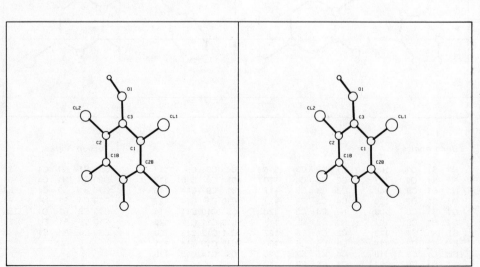

See also Sikka & Chidambaram, Acta Cryst., 23, 107, 1967.
P2$_1$/c   Z = 2   R = 0.170

TCLHQU   LB 6-2-31

Bond Lengths

Cl1	C1	1.74
Cl2	C2	1.72
C3	O1	1.35
C1	C3	1.40
C1	C2B	1.36
C2	C3	1.39

Bond Angles

Cl1	C1	C3	117
Cl1	C1	C2B	121
C3	C1	C2B	122
Cl2	C2	C3	119
Cl2	C2	C1B	121
C3	C2	C1B	120
O1	C3	C1	122
O1	C3	C2	119
C1	C3	C2	118

17.3   p - Nitrophenol

$C_6H_5NO_3$

(i)   P.Coppens, G.M.J.Schmidt, Acta Cryst., 18, 654, 1965 (β form)

(ii)   P.Coppens, G.M.J.Schmidt, Acta Cryst., 18, 62, 1965 (α form at 90°K)

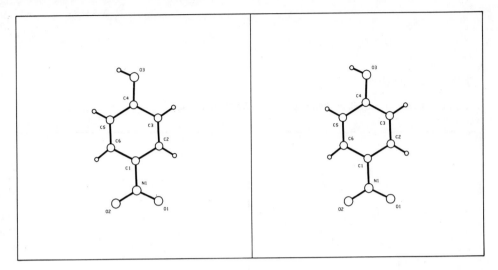

(i)

P2$_1$/a   Z = 4   R = 0.069

NITPOL   LB 6-5-42

(ii)

P2$_1$/n   Z = 4   R = 0.083

NITPOL01   LB 6-5-41

Bond Lengths

		(i)	(ii)			(i)	(ii)
N1	O1	1.24	1.23	C1	C6	1.39	1.38
N1	O2	1.24	1.24	C2	C3	1.38	1.38
C1	N1	1.45	1.44	C3	C4	1.40	1.39
C4	O3	1.36	1.35	C4	C5	1.40	1.39
C1	C2	1.39	1.39	C5	C6	1.38	1.38

Bond Angles

			(i)	(ii)				(i)	(ii)
O1	N1	O2	123	122	C2	C3	C4	120	120
O1	N1	C1	119	119	O3	C4	C3	116	117
O2	N1	C1	119	119	O3	C4	C5	123	122
N1	C1	C2	118	118	C3	C4	C5	120	121
N1	C1	C6	120	119	C4	C5	C6	120	119
C2	C1	C6	122	122	C1	C6	C5	119	119
C1	C2	C3	119	118					

Torsion Angles

				(i)	(ii)
C6	C1	N1	O2	−7	2

17.4   p - Nitrophenol (α form, at approx. 90 ° K)

$C_6H_5NO_3$

For complete entry see 17.3

17.5   Phenol (monoclinic)

C_6H_6O

C.Scheringer, Z. Kristallogr., 119, 273, 1963

No comparison of bond lengths is possible since they are not reported in the paper.
See also Gillier - Pandraud, Bull. Soc. Chim. Fr., 1988, 1967.
P2$_1$ Z = 6   R = 0.207

PHENOL10   LB 6-6-58

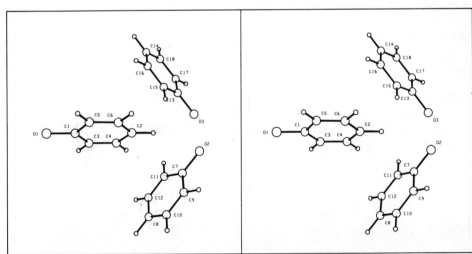

Bond Lengths

C1	O1	1.38	C7	O2	1.39	C13	O3	1.40
C1	C3	1.40	C7	C9	1.41	C13	C15	1.39
C1	C5	1.40	C7	C11	1.39	C13	C17	1.40
C2	C4	1.40	C8	C10	1.39	C14	C16	1.40
C2	C6	1.39	C8	C12	1.40	C14	C18	1.39
C3	C4	1.36	C9	C10	1.37	C15	C16	1.38
C5	C6	1.36	C11	C12	1.38	C17	C18	1.38

Bond Angles

O1	C1	C3	119	O2	C7	C9	120	O3	C13	C15	119
O1	C1	C5	119	O2	C7	C11	119	O3	C13	C17	119
C3	C1	C5	122	C9	C7	C11	121	C15	C13	C17	122
C4	C2	C6	121	C10	C8	C12	121	C16	C14	C18	122
C1	C3	C4	119	C7	C9	C10	120	C13	C15	C16	119
C2	C4	C3	119	C8	C10	C9	119	C14	C16	C15	119
C1	C5	C6	119	C7	C11	C12	119	C13	C17	C18	119
C2	C6	C5	120	C8	C12	C11	120	C14	C18	C17	119

17.6   Phenol hemihydrate

C_6H_6O , $0.5H_2O$

B.Meuthen, M.v. Stackelberg, Z. Elektrochem., 64, 387, 1960

The structure was determined in two dimensions only. Atomic coordinates were not reported in the paper.

Pbcn   Z = 8   R = 0.40

PHOLHH   LB 6-6-59

17.7   Catechol

$C_6H_6O_2$

J.Clastre, A.Lamarque, C. R. Acad. Sci., Fr., 260, 379, 1965

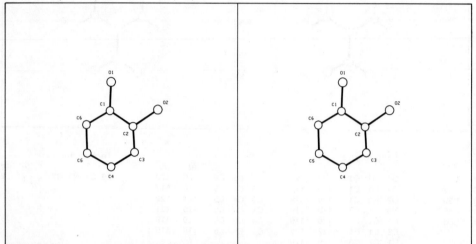

No comparison of bond lengths is possible since they are not reported in the paper.

See also Brown, Acta Cryst., 21, 170, 1966; Wunderlich & Mootz, Acta Cryst. (B), 27, 1684, 1971.

$P2_1/c$ Z = 4   R = 0.160

CATCOL   LB 6-6-58

Bond Lengths

C1	O1	1.42	C2	C3	1.30
C2	O2	1.51	C3	C4	1.39
C1	C2	1.41	C4	C5	1.40
C1	C6	1.39	C5	C6	1.41

Bond Angles

O1	C1	C2	120	C1	C2	C3	125
O1	C1	C6	122	C2	C3	C4	117
C2	C1	C6	117	C3	C4	C5	121
O2	C2	C1	114	C4	C5	C6	120
O2	C2	C3	119	C1	C6	C5	118

17.8   Phloroglucinol

$C_6H_6O_3$

K.Maartmann-Moe, Acta Cryst., 19, 155, 1965

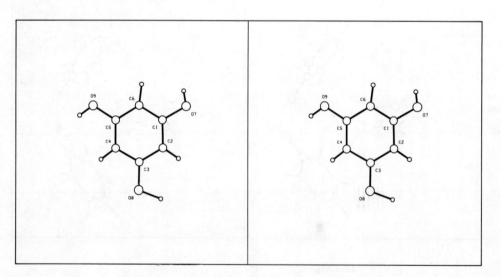

$P2_12_12_1$ Z = 4   R = 0.075

PHGLOL   LB 6-6-76

Bond Lengths

C1	O7	1.39	C2	C3	1.38
C3	O8	1.37	C3	C4	1.39
C5	O9	1.37	C4	C5	1.38
C1	C2	1.37	C5	C6	1.39
C1	C6	1.38			

Bond Angles

O7	C1	C2	118	O8	C3	C2	121	O9	C5	C4	121
O7	C1	C6	120	O8	C3	C4	118	O9	C5	C6	117
C2	C1	C6	122	C2	C3	C4	121	C4	C5	C6	121
C1	C2	C3	119	C3	C4	C5	118	C1	C6	C5	118

17.9   o - Aminophenol hydrochloride

$C_6H_8NO^+$, Cl^-

A.F.Cesur, J.P.G.Richards, Z. Kristallogr., 122, 283, 1965

$P2_1/c$ Z = 8   R = 0.110

AMPHCL   LB 6-8-23

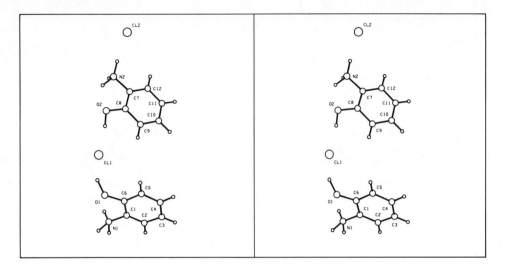

Bond Lengths

C1	N1	1.48	C7	N2	1.47
C6	O1	1.36	C8	O2	1.37
C1	C2	1.35	C7	C8	1.38
C1	C6	1.38	C7	C12	1.39
C2	C3	1.39	C8	C9	1.40
C3	C4	1.39	C9	C10	1.40
C4	C5	1.40	C10	C11	1.37
C5	C6	1.40	C11	C12	1.37

Bond Angles

N1	C1	C2	120		N2	C7	C8	117
N1	C1	C6	117		N2	C7	C12	121
C2	C1	C6	123		C8	C7	C12	122
C1	C2	C3	119		O2	C8	C7	118
C2	C3	C4	119		O2	C8	C9	123
C3	C4	C5	123		C7	C8	C9	119
C4	C5	C6	117		C8	C9	C10	119
O1	C6	C1	117		C9	C10	C11	121
O1	C6	C5	123		C10	C11	C12	121
C1	C6	C5	120		C7	C12	C11	118

17.10   2 - Aminoresorcinol hydrochloride

$C_6H_8NO_2^+$, Cl^-

A.F.Cesur, D.A.Price, J.P.G.Richards, Acta Cryst., 16, A61, 1963

Atomic coordinates were not reported in the paper.
$P2_1/n$ Z = 4   No R factor was given.

ARESRC

17.11   2,5 - Dimethylphenol

$C_8H_{10}O$

H.Gillier-Pandraud, Bull. Soc. Chim. Fr., 3267, 1965

$P2_1$ Z = 2   No R factor was given.

DMPHOL   LB 8-10-22

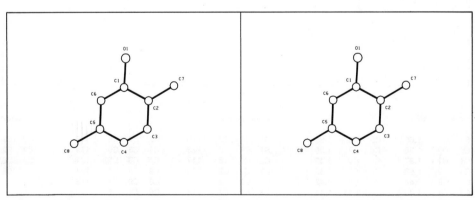

Bond Lengths

C1	O1	1.44	C3	C4	1.37
C1	C2	1.42	C4	C5	1.40
C1	C6	1.36	C5	C6	1.39
C2	C3	1.39	C5	C8	1.52
C2	C7	1.51			

Bond Angles

O1	C1	C2	115		C2	C3	C4	121
O1	C1	C6	122		C3	C4	C5	123
C2	C1	C6	123		C4	C5	C6	116
C1	C2	C3	115		C4	C5	C8	123
C1	C2	C7	123		C6	C5	C8	121
C3	C2	C7	122		C1	C6	C5	121

17.12 Quinhydrone (triclinic β form) $C_{12}H_{10}O_4$

T.Sakurai, Acta Cryst., 19, 320, 1965

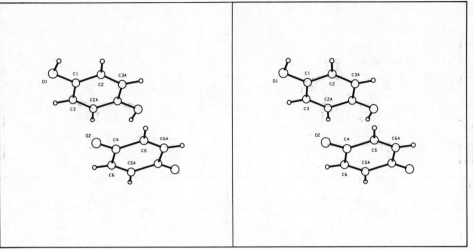

See also Sakurai, Acta Cryst. (B), 24, 403, 1968; Matsuda et al., Bull. Chem. Soc. Jap., 31, 611, 1958.
P-1   Z = 1   R = 0.101

QUIDON   LB 12-10-69

Bond Lengths

C1	O1	1.38	C4	O2	1.23
C1	C2	1.40	C4	C5	1.49
C1	C3	1.36	C4	C6	1.45
C2	C3A	1.39	C5	C6A	1.34

Bond Angles

O1	C1	C2	121	O2	C4	C5	120
O1	C1	C3	118	O2	C4	C6	121
C2	C1	C3	121	C5	C4	C6	119
C1	C2	C3A	119	C4	C5	C6A	120
C1	C3	C2A	120	C4	C6	C5A	121

17.13 4,4′ - Dihydroxythiobenzophenone monohydrate $C_{13}H_{10}O_2S$, H_2O

L.M.Manojlovic, I.G.Edmunds, Acta Cryst., 18, 543, 1965

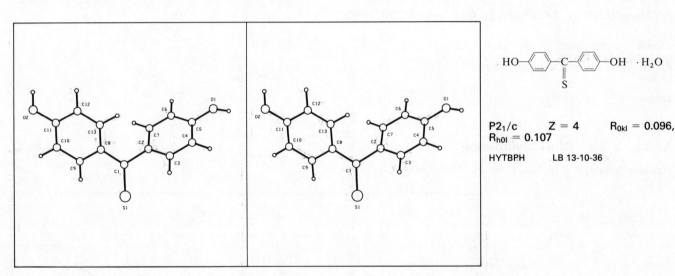

$P2_1/c$ Z = 4 $R_{0kl} = 0.096$, $R_{h0l} = 0.107$

HYTBPH   LB 13-10-36

Bond Lengths

S1	C1	1.65	C5	C6	1.36
C5	O1	1.38	C6	C7	1.38
C11	O2	1.37	C8	C9	1.43
C1	C2	1.53	C8	C13	1.39
C1	C8	1.48	C9	C10	1.42
C2	C3	1.40	C10	C11	1.41
C2	C7	1.43	C11	C12	1.41
C3	C4	1.37	C12	C13	1.40
C4	C5	1.42			

Bond Angles

S1	C1	C2	119	C2	C7	C6	119
S1	C1	C8	123	C1	C8	C9	119
C2	C1	C8	117	C1	C8	C13	121
C1	C2	C3	121	C9	C8	C13	121
C1	C2	C7	119	C8	C9	C10	118
C3	C2	C7	119	C9	C10	C11	120
C2	C3	C4	121	O2	C11	C10	117
C3	C4	C5	119	O2	C11	C12	121
O1	C5	C4	121	C10	C11	C12	122
O1	C5	C6	118	C11	C12	C13	118
C4	C5	C6	121	C8	C13	C12	122
C5	C6	C7	122				

Torsion Angles

C3	C2	C1	S1	−47
C7	C2	C1	C8	−47
C9	C8	C1	S1	−25
C13	C8	C1	C2	−29

17.14   4 - Bromo - 2,6 - di - t - butylphenol

$C_{14}H_{21}BrO$

M.Maze, C.Rerat, C. R. Acad. Sci., Fr., 259, 4612, 1964

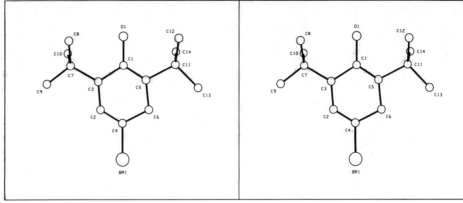

No comparison of bond lengths is possible since they are not reported in the paper.

$P2_12_12_1$ $Z = 2$ $R_{h0l} = 0.27$, $R_{h1l} = 0.27$, $R_{hk0} = 0.19$

BBPHOL   LB 14-21-1

Bond Lengths

Br1	C4	1.79		C5	C6	1.47
C1	O1	1.43		C5	C11	1.68
C1	C3	1.52		C7	C8	1.65
C1	C5	1.35		C7	C9	1.51
C2	C3	1.38		C7	C10	1.61
C2	C4	1.29		C11	C12	1.68
C3	C7	1.62		C11	C13	1.61
C4	C6	1.49		C11	C14	1.50

Bond Angles

O1	C1	C3	122	C2	C4	C6	123	C8	C7	C10	112
O1	C1	C5	123	C1	C5	C6	128	C9	C7	C10	100
C3	C1	C5	115	C1	C5	C11	120	C5	C11	C12	107
C3	C2	C4	125	C6	C5	C11	111	C5	C11	C13	107
C1	C3	C2	117	C4	C6	C5	110	C5	C11	C14	112
C1	C3	C7	119	C3	C7	C8	110	C12	C11	C13	116
C2	C3	C7	124	C3	C7	C9	114	C12	C11	C14	106
Br1	C4	C2	121	C3	C7	C10	109	C13	C11	C14	109
Br1	C4	C6	115	C8	C7	C9	111				

Torsion Angles

C1	C3	C7	C8	−55
C1	C3	C7	C9	179
C1	C3	C7	C10	68
C1	C5	C11	C12	56
C1	C5	C11	C13	−179
C1	C5	C11	C14	−60

17.15   p,p′ - Dimethoxybenzophenone

$C_{15}H_{14}O_3$

H.G.Norment, I.L.Karle, Acta Cryst., 15, 873, 1962

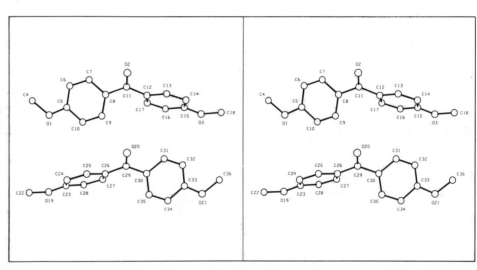

Published values of y(C36) = 0.0023 and y(C18) = 0.0123 are incorrect. The correct values are −0.0023 and −0.0123 respectively.

$P2_1/a$ $Z = 8$ $R = 0.18$

DMBOPN   LB 15-14-7

Bond Lengths

C4	O1	1.43		C22	O19	1.42
C5	O1	1.35		C23	O19	1.36
C11	O2	1.21		C29	O20	1.22
C15	O3	1.37		C33	O21	1.37
C18	O3	1.42		C36	O21	1.43
C5	C6	1.40		C23	C24	1.40
C5	C10	1.39		C23	C28	1.40
C6	C7	1.39		C24	C25	1.39
C7	C8	1.39		C25	C26	1.39
C8	C9	1.41		C26	C27	1.39
C8	C11	1.48		C26	C29	1.49
C9	C10	1.39		C27	C28	1.40
C11	C12	1.50		C29	C30	1.49
C12	C13	1.41		C30	C31	1.39
C12	C17	1.40		C30	C35	1.40
C13	C14	1.39		C31	C32	1.37
C14	C15	1.39		C32	C33	1.38
C15	C16	1.39		C33	C34	1.38
C16	C17	1.39		C34	C35	1.38

Bond Angles

C4	O1	C5	119	C13	C12	C17	119	C25	C26	C29	119
C15	O3	C18	118	C12	C13	C14	121	C27	C26	C29	123
O1	C5	C6	125	C13	C14	C15	119	C26	C27	C28	121
O1	C5	C10	116	O3	C15	C14	124	C23	C28	C27	119
C6	C5	C10	119	O3	C15	C16	114	O20	C29	C26	120
C5	C6	C7	120	C14	C15	C16	122	O20	C29	C30	119
C6	C7	C8	122	C15	C16	C17	118	C26	C29	C30	120
C7	C8	C9	117	C12	C17	C16	121	C29	C30	C31	119
C7	C8	C11	119					C29	C30	C35	123
C9	C8	C11	124	C22	O19	C23	118	C31	C30	C35	118
C8	C9	C10	121	C33	O21	C36	118	C30	C31	C32	122
C5	C10	C9	120	O19	C23	C24	125	C31	C32	C33	120
O2	C11	C8	119	O19	C23	C28	115	O21	C33	C32	125
O2	C11	C12	120	C24	C23	C28	120	O21	C33	C34	115
C8	C11	C12	122	C23	C24	C25	119	C32	C33	C34	120
C11	C12	C13	119	C24	C25	C26	122	C33	C34	C35	120
C11	C12	C17	122	C25	C26	C27	118	C30	C35	C34	121

Torsion Angles

C4	O1	C5	C10	−180
C9	C8	C11	C12	36
C8	C11	C12	C17	26
C14	C15	O3	C18	−5
C22	O19	C23	C24	2
C27	C26	C29	C30	−28
C26	C29	C30	C35	−36
C32	C33	O21	C36	0

17.16   4 - Methyl - 2,6 - di - t - butylphenol $C_{15}H_{24}O$

M.Maze, C.Rerat, C. R. Acad. Sci., Fr., 259, 4612, 1964

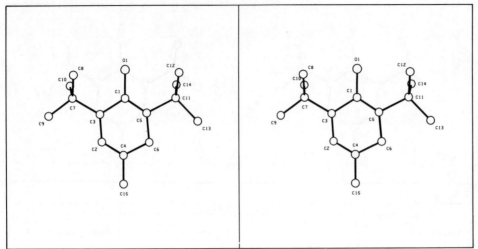

No comparison of bond lengths is possible since they are not reported in the paper.

$P2_12_12_1$ $Z = 4$ $R_{h0l} = 0.17$, $R_{hk0} = 0.21$

MBPHOL   LB 15-24-13

Bond Lengths

C1	O1	1.42		C5	C6	1.45		
C1	C3	1.52		C5	C11	1.68		
C1	C5	1.34		C7	C8	1.70		
C2	C3	1.37		C7	C9	1.50		
C2	C4	1.28		C7	C10	1.61		
C3	C7	1.61		C11	C12	1.67		
C4	C6	1.48		C11	C13	1.60		
C4	C15	1.41		C11	C14	1.50		

Bond Angles

O1	C1	C3	122		C6	C4	C15	115			
O1	C1	C5	123		C1	C5	C6	128			
C3	C1	C5	115		C1	C5	C11	120			
C3	C2	C4	125		C6	C5	C11	111			
C1	C3	C2	117		C4	C6	C5	110			
C1	C3	C7	119		C3	C7	C8	104			
C2	C3	C7	124		C3	C7	C9	115			
C2	C4	C6	124		C3	C7	C10	108			
C2	C4	C15	121		C8	C7	C9	113			

C8	C7	C10	116
C9	C7	C10	100
C5	C11	C12	107
C5	C11	C13	107
C5	C11	C14	112
C12	C11	C13	116
C12	C11	C14	106
C13	C11	C14	108

Torsion Angles

C1	C3	C7	C8	−57
C1	C3	C7	C9	179
C1	C3	C7	C10	67
C1	C5	C11	C12	56
C1	C5	C11	C13	−179
C1	C5	C11	C14	−60

17.17   Deoxyanisoin $C_{16}H_{16}O_3$

H.G.Norment, I.L.Karle, Acta Cryst., 15, 873, 1962

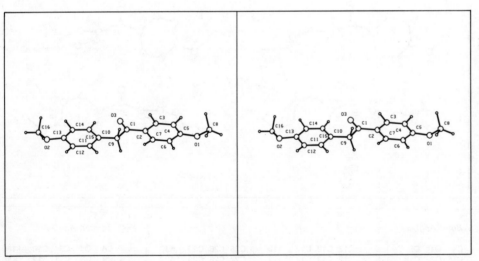

Published y coordinate for H83(relabelled H7) = 0.5. The correct value is 0.0.

$P2_1/c$ $Z = 2$ $R = 0.16$

DOXANN   LB 16-16-28

Bond Lengths

C5	O1	1.37		C4	C5	1.40	
C8	O1	1.43		C5	C6	1.39	
C13	O2	1.37		C6	C7	1.39	
C16	O2	1.43		C9	C10	1.53	
C1	O3	1.22		C10	C11	1.39	
C1	C2	1.50		C10	C15	1.39	
C1	C9	1.51		C11	C12	1.38	
C2	C3	1.40		C12	C13	1.40	
C2	C7	1.40		C13	C14	1.37	
C3	C4	1.39		C14	C15	1.40	

Bond Angles

C5	O1	C8	118		C3	C4	C5	119			
C13	O2	C16	116		O1	C5	C4	124			
O3	C1	C2	120		O1	C5	C6	115			
O3	C1	C9	124		C4	C5	C6	121			
C2	C1	C9	116		C5	C6	C7	119			
C1	C2	C3	119		C2	C7	C6	120			
C1	C2	C7	122		C1	C9	C10	114			
C3	C2	C7	119		C9	C10	C11	122			
C2	C3	C4	121		C9	C10	C15	119			

C11	C10	C15	119
C10	C11	C12	121
C11	C12	C13	120
O2	C13	C12	115
O2	C13	C14	125
C12	C13	C14	121
C13	C14	C15	119
C10	C15	C14	121

Torsion Angles

C14	C13	O2	C16	3
C11	C10	C9	C1	−64
C10	C9	C1	C2	175
C9	C1	C2	C7	1
C4	C5	O1	C8	4

18.1   Tetrabromo - p - benzoquinone

$C_6Br_4O_2$

Bromanil
I.Ueda, J. Phys. Soc. Jap., 16, 1185, 1961

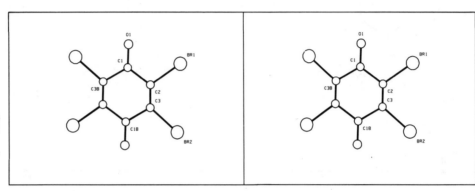

No comparison of bond lengths is possible since they are not reported in the paper.
$P2_1/a$ $Z = 2$ $R_{0kl} = 0.13$, $R_{h0l} = 0.15$, $R_{hk0} = 0.22$

TBBENQ   LB 6-0-13

Bond Lengths			Bond Angles							Torsion Angles		
Br1	C2	1.86	O1	C1	C2	124	C1	C2	C3	124	Br1 C2 C3 Br2	−22
Br2	C3	1.88	O1	C1	C3B	121	Br2	C3	C2	128		
C1	O1	1.15	C2	C1	C3B	115	Br2	C3	C1B	110		
C1	C2	1.45	Br1	C2	C1	110	C2	C3	C1B	120		
C1	C3B	1.43	Br1	C2	C3	124						
C2	C3	1.13										

18.2   Tetrachloro - p - benzoquinone

$C_6Cl_4O_2$

(i)   Chloranil
       S.S.C.Chu, G.A.Jeffrey, T.Sakurai, Acta Cryst., 15, 661, 1962

(ii)   Chloranil
       I.Ueda, J. Phys. Soc. Jap., 16, 1185, 1961

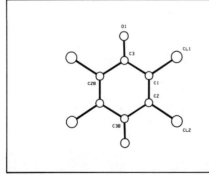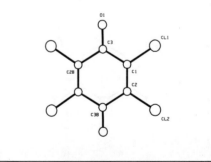

(i)

$P2_1/a$ $Z = 2$ $R = 0.125$

TCBENQ   LB 6-0-18

(ii)

$P2_1/a$ $Z = 2$ $R_{0kl} = 0.09$, $R_{h0l} = 0.13$, $R_{hk0} = 0.10$

TCBENQ01   LB 6-0-18

Bond Lengths		(i)	(ii)	Bond Angles			(i)	(ii)	Torsion Angles			(i)	(ii)
Cl1	C1	1.70	1.75	Cl1	C1	C2	122	125	Cl1 C1 C2 Cl2			−2	5
Cl2	C2	1.71	1.74	Cl1	C1	C3	116	114					
C3	O1	1.19	1.26	C2	C1	C3	121	121					
C1	C2	1.33	1.33	Cl2	C2	C1	122	121					
C1	C3	1.46	1.50	Cl2	C2	C3B	116	115					
C2	C3B	1.48	1.50	C1	C2	C3B	121	124					
				O1	C3	C1	123	123					
				O1	C3	C2B	120	122					
				C1	C3	C2B	117	114					

18.3　Tetrachloro - p - benzoquinone

$C_6Cl_4O_2$

For complete entry see 18.3

18.4　p - Benzoquinone

$C_6H_4O_2$

(i)　J.Trotter, Acta Cryst., 13, 86, 1960

(ii)　J.Trotter, Acta Cryst., 14, 553, 1961　(discussion)

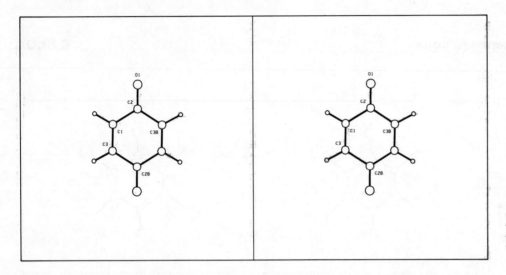

$P2_1/a$　$Z = 2$　$R = 0.095$

BNZQUI　　LB 6-4-66

Bond Lengths			Bond Angles			
C2	O1	1.22	C2	C1	C3	121
C1	C2	1.47	O1	C2	C1	121
C1	C3	1.31	O1	C2	C3B	121
C2	C3B	1.47	C1	C2	C3B	118
			C1	C3	C2B	121

18.5　p - Benzoquinone (discussion)

$C_6H_4O_2$

For complete entry see 18.4

18.6　Tetrahydroxy - p - benzoquinone dihydrate

$C_6H_4O_6$, $2H_2O$

H.P.Klug, Acta Cryst., 19, 983, 1965

$P2_1/c$　$Z = 2$　$R = 0.079$ ·

TOXBZQ　　LB 6-4-69

Bond Lengths			Bond Angles							
C1	O1	1.23	O1	C1	C2	121	C1	C2	C3B	119
C2	O2	1.34	O1	C1	C3	120	O3	C3	C1	118
C3	O3	1.34	C2	C1	C3	120	O3	C3	C2B	121
C1	C2	1.48	O2	C2	C1	114	C1	C3	C2B	121
C1	C3	1.48	O2	C2	C3B	127				
C2	C3B	1.34								

18.7 α - 2 - Chloro - 5 - methyl - p - benzoquinone - 4 - oxime (syn form)

$C_7H_6ClNO_2$

C.Romers, E.Fischmann, Acta Cryst., 13, 809, 1960

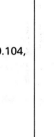

P2$_1$/c   Z = 4 $R_{0kl} = 0.104$,
$R_{1kl} = 0.187$

CLMBQO   LB 7-6-10

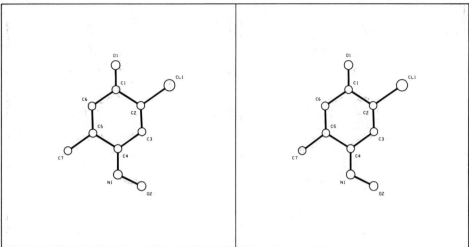

Bond Lengths

Cl1	C2	1.77	C2	C3	1.30
N1	O2	1.32	C3	C4	1.48
C4	N1	1.27	C4	C5	1.49
C1	O1	1.21	C5	C6	1.34
C1	C2	1.48	C5	C7	1.53
C1	C6	1.45			

Bond Angles

O2	N1	C4	115	N1	C4	C3	124
O1	C1	C2	122	N1	C4	C5	121
O1	C1	C6	122	C3	C4	C5	113
C2	C1	C6	115	C4	C5	C6	123
Cl1	C2	C1	114	C4	C5	C7	115
Cl1	C2	C3	121	C6	C5	C7	122
C1	C2	C3	123	C1	C6	C5	121
C2	C3	C4	121				

18.8 β - 2 - Chloro - p - benzoquinone - 4 - oxime acetate (anti form, at −140 °C)

$C_8H_6ClNO_3$

E.Fischmann, C.H.MacGillavry, C.Romers, Acta Cryst., 14, 759, 1961

P2$_1$/n   Z = 4 $R_{0kl} = 0.122$,
$R_{1k^{-}1} = 0.117$

CBOXAA   LB 8-6-7

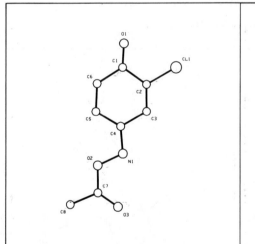
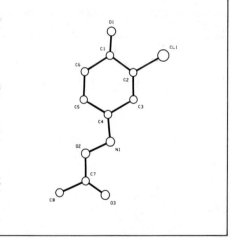

Bond Lengths

Cl1	C2	1.75	C1	C6	1.52
N1	O2	1.39	C2	C3	1.33
C4	N1	1.35	C3	C4	1.51
C1	O1	1.20	C4	C5	1.45
C7	O2	1.35	C5	C6	1.37
C7	O3	1.23	C7	C8	1.54
C1	C2	1.46			

Bond Angles

O2	N1	C4	109	N1	C4	C3	113
N1	O2	C7	114	N1	C4	C5	125
O1	C1	C2	121	C3	C4	C5	120
O1	C1	C6	125	C4	C5	C6	117
C2	C1	C6	114	C1	C6	C5	124
Cl1	C2	C1	117	O2	C7	O3	123
Cl1	C2	C3	118	O2	C7	C8	112
C1	C2	C3	125	O3	C7	C8	125
C2	C3	C4	118				

Torsion Angles

C5	C4	N1	O2	−10
C4	N1	O2	C7	−171
N1	O2	C7	C8	−169

18.9 α - 2 - Chloro - p - benzoquinone - 4 - oxime acetate (syn form, at −140 °C)

$C_8H_6ClNO_3$

E.Fischmann, C.H.MacGillavry, C.Romers, Acta Cryst., 14, 753, 1961

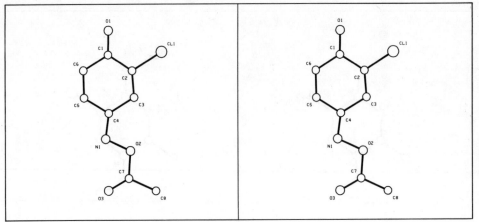

P2$_1$/a   Z = 4   R$_{hk0}$ = 0.14,
R$_{0kl}$ = 0.147

CBOXAS   LB 8-6-6

Bond Lengths

Cl1	C2	1.76	C1	C6	1.49
N1	O2	1.40	C2	C3	1.32
C4	N1	1.29	C3	C4	1.53
C1	O1	1.20	C4	C5	1.48
C7	O2	1.36	C5	C6	1.35
C7	O3	1.21	C7	C8	1.52
C1	C2	1.47			

Bond Angles

O2	N1	C4	108	Cl1	C2	C3	117	C4	C5	C6	122
N1	O2	C7	109	C1	C2	C3	128	C1	C6	C5	120
O1	C1	C2	122	C2	C3	C4	116	O2	C7	O3	124
O1	C1	C6	123	N1	C4	C3	128	O2	C7	C8	109
C2	C1	C6	115	N1	C4	C5	114	O3	C7	C8	127
Cl1	C2	C1	115	C3	C4	C5	118				

Torsion Angles

C5	C4	N1	O2	−180
C4	N1	O2	C7	169
N1	O2	C7	C8	179

18.10 β - 5 - (2′ - Chloroethoxy) - o - quinone - 2 - oxime (syn form)

$C_8H_8ClNO_3$

C.Romers, A.J.H.Umans, Kkl. Nederl. Akad. Wetensch., Proc., B, 63, 32, 1960

The structure was determined in two dimensions only.
Atomic coordinates were not reported in the paper.
P2$_1$/c   Z = 4   R$_{0kl}$ = 0.16,   R$_{1kl}$ = 0.20

CETOQO   LB 8-8-17

18.11   2,5 - Dimethyl - 1,4 - benzoquinone

$C_8H_8O_2$

D.Rabinovich, G.M.J.Schmidt, J. Chem. Soc., 2030, 1964

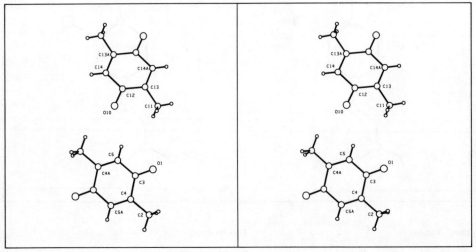

No comparison of bond lengths is possible since they are not reported in the paper.
See also Hirshfeld & Rabinovich, Acta Cryst., 23, 989, 1967.
P-1   Z = 2   R = 0.050

DMEBQU   LB 8-8-36

Bond Lengths

C3	O1	1.22	C12	O10	1.22
C2	C4	1.50	C11	C13	1.50
C3	C4	1.49	C12	C13	1.49
C3	C5	1.46	C12	C14	1.50
C4	C5A	1.34	C13	C14A	1.33

Bond Angles

O1	C3	C4	121	O10	C12	C13	121
O1	C3	C5	121	O10	C12	C14	107
C4	C3	C5	119	C13	C12	C14	132
C2	C4	C3	118	C11	C13	C12	118
C2	C4	C5A	123	C11	C13	C14A	123
C3	C4	C5A	119	C12	C13	C14A	119
C3	C5	C4A	123	C12	C14	C13A	109

18.12 β - 5 - n - Propoxy - o - benzoquinone - 2 - oxime (syn form, at −120 °C)

$C_9H_{11}NO_3$

C.Romers, Acta Cryst., 17, 1287, 1964

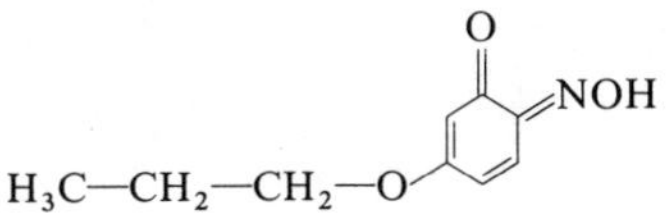

$P2_1/c$ $Z = 4$ $R = 0.116$

PBZQOX   LB 9-11-25

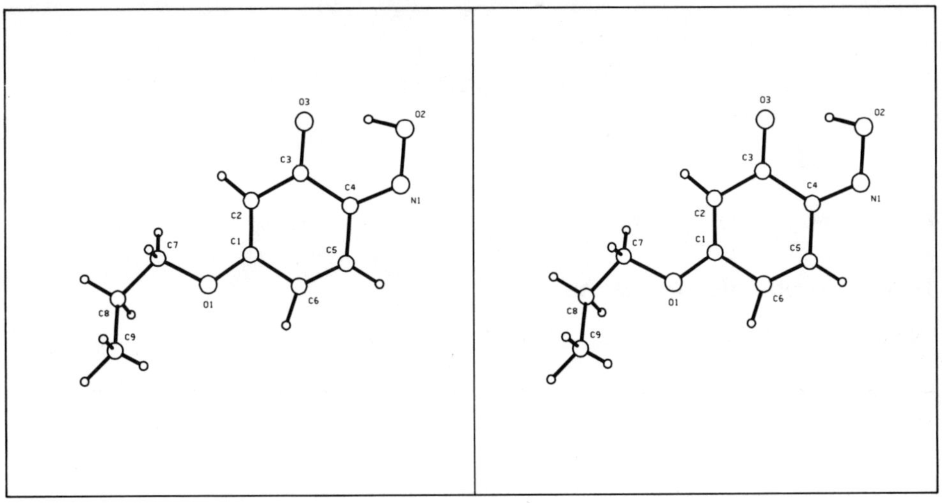

Bond Lengths

N1	O2	1.36	C2	C3	1.41
C4	N1	1.32	C3	C4	1.48
C1	O1	1.35	C4	C5	1.45
C7	O1	1.45	C5	C6	1.35
C3	O3	1.27	C7	C8	1.52
C1	C2	1.36	C8	C9	1.51
C1	C6	1.46			

Bond Angles

O2	N1	C4	117	C2	C3	C4	119
C1	O1	C7	118	N1	C4	C3	124
O1	C1	C2	125	N1	C4	C5	117
O1	C1	C6	112	C3	C4	C5	119
C2	C1	C6	123	C4	C5	C6	120
C1	C2	C3	120	C1	C6	C5	120
O3	C3	C2	123	O1	C7	C8	107
O3	C3	C4	119	C7	C8	C9	113

Torsion Angles

C2	C1	O1	C7	−2
C1	O1	C7	C8	178
O1	C7	C8	C9	62
C3	C4	N1	O2	−1

19.1   Hexachlorobenzene   C₆Cl₆

I.N.Strel'tsova, Yu.T.Struchkov, Zh. Strukt. Khim., 2, 312, 1961

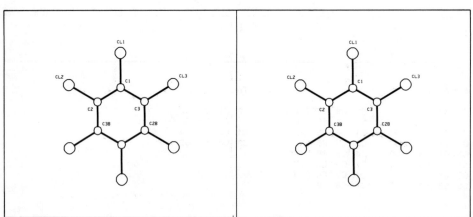

No comparison of bond lengths is possible since they are not reported in the paper.

P2₁/c   Z = 2 R_{h0l} = 0.15, R_{h1l} = 0.19

HCLBNZ   LB 6-0-20

Bond Lengths

Cl1	C1	1.72	C1	C2	1.40
Cl2	C2	1.71	C1	C3	1.40
Cl3	C3	1.71	C2	C3B	1.40

Bond Angles

Cl1	C1	C2	120	Cl2	C2	C1	120	Cl3	C3	C1	120
Cl1	C1	C3	120	Cl2	C2	C3B	120	Cl3	C3	C2B	120
C2	C1	C3	120	C1	C2	C3B	120	C1	C3	C2B	120

19.2   1, 2 - 4, 5 -Tetrabromobenzene   C₆H₂Br₄

(i)   G.Gafner, F.H.Herbstein, Acta Cryst., 17, 982, 1964 (γ form, stable above 46.5°C)

(ii)   G.Gafner, F.H.Herbstein, Acta Cryst., 13, 706, 1960 (β form, stable below 46.5°C)

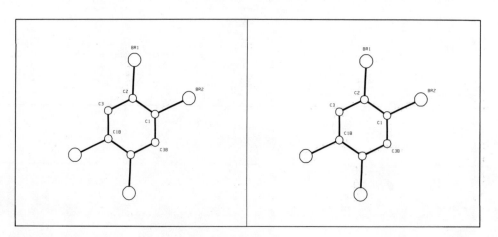

(i)

P2₁/a   Z = 2   R = 0.153

TETBBZ01   LB 6-2-16

(ii)

P2₁/a   Z = 2   R = 0.126

TETBBZ   LB 6-2-17

Bond Lengths

		(i)	(ii)
Br1	C2	1.84	1.89
Br2	C1	1.92	1.91
C1	C2	1.42	1.40
C1	C3B	1.37	1.38
C2	C3	1.36	1.41

Bond Angles

			(i)	(ii)
Br2	C1	C2	120	121
Br2	C1	C3B	118	114
C2	C1	C3B	122	124
Br1	C2	C1	122	122
Br1	C2	C3	121	118
C1	C2	C3	116	120
C2	C3	C1B	121	115

19.3   1,2 - 4,5 - Tetrabromobenzene (β form, stable below 46.5° C) $C_6H_2Br_4$

For complete entry see 19.2

19.4   1,3,5 - Tribromobenzene $C_6H_3Br_3$

H.J.Milledge, L.M.Pant, Acta Cryst., 13, 285, 1960

Isomorphous with 1,3,5 - trichlorobenzene.
$P2_12_12_1$ Z = 4 R_{hk0} = 0.095,
R_{0kl} = 0.096, R_{h0l} = 0.096

TBRMBZ   LB 6-3-6

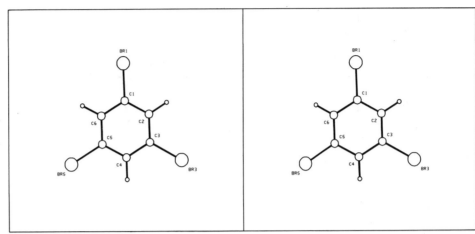

Bond Lengths

Br1	C1	1.86	C2	C3	1.39
Br3	C3	1.85	C3	C4	1.40
Br5	C5	1.86	C4	C5	1.40
C1	C2	1.40	C5	C6	1.39
C1	C6	1.40			

Bond Angles

Br1	C1	C2	120	C2	C3	C4	120
Br1	C1	C6	120	C3	C4	C5	120
C2	C1	C6	120	Br5	C5	C4	120
C1	C2	C3	120	Br5	C5	C6	120
Br3	C3	C2	120	C4	C5	C6	120
Br3	C3	C4	120	C1	C6	C5	120

19.5   1,3,5 - Trichlorobenzene $C_6H_3Cl_3$

(i)   H.J.Milledge, L.M.Pant, Acta Cryst., 13, 285, 1960

(ii)   H.J.Milledge, L.M.Pant, Acta Cryst., 13, 285, 1960 (at −183°C)

(i)
Isomorphous with 1,3,5 - tribromobenzene.
$P2_12_12_1$ Z = 4 R_{hk0} = 0.109,
R_{0kl} = 0.084

TCHLBZ   LB 6-3-12

(ii)

The structure was determined in two dimensions only. Atomic coordinates were not reported in the paper.
$P2_12_12_1$ Z = 4   No R factor was given.

TCHLBZ01   LB 6-3-12

Bond Lengths

Cl1	C1	1.71	C2	C3	1.41
Cl3	C3	1.71	C3	C4	1.37
Cl5	C5	1.71	C4	C5	1.38
C1	C2	1.37	C5	C6	1.39
C1	C6	1.40			

Bond Angles

Cl1	C1	C2	119	C2	C3	C4	121
Cl1	C1	C6	119	C3	C4	C5	120
C2	C1	C6	122	Cl5	C5	C4	121
C1	C2	C3	117	Cl5	C5	C6	120
Cl3	C3	C2	117	C4	C5	C6	119
Cl3	C3	C4	121	C1	C6	C5	120

19.6   1,3,5 - Trichlorobenzene (at − 183 ° C) $C_6H_3Cl_3$

For complete entry see 19.5

19.7   p - Dichlorobenzene (monoclinic form, at −140 ° C)   C₆H₄Cl₂

C.Panattoni, E.Frasson, S.Bezzi, Gazz. Chim. Ital., 93, 813, 1963

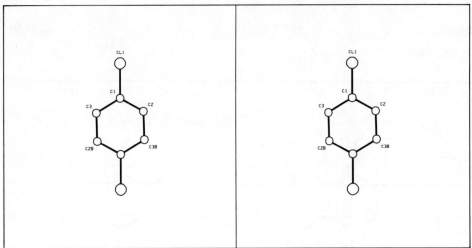

See also Croatto et al., Acta Cryst., 5, 825, 1952; Frasson et al., Acta Cryst., 12, 126, 1959; Housty & Clastre, Acta Cryst., 10, 695, 1957.
$P2_1/a$ $Z = 2$ $R_{h0l} = 0.10$, $R_{hk0} = 0.10$

DCLBEN03   LB 6-4-25

Bond Lengths			Bond Angles			
Cl1	C1	1.72	Cl1	C1	C2	118
C1	C2	1.37	Cl1	C1	C3	121
C1	C3	1.41	C2	C1	C3	121
C2	C3B	1.39	C1	C2	C3B	120
			C1	C3	C2B	119

19.8   Benzene   C₆H₆

(i)   G.E.Bacon, N.A.Curry, S.A.Wilson, Proc. R. Soc., A, 279, 98, 1964   (at −55°C neutron diffraction)

(ii)   G.E.Bacon, N.A.Curry, S.A.Wilson, Proc. R. Soc., A, 279, 98, 1964   (at −135°C neutron diffraction)

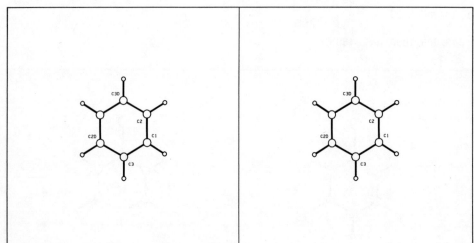

(i)

See also Cox et al., Proc. R. Soc., A, 247, 1, 1958; Piermarini et al., Science, 165, 1250, 1969; Fourme et al., Acta Cryst. (B), 27, 1275, 1971.
Pbca $Z = 4$ $R = 0.059$

BENZEN   LB 6-6-1

(ii)

Pbca $Z = 4$ $R = 0.076$

BENZEN01   LB 6-6-1

Bond Lengths		(i)	(ii)	Bond Angles			(i)	(ii)
C1	C2	1.39	1.39	C2	C1	C3	120	121
C1	C3	1.39	1.39	C2	C1	H1	123	121
C2	C3D	1.39	1.40	C3	C1	H1	117	119
C1	H1	1.06	1.09	C1	C2	C3D	120	120
C2	H2	1.08	1.09	C1	C2	H2	121	121
C3	H3	1.07	1.08	C1	C3	C2D	121	120
				C1	C3	H3	120	121

19.9   Benzene (at − 135 ° C, neutron diffraction)   C₆H₆

For complete entry see 19.8

19.10   m - Xylene tetrabromide

$C_8H_6Br_4$

I.N.Strel'tsova, Yu.T.Struchkov, Izvest. Akad. Nauk S. S. S. R., Ser. Khim., 250, 1961

No comparison of bond lengths is possible since they are not reported in the paper. There is statistical disorder of bromine atoms and methyl groups.
$P2_1/c$ $Z = 2$ $R_{h0l} = 0.127$, $R_{h1l} = 0.184$

MXYLTB   LB 8-6-5

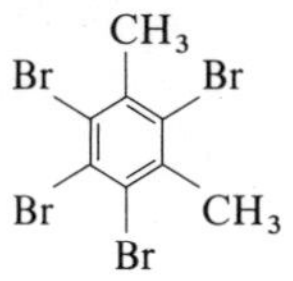

Bond Lengths			Bond Angles			
C1	C2	1.40	C2	C1	C3	120
C1	C3	1.40	C1	C2	C3B	120
C2	C3B	1.40	C1	C3	C2B	120

19.11   o - Bromobenzoylacetylene

C_9H_5BrO

G.Ferguson, J.Tyrrell, Chem. Communic., 195, 1965

Atomic coordinates were not reported in the paper.
$P2_12_12_1$ $Z = 4$ $R = 0.080$

BRBOAC   LB 9-5-1

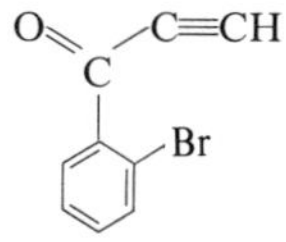

19.12   2,3,5,6 - Tetramethylbromobenzene (α form)

$C_{10}H_{13}Br$

G.Charbonneau, J.Baudour, J.-C.Messager, J.Meinnel,
Bull. Soc. Fr. Mineral. Cristallogr., 88, 147, 1965

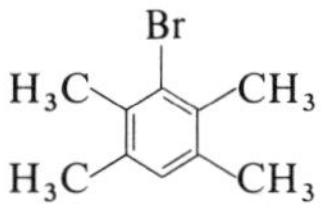

No comparison of bond lengths is possible since they are not reported in the paper. The published coordinates do not refer to the standard origin for space group $P2_12_12_1$. The standard coordinates are $x + 0.25$, y, $z + 0.25$.
$P2_12_12_1$ $Z = 4$ $R_{h0l} = 0.138$, $R_{hk0} = 0.183$

TMBRBZ   LB 10-13-1

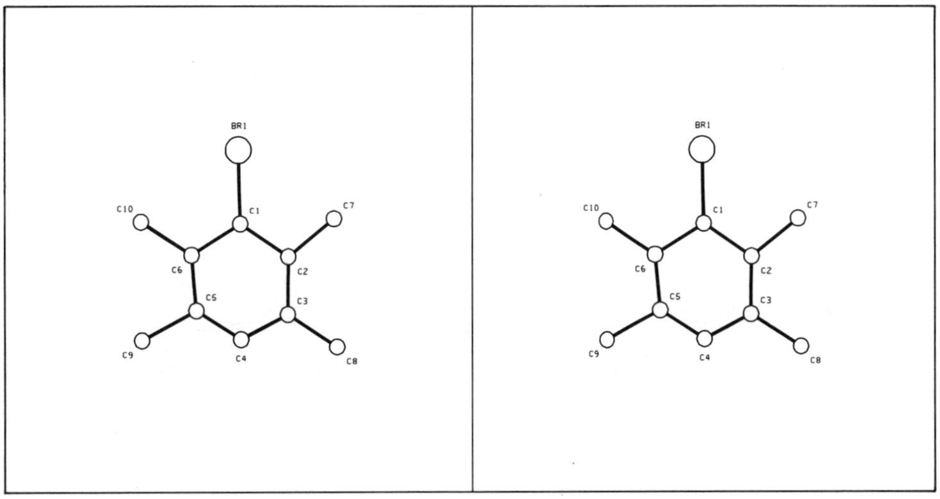

Bond Lengths					
Br1	C1	1.83	C3	C8	1.51
C1	C2	1.47	C4	C5	1.34
C1	C6	1.46	C5	C6	1.39
C2	C3	1.42	C5	C9	1.57
C2	C7	1.52	C6	C10	1.54
C3	C4	1.34			

Bond Angles							
Br1	C1	C2	125	C4	C3	C8	121
Br1	C1	C6	120	C3	C4	C5	121
C2	C1	C6	115	C4	C5	C6	127
C1	C2	C3	123	C4	C5	C9	121
C1	C2	C7	108	C6	C5	C9	112
C3	C2	C7	129	C1	C6	C5	116
C2	C3	C4	117	C1	C6	C10	117
C2	C3	C8	121	C5	C6	C10	127

19.13   2,3,5,6 - Tetramethylbromobenzene (β form)

$C_{10}H_{13}Br$

J.Baudour, J.-C.Messager, J.Meinnel, Bull. Soc. Fr. Mineral. Cristallogr., 88, 147, 1965

The structure was determined in two dimensions only. The bromine atom is disordered.
$P2_1/a$ $Z = 4$ $R_{h0l} = 0.22$

TMBRBZ01   LB 10-13-2

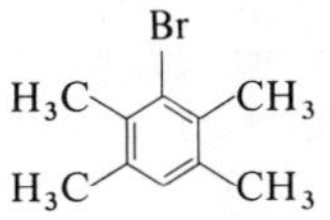

19.14 Biphenyl

$C_{12}H_{10}$

J.Trotter, Acta Cryst., 14, 1135, 1961

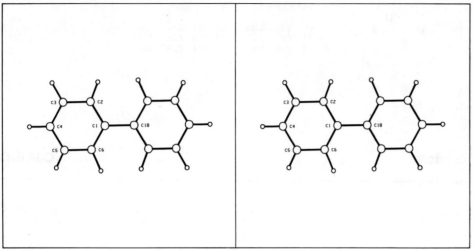

P2$_1$/a   Z = 2 R_{h0l} = 0.165,
R_{0kl} = 0.148

BIPHEN   LB 12-10-2

Bond Lengths

C1	C2	1.38	C3	C4	1.37
C1	C6	1.37	C4	C5	1.38
C1	C1B	1.51	C5	C6	1.41
C2	C3	1.42			

Bond Angles

C2	C1	C6	119	C2	C3	C4	120
C2	C1	C1B	121	C3	C4	C5	119
C6	C1	C1B	120	C4	C5	C6	121
C1	C2	C3	121	C1	C6	C5	121

Torsion Angles

C2	C1	C1B	C6B	0

19.15 Biphenyl

$C_{12}H_{10}$

A.Hargreaves, S.H.Rizvi, Acta Cryst., 15, 365, 1962

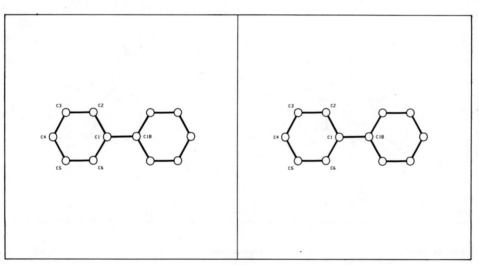

P2$_1$/a   Z = 2 R_{h0l} = 0.089,
R_{0kl} = 0.123, R_{hk0} = 0.146

BIPHEN01   LB 12-10-2

Bond Lengths

C1	C2	1.40	C3	C4	1.38
C1	C6	1.36	C4	C5	1.35
C1	C1B	1.51	C5	C6	1.42
C2	C3	1.42			

Bond Angles

C2	C1	C6	119	C2	C3	C4	119
C2	C1	C1B	120	C3	C4	C5	121
C6	C1	C1B	121	C4	C5	C6	119
C1	C2	C3	120	C1	C6	C5	121

Torsion Angles

C2	C1	C1B	C6B	1

19.16 Biphenyl

$C_{12}H_{10}$

G.B.Robertson, Nature, 191, 593, 1961

Atomic coordinates were not given. The refinement using diffractometer data gave very accurate bond lengths which are reported in the paper.

P2$_1$/c   Z = 2   R = 0.038

BIPHEN02   LB 12-10-2

19.17   Diphenyliodonium fluoroborate

$C_{12}H_{10}I^+$, BF_4^-

Yu.T.Struchkov, T.L.Hotsyanova, Izvest. Akad. Nauk S. S. S. R., Ser. Khim., 821, 1960

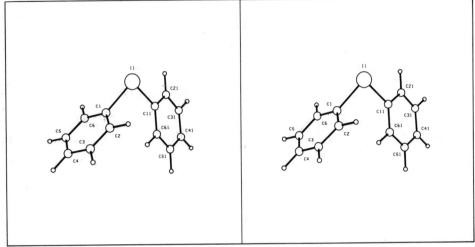

P2₁/c   Z = 4   No R factor was given.

DPIMFB   LB 12-10-13

Bond Lengths

I1	C1	2.05
I1	C11	2.02
C1	C2	1.41
C1	C6	1.39
C2	C3	1.40
C3	C4	1.39
C4	C5	1.41
C5	C6	1.40
C11	C21	1.39
C11	C61	1.42
C21	C31	1.40
C31	C41	1.42
C41	C51	1.40
C51	C61	1.39
B1	F1	1.44
B1	F2	1.43
B1	F3	1.41
B1	F4	1.45

Bond Angles

C1	I1	C11	94
I1	C1	C2	117
I1	C1	C6	122
C2	C1	C6	121
C1	C2	C3	121
C2	C3	C4	119
C3	C4	C5	121
C4	C5	C6	121
C1	C6	C5	119
I1	C11	C21	117
I1	C11	C61	121
C21	C11	C61	122
C11	C21	C31	119
C21	C31	C41	119
C31	C41	C51	121
C41	C51	C61	120
C11	C61	C51	119
F1	B1	F2	108
F1	B1	F3	109
F1	B1	F4	110
F2	B1	F3	110
F2	B1	F4	111
F3	B1	F4	109

Torsion Angles

C6	C1	I1	C11	−91
C61	C11	I1	C1	−29

19.18   Hexa(bromomethyl)benzene

$C_{12}H_{12}Br_6$

P.Marsau, Acta Cryst., 18, 851, 1965

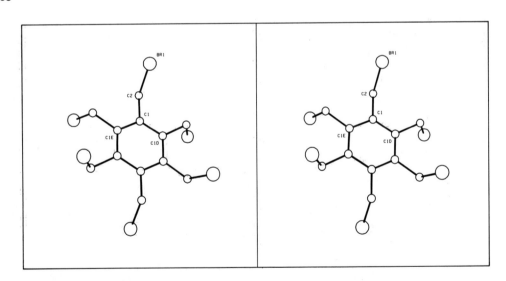

P-3   Z = 3   R = 0.087

HBMEBZ   LB 12-12-12

Bond Lengths

Br1	C2	1.98
C1	C2	1.54
C1	C1D	1.39

Bond Angles

C2	C1	C1D	120
C2	C1	C1E	120
Br1	C2	C1	111

Torsion Angles

C1D	C1	C2	Br1	−87

19.19   Benzil

C.J.Brown, R.Sadanaga, Acta Cryst., 18, 158, 1965

$C_{14}H_{10}O_2$

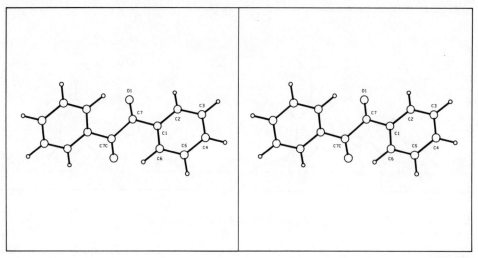

The space group could be the enantiomorphous $P3_221$.
$P3_121$ $Z = 3$ $R = 0.078$

BENZIL   LB 14-10-43

Bond Lengths

C7	O1	1.21	C3	C4	1.39	
C1	C2	1.38	C4	C5	1.40	
C1	C6	1.40	C5	C6	1.39	
C1	C7	1.48	C7	C7C	1.52	
C2	C3	1.39				

Bond Angles

C2	C1	C6	122	C4	C5	C6	120
C2	C1	C7	119	C1	C6	C5	118
C6	C1	C7	119	O1	C7	C1	122
C1	C2	C3	120	O1	C7	C7C	118
C2	C3	C4	118	C1	C7	C7C	119
C3	C4	C5	121				

Torsion Angles

C6	C1	C7	C7C	−9
C1	C7	C7C	O1C	−69
C1	C7	C7C	C1C	115
O1	C7	C7C	O1C	108

19.20   bis(m - Bromobenzoyl)methane

D.E.Williams, W.L.Dumke, R.E.Rundle, Acta Cryst., 15, 627, 1962

$C_{15}H_{10}Br_2O_2$

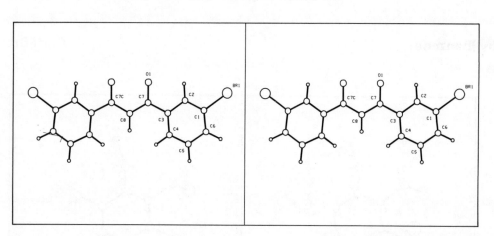

Pnca $Z = 8$ $R = 0.057$

BRBOYM   LB 15-10-3

Bond Lengths

Br1	C1	1.90	C3	C4	1.41	
C7	O1	1.31	C3	C7	1.46	
C1	C2	1.39	C4	C5	1.39	
C1	C6	1.37	C5	C6	1.40	
C2	C3	1.40	C7	C8	1.39	

Bond Angles

Br1	C1	C2	118	C3	C4	C5	120
Br1	C1	C6	119	C4	C5	C6	122
C2	C1	C6	123	C1	C6	C5	118
C1	C2	C3	119	O1	C7	C3	116
C2	C3	C4	119	O1	C7	C8	120
C2	C3	C7	119	C3	C7	C8	125
C4	C3	C7	122	C7	C8	C7C	122

Torsion Angles

C2	C3	C7	C8	−178
C3	C7	C8	C7C	−179

19.21   bis(m - Chlorobenzoyl)methane

G.R.Engebretson, R.E.Rundle, J. Amer. Chem. Soc., 86, 574, 1964

$C_{15}H_{10}Cl_2O_2$

15-10-3 $X = Br$
15-10-4 $X = Cl$

Using the published coordinates the two benzoyl moieties do not connect.
$Pca2_1$ $Z = 4$ $R = 0.058$

CLBOME   LB 15-10-4

20.1   Hexachlorocyclopropane   C₃Cl₆

T.Tanako, T.Chiba, Y.Sasada, M.Kakudo, S.Nozakura, S.Murahahi,
Bull. Chem. Soc. Jap., 38, 157, 1965

Atomic coordinates were not
reported in the paper.
P2₁/a   Z = 4   R = 0.14

HCCYPR   LB 3-0-4

20.2   Octachlorocyclobutane (refinement of data of Owen and Hoard, Acta Cryst., 4,172,1951)   C₄Cl₈

T.N.Margulis, Acta Cryst., 19, 857, 1965

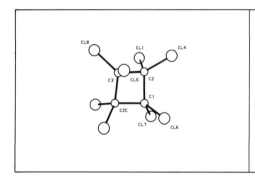

P2₁/m   Z = 2   R = 0.12

CLCBUT   LB 4-0-8

Bond Lengths			Bond Angles							Torsion Angles									
Cl1	C2	1.75	Cl6	C1	Cl7	109	Cl4	C2	C1	116	Cl6	C1	C2	Cl1	149	Cl1	C2	C3	Cl5	−150
Cl4	C2	1.76	Cl6	C1	C2	114	Cl4	C2	C3	117	Cl6	C1	C2	Cl4	23	Cl1	C2	C3	Cl8	−23
Cl5	C3	1.77	Cl7	C1	C2	115	C1	C2	C3	89	Cl6	C1	C2	C3	−97	Cl1	C2	C3	C2C	98
Cl6	C1	1.70	C2	C1	C2C	89	Cl5	C3	Cl8	109	Cl7	C1	C2	Cl1	22	Cl4	C2	C3	Cl5	−25
Cl7	C1	1.76	Cl1	C2	Cl4	108	Cl5	C3	C2	112	Cl7	C1	C2	Cl4	−104	Cl4	C2	C3	Cl8	102
Cl8	C3	1.72	Cl1	C2	C1	115	Cl8	C3	C2	118	Cl7	C1	C2	C3	136	Cl4	C2	C3	C2C	−137
C1	C2	1.57	Cl1	C2	C3	112	C2	C3	C2C	88	C2C	C1	C2	Cl1	−95	C1	C2	C3	Cl5	94
C2	C3	1.58									C2C	C1	C2	Cl4	138	C1	C2	C3	Cl8	−139
											C2C	C1	C2	C3	19	C1	C2	C3	C2C	−18

20.3   Cyclopentadiene (at −150° C)   C₅H₆

G.Liebling, R.E.Marsh, Acta Cryst., 19, 202, 1965

P2₁/n   Z = 4   R = 0.10

CPENAD   LB 5-6-1

Bond Lengths			Bond Angles			
C1	C2	1.27	C2	C1	C5	111
C1	C5	1.48	C1	C2	C3	112
C2	C3	1.44	C2	C3	C4	107
C3	C4	1.38	C3	C4	C5	108
C4	C5	1.51	C1	C5	C4	102

20.4   Dimethylfulvene (at −50 ° C) C_8H_{10}

N.Norman, B.Post, Acta Cryst., 14, 503, 1961

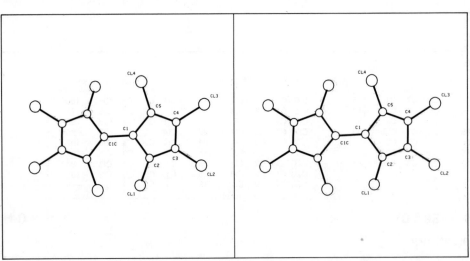

C2/c   Z = 4   R = 0.12

DMEFUL   LB 8-10-1

Bond Lengths			Bond Angles			
C1	C2	1.34	C2	C1	C3	127
C1	C3	1.44	C3	C1	C3A	106
C2	C5	1.52	C1	C2	C5	123
C3	C4	1.35	C5	C2	C5A	113
C4	C4A	1.44	C1	C3	C4	108
			C3	C4	C4A	109

20.5   1 - Methyl - 3 - imino - 4 - α - hydroxyethylidene cyclopent - 1 - ene - 2 - carbonamide hydrobromide monohydrate $C_8H_{13}N_2O_2{}^+$, Br^- , H_2O

G.L.Buchanan, J.A.Hamilton, T.A.Hamor, G.A.Sim, Acta Chem. Scand., 16, 776, 1962

Atomic coordinates were not reported in the paper.
P2₁/c   Z = 4   R = 0.153

MICPCA

20.6   Perchlorofulvalene $C_{10}Cl_8$

P.J.Wheatley, J. Chem. Soc., 4936, 1961

C2/c   Z = 4 R_{h0l} = 0.19, R_{hk0} = 0.19

CLFULV   LB 10-0-3

Bond Lengths			Bond Angles								Torsion Angles									
Cl1	C2	1.69	C2	C1	C5	106	C2	C3	C4	111	C5	C1	C2	Cl1	−168	Cl1	C2	C3	Cl2	−9
Cl2	C3	1.69	C2	C1	C1C	124	Cl3	C4	C3	126	C5	C1	C2	C3	−1	Cl1	C2	C3	C4	169
Cl3	C4	1.68	C5	C1	C1C	130	Cl3	C4	C5	124	C1C	C1	C2	Cl1	16	C1	C2	C3	Cl2	−176
Cl4	C5	1.70	Cl1	C2	C1	127	C3	C4	C5	110	C1C	C1	C2	C3	−177	C1	C2	C3	C4	1
C1	C2	1.48	Cl1	C2	C3	127	Cl4	C5	C1	124	C2	C1	C5	Cl4	−174	Cl2	C3	C4	Cl3	−13
C1	C5	1.47	C1	C2	C3	105	Cl4	C5	C4	128	C2	C1	C5	C4	0	Cl2	C3	C4	C5	175
C1	C1C	1.49	Cl2	C3	C2	125	C1	C5	C4	108	C1C	C1	C5	Cl4	3	C2	C3	C4	Cl3	170
C2	C3	1.39	Cl2	C3	C4	124					C1C	C1	C5	C4	176	C2	C3	C4	C5	−2
C3	C4	1.38									C2	C1	C1C	C2C	−145	Cl3	C4	C5	Cl4	2
C4	C5	1.36									C2	C1	C1C	C5C	39	Cl3	C4	C5	C1	−171
											C5	C1	C1C	C2C	39	C3	C4	C5	Cl4	174
											C5	C1	C1C	C5C	−136	C3	C4	C5	C1	1

20.7 2,2 - Dichloro - 3 - phenylcyclobutenone

$C_{10}H_6Cl_2O$

I.L.Karle, K.Britts, Z. Kristallogr., 121, 190, 1965

P2₁/c   Z = 4   R = 0.136

DCPCBU   LB 10-6-11

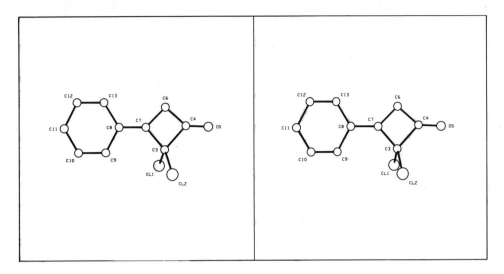

Bond Lengths

Cl1	C3	1.76	C7	C8	1.38
Cl2	C3	1.78	C8	C9	1.41
C4	O5	1.17	C8	C13	1.42
C3	C4	1.59	C9	C10	1.38
C3	C7	1.47	C10	C11	1.36
C4	C6	1.40	C11	C12	1.41
C6	C7	1.39	C12	C13	1.37

Bond Angles

Cl1	C3	Cl2	110	C3	C7	C8	132
Cl1	C3	C4	115	C6	C7	C8	135
Cl1	C3	C7	116	C7	C8	C9	120
Cl2	C3	C4	112	C7	C8	C13	122
Cl2	C3	C7	117	C9	C8	C13	119
C4	C3	C7	85	C8	C9	C10	120
O5	C4	C3	131	C9	C10	C11	120
O5	C4	C6	142	C10	C11	C12	121
C3	C4	C6	87	C11	C12	C13	119
C4	C6	C7	95	C8	C13	C12	121
C3	C7	C6	92				

Torsion Angles

Cl1	C3	C4	O5	−64	C4	C3	C7	C6	3
Cl1	C3	C4	C6	114	C4	C3	C7	C8	−176
Cl2	C3	C4	O5	63	O5	C4	C6	C7	180
Cl2	C3	C4	C6	−120	C3	C4	C6	C7	3
C7	C3	C4	O5	−180	C4	C6	C7	C3	−3
C7	C3	C4	C6	−3	C4	C6	C7	C8	176
Cl1	C3	C7	C6	−113	C3	C7	C8	C9	10
Cl1	C3	C7	C8	68	C3	C7	C8	C13	−169
Cl2	C3	C7	C6	115	C6	C7	C8	C9	−169
Cl2	C3	C7	C8	−64	C6	C7	C8	C13	12

20.8 Phenylcyclobutenedione

$C_{10}H_6O_2$

C.H.Wong, R.E.Marsh, V.Schomaker, Acta Cryst., 17, 131, 1964

P2₁/c   Z = 4   R = 0.08

PCBUTO   LB 10-6-22

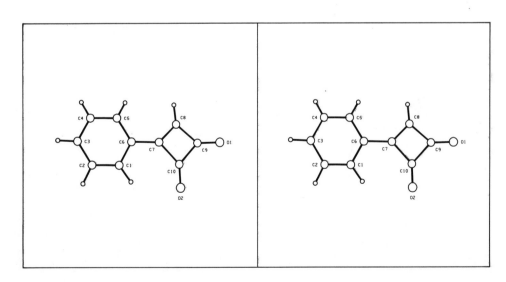

Bond Lengths

C9	O1	1.22	C5	C6	1.40
C10	O2	1.19	C6	C7	1.45
C1	C2	1.38	C7	C8	1.36
C1	C6	1.38	C7	C10	1.51
C2	C3	1.38	C8	C9	1.46
C3	C4	1.38	C9	C10	1.54
C4	C5	1.38			

Bond Angles

C2	C1	C6	120	C6	C7	C10	133
C1	C2	C3	121	C8	C7	C10	92
C2	C3	C4	119	C7	C8	C9	95
C3	C4	C5	121	O1	C9	C8	137
C4	C5	C6	120	O1	C9	C10	136
C1	C6	C5	119	C8	C9	C10	87
C1	C6	C7	120	O2	C10	C7	137
C5	C6	C7	121	O2	C10	C9	137
C6	C7	C8	135	C7	C10	C9	86

Torsion Angles

C1	C6	C7	C8	180	C8	C7	C10	O2	−179
C1	C6	C7	C10	0	C8	C7	C10	C9	0
C5	C6	C7	C8	1	C7	C8	C9	O1	180
C5	C6	C7	C10	−179	C7	C8	C9	C10	0
C6	C7	C8	C9	−180	O1	C9	C10	O2	−1
C10	C7	C8	C9	0	O1	C9	C10	C7	−180
C6	C7	C10	O2	1	C8	C9	C10	O2	179
C6	C7	C10	C9	180	C8	C9	C10	C7	0

20.9 1 - Cyclohexenyl - 1 - cyclobutenedione

$C_{10}H_{10}O_2$

I.L.Karle, K.Britts, S.Brenner, Acta Cryst., 17, 1506, 1964

P2$_1$/c   Z = 4   R = 0.15

CYHBUO   LB 10-10-50

Bond Lengths

C4	O1	1.17	C7	C8	1.35
C3	O2	1.23	C7	C12	1.50
C3	C4	1.55	C8	C9	1.50
C3	C6	1.48	C9	C10	1.55
C4	C5	1.49	C10	C11	1.54
C5	C6	1.39	C11	C12	1.53
C6	C7	1.43			

Bond Angles

O2	C3	C4	136	C5	C6	C7	133
O2	C3	C6	135	C6	C7	C8	116
C4	C3	C6	89	C6	C7	C12	119
O1	C4	C3	135	C8	C7	C12	124
O1	C4	C5	140	C7	C8	C9	121
C3	C4	C5	85	C8	C9	C10	114
C4	C5	C6	95	C9	C10	C11	110
C3	C6	C5	91	C10	C11	C12	110
C3	C6	C7	136	C7	C12	C11	112

Torsion Angles

O2	C3	C4	O1	1	C3	C6	C7	C8	−2
O2	C3	C4	C5	−180	C3	C6	C7	C12	−180
C6	C3	C4	O1	180	C5	C6	C7	C8	179
C6	C3	C4	C5	−1	C5	C6	C7	C12	1
O2	C3	C6	C5	180	C6	C7	C8	C9	−180
O2	C3	C6	C7	0	C12	C7	C8	C9	−2
C4	C3	C6	C5	1	C6	C7	C12	C11	163
C4	C3	C6	C7	−178	C8	C7	C12	C11	−14
O1	C4	C5	C6	−180	C7	C8	C9	C10	−14
C3	C4	C5	C6	1	C8	C9	C10	C11	45
C4	C5	C6	C3	−1	C9	C10	C11	C12	−62
C4	C5	C6	C7	178	C10	C11	C12	C7	46

20.10 1,3 - Di - isopropylidene cyclobutane - 2,4 - dione

$C_{10}H_{12}O_2$

A.Schuijff, Proefschr. Doct. Wiskde. Naturwet., Utrecht, 1962

Atomic coordinates were not|reported in the paper.
Pbcn   Z = 2   No R factor was given.

IPCBDO

20.11 1,2,3 - Tribromo - 6 - (o - methoxyphenyl) - fulvene

$C_{13}H_9Br_3O$

Y.Kato, Y.Sasada, M.Kakudo, Bull. Chem. Soc. Jap., 38, 1761, 1965

P2$_1$/c   Z = 4   R = 0.113

TBMFUL   LB 13-9-3

Bond Lengths

Br1	C1	1.84	C4	C5	1.46
Br2	C2	1.86	C5	C6	1.36
Br3	C3	1.87	C6	C7	1.49
C12	O1	1.39	C7	C8	1.42
C13	O1	1.46	C7	C12	1.38
C1	C2	1.29	C8	C9	1.36
C1	C5	1.49	C9	C10	1.42
C2	C3	1.48	C10	C11	1.42
C3	C4	1.32	C11	C12	1.44

Bond Angles

C12	O1	C13	120	C2	C3	C4	111	C7	C8	C9	120
Br1	C1	C2	127	C3	C4	C5	107	C8	C9	C10	120
Br1	C1	C5	125	C1	C5	C4	106	C9	C10	C11	123
C2	C1	C5	109	C1	C5	C6	122	C10	C11	C12	114
Br2	C2	C1	129	C4	C5	C6	132	O1	C12	C7	117
Br2	C2	C3	123	C5	C6	C7	124	O1	C12	C11	119
C1	C2	C3	108	C6	C7	C8	122	C7	C12	C11	124
Br3	C3	C2	124	C6	C7	C12	119				
Br3	C3	C4	125	C8	C7	C12	119				

Torsion Angles

C13	O1	C12	C7	172
C13	O1	C12	C11	−11
C1	C5	C6	C7	179
C4	C5	C6	C7	−6
C5	C6	C7	C8	−37
C5	C6	C7	C12	147

20.12   2,5 - Di - (p - iodobenzylidene)cyclopentanone $C_{19}H_{14}I_2O$

D.Mootz, K.Plieth, Z. Elektrochem., 65, 151, 1961

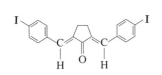

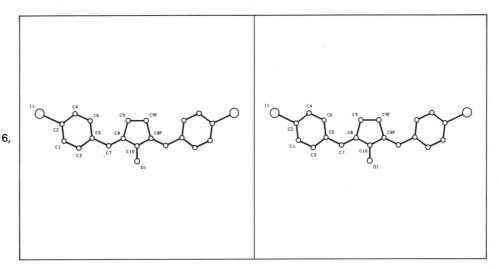

Abm2   Z = 4 $R_{0kl} = 0.16,$
$R_{hk0} = 0.18$

IBCPEO   LB 19-14-8

Bond Lengths

I1	C2	2.08	C5	C6	1.40
C10	O1	1.28	C5	C7	1.53
C1	C2	1.40	C7	C8	1.36
C1	C3	1.40	C8	C9	1.54
C2	C4	1.40	C8	C10	1.31
C3	C5	1.40	C9	C9F	1.51
C4	C6	1.40			

Bond Angles

C2	C1	C3	120	C4	C6	C5	120
I1	C2	C1	120	C5	C7	C8	130
I1	C2	C4	120	C7	C8	C9	128
C1	C2	C4	120	C7	C8	C10	128
C1	C3	C5	120	C9	C8	C10	99
C2	C4	C6	120	C8	C9	C9F	105
C3	C5	C6	120	O1	C10	C8	117
C3	C5	C7	120	C8	C10	C8F	127
C6	C5	C7	120				

Torsion Angles

C3	C5	C7	C8	162	C7	C8	C10	O1	0
C6	C5	C7	C8	−19	C7	C8	C10	C8F	180
C5	C7	C8	C9	29	C9	C8	C10	O1	158
C5	C7	C8	C10	−180	C9	C8	C10	C8F	−22
C7	C8	C9	C9F	168	C8	C9	C9F	C8F	0
C10	C8	C9	C9F	10					

20.13   1,2,3,4 - Tetraphenylcyclobutane (centrosymmetric form, refinement of data of Dunitz, Acta Cryst., 2,1,1949) $C_{28}H_{24}$

T.N.Margulis, Acta Cryst., 19, 857, 1965

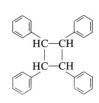

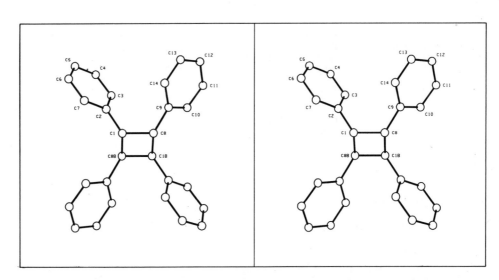

$P2_1/a$ Z = 2   R = 0.14

PHCBUT   LB 28-24-1

Bond Lengths

C1	C2	1.50	C6	C7	1.37
C1	C8	1.57	C8	C9	1.52
C1	C8B	1.57	C9	C10	1.39
C2	C3	1.41	C9	C14	1.39
C2	C7	1.41	C10	C11	1.39
C3	C4	1.40	C11	C12	1.39
C4	C5	1.38	C12	C13	1.39
C5	C6	1.42	C13	C14	1.39

Bond Angles

C2	C1	C8	123	C1	C8	C9	121
C2	C1	C8B	114	C1	C8	C1B	91
C8	C1	C8B	89	C9	C8	C1B	118
C1	C2	C3	122	C8	C9	C10	122
C1	C2	C7	119	C8	C9	C14	118
C3	C2	C7	119	C10	C9	C14	119
C2	C3	C4	120	C9	C10	C11	121
C3	C4	C5	120	C10	C11	C12	120
C4	C5	C6	121	C11	C12	C13	120
C5	C6	C7	120	C12	C13	C14	120
C2	C7	C6	121	C9	C14	C13	120

Torsion Angles

C8	C1	C2	C3	48	C2	C1	C8B	C1B	126
C8	C1	C2	C7	−134	C2	C1	C8B	C9B	−107
C8B	C1	C2	C3	−58	C8	C1	C8B	C1B	0
C8B	C1	C2	C7	120	C8	C1	C8B	C9B	127
C2	C1	C8	C9	5	C1	C8	C9	C10	−133
C2	C1	C8	C1B	−119	C1	C8	C9	C14	54
C8B	C1	C8	C9	124	C1B	C8	C9	C10	−23
C8B	C1	C8	C1B	0	C1B	C8	C9	C14	164

21.1   Cyclohexane - 1,4 - dione $C_6H_8O_2$

(i)   A.Mossel, C.Romers, Acta Cryst., 17, 1217, 1964 (at −140°C)

(ii)   P.Groth, O.Hassel, Acta Chem. Scand., 18, 923, 1964

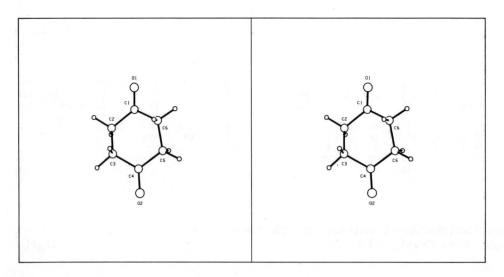

(i)

$P2_1$ Z = 2   R = 0.081

CYHEXO   LB 6-8-55

(ii)

$P2_1$ Z = 2   R = 0.069

CYHEXO01   LB 6-8-55

Bond Lengths			
		(i)	(ii)
C1	O1	1.21	1.22
C4	O2	1.21	1.22
C1	C2	1.53	1.51
C1	C6	1.51	1.51
C2	C3	1.54	1.55
C3	C4	1.50	1.50
C4	C5	1.52	1.51
C5	C6	1.53	1.56

Bond Angles				
			(i)	(ii)
O1	C1	C2	121	121
O1	C1	C6	123	122
C2	C1	C6	116	117
C1	C2	C3	113	112
C2	C3	C4	112	112
O2	C4	C3	122	122
O2	C4	C5	122	120
C3	C4	C5	116	117
C4	C5	C6	113	112
C1	C6	C5	111	110

Torsion Angles					
				(i)	(ii)
O1	C1	C2	C3	−169	168
C6	C1	C2	C3	12	−11
O1	C1	C6	C5	−139	140
C2	C1	C6	C5	41	−41
C1	C2	C3	C4	−52	52
C2	C3	C4	O2	−139	138
C2	C3	C4	C5	40	−39
O2	C4	C5	C6	−168	169
C3	C4	C5	C6	12	−14
C4	C5	C6	C1	−53	54

21.2   Cyclohexane - 1,4 - dione $C_6H_8O_2$

For complete entry see 21.1

21.3   trans - 1,4 - Dichlorocyclohexane (low temp. form) $C_6H_{10}Cl_2$

T.Dahl, O.Hassel, C.Romming, Acta Chem. Scand., 18, 2280, 1964

The structure is totally disordered.
$P4_2/mnm$ Z = 2   R = 0.186

TDCHCH   LB 6-10-15

21.4   myo - Inositol $C_6H_{12}O_6$

I.N.Rabinowitz, J.Kraut, Acta Cryst., 17, 159, 1964

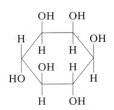

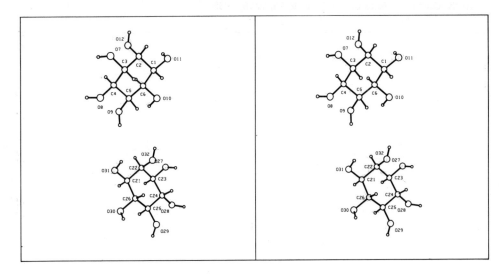

P2$_1$/c   Z = 8   R = 0.06

MYINOL   LB 6-12-85

Bond Lengths

C3	O7	1.43	C23	O27	1.44
C4	O8	1.42	C24	O28	1.42
C5	O9	1.43	C25	O29	1.44
C6	O10	1.43	C26	O30	1.43
C1	O11	1.42	C21	O31	1.43
C2	O12	1.43	C22	O32	1.44
C1	C2	1.53	C21	C22	1.52
C1	C6	1.51	C21	C26	1.52
C2	C3	1.53	C22	C23	1.53
C3	C4	1.52	C23	C24	1.52
C4	C5	1.52	C24	C25	1.51
C5	C6	1.52	C25	C26	1.51

Bond Angles

O11	C1	C2	111	O31	C21	C22	111
O11	C1	C6	113	O31	C21	C26	112
C2	C1	C6	110	C22	C21	C26	112
O12	C2	C1	110	O32	C22	C21	109
O12	C2	C3	110	O32	C22	C23	110
C1	C2	C3	110	C21	C22	C23	109
O7	C3	C2	110	O27	C23	C22	112
O7	C3	C4	112	O27	C23	C24	112
C2	C3	C4	110	C22	C23	C24	111
O8	C4	C3	109	O28	C24	C23	109
O8	C4	C5	111	O28	C24	C25	110
C3	C4	C5	110	C23	C24	C25	109
O9	C5	C4	110	O29	C25	C24	110
O9	C5	C6	109	O29	C25	C26	109
C4	C5	C6	112	C24	C25	C26	113
O10	C6	C1	108	O30	C26	C21	108
O10	C6	C5	110	O30	C26	C25	110
C1	C6	C5	111	C21	C26	C25	111

Torsion Angles

O11	C1	C2	O12	63	O31	C21	C22	O32	62
O11	C1	C2	C3	−175	O31	C21	C22	C23	−177
C6	C1	C2	O12	−63	C26	C21	C22	O32	−64
C6	C1	C2	C3	58	C26	C21	C22	C23	56
O11	C1	C6	O10	58	O31	C21	C26	O30	60
O11	C1	C6	C5	179	O31	C21	C26	C25	−179
C2	C1	C6	O10	−177	C22	C21	C26	O30	−175
C2	C1	C6	C5	−56	C22	C21	C26	C25	−54
O12	C2	C3	O7	−62	O32	C22	C23	O27	−65
O12	C2	C3	C4	62	O32	C22	C23	C24	61
C1	C2	C3	O7	176	C21	C22	C23	O27	176
C1	C2	C3	C4	−60	C21	C22	C23	C24	−59
O7	C3	C4	O8	−57	O27	C23	C24	O28	−56
O7	C3	C4	C5	−179	O27	C23	C24	C25	−177
C2	C3	C4	O8	180	C22	C23	C24	O28	178
C2	C3	C4	C5	59	C22	C23	C24	C25	58
O8	C4	C5	O9	62	O28	C24	C25	O29	63
O8	C4	C5	C6	−177	O28	C24	C25	C26	−175
C3	C4	C5	O9	−177	C23	C24	C25	O29	−178
C3	C4	C5	C6	−57	C23	C24	C25	C26	−55
O9	C5	C6	O10	−63	O29	C25	C26	O30	−64
O9	C5	C6	C1	177	O29	C25	C26	C21	176
C4	C5	C6	O10	176	C24	C25	C26	O30	173
C4	C5	C6	C1	56	C24	C25	C26	C21	54

21.5   myo - Inositol dihydrate $C_6H_{12}O_6$, $2H_2O$

T.R.Lomer, A.Miller, C.A.Beevers, Acta Cryst., 16, 264, 1963

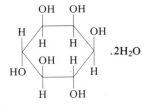

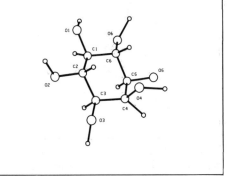

.2H$_2$O

P2$_1$/a   Z = 4   R = 0.20

MYTOLD   LB 6-12-86

Bond Lengths

C1	O1	1.40
C2	O2	1.46
C3	O3	1.48
C4	O4	1.43
C5	O5	1.46
C6	O6	1.44
C1	C2	1.53
C1	C6	1.50
C2	C3	1.50
C3	C4	1.50
C4	C5	1.46
C5	C6	1.52

Bond Angles

O1	C1	C2	107	O4	C4	C3	110
O1	C1	C6	110	O4	C4	C5	110
C2	C1	C6	110	C3	C4	C5	106
O2	C2	C1	107	O5	C5	C4	109
O2	C2	C3	110	O5	C5	C6	106
C1	C2	C3	107	C4	C5	C6	115
O3	C3	C2	109	O6	C6	C1	107
O3	C3	C4	107	O6	C6	C5	110
C2	C3	C4	115	C1	C6	C5	109

Torsion Angles

O1	C1	C2	O2	65	O2	C2	C3	O3	−63	O4	C4	C5	O5	58
O1	C1	C2	C3	−177	O2	C2	C3	C4	176	O4	C4	C5	C6	−62
C6	C1	C2	O2	−175	C1	C2	C3	O3	−179	C3	C4	C5	O5	176
C6	C1	C2	C3	−57	C1	C2	C3	C4	60	C3	C4	C5	C6	57
O1	C1	C6	O6	−66	O3	C3	C4	O4	−62	O5	C5	C6	O6	63
O1	C1	C6	C5	174	O3	C3	C4	C5	179	O5	C5	C6	C1	−179
C2	C1	C6	O6	176	C2	C3	C4	O4	60	C4	C5	C6	O6	−176
C2	C1	C6	C5	56	C2	C3	C4	C5	−59	C4	C5	C6	C1	−58

21.6   cis - 4 - Aminomethyl - cyclohexane carboxylic acid hydrobromide

$C_8H_{16}NO_2^+$, Br^-

P.Groth, O.Hassel, Acta Chem. Scand., 19, 1709, 1965

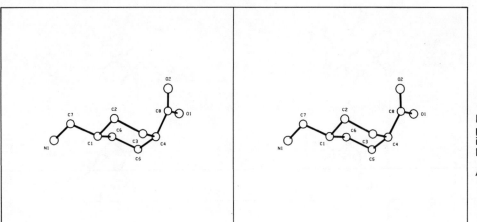

No comparison of bond lengths is possible since they are not reported in the paper.
$P2_1/c$ Z = 4   R = 0.065

AMHCAC   LB 8-16-6

Bond Lengths

C7	N1	1.51	C2	C3	1.59
C8	O1	1.31	C3	C4	1.49
C8	O2	1.25	C4	C5	1.51
C1	C2	1.57	C4	C8	1.51
C1	C6	1.48	C5	C6	1.50
C1	C7	1.53			

Bond Angles

C2	C1	C6	108	C5	C4	C8	114
C2	C1	C7	108	C4	C5	C6	115
C6	C1	C7	114	C1	C6	C5	112
C1	C2	C3	108	N1	C7	C1	111
C2	C3	C4	112	O1	C8	O2	120
C3	C4	C5	112	O1	C8	C4	115
C3	C4	C8	112	O2	C8	C4	126

Torsion Angles

C6	C1	C2	C3	−61	C2	C3	C4	C8	78
C7	C1	C2	C3	175	C3	C4	C5	C6	49
C2	C1	C6	C5	60	C8	C4	C5	C6	−79
C7	C1	C6	C5	−180	C3	C4	C8	O1	179
C2	C1	C7	N1	−175	C3	C4	C8	O2	0
C6	C1	C7	N1	65	C5	C4	C8	O1	−53
C1	C2	C3	C4	58	C5	C4	C8	O2	128
C2	C3	C4	C5	−51	C4	C5	C6	C1	−55

21.7   Dimethyl - 2,5 - dihydroxy - 1,4 - cyclohexadiene - 1,4 - dicarboxylate

$C_{10}H_{12}O_6$

(i)   P.Ganis, C.Pedone, P.A.Temussi,
Atti Accad. Nazion. Lincei, R. C., Cl. Sci. Fis. Mat. Nat., 35, 175, 1963   (form i)

(ii)   P.Ganis, C.Pedone, P.A.Temussi,
Atti Accad. Nazion. Lincei, R. C., Cl. Sci. Fis. Mat. Nat., 35, 68, 1963   (form ii)

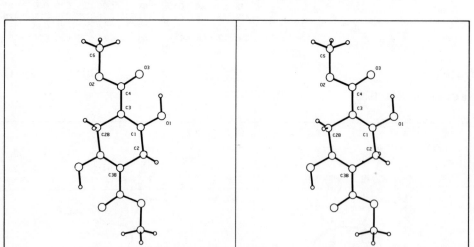

(i)

$P2_1/a$ Z = 2 $R_{h0l} = 0.148$, $R_{hk0} = 0.14$

DCHEXC   LB 10-12-50

(ii)

P-1   Z = 1 $R_{h0l} = 0.161$, $R_{hk0} = 0.125$

DCHEXC01   LB 10-12-51

Bond Lengths

		(i)	(ii)
C1	O1	1.37	1.36
		(1.30)	
C4	O2	1.31	1.34
C5	O2	1.48	1.50
			(1.45)
C4	O3	1.23	1.22
C1	C2	1.52	1.50
C1	C3	1.30	1.33
C2	C3B	1.49	1.49
C3	C4	1.46	1.43

Bond Angles

			(i)	(ii)
C4	O2	C5	113	117
O1	C1	C2	105	111
O1	C1	C3	122	123
C2	C1	C3	130	127
C1	C2	C3B	109	112
C1	C3	C4	123	120
C1	C3	C2B	120	121
C4	C3	C2B	116	119
O2	C4	O3	125	116
O2	C4	C3	114	114
O3	C4	C3	120	130

Torsion Angles

				(i)	(ii)					(i)	(ii)
C5	O2	C4	O3	−15	2	C2	C1	C3	C2B	13	4
C5	O2	C4	C3	179	177	C1	C2	C3B	C1B	11	−4
O1	C1	C2	C3B	−172	180	C1	C2	C3B	C4B	−177	176
C3	C1	C2	C3B	−12	4	C1	C3	C4	O2	−180	180
O1	C1	C3	C4	−17	0	C1	C3	C4	O3	14	−6
O1	C1	C3	C2B	171	179	C2B	C3	C4	O2	−7	0
C2	C1	C3	C4	−175	−175	C2B	C3	C4	O3	−174	174

21.8   Dimethyl - 2,5 - dihydroxy - 1,4 - cyclohexadiene - 1,4 - dicarboxylate (form ii)

$C_{10}H_{12}O_6$

For complete entry see 21.7

21.9   2,6 - Dibromo - 3,3,5,5 - tetramethylcyclohexanone

$C_{10}H_{16}Br_2O$

L.C.G.Goaman, D.F.Grant, Acta Cryst., 17, 1604, 1964

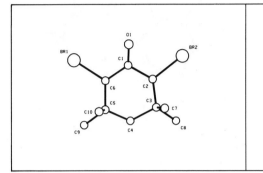 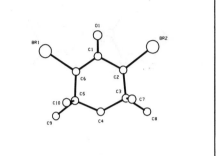

$P2_12_12_1$ Z = 4   R = 0.10

DBMECH   LB 10-16-10

Bond Lengths

Br1	C6	1.96	C3	C7	1.49
Br2	C2	1.96	C3	C8	1.48
C1	O1	1.20	C4	C5	1.49
C1	C2	1.55	C5	C6	1.57
C1	C6	1.48	C5	C9	1.57
C2	C3	1.55	C5	C10	1.45
C3	C4	1.55			

Bond Angles

O1	C1	C2	122	C7	C3	C8	107
O1	C1	C6	128	C3	C4	C5	120
C2	C1	C6	111	C4	C5	C6	104
Br2	C2	C1	110	C4	C5	C9	106
Br2	C2	C3	113	C4	C5	C10	118
C1	C2	C3	111	C6	C5	C9	107
C2	C3	C4	103	C6	C5	C10	114
C2	C3	C7	114	C9	C5	C10	108
C2	C3	C8	109	Br1	C6	C1	109
C4	C3	C7	115	Br1	C6	C5	113
C4	C3	C8	109	C1	C6	C5	111

Torsion Angles

O1	C1	C2	Br2	−6	C1	C2	C3	C8	170
O1	C1	C2	C3	119	C2	C3	C4	C5	−59
C6	C1	C2	Br2	172	C7	C3	C4	C5	66
C6	C1	C2	C3	−63	C8	C3	C4	C5	−174
O1	C1	C6	Br1	6	C3	C4	C5	C6	59
O1	C1	C6	C5	−119	C3	C4	C5	C9	171
C2	C1	C6	Br1	−172	C3	C4	C5	C10	−69
C2	C1	C6	C5	63	C4	C5	C6	Br1	−180
Br2	C2	C3	C4	178	C4	C5	C6	C1	−57
Br2	C2	C3	C7	52	C9	C5	C6	Br1	68
Br2	C2	C3	C8	−67	C9	C5	C6	C1	−168
C1	C2	C3	C4	54	C10	C5	C6	Br1	−51
C1	C2	C3	C7	−71	C10	C5	C6	C1	73

21.10   2 - Bromo - 3,3,5,5 - tetramethylcyclohexanone

$C_{10}H_{17}BrO$

L.C.G.Goaman, D.F.Grant, Acta Cryst., 17, 1604, 1964

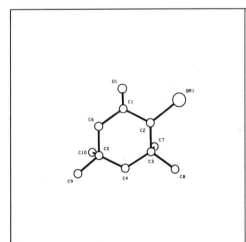 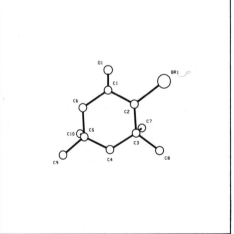

$P2_12_12_1$ Z = 4   R = 0.14

BRMECH   LB 10-17-1

Bond Lengths

Br1	C2	1.88	C3	C8	1.55
C1	O1	1.15	C4	C5	1.47
C1	C2	1.59	C5	C6	1.56
C1	C6	1.59	C5	C9	1.55
C2	C3	1.55	C5	C10	1.52
C3	C4	1.57			
C3	C7	1.59			

Bond Angles

O1	C1	C2	123	C4	C3	C8	108
O1	C1	C6	129	C7	C3	C8	106
C2	C1	C6	108	C3	C4	C5	121
Br1	C2	C1	111	C4	C5	C6	108
Br1	C2	C3	115	C4	C5	C9	107
C1	C2	C3	108	C4	C5	C10	113
C2	C3	C4	110	C6	C5	C9	105
C2	C3	C7	108	C6	C5	C10	111
C2	C3	C8	111	C9	C5	C10	112
C4	C3	C7	114	C1	C6	C5	110

Torsion Angles

O1	C1	C2	Br1	5	C1	C2	C3	C8	−172
O1	C1	C2	C3	−121	C2	C3	C4	C5	50
C6	C1	C2	Br1	−169	C7	C3	C4	C5	−72
C6	C1	C2	C3	64	C8	C3	C4	C5	171
O1	C1	C6	C5	120	C3	C4	C5	C6	−49
C2	C1	C6	C5	−66	C3	C4	C5	C9	−162
Br1	C2	C3	C4	−177	C3	C4	C5	C10	74
Br1	C2	C3	C7	−53	C4	C5	C6	C1	55
Br1	C2	C3	C8	63	C9	C5	C6	C1	169
C1	C2	C3	C4	−53	C10	C5	C6	C1	−69
C1	C2	C3	C7	71					

21.11   Bicyclohexylidene $C_{12}H_{20}$

K.Sasvari, M.Low, Acta Cryst., 19, 840, 1965

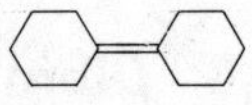

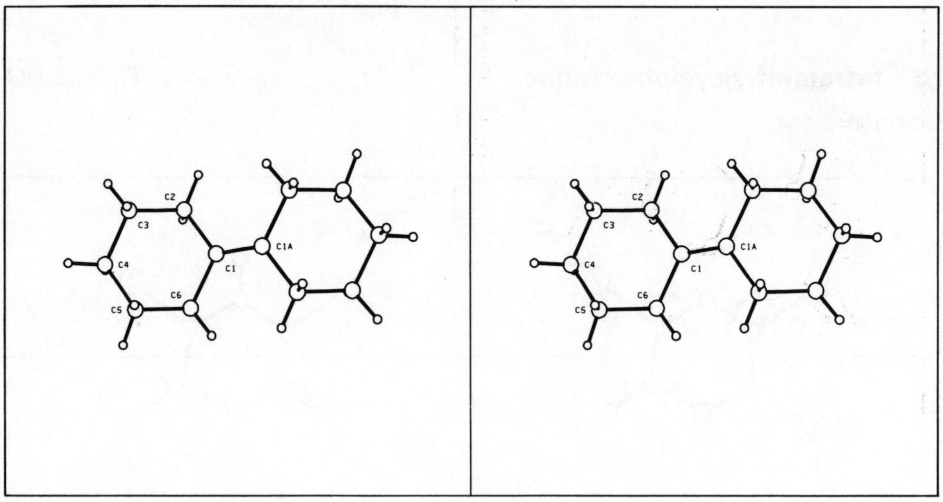

P-1   Z = 1   R = 0.116

BCHXEN   LB 12-20-1

Bond Lengths

C1	C2	1.51
C1	C6	1.53
C1	C1A	1.33
C2	C3	1.53
C3	C4	1.52
C4	C5	1.52
C5	C6	1.53

Bond Angles

C2	C1	C6	111
C2	C1	C1A	125
C6	C1	C1A	124
C1	C2	C3	112
C2	C3	C4	111
C3	C4	C5	111
C4	C5	C6	110
C1	C6	C5	112

Torsion Angles

C6	C1	C2	C3	55
C1A	C1	C2	C3	−125
C2	C1	C6	C5	−55
C1A	C1	C6	C5	124
C2	C1	C1A	C2A	−180
C2	C1	C1A	C6A	0
C6	C1	C1A	C2A	0
C6	C1	C1A	C6A	−180
C1	C2	C3	C4	−56
C2	C3	C4	C5	56
C3	C4	C5	C6	−56
C4	C5	C6	C1	56

22.1 Sodium tropolonate (refinement of data of Sasada and Nitta, Acta Cryst., 9,205,1956)

$C_7H_5O_2^-$, Na+

R.Shiono, Acta Cryst., 14, 42, 1961

Published values of y(C4) = 0.7074A and . z(C4) = −2.7666A. Comparison with the paper of Sasada and Nitta shows that these coordinates should be 0.7610 and −2.7703A respectively.
P2₁/c   Z = 4   R = 0.11

NATROP   LB 7-5-34

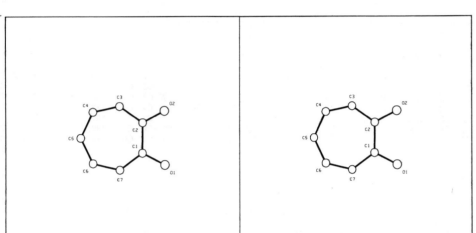

Bond Lengths			Bond Angles			
C1	O1	1.29	O1	C1	C2	116
C2	O2	1.28	O1	C1	C7	118
C1	C2	1.49	C2	C1	C7	126
C1	C7	1.41	O2	C2	C1	118
C2	C3	1.43	O2	C2	C3	118
C3	C4	1.38	C1	C2	C3	124
C4	C5	1.42	C2	C3	C4	134
C5	C6	1.39	C3	C4	C5	127
C6	C7	1.39	C4	C5	C6	128
			C5	C6	C7	130
			C1	C7	C6	131

22.2   7 - Bromo - 2 - methoxy tropone

$C_8H_7BrO_2$

K.Furukawa, Y.Sasada, A.Shimada, T.Watanabe, Bull. Chem. Soc. Jap., 37, 1871, 1964

Pn2₁a   Z = 4 R_{h0l} = 0.18,
R_{hk0} = 0.15

BMEOTR   LB 8-7-3

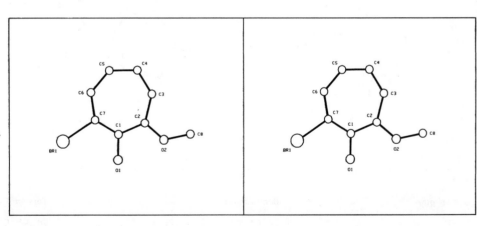

Bond Lengths						Bond Angles							Torsion Angles						
Br1	C7	1.96	C2	C3	1.45	C2	O2	C8	129	C2	C3	C4	134	C8	O2	C2	C1	−178	C2 C1 C7 C6	−31
C1	O1	1.25	C3	C4	1.39	O1	C1	C2	114	C3	C4	C5	122	C8	O2	C2	C3	4	O2 C2 C3 C4	173
C2	O2	1.30	C4	C5	1.42	O1	C1	C7	119	C4	C5	C6	131	O1	C1	C2	O2	7	C1 C2 C3 C4	−5
C8	O2	1.41	C5	C6	1.43	C2	C1	C7	124	C5	C6	C7	130	O1	C1	C2	C3	−175	C2 C3 C4 C5	−3
C1	C2	1.45	C6	C7	1.38	O2	C2	C1	118	Br1	C7	C1	117	C7	C1	C2	O2	−155	C3 C4 C5 C6	−4
C1	C7	1.41				O2	C2	C3	116	Br1	C7	C6	114	C7	C1	C2	C3	23	C4 C5 C6 C7	1
						C1	C2	C3	126	C1	C7	C6	127	O1	C1	C7	Br1	6	C5 C6 C7 Br1	−180
														O1	C1	C7	C6	168	C5 C6 C7 C1	18
														C2	C1	C7	Br1	167		

22.3   3 - Bromo - 2 - methoxy tropone

C₈H₇BrO₂

K.Furukawa, Y.Sasada, A.Shimada, T.Watanabe, Bull. Chem. Soc. Jap., 37, 1871, 1964

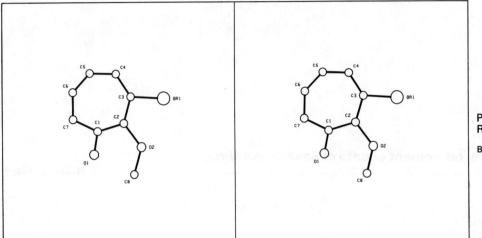

P2₁/a   Z = 4   R₀ₖₗ = 0.17,
Rₕₖ₀ = 0.15

BRMOTR   LB 8-7-2

Bond Lengths

Br1	C3	1.88	C2	C3	1.48
C1	O1	1.24	C3	C4	1.44
C2	O2	1.46	C4	C5	1.37
C8	O2	1.52	C5	C6	1.41
C1	C2	1.45	C6	C7	1.47
C1	C7	1.40			

Bond Angles

C2	O2	C8	126	Br1	C3	C2	110
O1	C1	C2	119	Br1	C3	C4	116
O1	C1	C7	105	C2	C3	C4	133
C2	C1	C7	136	C3	C4	C5	122
O2	C2	C1	110	C4	C5	C6	130
O2	C2	C3	124	C5	C6	C7	139
C1	C2	C3	125	C1	C7	C6	115

Torsion Angles

C8	O2	C2	C1	42	O2	C2	C3	C4	165
C8	O2	C2	C3	−129	C1	C2	C3	Br1	−169
O1	C1	C2	O2	16	C1	C2	C3	C4	−4
O1	C1	C2	C3	−174	Br1	C3	C4	C5	164
C7	C1	C2	O2	−166	C2	C3	C4	C5	0
C7	C1	C2	C3	4	C3	C4	C5	C6	2
O1	C1	C7	C6	177	C4	C5	C6	C7	0
C2	C1	C7	C6	−1	C5	C6	C7	C1	−2
O2	C2	C3	Br1	0					

22.4   1,3,5,7 - Cyclo - octatetraene carboxylic acid

C₉H₈O₂

D.P.Shoemaker, H.Kindler, W.G.Sly, R.C.Srivastava, J. Amer. Chem. Soc., 87, 482, 1965

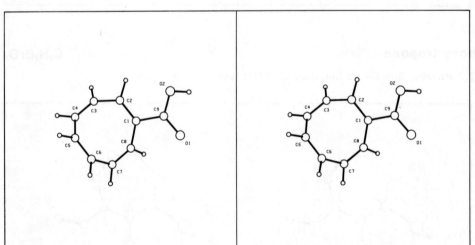

In the paper the value of β is given as 110° 9.5' in the abstract and 100° 9.5' in the main text. The former value is correct.
P2₁/c   Z = 4   R = 0.101

CYOCTC   LB 9-8-11

Bond Lengths

C9	O1	1.26	C3	C4	1.32
C9	O2	1.28	C4	C5	1.45
C1	C2	1.32	C5	C6	1.33
C1	C8	1.48	C6	C7	1.49
C1	C9	1.48	C7	C8	1.31
C2	C3	1.46			

Bond Angles

C2	C1	C8	126	C5	C6	C7	125
C2	C1	C9	119	C6	C7	C8	126
C8	C1	C9	115	C1	C8	C7	127
C1	C2	C3	127	O1	C9	O2	122
C2	C3	C4	126	O1	C9	C1	121
C3	C4	C5	127	O2	C9	C1	117
C4	C5	C6	127				

Torsion Angles

C8	C1	C2	C3	1	C8	C1	C9	O2	178
C9	C1	C2	C3	175	C1	C2	C3	C4	57
C2	C1	C8	C7	−58	C2	C3	C4	C5	−1
C9	C1	C8	C7	128	C3	C4	C5	C6	−56
C2	C1	C9	O1	−177	C4	C5	C6	C7	0
C2	C1	C9	O2	3	C5	C6	C7	C8	57
C8	C1	C9	O1	−3	C6	C7	C8	C1	−1

22.5 Calcium - 2,4,6,8 - cyclo - octatetraene - 1,2 - dicarboxylate dihydrate

$C_{10}H_6O_4^{2-}$, Ca^{2+} , $2H_2O$

D.A.Wright, K.Seff, D.P.Shoemaker, Acta Cryst., 16, A58, 1963

Atomic coordinates were not reported in the paper.
P-1   Z = 2   R = 0.086

CACOCT

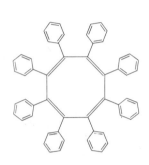

22.6 Octaphenylcyclo - octatetraene

$C_{56}H_{40}$

P.J.Wheatley, J. Chem. Soc., 3136, 1965

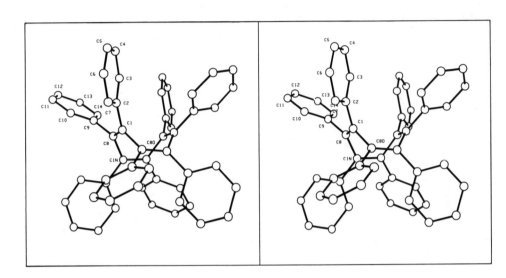

I4₁/a   Z = 4   R = 0.117

OPCYOC   LB 56-40-2

Bond Lengths

C1	C2	1.50	C6	C7	1.42
C1	C8	1.34	C8	C9	1.49
C1	C8O	1.49	C9	C10	1.41
C2	C3	1.41	C9	C14	1.40
C2	C7	1.41	C10	C11	1.40
C3	C4	1.43	C11	C12	1.41
C4	C5	1.39	C12	C13	1.39
C5	C6	1.39	C13	C14	1.43

Bond Angles

C2	C1	C8	124
C2	C1	C8O	116
C8	C1	C8O	119
C1	C2	C3	118
C1	C2	C7	121
C3	C2	C7	121
C2	C3	C4	118
C3	C4	C5	121
C4	C5	C6	120
C5	C6	C7	120
C2	C7	C6	119

C1	C8	C9	124
C1	C8	C1N	119
C9	C8	C1N	117
C8	C9	C10	120
C8	C9	C14	119
C10	C9	C14	121
C9	C10	C11	119
C10	C11	C12	121
C11	C12	C13	121
C12	C13	C14	119
C9	C14	C13	120

Torsion Angles

C8	C1	C2	C3	−49
C8	C1	C2	C7	134
C8O	C1	C2	C3	127
C8O	C1	C2	C7	−50
C2	C1	C8	C9	−9
C2	C1	C8	C1N	172
C8O	C1	C8	C9	174
C8O	C1	C8	C1N	−5

C2	C1	C8O	C1O	−105
C2	C1	C8O	C9O	74
C8	C1	C8O	C1O	71
C8	C1	C8O	C9O	−110
C1	C8	C9	C10	−48
C1	C8	C9	C14	136
C1N	C8	C9	C10	131
C1N	C8	C9	C14	−45

22.7 Octaphenylcyclo - octatetraene

$C_{56}H_{40}$

G.S.Pawley, W.N.Lipscomb, H.H.Freedman, J. Amer. Chem. Soc., 86, 4725, 1964

Atomic coordinates were not given but bond lengths were reported.
I4₁/a   Z = 4   R = 0.12

OPCYOC01   LB 56-40-2

23.1 cis,cis,cis - 1,4,7 - Cyclononatriene

C_9H_{12}

W.R.Roth, W.B.Bang, P.Goebel, R.L.Sass, R.B.Turner, A.P.Yu,
J. Amer. Chem. Soc., 86, 3178, 1964

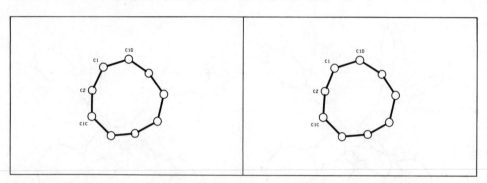

R3m   Z = 3   R = 0.12

CNONTR   LB 9-12-1

Bond Lengths			Bond Angles				Torsion Angles				
C1	C2	1.52	C2	C1	C1D	125	C1D	C1	C2	C1C	95
C1	C1D	1.35	C1	C2	C1C	108	C2	C1	C1D	C2A	0

23.2 Cyclononylamine hydrobromide

$C_9H_{20}N^+$, Br^-

R.F.Bryan, J.D.Dunitz, Helv. Chim. Acta, 43, 3, 1960

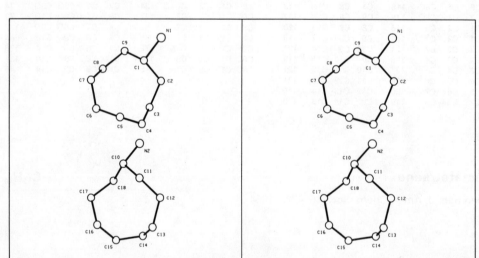

The asymmetric unit consists of two molecules which are conformational isomers.
P2₁/n   Z = 8   R = 0.13

CYNAMB   LB 9-20-3

Bond Lengths						Bond Angles							Torsion Angles						
C1	N1	1.48	C10	N2	1.49	N1	C1	C2	103	N2	C10	C11	104	N1	C1	C2	C3	175	N2 C10 C11 C12	−77
C1	C2	1.54	C10	C11	1.54	N1	C1	C9	105	N2	C10	C18	110	C9	C1	C2	C3	−73	C18 C10 C11 C12	45
C1	C9	1.55	C10	C18	1.53	C2	C1	C9	112	C11	C10	C18	117	N1	C1	C9	C8	−166	N2 C10 C18 C17	−163
C2	C3	1.53	C11	C12	1.54	C1	C2	C3	116	C10	C11	C12	118	C2	C1	C9	C8	83	C11 C10 C18 C17	78
C3	C4	1.51	C12	C13	1.53	C2	C3	C4	117	C11	C12	C13	117	C1	C2	C3	C4	−65	C10 C11 C12 C13	−95
C4	C5	1.53	C13	C14	1.51	C3	C4	C5	124	C12	C13	C14	117	C2	C3	C4	C5	67	C11 C12 C13 C14	95
C5	C6	1.52	C14	C15	1.52	C4	C5	C6	114	C13	C14	C15	120	C3	C4	C5	C6	48	C12 C13 C14 C15	−104
C6	C7	1.51	C15	C16	1.56	C5	C6	C7	121	C14	C15	C16	116	C4	C5	C6	C7	−94	C13 C14 C15 C16	25
C7	C8	1.53	C16	C17	1.58	C6	C7	C8	119	C15	C16	C17	111	C5	C6	C7	C8	86	C14 C15 C16 C17	90
C8	C9	1.53	C17	C18	1.53	C7	C8	C9	117	C16	C17	C18	113	C6	C7	C8	C9	−104	C15 C16 C17 C18	−61
						C1	C9	C8	112	C10	C18	C17	119	C7	C8	C9	C1	43	C16 C17 C18 C10	−81

23.3   1,6 - trans - Dibromocyclodecane

$C_{10}H_{18}Br_2$

J.D.Dunitz, H.P.Weber, Helv. Chim. Acta, 47, 951, 1964

$P2_1/c$ $Z = 2$ $R_{0kl} = 0.11$,
$R_{h0l} = 0.11$, $R_{hk0} = 0.13$

BRCDEC   LB 10-18-5

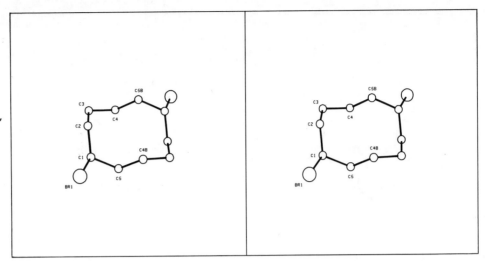

Bond Lengths			Bond Angles				Torsion Angles				
Br1	C1	1.92	Br1	C1	C2	115	Br1	C1	C2	C3	−165
C1	C2	1.53	Br1	C1	C5	108	C5	C1	C2	C3	68
C1	C5	1.54	C2	C1	C5	117	Br1	C1	C5	C4B	−71
C2	C3	1.52	C1	C2	C3	122	C2	C1	C5	C4B	60
C3	C4	1.54	C2	C3	C4	114	C1	C2	C3	C4	−70
C4	C5B	1.55	C3	C4	C5B	117	C2	C3	C4	C5B	−52
			C1	C5	C4B	116	C3	C4	C5B	C1B	152

23.4   Cyclodecylamine hydrochloride sesquihydrate

$C_{10}H_{22}N^+$, Cl^- , $1.5H_2O$

M.H.Mladeck, W.Nowacki, Helv. Chim. Acta, 47, 1280, 1964

$C2/c$ $Z = 4$ $R = 0.10$

CDECAC   LB 10-22-3

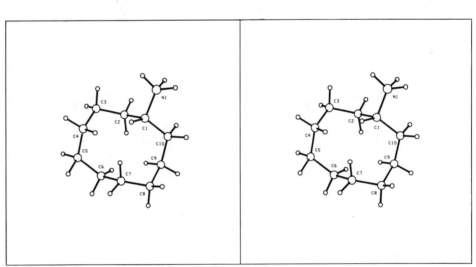

Bond Lengths			Bond Angles				Torsion Angles				
C1	N1	1.53	N1	C1	C2	109	N1	C1	C2	C3	−87
C1	C2	1.53	N1	C1	C10	107	C10	C1	C2	C3	153
C1	C10	1.54	C2	C1	C10	115	N1	C1	C10	C9	−178
C2	C3	1.56	C1	C2	C3	116	C2	C1	C10	C9	−57
C3	C4	1.54	C2	C3	C4	117	C1	C2	C3	C4	−54
C4	C5	1.53	C3	C4	C5	118	C2	C3	C4	C5	−68
C5	C6	1.55	C4	C5	C6	118	C3	C4	C5	C6	68
C6	C7	1.53	C5	C6	C7	115	C4	C5	C6	C7	54
C7	C8	1.56	C6	C7	C8	115	C5	C6	C7	C8	−151
C8	C9	1.55	C7	C8	C9	117	C6	C7	C8	C9	53
C9	C10	1.54	C8	C9	C10	118	C7	C8	C9	C10	69
			C1	C10	C9	117	C8	C9	C10	C1	−66

23.5   1,6 - trans - Diaminocyclodecane dihydrochloride (triclinic form) $C_{10}H_{24}N_2^{2+}$, $2Cl^-$

E.Huber-Buser, J.D.Dunitz, Helv. Chim. Acta, 44, 2027, 1961

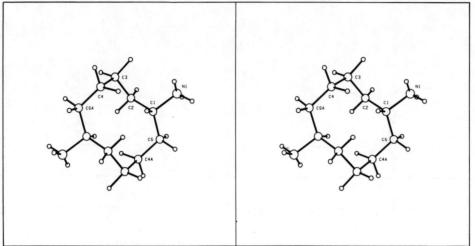

$2Cl^- \cdot 2H_2O$

See also Huber - Buser & Dunitz,
Helv. Chim. Acta, 49, 1821, 1966.
P-1   Z = 1   R = 0.11

ACDECT10   LB 10-24-3

Bond Lengths			Bond Angles				Torsion Angles				
C1	N1	1.53	N1	C1	C2	107	N1	C1	C2	C3	−86
C1	C2	1.54	N1	C1	C5	108	C5	C1	C2	C3	153
C1	C5	1.52	C2	C1	C5	115	N1	C1	C5	C4A	−172
C2	C3	1.55	C1	C2	C3	115	C2	C1	C5	C4A	−52
C3	C4	1.52	C2	C3	C4	116	C1	C2	C3	C4	−59
C4	C5A	1.53	C3	C4	C5A	119	C2	C3	C4	C5A	−67
			C1	C5	C4A	116	C3	C4	C5A	C1A	69

23.6   1,6 - cis - Diaminocyclodecane dihydrochloride dihydrate $C_{10}H_{24}N_2^{2+}$, $2Cl^-$, $2H_2O$

J.D.Dunitz, K.Venkatesan, Helv. Chim. Acta, 44, 2033, 1961

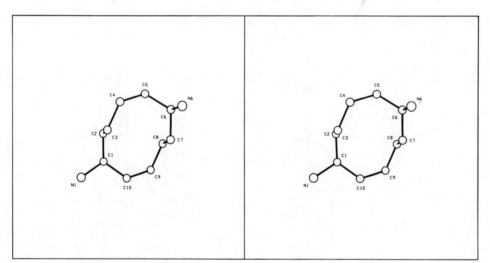

$\cdot 2\,Cl^- \cdot 2H_2O$

P2$_1$/c   Z = 4   R = 0.12
ACDECC   LB 10-24-4

Bond Lengths			Bond Angles				Torsion Angles				
C1	N1	1.55	N1	C1	C2	109	N1	C1	C2	C3	66
C6	N6	1.50	N1	C1	C10	105	C10	C1	C2	C3	−52
C1	C2	1.54	C2	C1	C10	116	N1	C1	C10	C9	168
C1	C10	1.53	C1	C2	C3	117	C2	C1	C10	C9	−72
C2	C3	1.52	C2	C3	C4	113	C1	C2	C3	C4	152
C3	C4	1.53	C3	C4	C5	119	C2	C3	C4	C5	−53
C4	C5	1.55	C4	C5	C6	120	C3	C4	C5	C6	−66
C5	C6	1.54	N6	C6	C5	110	C4	C5	C6	N6	−64
C6	C7	1.52	N6	C6	C7	109	C4	C5	C6	C7	61
C7	C8	1.55	C5	C6	C7	118	N6	C6	C7	C8	−174
C8	C9	1.54	C6	C7	C8	113	C5	C6	C7	C8	60
C9	C10	1.55	C7	C8	C9	114	C6	C7	C8	C9	−153
			C8	C9	C10	118	C7	C8	C9	C10	57
			C1	C10	C9	116	C8	C9	C10	C1	67

23.7   Cyclododecane (low temp. form)   C₁₂H₂₄

J.D.Dunitz, H.M.M.Shearer, Helv. Chim. Acta, 43, 18, 1960

The structure is totally disordered.
C2/m   Z = 2   R = 0.14

CDODEC   LB 12-24-1

23.8   5,11,17 - trisDehydro - (18)annulene   C₁₈H₁₂

N.A.Bailey, R.Mason, Proc. Chem. Soc., 356, 1964

The structure is totally disordered.
Pna2₁   Z = 4   R = 0.16

TDEHAN   LB 18-12-6

23.9   (18)Annulene (at 80 ° K)   C₁₈H₁₈

J.Bregman, F.L.Hirshfeld, D.Rabinovich, G.M.J.Schmidt, Acta Cryst., 19, 227 + , 1965

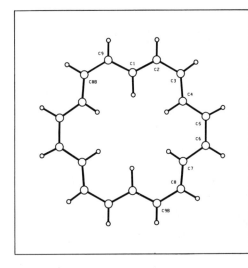

P2₁/a   Z = 2   R = 0.076

ANULEN   LB 18-18-1

Bond Lengths			Bond Angles				Torsion Angles			
C1	C2	1.39	C2	C1	C9	126	C9	C1	C2	C3	−178
C1	C9	1.39	C1	C2	C3	124	C2	C1	C9	C8B	174
C2	C3	1.41	C2	C3	C4	124	C1	C2	C3	C4	1
C3	C4	1.38	C3	C4	C5	128	C2	C3	C4	C5	−175
C4	C5	1.38	C4	C5	C6	123	C3	C4	C5	C6	178
C5	C6	1.43	C5	C6	C7	124	C4	C5	C6	C7	−4
C6	C7	1.38	C6	C7	C8	128	C5	C6	C7	C8	173
C7	C8	1.37	C7	C8	C9B	124	C6	C7	C8	C9B	−175
C8	C9B	1.42	C1	C9	C8B	124	C7	C8	C9B	C1B	2

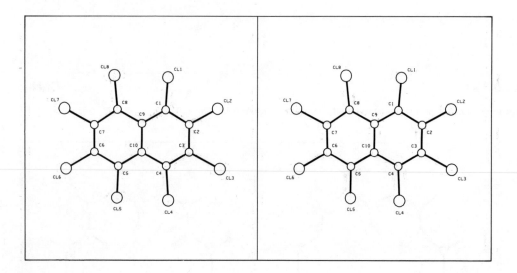

24.1   Octachloronaphthalene

$C_{10}Cl_8$

G.Gafner, F.H.Herbstein, Nature, 200, 130, 1963

$P2_1/a$ $Z = 4$ $R = 0.21$

OCLNAP   LB 10-0-2

Bond Lengths

Cl1	C1	1.72		C2	C3	1.38
Cl2	C2	1.72		C3	C4	1.35
Cl3	C3	1.75		C4	C10	1.42
Cl4	C4	1.72		C5	C6	1.41
Cl5	C5	1.70		C5	C10	1.40
Cl6	C6	1.72		C6	C7	1.36
Cl7	C7	1.74		C7	C8	1.40
Cl8	C8	1.69		C8	C9	1.45
C1	C2	1.41		C9	C10	1.41
C1	C9	1.41				

Bond Angles

Cl1	C1	C2	115		Cl6	C6	C5	120
Cl1	C1	C9	124		Cl6	C6	C7	120
C2	C1	C9	120		C5	C6	C7	120
Cl2	C2	C1	121		Cl7	C7	C6	120
Cl2	C2	C3	121		Cl7	C7	C8	118
C1	C2	C3	119		C6	C7	C8	122
Cl3	C3	C2	117		Cl8	C8	C7	117
Cl3	C3	C4	121		Cl8	C8	C9	125
C2	C3	C4	122		C7	C8	C9	118
Cl4	C4	C3	117		C1	C9	C8	124
Cl4	C4	C10	121		C1	C9	C10	119
C3	C4	C10	121		C8	C9	C10	118
Cl5	C5	C6	117		C4	C10	C5	123
Cl5	C5	C10	124		C4	C10	C9	117
C6	C5	C10	119		C5	C10	C9	120

Torsion Angles

Cl1	C1	C2	Cl2	1		C10	C5	C6	Cl6	−178
Cl1	C1	C2	C3	−178		C10	C5	C6	C7	3
C9	C1	C2	Cl2	178		Cl5	C5	C10	C4	−20
C9	C1	C2	C3	0		Cl5	C5	C10	C9	159
Cl1	C1	C9	C8	−16		C6	C5	C10	C4	164
Cl1	C1	C9	C10	165		C6	C5	C10	C9	−17
C2	C1	C9	C8	167		Cl6	C6	C7	Cl7	8
C2	C1	C9	C10	−12		Cl6	C6	C7	C8	−173
Cl2	C2	C3	Cl3	9		C5	C6	C7	Cl7	−173
Cl2	C2	C3	C4	−174		C5	C6	C7	C8	6
C1	C2	C3	Cl3	−172		Cl7	C7	C8	Cl8	−2
C1	C2	C3	C4	5		Cl7	C7	C8	C9	178
Cl3	C3	C4	Cl4	5		C6	C7	C8	Cl8	180
Cl3	C3	C4	C10	180		C6	C7	C8	C9	−1
C2	C3	C4	Cl4	−172		Cl8	C8	C9	C1	−11
C2	C3	C4	C10	3		Cl8	C8	C9	C10	167
Cl4	C4	C10	C5	−21		C7	C8	C9	C1	169
Cl4	C4	C10	C9	160		C7	C8	C9	C10	−13
C3	C4	C10	C5	164		C1	C9	C10	C4	19
C3	C4	C10	C9	−15		C1	C9	C10	C5	−160
Cl5	C5	C6	Cl6	6		C8	C9	C10	C4	−160
Cl5	C5	C6	C7	−173		C8	C9	C10	C5	21

24.2   1,5 - Dibromo - 4,8 - dichloronaphthalene $C_{10}H_4Br_2Cl_2$

M.A.Davydova, Yu.T.Struchkov, Zh. Strukt. Khim., 6, 113, 1965

For correct equation of least squares plane see Zh.Strukt.Khim.,9,547,1968. The bromine and chlorine atoms are disordered.

$P2_1/c$ Z = 4   R = 0.184

BCNPHL   LB 10-4-1

Bond Lengths

C1	C2	1.37	C5	C10	1.47
C1	C9	1.45	C6	C7	1.38
C2	C3	1.40	C7	C8	1.36
C3	C4	1.39	C8	C9	1.40
C4	C10	1.45	C9	C10	1.51
C5	C6	1.34			

Bond Angles

C2	C1	C9	120	C7	C8	C9	125
C1	C2	C3	127	C1	C9	C8	127
C2	C3	C4	115	C1	C9	C10	115
C3	C4	C10	124	C8	C9	C10	118
C6	C5	C10	119	C4	C10	C5	127
C5	C6	C7	127	C4	C10	C9	118
C6	C7	C8	116	C5	C10	C9	115

Torsion Angles

C9	C1	C2	C3	5	C6	C5	C10	C9	0
C2	C1	C9	C8	173	C5	C6	C7	C8	8
C2	C1	C9	C10	−8	C6	C7	C8	C9	−5
C1	C2	C3	C4	−5	C7	C8	C9	C1	179
C2	C3	C4	C10	9	C7	C8	C9	C10	0
C3	C4	C10	C5	176	C1	C9	C10	C4	11
C3	C4	C10	C9	−13	C1	C9	C10	C5	−176
C10	C5	C6	C7	−6	C8	C9	C10	C4	−170
C6	C5	C10	C4	172	C8	C9	C10	C5	3

24.3   1,4,5,8 - Tetrachloronaphthalene $C_{10}H_4Cl_4$

(i)   G.Gafner, F.H.Herbstein, Acta Cryst., 15, 1081, 1962

(ii)   M.A.Davydova, Yu.T.Struchkov, Zh. Strukt. Khim., 3, 184, 1962

(i)

Pccn   Z = 4   R = 0.146

TCNAPH   LB 10-4-10

(ii)

Pccn   Z = 4   R = 0.144

TCNAPH01   LB 10-4-10

Bond Lengths

		(i)	(ii)
Cl1	C2	1.73	1.76
Cl2	C4	1.75	1.73
C1	C2	1.34	1.33
C1	C5A	1.41	1.41
C2	C3	1.44	1.43
C3	C4	1.47	1.43
C3	C3A	1.42	1.44
C4	C5	1.34	1.35

Bond Angles

			(i)	(ii)
C2	C1	C5A	123	120
Cl1	C2	C1	114	113
Cl1	C2	C3	125	124
C1	C2	C3	120	123
C2	C3	C4	125	125
C2	C3	C3A	119	116
C4	C3	C3A	117	119
Cl2	C4	C3	123	124
Cl2	C4	C5	114	114
C3	C4	C5	123	121
C4	C5	C1A	119	120

24.4   1,4,5,8 - Tetrachloronaphthalene $C_{10}H_4Cl_4$

For complete entry see 24.3

24.5   2,6 - Dichloronaphthalene $C_{10}H_6Cl_2$

T.L.Khotsyanova, Yu.T.Struchkov, Zh. Strukt. Khim., 5, 404, 1964

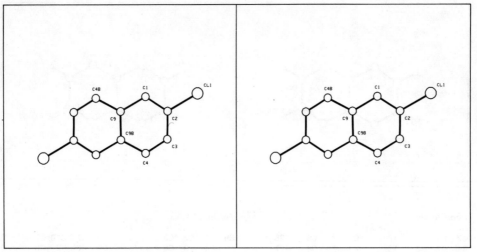

No comparison of bond lengths is possible since they are not reported in the paper.
$P2_1/c$ $Z = 2$ $R = 0.23$

DCNAPH   LB 10-6-9

Bond Lengths			Bond Angles			
Cl1	C2	1.79	C2	C1	C9	119
C1	C2	1.35	Cl1	C2	C1	119
C1	C9	1.48	Cl1	C2	C3	120
C2	C3	1.39	C1	C2	C3	121
C3	C4	1.33	C2	C3	C4	122
C4	C9B	1.42	C3	C4	C9B	121
C9	C9B	1.42	C1	C9	C4B	123
			C1	C9	C9B	118

24.6   1,5 - Dinitronaphthalene $C_{10}H_6N_2O_4$

J.Trotter, Acta Cryst., 13, 95, 1960

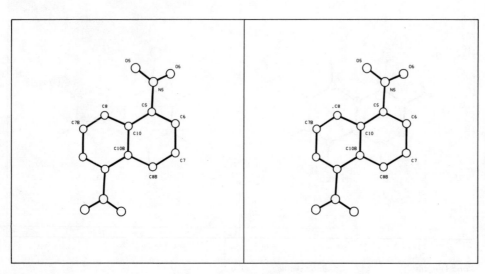

See also Sevastyanov et al., Zh. Fiz. Khim., 22, 1153, 1948.
$P2_1/a$ $Z = 2$ $R_{0kl} = 0.088$, $R_{h0l} = 0.169$, $R_{hk0} = 0.122$

DNNAPH   LB 10-6-17

Bond Lengths			Bond Angles				Torsion Angles				
N5	O5	1.19	O5	N5	O6	124	O5	N5	C5	C6	−136
N5	O6	1.23	O5	N5	C5	118	O5	N5	C5	C10	40
C5	N5	1.49	O6	N5	C5	117	O6	N5	C5	C6	55
C5	C6	1.39	N5	C5	C6	114	O6	N5	C5	C10	−130
C5	C10	1.40	N5	C5	C10	122					
C6	C7	1.41	C6	C5	C10	124					
C7	C8B	1.36	C5	C6	C7	117					
C8	C10	1.45	C6	C7	C8B	119					
C10	C10B	1.42	C10	C8	C7B	126					
			C5	C10	C8	126					
			C5	C10	C10B	120					
			C8	C10	C10B	114					

24.7   1,8 - Dinitronaphthalene (form i) $C_{10}H_6N_2O_4$

Z.A.Akopyan, A.I.Kitaigorodskij, Yu.T.Struchkov, Zh. Strukt. Khim., 6, 729, 1965

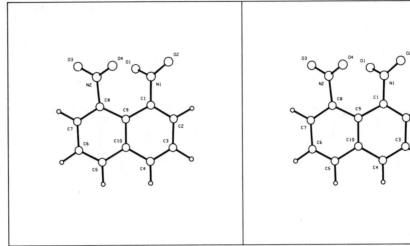

Published value of y(H7) = 0.394.
The correct value is −0.394.
$P2_12_12_1$ Z = 4   R = 0.165

DNTNAP10   LB 10-6-18

Bond Lengths

N1	O1	1.23	C3	C4	1.34
N1	O2	1.24	C4	C10	1.42
N2	O3	1.24	C5	C6	1.33
N2	O4	1.24	C5	C10	1.42
C1	N1	1.47	C6	C7	1.44
C8	N2	1.48	C7	C8	1.37
C1	C2	1.35	C8	C9	1.46
C1	C9	1.46	C9	C10	1.41
C2	C3	1.43			

Bond Angles

O1	N1	O2	122	C6	C5	C10	123
O1	N1	C1	120	C5	C6	C7	119
O2	N1	C1	118	C6	C7	C8	119
O3	N2	O4	127	N2	C8	C7	116
O3	N2	C8	116	N2	C8	C9	121
O4	N2	C8	117	C7	C8	C9	123
N1	C1	C2	118	C1	C9	C8	128
N1	C1	C9	118	C1	C9	C10	117
C2	C1	C9	122	C8	C9	C10	115
C1	C2	C3	119	C4	C10	C5	121
C2	C3	C4	122	C4	C10	C9	119
C3	C4	C10	121	C5	C10	C9	120

Torsion Angles

O1	N1	C1	C2	129	N1	C1	C9	C8	−21
O1	N1	C1	C9	−38	N1	C1	C9	C10	166
O2	N1	C1	C2	−46	C2	C1	C9	C8	173
O2	N1	C1	C9	147	C2	C1	C9	C10	−1
O3	N2	C8	C7	−38	N2	C8	C9	C1	−8
O3	N2	C8	C9	145	N2	C8	C9	C10	166
O4	N2	C8	C7	137	C7	C8	C9	C1	176
O4	N2	C8	C9	−40	C7	C8	C9	C10	−10

24.8   α - Naphthol $C_{10}H_8O$

B.Robinson, A.Hargreaves, Acta Cryst., 17, 944, 1964

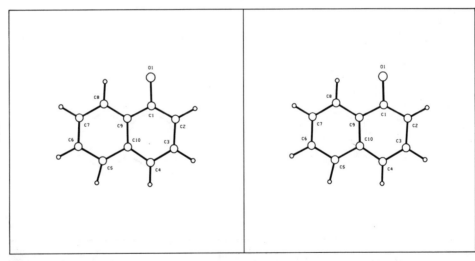

No comparison of bond lengths is possible since they are not reported in the paper.
$P2_1/a$ Z = 4   R = 0.12

NAPHOL   LB 10-8-25

Bond Lengths

C1	O1	1.40	C5	C6	1.43
C1	C2	1.41	C5	C10	1.46
C1	C9	1.38	C6	C7	1.40
C2	C3	1.44	C7	C8	1.43
C3	C4	1.36	C8	C9	1.41
C4	C10	1.38	C9	C10	1.40

Bond Angles

O1	C1	C2	120	C6	C7	C8	121
O1	C1	C9	116	C7	C8	C9	120
C2	C1	C9	124	C1	C9	C8	122
C1	C2	C3	114	C1	C9	C10	116
C2	C3	C4	123	C8	C9	C10	122
C3	C4	C10	118	C4	C10	C5	120
C6	C5	C10	123	C4	C10	C9	124
C5	C6	C7	117	C5	C10	C9	116

24.9   2 - Naphthoic acid

$C_{11}H_8O_2$

J.Trotter, Acta Cryst., 14, 101, 1961

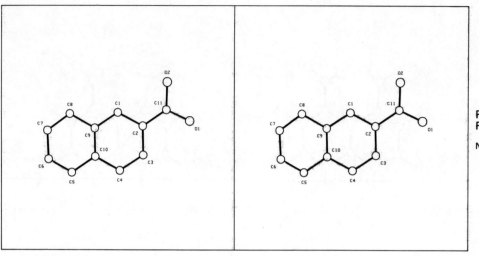

$P2_1/n$ Z = 4 $R_{h0l} = 0.159$, $R_{hk0} = 0.138$

NAPHAC   LB 11-8-14

Bond Lengths

C11	O1	1.33	C4	C10	1.43
C11	O2	1.36	C5	C6	1.36
C1	C2	1.44	C5	C10	1.44
C1	C9	1.40	C6	C7	1.42
C2	C3	1.43	C7	C8	1.41
C2	C11	1.44	C8	C9	1.47
C3	C4	1.42	C9	C10	1.39

Bond Angles

C2	C1	C9	120	C1	C9	C8	118
C1	C2	C3	118	C1	C9	C10	122
C1	C2	C11	120	C8	C9	C10	120
C3	C2	C11	122	C4	C10	C5	119
C2	C3	C4	121	C4	C10	C9	119
C3	C4	C10	120	C5	C10	C9	121
C6	C5	C10	119	O1	C11	O2	112
C5	C6	C7	121	O1	C11	C2	123
C6	C7	C8	122	O2	C11	C2	126
C7	C8	C9	116				

Torsion Angles

C1	C2	C11	O1	−178
C1	C2	C11	O2	2
C3	C2	C11	O1	0
C3	C2	C11	O2	−179

24.10   1 - Naphthoic acid

$C_{11}H_8O_2$

J.Trotter, Acta Cryst., 13, 732, 1960

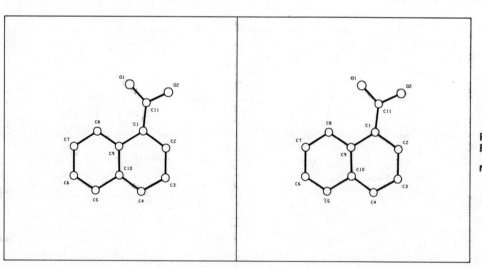

$P2_1/a$ Z = 4 $R_{h0l} = 0.127$, $R_{hk0} = 0.23$

NAPOAC   LB 11-8-13

Bond Lengths

C11	O1	1.25	C4	C10	1.38
C11	O2	1.28	C5	C6	1.34
C1	C2	1.44	C5	C10	1.43
C1	C9	1.45	C6	C7	1.43
C1	C11	1.40	C7	C8	1.42
C2	C3	1.46	C8	C9	1.35
C3	C4	1.40	C9	C10	1.42

Bond Angles

C2	C1	C9	113	C1	C9	C8	115
C2	C1	C11	118	C1	C9	C10	121
C9	C1	C11	128	C8	C9	C10	124
C1	C2	C3	124	C4	C10	C5	114
C2	C3	C4	119	C4	C10	C9	125
C3	C4	C10	117	C5	C10	C9	120
C6	C5	C10	116	O1	C11	O2	110
C5	C6	C7	122	O1	C11	C1	127
C6	C7	C8	121	O2	C11	C1	122
C7	C8	C9	115				

Torsion Angles

C2	C1	C11	O1	−171
C2	C1	C11	O2	1
C9	C1	C11	O1	20
C9	C1	C11	O2	−168

24.11   3 - Bromo - 1,8 - dimethylnaphthalene

M.B.Jameson, B.R.Penfold, J. Chem. Soc., 528, 1965

$C_{12}H_{11}Br$

P-1   Z = 2   R = 0.106

BDMNAP   LB 12-11-1

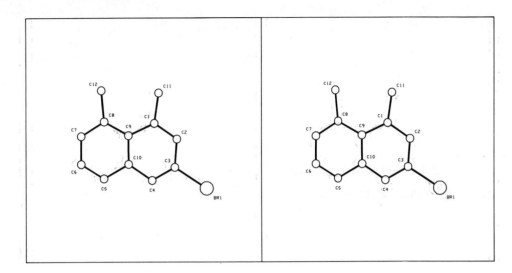

Bond Lengths

Br1	C3	1.92	C5	C6	1.36
C1	C2	1.39	C5	C10	1.44
C1	C9	1.45	C6	C7	1.39
C1	C11	1.51	C7	C8	1.38
C2	C3	1.40	C8	C9	1.41
C3	C4	1.33	C8	C12	1.52
C4	C10	1.43	C9	C10	1.42

Bond Angles

C2	C1	C9	122	C6	C7	C8	121
C2	C1	C11	115	C7	C8	C9	119
C9	C1	C11	123	C7	C8	C12	116
C1	C2	C3	120	C9	C8	C12	124
Br1	C3	C2	118	C1	C9	C8	127
Br1	C3	C4	120	C1	C9	C10	114
C2	C3	C4	122	C8	C9	C10	119
C3	C4	C10	119	C4	C10	C5	117
C6	C5	C10	119	C4	C10	C9	123
C5	C6	C7	121	C5	C10	C9	119

24.12   1, 5 - Dimethylnaphthalene ·

J.Beintema, Acta Cryst., 18, 647, 1965

$C_{12}H_{12}$

$P2_1/c$ Z = 4 $R_{0kl} = 0.093,$
$R_{h0l} = 0.141$

DIMNAP   LB 12-12-1

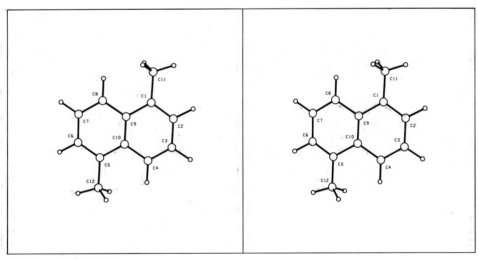

Bond Lengths

C1	C2	1.37	C5	C10	1.44
C1	C9	1.45	C5	C12	1.53
C1	C11	1.50	C6	C7	1.42
C2	C3	1.43	C7	C8	1.39
C3	C4	1.38	C8	C9	1.43
C4	C10	1.44	C9	C10	1.38
C5	C6	1.36			

Bond Angles

C2	C1	C9	117	C5	C6	C7	122
C2	C1	C11	121	C6	C7	C8	120
C9	C1	C11	122	C7	C8	C9	119
C1	C2	C3	122	C1	C9	C8	118
C2	C3	C4	121	C1	C9	C10	122
C3	C4	C10	118	C8	C9	C10	120
C6	C5	C10	118	C4	C10	C5	119
C6	C5	C12	120	C4	C10	C9	120
C10	C5	C12	122	C5	C10	C9	121

25.1   2,3 - Dichloro - 1,4 - naphthoquinone

$C_{10}H_4Cl_2O_2$

J.C.Metras, Acta Cryst., 14, 153, 1961

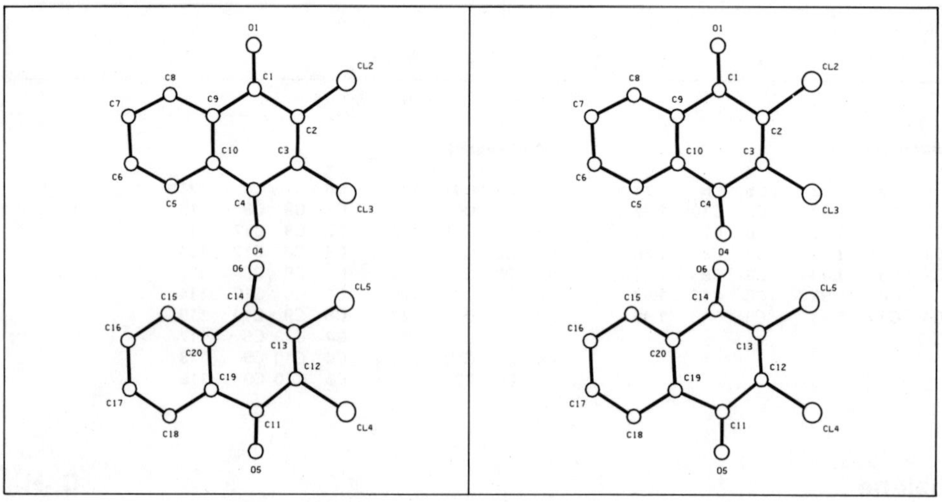

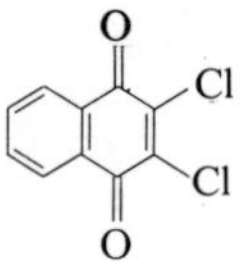

P-1   Z = 4   R = 0.11

DCLNAP   LB 10-4-9

Bond Lengths

Cl2	C2	1.76	Cl4	C12	1.78
Cl3	C3	1.70	Cl5	C13	1.71
C1	O1	1.23	C11	O5	1.17
C4	O4	1.22	C14	O6	1.20
C1	C2	1.50	C11	C12	1.49
C1	C9	1.43	C11	C19	1.49
C2	C3	1.32	C12	C13	1.35
C3	C4	1.48	C13	C14	1.47
C4	C10	1.42	C14	C20	1.49
C5	C6	1.37	C15	C16	1.40
C5	C10	1.39	C15	C20	1.43
C6	C7	1.36	C16	C17	1.40
C7	C8	1.38	C17	C18	1.43
C8	C9	1.41	C18	C19	1.44
C9	C10	1.36	C19	C20	1.43

Bond Angles

O1	C1	C2	123	O5	C11	C12	127
O1	C1	C9	120	O5	C11	C19	115
C2	C1	C9	117	C12	C11	C19	118
Cl2	C2	C1	113	Cl4	C12	C11	111
Cl2	C2	C3	126	Cl4	C12	C13	124
C1	C2	C3	121	C11	C12	C13	124
Cl3	C3	C2	119	Cl5	C13	C12	118
Cl3	C3	C4	119	Cl5	C13	C14	122
C2	C3	C4	121	C12	C13	C14	119
O4	C4	C3	116	O6	C14	C13	111
O4	C4	C10	128	O6	C14	C20	129
C3	C4	C10	116	C13	C14	C20	119
C6	C5	C10	125	C16	C15	C20	124
C5	C6	C7	120	C15	C16	C17	120
C6	C7	C8	113	C16	C17	C18	125
C7	C8	C9	128	C17	C18	C19	116
C1	C9	C8	123	C11	C19	C18	124
C1	C9	C10	121	C11	C19	C20	118
C8	C9	C10	116	C18	C19	C20	118
C4	C10	C5	120	C14	C20	C15	115
C4	C10	C9	123	C14	C20	C19	122
C5	C10	C9	116	C15	C20	C19	123

Torsion Angles

O5	C11	C12	Cl4	−13
O5	C11	C12	C13	175
C19	C11	C12	Cl4	173
C19	C11	C12	C13	1
O5	C11	C19	C18	1
O5	C11	C19	C20	−173
C12	C11	C19	C18	176
C12	C11	C19	C20	2
Cl4	C12	C13	Cl5	−3
Cl4	C12	C13	C14	−172
C11	C12	C13	Cl5	168
C11	C12	C13	C14	−2
Cl5	C13	C14	O6	−3
Cl5	C13	C14	C20	−170
C12	C13	C14	O6	166
C12	C13	C14	C20	−1

25.2   2 - Bromo - 1,4 - naphthoquinone $C_{10}H_5BrO_2$

J.Gaultier, C.Hauw, Acta Cryst., 18, 604, 1965

P2$_1$/c   Z = 4   R = 0.09

BRNAPQ   LB 10-5-1

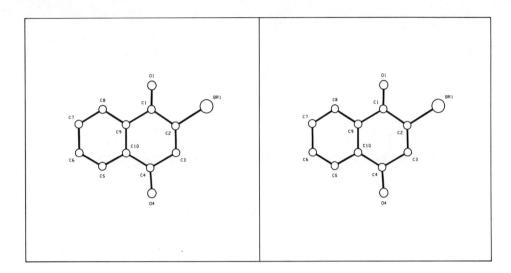

Bond Lengths

Br1	C2	1.87	C4	C10	1.44
C1	O1	1.19	C5	C6	1.36
C4	O4	1.25	C5	C10	1.39
C1	C2	1.48	C6	C7	1.42
C1	C9	1.50	C7	C8	1.42
C2	C3	1.33	C8	C9	1.41
C3	C4	1.52	C9	C10	1.40

Bond Angles

O1	C1	C2	122	C6	C5	C10	122
O1	C1	C9	121	C5	C6	C7	120
C2	C1	C9	117	C6	C7	C8	119
Br1	C2	C1	116	C7	C8	C9	118
Br1	C2	C3	120	C1	C9	C8	118
C1	C2	C3	124	C1	C9	C10	119
C2	C3	C4	118	C8	C9	C10	122
O4	C4	C3	116	C4	C10	C5	121
O4	C4	C10	125	C4	C10	C9	121
C3	C4	C10	120	C5	C10	C9	118

25.3   2 - Chloro - 3 - hydroxy - 1,4 - naphthoquinone $C_{10}H_5ClO_3$

J.Gaultier, C.Hauw, Acta Cryst., 19, 580, 1965

Pc   Z = 2   R = 0.11

CHNAPQ   LB 10-5-6

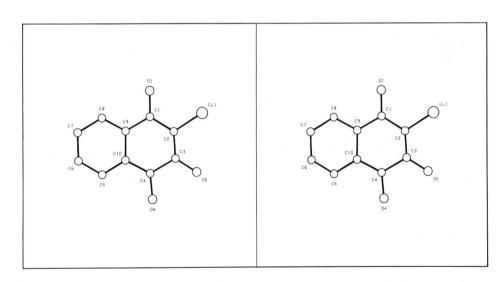

Bond Lengths

Cl1	C2	1.72	C4	C10	1.43
C1	O1	1.28	C5	C6	1.40
C4	O4	1.26	C5	C10	1.39
C3	O5	1.31	C6	C7	1.39
C1	C2	1.41	C7	C8	1.44
C1	C9	1.44	C8	C9	1.38
C2	C3	1.34	C9	C10	1.44
C3	C4	1.48			

Bond Angles

O1	C1	C2	122	C3	C4	C10	124
O1	C1	C9	118	C6	C5	C10	120
C2	C1	C9	120	C5	C6	C7	121
Cl1	C2	C1	118	C6	C7	C8	119
Cl1	C2	C3	118	C7	C8	C9	122
C1	C2	C3	124	C1	C9	C8	123
O5	C3	C2	124	C1	C9	C10	119
O5	C3	C4	120	C8	C9	C10	117
C2	C3	C4	116	C4	C10	C5	122
O4	C4	C3	114	C4	C10	C9	116
O4	C4	C10	122	C5	C10	C9	121

25.4   2 - Chloro - 3 - amino - 1,4 - naphthoquinone

J.Gaultier, C.Hauw, Acta Cryst., 19, 585, 1965

$C_{10}H_6ClNO_2$

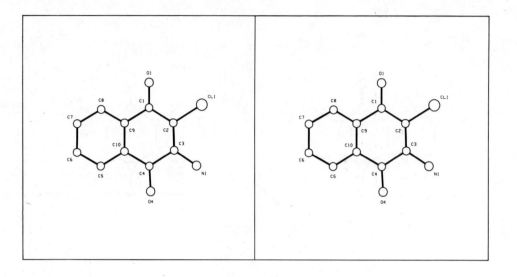

Pc   Z = 2   R = 0.11

CANAPQ   LB 10-6-5

Bond Lengths

Cl1	C2	1.71	C4	C10	1.46
C3	N1	1.37	C5	C6	1.41
C1	O1	1.25	C5	C10	1.42
C4	O4	1.23	C6	C7	1.41
C1	C2	1.44	C7	C8	1.43
C1	C9	1.46	C8	C9	1.39
C2	C3	1.35	C9	C10	1.40
C3	C4	1.50			

Bond Angles

O1	C1	C2	121	C3	C4	C10	119
O1	C1	C9	120	C6	C5	C10	120
C2	C1	C9	119	C5	C6	C7	119
Cl1	C2	C1	118	C6	C7	C8	119
Cl1	C2	C3	120	C7	C8	C9	122
C1	C2	C3	122	C1	C9	C8	121
N1	C3	C2	125	C1	C9	C10	121
N1	C3	C4	115	C8	C9	C10	118
C2	C3	C4	120	C4	C10	C5	120
O4	C4	C3	118	C4	C10	C9	119
O4	C4	C10	123	C5	C10	C9	121

25.5   1,4 - Naphthoquinone

J.Gaultier, C.Hauw, Acta Cryst., 18, 179, 1965

$C_{10}H_6O_2$

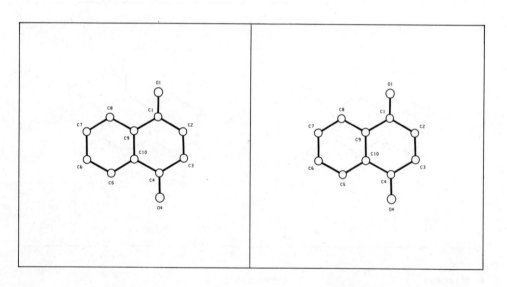

P2$_1$/c   Z = 4   R = 0.13

NAPHQU   LB 10-6-21

Bond Lengths

C1	O1	1.21	C5	C6	1.43
C4	O4	1.22	C5	C10	1.36
C1	C2	1.48	C6	C7	1.37
C1	C9	1.43	C7	C8	1.41
C2	C3	1.31	C8	C9	1.39
C3	C4	1.45	C9	C10	1.39
C4	C10	1.46			

Bond Angles

O1	C1	C2	119	C5	C6	C7	119
O1	C1	C9	119	C6	C7	C8	119
C2	C1	C9	122	C7	C8	C9	121
C1	C2	C3	121	C1	C9	C8	123
C2	C3	C4	118	C1	C9	C10	118
O4	C4	C3	118	C8	C9	C10	119
O4	C4	C10	119	C4	C10	C5	122
C3	C4	C10	123	C4	C10	C9	118
C6	C5	C10	122	C5	C10	C9	120

25.6   5,8 - Dihydroxy - 1,4 - naphthoquinone (form C) $C_{10}H_6O_4$

Naphthazarin
C.Pascard-Billy, Acta Cryst., 15, 519, 1962

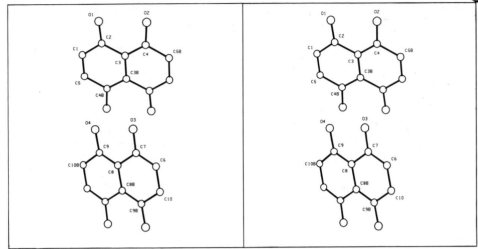

See also Cradwick & Hall, Acta Cryst. (B), 27, 1990, 1971.
$P2_1/n$ $Z = 4$ No R factor was given.

DHNAPH   LB 10-6-25

Bond Lengths

C2	O1	1.30	C7	O3	1.33
C4	O2	1.33	C9	O4	1.33
C1	C2	1.40	C6	C7	1.39
C1	C5	1.37	C6	C10	1.39
C2	C3	1.47	C7	C8	1.47
C3	C4	1.38	C8	C9	1.37
C3	C3B	1.46	C8	C8B	1.45
C4	C5B	1.47	C9	C10B	1.47

Bond Angles

C2	C1	C5	123	C7	C6	C10	122
O1	C2	C1	119	O3	C7	C6	120
O1	C2	C3	121	O3	C7	C8	119
C1	C2	C3	120	C6	C7	C8	121
C2	C3	C4	122	C7	C8	C9	122
C2	C3	C3B	117	C7	C8	C8B	115
C4	C3	C3B	121	C9	C8	C8B	122
O2	C4	C3	125	O4	C9	C8	123
O2	C4	C5B	114	O4	C9	C10B	116
C3	C4	C5B	121	C8	C9	C10B	121
C1	C5	C4B	119	C6	C10	C9B	118

25.7   5,8 - Dihydroxy - 1,4 - naphthoquinone (form A) $C_{10}H_6O_4$

Naphthazarin
C.Pascard-Billy, Bull. Soc. Chim. Fr., 2293, 1962

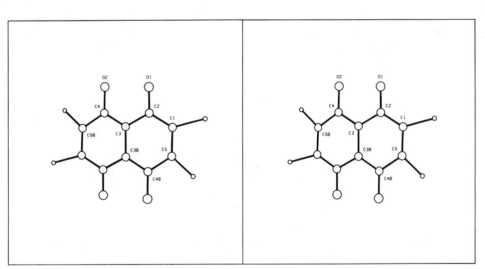

$P2_1/c$ $Z = 2$ $R_{0kl} = 0.169$, $R_{h0l} = 0.135$

DHNAPH01   LB 10-6-23

Bond Lengths

C2	O1	1.27
C4	O2	1.32
C1	C2	1.44
C1	C5	1.39
C2	C3	1.46
C3	C4	1.40
C3	C3B	1.50
C4	C5B	1.47

Bond Angles

C2	C1	C5	118
O1	C2	C1	121
O1	C2	C3	114
C1	C2	C3	125
C2	C3	C4	124
C2	C3	C3B	114
C4	C3	C3B	122
O2	C4	C3	120
O2	C4	C5B	120
C3	C4	C5B	120
C1	C5	C4B	121

25.8   5, 8 - Dihydroxy - 1, 4 - naphthoquinone (form B) $C_{10}H_6O_4$

Naphthazarin
C.Pascard-Billy, Bull. Soc. Chim. Fr., 2282, 1962

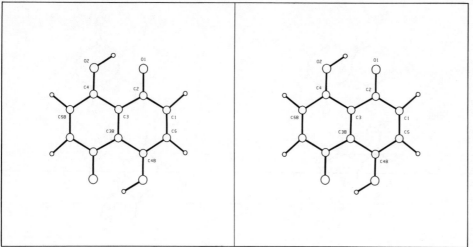

The authors conclude that the molecule is centrosymmetric.
$P2_1/c$ $Z = 2$ $R_{0kl} = 0.142$, $R_{h0l} = 0.148$

DHNAPH02   LB 10-6-24

Bond Lengths

C2	O1	1.33	C2	C3	1.44
C4	O2	1.29	C3	C4	1.48
C1	C2	1.40	C3	C3B	1.41
C1	C5	1.37	C4	C5B	1.45

Bond Angles

C2	C1	C5	120	C2	C3	C4	121	O2	C4	C5B	123
O1	C2	C1	119	C2	C3	C3B	119	C3	C4	C5B	118
O1	C2	C3	119	C4	C3	C3B	120	C1	C5	C4B	122
C1	C2	C3	122	O2	C4	C3	120				

25.9   5,8 - Dihydroxy - 1,4 - naphthoquinone (at $-140\,^\circ$C) $C_{10}H_6O_4$

Naphthazarin
P.Srivastava, Indian J. Phys., 35, 640, 1961

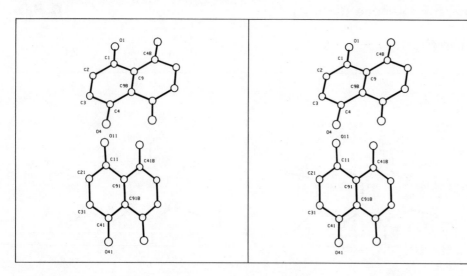

No comparison of bond lengths is possible since they are not reported in the paper.
$P2_1/c$ $Z = 4$ $R = 0.11$

DHNAPH03

Bond Lengths

C1	O1	1.29	C11	O11	1.28
C4	O4	1.30	C41	O41	1.27
C1	C2	1.40	C11	C21	1.42
C1	C9	1.44	C11	C91	1.44
C2	C3	1.41	C21	C31	1.40
C3	C4	1.45	C31	C41	1.45
C4	C9B	1.40	C41	C91B	1.42
C9	C9B	1.42	C91	C91B	1.41

Bond Angles

O1	C1	C2	118	O11	C11	C21	120
O1	C1	C9	121	O11	C11	C91	122
C2	C1	C9	121	C21	C11	C91	118
C1	C2	C3	123	C11	C21	C31	123
C2	C3	C4	116	C21	C31	C41	119
O4	C4	C3	114	O41	C41	C31	117
O4	C4	C9B	124	O41	C41	C91B	124
C3	C4	C9B	121	C31	C41	C91B	119
C1	C9	C4B	121	C11	C91	C41B	119
C1	C9	C9B	117	C11	C91	C91B	120

25.10   2 - Chloro - 3 - methyl - 1,4 - naphthoquinone

$C_{11}H_7ClO_2$

M.Breton, C. R. Acad. Sci., Fr., 258, 3489, 1964

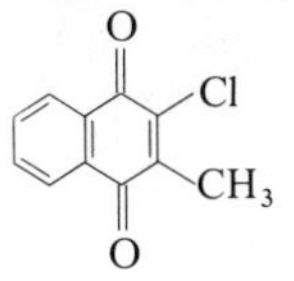

The structure is totally disordered.
P2$_1$/n   Z = 4   R = 0.146

CLMNQU   LB 11-7-2

25.11   3 - Hydroxy - 2 - methyl - 1,4 - naphthoquinone

$C_{11}H_8O_3$

J.Gaultier, C.Hauw, Acta Cryst., 19, 919, 1965

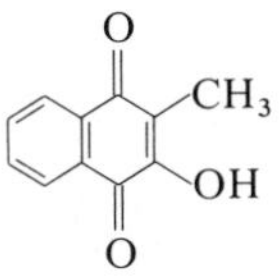

P2$_1$ Z = 2   R = 0.11

HMNAPQ10   LB 11-8-16

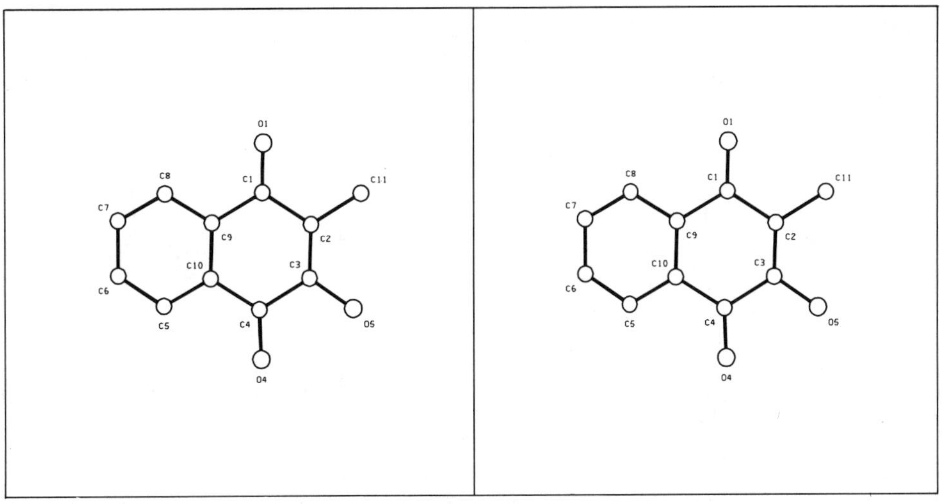

Bond Lengths

C1	O1	1.23	C4	C10	1.46
C4	O4	1.22	C5	C6	1.39
C3	O5	1.36	C5	C10	1.38
C1	C2	1.47	C6	C7	1.36
C1	C9	1.50	C7	C8	1.38
C2	C3	1.33	C8	C9	1.38
C2	C11	1.50	C9	C10	1.39
C3	C4	1.50			

Bond Angles

O1	C1	C2	121	C3	C4	C10	118
O1	C1	C9	121	C6	C5	C10	119
C2	C1	C9	118	C5	C6	C7	122
C1	C2	C3	120	C6	C7	C8	119
C1	C2	C11	117	C7	C8	C9	120
C3	C2	C11	122	C1	C9	C8	119
O5	C3	C2	122	C1	C9	C10	120
O5	C3	C4	115	C8	C9	C10	120
C2	C3	C4	123	C4	C10	C5	120
O4	C4	C3	119	C4	C10	C9	120
O4	C4	C10	124	C5	C10	C9	120

25.12   2 - Acetyl - 4,7,8 - trihydroxy - 6 - methoxy - 3 - methyl - 1,5 - naphthoquinone

$C_{14}H_{12}O_7$

M.Fehlmann, A.Niggli, Helv. Chim. Acta, 48, 305, 1965

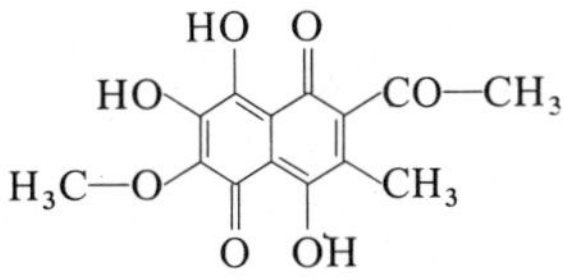

Atomic coordinates were not given
but bond lengths were reported.
P1   Z = 1   R = 0.14

AHMNAQ   LB 14-12-35

26.1 1,5 - Dibromoanthraquinone

$C_{14}H_6Br_2O_2$

L.A.Chetkina, G.A.Gol'der, Kristallografija, 8, 194, 1963

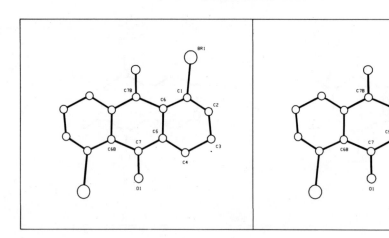

See also Chetkina & Gol'der, Kristallografija, 12, 404, 1967.
$P2_1/a$ Z = 2   R = 0.148

BANTRQ   LB 14-6-1

Bond Lengths

Br1	C1	2.01	C3	C4	1.50
C7	O1	1.35	C4	C5	1.36
C1	C2	1.31	C5	C6	1.44
C1	C6	1.36	C5	C7	1.39
C2	C3	1.35	C6	C7B	1.51

Bond Angles

Br1	C1	C2	116	C3	C4	C5	122	C1	C6	C7B	133
Br1	C1	C6	120	C4	C5	C6	120	C5	C6	C7B	111
C2	C1	C6	123	C4	C5	C7	122	O1	C7	C5	116
C1	C2	C3	128	C6	C5	C7	118	O1	C7	C6B	113
C2	C3	C4	111	C1	C6	C5	115	C5	C7	C6B	131

26.2 1,5 - Di - iodoanthraquinone

$C_{14}H_6I_2O_2$

L.A.Chetkina, G.A.Gol'der, Kristallografija, 8, 582, 1963

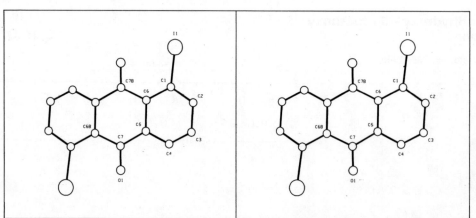

See also Chetkina & Gol'der, Kristallografija, 12, 404, 1967.
$P2_1/c$ Z = 2 $R_{h0l} = 0.175$,
$R_{h1l} = 0.193$, $R_{h2l} = 0.180$,
$R_{h3l} = 0.207$

IANTRQ   LB 14-6-8

Bond Lengths

I1	C1	2.01	C3	C4	1.29
C7	O1	1.21	C4	C5	1.35
C1	C2	1.39	C5	C6	1.51
C1	C6	1.43	C5	C7	1.49
C2	C3	1.45	C6	C7B	1.45

Bond Angles

I1	C1	C2	117	C3	C4	C5	126	C1	C6	C7B	127
I1	C1	C6	125	C4	C5	C6	117	C5	C6	C7B	115
C2	C1	C6	118	C4	C5	C7	123	O1	C7	C5	119
C1	C2	C3	121	C6	C5	C7	120	O1	C7	C6B	117
C2	C3	C4	120	C1	C6	C5	118	C5	C7	C6B	125

26.3 9 - Chloro - 10 - bromoanthracene

$C_{14}H_8BrCl$

M.Hospital, Acta Cryst., 14, 76, 1961

The structure is totally disordered.
P-1   Z = 2   No R factor was given.

CLBRAN   LB 14-8-2

26.4 10,10 - Dibromoanthrone

$C_{14}H_8Br_2O$

J.Silverman, N.F.Yannoni, Nature, 200, 64, 1963

P2$_1$/c   Z = 4   R = 0.175

DBRANO   LB 14-8-6

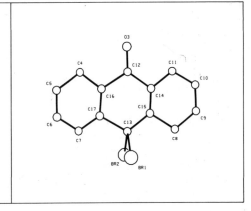

Bond Lengths

Br1	C13	2.03
Br2	C13	1.98
C12	O3	1.25
C4	C5	1.50
C4	C16	1.39
C5	C6	1.30
C6	C7	1.31
C7	C17	1.34
C8	C9	1.49
C8	C15	1.51
C9	C10	1.32
C10	C11	1.41
C11	C14	1.45
C12	C14	1.47
C12	C16	1.58
C13	C15	1.47
C13	C17	1.61
C14	C15	1.23
C16	C17	1.31

Bond Angles

C5	C4	C16	109	Br2	C13	C17	108
C4	C5	C6	124	C15	C13	C17	115
C5	C6	C7	123	C11	C14	C12	109
C6	C7	C17	116	C11	C14	C15	129
C9	C8	C15	110	C12	C14	C15	122
C8	C9	C10	125	C8	C15	C13	112
C9	C10	C11	120	C8	C15	C14	119
C10	C11	C14	114	C13	C15	C14	129
O3	C12	C14	126	C4	C16	C12	112
O3	C12	C16	120	C4	C16	C17	121
C14	C12	C16	114	C12	C16	C17	126
Br1	C13	Br2	105	C7	C17	C13	118
Br1	C13	C15	113	C7	C17	C16	127
Br1	C13	C17	105	C13	C17	C16	115
Br2	C13	C15	110				

Torsion Angles

C16	C4	C5	C6	−1	O3	C12	C14	C11	−2	Br1	C13	C17	C7	−60
C5	C4	C16	C12	179	O3	C12	C14	C15	−176	Br1	C13	C17	C16	121
C5	C4	C16	C17	1	C16	C12	C14	C11	174	Br2	C13	C17	C7	52
C4	C5	C6	C7	0	C16	C12	C14	C15	0	Br2	C13	C17	C16	−128
C5	C6	C7	C17	1	O3	C12	C16	C4	0	C15	C13	C17	C7	175
C6	C7	C17	C13	−180	O3	C12	C16	C17	178	C15	C13	C17	C16	−5
C6	C7	C17	C16	−1	C14	C12	C16	C4	−176	C11	C14	C15	C8	17
C15	C8	C9	C10	12	C14	C12	C16	C17	2	C11	C14	C15	C13	−177
C9	C8	C15	C13	175	Br1	C13	C15	C8	53	C12	C14	C15	C8	−171
C9	C8	C15	C14	−16	Br1	C13	C15	C14	−114	C12	C14	C15	C13	−4
C8	C9	C10	C11	−7	Br2	C13	C15	C8	−64	C4	C16	C17	C7	0
C9	C10	C11	C14	4	Br2	C13	C15	C14	129	C4	C16	C17	C13	179
C10	C11	C14	C12	177	C17	C13	C15	C8	174	C12	C16	C17	C7	−178
C10	C11	C14	C15	−10	C17	C13	C15	C14	7	C12	C16	C17	C13	1

26.5 Anthraquinone

$C_{14}H_8O_2$

B.V.R.Murty, Z. Kristallogr., 113, 445, 1960

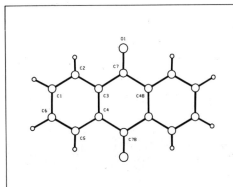
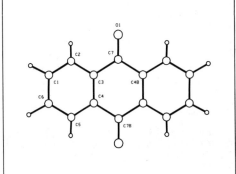

See also Lonsdale et al., Acta Cryst.,
20, 1, 1966; Prakash, Acta Cryst., 22,
439, 1967.
P2$_1$/a   Z = 2   R = 0.196

ANTQUO   LB 14-8-26

Bond Lengths

C7	O1	1.23	C3	C7	1.48
C1	C2	1.37	C4	C5	1.39
C1	C6	1.41	C4	C7B	1.48
C2	C3	1.39	C5	C6	1.38
C3	C4	1.37			

Bond Angles

C2	C1	C6	120	C3	C4	C5	119	O1	C7	C3	121
C1	C2	C3	120	C3	C4	C7B	122	O1	C7	C4B	122
C2	C3	C4	120	C5	C4	C7B	119	C3	C7	C4B	118
C2	C3	C7	119	C4	C5	C6	121				
C4	C3	C7	121	C1	C6	C5	119				

26.6   1,8 - Dihydroxyanthraquinone

$C_{14}H_8O_4$

A.Prakash, Z. Kristallogr., 122, 272, 1965

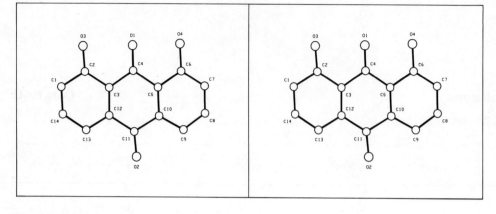

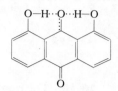

$P4_1$ $Z = 4$ $R = 0.159$

DHANQU   LB 14-8-32

Bond Lengths

C4	O1	1.25	C5	C6	1.44
C11	O2	1.25	C5	C10	1.41
C2	O3	1.27	C6	C7	1.41
C6	O4	1.35	C7	C8	1.34
C1	C2	1.43	C8	C9	1.38
C1	C14	1.34	C9	C10	1.41
C2	C3	1.49	C10	C11	1.49
C3	C4	1.49	C11	C12	1.50
C3	C12	1.37	C12	C13	1.38
C4	C5	1.50	C13	C14	1.44

Bond Angles

C2	C1	C14	119	C4	C5	C6	113	C5	C10	C11	118
O3	C2	C1	117	C4	C5	C10	126	C9	C10	C11	121
O3	C2	C3	126	C6	C5	C10	121	O2	C11	C10	115
C1	C2	C3	115	O4	C6	C5	121	O2	C11	C12	127
C2	C3	C4	114	O4	C6	C7	124	C10	C11	C12	117
C2	C3	C12	122	C5	C6	C7	115	C3	C12	C11	121
C4	C3	C12	124	C6	C7	C8	122	C3	C12	C13	120
O1	C4	C3	122	C7	C8	C9	124	C11	C12	C13	117
O1	C4	C5	125	C8	C9	C10	116	C12	C13	C14	116
C3	C4	C5	113	C5	C10	C9	121	C1	C14	C13	126

26.7   Anthracene

$C_{14}H_{10}$

(i)   R.Mason, Acta Cryst., 17, 547, 1964 (at 290°K)

(ii)   R.Mason, Acta Cryst., 17, 547, 1964 (at 95°K)

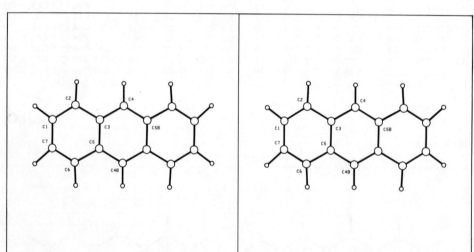

(i)

See also Mathieson et al., Acta Cryst., 3, 245, 1950; Ahmed & Cruickshank, Acta Cryst., 5, 852, 1952; Cruickshank, Acta Cryst., 9, 915, 1956; Sparks, Thesis, UCLA, 1958.
$P2_1/a$ $Z = 2$ $R = 0.043$

ANTCEN   LB 14-10-1

(ii)

$P2_1/a$ $Z = 2$ No R factor was given.

ANTCEN01   LB 14-10-1

Bond Lengths

		(i)	(ii)
C1	C2	1.37	1.37
C1	C7	1.41	1.43
C2	C3	1.45	1.45
C3	C4	1.41	1.39
C3	C5	1.42	1.43
C4	C5B	1.40	1.41
C5	C6	1.44	1.44
C6	C7	1.36	1.38

Bond Angles

			(i)	(ii)				(i)	(ii)
C2	C1	C7	122	122	C3	C5	C6	119	119
C1	C2	C3	119	119	C3	C5	C4B	120	119
C2	C3	C4	121	121	C6	C5	C4B	121	122
C2	C3	C5	119	120	C5	C6	C7	120	120
C4	C3	C5	120	120	C1	C7	C6	121	120
C3	C4	C5B	120	122					

26.8   Anthracene (at 95 ° K) $C_{14}H_{10}$

For complete entry see 26.7

26.9   Anthrone $C_{14}H_{10}O$

S.N.Srivastava, Acta Cryst., 17, 851, 1964

The structure is totally disordered.
$P2_1/a$ Z = 2   R = 0.17

ANTRON   LB 14-10-40

26.10   9 - Ethyl - 10 - bromoanthracene $C_{16}H_{13}Br$

C.Hauw, Acta Cryst., 13, 100, 1960

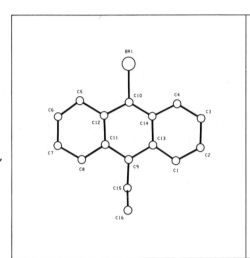

$P2_12_12_1$ Z = 4 R_{h0l} = 0.139,
R_{hk0} = 0.113

EBANTH   LB 16-13-1

Bond Lengths

Br1	C10	1.89	C8	C11	1.42
C1	C2	1.39	C9	C11	1.45
C1	C13	1.43	C9	C13	1.44
C2	C3	1.45	C9	C15	1.44
C3	C4	1.41	C10	C12	1.43
C4	C14	1.41	C10	C14	1.38
C5	C6	1.37	C11	C12	1.45
C5	C12	1.45	C13	C14	1.44
C6	C7	1.44	C15	C16	1.54
C7	C8	1.42			

Bond Angles

C2	C1	C13	119	C8	C11	C9	116
C1	C2	C3	119	C8	C11	C12	119
C2	C3	C4	120	C9	C11	C12	123
C3	C4	C14	123	C5	C12	C10	122
C6	C5	C12	115	C5	C12	C11	121
C5	C6	C7	126	C10	C12	C11	114
C6	C7	C8	118	C1	C13	C9	116
C7	C8	C11	119	C1	C13	C14	124
C11	C9	C15	120	C9	C13	C14	119
C13	C9	C15	123	C4	C14	C10	122
Br1	C10	C12	116	C4	C14	C13	114
Br1	C10	C14	122	C10	C14	C13	121
C12	C10	C14	122	C9	C15	C16	124

Torsion Angles

C13	C1	C2	C3	2	C15	C9	C13	C1	6
C2	C1	C13	C9	174	C15	C9	C13	C14	171
C2	C1	C13	C14	10	C11	C9	C15	C16	−81
C1	C2	C3	C4	−8	C13	C9	C15	C16	82
C2	C3	C4	C14	3	Br1	C10	C12	C5	−3
C3	C4	C14	C10	169	Br1	C10	C12	C11	−167
C3	C4	C14	C13	7	C14	C10	C12	C5	178
C12	C5	C6	C7	5	C14	C10	C12	C11	14
C6	C5	C12	C10	−174	Br1	C10	C14	C4	6
C6	C5	C12	C11	−11	Br1	C10	C14	C13	167
C5	C6	C7	C8	0	C12	C10	C14	C4	−175
C6	C7	C8	C11	1	C12	C10	C14	C13	−15
C7	C8	C11	C9	−170	C8	C11	C12	C5	13
C7	C8	C11	C12	−7	C8	C11	C12	C10	177
C13	C9	C11	C8	−170	C9	C11	C12	C5	175
C13	C9	C11	C12	27	C9	C11	C12	C10	−21
C15	C9	C11	C8	−6	C1	C13	C14	C4	−14
C15	C9	C11	C12	−169	C1	C13	C14	C10	−176
C11	C9	C13	C1	169	C9	C13	C14	C4	−178
C11	C9	C13	C14	−25	C9	C13	C14	C10	20

26.11   9,10 - Anthrahydroquinone dibenzoate $C_{28}H_{18}O_4$

J.Iball, K.J.H.Mackay, Acta Cryst., 15, 148, 1962

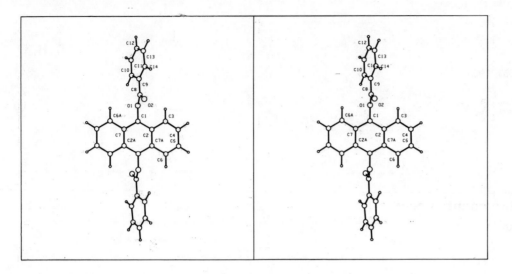

P-1   Z = 1   R = 0.09

ANTHQB   LB 28-18-4

Bond Lengths

C1	O1	1.40	C5	C6	1.39
C8	O1	1.39	C6	C7A	1.44
C8	O2	1.19	C8	C9	1.47
C1	C2	1.42	C9	C10	1.42
C1	C7	1.43	C9	C14	1.38
C2	C3	1.44	C10	C11	1.41
C2	C7A	1.42	C11	C12	1.37
C3	C4	1.35	C12	C13	1.29
C4	C5	1.44	C13	C14	1.41

Bond Angles

C1	O1	C8	118	C3	C4	C5	122	C8	C9	C10	120
O1	C1	C2	118	C4	C5	C6	120	C8	C9	C14	119
O1	C1	C7	120	C5	C6	C7A	119	C10	C9	C14	121
C2	C1	C7	123	C1	C7	C2A	118	C9	C10	C11	116
C1	C2	C3	123	C1	C7	C6A	121	C10	C11	C12	121
C1	C2	C7A	119	O1	C8	O2	122	C11	C12	C13	123
C3	C2	C7A	119	O1	C8	C9	113	C12	C13	C14	120
C2	C3	C4	120	O2	C8	C9	125	C9	C14	C13	119

Torsion Angles

C8	O1	C1	C2	−90
C8	O1	C1	C7	92
C1	O1	C8	O2	11
C1	O1	C8	C9	−177
O1	C8	C9	C10	20
O1	C8	C9	C14	−163
O2	C8	C9	C10	−169
O2	C8	C9	C14	9

27.1   Triketoindane (tetragonal form)

$C_9H_4O_3$

W.Bolton, Acta Cryst., 18, 5, 1965

Published value of z(H2) = 1.245.
The correct value is -1.245.
I4₁cd   Z = 8   R = 0.079

TIKIND   LB 9-4-3

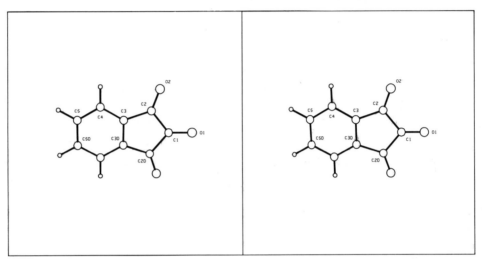

Bond Lengths

C1	O1	1.19	C3	C4	1.39
C2	O2	1.23	C3	C3D	1.39
C1	C2	1.53	C4	C5	1.37
C2	C3	1.48	C5	C5D	1.41

Bond Angles

O1	C1	C2	127	C2	C3	C4	129
C2	C1	C2D	105	C2	C3	C3D	110
O2	C2	C1	124	C4	C3	C3D	121
O2	C2	C3	129	C3	C4	C5	118
C1	C2	C3	107	C4	C5	C5D	121

27.2   Azulene

$C_{10}H_8$

J.M.Robertson, H.M.M.Shearer, G.A.Sim, D.G.Watson, Acta Cryst., 15, 1, 1962

The structure is totally disordered.
P2₁/a   Z = 2   R = 0.13

AZLENE   LB 10-8-1

27.3   Azulene (refinement)

$C_{10}H_8$

G.S.Pawley, Acta Cryst., 18, 560, 1965

The structure is totally disordered.
P2₁/a   Z = 2   R = 0.069

AZLENE01   LB 10-8-1

28.1   6,6 - Dibromo - 2,3 - 4,5 - dimethano - 2,4 - dinitro - cyclohexanone

$C_8H_6Br_2N_2O_5$

C.H.Stam, H.Evers, Rec. Trav. Chim. Pays-Bas, 84, 1496, 1965

$P2_1/n$ Z = 4   R = 0.111

BMNHXO   LB 8-6-4

Bond Lengths

Br1	C6	1.96
Br2	C6	1.99
N1	O2	1.25
N1	O3	1.20
N2	O4	1.24
N2	O5	1.24
C2	N1	1.46
C4	N2	1.45
C1	O1	1.21
C1	C2	1.50
C1	C6	1.50
C2	C3	1.52
C2	C7	1.52
C3	C4	1.46
C3	C7	1.50
C4	C5	1.53
C4	C8	1.50
C5	C6	1.47
C5	C8	1.51

Bond Angles

O2	N1	O3	121		N2	C4	C3	113
O2	N1	C2	119		N2	C4	C5	117
O3	N1	C2	120		N2	C4	C8	115
O4	N2	O5	121		C3	C4	C5	123
O4	N2	C4	119		C3	C4	C8	120
O5	N2	C4	120		C5	C4	C8	60
O1	C1	C2	121		C4	C5	C6	117
O1	C1	C6	121		C4	C5	C8	59
C2	C1	C6	117		C6	C5	C8	118
N1	C2	C1	113		Br1	C6	Br2	105
N1	C2	C3	116		Br1	C6	C1	109
N1	C2	C7	114		Br1	C6	C5	108
C1	C2	C3	119		Br2	C6	C1	107
C1	C2	C7	125		Br2	C6	C5	109
C3	C2	C7	59		C1	C6	C5	118
C2	C3	C4	117		C2	C7	C3	60
C2	C3	C7	60		C4	C8	C5	61
C4	C3	C7	121					

Torsion Angles

O2	N1	C2	C1	−59		O1	C1	C6	Br1	−18		C7	C3	C4	C8	−132
O2	N1	C2	C3	158		O1	C1	C6	Br2	95		C4	C3	C7	C2	106
O2	N1	C2	C7	92		O1	C1	C6	C5	−142		N2	C4	C5	C6	−146
O3	N1	C2	C1	123		C2	C1	C6	Br1	160		N2	C4	C5	C8	105
O3	N1	C2	C3	−20		C2	C1	C6	Br2	−87		C3	C4	C5	C6	1
O3	N1	C2	C7	−87		C2	C1	C6	C5	36		C3	C4	C5	C8	−108
O4	N2	C4	C3	3		N1	C2	C3	C4	144		C8	C4	C5	C6	108
O4	N2	C4	C5	153		N1	C2	C3	C7	−104		N2	C4	C8	C5	−108
O4	N2	C4	C8	−139		C1	C2	C3	C4	3		C3	C4	C8	C5	113
O5	N2	C4	C3	−177		C1	C2	C3	C7	116		C4	C5	C6	Br1	−148
O5	N2	C4	C5	−27		C7	C2	C3	C4	−112		C4	C5	C6	Br2	98
O5	N2	C4	C8	41		N1	C2	C7	C3	107		C4	C5	C6	C1	−24
O1	C1	C2	N1	11		C1	C2	C7	C3	−106		C8	C5	C6	Br1	−81
O1	C1	C2	C3	152		C2	C3	C4	N2	158		C8	C5	C6	Br2	166
O1	C1	C2	C7	−137		C2	C3	C4	C5	10		C8	C5	C6	C1	44
C6	C1	C2	N1	−168		C2	C3	C4	C8	−62		C6	C5	C8	C4	−106
C6	C1	C2	C3	−26		C7	C3	C4	N2	88						
C6	C1	C2	C7	45		C7	C3	C4	C5	−61						

28.2 Tricyclo(5.3.0.0²,⁶)decan - 3,8 - dione

$C_{10}H_{12}O_2$

T.N.Margulis, Acta Cryst., 18, 742, 1965

$P2_1/n$ Z = 2   R = 0.154

TCYDEC   LB 10-12-44

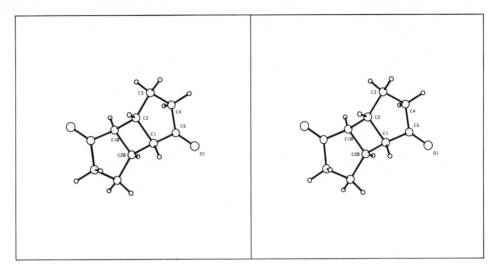

Bond Lengths			*Bond Angles*				*Torsion Angles*								
C5	O1	1.21	C2	C1	C5	105	C5	C1	C2	C3	−5	C2	C1	C2B	C3B	−110
C1	C2	1.54	C2	C1	C2B	89	C5	C1	C2	C1B	110	C5	C1	C2B	C1B	−106
C1	C5	1.51	C5	C1	C2B	109	C2B	C1	C2	C3	−115	C5	C1	C2B	C3B	144
C1	C2B	1.59	C1	C2	C3	108	C2B	C1	C2	C1B	0	C1	C2	C3	C4	15
C2	C3	1.55	C1	C2	C1B	91	C2	C1	C5	O1	172	C1B	C2	C3	C4	−84
C3	C4	1.53	C3	C2	C1B	113	C2	C1	C5	C4	−8	C2	C3	C4	C5	−20
C4	C5	1.49	C2	C3	C4	106	C2B	C1	C5	O1	−93	C3	C4	C5	O1	−162
			C3	C4	C5	106	C2B	C1	C5	C4	87	C3	C4	C5	C1	18
			O1	C5	C1	124	C2	C1	C2B	C1B	0					
			O1	C5	C4	124										
			C1	C5	C4	111										

28.3 2,3 - Dihydro 2,3 - methylene - 1,4 - naphthoquinone

$C_{11}H_8O_2$

W.K.Grant, J.C.Speakman, Acta Cryst., 15, 292, 1962

$P2_1/m$ Z = 2   R = 0.13

HYMNAP   LB 11-8-12

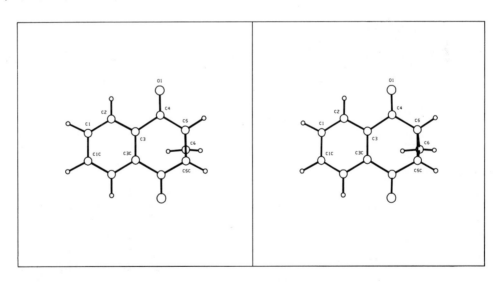

Bond Lengths			*Bond Angles*				*Torsion Angles*								
C4	O1	1.21	C2	C1	C1C	119	C1C	C1	C2	C3	0	C4	C3	C3C	C2C	176
C1	C2	1.38	C1	C2	C3	122	C2	C1	C1C	C2C	0	C4	C3	C3C	C4C	0
C1	C1C	1.40	C2	C3	C4	120	C1	C2	C3	C4	−177	O1	C4	C5	C6	−131
C2	C3	1.40	C2	C3	C3C	119	C1	C2	C3	C3C	0	O1	C4	C5	C5C	161
C3	C4	1.48	C4	C3	C3C	121	C2	C3	C4	O1	16	C3	C4	C5	C6	49
C3	C3C	1.40	O1	C4	C3	121	C2	C3	C4	C5	−164	C3	C4	C5	C5C	−19
C4	C5	1.48	O1	C4	C5	121	C3C	C3	C4	O1	−160	C4	C5	C6	C5C	−109
C5	C6	1.50	C3	C4	C5	118	C3C	C3	C4	C5	20	C4	C5	C5C	C6	106
C5	C5C	1.52	C4	C5	C6	117	C2	C3	C3C	C2C	0	C4	C5	C5C	C4C	0
			C4	C5	C5C	118	C2	C3	C3C	C4C	−176	C6	C5	C5C	C4C	−106
			C6	C5	C5C	59										
			C5	C6	C5C	61										

28.4 Acenaphthenequinone

$C_{12}H_6O_2$

T.C.W.Mak, J.Trotter, Acta Cryst., 16, 811, 1963

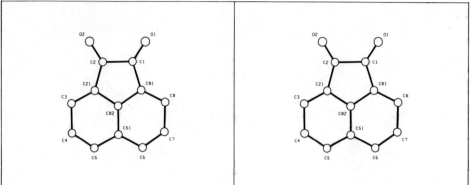

P2₁2₁2₁   Z = 4 R_{0kl} = 0.116, R_{hk0} = 0.139

ACNAQU   LB 12-6-7

Bond Lengths

C1	O1	1.18	C5	C51	1.39
C2	O2	1.20	C6	C7	1.37
C1	C2	1.53	C6	C51	1.40
C1	C81	1.48	C7	C8	1.45
C2	C21	1.47	C8	C81	1.37
C3	C4	1.45	C21	C82	1.41
C3	C21	1.36	C51	C82	1.41
C4	C5	1.37	C81	C82	1.42

Bond Angles

O1	C1	C2	125	C4	C5	C51	120	C5	C51	C82	118
O1	C1	C81	128	C7	C6	C51	118	C6	C51	C82	117
C2	C1	C81	107	C6	C7	C8	127	C1	C81	C8	133
O2	C2	C1	123	C7	C8	C81	113	C1	C81	C82	106
O2	C2	C21	130	C2	C21	C3	133	C8	C81	C82	122
C1	C2	C21	107	C2	C21	C82	106	C21	C82	C51	122
C4	C3	C21	117	C3	C21	C82	120	C21	C82	C81	115
C3	C4	C5	123	C5	C51	C6	125	C51	C82	C81	123

28.5 5 - Chloro - 6 - bromoacenaphthene

$C_{12}H_8BrCl$

R.L.Ávoyan, Yu.T.Struchkov, Zh. Strukt. Khim., 5, 407, 1964

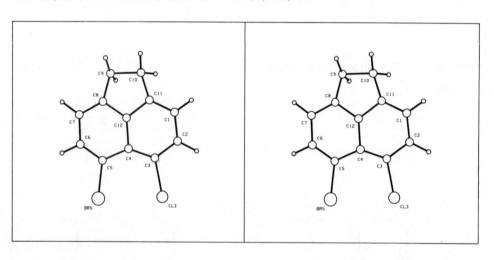

P-1   Z = 2   R = 0.190

CBACNP   LB 12-8-6

Bond Lengths

Br5	C5	1.89	C5	C6	1.38
Cl3	C3	1.94	C6	C7	1.45
C1	C2	1.42	C7	C8	1.37
C1	C11	1.42	C8	C9	1.43
C2	C3	1.42	C8	C12	1.45
C3	C4	1.42	C9	C10	1.56
C4	C5	1.45	C10	C11	1.42
C4	C12	1.51	C11	C12	1.46

Bond Angles

C2	C1	C11	121	Br5	C5	C4	120	C8	C9	C10	106
C1	C2	C3	119	Br5	C5	C6	118	C9	C10	C11	107
Cl3	C3	C2	114	C4	C5	C6	122	C1	C11	C10	133
Cl3	C3	C4	120	C5	C6	C7	126	C1	C11	C12	118
C2	C3	C4	126	C6	C7	C8	116	C10	C11	C12	109
C3	C4	C5	138	C7	C8	C9	133	C4	C12	C8	127
C3	C4	C12	112	C7	C8	C12	119	C4	C12	C11	123
C5	C4	C12	109	C9	C8	C12	108	C8	C12	C11	109

28.6 3,5 - Dibromoacenaphthene

$C_{12}H_8Br_2$

R.L.Avoyan, Yu.T.Struchkov, Zh. Strukt. Khim., 3, 605, 1962

The structure was determined in two dimensions only. Atomic coordinates were not reported in the paper.

Pca2₁   Z = 4 R_{hk0} = 0.20

DBACNP   LB 12-8-8

28.7 5,6 - Dichloroacenaphthene

C₁₂H₈Cl₂ → $C_{12}H_8Cl_2$

R.L.Avoyan, Yu.T.Struchkov, Zh. Strukt. Khim., 2, 719, 1961

C2/c   Z = 4   R = 0.11

DCACNP   LB 12-8-21

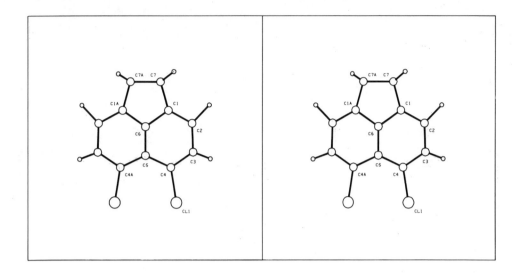

Bond Lengths

Cl1	C4	1.74
C1	C2	1.37
C1	C6	1.41
C1	C7	1.46
C2	C3	1.42
C3	C4	1.37
C4	C5	1.41
C5	C6	1.42
C7	C7A	1.54

Bond Angles

C2	C1	C6	118
C2	C1	C7	133
C6	C1	C7	109
C1	C2	C3	119
C2	C3	C4	122
Cl1	C4	C3	114
Cl1	C4	C5	124
C3	C4	C5	122
C4	C5	C6	115
C4	C5	C4A	131
C1	C6	C5	125
C1	C6	C1A	110
C1	C7	C7A	105

28.8 cis - 1,2 - Acenaphthenediol dinitrate

C₁₂H₈N₂O₆ → $C_{12}H_8N_2O_6$

T.C.W.Mak, J.Trotter, Acta Cryst., 17, 367, 1964

P2₁/c   Z = 4   R = 0.15

ANADON   LB 12-8-50

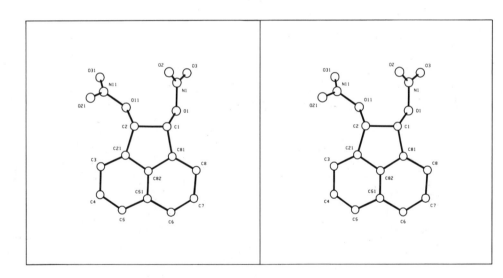

Bond Lengths

N1	O1	1.41
N1	O2	1.20
N1	O3	1.17
N11	O11	1.41
N11	O21	1.19
N11	O31	1.23
C1	O1	1.47
C2	O11	1.47
C1	C2	1.60
C1	C81	1.52
C2	C21	1.53
C3	C4	1.45
C3	C21	1.37
C4	C5	1.39
C5	C51	1.44
C6	C7	1.37
C6	C51	1.40
C7	C8	1.45
C8	C81	1.40
C21	C82	1.40
C51	C82	1.40
C81	C82	1.40

Bond Angles

O1	N1	O2	117
O1	N1	O3	111
O2	N1	O3	131
O11	N11	O21	116
O11	N11	O31	109
O21	N11	O31	133
N1	O1	C1	116
N11	O11	C2	115
O1	C1	C2	111
O1	C1	C81	105
C2	C1	C81	101
O11	C2	C1	107
O11	C2	C21	108
C1	C2	C21	107
C4	C3	C21	117
C3	C4	C5	123
C4	C5	C51	118
C7	C6	C51	118
C6	C7	C8	125
C7	C8	C81	115
C2	C21	C3	132
C2	C21	C82	106
C3	C21	C82	121
C5	C51	C6	124
C5	C51	C82	118
C6	C51	C82	118
C1	C81	C8	128
C1	C81	C82	111
C8	C81	C82	120
C21	C82	C51	123
C21	C82	C81	114
C51	C82	C81	123

Torsion Angles

O2	N1	O1	C1	−3
O3	N1	O1	C1	171
O21	N11	O11	C2	−12
O31	N11	O11	C2	179
N1	O1	C1	C2	80
N1	O1	C1	C81	−172
N11	O11	C2	C1	−143
N11	O11	C2	C21	102
O1	C1	C2	O11	−7
O1	C1	C2	C21	109
C81	C1	C2	O11	−118
C81	C1	C2	C21	−2

28.9 cis - 1,2 - Acenaphthenediol

$C_{12}H_{10}O_2$

J.Trotter, T.C.W.Mak, Acta Cryst., 16, 1032, 1963

In the paper C1 - O1 = 1.458A and C2 - O2 = 1.440A. These values should be interchanged.
$P2_1/c$ Z = 4   R = 0.15

ACNAOL   LB 12-10-63

Bond Lengths

C1	O1	1.44	C5	C10	1.39
C2	O2	1.46	C6	C7	1.31
C1	C2	1.60	C6	C10	1.46
C1	C11	1.49	C7	C8	1.52
C2	C9	1.46	C8	C11	1.40
C3	C4	1.45	C9	C12	1.40
C3	C9	1.41	C10	C12	1.47
C4	C5	1.32	C11	C12	1.41

Bond Angles

O1	C1	C2	112	C4	C5	C10	121	C5	C10	C12	114
O1	C1	C11	114	C7	C6	C10	119	C6	C10	C12	117
C2	C1	C11	103	C6	C7	C8	125	C1	C11	C8	130
O2	C2	C1	113	C7	C8	C11	116	C1	C11	C12	110
O2	C2	C9	111	C2	C9	C3	136	C8	C11	C12	120
C1	C2	C9	106	C2	C9	C12	110	C9	C12	C10	126
C4	C3	C9	119	C3	C9	C12	115	C9	C12	C11	112
C3	C4	C5	124	C5	C10	C6	128	C10	C12	C11	122

Torsion Angles

O1	C1	C2	O2	2
O1	C1	C2	C9	−120
C11	C1	C2	O2	125
C11	C1	C2	C9	3

28.10   Phenanthrene

$C_{14}H_{10}$

J.Trotter, Acta Cryst., 16, 605, 1963

See also Kay et al., Acta Cryst. (B), 27, 26, 1971.
$P2_1$ Z = 2   R = 0.137

PHENAN   LB 14-10-5

Bond Lengths

C1	C2	1.38	C7	C8	1.38
C1	C11	1.47	C8	C14	1.45
C2	C3	1.40	C9	C10	1.37
C3	C4	1.40	C9	C14	1.38
C4	C12	1.40	C10	C11	1.40
C5	C6	1.37	C11	C12	1.39
C5	C13	1.41	C12	C13	1.45
C6	C7	1.39	C13	C14	1.42

Bond Angles

C2	C1	C11	117	C1	C11	C12	120
C1	C2	C3	123	C10	C11	C12	120
C2	C3	C4	118	C4	C12	C11	120
C3	C4	C12	121	C4	C12	C13	121
C6	C5	C13	122	C11	C12	C13	119
C5	C6	C7	121	C5	C13	C12	125
C6	C7	C8	122	C5	C13	C14	116
C7	C8	C14	116	C12	C13	C14	119
C10	C9	C14	122	C8	C14	C9	117
C9	C10	C11	121	C8	C14	C13	123
C1	C11	C10	120	C9	C14	C13	119

28.11 Phenanthrene (refinement of data of Basak, Ind. J. Phys., 24,309,1950)

$C_{14}H_{10}$

R.Mason, Molec. Phys., 4, 413, 1961

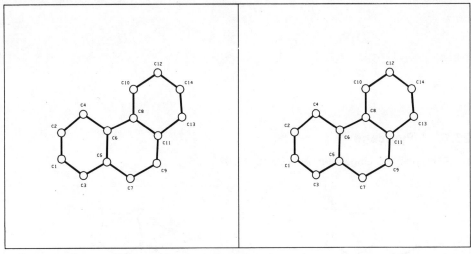

No comparison of bond lengths is possible since they are not reported in the paper.
P2$_1$ Z = 2   R = 0.12

PHENAN01   LB 14-10-5

Bond Lengths

C1	C2	1.30	C7	C9	1.54
C1	C3	1.39	C8	C10	1.41
C2	C4	1.45	C8	C11	1.52·
C3	C5	1.39	C9	C11	1.37
C4	C6	1.49	C10	C12	1.48
C5	C6	1.53	C11	C13	1.56
C5	C7	1.44	C12	C14	1.40
C6	C8	1.47	C13	C14	1.37

Bond Angles

C2	C1	C3	126	C6	C8	C10	115
C1	C2	C4	129	C6	C8	C11	120
C1	C3	C5	115	C10	C8	C11	124
C2	C4	C6	108	C7	C9	C11	121
C3	C5	C6	120	C8	C10	C12	123
C3	C5	C7	117	C8	C11	C9	122
C6	C5	C7	123	C8	C11	C13	108
C4	C6	C5	122	C9	C11	C13	128
C4	C6	C8	121	C10	C12	C14	112
C5	C6	C8	117	C11	C13	C14	120
C5	C7	C9	117	C12	C14	C13	130

29.1 Pyracene

$C_{14}H_{12}$

G.L.Simmons, E.C.Lingafelter, Acta Cryst., 14, 872, 1961

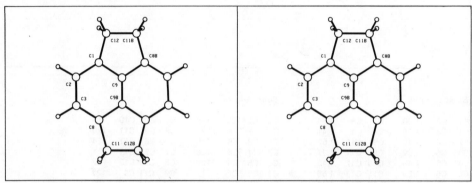

P2$_1$/n   Z = 2   R$_{h0l}$ = 0.060, R$_{hk0}$ = 0.077

PYRCEN   LB 14-12-2

Bond Lengths

C1	C2	1.38	C2	C3	1.44	C8	C9B	1.42
C1	C9	1.41	C3	C8	1.36	C9	C9B	1.34
C1	C12	1.54	C8	C11	1.54	C11	C12B	1.59

Bond Angles

C2	C1	C9	116	C2	C3	C8	121	C1	C9	C8B	115
C2	C1	C12	136	C3	C8	C11	136	C1	C9	C9B	122
C9	C1	C12	108	C3	C8	C9B	117	C8	C11	C12B	106
C1	C2	C3	121	C11	C8	C9B	107	C1	C12	C11B	105

29.2 tris(Trimethylene)benzene

$C_{15}H_{18}$

E.R.Boyko, P.A.Vaughan, Acta Cryst., 17, 152, 1964

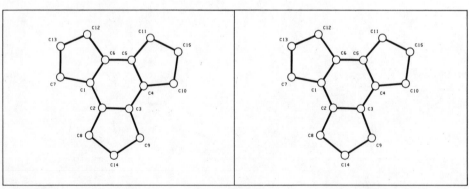

In the paper the value of b is given as 5.87A in the abstract and 5.07A in the main text. The former value is correct.

P2$_1$/c   Z = 4   R = 0.12

TMENBZ   LB 15-18-1

Bond Lengths

C1	C2	1.39
C1	C6	1.37
C1	C7	1.58
C2	C3	1.40
C2	C8	1.51
C3	C4	1.36
C3	C9	1.55
C4	C5	1.41
C4	C10	1.55
C5	C6	1.38
C5	C11	1.49
C6	C12	1.57
C7	C13	1.50
C8	C14	1.60
C9	C14	1.61
C10	C15	1.57
C11	C15	1.59
C12	C13	1.52

Bond Angles

C2	C1	C6	119	C6	C5	C11	131
C2	C1	C7	127	C1	C6	C5	123
C6	C1	C7	114	C1	C6	C12	109
C1	C2	C3	118	C5	C6	C12	127
C1	C2	C8	127	C1	C7	C13	100
C3	C2	C8	115	C2	C8	C14	101
C2	C3	C4	122	C3	C9	C14	101
C2	C3	C9	113	C4	C10	C15	102
C4	C3	C9	125	C5	C11	C15	104
C3	C4	C5	120	C6	C12	C13	102
C3	C4	C10	128	C7	C13	C12	114
C5	C4	C10	112	C8	C14	C9	111
C4	C5	C6	117	C10	C15	C11	107
C4	C5	C11	112				

Torsion Angles

C6	C1	C2	C3	−3	C1	C2	C8	C14	179	C4	C5	C6	C1	−3
C6	C1	C2	C8	−179	C3	C2	C8	C14	3	C4	C5	C6	C12	−178
C7	C1	C2	C3	−178	C2	C3	C4	C5	−1	C11	C5	C6	C1	174
C7	C1	C2	C8	6	C2	C3	C4	C10	180	C11	C5	C6	C12	0
C2	C1	C6	C5	4	C9	C3	C4	C5	179	C4	C5	C11	C15	−12
C2	C1	C6	C12	180	C9	C3	C4	C10	0	C6	C5	C11	C15	170
C7	C1	C6	C5	179	C2	C3	C9	C14	0	C1	C6	C12	C13	11
C7	C1	C6	C12	−5	C4	C3	C9	C14	180	C5	C6	C12	C13	−173
C2	C1	C7	C13	171	C3	C4	C5	C6	2	C1	C7	C13	C12	11
C6	C1	C7	C13	−3	C3	C4	C5	C11	−176	C2	C8	C14	C9	−3
C1	C2	C3	C4	2	C10	C4	C5	C6	−179	C3	C9	C14	C8	2
C1	C2	C3	C9	−178	C10	C4	C5	C11	3	C4	C10	C15	C11	−15
C8	C2	C3	C4	178	C3	C4	C10	C15	−173	C5	C11	C15	C10	17
C8	C2	C3	C9	−2	C5	C4	C10	C15	8	C6	C12	C13	C7	−14

29.3   3,6 - Dichloro - 1 - 2,4 - 5 - dibenzpentalene   C₁₆H₈Cl₂

A.Schuijff, Proefschr. Doct. Wiskde. Naturwet., Utrecht, 1962

The structure was determined in two dimensions only. Atomic coordinates were not reported in the paper.
C2/c   Z = 4   No R factor was given.

DCDBPL

29.4   Acepleiadylene   C₁₆H₁₀

A.W.Hanson, Acta Cryst., 13, 215, 1960

The structure is totally disordered.
P2₁/a   Z = 4   R = 0.18

ACPLDL   LB 16-10-1

29.5   Pyrene   C₁₆H₁₀

A.Camerman, J.Trotter, Acta Cryst., 18, 636, 1965

See also Allman, Z. Kristallogr., 132, 129, 1970.
P2₁/a   Z = 4   R = 0.11

PYRENE   LB 16-10-4

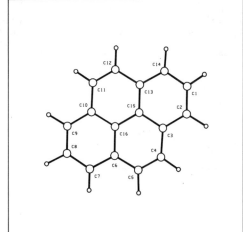

Bond Lengths

C1	C2	1.37	C8	C9	1.35
C1	C14	1.39	C9	C10	1.42
C2	C3	1.41	C10	C11	1.43
C3	C4	1.44	C10	C16	1.41
C3	C15	1.42	C11	C12	1.31
C4	C5	1.32	C12	C13	1.47
C5	C6	1.41	C13	C14	1.42
C6	C7	1.41	C13	C15	1.38
C6	C16	1.43	C15	C16	1.41
C7	C8	1.39			

Bond Angles

C2	C1	C14	122	C6	C7	C8	120	C14	C13	C15	120
C1	C2	C3	120	C7	C8	C9	122	C1	C14	C13	119
C2	C3	C4	123	C8	C9	C10	120	C3	C15	C13	121
C2	C3	C15	119	C9	C10	C11	122	C3	C15	C16	119
C4	C3	C15	118	C9	C10	C16	120	C13	C15	C16	120
C3	C4	C5	122	C11	C10	C16	119	C6	C16	C10	120
C4	C5	C6	122	C10	C11	C12	122	C6	C16	C15	120
C5	C6	C7	123	C11	C12	C13	120	C10	C16	C15	120
C5	C6	C16	119	C12	C13	C14	121				
C7	C6	C16	118	C12	C13	C15	119				

29.6   1,2 - Cyclopentenophenanthrene

$C_{17}H_{13}$

R.F.Entwistle, J.Iball, Z. Kristallogr., 116, 251, 1961

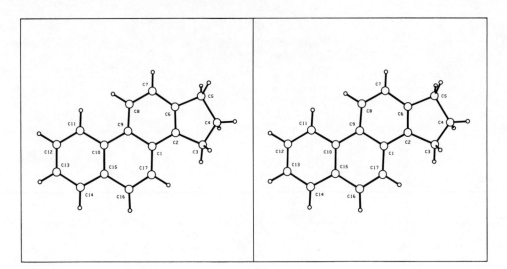

$P2_1/a$ Z = 4   R = 0.10

CPPHEN   LB 17-14-1

Bond Lengths

C1	C2	1.42	C8	C9	1.41
C1	C9	1.45	C9	C10	1.43
C1	C17	1.44	C10	C11	1.43
C2	C3	1.52	C10	C15	1.45
C2	C6	1.36	C11	C12	1.39
C3	C4	1.55	C12	C13	1.37
C4	C5	1.57	C13	C14	1.40
C5	C6	1.51	C14	C15	1.40
C6	C7	1.44	C15	C16	1.45
C7	C8	1.41	C16	C17	1.35

Bond Angles

C2	C1	C9	119	C2	C6	C7	123	C10	C11	C12	120
C2	C1	C17	122	C5	C6	C7	124	C11	C12	C13	120
C9	C1	C17	118	C6	C7	C8	116	C12	C13	C14	122
C1	C2	C3	127	C7	C8	C9	124	C13	C14	C15	120
C1	C2	C6	121	C1	C9	C8	118	C10	C15	C14	118
C3	C2	C6	112	C1	C9	C10	119	C10	C15	C16	121
C2	C3	C4	101	C8	C9	C10	124	C14	C15	C16	121
C3	C4	C5	108	C9	C10	C11	121	C15	C16	C17	118
C4	C5	C6	101	C9	C10	C15	120	C1	C17	C16	124
C2	C6	C5	113	C11	C10	C15	119				

Torsion Angles

C1	C2	C3	C4	169
C6	C2	C3	C4	−9
C1	C2	C6	C5	177
C1	C2	C6	C7	5
C3	C2	C6	C5	−4
C3	C2	C6	C7	−176
C2	C3	C4	C5	19
C3	C4	C5	C6	−21
C4	C5	C6	C2	16
C4	C5	C6	C7	−172

29.7   Benzo(c)phenanthrene

$C_{18}H_{12}$

F.L.Hirshfeld, S.Sandler, G.M.J.Schmidt, J. Chem. Soc., 2108, 1963

$P2_12_12_1$ Z = 4   R = 0.090

BZPHAN   LB 18-12-4

Torsion Angles

C1	C7	C8	C4	−10
C1	C7	C8	C5	168
C9	C7	C8	C4	176
C9	C7	C8	C5	−7
C1	C7	C9	C10	−160
C1	C7	C9	C17	20
C8	C7	C9	C10	14
C8	C7	C9	C17	−166
C7	C9	C17	C11	17
C7	C9	C17	C18	−168
C10	C9	C17	C11	−162
C10	C9	C17	C18	13
C9	C17	C18	C14	176
C9	C17	C18	C15	−7
C11	C17	C18	C14	−8
C11	C17	C18	C15	169

Bond Lengths

C1	C2	1.38	C9	C17	1.44
C1	C7	1.43	C10	C16	1.43
C2	C3	1.41	C11	C12	1.38
C3	C4	1.38	C11	C17	1.44
C4	C8	1.39	C12	C13	1.40
C5	C6	1.35	C13	C14	1.36
C5	C8	1.44	C14	C18	1.39
C6	C10	1.43	C15	C16	1.33
C7	C8	1.43	C15	C18	1.44
C7	C9	1.45	C17	C18	1.44
C9	C10	1.41			

Bond Angles

C2	C1	C7	121	C4	C8	C7	121	C12	C13	C14	119
C1	C2	C3	121	C5	C8	C7	119	C13	C14	C18	122
C2	C3	C4	118	C7	C9	C10	118	C16	C15	C18	121
C3	C4	C8	121	C7	C9	C17	125	C10	C16	C15	121
C6	C5	C8	120	C10	C9	C17	118	C9	C17	C11	124
C5	C6	C10	122	C6	C10	C9	120	C9	C17	C18	120
C1	C7	C8	116	C6	C10	C16	119	C11	C17	C18	116
C1	C7	C9	124	C9	C10	C16	121	C14	C18	C15	121
C8	C7	C9	120	C12	C11	C17	121	C14	C18	C17	120
C4	C8	C5	120	C11	C12	C13	121	C15	C18	C17	118

29.8 Chrysene $C_{18}H_{12}$

D.M.Burns, J.Iball, Proc. R. Soc., A, 257, 491, 1960

I2/c   Z = 4   R = 0.08

CRYSEN   LB 18-12-3

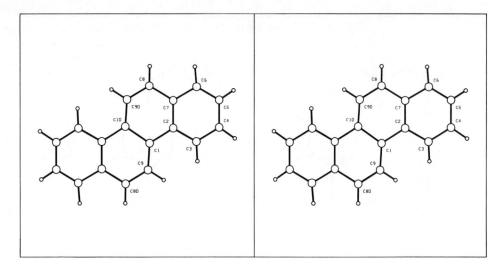

Bond Lengths

C1	C2	1.47	C4	C5	1.39
C1	C9	1.36	C5	C6	1.36
C1	C1D	1.52	C6	C7	1.43
C2	C3	1.40	C7	C8	1.46
C2	C7	1.41	C8	C9D	1.37
C3	C4	1.38			

Bond Angles

C2	C1	C9	124	C4	C5	C6	120
C2	C1	C1D	114	C5	C6	C7	120
C9	C1	C1D	121	C2	C7	C6	119
C1	C2	C3	120	C2	C7	C8	121
C1	C2	C7	121	C6	C7	C8	119
C3	C2	C7	119	C7	C8	C9D	118
C2	C3	C4	121	C1	C9	C8D	124
C3	C4	C5	120				

29.9 Tetracene (for full structural details see Robertson et al., Acta Cryst., 14,697,1961) $C_{18}H_{12}$

R.B.Campbell, J.M.Robertson, J.Trotter, Acta Cryst., 15, 289, 1962

No comparison of bond lengths is possible since they are not reported in the paper.

P-1   Z = 2 R_{0kl} = 0.107, R_{h0l} = 0.098

TETCEN   LB 18-12-2

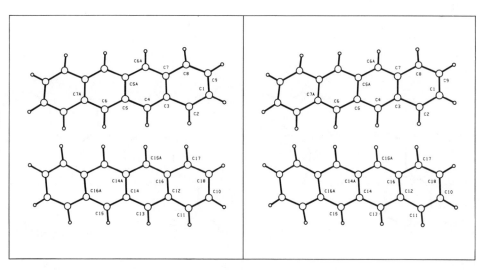

Bond Lengths

C1	C2	1.37	C10	C11	1.38
C1	C9	1.45	C10	C18	1.48
C2	C3	1.47	C11	C12	1.42
C3	C4	1.35	C12	C13	1.41
C3	C7	1.40	C12	C16	1.44
C4	C5	1.43	C13	C14	1.43
C5	C6	1.37	C14	C15	1.38
C5	C5A	1.46	C14	C14A	1.46
C6	C7A	1.40	C15	C16A	1.40
C7	C8	1.44	C16	C17	1.36
C8	C9	1.41	C17	C18	1.35

Bond Angles

C2	C1	C9	122	C11	C10	C18	120
C1	C2	C3	120	C10	C11	C12	118
C2	C3	C4	121	C11	C12	C13	121
C2	C3	C7	119	C11	C12	C16	122
C4	C3	C7	120	C13	C12	C16	117
C3	C4	C5	122	C12	C13	C14	124
C4	C5	C6	124	C13	C14	C15	124
C4	C5	C5A	118	C13	C14	C14A	117
C6	C5	C5A	118	C15	C14	C14A	119
C5	C6	C7A	123	C14	C15	C16A	123
C3	C7	C8	120	C12	C16	C17	116
C3	C7	C6A	120	C12	C16	C15A	120
C8	C7	C6A	120	C17	C16	C15A	124
C7	C8	C9	121	C16	C17	C18	126
C1	C9	C8	118	C10	C18	C17	118

29.10   Triphenylene

$C_{18}H_{12}$

F.R.Ahmed, J.Trotter, Acta Cryst., 16, 503, 1963

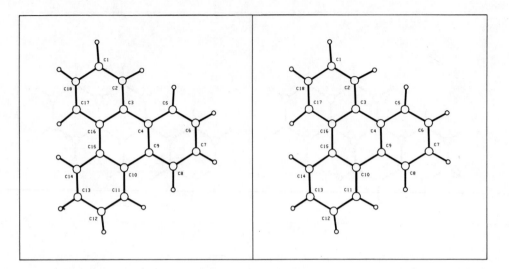

$P2_12_12_1$ Z = 4   R = 0.10

TRIPHE   LB 18-12-5

Bond Lengths

C1	C2	1.39	C5	C6	1.36	C11	C12	1.38
C1	C18	1.41	C6	C7	1.39	C12	C13	1.41
C2	C3	1.41	C7	C8	1.40	C13	C14	1.37
C3	C4	1.44	C8	C9	1.40	C14	C15	1.42
C3	C16	1.42	C9	C10	1.47	C15	C16	1.43
C4	C5	1.43	C10	C11	1.43	C16	C17	1.40
C4	C9	1.41	C10	C15	1.41	C17	C18	1.37

Bond Angles

C2	C1	C18	118	C6	C7	C8	120	C12	C13	C14	121
C1	C2	C3	122	C7	C8	C9	120	C13	C14	C15	122
C2	C3	C4	122	C4	C9	C8	120	C10	C15	C14	118
C2	C3	C16	119	C4	C9	C10	119	C10	C15	C16	120
C4	C3	C16	119	C8	C9	C10	121	C14	C15	C16	122
C3	C4	C5	122	C9	C10	C11	120	C3	C16	C15	121
C3	C4	C9	121	C9	C10	C15	120	C3	C16	C17	118
C5	C4	C9	117	C11	C10	C15	120	C15	C16	C17	122
C4	C5	C6	122	C10	C11	C12	121	C16	C17	C18	123
C5	C6	C7	120	C11	C12	C13	119	C1	C18	C17	120

29.11   2,8 - Dihydroxy - 5,6,11,12,4b,10b - hexahydrochrysene

$C_{18}H_{18}O_2$

M.Ehrenberg, Acta Cryst., 16, 215, 1963

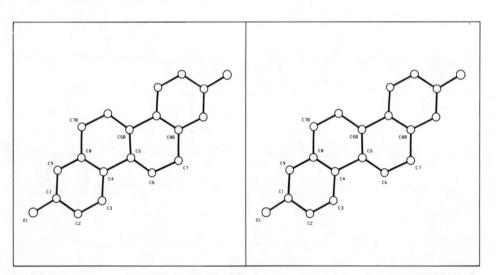

$P2_1/a$ Z = 2   R = 0.11

DOXCRY   LB 18-18-28

Bond Lengths

C1	O1	1.40
C1	C2	1.38
C1	C9	1.41
C2	C3	1.41
C3	C4	1.43
C4	C5	1.57
C4	C8	1.34
C5	C6	1.56
C5	C5B	1.51
C6	C7	1.57
C7	C8B	1.54
C8	C9	1.43

Bond Angles

O1	C1	C2	117
O1	C1	C9	122
C2	C1	C9	121
C1	C2	C3	119
C2	C3	C4	120
C3	C4	C5	118
C3	C4	C8	119
C5	C4	C8	122
C4	C5	C6	113
C4	C5	C5B	110
C6	C5	C5B	108
C5	C6	C7	107
C6	C7	C8B	113
C4	C8	C7B	122
C4	C8	C9	122
C9	C8	C7B	116
C1	C9	C8	118

Torsion Angles

O1	C1	C2	C3	−179	C5	C4	C8	C9	179
C9	C1	C2	C3	1	C5	C4	C8	C7B	6
O1	C1	C9	C8	176	C4	C5	C6	C7	−169
C2	C1	C9	C8	−3	C5B	C5	C6	C7	69
C1	C2	C3	C4	−3	C4	C5	C5B	C4B	180
C2	C3	C4	C5	179	C4	C5	C5B	C6B	56
C2	C3	C4	C8	8	C6	C5	C5B	C4B	−56
C3	C4	C5	C6	43	C6	C5	C5B	C6B	−180
C3	C4	C5	C5B	164	C5	C6	C7	C8B	−49
C8	C4	C5	C6	−147	C6	C7	C8B	C4B	19
C8	C4	C5	C5B	−25	C6	C7	C8B	C9B	−168
C3	C4	C8	C9	−11	C4	C8	C9	C1	9
C3	C4	C8	C7B	177	C7B	C8	C9	C1	−179

29.12   2,7 - Dimethylperhydropyrene

$C_{18}H_{30}$

A.Immirzi, Atti Accad. Nazion. Lincei, R. C., Cl. Sci. Fis. Mat. Nat., 37, 178, 1964

The published coordinates do not
provide connections for bonds
C13 - C15 and C12 - C16.
$P2_1/c$ Z = 2   R = 0.10

PHYPYR   LB 18-30-2

29.13   2' - Methyl - 1,2 - benzanthraquinone (form i)

$C_{19}H_{12}O_2$

R.P.Ferrier, J.Iball, Acta Cryst., 16, 513, 1963

$P2_1$ Z = 2   R = 0.071

MBZANQ   LB 19-12-7

Bond Lengths

C1	O1	1.21	C9	C10	1.42	
C8	O2	1.22	C9	C18	1.41	
C1	C2	1.46	C10	C11	1.44	
C1	C18	1.52	C10	C15	1.41	
C2	C3	1.42	C11	C12	1.37	
C2	C7	1.40	C12	C13	1.39	
C3	C4	1.38	C12	C19	1.51	
C4	C5	1.38	C13	C14	1.37	
C5	C6	1.38	C14	C15	1.44	
C6	C7	1.38	C15	C16	1.41	
C7	C8	1.51	C16	C17	1.37	
C8	C9	1.48	C17	C18	1.39	

Bond Angles

O1	C1	C2	123	C5	C6	C7	120	C10	C9	C18	118	C13	C14	C15	120
O1	C1	C18	119	C2	C7	C6	121	C9	C10	C11	124	C10	C15	C14	119
C2	C1	C18	118	C2	C7	C8	120	C9	C10	C15	118	C10	C15	C16	122
C1	C2	C3	120	C6	C7	C8	119	C11	C10	C15	118	C14	C15	C16	119
C1	C2	C7	122	O2	C8	C7	117	C10	C11	C12	122	C15	C16	C17	119
C3	C2	C7	119	O2	C8	C9	124	C11	C12	C13	120	C16	C17	C18	120
C2	C3	C4	120	C7	C8	C9	120	C11	C12	C19	121	C1	C18	C9	122
C3	C4	C5	121	C8	C9	C10	123	C13	C12	C19	119	C1	C18	C17	116
C4	C5	C6	121	C8	C9	C18	119	C12	C13	C14	122	C9	C18	C17	122

29.14   5 - Methyl - 1,2 - benzanthraquinone

$C_{19}H_{12}O_2$

R.P.Ferrier, J.Iball, Acta Cryst., 16, 269, 1963

$P2_1nb$ Z = 4   R = 0.082

MEBZAN   LB 19-12-10

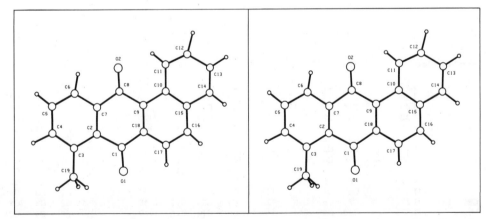

Bond Lengths

C1	O1	1.22	C8	C9	1.50	
C8	O2	1.21	C9	C10	1.47	
C1	C2	1.51	C9	C18	1.39	
C1	C18	1.48	C10	C11	1.46	
C2	C3	1.42	C10	C15	1.39	
C2	C7	1.40	C11	C12	1.36	
C3	C4	1.37	C12	C13	1.43	
C3	C19	1.47	C13	C14	1.37	
C4	C5	1.38	C14	C15	1.47	
C5	C6	1.38	C15	C16	1.38	
C6	C7	1.41	C16	C17	1.39	
C7	C8	1.47	C17	C18	1.40	

Bond Angles

O1	C1	C2	120	C3	C4	C5	124	C8	C9	C10	122	C13	C14	C15	122
O1	C1	C18	119	C4	C5	C6	118	C8	C9	C18	118	C10	C15	C14	119
C2	C1	C18	120	C5	C6	C7	121	C10	C9	C18	119	C10	C15	C16	123
C1	C2	C3	124	C2	C7	C6	119	C9	C10	C11	122	C14	C15	C16	119
C1	C2	C7	116	C2	C7	C8	125	C9	C10	C15	117	C15	C16	C17	120
C3	C2	C7	120	C6	C7	C8	116	C10	C11	C12	121	C16	C17	C18	120
C2	C3	C4	117	O2	C8	C7	120	C11	C10	C15	121	C1	C18	C9	123
C2	C3	C19	121	O2	C8	C9	121	C11	C12	C13	125	C1	C18	C17	117
C4	C3	C19	122	C7	C8	C9	118	C12	C13	C14	117	C9	C18	C17	121

29.15   9,10 - Dimethyl - 1,2 - benzanthracene

C₂₀H₁₆ → $C_{20}H_{16}$

D.Sayre, P.H.Friedlander, Nature, 187, 139, 1960

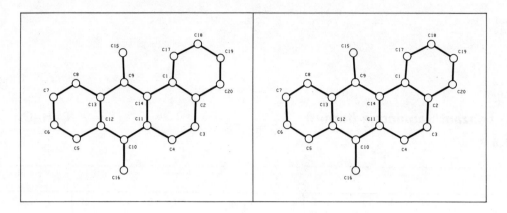

P2₁nb   Z = 4   R = 0.135

BENANT   LB 20-16-1

Bond Lengths

C1	C2	1.42	C6	C7	1.39	C10	C12	1.40
C1	C14	1.48	C7	C8	1.38	C10	C16	1.53
C1	C17	1.40	C8	C13	1.43	C11	C14	1.45
C2	C3	1.41	C9	C13	1.44	C12	C13	1.42
C2	C20	1.44	C9	C14	1.39	C17	C18	1.40
C3	C4	1.34	C9	C15	1.50	C18	C19	1.40
C4	C11	1.44	C10	C11	1.39	C19	C20	1.35
C5	C6	1.35						
C5	C12	1.45						

Bond Angles

C2	C1	C14	118	C5	C6	C7	121	C4	C11	C10	121	C1	C14	C9	123
C2	C1	C17	119	C6	C7	C8	120	C4	C11	C14	119	C1	C14	C11	117
C14	C1	C17	123	C7	C8	C13	121	C10	C11	C14	120	C9	C14	C11	120
C1	C2	C3	121	C13	C9	C14	118	C5	C12	C10	123	C1	C17	C18	121
C1	C2	C20	117	C13	C9	C15	118	C5	C12	C13	117	C17	C18	C19	119
C3	C2	C20	121	C14	C9	C15	124	C10	C12	C13	120	C18	C19	C20	121
C2	C3	C4	121	C11	C10	C12	120	C8	C13	C9	121	C2	C20	C19	122
C3	C4	C11	122	C11	C10	C16	121	C8	C13	C12	119				
C6	C5	C12	122	C12	C10	C16	119	C9	C13	C12	121				

29.16   9,10 - Dimethyl - 1,2 - benzanthracene (refinement of data of Sayre and Friedlander, Nature, 187,139,1960)

C₂₀H₁₆ → $C_{20}H_{16}$

J.Iball, Nature, 201, 916, 1964

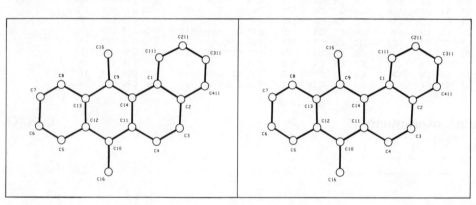

P2₁nb   Z = 4   R = 0.070

BENANT01   LB 20-16-1

Bond Lengths

C1	C2	1.42
C1	C14	1.48
C1	C111	1.40
C2	C3	1.42
C2	C411	1.42
C3	C4	1.34
C4	C11	1.45
C5	C6	1.35
C5	C12	1.44
C6	C7	1.47 (1.41)
C7	C8	1.27 (1.37)
C8	C13	1.42
C9	C13	1.43
C9	C14	1.39
C9	C15	1.51
C10	C11	1.39
C10	C12	1.41
C10	C16	1.52
C11	C14	1.45
C12	C13	1.43
C111	C211	1.38
C211	C311	1.41
C311	C411	1.36

Bond Angles

C2	C1	C14	118	C12	C10	C16	120
C2	C1	C111	118	C4	C11	C10	121
C14	C1	C111	123	C4	C11	C14	118
C1	C2	C3	120	C10	C11	C14	121
C1	C2	C411	118	C5	C12	C10	123
C3	C2	C411	121	C5	C12	C13	118
C2	C3	C4	121	C10	C12	C13	120
C3	C4	C11	122	C8	C13	C9	121
C6	C5	C12	122	C8	C13	C12	119
C5	C6	C7	117	C9	C13	C12	120
C6	C7	C8	123	C1	C14	C9	123
C7	C8	C13	122	C1	C14	C11	118
C13	C9	C14	119	C9	C14	C11	119
C13	C9	C15	118	C1	C111	C211	121
C14	C9	C15	123	C111	C211	C311	120
C11	C10	C12	119	C211	C311	C411	119
C11	C10	C16	121	C2	C411	C311	122

Torsion Angles

C14	C1	C2	C3	7	C15	C9	C13	C8	12
C14	C1	C2	C411	−178	C15	C9	C13	C12	−168
C111	C1	C2	C3	−168	C13	C9	C14	C1	166
C111	C1	C2	C411	7	C13	C9	C14	C11	−15
C2	C1	C14	C9	162	C15	C9	C14	C1	−18
C2	C1	C14	C11	−16	C15	C9	C14	C11	160
C111	C1	C14	C9	−22	C12	C10	C11	C4	176
C111	C1	C14	C11	159	C12	C10	C11	C14	−2
C2	C1	C111	C211	−5	C16	C10	C11	C4	−4
C14	C1	C111	C211	180	C16	C10	C11	C14	178
C1	C2	C3	C4	5	C11	C10	C12	C5	175
C411	C2	C3	C4	−170	C11	C10	C12	C13	−6
C1	C2	C411	C311	−3	C16	C10	C12	C5	−5
C3	C2	C411	C311	172	C16	C10	C12	C13	174
C2	C3	C4	C11	−8	C4	C11	C14	C1	14
C3	C4	C11	C10	−179	C4	C11	C14	C9	−165
C3	C4	C11	C14	−2	C10	C11	C14	C1	−169
C12	C5	C6	C7	−2	C10	C11	C14	C9	13
C6	C5	C12	C10	180	C5	C12	C13	C8	2
C6	C5	C12	C13	1	C5	C12	C13	C9	−178
C5	C6	C7	C8	0	C10	C12	C13	C8	−177
C6	C7	C8	C13	3	C10	C12	C13	C9	4
C7	C8	C13	C9	176	C1	C111	C211	C311	−1
C7	C8	C13	C12	−3	C111	C211	C311	C411	5
C14	C9	C13	C8	−172	C211	C311	C411	C2	−3
C14	C9	C13	C12	7					

29.17   1,12 - Dimethylbenzo(c)phenanthrene (at 80 ° K)   C₂₀H₁₆

F.L.Hirshfeld, S.Sandler, G.M.J.Schmidt, J. Chem. Soc., 2108, 1963

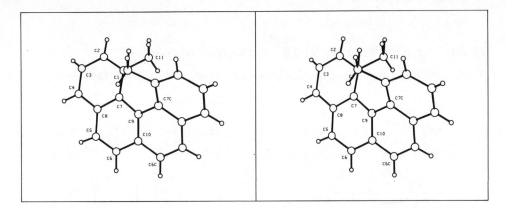

Pbna   Z = 4   R = 0.104

DMBPHA   LB 20-16-2

Bond Lengths

C1	C2	1.40
C1	C7	1.44
C1	C11	1.51
C2	C3	1.39
C3	C4	1.38
C4	C8	1.41
C5	C6	1.37
C5	C8	1.44
C6	C10	1.43
C7	C8	1.41
C7	C9	1.45
C9	C10	1.41

Bond Angles

C2	C1	C7	118
C2	C1	C11	118
C7	C1	C11	123
C1	C2	C3	123
C2	C3	C4	119
C3	C4	C8	120
C6	C5	C8	119
C5	C6	C10	121
C1	C7	C8	118

C1	C7	C9	123
C8	C7	C9	118
C4	C8	C5	119
C4	C8	C7	121
C5	C8	C7	120
C7	C9	C10	117
C7	C9	C7C	126
C6	C10	C9	120
C6	C10	C6C	120

Torsion Angles

C7	C1	C2	C3	−1
C11	C1	C2	C3	170
C2	C1	C7	C8	10
C2	C1	C7	C9	−178
C11	C1	C7	C8	−161
C11	C1	C7	C9	12
C1	C2	C3	C4	−6
C2	C3	C4	C8	4
C3	C4	C8	C5	−168

C3	C4	C8	C7	6
C8	C5	C6	C10	10
C6	C5	C8	C4	168
C6	C5	C8	C7	−5
C5	C6	C10	C9	2
C5	C6	C10	C6C	−178
C1	C7	C8	C4	−12
C1	C7	C8	C5	161
C9	C7	C8	C4	175

C9	C7	C8	C5	−12
C1	C7	C9	C10	−149
C1	C7	C9	C7C	31
C8	C7	C9	C10	23
C8	C7	C9	C7C	−157
C7	C9	C10	C6	−18
C7	C9	C10	C6C	162
C7C	C9	C10	C6	162
C7C	C9	C10	C6C	−18

29.18   2,7 - Diacetoxy - trans.- 15,16 - dimethyl - 15,16 - dihydropyrene   C₂₂H₂₀O₄

(i)   A.W.Hanson, Acta Cryst., 18, 599, 1965

(ii) A.W.Hanson, Acta Cryst., 18, 599, 1965 (at −130°C)

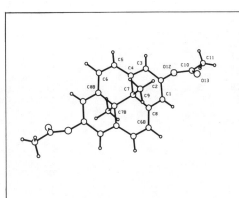

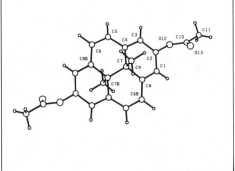

(i) P2₁/a   Z = 2   R = 0.044

DAMHPY   LB 22-20-14

(ii) P2₁/a   Z = 2   R = 0.099

DAMHPY01   LB 22-20-14

Bond Lengths

		(i)	(ii)
C2	O12	1.41	1.42
C10	O12	1.36	1.37
C10	O13	1.19	1.19
C1	C2	1.39	1.39
C1	C8	1.38	1.39
C2	C3	1.39	1.39
C3	C4	1.39	1.40
C4	C5	1.40	1.40
C4	C7	1.52	1.52
C5	C6	1.39	1.39
C6	C8B	1.40	1.41
C7	C8	1.52	1.52
C7	C9	1.56	1.56
C7	C7B	1.53	1.55
C10	C11	1.48	1.51

Bond Angles

			(i)	(ii)
C2	O12	C10	119	118
C2	C1	C8	120	120
O12	C2	C1	119	119
O12	C2	C3	116	115
C1	C2	C3	124	125
C2	C3	C4	120	120
C3	C4	C5	124	124
C3	C4	C7	118	118
C5	C4	C7	117	118
C4	C5	C6	122	122
C5	C6	C8B	122	122
C4	C7	C8	114	115
C4	C7	C9	105	106
C4	C7	C7B	110	110
C8	C7	C9	105	105
C8	C7	C7B	110	110
C9	C7	C7B	111	111
C1	C8	C7	119	118
C1	C8	C6B	124	124
C7	C8	C6B	117	117
O12	C10	O13	123	123
O12	C10	C11	111	110
O13	C10	C11	126	127

Torsion Angles

				(i)	(ii)
C10	O12	C2	C1	−68	−65
C10	O12	C2	C3	121	123
C2	O12	C10	O13	−2	−2
C2	O12	C10	C11	179	178
C8	C1	C2	O12	−175	−175
C8	C1	C2	C3	−4	−5
C2	C1	C8	C7	−9	−9
C2	C1	C8	C6B	178	178
O12	C2	C3	C4	175	174
C1	C2	C3	C4	3	4
C2	C3	C4	C5	−176	−176
C2	C3	C4	C7	11	11
C3	C4	C5	C6	179	179
C7	C4	C5	C6	−8	−8
C3	C4	C7	C8	−23	−24
C3	C4	C7	C9	92	92
C3	C4	C7	C7B	−148	−148
C5	C4	C7	C8	164	164
C5	C4	C7	C9	−82	−81

				(i)	(ii)
C5	C4	C7	C7B	39	39
C4	C5	C6	C8B	−8	−8
C5	C6	C8B	C1B	178	178
C5	C6	C8B	C7B	−9	−9
C4	C7	C8	C1	22	23
C4	C7	C8	C6B	−165	−164
C9	C7	C8	C1	−93	−93
C9	C7	C8	C6B	81	80
C7B	C7	C8	C1	147	147
C7B	C7	C8	C6B	−40	−39
C4	C7	C7B	C4B	−53	−52
C4	C7	C7B	C9B	63	63
C8	C7	C7B	C4B	53	52
C8	C7	C7B	C8B	−180	−180
C8	C7	C7B	C9B	−64	−65
C9	C7	C7B	C4B	−63	−63
C9	C7	C7B	C8B	64	65
C9	C7	C7B	C9B	−180	−180

29.19   2,7 - Diacetoxy - trans - 15,16 - dimethyl - 15,16 - dihydropyrene (at −130 °C)

For complete entry see 29.18

$C_{22}H_{20}O_4$

29.20   5,6 - Dichloro - 11,12 - diphenylnaphthacene

R.L.Avoyan, A.I.Kitaigorodskij, Yu.T.Struchkov, Zh. Strukt. Khim., 5, 420, 1964

$C_{30}H_{18}Cl_2$

I2/c   Z = 4   R = 0.14

CPNPCN   LB 30-18-3

Bond Lengths

Cl1	C2	1.80	C8	C9	1.41
C1	C2	1.42	C9	C10	1.41
C1	C10	1.46	C9	C11	1.47
C2	C3	1.32	C11	C12	1.48
C3	C4	1.50	C11	C16	1.37
C3	C8	1.46	C12	C13	1.37
C4	C5	1.32	C13	C14	1.37
C5	C6	1.43	C14	C15	1.42
C6	C7	1.36	C15	C16	1.37
C7	C8	1.45			

Bond Angles

C2	C1	C10	113	C7	C8	C9	122
C2	C1	C2B	133	C8	C9	C10	121
Cl1	C2	C1	118	C8	C9	C11	119
Cl1	C2	C3	114	C10	C9	C11	120
C1	C2	C3	129	C1	C10	C9	118
C2	C3	C4	128	C9	C10	C9B	123
C2	C3	C8	115	C9	C11	C12	120
C4	C3	C8	117	C9	C11	C16	118
C3	C4	C5	121	C12	C11	C16	121
C4	C5	C6	120	C11	C12	C13	113
C5	C6	C7	123	C12	C13	C14	127
C6	C7	C8	120	C13	C14	C15	116
C3	C8	C7	118	C14	C15	C16	121
C3	C8	C9	119	C11	C16	C15	120

Torsion Angles

C10	C1	C2	Cl1	167	C6	C7	C8	C9	174
C10	C1	C2	C3	−11	C3	C8	C9	C10	−2
C2B	C1	C2	Cl1	−13	C3	C8	C9	C11	−179
C2B	C1	C2	C3	169	C7	C8	C9	C10	−174
C2	C1	C10	C9	21	C7	C8	C9	C11	9
C2	C1	C10	C9B	−159	C8	C9	C10	C1	−16
C2B	C1	C10	C9	−159	C8	C9	C10	C9B	164
C2B	C1	C10	C9B	21	C11	C9	C10	C1	161
Cl1	C2	C3	C4	1	C11	C9	C10	C9B	−19
Cl1	C2	C3	C8	176	C8	C9	C11	C12	−70
C1	C2	C3	C4	179	C8	C9	C11	C16	101
C1	C2	C3	C8	−6	C10	C9	C11	C12	113
C2	C3	C4	C5	176	C10	C9	C11	C16	−75
C8	C3	C4	C5	1	C9	C11	C12	C13	180
C2	C3	C8	C7	−175	C16	C11	C12	C13	8
C2	C3	C8	C9	13	C9	C11	C16	C15	−176
C4	C3	C8	C7	1	C12	C11	C16	C15	−5
C4	C3	C8	C9	−172	C11	C12	C13	C14	−6
C3	C4	C5	C6	−6	C12	C13	C14	C15	0
C4	C5	C6	C7	9	C13	C14	C15	C16	4
C5	C6	C7	C8	−7	C14	C15	C16	C11	−2
C6	C7	C8	C3	2					

30.1 Perylene (β form)

$C_{20}H_{12}$

J.Tanaka, Bull. Chem. Soc. Jap., 36, 1237, 1963

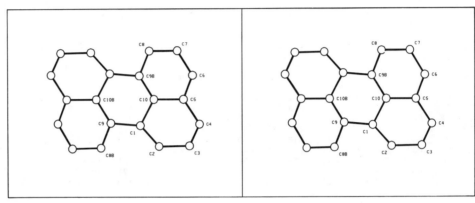

No comparison of bond lengths is possible since they are not reported in the paper.
See also Kerr, Acta Cryst., 21, A119, 1966.

$P2_1/a$ $Z = 2$ $R_{0kl} = 0.27$, $R_{h0l} = 0.17$

PERLEN   LB 20-12-4

Bond Lengths

C1	C2	1.42	C5	C6	1.27
C1	C9	1.48	C5	C10	1.52
C1	C10	1.46	C6	C7	1.44
C2	C3	1.54	C7	C8	1.46
C3	C4	1.18	C8	C9B	1.32
C4	C5	1.47	C9	C10B	1.37

Bond Angles

C2	C1	C9	137	C4	C5	C6	125	C1	C9	C8B	108
C2	C1	C10	109	C4	C5	C10	124	C1	C9	C10B	127
C9	C1	C10	113	C6	C5	C10	111	C1	C10	C5	118
C1	C2	C3	132	C5	C6	C7	127	C1	C10	C9B	119
C2	C3	C4	116	C6	C7	C8	120	C5	C10	C9B	123
C3	C4	C5	121	C7	C8	C9B	113				

30.2 Perylene (α form)

$C_{20}H_{12}$

A.Camerman, J.Trotter, Proc. R. Soc., A, 279, 129, 1964

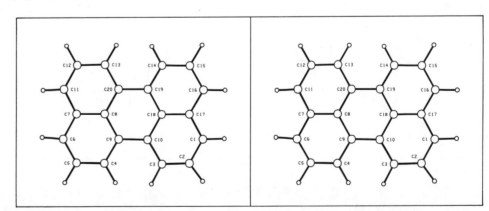

$P2_1/a$ $Z = 4$ $R = 0.081$

PERLEN01   LB 20-12-4

Bond Lengths

C1	C2	1.36	C7	C8	1.42	C13	C20	1.41
C1	C17	1.41	C7	C11	1.39	C14	C15	1.42
C2	C3	1.41	C8	C9	1.44	C14	C19	1.39
C3	C10	1.40	C8	C20	1.40	C15	C16	1.37
C4	C5	1.42	C9	C10	1.46	C16	C17	1.38
C4	C9	1.39	C10	C18	1.43	C17	C18	1.42
C5	C6	1.37	C11	C12	1.37	C18	C19	1.43
C6	C7	1.41	C12	C13	1.42	C19	C20	1.48

Bond Angles

C2	C1	C17	122	C7	C8	C9	119	C7	C11	C12	122	C10	C18	C17	121
C1	C2	C3	121	C7	C8	C20	121	C11	C12	C13	121	C10	C18	C19	121
C2	C3	C10	120	C9	C8	C20	120	C12	C13	C20	119	C17	C18	C19	118
C5	C4	C9	120	C4	C9	C8	119	C15	C14	C19	121	C14	C19	C18	119
C4	C5	C6	121	C4	C9	C10	120	C14	C15	C16	120	C14	C19	C20	122
C5	C6	C7	120	C8	C9	C10	121	C15	C16	C17	120	C18	C19	C20	119
C6	C7	C8	120	C3	C10	C9	123	C1	C17	C16	121	C8	C20	C13	120
C6	C7	C11	122	C3	C10	C18	118	C1	C17	C18	118	C8	C20	C19	121
C8	C7	C11	118	C9	C10	C18	119	C16	C17	C18	121	C13	C20	C19	120

30.3   20 - Methylcholanthrene $C_{21}H_{16}$

J.Iball, S.G.G.MacDonald, Z. Kristallogr., 114, 439, 1960

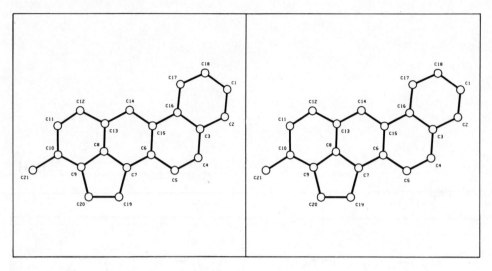

$P2_1/c$ Z = 4   R = 0.15

MCHLAN10   LB 21-16-2

Bond Lengths

C1	C2	1.36	C7	C8	1.41	C12	C13	1.44
C1	C18	1.42	C7	C19	1.51	C13	C14	1.42
C2	C3	1.41	C8	C9	1.41	C14	C15	1.40
C3	C4	1.43	C8	C13	1.38	C15	C16	1.46
C3	C16	1.43	C9	C10	1.35	C16	C17	1.40
C4	C5	1.37	C9	C20	1.53	C17	C18	1.40
C5	C6	1.44	C10	C11	1.43	C19	C20	1.55
C6	C7	1.40	C10	C21	1.50			
C6	C15	1.44	C11	C12	1.38			

Bond Angles

C2	C1	C18	120	C6	C7	C8	119	C9	C10	C21	123	C14 C15 C16 120
C1	C2	C3	121	C6	C7	C19	132	C11	C10	C21	120	C3 C16 C15 118
C2	C3	C4	119	C8	C7	C19	109	C10	C11	C12	123	C3 C16 C17 119
C2	C3	C16	120	C7	C8	C9	112	C11	C12	C13	120	C15 C16 C17 123
C4	C3	C16	121	C7	C8	C13	123	C8	C13	C12	115	C16 C17 C18 121
C3	C4	C5	121	C9	C8	C13	125	C8	C13	C14	119	C1 C18 C17 120
C4	C5	C6	121	C8	C9	C10	120	C12	C13	C14	126	C7 C19 C20 105
C5	C6	C7	121	C8	C9	C20	109	C13	C14	C15	120	C9 C20 C19 105
C5	C6	C15	120	C10	C9	C20	131	C6	C15	C14	120	
C7	C6	C15	119	C9	C10	C11	117	C6	C15	C16	120	

30.4   Pentacene (for full structural details see Campbell et al., Acta Cryst., 14,705,1961) $C_{22}H_{14}$

R.B.Campbell, J.M.Robertson, J.Trotter, Acta Cryst., 15, 289, 1962

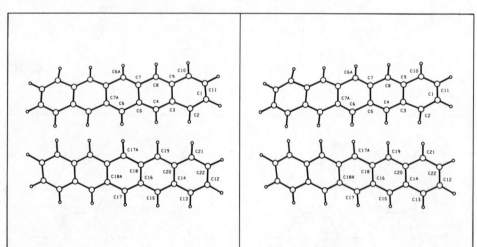

No comparison of bond lengths is possible since they are not reported in the paper.

P-1   Z = 2 R_{0kl} = 0.104, R_{h0l} = 0.182

PENCEN   LB 22-14-6

Bond Lengths

C1	C2	1.35	C12	C13	1.36
C1	C11	1.37	C12	C22	1.48
C2	C3	1.44	C13	C14	1.42
C3	C4	1.35	C14	C15	1.41
C3	C9	1.41	C14	C20	1.47
C4	C5	1.38	C15	C16	1.42
C5	C6	1.43	C16	C17	1.39
C5	C7	1.42	C16	C18	1.48
C6	C7A	1.34	C17	C18A'	1.41
C7	C8	1.46	C18	C19	1.36
C8	C9	1.36	C19	C20	1.38
C9	C10	1.43	C20	C21	1.40
C10	C11	1.36	C21	C22	1.35

Bond Angles

C2	C1	C11	119	C5	C7	C8	114	C13	C12	C22	119	C16	C18	C19	117
C1	C2	C3	123	C5	C7	C6A	124	C12	C13	C14	123	C16	C18	C17A	117
C2	C3	C4	126	C8	C7	C6A	121	C13	C13	C14	C15	122	C19	C18	C17A	125
C2	C3	C9	117	C7	C8	C9	123	C13	C14	C20	118	C18	C19	C20	127
C4	C3	C9	116	C3	C9	C8	120	C15	C14	C20	120	C14	C20	C19	116
C3	C4	C5	126	C3	C9	C10	117	C14	C15	C16	121	C14	C20	C21	117
C4	C5	C6	123	C8	C9	C10	122	C15	C16	C17	123	C19	C20	C21	127
C4	C5	C7	119	C9	C10	C11	122	C15	C16	C18	118	C20	C21	C22	126
C6	C5	C7	116	C1	C11	C10	122	C17	C16	C18	119	C12	C22	C21	117
C5	C6	C7A	118					C16	C17	C18A	124				

30.5   9,10 - Dihydro - 1,2,5,6 - dibenzanthracene (analysis of planarity using data of Iball and Young, Acta Cryst., 11,476,1958)

$C_{22}H_{16}$

F.H.Herbstein, Acta Cryst., 14, 77, 1961

For structural details see paper by
Iball & Young, Acta Cryst., 11, 476, 1958.

HDBANT   LB 22-16-1

30.6   Coronene

$C_{24}H_{12}$

J.K.Fawcett, J.Trotter, Proc. R. Soc., A, 289, 366, 1965

See also Robertson & White, J. Chem. Soc., 607, 1945.
$P2_1/a$ $Z = 2$ $R = 0.157$

CORONE   LB 24-12-1

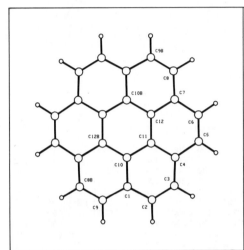
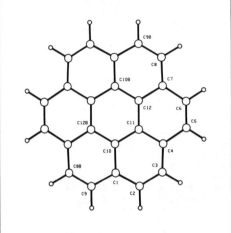

Bond Lengths

C1	C2	1.41	C6	C7	1.41					
C1	C9	1.42	C7	C8	1.41					
C1	C10	1.42	C7	C12	1.43					
C2	C3	1.35	C8	C9B	1.35					
C3	C4	1.41	C10	C11	1.42					
C4	C5	1.41	C10	C12B	1.42					
C4	C11	1.44	C11	C12	1.43					
C5	C6	1.33								

Bond Angles

C2	C1	C9	124	C3	C4	C11	117	C8	C7	C12	118	C4	C11	C10	121
C2	C1	C10	118	C5	C4	C11	118	C7	C8	C9B	122	C4	C11	C12	119
C9	C1	C10	118	C4	C5	C6	122	C1	C9	C8B	122	C10	C11	C12	120
C1	C2	C3	122	C5	C6	C7	123	C1	C10	C11	120	C7	C12	C11	121
C2	C3	C4	123	C6	C7	C8	125	C1	C10	C12B	121	C7	C12	C10B	119
C3	C4	C5	125	C6	C7	C12	117	C11	C10	C12B	120	C11	C12	C10B	120

30.7   1,2 - 7,8 - Dibenzocoronene

$C_{32}H_{16}$

J.M.Robertson, J.Trotter, J. Chem. Soc., 1115, 1961

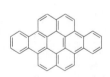

C2/c   Z = 4 $R_{h0l} = 0.12,$
$R_{h1l} = 0.17$

DBZCOR   LB 32-16-1

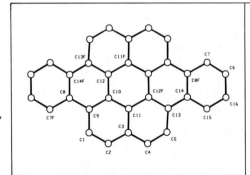
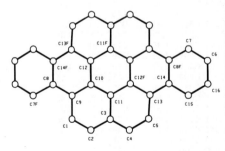

Bond Lengths

C1	C2	1.37	C8	C9	1.40
C1	C9	1.42	C8	C14F	1.42
C2	C3	1.38	C9	C10	1.39
C3	C4	1.39	C10	C11	1.41
C3	C11	1.45	C10	C12	1.43
C4	C5	1.39	C11	C12F	1.42
C5	C13	1.45	C12	C13F	1.40
C6	C7	1.36	C13	C14	1.37
C6	C16	1.42	C14	C15	1.41
C7	C8F	1.41	C15	C16	1.40

Bond Angles

C2	C1	C9	118	C9	C8	C14F	118	C10	C12	C11F	118
C1	C2	C3	124	C1	C9	C8	118	C10	C12	C13F	119
C2	C3	C4	124	C1	C9	C10	119	C5	C13	C14	122
C2	C3	C11	119	C8	C9	C10	123	C5	C13	C12F	115
C4	C3	C11	117	C9	C10	C11	124	C14	C13	C12F	123
C3	C4	C5	123	C9	C10	C12	118	C13	C14	C15	120
C4	C5	C13	122	C11	C10	C12	118	C13	C14	C8F	119
C7	C6	C16	121	C3	C11	C10	116	C15	C14	C8F	120
C6	C7	C8F	121	C3	C11	C12F	120	C14	C15	C16	120
C9	C8	C7F	123	C10	C11	C12F	123	C6	C16	C15	118

30.8 Dibenzanthrone

$C_{34}H_{16}O_2$

W.Bolton, H.P.Stadler, Acta Cryst., 17, 1015, 1964

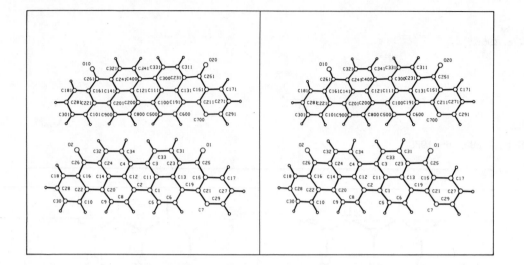

$P2_1$ Z = 4   R = 0.12

DIBANT   LB 34-16-2

Bond Lengths

C261	O10	1.27	C25	O1	1.21
C251	O20	1.28	C26	O2	1.26
C100	C111	1.46	C1	C2	1.44
C100	C200	1.46	C1	C5	1.37
C100	C500	1.39	C1	C11	1.42
C101	C221	1.40	C2	C8	1.41
C101	C301	1.33	C2	C12	1.48
C111	C131	1.42	C3	C4	1.47
C111	C300	1.47	C3	C11	1.42
C121	C141	1.39	C3	C33	1.39
C121	C200	1.43	C4	C12	1.39
C121	C400	1.40	C4	C34	1.36
C131	C191	1.40	C5	C6	1.41
C131	C231	1.45	C6	C19	1.43
C141	C201	1.47	C7	C21	1.38
C141	C241	1.46	C7	C29	1.38
C151	C171	1.40	C8	C9	1.40
C151	C211	1.39	C9	C20	1.36
C151	C251	1.49	C10	C22	1.43
C161	C181	1.42	C10	C30	1.36
C161	C221	1.41	C11	C13	1.44
C161	C261	1.48	C12	C14	1.42
C171	C271	1.38	C13	C19	1.44
C181	C281	1.39	C13	C23	1.40
C191	C211	1.47	C14	C20	1.43
C191	C600	1.39	C14	C24	1.44
C200	C800	1.43	C15	C17	1.45
C201	C221	1.47	C15	C21	1.42
C201	C900	1.40	C15	C25	1.45
C211	C700	1.40	C16	C18	1.40
C231	C251	1.48	C16	C22	1.44
C231	C311	1.41	C16	C26	1.41
C241	C261	1.42	C17	C27	1.38
C241	C321	1.38	C18	C28	1.40
C271	C291	1.40	C19	C21	1.40
C281	C301	1.42	C20	C22	1.47
C291	C700	1.39	C23	C25	1.51
C300	C331	1.38	C23	C31	1.32
C300	C400	1.50	C24	C26	1.49
C311	C331	1.37	C24	C32	1.36
C321	C341	1.40	C27	C29	1.45
C341	C400	1.37	C28	C30	1.36
C500	C600	1.37	C31	C33	1.43
C800	C900	1.38	C32	C34	1.40

Bond Angles

C111	C100	C200	119	C151	C251	C231	117	C4	C12	C14	121
C111	C100	C500	118	O10	C261	C161	122	C11	C13	C19	120
C200	C100	C500	124	O10	C261	C241	120	C11	C13	C23	120
C221	C101	C301	120	C161	C261	C241	118	C19	C13	C23	120
C100	C111	C131	119	C171	C271	C291	119	C12	C14	C20	121
C100	C111	C300	120	C181	C281	C301	120	C12	C14	C24	118
C131	C111	C300	121	C271	C291	C700	120	C20	C14	C24	121
C141	C121	C200	119	C111	C300	C331	119	C17	C15	C21	119
C141	C121	C400	119	C111	C300	C400	119	C17	C15	C25	118
C200	C121	C400	122	C331	C300	C400	123	C21	C15	C25	123
C111	C131	C191	122	C101	C301	C281	122	C18	C16	C22	118
C111	C131	C231	117	C231	C311	C331	122	C18	C16	C26	119
C191	C131	C231	121	C241	C321	C341	123	C22	C16	C26	122
C121	C141	C201	121	C300	C331	C311	122	C15	C17	C27	124
C121	C141	C241	121	C321	C341	C400	119	C16	C18	C28	122
C201	C141	C241	118	C121	C400	C300	119	C6	C19	C13	118
C171	C151	C211	119	C121	C400	C341	121	C6	C19	C21	120
C171	C151	C251	119	C300	C400	C341	119	C13	C19	C21	122
C211	C151	C251	122	C100	C500	C600	122	C9	C20	C14	119
C181	C161	C221	121	C191	C600	C500	123	C9	C20	C22	121
C181	C161	C261	117	C211	C700	C291	120	C14	C20	C22	120
C221	C161	C261	122	C200	C800	C900	122	C7	C21	C15	117
C151	C171	C271	121	C201	C900	C800	120	C7	C21	C19	124
C161	C181	C281	118					C15	C21	C19	119
C131	C191	C211	121	C2	C1	C5	121	C10	C22	C16	117
C131	C191	C600	118	C2	C1	C11	119	C10	C22	C20	124
C211	C191	C600	121	C5	C1	C11	120	C16	C22	C20	119
C100	C200	C121	121	C1	C2	C8	123	C13	C23	C25	120
C100	C200	C800	120	C1	C2	C12	120	C13	C23	C31	122
C121	C200	C800	119	C8	C2	C12	117	C25	C23	C31	118
C141	C201	C221	120	C4	C3	C11	120	C14	C24	C26	119
C141	C201	C900	119	C4	C3	C33	122	C14	C24	C32	119
C221	C201	C900	121	C11	C3	C33	119	C26	C24	C32	122
C151	C211	C191	119	C3	C4	C12	119	O1	C25	C15	126
C151	C211	C700	120	C3	C4	C34	121	O1	C25	C23	118
C191	C211	C700	121	C12	C4	C34	120	C15	C25	C23	116
C101	C221	C161	119	C1	C5	C6	122	O2	C26	C16	124
C101	C221	C201	121	C5	C5	C6	120	O2	C26	C24	117
C161	C221	C201	120	C21	C7	C29	123	C16	C26	C24	119
C131	C231	C251	119	C2	C8	C9	122	C17	C27	C29	115
C131	C231	C311	120	C8	C9	C20	122	C18	C28	C30	120
C251	C231	C311	121	C22	C10	C30	122	C7	C29	C27	122
C141	C241	C261	122	C1	C11	C3	122	C10	C30	C28	120
C141	C241	C321	116	C1	C11	C13	120	C23	C31	C33	119
C261	C241	C321	121	C3	C11	C13	118	C24	C32	C34	122
O20	C251	C151	124	C2	C12	C4	120	C3	C33	C31	122
O20	C251	C231	119	C2	C12	C14	118	C4	C34	C32	121

30.9   Isodibenzanthrone $C_{34}H_{16}O_2$

W.Bolton, Acta Cryst., 17, 1020, 1964

$P2_1/c$ Z = 2   R = 0.12

IDBANT   LB 34-16-1

Bond Lengths

C16	O1	1.25	C25	O2	1.24
C1	C4	1.36	C18	C21	1.38
C1	C6	1.40	C18	C24	1.41
C2	C3	1.43	C18	C25	1.46
C2	C6	1.34	C19	C20	1.38
C2	C7B	1.44	C19	C23	1.46
C3	C7	1.45	C19	C24	1.43
C3	C8	1.41	C20	C22	1.42
C4	C8	1.42	C20	C23B	1.44
C4	C9	1.47	C21	C22	1.41
C5	C9	1.38	C23	C28	1.41
C5	C10	1.39	C23	C20B	1.44
C7	C11	1.41	C24	C27	1.44
C7	C2B	1.44	C25	C26	1.42
C8	C12	1.44	C26	C29	1.40
C9	C13	1.38	C26	C30	1.42
C10	C14	1.40	C27	C30	1.42
C11	C15	1.37	C27	C31	1.37
C12	C15	1.35	C28	C31	1.39
C12	C16	1.48	C29	C32	1.38
C13	C16	1.46	C30	C33	1.42
C13	C17	1.36	C32	C34	1.41
C14	C17	1.37	C33	C34	1.39

Bond Angles

C4	C1	C6	122	C8	C12	C16	116	C19	C23	C20B	118
C3	C2	C6	118	C15	C12	C16	122	C28	C23	C20B	123
C3	C2	C7B	120	C9	C13	C16	120	C18	C24	C19	116
C6	C2	C7B	122	C9	C13	C17	122	C18	C24	C27	121
C2	C3	C7	120	C16	C13	C17	118	C19	C24	C27	123
C2	C3	C8	119	C10	C14	C17	122	O2	C25	C18	118
C7	C3	C8	121	C11	C15	C12	122	O2	C25	C26	121
C1	C4	C8	117	O1	C16	C12	115	C18	C25	C26	120
C1	C4	C9	123	O1	C16	C13	123	C25	C26	C29	120
C8	C4	C9	120	C12	C16	C13	121	C25	C26	C30	120
C9	C5	C10	121	C13	C17	C14	119	C29	C26	C30	119
C1	C6	C2	123					C24	C27	C30	120
C3	C7	C11	118	C21	C18	C24	121	C24	C27	C31	117
C3	C7	C2B	120	C21	C18	C25	120	C30	C27	C31	123
C11	C7	C2B	122	C24	C18	C25	119	C23	C28	C31	122
C3	C8	C4	122	C20	C19	C23	120	C26	C29	C32	122
C3	C8	C12	116	C20	C19	C24	124	C26	C30	C27	120
C4	C8	C12	122	C23	C19	C24	117	C26	C30	C33	118
C4	C9	C5	121	C19	C20	C22	119	C27	C30	C33	123
C4	C9	C13	120	C19	C20	C23B	122	C27	C31	C28	122
C5	C9	C13	118	C22	C20	C23B	119	C29	C32	C34	120
C5	C10	C14	117	C18	C21	C22	122	C30	C33	C34	123
C7	C11	C15	120	C20	C22	C21	118	C32	C34	C33	118
C8	C12	C15	122	C19	C23	C28	118				

30.10 Quaterrylene

$C_{40}H_{20}$

H.N.Shrivastava, J.C.Speakman, Proc. R. Soc., A, 257, 477, 1960

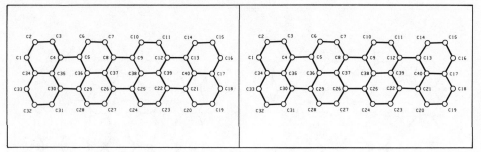

Isotypic with perylene.
$P2_1/a$ $Z = 4$ $R_{h0l} = 0.11$,
$R_{hk0} = 0.23$

QUATER   LB 40-20-1

Bond Lengths

C1	C2	1.38	C12	C39	1.38	C25	C26	1.54
C1	C34	1.39	C13	C14	1.39	C25	C38	1.40
C2	C3	1.42	C13	C40	1.41	C26	C27	1.37
C3	C4	1.42	C14	C15	1.42	C27	C28	1.44
C4	C5	1.56	C15	C16	1.37	C28	C29	1.34
C4	C35	1.42	C16	C17	1.40	C29	C30	1.51
C5	C6	1.36	C17	C18	1.36	C29	C36	1.42
C5	C36	1.42	C17	C40	1.45	C30	C31	1.41
C6	C7	1.38	C18	C19	1.36	C30	C35	1.36
C7	C8	1.39	C19	C20	1.45	C31	C32	1.42
C8	C9	1.52	C20	C21	1.40	C32	C33	1.38
C8	C37	1.40	C21	C22	1.53	C33	C34	1.41
C9	C10	1.40	C21	C40	1.40	C34	C35	1.42
C9	C38	1.42	C22	C23	1.40	C36	C37	1.44
C10	C11	1.42	C22	C39	1.39	C38	C39	1.42
C11	C12	1.36	C23	C24	1.46			
C12	C13	1.52	C24	C25	1.36			

Bond Angles

C2	C1	C34	122	C11	C12	C39	119	C22	C23	C24	121	C1	C34	C35	119
C1	C2	C3	121	C13	C12	C39	120	C23	C24	C25	118	C33	C34	C35	118
C2	C3	C4	117	C12	C13	C14	122	C24	C25	C26	119	C4	C35	C30	122
C3	C4	C5	117	C12	C13	C40	120	C24	C25	C38	120	C4	C35	C34	118
C3	C4	C35	123	C14	C13	C40	118	C26	C25	C38	121	C30	C35	C34	120
C5	C4	C35	120	C13	C14	C15	124	C25	C26	C27	121	C5	C36	C29	124
C4	C5	C6	122	C14	C15	C16	117	C25	C26	C37	120	C5	C36	C37	115
C4	C5	C36	115	C15	C16	C17	122	C27	C26	C37	120	C29	C36	C37	120
C6	C5	C36	123	C16	C17	C18	121	C26	C27	C28	121	C8	C37	C26	120
C5	C6	C7	119	C16	C17	C40	119	C27	C28	C29	121	C8	C37	C36	121
C6	C7	C8	122	C18	C17	C40	120	C28	C29	C30	122	C26	C37	C36	118
C7	C8	C9	122	C17	C18	C19	120	C28	C29	C36	120	C9	C38	C25	119
C7	C8	C37	119	C18	C19	C20	121	C30	C29	C36	118	C9	C38	C39	119
C9	C8	C37	119	C19	C20	C21	119	C29	C30	C31	118	C25	C38	C39	123
C8	C9	C10	121	C20	C21	C22	122	C29	C30	C35	121	C12	C39	C22	119
C8	C9	C38	121	C20	C21	C40	119	C31	C30	C35	121	C12	C39	C38	122
C10	C9	C38	118	C22	C21	C40	119	C30	C31	C32	121	C22	C39	C38	118
C9	C10	C11	121	C21	C22	C23	119	C31	C32	C33	116	C13	C40	C17	120
C10	C11	C12	121	C21	C22	C39	121	C32	C33	C34	124	C13	C40	C21	120
C11	C12	C13	121	C23	C22	C39	120	C1	C34	C33	123	C17	C40	C21	120

30.11 1,12 - 2,3 - 4,5 - 6,7 - 8,9 - 10,11 - Hexabenzcoronene

$C_{42}H_{18}$

J.M.Robertson, J.Trotter, J. Chem. Soc., 1280, 1961

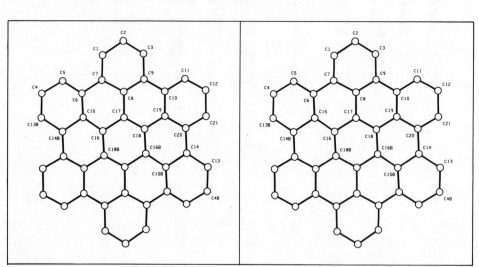

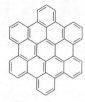

$P2_1/a$ $Z = 2$ $R = 0.12$

HBZCOR   LB 42-18-1

Bond Lengths

C1	C2	1.44	C10	C19	1.40			
C1	C7	1.40	C11	C12	1.39			
C2	C3	1.39	C12	C21	1.46			
C3	C9	1.42	C13	C14	1.47			
C4	C5	1.41	C14	C20	1.41			
C4	C13B	1.37	C14	C15B	1.47			
C5	C6	1.35	C15	C16	1.40			
C6	C7	1.40	C16	C17	1.44			
C6	C15	1.37	C16	C18B	1.37			
C7	C8	1.43	C17	C18	1.37			
C8	C9	1.37	C18	C19	1.39			
C8	C17	1.46	C19	C20	1.40			
C9	C10	1.42	C20	C21	1.38			
C10	C11	1.38						

Bond Angles

C2	C1	C7	125	C3	C9	C10	120	C15	C16	C18B	126
C1	C2	C3	115	C8	C9	C10	120	C17	C16	C18B	119
C2	C3	C9	122	C9	C10	C11	120	C8	C17	C16	122
C5	C4	C13B	121	C9	C10	C19	119	C8	C17	C18	119
C4	C5	C6	118	C11	C10	C19	121	C16	C17	C18	120
C5	C6	C7	117	C10	C11	C12	121	C17	C18	C19	121
C5	C6	C15	125	C11	C12	C21	119	C17	C18	C16B	121
C7	C6	C15	119	C14	C13	C4B	121	C19	C18	C16B	118
C1	C7	C6	123	C13	C14	C20	125	C10	C19	C18	121
C1	C7	C8	115	C13	C14	C15B	115	C10	C19	C20	118
C6	C7	C8	121	C20	C14	C15B	120	C18	C19	C20	121
C7	C8	C9	122	C6	C15	C16	126	C14	C20	C19	121
C7	C8	C17	117	C6	C15	C14B	119	C14	C20	C21	117
C9	C8	C17	121	C16	C15	C14B	115	C19	C20	C21	122
C3	C9	C8	120	C15	C16	C17	115	C12	C21	C20	119

31.1 Dodecafluoro - tricyclo(3,3,0,0^{2,6})octane

C_8F_{12}

I.L.Karle, J.Karle, T.B.Owen, J.L.Hoard, Acta Cryst., 18, 345, 1965

The structure is totally disordered.
P-1   Z = 1   R = 0.177

FTCYOC   LB 8-0-6

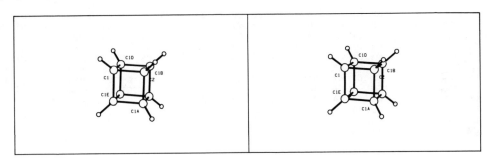

$$CF_2\text{---}CF\text{---}CF\text{---}CF_2$$
$$CF_2\text{---}CF\text{---}CF\text{---}CF_2$$

31.2 Cubane

C_8H_8

E.B.Fleischer, J. Amer. Chem. Soc., 86, 3889, 1964

R-3   Z = 1   R = 0.07

CUBANE   LB 8-8-1

Bond Lengths			Bond Angles			
C1	C2	1.55	C2	C1	C1D	90
C1	C1D	1.55	C1	C2	C1A	89

Torsion Angles

C1D	C1	C2	C1A	−90	C2	C1	C1D	C1B	0
C1D	C1	C2	C1B	0	C2	C1	C1D	C2C	91
C1E	C1	C2	C1A	0	C1E	C1	C1D	C1B	−90
C1E	C1	C2	C1B	90	C1E	C1	C1D	C2C	0

31.3 3 - Bromo - 6,6 - dimethyl - norpinan - 2 - one

$C_9H_{13}BrO$

Y.Barrans, C. R. Acad. Sci., Fr., 259, 796, 1964

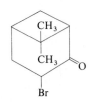

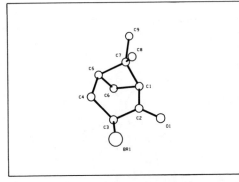

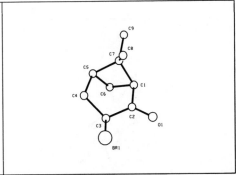

$P2_12_12_1$ Z = 4   R = 0.10

BMNOPO   LB 9-13-1

Bond Lengths			Bond Angles								
Br1	C3	1.98	C2	C1	C6	107	C4	C5	C6	110
C2	O1	1.24	C2	C1	C7	102	C4	C5	C7	107
C1	C2	1.50	C6	C1	C7	86	C6	C5	C7	86
C1	C6	1.61	O1	C2	C1	118	C1	C6	C5	88
C1	C7	1.61	O1	C2	C3	123	C1	C7	C5	89
C2	C3	1.47	C1	C2	C3	118	C1	C7	C8	118
C3	C4	1.60	Br1	C3	C2	110	C1	C7	C9	110
C4	C5	1.56	Br1	C3	C4	109	C5	C7	C8	118
C5	C6	1.62	C2	C3	C4	112	C5	C7	C9	109
C5	C7	1.60	C3	C4	C5	109	C8	C7	C9	111
C7	C8	1.55								
C7	C9	1.57								

Torsion Angles

C6	C1	C2	O1	151	C6	C1	C7	C8	146	C4	C5	C6	C1	−82
C6	C1	C2	C3	−23	C6	C1	C7	C9	−85	C7	C5	C6	C1	24
C7	C1	C2	O1	−120	O1	C2	C3	Br1	30	C4	C5	C7	C1	85
C7	C1	C2	C3	66	O1	C2	C3	C4	151	C4	C5	C7	C8	−37
C2	C1	C6	C5	77	C1	C2	C3	Br1	−157	C4	C5	C7	C9	−164
C7	C1	C6	C5	−24	C1	C2	C3	C4	−36	C6	C5	C7	C1	−24
C2	C1	C7	C5	−82	Br1	C3	C4	C5	152	C6	C5	C7	C8	−146
C2	C1	C7	C8	40	C2	C3	C4	C5	30	C6	C5	C7	C9	86
C2	C1	C7	C9	168	C3	C4	C5	C6	31					
C6	C1	C7	C5	25	C3	C4	C5	C7	−61					

31.4   3 - Chloro - 6,6 - dimethyl - norpinan - 2 - one $C_9H_{13}ClO$

Y.Barrans, C. R. Acad. Sci., Fr., 259, 796, 1964

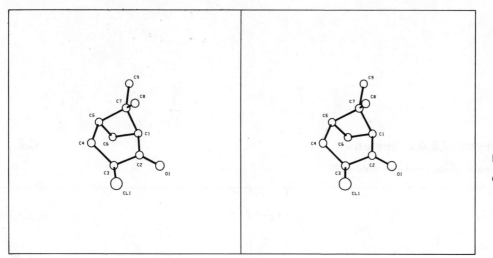

$P2_12_12_1$ Z = 4   R = 0.095

CMNOPO   LB 9-13-2

Bond Lengths

Cl1	C3	1.82
C2	O1	1.20
C1	C2	1.51
C1	C6	1.58
C1	C7	1.60
C2	C3	1.47
C3	C4	1.59
C4	C5	1.56
C5	C6	1.63
C5	C7	1.62
C7	C8	1.55
C7	C9	1.53

Bond Angles

C2	C1	C6	106		C4	C5	C6	110
C2	C1	C7	104		C4	C5	C7	110
C6	C1	C7	89		C6	C5	C7	87
O1	C2	C1	121		C1	C6	C5	87
O1	C2	C3	122		C1	C7	C5	86
C1	C2	C3	116		C1	C7	C8	116
Cl1	C3	C2	111		C1	C7	C9	111
Cl1	C3	C4	108		C5	C7	C8	118
C2	C3	C4	115		C5	C7	C9	110
C3	C4	C5	106		C8	C7	C9	113

Torsion Angles

C6	C1	C2	O1	146		C6	C1	C7	C8	144		C4	C5	C6	C1	−85
C6	C1	C2	C3	−26		C6	C1	C7	C9	−86		C7	C5	C6	C1	25
C7	C1	C2	O1	−121		O1	C2	C3	Cl1	29		C4	C5	C7	C1	86
C7	C1	C2	C3	67		O1	C2	C3	C4	152		C4	C5	C7	C8	−32
C2	C1	C6	C5	79		C1	C2	C3	Cl1	−158		C4	C5	C7	C9	−164
C7	C1	C6	C5	−25		C1	C2	C3	C4	−36		C6	C5	C7	C1	−24
C2	C1	C7	C5	−82		Cl1	C3	C4	C5	154		C6	C5	C7	C8	−141
C2	C1	C7	C8	38		C2	C3	C4	C5	31		C6	C5	C7	C9	86
C2	C1	C7	C9	168		C3	C4	C5	C6	32						
C6	C1	C7	C5	25		C3	C4	C5	C7	−62						

31.5   Adamantane $C_{10}H_{16}$

For complete entry see 31.6

31.6   Adamantane $C_{10}H_{16}$

(i)   C.E.Nordman, D.J.Schmitkons, Acta Cryst., 18, 764, 1965 (at −110°C)

(ii)   C.E.Nordman, D.J.Schmitkons, Acta Cryst., 18, 764, 1965

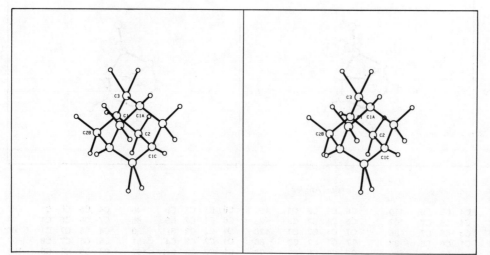

(i)

$P-42_1c$ Z = 2   R = 0.080

ADAMAN01   LB 10-16-1

(ii)

The structure is totally disordered. See also Donohue & Goodman, Acta Cryst., 22, 352, 1967.

Fm3m   Z = 2   R = 0.131

ADAMAN   LB 10-16-1

Bond Lengths

C1	C2	1.56
C1	C3	1.47
C1	C2B	1.53

Bond Angles

C2	C1	C3	109		C1	C2	C1C	110
C2	C1	C2B	108		C1	C3	C1A	117
C3	C1	C2B	107					

Torsion Angles

C3	C1	C2	C1C	54		C2B	C1	C3	C1A	60
C2B	C1	C2	C1C	−61		C2	C1	C2B	C1B	58
C2	C1	C3	C1A	−57		C3	C1	C2B	C1B	−60

31.7 1,6 - Methano - cyclodecapentaene - 2 - carboxylic acid $C_{12}H_{10}O_2$

M.Dobler, J.D.Dunitz, Helv. Chim. Acta, 48, 1429, 1965

P112₁/b Z = 4 R = 0.068

MCCARA LB 12-10-67

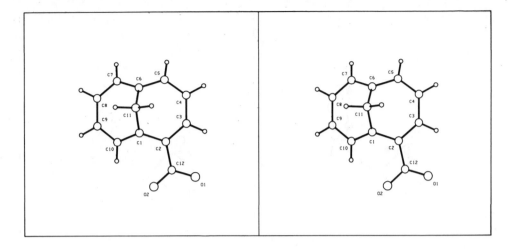

Bond Lengths

C12	O1	1.27	C4	C5	1.39
C12	O2	1.26	C5	C6	1.41
C1	C2	1.43	C6	C7	1.40
C1	C10	1.40	C6	C11	1.48
C1	C11	1.48	C7	C8	1.38
C2	C3	1.38	C8	C9	1.42
C2	C12	1.49	C9	C10	1.38
C3	C4	1.41			

Bond Angles

C2	C1	C10	129	C5	C6	C11	117
C2	C1	C11	114	C7	C6	C11	117
C10	C1	C11	116	C6	C7	C8	122
C1	C2	C3	122	C7	C8	C9	127
C3	C2	C12	118	C8	C9	C10	128
C2	C3	C4	130	C1	C10	C9	122
C3	C4	C5	126	C1	C11	C6	100
C4	C5	C6	123	O1	C12	O2	122
C5	C6	C7	126	O1	C12	C2	118
				O2	C12	C2	120

Torsion Angles

C10	C1	C2	C3	142	C3	C2	C12	O2	−175
C10	C1	C2	C12	−32	C2	C3	C4	C5	1
C11	C1	C2	C3	−30	C3	C4	C5	C6	20
C11	C1	C2	C12	155	C4	C5	C6	C7	−148
C2	C1	C10	C9	−148	C4	C5	C6	C11	24
C11	C1	C10	C9	24	C5	C6	C7	C8	146
C2	C1	C11	C6	89	C11	C6	C7	C8	−27
C10	C1	C11	C6	−85	C5	C6	C11	C1	−86
C1	C2	C3	C4	−18	C7	C6	C11	C1	87
C12	C2	C3	C4	157	C6	C7	C8	C9	−20
C1	C2	C12	O1	−178	C7	C8	C9	C10	1
C1	C2	C12	O2	0	C8	C9	C10	C1	21
C3	C2	C12	O1	7					

31.8 anti - 7 - Norbornenyl p - bromobenzoate $C_{14}H_{13}BrO_2$

A.C.Macdonald, J.Trotter, Acta Cryst., 19, 456, 1965

P2₁/a Z = 4 R = 0.18

NOBEBB LB 14-13-3

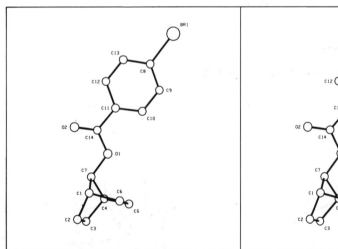

Bond Lengths

Br1	C8	1.90	C4	C7	1.53
C7	O1	1.44	C5	C6	1.56
C14	O1	1.34	C8	C9	1.39
C14	O2	1.20	C8	C13	1.38
C1	C2	1.52	C9	C10	1.37
C1	C6	1.58	C10	C11	1.39
C1	C7	1.50	C11	C12	1.40
C2	C3	1.34	C11	C14	1.44
C3	C4	1.51	C12	C13	1.39
C4	C5	1.56			

Bond Angles

C7	O1	C14	117	Br1	C8	C9	120
C2	C1	C6	104	Br1	C8	C13	120
C2	C1	C7	100	C9	C8	C13	120
C6	C1	C7	102	C8	C9	C10	119
C1	C2	C3	108	C9	C10	C11	123
C2	C3	C4	107	C10	C11	C12	118
C3	C4	C5	107	C10	C11	C14	124
C3	C4	C7	99	C12	C11	C14	118
C5	C4	C7	100	C11	C12	C13	120
C4	C5	C6	104	C8	C13	C12	121
C1	C6	C5	101	O1	C14	O2	124
O1	C7	C1	114	O1	C14	C11	114
O1	C7	C4	109	O2	C14	C11	123
C1	C7	C4	96				

Torsion Angles

C14	O1	C7	C1	−91	C1	C2	C3	C4	4
C14	O1	C7	C4	164	C2	C3	C4	C5	67
C6	C1	C2	C3	−75	C2	C3	C4	C7	−36
C7	C1	C2	C3	30	C3	C4	C5	C6	−66
C2	C1	C6	C5	69	C7	C4	C5	C6	36
C7	C1	C6	C5	−34	C3	C4	C7	O1	170
C2	C1	C7	O1	−164	C3	C4	C7	C1	52
C2	C1	C7	C4	−50	C5	C4	C7	O1	61
C6	C1	C7	O1	−57	C5	C4	C7	C1	−57
C6	C1	C7	C4	57	C4	C5	C6	C1	−2

31.9 anti - 8 - Tricyclo(3,2,1,0^{2,4})octyl p - bromobenzenesulfonate

C$_{14}$H$_{15}$BrO$_3$S

A.C.Macdonald, J.Trotter, Acta Cryst., 18, 243, 1965

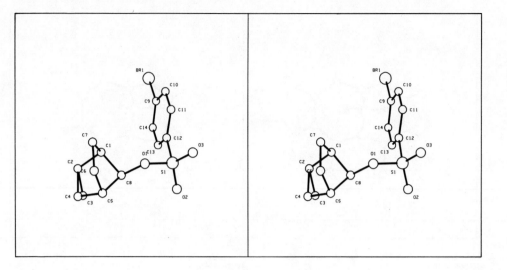

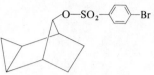

C2/c   Z = 8   R = 0.093

TCYOCB   LB 14-15-2

Bond Lengths

Br1	C9	1.90	C3	C4	1.50
S1	O1	1.56	C4	C5	1.55
S1	O2	1.44	C5	C6	1.52
S1	O3	1.44	C5	C8	1.51
S1	C12	1.77	C6	C7	1.55
C8	O1	1.48	C9	C10	1.39
C1	C2	1.52	C9	C14	1.42
C1	C7	1.60	C10	C11	1.37
C1	C8	1.51	C11	C12	1.43
C2	C3	1.51	C12	C13	1.37
C2	C4	1.54	C13	C14	1.34

Bond Angles

O1	S1	O2	110	C4	C5	C8	101
O1	S1	O3	104	C6	C5	C8	101
O1	S1	C12	102	C5	C6	C7	103
O2	S1	O3	120	C1	C7	C6	103
O2	S1	C12	109	O1	C8	C1	111
O3	S1	C12	110	O1	C8	C5	110
S1	O1	C8	119	C1	C8	C5	97
C2	C1	C7	105	Br1	C9	C10	119
C2	C1	C8	103	Br1	C9	C14	118
C7	C1	C8	99	C10	C9	C14	122
C1	C2	C3	119	C9	C10	C11	119
C1	C2	C4	104	C10	C11	C12	118
C3	C2	C4	59	S1	C12	C11	118
C2	C3	C4	62	S1	C12	C13	121
C2	C4	C3	59	C11	C12	C13	121
C2	C4	C5	103	C12	C13	C14	121
C3	C4	C5	120	C9	C14	C13	118
C4	C5	C6	107				

Torsion Angles

S1	O1	C8	C1	−113	C1	C2	C4	C5	1
S1	O1	C8	C5	141	C3	C2	C4	C5	117
C7	C1	C2	C3	−133	C2	C3	C4	C5	−88
C7	C1	C2	C4	−71	C2	C4	C5	C6	72
C8	C1	C2	C3	−29	C2	C4	C5	C8	−34
C8	C1	C2	C4	33	C3	C4	C5	C6	135
C2	C1	C7	C6	72	C3	C4	C5	C8	29
C8	C1	C7	C6	−33	C4	C5	C6	C7	−70
C2	C1	C8	O1	−168	C8	C5	C6	C7	36
C2	C1	C8	C5	−53	C4	C5	C8	O1	168
C7	C1	C8	O1	−60	C4	C5	C8	C1	53
C7	C1	C8	C5	55	C6	C5	C8	O1	58
C1	C2	C3	C4	89	C6	C5	C8	C1	−58
C1	C2	C4	C3	−116	C5	C6	C7	C1	−1

31.10 Congressane

C$_{14}$H$_{20}$

I.L.Karle, J.Karle, J. Amer. Chem. Soc., 87, 918, 1965

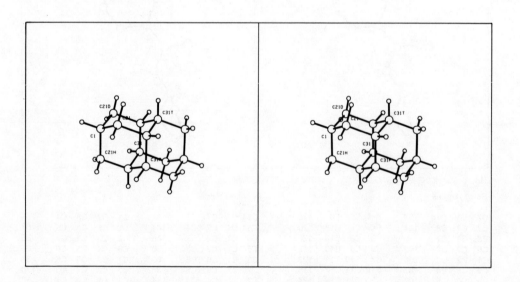

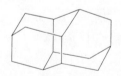

Pa3   Z = 4   R = 0.11

CONGRS   LB 14-20-1

Bond Lengths

C1	C21	1.54
C21	C31	1.53
C31	C31P	1.53

Bond Angles

C21	C1	C21D	109
C1	C21	C31	110
C21	C31	C31P	110
C21	C31	C31T	110

Torsion Angles

C21D	C1	C21	C31	−59	C21	C31	C31P	C21P	−180
C21H	C1	C21	C31	59	C21	C31	C31P	C31H	59
C1	C21	C31	C31P	−60	C31T	C31	C31P	C21P	59
C1	C21	C31	C31T	60	C31T	C31	C31P	C31H	−62

31.11   (2.2)Paracyclophane diolefin $C_{16}H_{12}$

C.L.Coulter, K.N.Trueblood, Acta Cryst., 16, 667, 1963

$P2_1/c$ Z = 2   R = 0.12

PCYDOL   LB 16-12-2

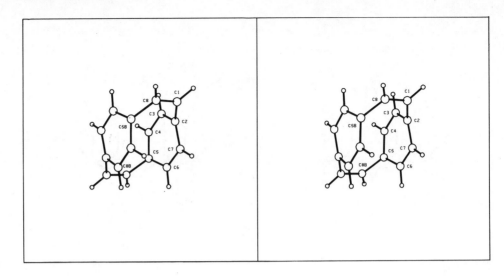

Bond Lengths				
C1	C2	1.51	C4 C5	1.40
C1	C8	1.34	C5 C6	1.39
C2	C3	1.41	C5 C8B	1.52
C2	C7	1.39	C6 C7	1.40
C3	C4	1.39		

Bond Angles							
C2	C1	C8	119	C4	C5	C6	118
C1	C2	C3	120	C4	C5	C8B	120
C1	C2	C7	120	C6	C5	C8B	120
C3	C2	C7	117	C5	C6	C7	120
C2	C3	C4	120	C2	C7	C6	121
C3	C4	C5	120	C1	C8	C5B	119

Torsion Angles									
C8	C1	C2	C3	82	C3	C4	C5	C6	−16
C8	C1	C2	C7	−80	C3	C4	C5	C8B	146
C2	C1	C8	C5B	−1	C4	C5	C6	C7	17
C1	C2	C3	C4	−147	C8B	C5	C6	C7	−146
C7	C2	C3	C4	15	C4	C5	C8B	C1B	−82
C1	C2	C7	C6	147	C6	C5	C8B	C1B	80
C3	C2	C7	C6	−15	C5	C6	C7	C2	−1
C2	C3	C4	C5	0					

31.12   Di - p - xylylene $C_{16}H_{16}$

(i)   K.Lonsdale, H.J.Milledge, K.V.Krishna Rao, Proc. R. Soc., A, 255, 82, 1960 (at 291°K)

(ii)   K.Lonsdale, H.J.Milledge, K.V.Krishna Rao, Proc. R. Soc., A, 255, 82, 1960 (at 93°K)

(i)

No comparison of bond lengths is possible since they are not reported in the paper.
See also Hope et al., Amer. Cryst. Assoc., Abstr. Papers (Winter Meeting), 42, 1970.
$P4_2/mnm$ Z = 2   R = 0.105

DXYLEN   LB 16-16-4

(ii)

No comparison of bond lengths is possible since they are not reported in the paper.
$P4_2/mnm$ Z = 2   R = 0.105

DXYLEN01   LB 16-16-4

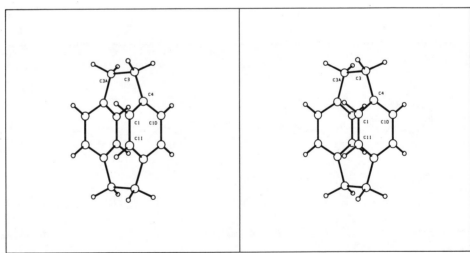

Bond Lengths		(i)	(ii)
C1	C4	1.38	1.39
C1	C1I	1.42	1.41
C3	C4	1.55	1.53
C3	C3A	1.63	1.56

Bond Angles			(i)	(ii)
C4	C1	C1I	119	120
C4	C3	C3A	111	113
C1	C4	C3	120	120
C1	C4	C1D	120	118

Torsion Angles				(i)	(ii)
C1I	C1	C4	C3	156	154
C1I	C1	C4	C1D	−16	−16
C4	C1	C1I	C4I	0	0
C3A	C3	C4	C1	−86	−85
C3A	C3	C4	C1D	86	85
C4	C3	C3A	C4A	0	0

31.13   Di - p - xylylene (at 93 ° K) $C_{16}H_{16}$

For complete entry see 31.12

31.14   trans - 1,4 - 5,8 - Dimethylene - cis,anti,cis - perhydroanthraquinone $C_{16}H_{20}O_2$

H.G.Norment, Acta Cryst., 18, 627, 1965

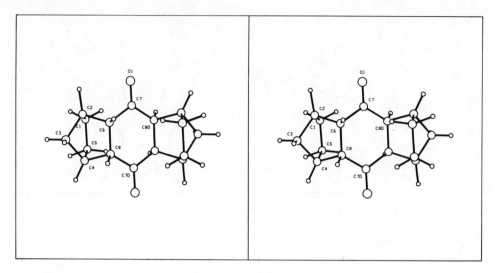

Pcab   Z = 4   R = 0.10

DMHANQ   LB 16-20-16

Bond Lengths

C7	O1	1.21
C1	C2	1.56
C1	C5	1.56
C2	C3	1.55
C2	C6	1.57
C3	C4	1.54
C4	C5	1.58
C4	C8	1.56
C6	C7	1.54
C6	C8	1.54
C7	C8D	1.51

Bond Angles

C2	C1	C5	104
C1	C2	C3	101
C1	C2	C6	107
C3	C2	C6	99
C2	C3	C4	96
C3	C4	C5	102
C3	C4	C8	100
C5	C4	C8	108
C1	C5	C4	103
C2	C6	C7	111
C2	C6	C8	105
C7	C6	C8	119
O1	C7	C6	120
O1	C7	C8D	120
C6	C7	C8D	120
C4	C8	C6	103
C4	C8	C7D	113
C6	C8	C7D	121

Torsion Angles

C5	C1	C2	C3	−35
C5	C1	C2	C6	68
C2	C1	C5	C4	2
C1	C2	C3	C4	55
C6	C2	C3	C4	−55
C1	C2	C6	C7	58
C1	C2	C6	C8	−72
C3	C2	C6	C7	162
C3	C2	C6	C8	32
C2	C3	C4	C5	−54
C2	C3	C4	C8	57
C3	C4	C5	C1	33
C8	C4	C5	C1	−72
C3	C4	C8	C6	−37
C3	C4	C8	C7D	−169
C5	C4	C8	C6	69
C5	C4	C8	C7D	−63
C2	C6	C7	O1	54
C2	C6	C7	C8D	−127
C8	C6	C7	O1	176
C8	C6	C7	C8D	−4
C2	C6	C8	C4	3
C2	C6	C8	C7D	129
C7	C6	C8	C4	−122
C7	C6	C8	C7D	4
O1	C7	C8D	C4D	62
O1	C7	C8D	C6D	−176
C6	C7	C8D	C4D	−118
C6	C7	C8D	C6D	4

31.15   1 - p - Bromobenzenesulfonyloxymethyl - 5 - methyl - bicyclo(3.3.1)nonan - 9 - ol $C_{17}H_{23}BrO_4S$

W.A.C.Brown, J.Martin, G.A.Sim, J. Chem. Soc., 1844, 1965

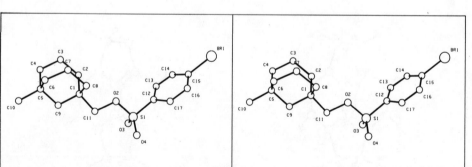

The hydroxyl oxygen atom is disordered.
P-1   Z = 2   R = 0.129

BICNOL   LB 17-23-2

Bond Lengths

Br1	C15	1.87	
S1	O2	1.57	
S1	O3	1.42	
S1	O4	1.45	
S1	C12	1.72	
C11	O2	1.48	
C1	C2	1.57	
C1	C8	1.55	
C1	C9	1.51	
C1	C11	1.52	
C2	C3	1.52	
C3	C4	1.48	
C4	C5	1.58
C5	C6	1.54
C5	C9	1.53
C5	C10	1.54
C6	C7	1.51
C7	C8	1.57
C12	C13	1.38
C12	C17	1.43
C13	C14	1.30
C14	C15	1.42
C15	C16	1.40
C16	C17	1.34

Bond Angles

O2	S1	O3	110
O2	S1	O4	110
O2	S1	C12	100
O3	S1	O4	114
O3	S1	C12	111
O4	S1	C12	111
S1	O2	C11	114
C2	C1	C8	113
C2	C1	C9	109
C2	C1	C11	110
C8	C1	C9	110
C8	C1	C11	109
C9	C1	C11	106
C1	C2	C3	113
C2	C3	C4	116
C3	C4	C5	115
C4	C5	C6	112
C4	C5	C9	109
C4	C5	C10	109
C6	C5	C9	109
C6	C5	C10	109
C9	C5	C10	110
C5	C6	C7	115
C6	C7	C8	114
C1	C8	C7	112
C1	C9	C5	111
O2	C11	C1	107
S1	C12	C13	121
S1	C12	C17	118
C13	C12	C17	120
C12	C13	C14	120
C13	C14	C15	121
Br1	C15	C14	120
Br1	C15	C16	120
C14	C15	C16	121
C15	C16	C17	119
C12	C17	C16	119

Torsion Angles

C8	C1	C2	C3	−70
C9	C1	C2	C3	52
C11	C1	C2	C3	168
C2	C1	C8	C7	70
C9	C1	C8	C7	−52
C11	C1	C8	C7	−168
C2	C1	C9	C5	−62
C8	C1	C9	C5	63
C11	C1	C9	C5	−180
C2	C1	C11	O2	67
C8	C1	C11	O2	−58
C9	C1	C11	O2	−176
C1	C2	C3	C4	−44
C2	C3	C4	C5	44
C3	C4	C5	C6	70
C3	C4	C5	C9	−50
C3	C4	C5	C10	−170
C4	C5	C6	C7	−68
C9	C5	C6	C7	52
C10	C5	C6	C7	172
C4	C5	C9	C1	60
C6	C5	C9	C1	−62
C10	C5	C9	C1	179
C5	C6	C7	C8	−45
C6	C7	C8	C1	44

31.16   4,12 - Dimethyl(2,2)metacyclophane

$C_{18}H_{20}$

A.W.Hanson, Acta Cryst., 15, 956, 1962

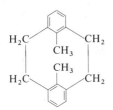

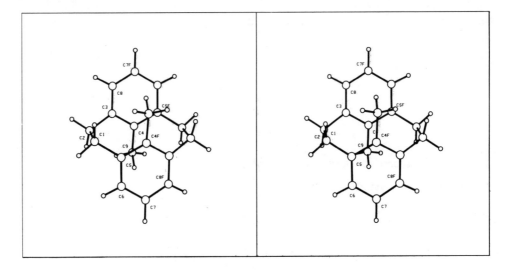

C2/c   Z = 4   R = 0.06

DMMCPH   LB 18-20-1

Bond Lengths

C1	C2	1.57
C1	C5	1.52
C2	C3	1.52
C3	C4	1.41
C3	C8	1.39
C4	C9	1.50
C4	C5F	1.41
C5	C6	1.40
C6	C7	1.39
C7	C8F	1.39

Bond Angles

C2	C1	C5	111	C9	C4	C5F	121
C1	C2	C3	112	C1	C5	C6	120
C2	C3	C4	120	C1	C5	C4F	120
C2	C3	C8	120	C6	C5	C4F	119
C4	C3	C8	119	C5	C6	C7	121
C3	C4	C9	121	C6	C7	C8F	119
C3	C4	C5F	119	C3	C8	C7F	121

Torsion Angles

C5	C1	C2	C3	−56	C4	C3	C8	C7F	−4
C2	C1	C5	C6	−89	C3	C4	C5F	C1F	153
C2	C1	C5	C4F	81	C3	C4	C5F	C6F	−17
C1	C2	C3	C4	79	C9	C4	C5F	C1F	−27
C1	C2	C3	C8	−89	C9	C4	C5F	C6F	162
C2	C3	C4	C9	29	C1	C5	C6	C7	166
C2	C3	C4	C5F	−151	C4F	C5	C6	C7	−4
C8	C3	C4	C9	−163	C5	C6	C7	C8F	−8
C8	C3	C4	C5F	17	C6	C7	C8F	C3F	8
C2	C3	C8	C7F	164					

31.17   (3.3)Paracyclophane

$C_{18}H_{20}$

P.K.Gantzel, K.N.Trueblood, Acta Cryst., 18, 958, 1965

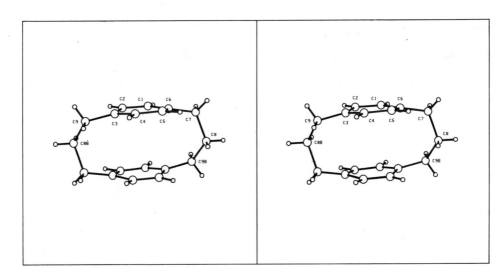

P2₁/n   Z = 2   R = 0.11

PCYCPH   LB 18-20-5

Bond Lengths

C1	C2	1.38
C1	C6	1.39
C2	C3	1.39
C3	C4	1.39
C3	C9	1.52
C4	C5	1.38
C5	C6	1.39
C6	C7	1.51
C7	C8	1.54
C8	C9B	1.52

Bond Angles

C2	C1	C6	121	C1	C6	C5	117
C1	C2	C3	122	C1	C6	C7	121
C2	C3	C4	117	C5	C6	C7	122
C2	C3	C9	122	C6	C7	C8	114
C4	C3	C9	121	C7	C8	C9B	117
C3	C4	C5	121	C3	C9	C8B	116
C4	C5	C6	121				

Torsion Angles

C6	C1	C2	C3	−1	C4	C3	C9	C8B	−128
C2	C1	C6	C5	−7	C3	C4	C5	C6	−1
C2	C1	C6	C7	168	C4	C5	C6	C1	8
C1	C2	C3	C4	8	C4	C5	C6	C7	−166
C1	C2	C3	C9	−169	C1	C6	C7	C8	−106
C2	C3	C4	C5	−7	C5	C6	C7	C8	68
C9	C3	C4	C5	170	C6	C7	C8	C9B	65
C2	C3	C9	C8B	49	C7	C8	C9B	C3B	−70

32.1   Sodium tetrazolate monohydrate

G.J.Palenik, Acta Cryst., 16, 596, 1963

CHN_4^- , Na^+ , H_2O

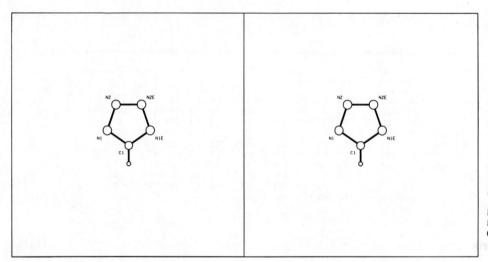

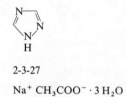

Pmcm   Z = 2   R = 0.05

NATETZ   LB 1-1-13

Bond Lengths			Bond Angles			
N1	N2	1.35	N2	N1	C1	104
N2	N2E	1.31	N1	N2	N2E	109
C1	N1	1.33	N1	C1	N1E	112

32.2   1,2,4 - Triazole

H.Deuschl, Ber. Bunsengesellsch. Phys. Chem., 69, 550, 1965

$C_2H_3N_3$

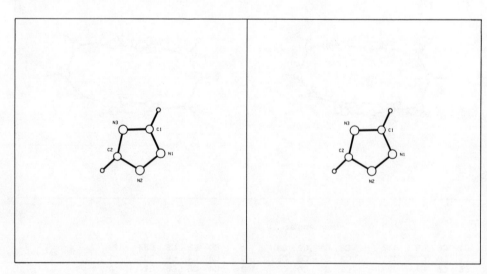

2-3-27

$Na^+ CH_3COO^- \cdot 3 H_2O$

See also Goldstein et al., Acta Cryst. (B), 25, 135, 1969.
Pbca   Z = 8   R = 0.195

TRAZOL   LB 2-3-26

Bond Lengths			Bond Angles			
N1	N2	1.35	N2	N1	C1	102
C1	N1	1.33	N1	N2	C2	112
C2	N2	1.34	C1	N3	C2	104
C1	N3	1.35	N1	C1	N3	114
C2	N3	1.35	N2	C2	N3	107

32.3 Pyrazole

$C_3H_4N_2$

H.W.W.Ehrlich, Acta Cryst., 13, 946, 1960

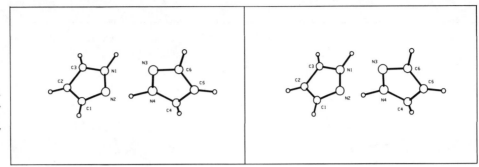

See also Berthou et al., Acta Cryst.
(B), 26, 1880, 1970; Larsen et al.,
Acta Chem. Scand., 24, 3248, 1970.
P2₁cn   Z = 8 R_{hk0} = 0.085,
R_{0kl} = 0.132, R_{h0l} = 0.113

PYRZOL   LB 3-4-7

Bond Lengths

N1	N2	1.36	N3	N4	1.36
C3	N1	1.30	C6	N3	1.35
C1	N2	1.34	C4	N4	1.33
C1	C2	1.34	C4	C5	1.41
C2	C3	1.42	C5	C6	1.33

Bond Angles

N2	N1	C3	112	N4	N3	C6	108
N1	N2	C1	103	N3	N4	C4	107
N2	C1	C2	114	N4	C4	C5	109
C1	C2	C3	103	C4	C5	C6	105
N1	C3	C2	107	N3	C6	C5	111

32.4 Pyrazoline hydrochloride

$C_3H_7N_2{}^+$, Cl^-

M.Nardelli, G.Fava, Acta Cryst., 15, 214, 1962

Pnma   Z = 4   R = 0.09

PYZOLC   LB 3-7-5

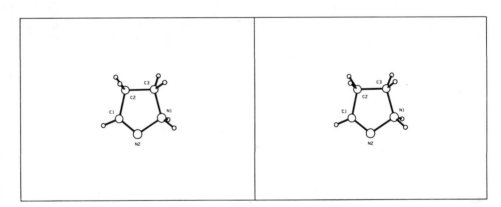

Bond Lengths

N1	N2	1.47
C3	N1	1.50
C1	N2	1.26
C1	C2	1.47
C2	C3	1.47

Bond Angles

N2	N1	C3	108
N1	N2	C1	107
N2	C1	C2	117
C1	C2	C3	103
N1	C3	C2	105

32.5 dl - Allantoin

$C_4H_6N_4O_3$

D.Mootz, Acta Cryst., 19, 726, 1965

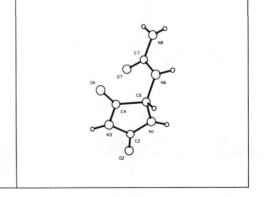

P2₁/c   Z = 4   R = 0.087

ALATIN   LB 4-6-48

Bond Lengths

C2	N1	1.34	C7	N8	1.34
C5	N1	1.46	C2	O2	1.22
C2	N3	1.40	C4	O4	1.21
C4	N3	1.36	C7	O7	1.25
C5	N6	1.43	C4	C5	1.53
C7	N6	1.37			

Bond Angles

C2	N1	C5	113	N3	C2	O2	125
C2	N3	C4	112	N3	C4	O4	126
C5	N6	C7	120	N3	C4	C5	107
N1	C2	N3	108	O4	C4	C5	127
N1	C2	O2	128	N1	C5	N6	116

N1	C5	C4	101
N6	C5	C4	114
N6	C7	N8	117
N6	C7	O7	120
N8	C7	O7	123

Torsion Angles

C7	N6	C5	N1	71
C7	N6	C5	C4	−46
C5	N6	C7	N8	178
C5	N6	C7	O7	−4

32.6 3 - Methoxycarbonyl - trans - 3,5 - dimethyl - Δ^1 - pyrazoline hydrobromide

$C_7H_{13}N_2O_2^+$, Br^-

H.Luth, J.Trotter, Acta Cryst., 19, 614, 1965

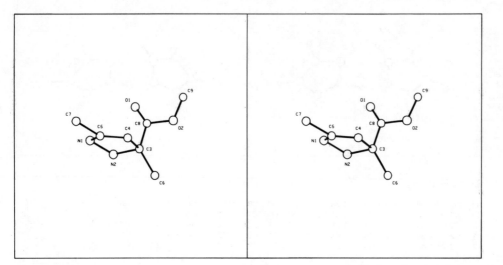

P2$_1$/c   Z = 4   R = 0.116

MEPAZB   LB 7-13-3

Bond Lengths

N1	N2	1.48	C3	C4	1.62
C5	N1	1.48	C3	C6	1.54
C3	N2	1.58	C3	C8	1.48
C8	O1	1.26	C4	C5	1.42
C8	O2	1.40	C5	C7	1.61
C9	O2	1.40			

Bond Angles

N2	N1	C5	94	C6	C3	C8	129
N1	N2	C3	117	C3	C4	C5	102
C8	O2	C9	114	N1	C5	C4	124
N2	C3	C4	99	N1	C5	C7	107
N2	C3	C6	110	C4	C5	C7	128
N2	C3	C8	101	O1	C8	O2	120
C4	C3	C6	113	O1	C8	C3	134
C4	C3	C8	101	O2	C8	C3	106

Torsion Angles

C5	N1	N2	C3	−23	C8	C3	C4	C5	95
N2	N1	C5	C4	18	N2	C3	C8	O1	17
N2	N1	C5	C7	−176	N2	C3	C8	O2	−162
N1	N2	C3	C4	21	C4	C3	C8	O1	−84
N1	N2	C3	C6	139	C4	C3	C8	O2	97
N1	N2	C3	C8	−82	C6	C3	C8	O1	144
C9	O2	C8	O1	4	C6	C3	C8	O2	−35
C9	O2	C8	C3	−177	C3	C4	C5	N1	−6
N2	C3	C4	C5	−8	C3	C4	C5	C7	−170
C6	C3	C4	C5	−124					

32.7 meso - 1,4 - Diaziridinyl - 2,3 - butanediol

$C_8H_{16}N_2O_2$

E.S.Gould, R.A.Pasternak, J. Amer. Chem. Soc., 83, 2658, 1961

P2$_1$/c   Z = 2   R = 0.13

DAZBOL   LB 8-16-37

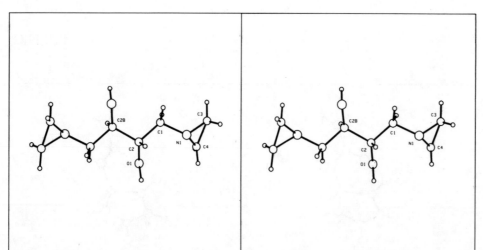

Bond Lengths

C1	N1	1.50
C3	N1	1.51
C4	N1	1.47
C2	O1	1.44
C1	C2	1.51
C2	C2B	1.56
C3	C4	1.47

Bond Angles

C1	N1	C3	112	O1	C2	C2B	109
C1	N1	C4	113	C1	C2	C2B	110
C3	N1	C4	59	N1	C3	C4	59
N1	C1	C2	110	N1	C4	C3	62
O1	C2	C1	109				

Torsion Angles

C3	N1	C1	C2	162	N1	C1	C2	C2B	172
C4	N1	C1	C2	97	O1	C2	C2B	O1B	180
C1	N1	C3	C4	−104	O1	C2	C2B	C1B	61
C1	N1	C4	C3	103	C1	C2	C2B	O1B	−61
N1	C1	C2	O1	−69	C1	C2	C2B	C1B	−180

32.8   1 - (4 - Chlorobenzyl) - 1 - nitrosyl - 2 - (4,5 - dihydro - 2 - imidazolyl) - hydrazine monohydrate

$C_{10}H_{12}ClN_5O$, H_2O

G.J.Palenik, Acta Cryst., 19, 47, 1965

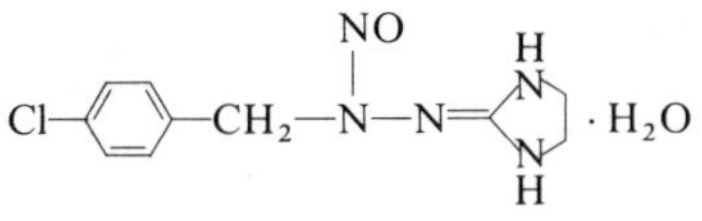

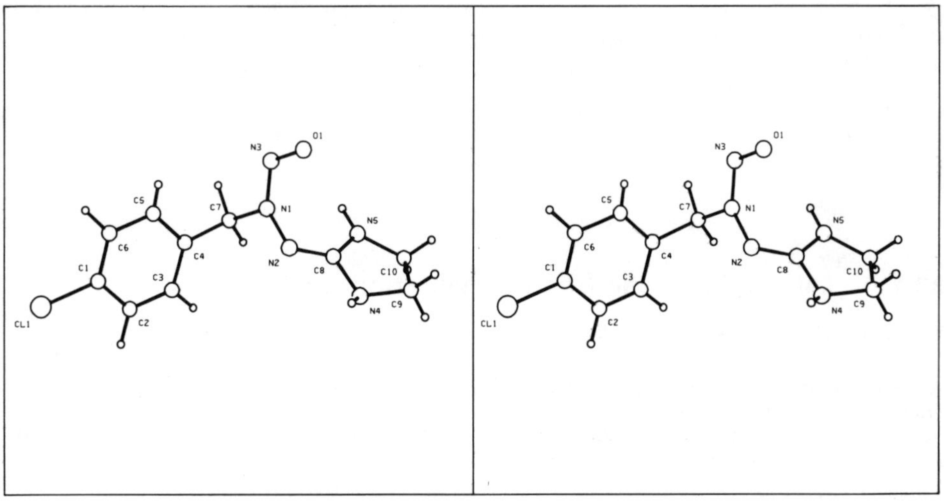

$P2_1/c$ Z = 4   R = 0.096

CNHYDM   LB 10-12-9

Bond Lengths

Cl1	C1	1.73	C10	N5	1.46
N1	N2	1.39	C1	C2	1.38
N1	N3	1.30	C1	C6	1.38
N3	O1	1.25	C2	C3	1.35
C7	N1	1.47	C3	C4	1.38
C8	N2	1.30	C4	C5	1.38
C8	N4	1.36	C4	C7	1.53
C9	N4	1.45	C5	C6	1.39
C8	N5	1.33	C9	C10	1.49

Bond Angles

N2	N1	N3	125
N2	N1	C7	118
N3	N1	C7	116
N1	N2	C8	114
N1	N3	O1	115
C8	N4	C9	109
C8	N5	C10	110
Cl1	C1	C2	120
Cl1	C1	C6	120
C2	C1	C6	120
C1	C2	C3	121
C2	C3	C4	120

C3	C4	C5	119
C3	C4	C7	120
C5	C4	C7	120
C4	C5	C6	121
C1	C6	C5	119
N1	C7	C4	112
N2	C8	N4	120
N2	C8	N5	130
N4	C8	N5	110
N4	C9	C10	102
N5	C10	C9	103

Torsion Angles

N3	N1	N2	C8	−84
C7	N1	N2	C8	108
N2	N1	N3	O1	9
C7	N1	N3	O1	177
N2	N1	C7	C4	66
N3	N1	C7	C4	−103
N1	N2	C8	N4	−178
N1	N2	C8	N5	−1
C9	N4	C8	N2	−167

C9	N4	C8	N5	16
C8	N4	C9	C10	−25
C10	N5	C8	N2	−176
C10	N5	C8	N4	1
C8	N5	C10	C9	−17
C3	C4	C7	N1	−115
C5	C4	C7	N1	70
N4	C9	C10	N5	24

33.1 Diketopiperazine (thermal vibration analysis)

$C_4H_6N_2O_2$

K.Lonsdale, Acta Cryst., 14, 37, 1961

Atomic coordinates were not reported in the paper.
Thermal vibration analysis.
See also Degeilh & Marsh, Acta Cryst., 12, 1007, 1959.
P2$_1$/a   Z = 2   No R factor was given.

DIKPIP   LB 4-6-46

33.2 Piperazine dihydrochloride monohydrate

$C_4H_{12}N_2^{2+}$, 2Cl$^-$, H_2O

C.Rerat, Acta Cryst., 13, 459, 1960

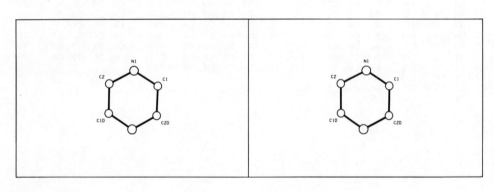

A2/a   Z = 4   R = 0.28

PIPAZC   LB 4-12-22

Bond Lengths			Bond Angles				Torsion Angles			
C1	N1	1.49	C1	N1	C2	111	C2	N1	C1	C2D	57
C2	N1	1.51	N1	C1	C2D	113	C1	N1	C2	C1D	−55
C1	C2D	1.53	N1	C2	C1D	109	N1	C1	C2D	N1D	−56

33.3 Pyrazinamide (α form)

$C_5H_5N_3O$

Y.Takaki, Y.Sasada, T.Watanabe, Acta Cryst., 13, 693, 1960

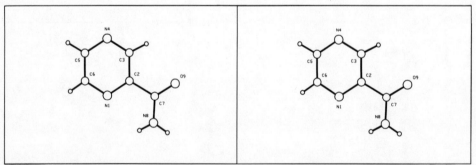

P2$_1$/a   Z = 4 R_{hk0} = 0.068,
R_{h0l} = 0.070

PYRZIN   LB 5-5-22

Bond Lengths						Bond Angles								Torsion Angles				
C2	N1	1.34	C7	O9	1.24	C2	N1	C6	115	N4	C5	C6	122	N1	C2	C7	N8	−2
C6	N1	1.35	C2	C3	1.38	C3	N4	C5	116	N1	C6	C5	122	N1	C2	C7	O9	174
C3	N4	1.33	C2	C7	1.50	N1	C2	C3	122	N8	C7	O9	123	C3	C2	C7	N8	178
C5	N4	1.35	C5	C6	1.37	N1	C2	C7	117	N8	C7	C2	118	C3	C2	C7	O9	−6
C7	N8	1.31				C3	C2	C7	121	O9	C7	C2	119					
						N4	C3	C2	123									

33.4 6 - Amido - 3 - pyridazone

$C_5H_5N_3O_2$

P.Cucka, Acta Cryst., 16, 318, 1963

P2$_1$/a   Z = 4   R = 0.106

AMIPYZ   LB 5-5-25

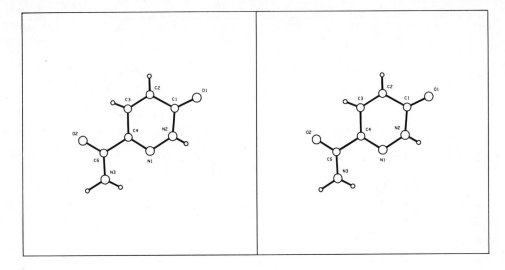

Bond Lengths

N1	N2	1.35	C5	O2	1.24
C4	N1	1.30	C1	C2	1.43
C1	N2	1.37	C2	C3	1.34
C5	N3	1.31	C3	C4	1.40
C1	O1	1.24	C4	C5	1.50

Bond Angles

N2	N1	C4	116	C1	C2	C3	120	N3	C5	O2	123
N1	N2	C1	127	C2	C3	C4	120	N3	C5	C4	118
N2	C1	O1	119	N1	C4	C3	123	O2	C5	C4	119
N2	C1	C2	114	N1	C4	C5	118				
O1	C1	C2	127	C3	C4	C5	120				

Torsion Angles

N1	C4	C5	N3	3
N1	C4	C5	O2	−177
C3	C4	C5	N3	−177
C3	C4	C5	O2	2

33.5 Pyridinium tetrafluoroarsenate

$C_5H_6N^+$, AsF_4O^-

H.Dunken, W.Haase, Z. Chem., 4, 156, 1964

The structure is totally disorded.
P-1   Z = 2   No R factor was
given.

PYRFAS   LB 5-6-2

33.6 Pyridine hydrochloride

$C_5H_6N^+$, Cl^-

C.Rerat, Acta Cryst., 15, 427, 1962

P2$_1$/m   Z = 2   R = 0.26

PYRHCL   LB 5-6-6

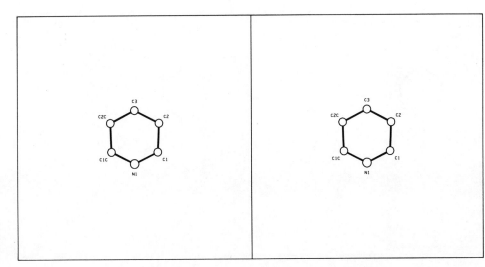

Bond Lengths

C1	N1	1.32
C1	C2	1.42
C2	C3	1.39

Bond Angles

C1	N1	C1C	127
N1	C1	C2	119
C1	C2	C3	114
C2	C3	C2C	126

33.7   Pyridine hydrogen nitrate

$C_5H_6N^+$, NO_3^-

A.J.Serewicz, B.K.Robertson, E.A.Meyers, J. Phys. Chem., 69, 1915, 1965

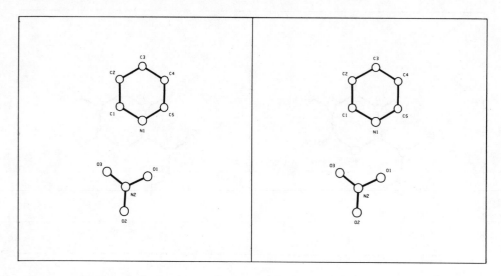

$P2_1/c$ $Z = 4$ $R = 0.085$

PYRDHN   LB 5-6-23

Bond Lengths			Bond Angles			
N2	O1	1.26	O1	N2	O2	119
N2	O2	1.21	O1	N2	O3	118
N2	O3	1.22	O2	N2	O3	123
C1	N1	1.35	C1	N1	C5	120
C5	N1	1.31	N1	C1	C2	120
C1	C2	1.35	C1	C2	C3	119
C2	C3	1.35	C2	C3	C4	120
C3	C4	1.34	C3	C4	C5	120
C4	C5	1.36	N1	C5	C4	120

33.8   Pyridine tetrabromorhenate(ii) (α form)

$C_5H_6N^+$, HBr_4Re^-

P.A.Koz'Min, V.G.Kuznetsov, Z.V.Popova, Zh. Strukt. Khim., 6, 651, 1965

The pyridinium cation is disordered.

I4/mmm   Z = 4   R = 0.142

PYBRRE   LB 5-7-3

33.9   Pyridine tetrabromorhenate(ii) (β form)

$C_5H_6N^+$, HBr_4Re^-

P.A.Koz'Min, V.G.Kuznetsov, Z.V.Popova, Zh. Strukt. Khim., 6, 651, 1965

The pyridinium cation is disordered.

Cccm   Z = 8   No R factor was given.

PYBRRE01   LB 5-7-3

33.10   Pyridinium rhenium(ii) tetrachloride

$2C_5H_6N^+$, $2H^+$, $Cl_8Re_2^{4-}$

V.G.Kuznetsov, P.A.Koz'Min, Zh. Strukt. Khim., 4, 55, 1963

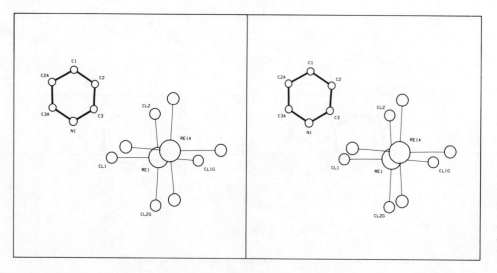

Cmmm   Z = 4   R = 0.15

PYRDRE   LB 5-7-5

Bond Lengths						Bond Angles						
Re1	Re1A	2.22	C3	N1	1.34	Cl1	Re1	Cl2	86	C3	N1	C3A	117
Re1	Cl1	2.43	C1	C2	1.40	Cl1	Re1	Cl1G	149	C2	C1	C2A	117
Re1	Cl2	2.43	C2	C3	1.39	Cl2	Re1	Cl2G	148	C1	C2	C3	119
										N1	C3	C2	124

33.11 Pyridine oxide hydrochloride

$C_5H_6NO^+, Cl^-$

G.Tsoucaris, Acta Cryst., 14, 914, 1961

The atomic coordinates result from
a three - dimensional refinement
but no details are given.
$P2_12_12_1$ $Z = 4$ $R_{hk0} = 0.20$,
$R_{h0l} = 0.24$

PYOHCL   LB 5-6-7

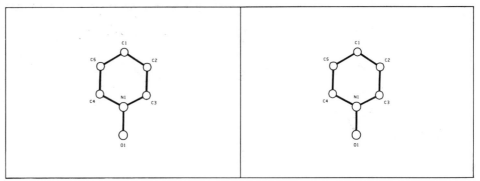

Bond Lengths

N1	O1	1.38	C1	C5	1.40
C3	N1	1.30	C2	C3	1.40
C4	N1	1.36	C4	C5	1.37
C1	C2	1.37			

Bond Angles

O1	N1	C3	116	C1	C2	C3	121
O1	N1	C4	117	N1	C3	C2	117
C3	N1	C4	127	N1	C4	C5	116
C2	C1	C5	118	C1	C5	C4	121

33.12 Piperidine hydrochloride

$C_5H_{12}N^+, Cl^-$

C.Rerat, Acta Cryst., 13, 72, 1960

Pcmb $Z = 4$ $R = 0.26$

PIPDCL   LB 5-12-7

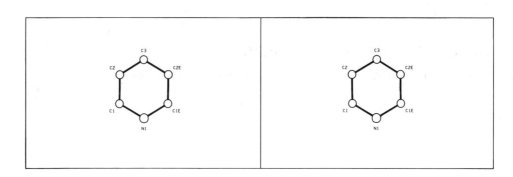

Bond Lengths

C1	N1	1.50
C1	C2	1.51
C2	C3	1.50

Bond Angles

C1	N1	C1E	112
N1	C1	C2	110
C1	C2	C3	113
C2	C3	C2E	110

Torsion Angles

C1E	N1	C1	C2	−55
N1	C1	C2	C3	55
C1	C2	C3	C2E	−53

33.13 Picolinic acid hydrochloride

$C_6H_6NO_2^+, Cl^-$

A.Laurent, Acta Cryst., 18, 799, 1965

Pbmm $Z = 4$ $R = 0.147$

PICACC   LB 6-6-15

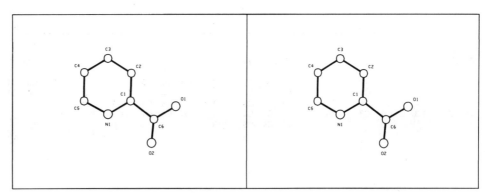

Bond Lengths

C1	N1	1.32	C1	C6	1.50
C5	N1	1.39	C2	C3	1.40
C6	O1	1.30	C3	C4	1.38
C6	O2	1.17	C4	C5	1.39
C1	C2	1.36			

Bond Angles

C1	N1	C5	122	C1	C2	C3	119	O1	C6	O2	125
N1	C1	C2	122	C2	C3	C4	119	O1	C6	C1	114
N1	C1	C6	113	C3	C4	C5	121	O2	C6	C1	121
C2	C1	C6	125	N1	C5	C4	118				

Torsion Angles

N1	C1	C6	O1	180
N1	C1	C6	O2	0
C2	C1	C6	O1	0
C2	C1	C6	O2	180

33.14   4 - Picoline - iodine complex

$C_6H_7I_2N$

O.Hassel, C.Romming, T.Tufte, Acta Chem. Scand., 15, 967, 1961

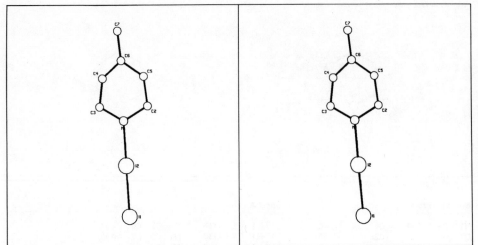

Published value of $y(C4) = 0.019$. The correct value is 0.251 (private communication).
$P2_1/c$ $Z = 4$ $R_{0kl} = 0.12$, $R_{h0l} = 0.16$

PICOLI   LB 6-7-6

Bond Lengths

I1	I2	2.82	C3	C4	1.41
I2	N1	2.32	C4	C6	1.31
C2	N1	1.43	C5	C6	1.40
C3	N1	1.41	C6	C7	1.47
C2	C5	1.47			

Bond Angles

I1	I2	N1	176	N1	C2	C5	113	C4	C6	C5	101
I2	N1	C2	117	N1	C3	C4	114	C4	C6	C7	125
I2	N1	C3	122	C3	C4	C6	138	C5	C6	C7	131
C2	N1	C3	119	C2	C5	C6	132				

33.15   3 - Pyridylcarbinol hydrochloride

$C_6H_8NO^+$, Cl^-

D.Kupfer, G.Tsoucaris, Bull. Soc. Fr. Mineral. Cristallogr., 87, 57, 1964

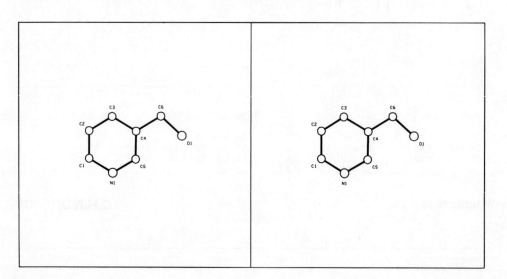

$P\text{-}1$ $Z = 2$ $R = 0.113$

PYDOHC

Bond Lengths

C1	N1	1.39	C2	C3	1.36
C5	N1	1.35	C3	C4	1.43
C6	O1	1.45	C4	C5	1.39
C1	C2	1.37	C4	C6	1.46

Bond Angles

C1	N1	C5	120	C3	C4	C6	120
N1	C1	C2	120	C5	C4	C6	121
C1	C2	C3	121	N1	C5	C4	121
C2	C3	C4	119	O1	C6	C4	108
C3	C4	C5	119				

Torsion Angles

C3	C4	C6	O1	180
C5	C4	C6	O1	1

33.16   Isonicotinic acid hydrazide dihydrochloride (form i)

$C_6H_9N_3O^{2+}$, $2Cl^-$

D.Kupfer, G.Tsoucaris, Bull. Soc. Fr. Mineral. Cristallogr., 87, 57, 1964

CO—NH—NH₃⁺

$CO-NH-NH_3^+$

· 2 Cl⁻

$P2_1/n$ Z = 4   No R factor was given.

INAHZC   LB 6-9-9

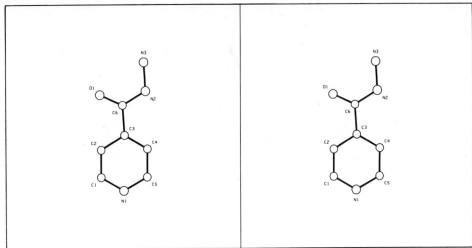

Bond Lengths

N2	N3	1.44	C1	C2	1.33	
C1	N1	1.33			(1.40)	
C5	N1	1.37	C2	C3	1.40	
C6	N2	1.35	C3	C4	1.36	
C6	O1	1.27	C3	C6	1.49	
			C4	C5	1.39	

Bond Angles

C1	N1	C5	122	C4	C3	C6	123
N3	N2	C6	116	C3	C4	C5	119
N1	C1	C2	119	N1	C5	C4	119
C1	C2	C3	122	N2	C6	O1	126
C2	C3	C4	119	N2	C6	C3	117
C2	C3	C6	118	O1	C6	C3	117

Torsion Angles

N3	N2	C6	O1	−5
N3	N2	C6	C3	177
C2	C3	C6	N2	164
C2	C3	C6	O1	−14
C4	C3	C6	N2	−19
C4	C3	C6	O1	163

33.17   Isonicotinic acid hydrazide dihydrochloride (form ii)

$C_6H_9N_3O^{2+}$, $2Cl^-$

D.Kupfer, G.Tsoucaris, Bull. Soc. Fr. Mineral. Cristallogr., 87, 57, 1964

$CO-NH-NH_3^+$

2 Cl⁻

$P2_1/a$ Z = 4   R = 0.19

INAHZC01   LB 6-9-9

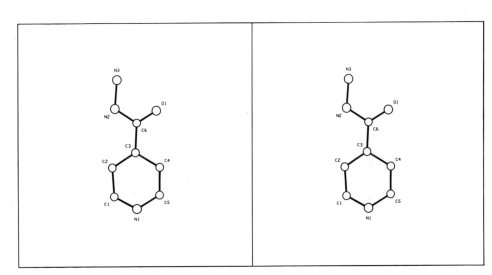

Bond Lengths

N2	N3	1.41	C1	C2	1.44
C1	N1	1.31	C2	C3	1.40
C5	N1	1.34	C3	C4	1.43
C6	N2	1.35	C3	C6	1.47
C6	O1	1.22	C4	C5	1.37

Bond Angles

C1	N1	C5	122	C4	C3	C6	118
N3	N2	C6	118	C3	C4	C5	119
N1	C1	C2	121	N1	C5	C4	122
C1	C2	C3	118	N2	C6	O1	118
C2	C3	C4	118	N2	C6	C3	118
C2	C3	C6	124	O1	C6	C3	124

Torsion Angles

N3	N2	C6	O1	−3
N3	N2	C6	C3	174
C2	C3	C6	N2	24
C2	C3	C6	O1	−159
C4	C3	C6	N2	−154
C4	C3	C6	O1	22

33.18   3 - Picolylamine dihydrochloride

$C_6H_{10}N_2^{2+}$, $2Cl^-$

F.Genet, Bull. Soc. Fr. Mineral. Cristallogr., 88, 463, 1965

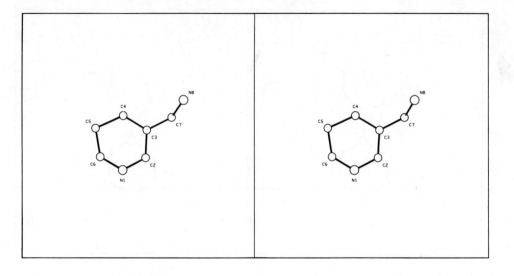

$P2_1/a$ $Z = 4$ $R = 0.16$

PICAMC   LB 6-10-18

Bond Lengths

C2	N1	1.34
C6	N1	1.34
C7	N8	1.46
C2	C3	1.38
C3	C4	1.42
C3	C7	1.48
C4	C5	1.56
		(1.38)
C5	C6	1.44
		(1.36)

Bond Angles

C2	N1	C6	124
N1	C2	C3	120
C2	C3	C4	117
C2	C3	C7	120
C4	C3	C7	123
C3	C4	C5	126
C4	C5	C6	104
N1	C6	C5	127
N8	C7	C3	114

Torsion Angles

C2	C3	C7	N8	−110
C4	C3	C7	N8	70

33.19   Pyridinium dicyanomethylide

$C_8H_5N_3$

C.Bugg, R.L.Sass, Acta Cryst., 18, 591, 1965

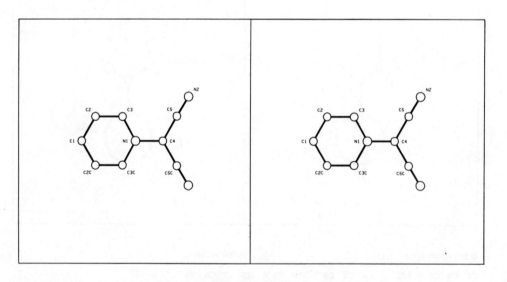

$P2_1/m$ $Z = 2$ $R = 0.129$

PYRCYM   LB 8-5-13

Bond Lengths

C3	N1	1.37
C4	N1	1.40
C5	N2	1.13
C1	C2	1.39
C2	C3	1.39
C4	C5	1.42

Bond Angles

C3	N1	C4	119
C3	N1	C3C	121
C2	C1	C2C	119
C1	C2	C3	120
N1	C3	C2	119
N1	C4	C5	121
C5	C4	C5C	119
N2	C5	C4	179

Torsion Angles

C3	N1	C4	C5	3
C3	N1	C4	C5C	178
C3C	N1	C4	C5	−178
C3C	N1	C4	C5C	−3

33.20 N - n - Propyl - 1,4 - dihydronicotinamide

$C_9H_{14}N_2O$

H.Koyama, Z. Kristallogr., 118, 51, 1963

P2$_1$/a   Z = 4   R = 0.18

PRHNCA   LB 9-14-7

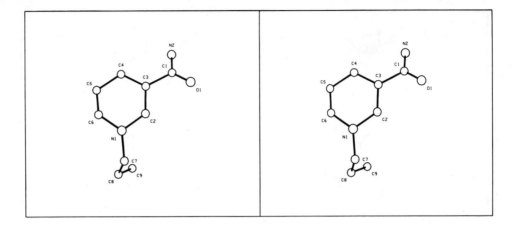

Bond Lengths

C2	N1	1.45	C2	C3	1.38
C6	N1	1.45	C3	C4	1.45
C7	N1	1.47	C4	C5	1.49
C1	N2	1.33	C5	C6	1.30
C1	O1	1.21	C7	C8	1.48
C1	C3	1.49	C8	C9	1.49

Bond Angles

C2	N1	C6	109	C1	C3	C4	124
C2	N1	C7	120	C2	C3	C4	118
C6	N1	C7	129	C3	C4	C5	118
N2	C1	O1	131	C4	C5	C6	117
N2	C1	C3	113	N1	C6	C5	131
O1	C1	C3	116	C7	C8	C9	124
N1	C2	C3	126				
C1	C3	C2	117				

Torsion Angles

C2	N1	C7	C8	−101
C6	N1	C7	C8	64
N2	C1	C3	C2	150
N2	C1	C3	C4	−26
O1	C1	C3	C2	−22
O1	C1	C3	C4	161
N1	C7	C8	C9	58

33.21 4,4' - Bipyridyl dihydrobromide

$C_{10}H_{10}N_2^{2+}$, 2Br$^-$

B.Mestvedt, Acta Cryst., 13, 1043, 1960

Atomic coordinates were not reported in the paper.
P-1   Z = 1   No R factor was given.

BPYRDB

$$H^+N \; / \; N^+H \quad .2Br^-$$

33.22 2,2' - Pyridil

$C_{12}H_8N_2O_2$

S.Hirokawa, T.Ashida, Acta Cryst., 14, 774, 1961

See also Ashida & Hirokawa, Acta Cryst. (B), 26, 454, 1970.
P2$_1$/n   Z = 4   R = 0.16

PYRDIL   LB 12-8-47

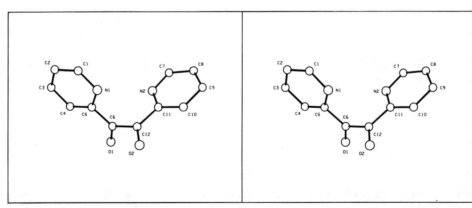

Bond Lengths

C1	N1	1.35	C4	C5	1.37
C5	N1	1.36	C5	C6	1.48
C7	N2	1.34	C6	C12	1.52
C11	N2	1.32	C7	C8	1.38
C6	O1	1.22	C8	C9	1.41
C12	O2	1.23	C9	C10	1.40
C1	C2	1.40	C10	C11	1.40
C2	C3	1.34	C11	C12	1.48
C3	C4	1.42			

Bond Angles

C1	N1	C5	117	C5	C6	C12	118
C7	N2	C11	120	N2	C7	C8	119
N1	C1	C2	122	C7	C8	C9	122
C1	C2	C3	120	C8	C9	C10	117
C2	C3	C4	120	C9	C10	C11	118
C3	C4	C5	116	N2	C11	C10	124
N1	C5	C4	125	N2	C11	C12	116
N1	C5	C6	114	C10	C11	C12	120
C4	C5	C6	121	O2	C12	C6	118
O1	C6	C5	124	O2	C12	C11	124
O1	C6	C12	119	C6	C12	C11	117

Torsion Angles

N1	C5	C6	O1	179	C5	C6	C12	O2	98
N1	C5	C6	C12	3	C5	C6	C12	C11	−87
C4	C5	C6	O1	−1	N2	C11	C12	O2	179
C4	C5	C6	C12	−178	N2	C11	C12	C6	4
O1	C6	C12	O2	−78	C10	C11	C12	O2	−3
O1	C6	C12	C11	97	C10	C11	C12	C6	−178

33.23 α - Pyridoin

$C_{12}H_{10}N_2O_2$

T.Ashida, S.Hirokawa, Y.Okaya, Acta Cryst., 18, 122, 1965

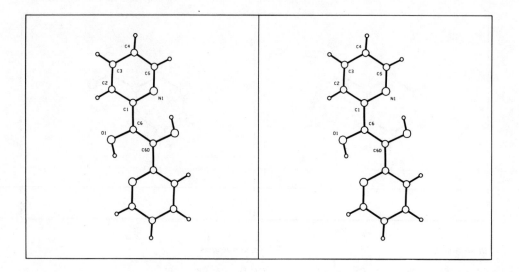

C2/c Z = 4 R = 0.113

PYRDON LB 12-10-56

Bond Lengths

C1	N1	1.35	C2	C3	1.38
C5	N1	1.33	C3	C4	1.38
C6	O1	1.37	C4	C5	1.38
C1	C2	1.40	C6	C6D	1.37
C1	C6	1.46			

Bond Angles

C1	N1	C5	119	C3	C4	C5	119
N1	C1	C2	121	N1	C5	C4	123
N1	C1	C6	118	O1	C6	C1	114
C2	C1	C6	121	O1	C6	C6D	123
C1	C2	C3	119	C1	C6	C6D	124
C2	C3	C4	119				

Torsion Angles

N1	C1	C6	O1	180	O1	C6	C6D O1D	−180
N1	C1	C6	C6D	−1	O1	C6	C6D C1D	−1
C2	C1	C6	O1	0	C1	C6	C6D O1D	1
C2	C1	C6	C6D	179	C1	C6	C6D C1D	180

33.24 α - Bromo - γ - phenyl - γ - ethylglutaconimide

$C_{13}H_{12}BrNO_2$

M.Bonamico, F.Coppola, G.Giacomello, A.Vaciago, L.Zambonelli,
Gazz. Chim. Ital., 92, 1319, 1962

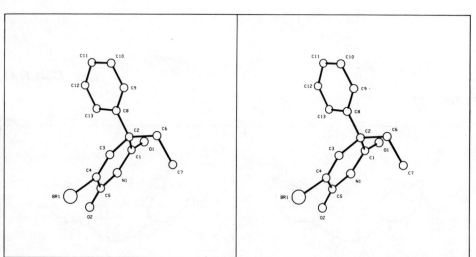

$P2_1/c$ Z = 4 R_{hk0} = 0.132,
R_{0kl} = 0.124, R_{h0l} = 0.149

BPEGIM

Bond Lengths

Br1	C4	1.84	C3	C4	1.32
C1	N1	1.43	C4	C5	1.38
C5	N1	1.50	C6	C7	1.60
C1	O1	1.22	C8	C9	1.42
C5	O2	1.26	C8	C13	1.38
C1	C2	1.51	C9	C10	1.37
C2	C3	1.55	C10	C11	1.38
C2	C6	1.56	C11	C12	1.40
C2	C8	1.47	C12	C13	1.35

Bond Angles

C1	N1	C5	125	C3	C4	C5	118
N1	C1	O1	117	N1	C5	O2	112
N1	C1	C2	119	N1	C5	C4	117
O1	C1	C2	125	O2	C5	C4	130
C1	C2	C3	109	C2	C6	C7	112
C1	C2	C6	112	C2	C8	C9	119
C1	C2	C8	109	C2	C8	C13	120
C3	C2	C6	109	C9	C8	C13	121
C3	C2	C8	104	C8	C9	C10	118
C6	C2	C8	114	C9	C10	C11	120
C2	C3	C4	132	C10	C11	C12	122
Br1	C4	C3	127	C11	C12	C13	119
Br1	C4	C5	115	C8	C13	C12	120

Torsion Angles

C5	N1	C1	O1	176	C3	C2	C6	C7	74
C5	N1	C1	C2	−5	C8	C2	C6	C7	−170
C1	N1	C5	O2	178	C1	C2	C8	C9	−145
C1	N1	C5	C4	7	C1	C2	C8	C13	38
N1	C1	C2	C3	1	C3	C2	C8	C9	100
N1	C1	C2	C6	121	C3	C2	C8	C13	−77
N1	C1	C2	C8	−112	C6	C2	C8	C9	−19
O1	C1	C2	C3	−179	C6	C2	C8	C13	164
O1	C1	C2	C6	−59	C2	C3	C4	Br1	−176
O1	C1	C2	C8	68	C2	C3	C4	C5	3
C1	C2	C3	C4	0	Br1	C4	C5	N1	173
C6	C2	C3	C4	−122	Br1	C4	C5	O2	5
C8	C2	C3	C4	116	C3	C4	C5	N1	−6
C1	C2	C6	C7	−45	C3	C4	C5	O2	−175

33.25   α - Ethyl - α - phenyl - α' - iodoglutarimide $C_{13}H_{14}INO_2$

M.Bonamico, F.Coppola, G.Giacomello, Gazz. Chim. Ital., 91, 193, 1961

$P2_1/c$ Z = 4 R_{hk0} = 0.13,
R_{0kl} = 0.17

EPIGAM   LB 13-14-3

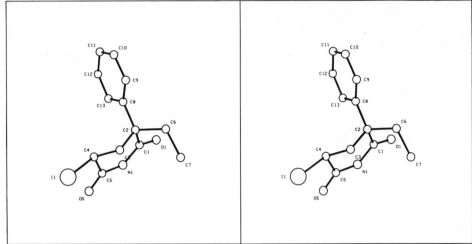

Bond Lengths

I1	C4	2.15	C3	C4	1.56
C1	N1	1.39	C4	C5	1.51
C5	N1	1.32	C6	C7	1.56
C1	O1	1.23	C8	C9	1.40
C5	O5	1.21	C8	C13	1.41
C1	C2	1.55	C9	C10	1.40
C2	C3	1.55	C10	C11	1.42
C2	C6	1.60	C11	C12	1.43
C2	C8	1.54	C12	C13	1.41

Bond Angles

C1	N1	C5	129	C3	C4	C5	107
N1	C1	O1	119	N1	C5	O5	125
C5	N1	C2	117	N1	C5	C4	114
O1	C1	C2	124	O5	C5	C4	121
C1	C2	C3	106	C2	C6	C7	115
C1	C2	C6	100	C2	C8	C9	121
C1	C2	C8	113	C2	C8	C13	118
C3	C2	C6	106	C9	C8	C13	121
C3	C2	C8	116	C8	C9	C10	119
C6	C2	C8	114	C9	C10	C11	121
C2	C3	C4	107	C10	C11	C12	118
I1	C4	C3	103	C11	C12	C13	121
I1	C4	C5	118	C8	C13	C12	119

Torsion Angles

C5	N1	C1	O1	−176	C3	C2	C6	C7	59
C5	N1	C1	C2	5	C8	C2	C6	C7	−172
C1	N1	C5	O5	−179	C1	C2	C8	C9	−158
C1	N1	C5	C4	4	C1	C2	C8	C13	26
N1	C1	C2	C3	24	C3	C2	C8	C9	79
N1	C1	C2	C6	134	C3	C2	C8	C13	−97
N1	C1	C2	C8	−104	C6	C2	C8	C9	−44
O1	C1	C2	C3	−155	C6	C2	C8	C13	139
O1	C1	C2	C6	−45	C2	C3	C4	I1	−166
O1	C1	C2	C8	76	C2	C3	C4	C5	70
C1	C2	C3	C4	−59	I1	C4	C5	N1	−156
C6	C2	C3	C4	−165	I1	C4	C5	O5	27
C8	C2	C3	C4	68	C3	C4	C5	N1	−41
C1	C2	C6	C7	−51	C3	C4	C5	O5	142

33.26   N - Benzyl - 1,4 - dihydronicotinamide $C_{13}H_{14}N_2O$

I.L.Karle, Acta Cryst., 14, 497, 1961

$P2_1/c$ Z = 4   R = 0.22

BDHNIC   LB 13-14-4

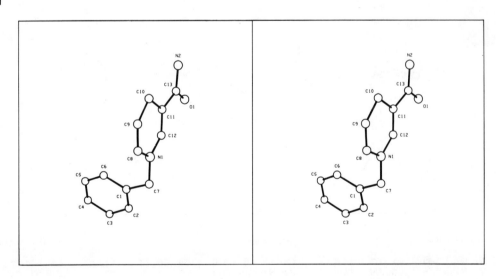

Bond Lengths

C7	N1	1.44	C3	C4	1.40
C8	N1	1.43	C4	C5	1.35
C12	N1	1.38	C5	C6	1.37
C13	N2	1.32	C8	C9	1.32
C13	O1	1.25	C9	C10	1.53
C1	C2	1.37	C10	C11	1.51
C1	C6	1.39	C11	C12	1.32
C1	C7	1.52	C11	C13	1.47
C2	C3	1.40			

Bond Angles

C7	N1	C8	121	C3	C4	C5	119
C7	N1	C12	122	C4	C5	C6	122
C8	N1	C12	117	C1	C6	C5	120
C2	C1	C6	118	N1	C7	C1	116
C2	C1	C7	118	N1	C8	C9	122
C6	C1	C7	123	C8	C9	C10	124
C1	C2	C3	121	C9	C10	C11	109
C2	C3	C4	120	C10	C11	C12	123

C10	C11	C13	120
C12	C11	C13	116
N1	C12	C11	124
N2	C13	O1	121
N2	C13	C11	118
O1	C13	C11	121

Torsion Angles

C8	N1	C7	C1	92
C12	N1	C7	C1	−87
C2	C1	C7	N1	157
C6	C1	C7	N1	−22
C10	C11	C13	N2	1
C10	C11	C13	O1	−177
C12	C11	C13	N2	−178
C12	C11	C13	O1	4

33.27 β - DL - 1,3 - Dimethyl - 4 - phenyl - 4 - propionoxy - piperidine hydrobromide

$C_{16}H_{24}NO_2^+$, Br^-

DL - Betaprodine hydrobromide
F.R.Ahmed, W.H.Barnes, L.Di M.Masironi, Acta Cryst., 16, 237, 1963

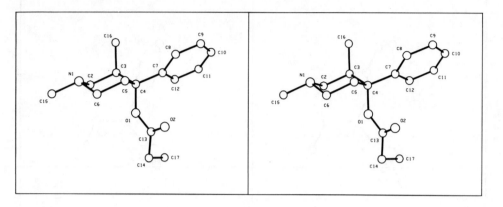

Pbca   Z = 8   R = 0.09

PRODBR   LB 16-24-3

Bond Lengths

C2	N1	1.48		C4	C7	1.53
C6	N1	1.51		C5	C6	1.52
C15	N1	1.50		C7	C8	1.38
C4	O1	1.46		C7	C12	1.39
C13	O1	1.34		C8	C9	1.39
C13	O2	1.19		C9	C10	1.37
C2	C3	1.53		C10	C11	1.36
C3	C4	1.55		C11	C12	1.41
C3	C16	1.55		C13	C14	1.52
C4	C5	1.53		C14	C17	1.52

Bond Angles

C2	N1	C6	112		C4	C5	C6	112
C2	N1	C15	110		N1	C6	C5	110
C6	N1	C15	111		C4	C7	C8	123
C4	O1	C13	120		C4	C7	C12	119
N1	C2	C3	112		C8	C7	C12	119
C2	C3	C4	110		C7	C8	C9	121
C2	C3	C16	111		C8	C9	C10	121
C4	C3	C16	114		C9	C10	C11	119
O1	C4	C3	102		C10	C11	C12	122
O1	C4	C5	111		C7	C12	C11	119
O1	C4	C7	109		O1	C13	O2	126
C3	C4	C5	109		O1	C13	C14	108
C3	C4	C7	111		O2	C13	C14	126
C5	C4	C7	114		C13	C14	C17	111

Torsion Angles

C6	N1	C2	C3	−56		C16	C3	C4	C5	71
C15	N1	C2	C3	−180		C16	C3	C4	C7	−56
C2	N1	C6	C5	56		O1	C4	C5	C6	−53
C15	N1	C6	C5	180		C3	C4	C5	C6	58
C13	O1	C4	C3	−180		C7	C4	C5	C6	−177
C13	O1	C4	C5	−64		O1	C4	C7	C8	−147
C13	O1	C4	C7	63		O1	C4	C7	C12	38
C4	O1	C13	O2	5		C3	C4	C7	C8	102
C4	O1	C13	C14	−178		C3	C4	C7	C12	−73
N1	C2	C3	C4	55		C5	C4	C7	C8	−22
N1	C2	C3	C16	−72		C5	C4	C7	C12	163
C2	C3	C4	O1	62		C4	C5	C6	N1	−58
C2	C3	C4	C5	−55		O1	C13	C14	C17	175
C2	C3	C4	C7	178		O2	C13	C14	C17	−8
C16	C3	C4	O1	−172					

33.28 β - DL - 1,3 - Dimethyl - 4 - phenyl - 4 - propionoxy - piperidine hydrochloride

$C_{16}H_{24}NO_2^+$, Cl^-

DL - Betaprodine hydrochloride
F.R.Ahmed, W.H.Barnes, Acta Cryst., 16, 1249, 1963

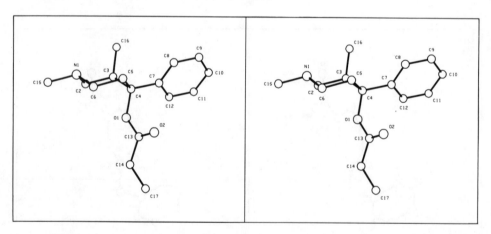

P2₁/c   Z = 4   R = 0.096

PROCLB   LB 16-24-5

Bond Lengths

C2	N1	1.49		C4	C7	1.52
C6	N1	1.50		C5	C6	1.52
C15	N1	1.49		C7	C8	1.39
C4	O1	1.48		C7	C12	1.38
C13	O1	1.36		C8	C9	1.39
C13	O2	1.20		C9	C10	1.37
C2	C3	1.52		C10	C11	1.35
C3	C4	1.55		C11	C12	1.41
C3	C16	1.52		C13	C14	1.48
C4	C5	1.52		C14	C17	1.52

Bond Angles

C2	N1	C6	110		C4	C5	C6	112
C2	N1	C15	110		N1	C6	C5	111
C6	N1	C15	111		C4	C7	C8	123
C4	O1	C13	121		C4	C7	C12	120
N1	C2	C3	112		C8	C7	C12	117
C2	C3	C4	111		C7	C8	C9	122
C2	C3	C16	112		C8	C9	C10	119
C4	C3	C16	113		C9	C10	C11	121
O1	C4	C3	102		C10	C11	C12	120
O1	C4	C5	110		C7	C12	C11	121
O1	C4	C7	109		O1	C13	O2	123
C3	C4	C5	109		O1	C13	C14	111
C3	C4	C7	112		O2	C13	C14	126
C5	C4	C7	115		C13	C14	C17	111

Torsion Angles

C6	N1	C2	C3	−58		C16	C3	C4	C5	73
C15	N1	C2	C3	179		C16	C3	C4	C7	−55
C2	N1	C6	C5	58		O1	C4	C5	C6	−55
C15	N1	C6	C5	−180		C3	C4	C5	C6	55
C13	O1	C4	C3	−179		C7	C4	C5	C6	−178
C13	O1	C4	C5	−63		O1	C4	C7	C8	−138
C13	O1	C4	C7	63		O1	C4	C7	C12	43
C4	O1	C13	O2	4		C3	C4	C7	C8	111
C4	O1	C13	C14	−176		C3	C4	C7	C12	−68
N1	C2	C3	C4	56		C5	C4	C7	C8	−15
N1	C2	C3	C16	−71		C5	C4	C7	C12	167
C2	C3	C4	O1	62		C4	C5	C6	N1	−58
C2	C3	C4	C5	−54		O1	C13	C14	C17	80
C2	C3	C4	C7	178		O2	C13	C14	C17	−100
C16	C3	C4	O1	−171					

33.29 α - DL - 1,3 - Dimethyl - 4 - phenyl - 4 - propionoxy - piperidine hydrochloride

$C_{16}H_{24}NO_2^+$, Cl^-

DL - Alphaprodine hydrochloride
G.Kartha, F.R.Ahmed, W.H.Barnes, Acta Cryst., 13, 525, 1960

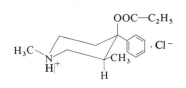

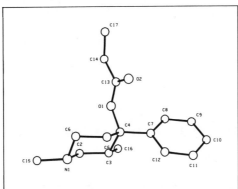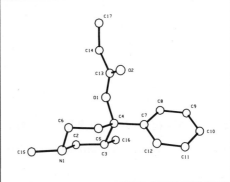

P2₁/c   Z = 4   R = 0.16

PRODCL   LB 16-24-4

Bond Lengths

C2	N1	1.50	C4	C7	1.53
C6	N1	1.50	C5	C6	1.51
C15	N1	1.53	C7	C8	1.38
C4	O1	1.46	C7	C12	1.38
C13	O1	1.35	C8	C9	1.37
C13	O2	1.22	C9	C10	1.39
C2	C3	1.52	C10	C11	1.38
C3	C4	1.56	C11	C12	1.38
C3	C16	1.54	C13	C14	1.49
C4	C5	1.54	C14	C17	1.51

Bond Angles

C2	N1	C6	111	C4	C5	C6	112
C2	N1	C15	110	N1	C6	C5	109
C6	N1	C15	111	C4	C7	C8	122
C4	O1	C13	120	C4	C7	C12	121
N1	C2	C3	111	C8	C7	C12	117
C2	C3	C4	112	C7	C8	C9	123
C2	C3	C16	108	C8	C9	C10	120
C4	C3	C16	115	C9	C10	C11	118
O1	C4	C3	104	C10	C11	C12	120
O1	C4	C5	110	C7	C12	C11	122
O1	C4	C7	111	O1	C13	O2	124
C3	C4	C5	108	O1	C13	C14	111
C3	C4	C7	111	O2	C13	C14	125
C5	C4	C7	113	C13	C14	C17	113

Torsion Angles

C6	N1	C2	C3	59	C16	C3	C4	C5	175
C15	N1	C2	C3	−177	C16	C3	C4	C7	−60
C2	N1	C6	C5	−61	O1	C4	C5	C6	57
C15	N1	C6	C5	176	C3	C4	C5	C6	−55
C13	O1	C4	C3	176	C7	C4	C5	C6	−178
C13	O1	C4	C5	60	O1	C4	C7	C8	−28
C13	O1	C4	C7	−65	O1	C4	C7	C12	158
C4	O1	C13	O2	1	C3	C4	C7	C8	87
C4	O1	C13	C14	−178	C3	C4	C7	C12	−87
N1	C2	C3	C4	−55	C5	C4	C7	C8	−152
N1	C2	C3	C16	178	C5	C4	C7	C12	34
C2	C3	C4	O1	−64	C4	C5	C6	N1	60
C2	C3	C4	C5	52	O1	C13	C14	C17	171
C2	C3	C4	C7	177	O2	C13	C14	C17	−8
C16	C3	C4	O1	59					

33.30   s - Triphenyltriazine

$C_{21}H_{15}N_3$

A.Damiani, E.Giglio, A.Ripamonti, Acta Cryst., 19, 161, 1965

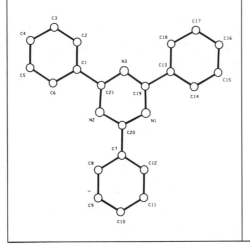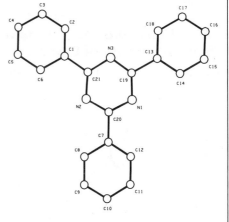

P2₁/c   Z = 4   R = 0.114

TPTRAZ   LB 21-15-3

Bond Lengths

C19	N1	1.32	C7	C12	1.38
C20	N1	1.35	C7	C20	1.47
C20	N2	1.32	C8	C9	1.38
C21	N2	1.33	C9	C10	1.37
C19	N3	1.32	C10	C11	1.40
C21	N3	1.36	C11	C12	1.38
C1	C2	1.38	C13	C14	1.40
C1	C6	1.41	C13	C18	1.40
C1	C21	1.47	C13	C19	1.49
C2	C3	1.38	C14	C15	1.40
C3	C4	1.39	C15	C16	1.39
C4	C5	1.37	C16	C17	1.40
C5	C6	1.38	C17	C18	1.40
C7	C8	1.41			

Bond Angles

C19	N1	C20	116	C8	C7	C20	120
C20	N2	C21	116	C12	C7	C20	122
C19	N3	C21	115	C7	C8	C9	120
C2	C1	C6	119	C8	C9	C10	120
C2	C1	C21	122	C9	C10	C11	120
C6	C1	C21	119	C10	C11	C12	120
C1	C2	C3	121	C7	C12	C11	121
C2	C3	C4	119	C14	C13	C18	121
C3	C4	C5	120	C14	C13	C19	119
C4	C5	C6	122	C18	C13	C19	120
C1	C6	C5	119	C13	C14	C15	119
C8	C7	C12	119	C14	C15	C16	121

C15	C16	C17	120
C16	C17	C18	119
C13	C18	C17	120
N1	C19	N3	126
N1	C19	C13	117
N3	C19	C13	117
N1	C20	N2	124
N1	C20	C7	117
N2	C20	C7	119
N2	C21	N3	124
N2	C21	C1	119
N3	C21	C1	117

Torsion Angles

C2	C1	C21	N2	−175
C2	C1	C21	N3	6
C6	C1	C21	N2	7
C6	C1	C21	N3	−172
C8	C7	C20	N1	170
C8	C7	C20	N2	−12
C12	C7	C20	N1	−9
C12	C7	C20	N2	169
C14	C13	C19	N1	−6
C14	C13	C19	N3	172
C18	C13	C19	N1	175
C18	C13	C19	N3	−7

34.1 Octahydro - 1,3,5,7 - tetranitro - 1,3,5,7 - tetrazocine (α form)

$C_4H_8N_8O_8$

H.H.Cady, A.C.Larson, D.T.Cromer, Acta Cryst., 16, 617, 1963

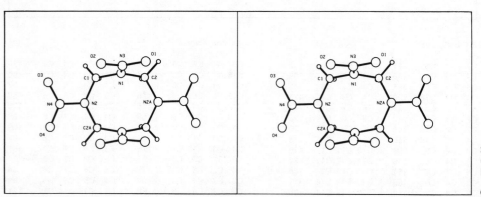

See also Choi & Boutin, Acta Cryst. (B), 26, 1235, 1970.
Fdd2 Z = 8 R = 0.035

OCHTET   LB 4-8-82

Bond Lengths

N1	N3	1.35	N4	O4	1.22
N2	N4	1.37	C1	N1	1.44
N3	O1	1.24	C2	N1	1.45
N3	O2	1.21	C1	N2	1.45
N4	O3	1.24	C2A	N2	1.47

Bond Angles

N3	N1	C1	117	N1	N3	O2	119
N3	N1	C2	119	O1	N3	O2	125
C1	N1	C2	124	N2	N4	O3	118
N4	N2	C1	120	N2	N4	O4	117
N4	N2	C2A	119	O3	N4	O4	125
C1	N2	C2A	120	N1	C1	N2	113
N1	N3	O1	116	N1	C2	N2A	111

Torsion Angles

C1	N1	N3	O1	179	C1	N2	N4	O3	−5
C1	N1	N3	O2	1	C1	N2	N4	O4	176
C2	N1	N3	O1	3	C2A	N2	N4	O3	−171
C2	N1	N3	O2	−175	C2A	N2	N4	O4	10
N3	N1	C1	N2	−75	N4	N2	C1	N1	129
C2	N1	C1	N2	101	C2A	N2	C1	N1	−65
N3	N1	C2	N2A	71	N4	N2	C2A	N1A	−126
C1	N1	C2	N2A	−105	C1	N2	C2A	N1A	68

34.2 Octahydro - 1,3,5,7 - tetranitro - 1,3,5,7 - tetrazocine (β form, refinement of data of Eiland and Pepinsky, Z.Krist., 106,273,1955)

$C_4H_8N_8O_8$

H.H.Cady, A.C.Larson, D.T.Cromer, Acta Cryst., 16, 617, 1963

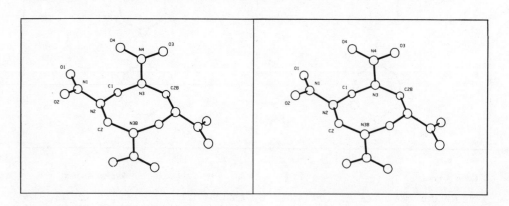

P2$_1$/c Z = 2 R = 0.13

OCHTET01   LB 4-8-83

Bond Lengths

N1	N2	1.41	N4	O4	1.22
N3	N4	1.37	C1	N2	1.43
N1	O1	1.22	C2	N2	1.45
N1	O2	1.23	C1	N3	1.46
N4	O3	1.22	C2B	N3	1.43

Bond Angles

N2	N1	O1	120	N4	N3	C2B	117
N2	N1	O2	116	C1	N3	C2B	124
O1	N1	O2	124	N3	N4	O3	115
N1	N2	C1	116	N3	N4	O4	117
N1	N2	C2	114	O3	N4	O4	128
C1	N2	C2	125	N2	C1	N3	111
N4	N3	C1	117	N2	C2	N3B	109

Torsion Angles

O1	N1	N2	C1	23	C1	N3	N4	O3	−180
O1	N1	N2	C2	−180	C1	N3	N4	O4	1
O2	N1	N2	C1	−161	C2B	N3	N4	O3	−11
O2	N1	N2	C2	−4	C2B	N3	N4	O4	170
N1	N2	C1	N3	113	N4	N3	C1	N2	−76
C2	N2	C1	N3	−42	C2B	N3	C1	N2	117
N1	N2	C2	N3B	−173	N4	N3	C2B	N2B	89
C1	N2	C2	N3B	−18	C1	N3	C2B	N2B	−103

34.3   Azacyclo - octane hydrobromide

$C_7H_{16}N^+$, Br^-

J.D.Dunitz, V.Prelog, Angew. Chem., 72, 896, 1960

The structure was determined in two dimensions only. Atomic coordinates were not reported in the paper.
Abm2   Z = 4   No R factor was given.

AZACOC

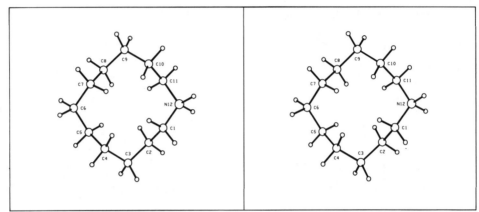

34.4   Azacyclododecane hydrochloride

$C_{11}H_{24}N^+$, Cl^-

J.D.Dunitz, H.P.Weber, Helv. Chim. Acta, 47, 1138, 1964

Published value of x(H2) = 0.770. The correct value is 0.077.
P-1   Z = 2   R = 0.11

AZDODC   LB 11-24-4

Bond Lengths

C1	N12	1.53	C5	C6	1.54
C11	N12	1.54	C6	C7	1.54
C1	C2	1.53	C7	C8	1.53
C2	C3	1.55	C8	C9	1.53
C3	C4	1.55	C9	C10	1.53
C4	C5	1.54	C10	C11	1.55

Bond Angles

C1	N12	C11	115	C5	C6	C7	116
N12	C1	C2	113	C6	C7	C8	111
C1	C2	C3	113	C7	C8	C9	112
C2	C3	C4	112	C8	C9	C10	112
C3	C4	C5	111	C9	C10	C11	113
C4	C5	C6	113	N12	C11	C10	112

Torsion Angles

C11	N12	C1	C2	68	C4	C5	C6	C7	66
C1	N12	C11	C10	70	C5	C6	C7	C8	71
N12	C1	C2	C3	−168	C6	C7	C8	C9	−169
C1	C2	C3	C4	64	C7	C8	C9	C10	67
C2	C3	C4	C5	71	C8	C9	C10	C11	69
C3	C4	C5	C6	−154	C9	C10	C11	N12	−155

34.5   1,8 - Diazacyclotetradecane dihydrobromide

$C_{12}H_{28}N_2^{2+}$, $2Br^-$

J.D.Dunitz, E.F.Meyer, Helv. Chim. Acta, 48, 1441, 1965

No comparison of bond lengths is possible since they are not reported in the paper.
Pccn   Z = 4   R = 0.061

DIAHBR   LB 12-28-5

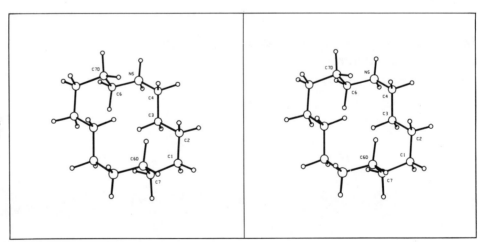

Bond Lengths

C4	N5	1.41
C6	N5	1.52
C1	C2	1.49
C1	C7	1.57
C2	C3	1.52
C3	C4	1.56
C6	C7D	1.50

Bond Angles

C4	N5	C6	116
C2	C1	C7	115
C1	C2	C3	114
C2	C3	C4	113
N5	C4	C3	115
N5	C6	C7D	112
C1	C7	C6D	111

Torsion Angles

C6	N5	C4	C3	59
C4	N5	C6	C7D	65
C7	C1	C2	C3	−54
C2	C1	C7	C6D	−64
C1	C2	C3	C4	173
C2	C3	C4	N5	−177
N5	C6	C7D	C1D	−172

35.1   8 - Azaguanine monohydrate

$C_4H_4N_6O$, H_2O

W.M.Macintyre, P.Singh, M.S.Werkema, Biophys. J., 5, 697, 1965

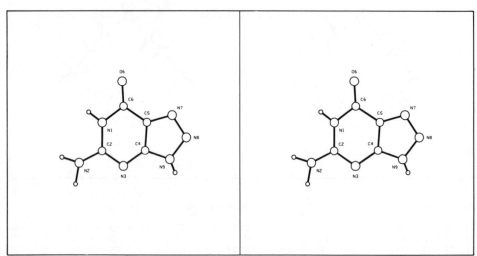

See also Sletten et al., Acta Cryst.
(B), 24, 1692, 1968.
P2₁/c   Z = 4   R = 0.12

AZGUAN   LB 4-4-51

Bond Lengths

N7	N8	1.31	C4	N3	1.35
N8	N9	1.37	C5	N7	1.34
C2	N1	1.40	C4	N9	1.34
C6	N1	1.37	C6	O6	1.23
C2	N2	1.32	C4	C5	1.39
C2	N3	1.33	C5	C6	1.44

Bond Angles

C2	N1	C6	126	N1	C2	N3	123	N7	C5	C6	131
C2	N3	C4	112	N2	C2	N3	120	C4	C5	C6	119
N8	N7	C5	108	N3	C4	N9	128	N1	C6	O6	122
N7	N8	N9	108	N3	C4	C5	128	N1	C6	C5	111
N8	N9	C4	110	N9	C4	C5	104	O6	C6	C5	127
N1	C2	N2	116	N7	C5	C4	110				

35.2   Rubidium 1,3a,4,6a - tetra - azapentalene 2,5 - dicarboxylate dihydrate

$C_6H_2N_4O_4^{2-}$, $2Rb^+$, $2H_2O$

M.Brufani, W.Fedeli, G.Giacomello, A.Vaciago, Ric. Sci., 2, A, 3, 1237, 1963

$$2 Rb^+ \left(OOC - \overset{N-N}{\underset{N-N}{}} - COO \right)^{2-} \cdot 2 H_2O$$

Atomic coordinates were not
reported in the paper.
P2₁/c   Z = 2 R_{hol} = 0.12

RBAZPC   LB 6-2-39

35.3   2,5 - Dimethyl - 3,6 - dibromo - 1,3a,4,6a - tetra - azapentalene $C_6H_6Br_2N_4$

M.Brufani, W.Fedeli, G.Giacomello, A.Vaciago, Gazz. Chim. Ital., 93, 1571, 1963

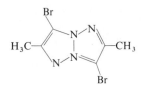

Pca2$_1$ Z = 4 R_{hk0} = 0.12,
R_{h0l} = 0.10

DAZPEN   LB 6-6-11

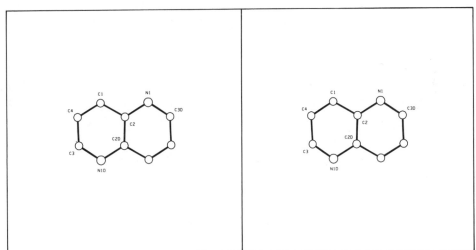

Bond Lengths

Br1	C2	1.93
Br2	C4	1.79
N1	N2	1.40
N2	N3	1.36
N3	N4	1.41
C1	N1	1.35
C4	N2	1.33
C2	N3	1.46
C3	N4	1.40
C1	C2	1.31
C1	C5	1.49
C3	C4	1.34
C3	C6	1.50

Bond Angles

N2	N1	C1	97
N1	N2	N3	115
N1	N2	C4	133
N3	N2	C4	111
N2	N3	N4	112
N2	N3	C2	102
N4	N3	C2	146
N3	N4	C3	96
N1	C1	C2	119
N1	C1	C5	113

C2	C1	C5	124
Br1	C2	N3	114
Br1	C2	C1	140
N3	C2	C1	102
N4	C3	C4	119
N4	C3	C6	109
C4	C3	C6	133
Br2	C4	N2	129
Br2	C4	C3	129
N2	C4	C3	102

Torsion Angles

C1	N1	N2	N3	2
C1	N1	N2	C4	170
N2	N1	C1	C2	12
N2	N1	C1	C5	171
N1	N2	N3	N4	166
N1	N2	N3	C2	−12
C4	N2	N3	N4	−5
C4	N2	N3	C2	177
N1	N2	C4	Br2	3
N1	N2	C4	C3	−171

N3	N2	C4	Br2	172
N3	N2	C4	C3	−2
N2	N3	N4	C3	9
C2	N3	N4	C3	−174
N2	N3	C2	Br1	179
N2	N3	C2	C1	17
N4	N3	C2	Br1	2
N4	N3	C2	C1	−159
N3	N4	C3	C4	−12
N3	N4	C3	C6	166

N1	C1	C2	Br1	−174
N1	C1	C2	N3	−19
C5	C1	C2	Br1	30
C5	C1	C2	N3	−176
N4	C3	C4	Br2	−165
N4	C3	C4	N2	9
C6	C3	C4	Br2	18
C6	C3	C4	N2	−168

35.4   1,5 - Naphthyridine dihydrate (orthorhombic form) $C_8H_6N_2$, $2H_2O$

M.Brufani, D.Duranti, G.Giacomello, L.Zambonelli, Gazz. Chim. Ital., 91, 287, 1961

Published value of y(C1) = 0.1539.
The correct value is −0.1539.
See also Brufani et al., Atti Accad.
Nazion. Lincei, R. C., Cl. Sci. Fis.
Mat. Nat., 40, 187, 1966.
Pbca   Z = 4 R_{h0l} = 0.114,
R_{0kl} = 0.156

NAPYDH   LB 8-6-13

Bond Lengths

C2	N1	1.38
C3D	N1	1.33
C1	C2	1.43
C1	C4	1.38
C2	C2D	1.41
C3	C4	1.40

Bond Angles

C2	N1	C3D	116
C2	C1	C4	120
N1	C2	C1	120
N1	C2	C2D	123
C1	C2	C2D	117
C1	C4	C3	118

35.5   Rubidium 2,5 - dimethyl - 1,3a,4,6a - tetra - azapentalene 3,6 - dicarboxylate dihydrate $C_8H_6N_4O_4{}^{2-}$, $2Rb^+$, $2H_2O$

M.Brufani, W.Fedeli, G.Giacomello, A.Vaciago, Gazz. Chim. Ital., 93, 1556, 1963

The structure was determined in
two dimensions only. Atomic
coordinates were not reported in
the paper.
P2$_1$/c   Z = 2 R_{0kl} = 0.08,
R_{h0l} = 0.18

RMAZPC   LB 8-6-17

35.6   iso - Quinoline hydrochloride

$C_9H_8N^+$, Cl^-

F.Genet, Bull. Soc. Fr. Mineral. Cristallogr., 88, 463, 1965

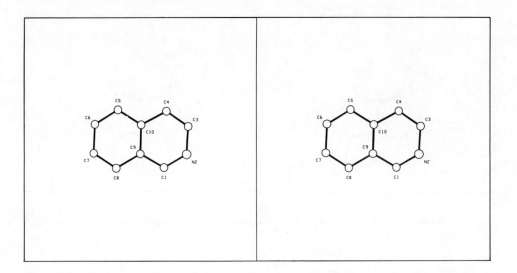

$P2_1/a$ $Z = 4$ $R = 0.15$

IQUINC   LB 9-8-3

Bond Lengths

C1	N2	1.34	C5	C10	1.40
C3	N2	1.39	C6	C7	1.44
C1	C9	1.38			(1.34)
C3	C4	1.35	C7	C8	1.38
C4	C10	1.45	C8	C9	1.42
C5	C6	1.39	C9	C10	1.45
		(1.44)			

Bond Angles

C1	N2	C3	122	C7	C8	C9	118
N2	C1	C9	122	C1	C9	C8	121
N2	C3	C4	121	C1	C9	C10	117
C3	C4	C10	118	C8	C9	C10	121
C6	C5	C10	117	C4	C10	C5	121
C5	C6	C7	124	C4	C10	C9	119
C6	C7	C8	119	C5	C10	C9	120

35.7   iso - Quinoline hydrochloride monohydrate

$C_9H_8N^+$, Cl^- , H_2O

F.Genet, Bull. Soc. Fr. Mineral. Cristallogr., 88, 463, 1965

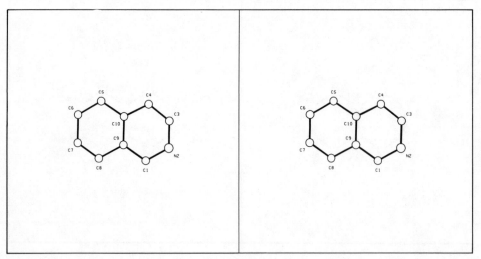

Published value of y(C3) = -0.01.
The correct value is -0.21.
P-1 $Z = 2$ $R = 0.18$

IQUICM   LB 9-8-4

Bond Lengths

C1	N2	1.34	C5	C6	1.37
C3	N2	1.33	C5	C10	1.39
		(1.38)	C6	C7	1.39
C1	C9	1.38	C7	C8	1.34
C3	C4	1.35	C8	C9	1.41
C4	C10	1.41	C9	C10	1.40

Bond Angles

C1	N2	C3	119	C7	C8	C9	118
N2	C1	C9	118	C1	C9	C8	118
N2	C3	C4	126	C1	C9	C10	123
C3	C4	C10	117	C8	C9	C10	119
C6	C5	C10	118	C4	C10	C5	121
C5	C6	C7	120	C4	C10	C9	116
C6	C7	C8	123	C5	C10	C9	122

35.8   2 - Amino - 5 - propyl - 7 - methyl - s - triazolo - (2,3,c) - pyrimidine hydrochloride

$C_9H_{14}N_5^+$, Cl^-

P.G.Owston, J.M.Rowe, Acta Cryst., 15, 231, 1962

C2/c   Z = 8   R = 0.24

AZPMHC   LB 9-14-3

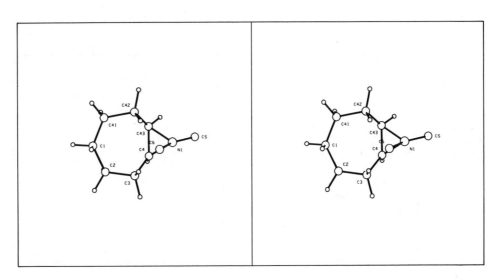

Bond Lengths

N3	N4	1.35	C2	N10	1.37
C2	N1	1.36	C5	C11	1.44
C9	N1	1.35	C7	C8	1.30
C2	N3	1.35	C7	C14	1.57
C5	N4	1.38	C8	C9	1.42
C9	N4	1.35	C11	C12	1.54
C5	N6	1.27	C12	C13	1.57
C7	N6	1.40			

Bond Angles

C2	N1	C9	107	N1	C2	N10	124	C8	C7	C14	122
N4	N3	C2	105	N3	C2	N10	125	C7	C8	C9	118
N3	N4	C5	123	N4	C5	N6	117	N1	C9	N4	107
N3	N4	C9	111	N4	C5	C11	118	N1	C9	C8	137
C5	N4	C9	124	N6	C5	C11	125	N4	C9	C8	117
C5	N6	C7	121	N6	C7	C8	123	C5	C11	C12	112
N1	C2	N3	110	N6	C7	C14	115	C11	C12	C13	110

Torsion Angles

N4	C5	C11	C12	−174
N6	C5	C11	C12	−1
C5	C11	C12	C13	−178

35.9   8,8 - Dimethyl - 8 - azoniabicyclo(5.1.0)octane iodide

$C_9H_{18}N^+$, I^-

L.M.Trefonas, R.Towns, J. Heterocycl. Chem., 1, 19, 1965

Pna2₁   Z = 4   R = 0.14

DMAZOI   LB 9-18-8

Bond Lengths

C4	N1	1.53
C5	N1	1.56
C6	N1	1.52
C43	N1	1.54
C1	C2	1.55
C1	C41	1.50
C2	C3	1.53
C3	C4	1.49
C4	C43	1.50
C41	C42	1.56
C42	C43	1.49

Bond Angles

C4	N1	C5	114	N1	C4	C3	114
C4	N1	C6	86	N1	C4	C43	61
C4	N1	C43	58	C3	C4	C43	124
C5	N1	C6	156	C1	C41	C42	119
C5	N1	C43	108	C41	C42	C43	107
C6	N1	C43	93	N1	C43	C4	61
C2	C1	C41	125	N1	C43	C42	111
C1	C2	C3	113	C4	C43	C42	122
C2	C3	C4	108				

Torsion Angles

C5	N1	C4	C3	146	C2	C1	C41	C42	−51
C5	N1	C4	C43	−97	C1	C2	C3	C4	−76
C6	N1	C4	C3	−22	C2	C3	C4	N1	140
C6	N1	C4	C43	96	C2	C3	C4	C43	69
C43	N1	C4	C3	−117	N1	C4	C43	C42	−98
C4	N1	C43	C42	116	C3	C4	C43	N1	101
C5	N1	C43	C4	108	C3	C4	C43	C42	3
C5	N1	C43	C42	−136	C1	C41	C42	C43	71
C6	N1	C43	C4	−83	C41	C42	C43	N1	−134
C6	N1	C43	C42	32	C41	C42	C43	C4	−67
C41	C1	C2	C3	53					

35.10   3 - Indolylacetic acid

$C_{10}H_9NO_2$

I.L.Karle, K.Britts, P.Gum, Acta Cryst., 17, 496, 1964

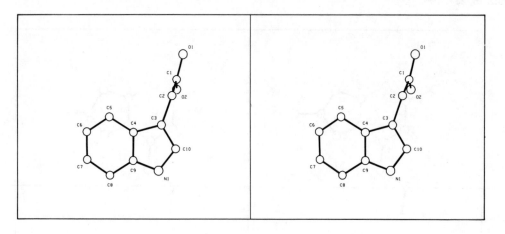

$P2_1/c$ Z = 4   R = 0.18

INACET   LB 10-9-23

Bond Lengths

C9	N1	1.38	C3	C10	1.34
C10	N1	1.40	C4	C5	1.43
C1	O1	1.30	C4	C9	1.41
C1	O2	1.22	C5	C6	1.41
C1	C2	1.49	C6	C7	1.39
C2	C3	1.51	C7	C8	1.41
C3	C4	1.47	C8	C9	1.42

Bond Angles

C9	N1	C10	108	C4	C3	C10	107
O1	C1	O2	123	C3	C4	C5	134
O1	C1	C2	113	C3	C4	C9	106
O2	C1	C2	124	C5	C4	C9	120
C1	C2	C3	115	C4	C5	C6	117
C2	C3	C4	125	C5	C6	C7	122
C2	C3	C10	128	C6	C7	C8	123

C7	C8	C9	115
N1	C9	C4	108
N1	C9	C8	128
C4	C9	C8	123
N1	C10	C3	110

Torsion Angles

O1	C1	C2	C3	174
O2	C1	C2	C3	−12
C1	C2	C3	C4	−86
C1	C2	C3	C10	98

35.11   5 - Hydroxytryptamine creatinine sulfate monohydrate

$C_{10}H_{13}N_2O^+$, $C_4H_8N_3O^+$, O_4S^{2-} , H_2O

I.L.Karle, K.S.Dragonette, S.A.Brenner, Acta Cryst., 19, 713, 1965

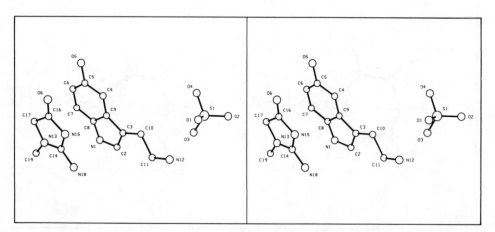

$C2/c$ Z = 8   R = 0.185

HTRCRS   LB 14-21-3

Bond Lengths

S1	O1	1.46	C5	C6	1.38
S1	O2	1.48	C6	C7	1.40
S1	O3	1.48	C7	C8	1.43
S1	O4	1.51	C8	C9	1.40
			C10	C11	1.53
C2	N1	1.39			
C8	N1	1.39	C14	N13	1.31
C11	N12	1.51	C17	N13	1.49
C5	O5	1.38	C19	N13	1.47
C2	C3	1.37	C14	N15	1.38
C3	C9	1.47	C16	N15	1.41
C3	C10	1.48	C14	N18	1.34
C4	C5	1.42	C16	O6	1.22
C4	C9	1.41	C16	C17	1.49

Bond Angles

O1	S1	O2	110	O5	C5	C4	116
O1	S1	O3	109	O5	C5	C6	122
O1	S1	O4	111	C4	C5	C6	122
O2	S1	O3	111	C5	C6	C7	122
O2	S1	O4	108	C6	C7	C8	116
O3	S1	O4	107	N1	C8	C7	128
				N1	C8	C9	110
C2	N1	C8	106	C7	C8	C9	122
N1	C2	C3	113	C3	C9	C4	132
C2	C3	C9	104	C3	C9	C8	107
C2	C3	C10	131	C4	C9	C8	121
C9	C3	C10	125	C3	C10	C11	111
C5	C4	C9	117	N12	C11	C10	108

C14	N13	C17	110
C14	N13	C19	128
C17	N13	C19	122
C14	N15	C16	108
N13	C14	N15	113
N13	C14	N18	126
N15	C14	N18	121
N15	C16	O6	123
N15	C16	C17	108
O6	C16	C17	129
N13	C17	C16	102

Torsion Angles

C2	C3	C10	C11	−9
C9	C3	C10	C11	167
C3	C10	C11	N12	−173

35.12　9,9 - Dimethyl - 9 - azoniabicyclo(6.1.0)nonane iodide

$C_{10}H_{20}N^+$, I^-

L.M.Trefonas, R.Majeste, Tetrahedron, 19, 929, 1963

The structure is totally disordered.
Pmn2$_1$　Z = 2　R = 0.13

MAZNOI　　LB 10-20-11

35.13　7 - (p - Iodobenzenesulfonyl) - 7 - azabicyclo(4.1.0)heptane

$C_{12}H_{14}INO_2S$

L.M.Trefonas, R.Majeste, J. Heterocycl. Chem., 2, 80, 1965

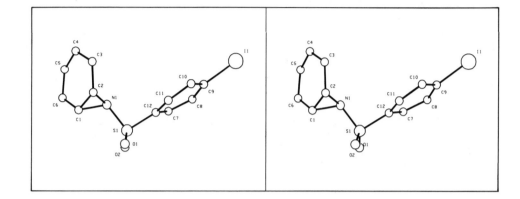

P2$_1$/n　Z = 4　R = 0.115

IBSAZH　　LB 12-14-17

Bond Lengths

I1	C9	2.05	C3	C4	1.51
S1	N1	1.66	C4	C5	1.49
S1	O1	1.47	C5	C6	1.47
S1	O2	1.37	C7	C8	1.42
S1	C12	1.72	C7	C12	1.45
C1	N1	1.50	C8	C9	1.43
C2	N1	1.53	C9	C10	1.51
C1	C2	1.48	C10	C11	1.39
C1	C6	1.49	C11	C12	1.40
C2	C3	1.49			

Bond Angles

N1	S1	O1	115	C2	C3	C4	115
N1	S1	O2	108	C3	C4	C5	122
N1	S1	C12	98	C4	C5	C6	121
O1	S1	O2	116	C1	C6	C5	116
O1	S1	C12	107	C8	C7	C12	121
O2	S1	C12	112	C7	C8	C9	118
S1	N1	C1	116	I1	C9	C8	119
S1	N1	C2	114	I1	C9	C10	120
C1	N1	C2	59	C8	C9	C10	121
N1	C1	C2	62	C9	C10	C11	116
N1	C1	C6	112	C10	C11	C12	123
C2	C1	C6	122	S1	C12	C7	118
N1	C2	C1	60	S1	C12	C11	123
N1	C2	C3	113	C7	C12	C11	119
C1	C2	C3	122				

Torsion Angles

O1	S1	N1	C1	−50	C2	N1	C1	C6	115
O1	S1	N1	C2	15	S1	N1	C2	C1	−107
O2	S1	N1	C1	80	S1	N1	C2	C3	138
O2	S1	N1	C2	146	C1	N1	C2	C3	−115
C12	S1	N1	C1	−163	N1	C1	C2	C3	100
C12	S1	N1	C2	−98	C6	C1	C2	N1	−99
N1	S1	C12	C7	−94	C6	C1	C2	C3	0
N1	S1	C12	C11	90	N1	C1	C6	C5	−60
O1	S1	C12	C7	146	C2	C1	C6	C5	9
O1	S1	C12	C11	−29	N1	C2	C3	C4	67
O2	S1	C12	C7	19	C1	C2	C3	C4	−1
O2	S1	C12	C11	−157	C2	C3	C4	C5	−7
S1	N1	C1	C2	104	C3	C4	C5	C6	17
S1	N1	C1	C6	−141	C4	C5	C6	C1	−17

35.14　5 - Iodo - 2 - phthalimidobenzoic acid monohydrate

$C_{15}H_8INO_4$, H_2O

R.M.Mayer, M.R.A.Pratt, Acta Cryst., 16, 1086, 1963

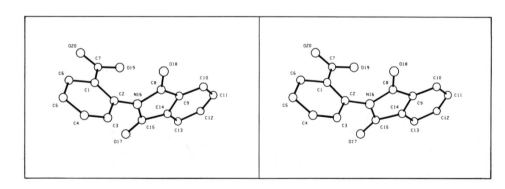

The iodine atom is disordered.
P-1　Z = 2　R = 0.10

IPTBZA　　LB 15-8-3

Bond Lengths

C2	N16	1.43	C3	C4	1.34
C8	N16	1.43	C4	C5	1.45
C15	N16	1.22	C5	C6	1.33
C15	O17	1.30	C8	C9	1.56
C8	O18	1.16	C9	C10	1.36
C7	O19	1.30	C9	C14	1.33
C7	O20	1.20	C10	C11	1.36
C1	C2	1.37	C11	C12	1.32
C1	C6	1.42	C12	C13	1.37
C1	C7	1.39	C13	C14	1.40
C2	C3	1.44	C14	C15	1.59

Bond Angles

C2	N16	C8	120	C4	C5	C6	123
C2	N16	C15	130	C1	C6	C5	116
C8	N16	C15	110	O19	C7	O20	125
C2	C1	C6	124	O19	C7	C1	119
C2	C1	C7	121	O20	C7	C1	116
C6	C1	C7	114	N16	C8	O18	126
N16	C2	C1	123	N16	C8	C9	104
N16	C2	C3	123	O18	C8	C9	129
C1	C2	C3	114	C8	C9	C10	129
C2	C3	C4	124	C8	C9	C14	108
C3	C4	C5	115	C10	C9	C14	123
				C9	C10	C11	117
				C10	C11	C12	120
				C11	C12	C13	125
				C12	C13	C14	114
				C9	C14	C13	121
				C9	C14	C15	103
				C13	C14	C15	136
				N16	C15	O17	128
				N16	C15	C14	113
				O17	C15	C14	116

Torsion Angles

C8	N16	C2	C1	96
C8	N16	C2	C3	−88
C15	N16	C2	C1	−93
C15	N16	C2	C3	83
C2	C1	C7	O19	−7
C2	C1	C7	O20	179
C6	C1	C7	O19	178
C6	C1	C7	O20	3

35.15   1 - (5' - Bromo - 2' - hydroxy - 4' - methoxyphenyl) - 3 - oxo - isoindolo - 1 - en

$C_{15}H_{10}BrNO_3$

N.E.Taylor, Acta Cryst., 14, 893, 1961

The structure was determined in two dimensions only. Atomic coordinates were not reported in the paper.

P-1   Z = 2 R_{0kl} = 0.17

BROXIN   LB 15-10-2

35.16   Indirubine

$C_{16}H_{10}N_2O_2$

H.Pandraud, Acta Cryst., 14, 901, 1961

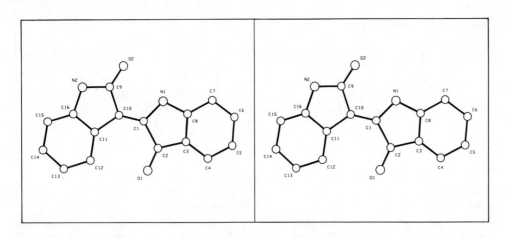

$P2_12_12_1$ Z = 4   R = 0.10

INDRUB   LB 16-10-17

Bond Lengths

C1	N1	1.40	C2	C3	1.48	C10	C11	1.51
C8	N1	1.40	C3	C4	1.38	C11	C12	1.41
C9	N2	1.38	C3	C8	1.39	C11	C16	1.41
C16	N2	1.40	C4	C5	1.41	C12	C13	1.42
C2	O1	1.21	C5	C6	1.41	C13	C14	1.41
C9	O2	1.25	C6	C7	1.41	C14	C15	1.41
C1	C2	1.53	C7	C8	1.44	C15	C16	1.36
C1	C10	1.31	C9	C10	1.48			

Bond Angles

C1	N1	C8	110	C2	C3	C8	106	N2	C9	O2	126	C11	C12	C13	116
C9	N2	C16	111	C4	C3	C8	123	N2	C9	C10	108	C12	C13	C14	121
N1	C1	C2	106	C3	C4	C5	117	O2	C9	C10	126	C13	C14	C15	122
N1	C1	C10	123	C4	C5	C6	122	C1	C10	C9	122	C14	C15	C16	116
C2	C1	C10	132	C5	C6	C7	121	C1	C10	C11	133	N2	C16	C11	110
O1	C2	C1	126	C6	C7	C8	116	C9	C10	C11	105	N2	C16	C15	126
O1	C2	C3	128	N1	C8	C3	112	C10	C11	C12	133	C11	C16	C15	124
C1	C2	C3	106	N1	C8	C7	126	C10	C11	C16	107				
C2	C3	C4	131	C3	C8	C7	122	C12	C11	C16	120				

35.17   Isoindigo

$C_{16}H_{10}N_2O_2$

H.von Eller-Pandraud, Acta Cryst., 13, 936, 1960

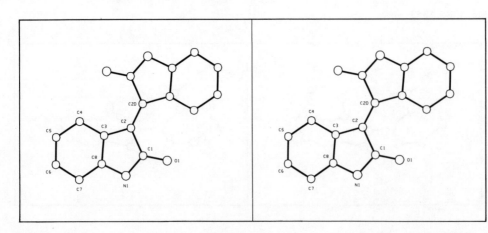

C2/m   Z = 2   No R factor was given.

ISOIND   LB 16-10-16

Bond Lengths

C1	N1	1.33	C3	C4	1.43
C8	N1	1.37	C3	C8	1.40
C1	O1	1.26	C4	C5	1.43
C1	C2	1.50	C5	C6	1.34
C2	C3	1.44	C6	C7	1.41
C2	C2D	1.34	C7	C8	1.39

Bond Angles

C1	N1	C8	108	C3	C2	C2D	132	C5	C6	C7	121
N1	C1	O1	121	C2	C3	C4	136	C6	C7	C8	114
N1	C1	C2	113	C2	C3	C8	110	N1	C8	C3	110
O1	C1	C2	126	C4	C3	C8	114	N1	C8	C7	121
C1	C2	C3	100	C3	C4	C5	119	C3	C8	C7	129
C1	C2	C2D	128	C4	C5	C6	123				

35.18   6,6 - Diphenyl - 3,3 - diethyl - 3 - azabicyclo(3.1.0)hexane bromide monohydrate

$C_{21}H_{26}N^+$, Br^- , H_2O

F.R.Ahmed, E.J.Gabe, Acta Cryst., 17, 603, 1964

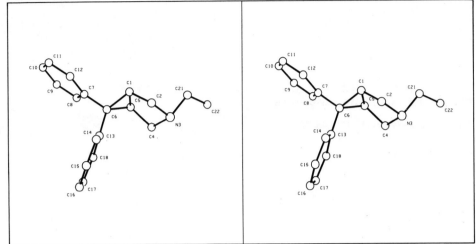

One of the ethyl groups is disordered.

$P2_1/n$ Z = 4   R = 0.114

DAZHEB   LB 21-26-1

Bond Lengths

C2	N3	1.53	C8	C9	1.39
C4	N3	1.52	C9	C10	1.38
C21	N3	1.53	C10	C11	1.38
C1	C2	1.50	C11	C12	1.39
C1	C5	1.53	C13	C14	1.39
C1	C6	1.51	C13	C18	1.40
C4	C5	1.51	C14	C15	1.39
C5	C6	1.52	C15	C16	1.39
C6	C7	1.51	C16	C17	1.39
C6	C13	1.50	C17	C18	1.39
C7	C8	1.39	C21	C22	1.52
C7	C12	1.39			

Bond Angles

C2	N3	C4	104	C6	C7	C8	121
C2	N3	C21	107	C6	C7	C12	120
C4	N3	C21	109	C8	C7	C12	119
C2	C1	C5	107	C7	C8	C9	120
C2	C1	C6	121	C8	C9	C10	120
C5	C1	C6	60	C9	C10	C11	120
N3	C2	C1	105	C10	C11	C12	120
N3	C4	C5	105	C7	C12	C11	120
C1	C5	C4	106	C6	C13	C14	121
C1	C5	C6	60	C6	C13	C18	119
C4	C5	C6	119	C14	C13	C18	119
C1	C6	C5	60	C13	C14	C15	121
C1	C6	C7	114	C14	C15	C16	120
C1	C6	C13	123	C15	C16	C17	120
C5	C6	C7	115	C16	C17	C18	120
C5	C6	C13	121	C13	C18	C17	120
C7	C6	C13	113	N3	C21	C22	116

Torsion Angles

C4	N3	C2	C1	−34	C1	C5	C6	C7	105
C21	N3	C2	C1	82	C1	C5	C6	C13	−113
C2	N3	C4	C5	35	C4	C5	C6	C1	93
C21	N3	C4	C5	−79	C4	C5	C6	C7	−162
C2	N3	C21	C22	176	C4	C5	C6	C13	−20
C4	N3	C21	C22	−72	C1	C6	C7	C8	120
C5	C1	C2	N3	20	C1	C6	C7	C12	−62
C6	C1	C2	N3	85	C5	C6	C7	C8	53
C2	C1	C5	C4	2	C5	C6	C7	C12	−129
C2	C1	C5	C6	116	C13	C6	C7	C8	−92
C6	C1	C5	C4	−114	C13	C6	C7	C12	86
C2	C1	C6	C5	−93	C1	C6	C13	C14	48
C2	C1	C6	C7	161	C1	C6	C13	C18	−138
C2	C1	C6	C13	16	C5	C6	C13	C14	121
C5	C1	C6	C7	−106	C5	C6	C13	C18	−65
C5	C1	C6	C13	110	C7	C6	C13	C14	−97
N3	C4	C5	C1	−23	C7	C6	C13	C18	77
N3	C4	C5	C6	−87					

36.1 Dodecahydro - 1,4,7,9b - tetra - azaphenalene trihydrochloride hemihydrate

A.E.Smith, Acta Cryst., 19, 248, 1965

$C_9H_{21}N_4{}^{3+}$, $3Cl^-$, $0.5H_2O$

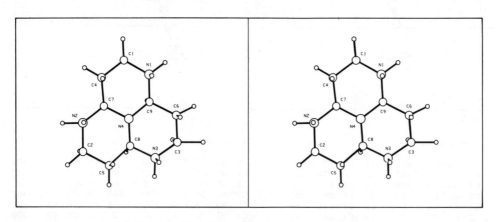

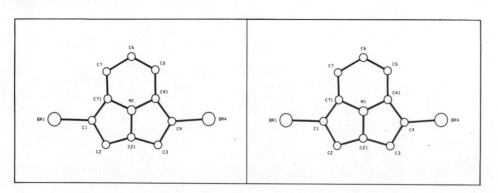

$Pna2_1$ $Z = 4$ $R = 0.093$

HAZPEN   LB 9-21-2

Bond Lengths

C1	N1	1.53	C9	N4	1.48
C9	N1	1.50	C1	C4	1.55
C2	N2	1.51	C2	C5	1.52
C7	N2	1.48	C3	C6	1.49
C3	N3	1.48	C4	C7	1.53
C8	N3	1.45	C5	C8	1.54
C7	N4	1.47	C6	C9	1.56
C8	N4	1.45			

Bond Angles

C1	N1	C9	109	C3	C6	C9	110
C2	N2	C7	114	N2	C7	N4	107
C3	N3	C8	116	N2	C7	C4	105
C7	N4	C8	111	N4	C7	C4	110
C7	N4	C9	109	N3	C8	N4	110
C8	N4	C9	111	N3	C8	C5	109
N1	C1	C4	105	N4	C8	C5	114
N2	C2	C5	110	N1	C9	N4	107
N3	C3	C6	105	N1	C9	C6	106
C1	C4	C7	108	N4	C9	C6	107
C2	C5	C8	109				

Torsion Angles

C9	N1	C1	C4	65	C9	N4	C8	N3	56
C1	N1	C9	N4	−67	C9	N4	C8	C5	179
C1	N1	C9	C6	180	C7	N4	C9	N1	64
C7	N2	C2	C5	56	C7	N4	C9	C6	177
C2	N2	C7	N4	−60	C8	N4	C9	N1	−173
C2	N2	C7	C4	−177	C8	N4	C9	C6	−60
C8	N3	C3	C6	58	N1	C1	C4	C7	−60
C3	N3	C8	N4	−56	N2	C2	C5	C8	−49
C3	N3	C8	C5	178	N3	C3	C6	C9	−60
C8	N4	C7	N2	60	C1	C4	C7	N2	177
C8	N4	C7	C4	174	C1	C4	C7	N4	61
C9	N4	C7	N2	−177	C2	C5	C8	N3	176
C9	N4	C7	C4	−63	C2	C5	C8	N4	53
C7	N4	C8	N3	178	C3	C6	C9	N1	177
C7	N4	C8	C5	−59	C3	C6	C9	N4	63

36.2 1,4 - Dibromo - cycl(3,2,2)azine

A.W.Hanson, Acta Cryst., 14, 124, 1961

$C_{10}H_5Br_2N$

$P2_1/n$ $Z = 4$ $R = 0.09$

DBRCYC   LB 10-5-2

Bond Lengths

Br1	C1	1.93	C1	C2	1.39	C4	C41	1.40
Br4	C4	1.89	C1	C71	1.34	C5	C6	1.39
C21	N1	1.33	C2	C21	1.37	C5	C41	1.41
C41	N1	1.38	C3	C4	1.36	C6	C7	1.48
C71	N1	1.35	C3	C21	1.43	C7	C71	1.35

Bond Angles

C21	N1	C41	115	C1	C2	C21	105	C5	C6	C7	123	N1	C41	C5	114
C21	N1	C71	114	C4	C3	C21	106	C6	C7	C71	117	C4	C41	C5	144
C41	N1	C71	131	Br4	C4	C3	125	N1	C21	C2	106	N1	C71	C1	103
Br1	C1	C2	123	Br4	C4	C41	123	N1	C21	C3	105	N1	C71	C7	117
Br1	C1	C71	126	C3	C4	C41	111	C2	C21	C3	149	C1	C71	C7	140
C2	C1	C71	112	C6	C5	C41	118	N1	C41	C4	102				

206

36.3   5 - Keto - 1,5 - dihydrobenz(cd)indole

$C_{11}H_7NO$

M.E.Burke, Dissert. Abstr., 25, 6249, 1965

Atomic coordinates were not reported in the paper.
P2$_1$/c   Z = 4   R = 0.071

HBZIND   LB 11-8-4

36.4   1,4,6,9 - Tetrachlorophenazine

$C_{12}H_4Cl_4N_2$

V.Riganti, S.Locchi, R.Curti, B.Bovio, J. Heterocycl. Chem., 2, 176, 1965

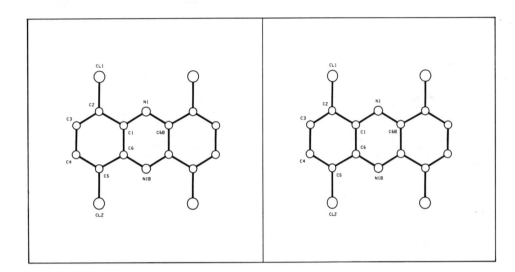

P2$_1$/n   Z = 2   R = 0.106

TCLPHZ   LB 12-4-2

Bond Lengths

Cl1	C2	1.71	C1	C6	1.45
Cl2	C5	1.73	C2	C3	1.35
C1	N1	1.34	C3	C4	1.43
C6B	N1	1.34	C4	C5	1.37
C1	C2	1.44	C5	C6	1.42

Bond Angles

C1	N1	C6B	118	C2	C3	C4	122
N1	C1	C2	119	C3	C4	C5	120
N1	C1	C6	121	Cl2	C5	C4	120
C2	C1	C6	119	Cl2	C5	C6	118
Cl1	C2	C1	119	C4	C5	C6	121
Cl1	C2	C3	122	C1	C6	C5	118
C1	C2	C3	119				

36.5   2,3,7,8 - Tetrachlorophenazine

$C_{12}H_4Cl_4N_2$

V.Riganti, S.Locchi, R.Curti, B.Bovio, J. Heterocycl. Chem., 2, 87, 1965

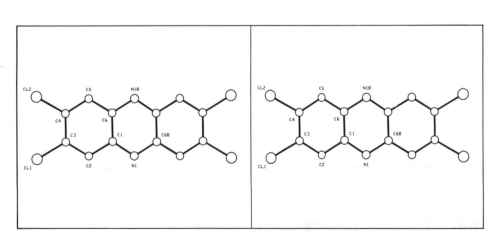

P2$_1$/c   Z = 2   R = 0.11

TCPHAZ   LB 12-4-3

Bond Lengths

Cl1	C3	1.73	C1	C6	1.43
Cl2	C4	1.73	C2	C3	1.38
C1	N1	1.34	C3	C4	1.42
C6B	N1	1.37	C4	C5	1.41
C1	C2	1.44	C5	C6	1.42

Bond Angles

C1	N1	C6B	116	C2	C3	C4	122
N1	C1	C2	116	Cl2	C4	C3	120
N1	C1	C6	124	Cl2	C4	C5	119
C2	C1	C6	119	C3	C4	C5	121
C1	C2	C3	119	C4	C5	C6	118
Cl1	C3	C2	119	C1	C6	C5	121
Cl1	C3	C4	119				

36.6 N - Oxyphenazine

R.Curti, V.Riganti, S.Locchi, Acta Cryst., 14, 133, 1961

C₁₂H₈N₂O

The structure is totally disordered.
P2₁/c   Z = 2   R$_{h0l}$ = 0.19,
R$_{hk0}$ = 0.17, R$_{h1l}$ = 0.17, R$_{h2l}$ = 0.16

OXYPHE   LB 12-8-44

36.7 Phenazine - 5,10 - dioxide

Y.Namba, T.Oda, T.Watanabe, Bull. Chem. Soc. Jap., 36, 1364, 1963

C₁₂H₈N₂O₂

P2₁/c   Z = 2   R$_{h0l}$ = 0.16,
R$_{0kl}$ = 0.15

PHAZOX   LB 12-8-46

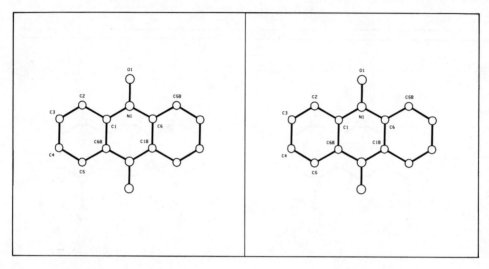

Bond Lengths			Bond Angles			
N1	O1	1.33	O1	N1	C1	120
C1	N1	1.34	O1	N1	C6	117
C6	N1	1.36	C1	N1	C6	123
C1	C2	1.44	N1	C1	C2	121
C1	C6B	1.45	N1	C1	C6B	121
C2	C3	1.36	C2	C1	C6B	118
C3	C4	1.43	C1	C2	C3	121
C4	C5	1.39	C2	C3	C4	121
C5	C6B	1.39	C3	C4	C5	119
			C4	C5	C6B	121
			N1	C6	C1B	117
			N1	C6	C5B	124

36.8 Phenazine - 5,10 - dioxide

V.Riganti, R.Curti, A.Coda, Ric. Sci., 1, 30, 1570, 1960

C₁₂H₈N₂O₂

P2₁/c   Z = 2   R = 0.153

PHAZOX01   LB 12-8-46

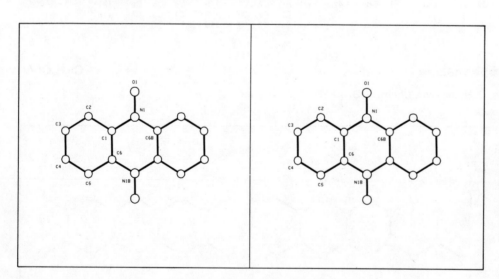

Bond Lengths			Bond Angles			
N1	O1	1.26	O1	N1	C1	120
C1	N1	1.35	O1	N1	C6B	120
C6B	N1	1.35	C1	N1	C6B	120
C1	C2	1.39	N1	C1	C2	119
C1	C6	1.41	N1	C1	C6	119
C2	C3	1.39	C2	C1	C6	122
C3	C4	1.40	C1	C2	C3	118
C4	C5	1.38	C2	C3	C4	120
C5	C6	1.40	C3	C4	C5	121
			C4	C5	C6	119
			C1	C6	C5	119

36.9 Dibenzo - 1,3a,4,6a - tetra - azapentalene

M.E.Burke, R.A.Sparks, K.N.Trueblood, Acta Cryst., 16, A64, 1963

C₁₂H₈N₄

Atomic coordinates were not reported in the paper.
C2/c   Z = 4   R = 0.08

TAZPEN   LB 12-8-54

36.10 Acridine (form ii)

$C_{13}H_9N$

D.C.Phillips, F.R.Ahmed, W.H.Barnes, Acta Cryst., 13, 365, 1960

See also Phillips, Acta Cryst., 9, 237, 1956.

$P2_1/a$ $Z = 8$ $R = 0.146$

ACRDIN   LB 13-9-11

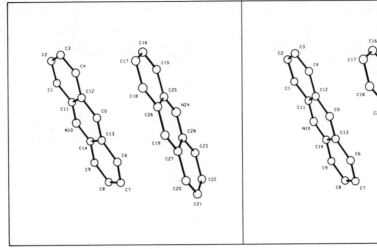

Bond Lengths

C11	N10	1.34	C7	C8	1.42	C17	C18	1.35
C14	N10	1.35	C8	C9	1.36	C18	C26	1.43
C1	C2	1.35	C9	C14	1.42	C19	C26	1.39
C1	C11	1.43	C11	C12	1.43	C19	C27	1.40
C2	C3	1.43	C13	C14	1.43	C20	C21	1.35
C3	C4	1.35				C20	C27	1.44
C4	C12	1.43	C25	N24	1.34	C21	C22	1.44
C5	C12	1.40	C28	N24	1.34	C22	C23	1.36
C5	C13	1.39	C15	C16	1.37	C23	C28	1.42
C6	C7	1.38	C15	C25	1.43	C25	C26	1.44
C6	C13	1.43	C16	C17	1.42	C27	C28	1.43

Bond Angles

C11	N10	C14	118	C5	C12	C11	118	C20	C21	C22	121
C2	C1	C11	121	C5	C13	C6	122	C21	C22	C23	120
C1	C2	C3	121	C5	C13	C14	119	C22	C23	C28	121
C2	C3	C4	120	C6	C13	C14	119	N24	C25	C15	119
C3	C4	C12	120	N10	C14	C9	118	N24	C25	C26	124
C12	C5	C13	119	N10	C14	C13	123	C15	C25	C26	118
C7	C6	C13	120	C9	C14	C13	119	C18	C26	C19	122
C6	C7	C8	120					C18	C26	C25	120
C7	C8	C9	122	C25	N24	C28	118	C19	C26	C25	118
C8	C9	C14	120	C16	C15	C25	120	C19	C27	C20	124
N10	C11	C1	118	C15	C16	C17	121	C19	C27	C28	118
N10	C11	C12	124	C16	C17	C18	121	C20	C27	C28	118
C1	C11	C12	118	C17	C18	C26	120	N24	C28	C23	118
C4	C12	C5	123	C26	C19	C27	119	N24	C28	C27	123
C4	C12	C11	119	C21	C20	C27	121	C23	C28	C27	119

36.11 asym - α,β - Naphthazine

$C_{20}H_{12}N_2$

B.Bovio, S.Locchi, Z. Kristallogr., 121, 306, 1965

$P2_1/c$ $Z = 2$ $R = 0.098$

NAAZAS   LB 20-12-12

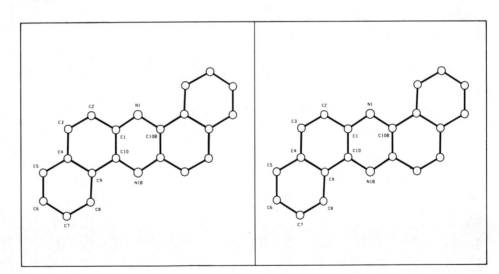

Bond Lengths

C1	N1	1.35	C4	C9	1.45
C10B	N1	1.34	C5	C6	1.39
C1	C2	1.44	C6	C7	1.41
C1	C10	1.41	C7	C8	1.41
C2	C3	1.37	C8	C9	1.42
C3	C4	1.46	C9	C10	1.43
C4	C5	1.43			

Bond Angles

C1	N1	C10B	116	C3	C4	C5	120	C7	C8	C9	122
N1	C1	C2	118	C3	C4	C9	119	C4	C9	C8	117
N1	C1	C10	123	C5	C4	C9	121	C4	C9	C10	119
C2	C1	C10	119	C4	C5	C6	119	C8	C9	C10	123
C1	C2	C3	122	C5	C6	C7	122	C1	C10	C9	120
C2	C3	C4	120	C6	C7	C8	119				

36.12   1,2,8,9 - Dibenzacridine

$C_{21}H_{13}N$

R.Mason, Proc. R. Soc., A, 258, 302, 1960

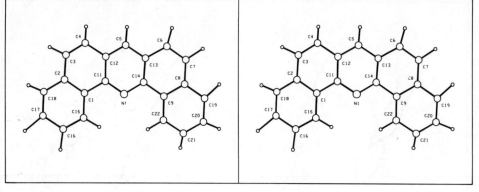

$Pna2_1$ $Z = 4$ $R_{hol} = 0.054$,
$R_{0kl} = 0.054$, $R_{hk0} = 0.054$

BNZACR   LB 21-13-3

Bond Lengths

C11	N1	1.35	C7	C8	1.42	
C14	N1	1.35	C8	C9	1.42	
C1	C2	1.43	C8	C19	1.43	
C1	C11	1.45	C9	C14	1.46	
C1	C15	1.44	C9	C22	1.38	
C2	C3	1.42	C11	C12	1.42	
C2	C18	1.43	C13	C14	1.41	
C3	C4	1.35	C15	C16	1.39	
C4	C12	1.48	C16	C17	1.43	
C5	C12	1.37	C17	C18	1.39	
C5	C13	1.40	C19	C20	1.36	
C6	C7	1.38	C20	C21	1.38	
C6	C13	1.44	C21	C22	1.41	

Bond Angles

C11	N1	C14	117	C7	C8	C19	121	C6	C13	C14	122
C2	C1	C11	118	C9	C8	C19	118	N1	C14	C9	117
C2	C1	C15	121	C8	C9	C14	118	N1	C14	C13	124
C11	C1	C15	121	C8	C9	C22	120	C9	C14	C13	119
C1	C2	C3	120	C14	C9	C22	122	C1	C15	C16	120
C1	C2	C18	117	N1	C11	C1	118	C15	C16	C17	120
C3	C2	C18	123	N1	C11	C12	123	C16	C17	C18	120
C2	C3	C4	124	C1	C11	C12	119	C2	C18	C17	122
C3	C4	C12	118	C4	C12	C5	119	C8	C19	C20	120
C12	C5	C13	118	C4	C12	C11	121	C19	C20	C21	122
C7	C6	C13	119	C5	C12	C11	120	C20	C21	C22	119
C6	C7	C8	121	C5	C13	C6	120	C9	C22	C21	121
C7	C8	C9	121	C5	C13	C14	118				

36.13   Di(6 - phenanthridyl)methane

$C_{27}H_{18}N_2$

H.Poppe, W.Hoppe, Z. Kristallogr., 122, 298, 1965

No comparison of bond lengths is possible since they are not reported in the paper. Published z coordinate for N1'(relabelled N11) = −0.098. The correct value is 0.098.
See also van Thuijl & Romers, Rec. Trav. Chim. Pays - Bas, 87, 5, 1968.

Pc $Z = 2$ $R_{0kl} = 0.127$,
$R_{hk0} = 0.13$, $R_{hol} = 0.23$

PHANME   LB 27-18-2

Bond Lengths

C2	N1	1.46	C13	C14	1.35	
C14	N1	1.39	C14	C151	1.37	
C21	N11	1.48	C21	C31	1.43	
C141	N11	1.21	C21	C71	1.41	
C2	C3	1.42	C31	C41	1.64	
C2	C7	1.32	C41	C51	1.37	
C3	C4	1.56	C51	C61	1.22	
C4	C5	1.24	C61	C71	1.57	
C5	C6	1.49	C71	C81	1.45	
C6	C7	1.53	C81	C91	1.32	
C7	C8	1.47	C81	C131	1.55	
C8	C9	1.33	C91	C101	1.37	
C8	C13	1.42	C101	C111	1.42	
C9	C10	1.48	C111	C121	1.31	
C10	C11	1.33	C121	C131	1.44	
C11	C12	1.25	C131	C141	1.46	
C12	C13	1.42	C141	C151	1.62	

Bond Angles

C2	N1	C14	106	C10	C11	C12	114	C61	C71	C81	120
C21	N11	C141	118	C11	C12	C13	131	C71	C81	C91	131
N1	C2	C3	110	C8	C13	C12	111	C71	C81	C131	113
N1	C2	C7	131	C8	C13	C14	121	C91	C81	C131	113
C3	C2	C7	119	C12	C13	C14	126	C81	C91	C101	128
C2	C3	C4	118	N1	C14	C13	129	C91	C101	C111	117
C3	C4	C5	118	N1	C14	C151	109	C101	C111	C121	121
C4	C5	C6	128	C13	C14	C151	122	C111	C121	C131	121
C5	C6	C7	109	N11	C21	C31	117	C81	C131	C121	117
C2	C7	C6	127	N11	C21	C71	115	C81	C131	C141	110
C2	C7	C8	118	C31	C21	C71	127	C121	C131	C141	132
C6	C7	C8	116	C21	C31	C41	110	N11	C141	C131	135
C7	C8	C9	125	C31	C41	C51	121	N11	C141	C151	111
C7	C8	C13	114	C41	C51	C61	122	C131	C141	C151	114
C9	C8	C13	121	C51	C61	C71	126	C14	C151	C141	128
C8	C9	C10	118	C21	C71	C61	112				
C9	C10	C11	121	C21	C71	C81	127				

Torsion Angles

N1	C14	C151	C141	−1
C13	C14	C151	C141	176
N11	C141	C151	C14	6
C131	C141	C151	C14	−179

37.1   Triethylenediamine

$C_6H_{12}N_2$

T.Wada, E.Kishida, Y.Tomiie, H.Suga, S.Seki, I.Nitta, Bull. Chem. Soc. Jap., 33, 1317, 1960

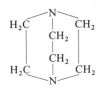

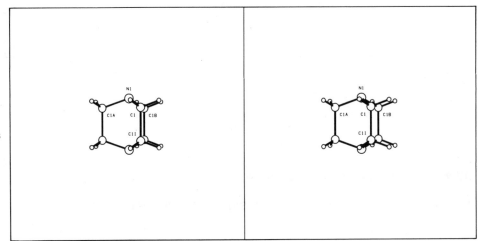

$P6_3/m$ $Z = 2$ No R factor was given.

TETDAM   LB 6-12-30

Bond Lengths

C1	N1	1.46
C1	C1I	1.59

Bond Angles

C1	N1	C1A	110
N1	C1	C1I	109

Torsion Angles

C1A	N1	C1	C1I	61
C1B	N1	C1	C1I	−61
N1	C1	C1I	N1I	0

37.2   Triethylenediamine (refined as sp. gp. no. 176)

$C_6H_{12}N_2$

G.S.Weiss, A.S.Parkes, R.E.Nixon, R.E.Hughes, J. Chem. Phys., 41, 3759, 1964

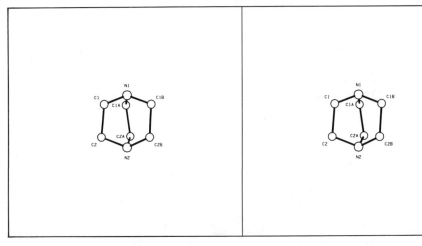

No comparison of bond lengths is possible since they are not reported in the paper.
$P6_3$ $Z = 2$ $R = 0.116$

TETDAM01   LB 6-12-30

Bond Lengths

C1	N1	1.43
C2	N2	1.49
C1	C2	1.61

Bond Angles

C1	N1	C1A	110
C2	N2	C2A	109
N1	C1	C2	109
N2	C2	C1	108

Torsion Angles

C1A	N1	C1	C2	52
C1B	N1	C1	C2	−70
C2A	N2	C2	C1	−68
C2B	N2	C2	C1	51
N1	C1	C2	N2	15

37.3   Triethylenediamine (refined as sp. gp. no. 173) $C_6H_{12}N_2$

G.S.Weiss, A.S.Parkes, R.E.Nixon, R.E.Hughes, J. Chem. Phys., 41, 3759, 1964

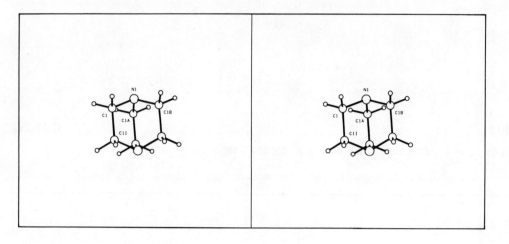

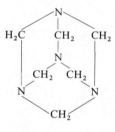

$P6_3/m$ $Z = 2$ $R = 0.133$

TETDAM02   LB 6-12-30

Bond Lengths			Bond Angles				Torsion Angles				
C1	N1	1.46	C1	N1	C1A	109	C1A	N1	C1	C1I	59
C1	C1I	1.57	N1	C1	C1I	110	C1B	N1	C1	C1I	−59
							N1	C1	C1I	N1I	0

37.4   Hexamethylenetetramine $C_6H_{12}N_4$

(i)   L.N.Becka, D.W.J.Cruickshank, Proc. R. Soc., A, 273, 435, 1963 (298°K Cu radiation)

(ii)   L.N.Becka, D.W.J.Cruickshank, Proc. R. Soc., A, 273, 435, 1963 (100°K Cu radiation)

(iii)   L.N.Becka, D.W.J.Cruickshank, Proc. R. Soc., A, 273, 435, 1963 (34°K Cu radiation)

(iv)   L.N.Becka, D.W.J.Cruickshank, Proc. R. Soc., A, 273, 435, 1963 (298°K Mo radiation)

(v)   L.N.Becka, D.W.J.Cruickshank, Proc. R. Soc., A, 273, 435, 1963 (100°K Mo radiation)

(vi)   L.N.Becka, D.W.J.Cruickshank, Proc. R. Soc., A, 273, 435, 1963 (34°K Mo radiation)

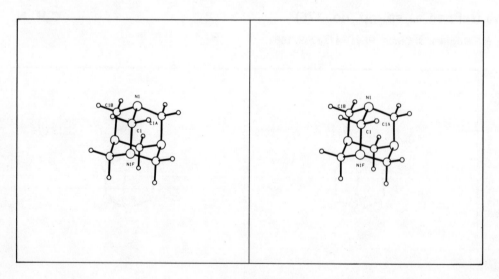

(i)   I-43m $Z = 2$ $R = 0.065$

HXMTAM   LB 6-12-41

(ii)   I-43m $Z = 2$ $R = 0.066$

HXMTAM01   LB 6-12-41

(iii)   I-43m $Z = 2$ $R = 0.063$

HXMTAM02   LB 6-12-41

(iv)   I-43m $Z = 2$ $R = 0.028$

HXMTAM03   LB 6-12-41

(v)   I-43m $Z = 2$ $R = 0.047$

HXMTAM04   LB 6-12-41

(vi)   I-43m $Z = 2$ $R = 0.041$

HXMTAM05   LB 6-12-41

Bond Lengths		(i)	(ii)	(iii)	(iv)	(v)	(vi)
C1	N1	1.46	1.47	1.47	1.47	1.47	1.48

Bond Angles			(i)	(ii)	(iii)	(iv)	(v)	(vi)
C1	N1	C1A	107	109	107	107	107	107
N1	C1	N1F	113	110	114	114	113	114

Torsion Angles				(i)	(ii)	(iii)	(iv)	(v)	(vi)
C1A	N1	C1	N1F	−58	−60	−57	−58	−58	−57
C1B	N1	C1	N1F	58	60	57	58	58	57

37.5   Hexamethylenetetramine (at 100 ° K, Cu radiation) $C_6H_{12}N_4$

For complete entry see 37.4

37.6   Hexamethylenetetramine (at 34 ° K,Cu radiation)

$C_6H_{12}N_4$

For complete entry see 37.4

37.7   Hexamethylenetetramine (at 298 ° K,Mo radiation)

$C_6H_{12}N_4$

For complete entry see 37.4

37.8   Hexamethylenetetramine (at 100 ° K,Mo radiation)

$C_6H_{12}N_4$

For complete entry see 37.4

37.9   Hexamethylenetetramine (at 34 ° K,Mo radiation)

$C_6H_{12}N_4$

For complete entry see 37.4

37.10   3 - Azabicyclo(3.3.1)nonane hydrobromide

$C_8H_{16}N^+$, Br^-

M.Dobler, J.D.Dunitz, Helv. Chim. Acta, 47, 695, 1964

$H_2C—\overset{\overset{\displaystyle H}{|}}{C}—CH_2$

$H_2C\quad CH_2\ NH_2^+ \cdot Br^-$

$H_2C—\underset{\underset{\displaystyle H}{|}}{C}—CH_2$

P-42₁c   Z = 8   R = 0.08

AZNONB   LB 8-16-4

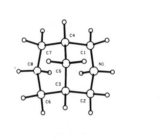

Bond Lengths

C1	N1	1.44	C3	C6	1.56
C2	N1	1.52	C4	C5	1.56
C1	C4	1.52	C4	C7	1.51
C2	C3	1.47	C6	C8	1.54
C3	C5	1.56	C7	C8	1.43

Bond Angles

C1	N1	C2	111	C1	C4	C7	115
N1	C1	C4	114	C5	C4	C7	112
N1	C2	C3	112	C3	C5	C4	101
C2	C3	C5	109	C3	C6	C8	112
C2	C3	C6	115	C4	C7	C8	118
C5	C3	C6	114	C6	C8	C7	112
C1	C4	C5	107				

Torsion Angles

C2	N1	C1	C4	−50	C2	C3	C6	C8	−73
C1	N1	C2	C3	50	C5	C3	C6	C8	55
N1	C1	C4	C5	62	C1	C4	C5	C3	−67
N1	C1	C4	C7	−63	C7	C4	C5	C3	60
N1	C2	C3	C5	−62	C1	C4	C7	C8	65
N1	C2	C3	C6	68	C5	C4	C7	C8	−58
C2	C3	C5	C4	69	C3	C6	C8	C7	−41
C6	C3	C5	C4	−61	C4	C7	C8	C6	45

37.11   N,N' - Dimethyl - 4,8 - diaza - tricyclo(4.2.2.2²,⁵) dodeca - 9,11 - dien - 3,7 - dione

$C_{12}H_{14}N_2O_2$

M.Laing, Proc. Chem. Soc., 343, 1964

Atomic coordinates were not given
but bond lengths were reported.
P2₁/c   Z = 2   R = 0.09

MAZDOD   LB 12-14-18

37.12   2 - Ethoxycarbonyl - 4 - bromo - 3 - methoxy - 8,8,9,9 - tetracyano - 2 - azabicyclo (3.2.2) non - 6 - ene

$C_{16}H_{14}BrN_5O_3$

J.H. van den Hende, A.S.Kende, Chem. Communic., 384, 1965.

Atomic coordinates were not given
but bond lengths were reported.
P2₁/n   Z = 4   R = 0.11

EAZNON   LB 16-14-7

38.1 Trioxane

C₃H₆O₃

V.Busetti, M.Mammi, G.Carazzolo, Z. Kristallogr., 119, 310, 1963

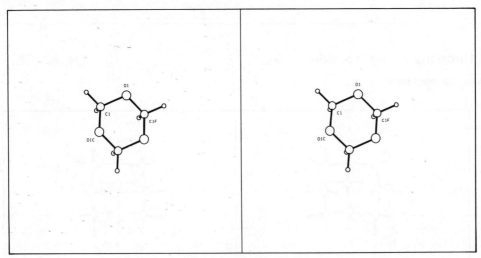

See also Busetti et al.,Acta Cryst. (B), 25, 1191, 1969.
R3c   Z = 6   R = 0.067

TROXAN   LB 3-6-39

Bond Lengths			Bond Angles			
C1	O1	1.43	C1	O1	C1F	108
C1F	O1	1.43	O1	C1	O1C	108

Torsion Angles

C1F	O1	C1	O1C	64
C1	O1	C1F	O1F	−64

38.2 trans - 2,3 - Dibromo - 1,4 - dioxane

C₄H₆Br₂O₂

C.Altona, C.Knobler, C.Romers, Rec. Trav. Chim. Pays-Bas, 82, 1089, 1963

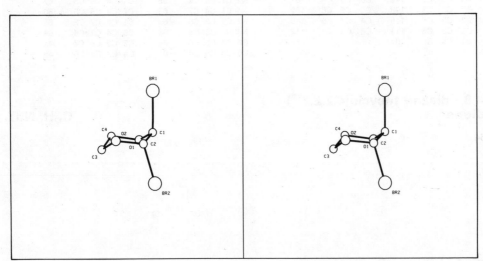

No comparison of bond lengths is possible since they are not reported in the paper.
P2₁2₁2₁   Z = 4   R₀ₖₗ = 0.07,
Rₕₒₗ = 0.13

DBRDOX   LB 4-6-11

Bond Lengths						Bond Angles							Torsion Angles									
Br1	C1	2.06	C2	O2	1.37	C1	O1	C4	110	Br2	C2	O2	113	C4	O1	C1	Br1	−73	Br1	C1	C2	Br2	−162
Br2	C2	1.98	C3	O2	1.43	C2	O2	C3	115	Br2	C2	C1	105	C4	O1	C1	C2	49	Br1	C1	C2	O2	76
C1	O1	1.38	C1	C2	1.48	Br1	C1	O1	110	O2	C2	C1	112	C1	O1	C4	C3	−54	O1	C1	C2	Br2	74
C4	O1	1.50	C3	C4	1.44	Br1	C1	C2	107	O2	C3	C4	110	C3	O2	C2	Br2	−68	O1	C1	C2	O2	−48
						O1	C1	C2	116	O1	C4	C3	112	C3	O2	C2	C1	49	O2	C3	C4	O1	56
														C2	O2	C3	C4	−55					

38.3   cis - 2,3 - Dichloro - 1,4 - dioxane $C_4H_6Cl_2O_2$

C.Altona, C.Romers, Acta Cryst., 16, 1225, 1963

$P2_12_12_1$ $Z = 4$ $R_{0kl} = 0.06$,
$R_{h0l} = 0.07$, $R_{hk0} = 0.07$

CDCDOX   LB 4-6-21

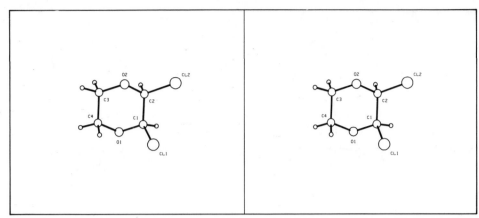

Bond Lengths

Cl1	C1	1.82		C2	O2	1.42
Cl2	C2	1.78		C3	O2	1.47
C1	O1	1.39		C1	C2	1.53
C4	O1	1.47		C3	C4	1.51

Bond Angles

C1	O1	C4	112		Cl2	C2	O2	105
C2	O2	C3	109		Cl2	C2	C1	112
Cl1	C1	O1	111		O2	C2	C1	112
Cl1	C1	C2	112		O2	C3	C4	109
O1	C1	C2	111		O1	C4	C3	111

Torsion Angles

C4	O1	C1	Cl1	71		Cl1	C1	C2	Cl2	50
C4	O1	C1	C2	−54		Cl1	C1	C2	O2	−68
C1	O1	C4	C3	57		O1	C1	C2	Cl2	175
C3	O2	C2	Cl2	179		O1	C1	C2	O2	57
C3	O2	C2	C1	−59		O2	C3	C4	O1	−58
C2	O2	C3	C4	59						

38.4   trans - 2,5 - Dichloro - 1,4 - dioxane $C_4H_6Cl_2O_2$

(i)   C.Altona, C.Knobler, C.Romers, Acta Cryst., 16, 1217, 1963   (Mo radiation)

(ii)   C.Altona, C.Knobler, C.Romers, Acta Cryst., 16, 1217, 1963   (at −125°C Mo radiation)

(iii)   C.Altona, C.Knobler, C.Romers, Acta Cryst., 16, 1217, 1963   (at −125°C Cu radiation)

(i)   P-1 $Z = 1$ $R_{0kl} = 0.06$,
$R_{hk0} = 0.08$

    DCLDXN   LB 4-6-23

(ii)   P-1 $Z = 1$ $R_{0kl} = 0.06$,
$R_{hk0} = 0.07$

    DCLDXN01   LB 4-6-23

(iii)   P-1 $Z = 1$ $R = 0.077$

    DCLDXN02   LB 4-6-23

Bond Lengths

		(i)	(ii)	(iii)
Cl1	C1	1.86	1.85	1.85
C1	O1	1.42	1.41	1.39
C2A	O1	1.39	1.42	1.43
C1	C2	1.52	1.50	1.51

Bond Angles

			(i)	(ii)	(iii)
C1	O1	C2A	114	114	113
Cl1	C1	O1	110	110	110
Cl1	C1	C2	108	109	110
O1	C1	C2	111	112	112

Torsion Angles

				(i)	(ii)	(iii)
C2A	O1	C1	Cl1	−69	−70	−70
C2A	O1	C1	C2	51	51	52
C1	O1	C2A	C1A	−51	−51	−52
Cl1	C1	C2	O1A	71	71	71
O1	C1	C2	O1A	−50	−50	−52

38.5   trans - 2,5 - Dichloro - 1,4 - dioxane (at −125 ° C, Mo radiation) $C_4H_6Cl_2O_2$

For complete entry see 38.4

38.6   trans - 2,5 - Dichloro - 1,4 - dioxane (at −125 ° C, Cu radiation) $C_4H_6Cl_2O_2$

For complete entry see 38.4

38.7   trans - 2,3 - Dichloro - 1,4 - dioxane $C_4H_6Cl_2O_2$

C.Altona, C.Romers, Rec. Trav. Chim. Pays-Bas, 82, 1080, 1963

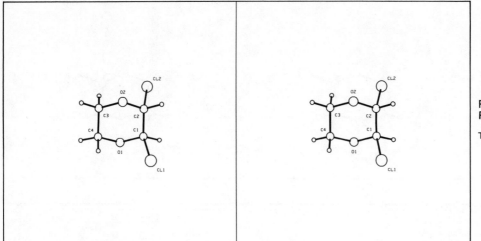

P2$_1$/c   Z = 4   R$_{0kl}$ = 0.09,
R$_{h0l}$ = 0.10, R$_{1kl}$ = 0.12

TDCDOX   LB 4-6-22

Bond Lengths

Cl1	C1	1.84	C2	O2	1.37	
Cl2	C2	1.83	C3	O2	1.44	
C1	O1	1.40	C1	C2	1.48	
C4	O1	1.42	C3	C4	1.50	

Bond Angles

C1	O1	C4	113	Cl2	C2	O2	112
C2	O2	C3	112	Cl2	C2	C1	107
Cl1	C1	O1	111	O2	C2	C1	115
Cl1	C1	C2	106	O2	C3	C4	112
O1	C1	C2	113	O1	C4	C3	111

Torsion Angles

C4	O1	C1	Cl1	70	Cl1	C1	C2	Cl2	162
C4	O1	C1	C2	−48	Cl1	C1	C2	O2	−73
C1	O1	C4	C3	52	O1	C1	C2	Cl2	−76
C3	O2	C2	Cl2	71	O1	C1	C2	O2	48
C3	O2	C2	C1	−51	O2	C3	C4	O1	−54
C2	O2	C3	C4	54					

38.8   Tetrahydrofuran - 3,3,4,4 - tetrol $C_4H_8O_5$

A.D.Mighell, R.A.Jacobson, Acta Cryst., 17, 1554, 1964

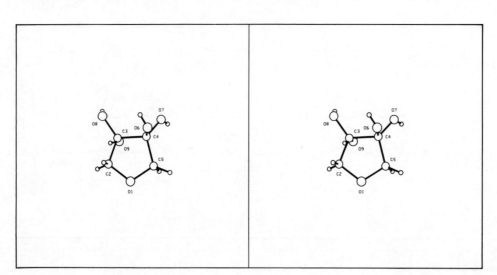

P-42$_1$c   Z = 8   R = 0.11

TFUROL   LB 4-8-96

Bond Lengths

C2	O1	1.41
C5	O1	1.43
C4	O6	1.37
C4	O7	1.38
C3	O8	1.38
C3	O9	1.40
C2	C3	1.52
C3	C4	1.56
C4	C5	1.50

Bond Angles

C2	O1	C5	110	O6	C4	O7	109
O1	C2	C3	106	O6	C4	C3	109
O8	C3	O9	113	O6	C4	C5	108
O8	C3	C2	111	O7	C4	C3	115
O8	C3	C4	114	O7	C4	C5	116
O9	C3	C2	113	C3	C4	C5	100
O9	C3	C4	105	O1	C5	C4	106
C2	C3	C4	100				

Torsion Angles

C5	O1	C2	C3	14	O9	C3	C4	O7	47
C2	O1	C5	C4	13	O9	C3	C4	C5	−78
O1	C2	C3	O8	−154	C2	C3	C4	O6	−73
O1	C2	C3	O9	78	C2	C3	C4	O7	165
O1	C2	C3	C4	−33	C2	C3	C4	C5	40
O8	C3	C4	O6	45	O6	C4	C5	O1	81
O8	C3	C4	O7	−77	O7	C4	C5	O1	−157
O8	C3	C4	C5	158	C3	C4	C5	O1	−33
O9	C3	C4	O6	169					

38.9   α - Furoic acid

$C_5H_4O_3$

P.Hudson, Acta Cryst., 15, 919, 1962

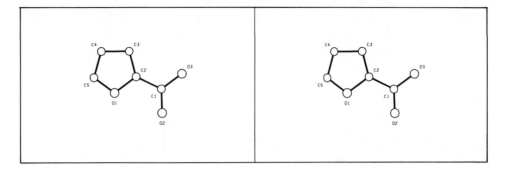

P-1   Z = 2   R = 0.082

FRANAC   LB 5-4-12

Bond Lengths

C2	O1	1.37	C1	C2	1.41
C5	O1	1.29	C2	C3	1.31
C1	O2	1.18	C3	C4	1.45
C1	O3	1.29	C4	C5	1.35

Bond Angles

C2	O1	C5	109		O1	C2	C3	110
O2	C1	O3	123		C1	C2	C3	130
O2	C1	C2	117		C2	C3	C4	105
O3	C1	C2	119		C3	C4	C5	106
O1	C2	C1	120		O1	C5	C4	110

Torsion Angles

O2	C1	C2	O1	8
O2	C1	C2	C3	−176
O3	C1	C2	O1	−180
O3	C1	C2	C3	−4

38.10   α - Methyltetronic acid

$C_5H_6O_3$

S.G.G.MacDonald, A.B.Alleyne, Acta Cryst., 16, 520, 1963

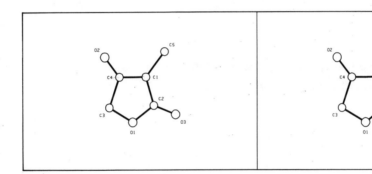

P2₁/c   Z = 4   R = 0.14

MTETAC   LB 5-6-26

Bond Lengths

C2	O1	1.36	C1	C2	1.47
C3	O1	1.41	C1	C4	1.37
C4	O2	1.24	C1	C5	1.57
C2	O3	1.21	C3	C4	1.59

Bond Angles

C2	O1	C3	111		O1	C2	O3	121		O2	C4	C1	127
C2	C1	C4	106		O1	C2	C1	112		O2	C4	C3	124
C2	C1	C5	127		O3	C2	C1	128		C1	C4	C3	109
C4	C1	C5	127		O1	C3	C4	102					

38.11   Furan - 3,4 - dicarboxylic acid

$C_6H_4O_5$

D.E.Williams, R.E.Rundle, J. Amer. Chem. Soc., 86, 1660, 1964

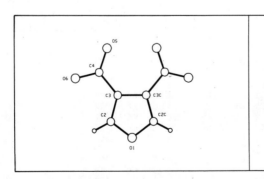
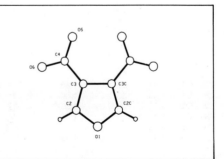

P112₁/m   Z = 2   R = 0.047

FURDCB   LB 6-4-68

Bond Lengths

C2	O1	1.36	C2	C3	1.35
C4	O5	1.26	C3	C4	1.47
C4	O6	1.25	C3	C3C	1.45

Bond Angles

C2	O1	C2C	107		C4	C3	C3C	130
O1	C2	C3	111		O5	C4	O6	121
C2	C3	C4	124		O5	C4	C3	121
C2	C3	C3C	106		O6	C4	C3	118

Torsion Angles

C2	C3	C4	O5	176
C2	C3	C4	O6	−4
C3C	C3	C4	O5	−4
C3C	C3	C4	O6	177

38.12   2,6 - Dimethyl - γ - pyrone hydrobromide monohydrate

H.Hope, Acta Chem. Scand., 19, 217, 1965

$C_7H_9O_2{}^+$, Br^- , H_2O

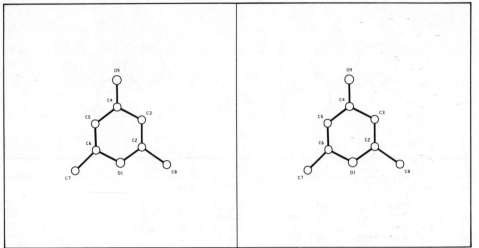

P-1   Z = 2 R_{0kl} = 0.11,
R_{h0l} = 0.076

DIMPYB   LB 7-9-5

Bond Lengths

C2	O1	1.34	C3	C4	1.41	
C6	O1	1.39	C4	C5	1.39	
C4	O9	1.32	C5	C6	1.31	
C2	C3	1.35	C6	C7	1.48	
C2	C8	1.54				

Bond Angles

C2	O1	C6	119	C2	C3	C4	117	C4	C5	C6	124
O1	C2	C3	124	O9	C4	C3	117	O1	C6	C5	118
O1	C2	C8	112	O9	C4	C5	126	O1	C6	C7	111
C3	C2	C8	124	C3	C4	C5	117	C5	C6	C7	131

38.13   3 - Bromo - 4 - hydroxycoumarin monohydrate

J.Gaultier, C.Hauw, Acta Cryst., 19, 927, 1965

$C_9H_5BrO_3$, H_2O

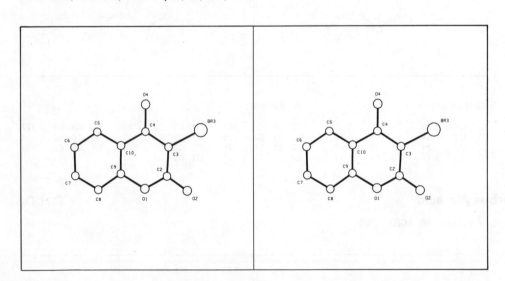

P2$_1$/n   Z = 4   R = 0.09

BHCOUM   LB 9-5-2

Bond Lengths

Br3	C3	1.88	C4	C10	1.43
C2	O1	1.31	C5	C6	1.40
C9	O1	1.43	C5	C10	1.40
C2	O2	1.27	C6	C7	1.39
C4	O4	1.34	C7	C8	1.36
C2	C3	1.43	C8	C9	1.39
C3	C4	1.41	C9	C10	1.39

Bond Angles

C2	O1	C9	121	C6	C5	C10	118
O1	C2	O2	117	C5	C6	C7	121
O1	C2	C3	121	C6	C7	C8	122
O2	C2	C3	122	C7	C8	C9	117
Br3	C3	C2	119	O1	C9	C8	116
Br3	C3	C4	121	O1	C9	C10	121
C2	C3	C4	119	C8	C9	C10	124
O4	C4	C3	122	C4	C10	C5	123
O4	C4	C10	119	C4	C10	C9	119
C3	C4	C10	119	C5	C10	C9	119

38.14 Glycolic acid - 2 - methyl - 4,5,6 - trichlorocyclohex - 2 - en - 1 - one ester acetal

$C_9H_9Cl_3O_3$

C.O.Haagensen, J.Danielsen, Acta Chem. Scand., 18, 581, 1964

$P2_12_12_1$ $Z = 4$ $R_{hk0} = 0.19$,
$R_{0kl} = 0.21$

GYHEXA   LB 9-9-6

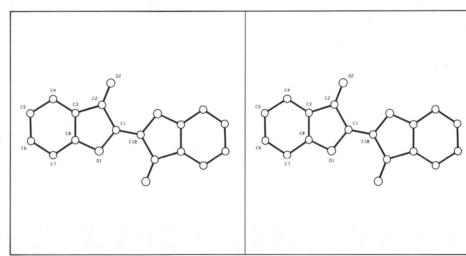

Bond Lengths

Cl1	C4	1.95
Cl2	C5	1.78
Cl3	C6	1.87
C1	O1	1.48
C8	O1	1.50
C1	O2	1.44
C7	O2	1.34
C7	O3	1.21
C1	C2	1.44
C1	C6	1.49
C2	C3	1.33
C2	C9	1.52
C3	C4	1.49
C4	C5	1.54
C5	C6	1.47
C7	C8	1.41

Bond Angles

C1	O1	C8	106	Cl1	C4	C5	109
C1	O2	C7	111	C3	C4	C5	117
O1	C1	O2	104	Cl2	C5	C4	112
O1	C1	C2	108	Cl2	C5	C6	113
O1	C1	C6	110	C4	C5	C6	107
O2	C1	C2	113	Cl3	C6	C1	111
O2	C1	C6	111	Cl3	C6	C5	109
C2	C1	C6	112	C1	C6	C5	112
C1	C2	C3	125	O2	C7	O3	120
C1	C2	C9	115	O2	C7	C8	110
C3	C2	C9	119	O3	C7	C8	128
C2	C3	C4	118	O1	C8	C7	106
Cl1	C4	C3	103				

Torsion Angles

C8	O1	C1	O2	−11	O2	C1	C2	C9	−44	C2	C3	C4	C5	14
C8	O1	C1	C2	−131	C6	C1	C2	C3	21	Cl1	C4	C5	Cl2	−49
C8	O1	C1	C6	107	C6	C1	C2	C9	−169	Cl1	C4	C5	C6	75
C1	O1	C8	C7	2	O1	C1	C6	Cl3	−54	C3	C4	C5	Cl2	−166
C7	O2	C1	O1	17	O1	C1	C6	C5	68	C3	C4	C5	C6	−42
C7	O2	C1	C2	134	O2	C1	C6	Cl3	60	Cl2	C5	C6	Cl3	−52
C7	O2	C1	C6	−100	O2	C1	C6	C5	−178	Cl2	C5	C6	C1	−175
C1	O2	C7	O3	178	C2	C1	C6	Cl3	−174	C4	C5	C6	Cl3	−176
C1	O2	C7	C8	−17	C2	C1	C6	C5	−52	C4	C5	C6	C1	61
O1	C1	C2	C3	−100	C1	C2	C3	C4	−3	O2	C7	C8	O1	8
O1	C1	C2	C9	70	C9	C2	C3	C4	−172	O3	C7	C8	O1	173
O2	C1	C2	C3	146	C2	C3	C4	Cl1	−107					

38.15 Oxindigo

$C_{16}H_8O_4$

H.Pandraud, Acta Cryst., 15, 1131, 1962

$P2_1/c$ $Z = 2$ No R factor was given.

OXINGO   LB 16-8-17

Bond Lengths

C1	O1	1.39	C3	C4	1.40
C8	O1	1.39	C3	C8	1.38
C2	O2	1.23	C4	C5	1.41
C1	C2	1.48	C5	C6	1.40
C1	C1B	1.34	C6	C7	1.38
C2	C3	1.47	C7	C8	1.41

Bond Angles

C1	O1	C8	106	C4	C3	C8	121
O1	C1	C2	110	C3	C4	C5	117
O1	C1	C1B	119	C4	C5	C6	120
C2	C1	C1B	130	C5	C6	C7	123
O2	C2	C1	128	C6	C7	C8	115
O2	C2	C3	129	O1	C8	C3	114
C1	C2	C3	104	O1	C8	C7	123
C2	C3	C4	133	C3	C8	C7	123
C2	C3	C8	106				

38.16   2,4,6 - Tricyclohexyl - trioxane $C_{21}H_{36}O_3$

G.Diana, P.Ganis, Atti Accad. Nazion. Lincei, R. C., Cl. Sci. Fis. Mat. Nat., 35, 80, 1963

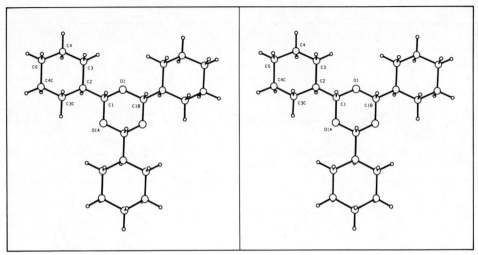

$P6_3cm$ Z = 2 R_{hk0} = 0.113,
R_{h0l} = 0.148

TCHXTO   LB 21-36-9

Bond Lengths

C1	O1	1.43
C1	C2	1.54
C2	C3	1.54
C3	C4	1.54
C4	C5	1.54

Bond Angles

C1	O1	C1B	109	C3	C2	C3C	109
O1	C1	O1A	109	C2	C3	C4	109
O1	C1	C2	109	C3	C4	C5	109
C1	C2	C3	109	C4	C5	C4C	109

Torsion Angles

C1B	O1	C1	O1A	−60	O1A	C1	C2	C3C	60
C1B	O1	C1	C2	−180	C1	C2	C3	C4	180
O1	C1	C2	C3	−60	C3C	C2	C3	C4	−60
O1	C1	C2	C3C	−180	C2	C3	C4	C5	60
O1A	C1	C2	C3	180	C3	C4	C5	C4C	−60

38.17   9,9' - Dixanthenylidene (α form) $C_{26}H_{16}O_2$

J.F.D.Mills, S.C.Nyburg, J. Chem. Soc., 308, 1963

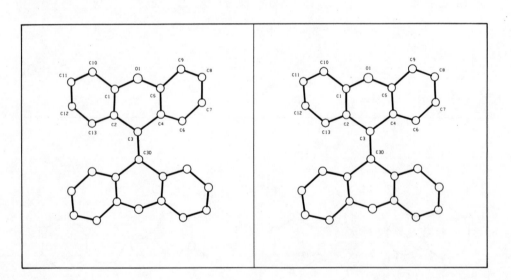

A2/n   Z = 4   R = 0.208

DIXTEN   LB 26-16-7

Bond Lengths

C1	O1	1.37	C4	C6	1.40
C5	O1	1.36	C5	C9	1.40
C1	C2	1.39	C6	C7	1.39
C1	C10	1.41	C7	C8	1.39
C2	C3	1.49	C8	C9	1.37
C2	C13	1.41	C10	C11	1.37
C3	C4	1.48	C11	C12	1.39
C3	C3D	1.37	C12	C13	1.39
C4	C5	1.39			

Bond Angles

C1	O1	C5	117	C5	C4	C6	116
O1	C1	C2	120	O1	C5	C4	120
O1	C1	C10	119	O1	C5	C9	117
C2	C1	C10	121	C4	C5	C9	123
C1	C2	C3	117	C4	C6	C7	121
C1	C2	C13	119	C6	C7	C8	121
C3	C2	C13	124	C7	C8	C9	119
C2	C3	C4	109	C5	C9	C8	119
C2	C3	C3D	126	C1	C10	C11	118
C4	C3	C3D	125	C10	C11	C12	121
C3	C4	C5	118	C11	C12	C13	120
C3	C4	C6	126	C2	C13	C12	119

Torsion Angles

C5	O1	C1	C2	30
C5	O1	C1	C10	−148
C1	O1	C5	C4	−31
C1	O1	C5	C9	144
C1	C2	C3	C4	−38
C1	C2	C3	C3D	141
C13	C2	C3	C4	141
C13	C2	C3	C3D	−40
C2	C3	C4	C5	37
C2	C3	C4	C6	−140
C3D	C3	C4	C5	−142
C3D	C3	C4	C6	41

38.18   9,9' - Dixanthenylidene (β form) $C_{26}H_{16}O_2$

J.F.D.Mills, S.C.Nyburg, J. Chem. Soc., 308, 1963

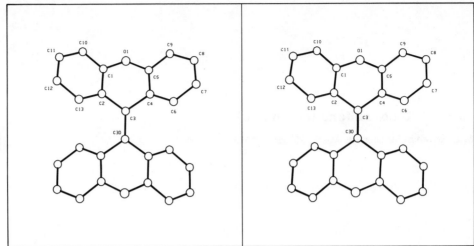

Published y coordinate for g (relabelled C6) = 0.052. The correct value is −0.052.
C2/c   Z = 4   R = 0.21

DIXTEN01   LB 26-16-8

Bond Lengths

C1	O1	1.40	
C5	O1	1.40	
C1	C2	1.40	
C1	C10	1.38	
C2	C3	1.49	
C2	C13	1.37	
C3	C4	1.49	
C3	C3D	1.40	
C4	C5	1.37	

C4	C6	1.39
C5	C9	1.37
C6	C7	1.41
C7	C8	1.39
C8	C9	1.40
C10	C11	1.37
C11	C12	1.39
C12	C13	1.40

Bond Angles

C1	O1	C5	115
O1	C1	C2	121
O1	C1	C10	116
C2	C1	C10	122
C1	C2	C3	116
C1	C2	C13	117
C3	C2	C13	127
C2	C3	C4	111

C2	C3	C3D	124
C4	C3	C3D	125
C3	C4	C5	116
C3	C4	C6	124
C5	C4	C6	119
O1	C5	C4	122
O1	C5	C9	116
C4	C5	C9	123

C4	C6	C7	118
C6	C7	C8	122
C7	C8	C9	118
C5	C9	C8	120
C1	C10	C11	119
C10	C11	C12	120
C11	C12	C13	119
C2	C13	C12	122

Torsion Angles

C5	O1	C1	C2	−30
C5	O1	C1	C10	150
C1	O1	C5	C4	28
C1	O1	C5	C9	−149
C1	C2	C3	C4	38
C1	C2	C3	C3D	−144
C13	C2	C3	C4	−137
C13	C2	C3	C3D	40
C2	C3	C4	C5	−40
C2	C3	C4	C6	138
C3D	C3	C4	C5	142
C3D	C3	C4	C6	−40

39.1   Thiete sulfone (at −40 °C) $C_3H_4O_2S$

M.Z.Lowenstein, Dissert. Abstr., 26, 2500, 1965

Atomic coordinates were not reported in the paper.
Ama2   Z = 4   No R factor was given.

THIETS   LB 3-4-16

39.2   3,5 - Diamino - 1,2 - dithiolium iodide $C_3H_5N_2S_2^+$, I^-

A.Hordvik, Acta Chem. Scand., 19, 1039, 1965

The structure was determined in two dimensions only. Atomic coordinates were not reported in the paper.
Pnma   Z = 4   R = 0.11

DATOLI   LB 3-5-5

39.3   trans - 2,3 - Dichloro - 1,4 - dithiane (at −180 °C) $C_4H_6Cl_2S_2$

H.T.Kalff, C.Romers, Acta Cryst., 18, 164, 1965

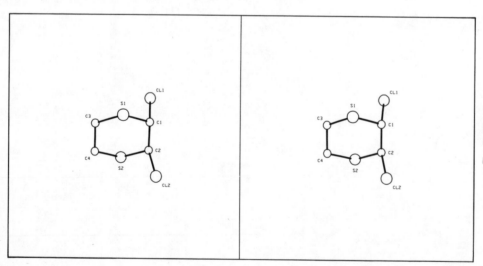

Pn   Z = 2 R_{0k0} = 0.069,
R-$_{h0l}$ = 0.061, R_{h0l} = 0.081

DCLDTH   LB 4-6-24

Bond Lengths

Cl1	C1	1.81	S2	C2	1.78
Cl2	C2	1.80	S2	C4	1.84
S1	C1	1.80	C1	C2	1.54
S1	C3	1.84	C3	C4	1.47

Bond Angles

C1	S1	C3	100	Cl2	C2	S2	113
C2	S2	C4	101	Cl2	C2	C1	107
Cl1	C1	S1	111	S2	C2	C1	117
Cl1	C1	C2	108	S1	C3	C4	114
S1	C1	C2	115	S2	C4	C3	111

Torsion Angles

C3	S1	C1	Cl1	69	Cl1	C1	C2	Cl2	167
C3	S1	C1	C2	−53	Cl1	C1	C2	S2	−65
C1	S1	C3	C4	62	S1	C1	C2	Cl2	−69
C4	S2	C2	Cl2	71	S1	C1	C2	S2	59
C4	S2	C2	C1	−54	S1	C3	C4	S2	−71
C2	S2	C4	C3	60					

39.4   1,4 - Diselenane tetrachloride

$C_4H_8Cl_4Se_2$

A.Amendola, E.S.Gould, B.Post, Inorg. Chem., 3, 1199, 1964

The published coordinates give incorrect connectivity.
Pbca   Z = 4   R = 0.17

DISECL   LB 4-8-31

39.5   Tetrahydroselenophene - iodine complex

$C_4H_8I_2Se$

H.Hope, J.D.McCullough, Acta Cryst., 17, 712, 1964

Carbon atoms C5 and C6 are disordered.
Pnma   Z = 4   R = 0.063

THSELI   LB 4-8-44

39.6   1,4 - Dithiane - iodine complex

$C_4H_8I_4S_2$

G.Y.Chao, J.D.McCullough, Acta Cryst., 13, 727, 1960

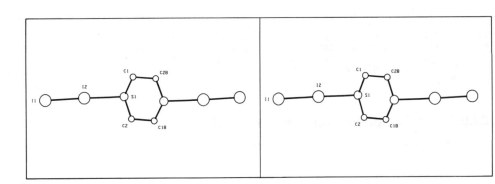

P2₁/c   Z = 2   R = 0.08

DTHINI   LB 4-8-47

Bond Lengths			Bond Angles				Torsion Angles				
I1	I2	2.79	I1	I2	S1	178	I1	I2	S1	C1	−86
I2	S1	2.87	I2	S1	C1	101	I1	I2	S1	C2	17
S1	C1	1.79	I2	S1	C2	96	I2	S1	C1	C2B	159
S1	C2	1.83	C1	S1	C2	102	C2	S1	C1	C2B	60
C1	C2B	1.55	S1	C1	C2B	110	I2	S1	C2	C1B	−164
			S1	C2	C1B	113	C1	S1	C2	C1B	−62
							S1	C1	C2B	S1B	−67

39.7   1,4 - Diselenane - iodine complex

$C_4H_8I_4Se_2$

G.Y.Chao, J.D.McCullough, Acta Cryst., 14, 940, 1961

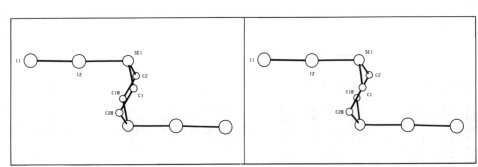

P2₁/c   Z = 2   R = 0.095

DSEIOD   LB 4-8-48

Bond Lengths			Bond Angles				Torsion Angles				
I1	I2	2.87	I1	I2	Se1	179	I1	I2	Se1	C1	116
I2	Se1	2.83	I2	Se1	C1	101	I1	I2	Se1	C2	−141
Se1	C1	1.95	I2	Se1	C2	101	I2	Se1	C1	C2B	46
Se1	C2	1.98	C1	Se1	C2	100	C2	Se1	C1	C2B	−58
C1	C2B	1.57	Se1	C1	C2B	117	I2	Se1	C2	C1B	−49
			Se1	C2	C1B	113	C1	Se1	C2	C1B	54
							Se1	C1	C2B	Se1B	64

39.8 1,4 - Dithiane - disulfoxide (β form)

H.Montgomery, Acta Cryst., 13, 381, 1960

$C_4H_8O_2S_2$

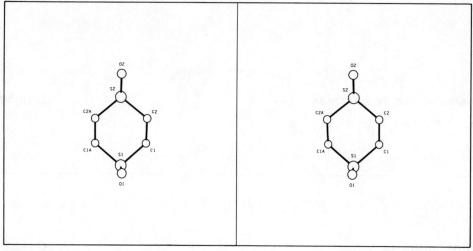

To obtain agreement between calculated and reported bond lengths the authors origin was shifted by 0.25, 0, 0. Published value of $z(O2) = 0.706$. The correct value is 0.746.

Pmn2$_1$ Z = 2 $R_{hk0} = 0.149$, $R_{0kl} = 0.145$

DTHDSX

Bond Lengths			Bond Angles				Torsion Angles				
S1	O1	1.43	O1	S1	C1	111	O1	S1	C1	C2	−55
S1	C1	1.79	C1	S1	C1A	97	C1A	S1	C1	C2	61
S2	O2	1.40	O2	S2	C2	109	O2	S2	C2	C1	175
S2	C2	1.77	C2	S2	C2A	98	C2A	S2	C2	C1	62
C1	C2	1.47	S1	C1	C2	113	S1	C1	C2	S2	−71
			S2	C2	C1	113					

39.9 β - Thiophenic acid (at −170 °C)

P.Hudson, J.H.Robertson, Acta Cryst., 17, 1497, 1964

$C_5H_4O_2S$

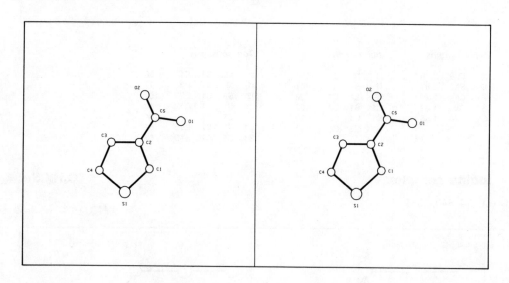

C2/c   Z = 8   R = 0.128

THIPAC   LB 5-4-10

Bond Lengths			Bond Angles				Torsion Angles				
S1	C1	1.71	C1	S1	C4	98	C1	C2	C5	O1	−5
S1	C4	1.70	S1	C1	C2	110	C1	C2	C5	O2	176
C5	O1	1.33	C1	C2	C3	112	C3	C2	C5	O1	176
C5	O2	1.24	C1	C2	C5	125	C3	C2	C5	O2	−3
C1	C2	1.41	C3	C2	C5	123					
C2	C3	1.44	C2	C3	C4	113					
C2	C5	1.48	S1	C4	C3	106					
C3	C4	1.51	O1	C5	O2	123					
			O1	C5	C2	115					
			O2	C5	C2	121					

39.10   α - Thiophene - carboxylic acid   C₅H₄O₂S

M.Nardelli, G.Fava, G.Giraldi, Acta Cryst., 15, 737, 1962

P2₁/c   Z = 4   R = 0.11

TPENAC   LB 5-4-9

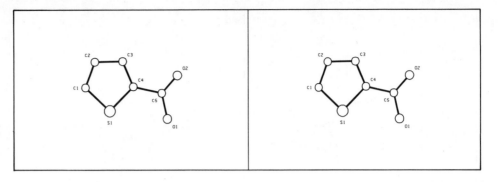

Bond Lengths

S1	C1	1.70	C1	C2	1.36
S1	C4	1.69	C2	C3	1.41
C5	O1	1.29	C3	C4	1.36
C5	O2	1.20	C4	C5	1.48

Bond Angles

C1	S1	C4	92	S1	C4	C5	122
S1	C1	C2	112	C3	C4	C5	126
C1	C2	C3	112	O1	C5	O2	125
C2	C3	C4	112	O1	C5	C4	115
S1	C4	C3	112	O2	C5	C4	120

Torsion Angles

S1	C4	C5	O1	1
S1	C4	C5	O2	−179
C3	C4	C5	O1	180
C3	C4	C5	O2	−1

39.11   α - Thiophene - carboxylic acid (at − 170 ° C)   C₅H₄O₂S

P.Hudson, J.H.Robertson, Acta Cryst., 15, 913, 1962

Atomic coordinates were not reported in the paper. The authors have published the differences between their coordinates and those of Nardelli et al. (see 39.10). Using the coordinates calculated from the difference table the carboxylic acid group does not connect with the thiophene ring.
P2₁/c   Z = 4   No R factor was given.

TPENAC01   LB 5-4-9

39.12   α - Selenophene - carboxylic acid   C₅H₄O₂Se

M.Nardelli, G.Fava, G.Giraldi, Acta Cryst., 15, 737, 1962

P2₁/c   Z = 4   R = 0.085

SELCBX   LB 5-4-11

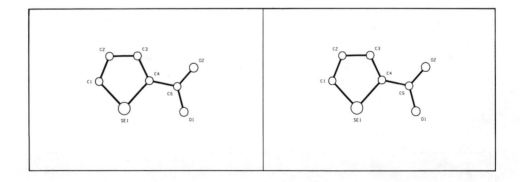

Bond Lengths

Se1	C1	1.85	C1	C2	1.36
Se1	C4	1.87	C2	C3	1.42
C5	O1	1.30	C3	C4	1.36
C5	O2	1.27	C4	C5	1.44

Bond Angles

C1	Se1	C4	87	Se1	C4	C5	121
Se1	C1	C2	112	C3	C4	C5	128
C1	C2	C3	114	O1	C5	O2	122
C2	C3	C4	116	O1	C5	C4	118
Se1	C4	C3	111	O2	C5	C4	120

Torsion Angles

Se1	C4	C5	O1	5
Se1	C4	C5	O2	−179
C3	C4	C5	O1	−179
C3	C4	C5	O2	−2

39.13 DL - 1,2 - Dithiane - 3,6 - dicarboxylic acid

$C_6H_8O_4S_2$

O.Foss, K.Johnsen, T.Reistad, Acta Chem. Scand., 18, 2345, 1964

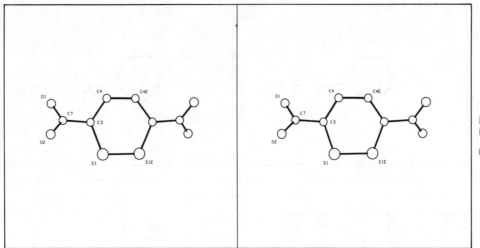

I2/c   Z = 4 R_{h0l} = 0.088, R_{hk0} = 0.093

DTHIAC   LB 6-8-61

Bond Lengths			Bond Angles				Torsion Angles				
S1	S1E	2.07	S1	C3	C4	110	C3	S1	S1E	C3E	60
S1	C3	1.85	S1	C3	C7	109	S1E	S1	C3	C4	−63
C7	O1	1.28	C4	C3	C7	116	S1E	S1	C3	C7	169
C7	O2	1.31	C3	C4	C4E	117	S1	C3	C4	C4E	63
C3	C4	1.53	O1	C7	O2	122	C7	C3	C4	C4E	−173
C3	C7	1.44	O1	C7	C3	117	S1	C3	C7	O1	−164
C4	C4E	1.53	O2	C7	C3	121	S1	C3	C7	O2	23
							C4	C3	C7	O1	71
							C4	C3	C7	O2	−102
							C3	C4	C4E	C3E	−62

39.14 DL - 1,2 - Diselenane - 3,6 - dicarboxylic acid

$C_6H_8O_4Se_2$

O.Foss, K.Johnsen, T.Reistad, Acta Chem. Scand., 18, 2345, 1964

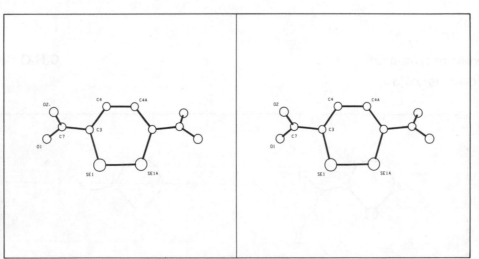

C2/c   Z = 4 R_{h0l} = 0.089, R_{hk0} = 0.068

DSELAC   LB 6-8-63

Bond Lengths			Bond Angles				Torsion Angles				
Se1	Se1A	2.32	Se1	C3	C4	112	C3	Se1	Se1A	C3A	57
Se1	C3	1.97	Se1	C3	C7	106	Se1A	Se1	C3	C4	−61
C7	O1	1.26	C4	C3	C7	116	Se1A	Se1	C3	C7	172
C7	O2	1.37	C3	C4	C4A	121	Se1	C3	C4	C4A	62
C3	C4	1.51	O1	C7	O2	123	C7	C3	C4	C4A	−177
C3	C7	1.46	O1	C7	C3	120	Se1	C3	C7	O1	−80
C4	C4A	1.48	O2	C7	C3	116	Se1	C3	C7	O2	95
							C4	C3	C7	O1	155
							C4	C3	C7	O2	−30
							C3	C4	C4A	C3A	−59

39.15   2,3 - Dimethyl - dithiofurophthene

$C_7H_8OS_2$

M.Mammi, R.Bardi, G.Traverso, S.Bezzi, Nature, 192, 1282, 1961

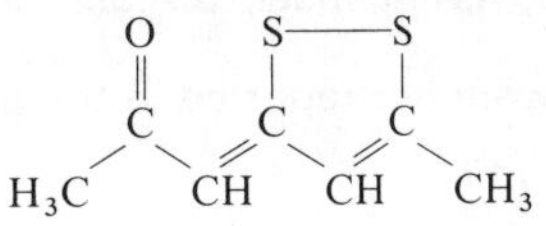

Atomic coordinates were not given
but bond lengths were reported.
P2$_1$/c   Z = 4 R_{h0l} = 0.13,
R_{0kl} = 0.21

DMETHF   LB 7-8-15

39.16   2,5 - Dimethyl - thiothiophthene

$C_7H_8S_3$

M.Mammi, R.Zannetti, Gazz. Chim. Ital., 92, 437, 1962

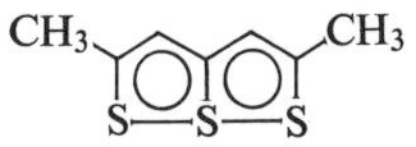

Atomic coordinates were not
reported in the paper.
See also Leung & Nyburg, J. Chem.
Soc. (D), 137, 1969.
Pnma   Z = 4 R_{hk0} = 0.48,
R_{0kl} = 0.39

MTHOPH

39.17   Tetracyano - 1,4 - dithiin

$C_8N_4S_2$

W.A.Dollase, J. Amer. Chem. Soc., 87, 979, 1965

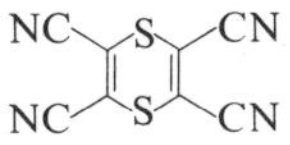

P2$_1$/n   Z = 4   R = 0.117

TCYDIT   LB 8-0-12

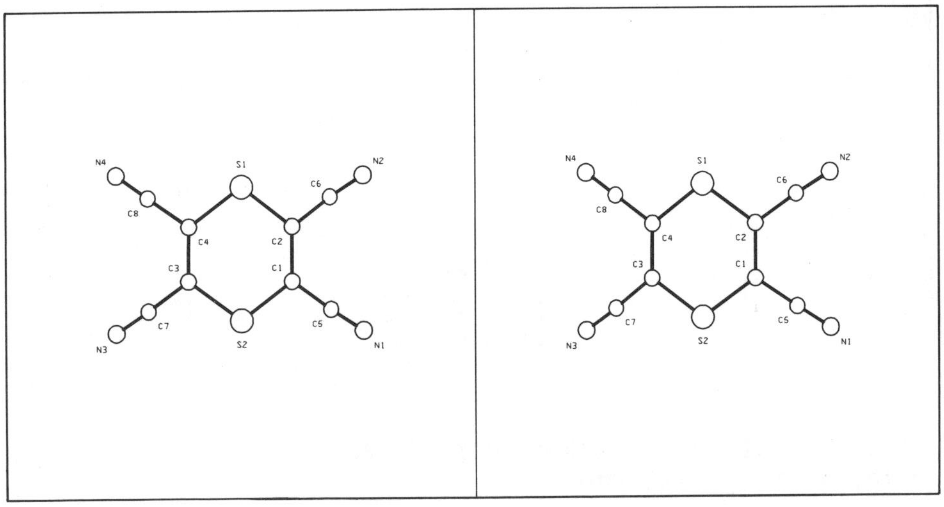

Bond Lengths

S1	C2	1.75	C8	N4	1.15
S1	C4	1.76	C1	C2	1.35
S2	C1	1.76	C1	C5	1.43
S2	C3	1.75	C2	C6	1.44
C5	N1	1.14	C3	C4	1.34
C6	N2	1.15	C3	C7	1.43
C7	N3	1.16	C4	C8	1.42

Bond Angles

C2	S1	C4	97		S2	C3	C7	116
C1	S2	C3	97		C4	C3	C7	121
S2	C1	C2	121		S1	C4	C3	122
S2	C1	C5	118		S1	C4	C8	117
C2	C1	C5	120		C3	C4	C8	121
S1	C2	C1	122		N1	C5	C1	177
S1	C2	C6	117		N2	C6	C2	175
C1	C2	C6	121		N3	C7	C3	178
S2	C3	C4	122		N4	C8	C4	179

Torsion Angles

C4	S1	C2	C1	−44		S2	C1	C2	S1	−2
C4	S1	C2	C6	132		S2	C1	C2	C6	−178
C2	S1	C4	C3	46		C5	C1	C2	S1	179
C2	S1	C4	C8	−133		C5	C1	C2	C6	2
C3	S2	C1	C2	46		S2	C3	C4	S1	−2
C3	S2	C1	C5	−134		S2	C3	C4	C8	177
C1	S2	C3	C4	−44		C7	C3	C4	S1	−175
C1	S2	C3	C7	129		C7	C3	C4	C8	4

39.18   3 - Bromo - 2,7 - dinitrothionaphthen - 5 - diazo - 4 - oxide

$C_8HBrN_4O_5S$

I.Brown, M.Martin-Smith, S.T.Reid, C.C.Scott, G.A.Sim, Chem. and Industry, 982, 1962

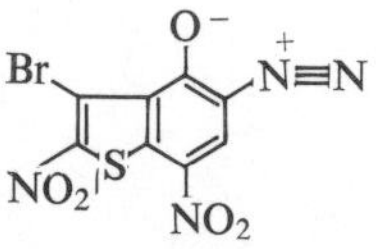

Atomic coordinates were not
reported in the paper.
P-1 Z = 2 R = 0.18

BNSNAO

227

39.19   1,6 - Dithiacyclodeca - 3,8 - diyne

$C_8H_8S_2$

G.Eglington, I.A.Lardy, R.A.Raphael, G.A.Sim, J. Chem. Soc., 1154, 1964

Atomic coordinates were not reported in the paper.

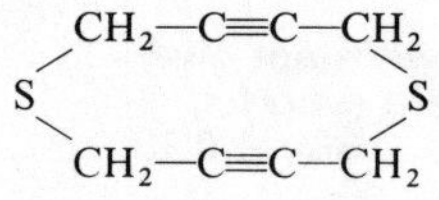

$P2_1/c$ Z = 2   R = 0.17

DSCYDY   LB 8-8-50

39.20   3 - Phenyl - 1,2 - dithiolium iodide

$C_9H_7S_2^+$, I^-

A.Hordvik, H.M.Kjoge, Acta Chem. Scand., 19, 935, 1965

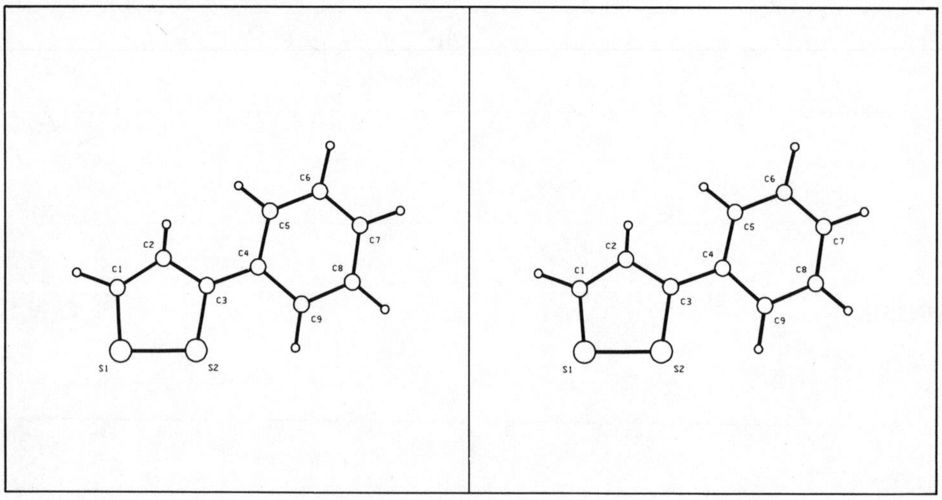

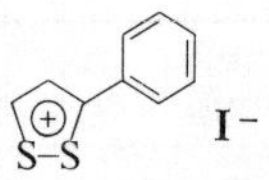

$P2_1/c$ Z = 4   R = 0.10

PEDTIO   LB 9-7-19

Bond Lengths

S1	S2	2.00	C4	C5	1.43	
S1	C1	1.67	C4	C9	1.44	
S2	C3	1.71	C5	C6	1.37	
C1	C2	1.39	C6	C7	1.33	
C2	C3	1.39	C7	C8	1.42	
C3	C4	1.40	C8	C9	1.40	

Bond Angles

S2	S1	C1	94	C3	C4	C9	121
S1	S2	C3	97	C5	C4	C9	117
S1	C1	C2	119	C4	C5	C6	124
C1	C2	C3	115	C5	C6	C7	118
S2	C3	C2	115	C6	C7	C8	122
S2	C3	C4	120	C7	C8	C9	121
C2	C3	C4	124	C4	C9	C8	117
C3	C4	C5	121				

Torsion Angles

S2	C3	C4	C5	154
S2	C3	C4	C9	−17
C2	C3	C4	C5	−39
C2	C3	C4	C9	150

39.21   2 - (2 - Methylsulfonylprop - 1 - ene) - 4 - methylsulfonyl - thiophene

$C_9H_{12}O_4S_3$

M.Mammi, C.Garbuglio, A.de Pace, Acta Cryst., 16, A54, 1963

Atomic coordinates were not reported in the paper.

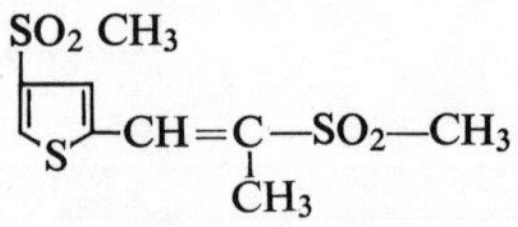

Fdd2   Z = 16   R = 0.17

MSPMST

40.1   5 - Chlorobenzfurazan - 1 - oxide

$C_6H_3ClN_2O_2$

D.Britton, W.E.Noland, J. Org. Chem., 27, 3218, 1962

P2$_1$/n   Z = 4   R = 0.136

CBFUZO   LB 6-3-7

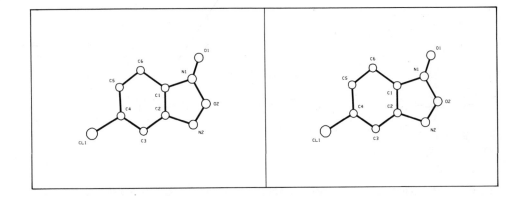

Bond Lengths

Cl1	C4	1.72	C1	C2	1.36
N1	O1	1.11	C1	C6	1.52
N1	O2	1.40	C2	C3	1.36
N2	O2	1.23	C3	C4	1.37
C1	N1	1.46	C4	C5	1.42
C2	N2	1.51	C5	C6	1.35

Bond Angles

O1	N1	O2	131	N1	C1	C6	128	Cl1	C4	C3	116
O1	N1	C1	126	C2	C1	C6	125	Cl1	C4	C5	118
O2	N1	C1	103	N2	C2	C1	109	C3	C4	C5	126
O2	N2	C2	104	N2	C2	C3	127	C4	C5	C6	125
N1	O2	N2	118	C1	C2	C3	124	C1	C6	C5	108
N1	C1	C2	107	C2	C3	C4	112				

40.2   N - (p - Bromophenyl) - sydnone

$C_8H_5BrN_2O_2$

H.Barnighausen, F.Jellinek, J.Munnik, A.Vos, Acta Cryst., 16, 471, 1963

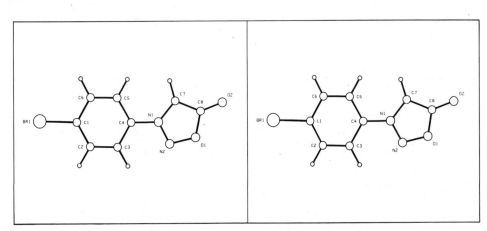

P-1   Z = 2   R = 0.082

BROPSY   LB 8-5-2

Bond Lengths

Br1	C1	1.89	C1	C2	1.38
N1	N2	1.34	C1	C6	1.42
N2	O1	1.37	C2	C3	1.38
C4	N1	1.41	C3	C4	1.40
C7	N1	1.38	C4	C5	1.41
C8	O1	1.42	C5	C6	1.37
C8	O2	1.20	C7	C8	1.41

Bond Angles

N2	N1	C4	118	C2	C1	C6	120	C1	C6	C5	119
N2	N1	C7	115	C1	C2	C3	121	N1	C7	C8	105
C4	N1	C7	127	C2	C3	C4	119	O1	C8	O2	119
N1	N2	O1	104	N1	C4	C3	121	O1	C8	C7	105
N2	O1	C8	111	N1	C4	C5	119	O2	C8	C7	136
Br1	C1	C2	122	C3	C4	C5	120				
Br1	C1	C6	118	C4	C5	C6	120				

Torsion Angles

N2	N1	C4	C3	28
N2	N1	C4	C5	−153
C7	N1	C4	C3	−153
C7	N1	C4	C5	27

40.3 Perkinamine hydrochloride

$C_8H_{14}NO^+$, Cl^-

B.Rerat, C.Rerat, Acta Cryst., 17, 1119, 1964

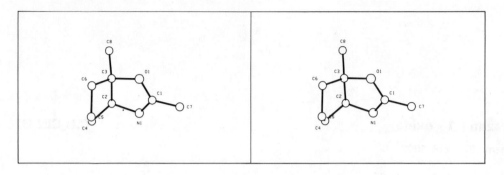

$P2_12_12_1$ Z = 4 R = 0.20

PEKAMC   LB 8-14-10

Bond Lengths

C1	N1	1.29
C2	N1	1.53
C1	O1	1.33
C3	O1	1.52
C1	C7	1.47
C2	C3	1.59
C2	C4	1.45
C3	C6	1.53
C3	C8	1.53
C4	C5	1.56
C5	C6	1.48

Bond Angles

C1	N1	C2	112		O1	C3	C6	108
C1	O1	C3	109		O1	C3	C8	105
N1	C1	O1	115		C2	C3	C6	105
N1	C1	C7	124		C2	C3	C8	119
O1	C1	C7	122		C6	C3	C8	116
N1	C2	C3	100		C2	C4	C5	103
N1	C2	C4	117		C4	C5	C6	101
C3	C2	C4	105		C3	C6	C5	104
O1	C3	C2	103					

Torsion Angles

C2	N1	C1	O1	−6		C1	O1	C3	C8	−126		C3	C2	C4	C5	−31
C2	N1	C1	C7	176		N1	C2	C3	O1	−3		O1	C3	C6	C5	−86
C1	N1	C2	C3	5		N1	C2	C3	C6	−116		C2	C3	C6	C5	24
C1	N1	C2	C4	−107		N1	C2	C3	C8	113		C8	C3	C6	C5	157
C3	O1	C1	N1	4		C4	C2	C3	O1	119		C2	C4	C5	C6	47
C3	O1	C1	C7	−178		C4	C2	C3	C6	5		C4	C5	C6	C3	−43
C1	O1	C3	C2	−1		C4	C2	C3	C8	−126					
C1	O1	C3	C6	110		N1	C2	C4	C5	78					

40.4   2 - Methyl - 4 - chloromethyl - 5 - p - nitrophenyl - oxazole

$C_{11}H_9ClN_2O_3$

V.Albano, P.L.Bellon, F.Pompa, V.Scatturin, Ric. Sci., 33, 1143, 1963

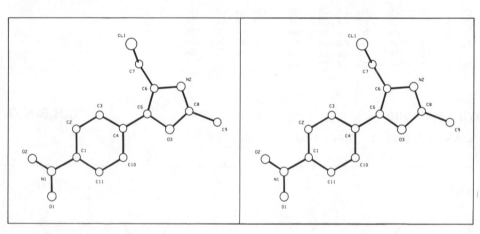

Published value of z(Cl1) = −0.0081. The correct value is 0.0081 (private communication).
$P2_1/c$ Z = 4   R = 0.18

MPHOXZ   LB 11-9-5

Bond Lengths

Cl1	C7	1.85		C1	C11	1.40
N1	O1	1.24		C2	C3	1.40
N1	O2	1.19		C3	C4	1.38
C1	N1	1.46		C4	C5	1.44
C6	N2	1.39		C4	C10	1.43
C8	N2	1.32		C5	C6	1.36
C5	O3	1.38		C6	C7	1.49
C8	O3	1.36		C8	C9	1.54
C1	C2	1.39		C10	C11	1.42

Bond Angles

O1	N1	O2	123		C2	C3	C4	122		C5	C6	C7	133
O1	N1	C1	116		C3	C4	C5	122		Cl1	C7	C6	110
O2	N1	C1	121		C3	C4	C10	119		N2	C8	O3	114
C6	N2	C8	105		C5	C4	C10	119		N2	C8	C9	129
C5	O3	C8	104		O3	C5	C4	117		O3	C8	C9	117
N1	C1	C2	117		O3	C5	C6	108		C4	C10	C11	120
N1	C1	C11	120		C4	C5	C6	135		C1	C11	C10	118
C2	C1	C11	122		N2	C6	C5	109					
C1	C2	C3	119		N2	C6	C7	118					

Torsion Angles

O1	N1	C1	C2	−174
O1	N1	C1	C11	6
O2	N1	C1	C2	7
O2	N1	C1	C11	−173
C3	C4	C5	O3	169
C3	C4	C5	C6	−17
C10	C4	C5	O3	−6
C10	C4	C5	C6	167
N2	C6	C7	Cl1	−92
C5	C6	C7	Cl1	86

40.5   2,4 - Dimethyl - 5 - p - nitrophenyl oxazole

$C_{11}H_{10}N_2O_3$

V.Albano, P.L.Bellon, F.Pompa, V.Scatturin, Acta Cryst., 16, A63, 1963

Atomic coordinates were not reported in the paper.
$P2_1$ Z = 2   No R factor was given.

MNPOXZ   LB 11-10-7

40.6   3 - Benzoylanthranil

$C_{14}H_9NO_2$

M.Sundaralingam, G.A.Jeffrey, Acta Cryst., 15, 1035, 1962

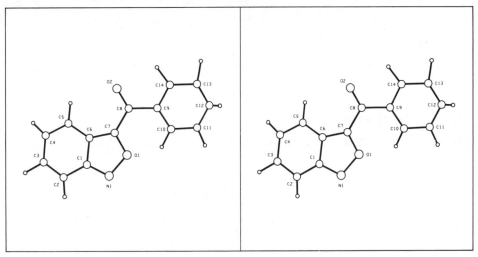

Further refinement (R = 0.053) was reported by Sundaralingam and Jensen, Acta Cryst., 16, A61, 1963 but no coordinates have been published. Published value of z(C2) = 0.4344. The correct value is 0.4244.

P2₁/c   Z = 4   R = 0.090

BENZAN   LB 14-9-12

Bond Lengths

N1	O1	1.41		C6	C7	1.39
C1	N1	1.34		C7	C8	1.47
C7	O1	1.36		C8	C9	1.52
C8	O2	1.22		C9	C10	1.40
C1	C2	1.39		C9	C14	1.40
C1	C6	1.43		C10	C11	1.39
C2	C3	1.36		C11	C12	1.37
C3	C4	1.43		C12	C13	1.37
C4	C5	1.38		C13	C14	1.42
C5	C6	1.42				

Bond Angles

O1	N1	C1	105		C1	C6	C5	120		C8	C9	C10	123
N1	O1	C7	111		C1	C6	C7	104		C8	C9	C14	118
N1	C1	C2	126		C5	C6	C7	135		C10	C9	C14	120
N1	C1	C6	112		O1	C7	C6	108		C9	C10	C11	120
C2	C1	C6	122		O1	C7	C8	121		C10	C11	C12	120
C1	C2	C3	117		C6	C7	C8	130		C11	C12	C13	121
C2	C3	C4	123		O2	C8	C7	119		C12	C13	C14	120
C3	C4	C5	120		O2	C8	C9	120		C9	C14	C13	119
C4	C5	C6	118		C7	C8	C9	121					

Torsion Angles

O1	C7	C8	O2	−170
O1	C7	C8	C9	8
C6	C7	C8	O2	8
C6	C7	C8	C9	−174
O2	C8	C9	C10	−149
O2	C8	C9	C14	29
C7	C8	C9	C10	32
C7	C8	C9	C14	−150

40.7   1,4 - bis - 2 - (5 - Phenyloxazolyl)benzene

$C_{24}H_{16}N_2O_2$

I.Ambats, R.E.Marsh, Acta Cryst., 19, 942, 1965

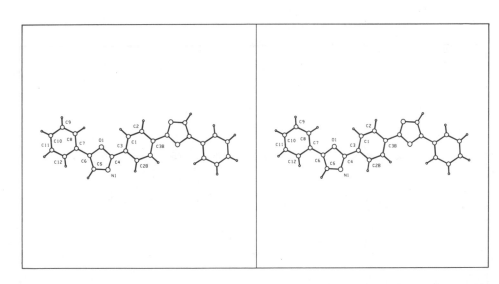

P2₁/c   Z = 2   R = 0.058

PHOXBZ   LB 24-16-7

Bond Lengths

C4	N1	1.29		C5	C6	1.35
C5	N1	1.38		C6	C7	1.45
C4	O1	1.36		C7	C8	1.39
C6	O1	1.38		C7	C12	1.40
C1	C2	1.38		C8	C9	1.38
C1	C3	1.40		C9	C10	1.38
C2	C3B	1.40		C10	C11	1.37
C3	C4	1.46		C11	C12	1.38

Bond Angles

C4	N1	C5	104		N1	C4	C3	128		C8	C7	C12	119
C4	O1	C6	105		O1	C4	C3	118		C7	C8	C9	120
C2	C1	C3	120		N1	C5	C6	110		C8	C9	C10	121
C1	C2	C3B	120		O1	C6	C5	107		C9	C10	C11	120
C1	C3	C4	122		O1	C6	C7	118		C10	C11	C12	120
C1	C3	C2B	119		C5	C6	C7	135		C7	C12	C11	120
C4	C3	C2B	119		C6	C7	C8	121					
N1	C4	O1	114		C6	C7	C12	120					

Torsion Angles

C1	C3	C4	N1	177
C1	C3	C4	O1	−3
C2B	C3	C4	N1	−3
C2B	C3	C4	O1	176
O1	C6	C7	C8	−6
O1	C6	C7	C12	174
C5	C6	C7	C8	173
C5	C6	C7	C12	−7

41.1 Xanthan hydride

C₂H₂N₂S₃

R.H.Stanford Junior, Acta Cryst., 16, 1157, 1963

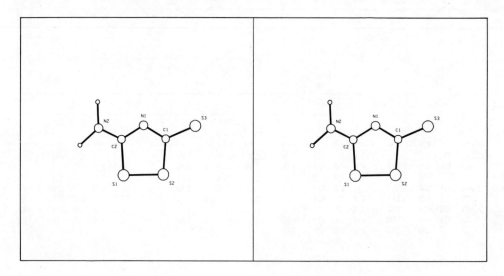

P2₁/c   Z = 4   R = 0.069

XANHYD   LB 2-2-27

Bond Lengths			Bond Angles			
S1	S2	2.05	S2	S1	C2	92
S1	C2	1.77	S1	S2	C1	95
S2	C1	1.76	C1	N1	C2	118
S3	C1	1.65	S2	C1	S3	117
C1	N1	1.33	S2	C1	N1	116
C2	N1	1.33	S3	C1	N1	126
C2	N2	1.30	S1	C2	N1	118
			S1	C2	N2	119
			N1	C2	N2	123

41.2 Xanthan hydride

C₂H₂N₂S₃

A.Hordvik, Acta Chem. Scand., 17, 2575, 1963

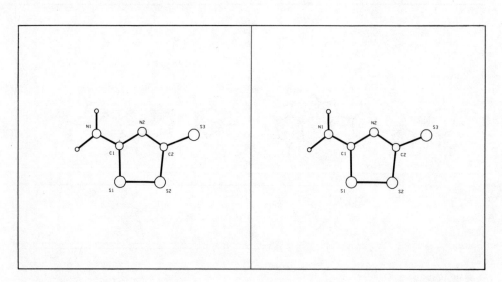

P2₁/c   Z = 4   R = 0.062

XANHYD01   LB 2-2-27

Bond Lengths			Bond Angles			
S1	S2	2.06	S2	S1	C1	92
S1	C1	1.76	S1	S2	C2	95
S2	C2	1.76	C1	N2	C2	116
S3	C2	1.65	S1	C1	N1	119
C1	N1	1.31	S1	C1	N2	119
C1	N2	1.36	N1	C1	N2	122
C2	N2	1.35	S2	C2	S3	117
			S2	C2	N2	117
			S3	C2	N2	126

41.3   Thiuret hydrobromide

$C_2H_4N_3S_2^+$, Br^-

A.Hordvik, S.Joys, Acta Chem. Scand., 19, 1539, 1965

P2$_1$/c   Z = 4   R = 0.09

TURETB   LB 2-4-8

Bond Lengths			Bond Angles			
S1	S2	2.08	S2	S1	C1	93
S1	C1	1.72	S1	S2	C2	91
S2	C2	1.74	C1	N2	C2	112
C1	N1	1.32	S1	C1	N1	119
C1	N2	1.35	S1	C1	N2	121
C2	N2	1.33	N1	C1	N2	120
C2	N3	1.37	S2	C2	N2	122
			S2	C2	N3	118
			N2	C2	N3	120

41.4   Rhodanine

$C_3H_3NOS_2$

D.van der Helm, A.E.Lessor, L.L.Merritt, Acta Cryst., 15, 1227, 1962

P2$_1$/n   Z = 4   R = 0.14

RHODIN   LB 3-3-16

Bond Lengths			Bond Angles			
S1	C1	1.64	C1	S2	C3	93
S2	C1	1.74	C1	N1	C2	117
S2	C3	1.82	S1	C1	S2	124
C1	N1	1.37	S1	C1	N1	124
C2	N1	1.38	S2	C1	N1	112
C2	O1	1.23	N1	C2	O1	124
C2	C3	1.51	N1	C2	C3	112
			O1	C2	C3	124
			S2	C3	C2	106

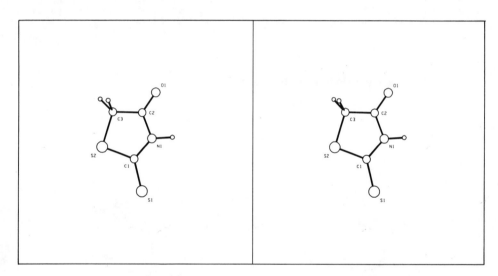

41.5   2 - (2′ - Hydroxyethylamino) - 2 - thiazoline

$C_5H_{10}N_2OS$

R.A.L.Miller, J.M.Robertson, G.A.Sim, R.C.Clapp, L.Long, T.Hasselstrom,
Nature, 202, 287, 1964

Atomic coordinates were not given
but bond lengths were reported.
P2$_1$/c   Z = 4   R = 0.15

HETHAZ   LB 5-10-7

41.6   3 - Methylbenzothiazoline - 2 - thione   C₈H₇NS₂

P.J.Wheatley, J. Chem. Soc., 4379, 1961

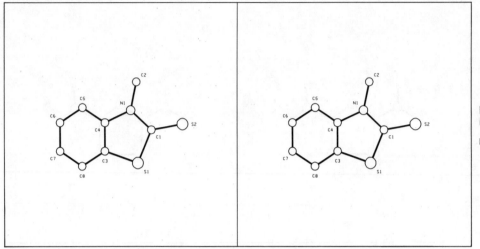

P2₁   Z = 2   R_{h0l} = 0.11,
R_{0kl} = 0.11

MBZTZS   LB 8-7-11

Bond Lengths

S1	C1	1.77	C3	C4	1.41
S1	C3	1.78	C3	C8	1.38
S2	C1	1.63	C4	C5	1.36
C1	N1	1.43	C5	C6	1.38
C2	N1	1.43	C6	C7	1.41
C4	N1	1.45	C7	C8	1.36

Bond Angles

C1	S1	C3	94	S2	C1	N1	128	C3	C4	C5	123
C1	N1	C2	120	S1	C3	C4	109	C4	C5	C6	115
C1	N1	C4	113	S1	C3	C8	129	C5	C6	C7	122
C2	N1	C4	126	C4	C3	C8	122	C6	C7	C8	123
S1	C1	S2	123	N1	C4	C3	115	C3	C8	C7	115
S1	C1	N1	109	N1	C4	C5	123				

41.7   2 - Methylthiobenzothiazole   C₈H₇NS₂

P.J.Wheatley, J. Chem. Soc., 3636, 1962

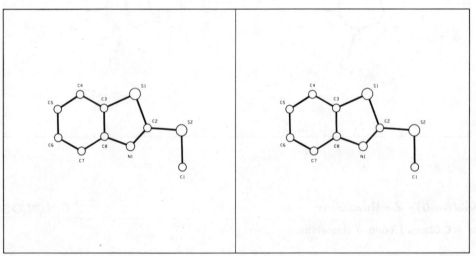

P2₁/c   Z = 4   R_{h0l} = 0.10,
R_{hk0} = 0.07

MESBSZ   LB 8-7-12

Bond Lengths

S1	C2	1.78	C3	C4	1.40
S1	C3	1.73	C3	C8	1.40
S2	C1	1.82	C4	C5	1.37
S2	C2	1.77	C5	C6	1.40
C2	N1	1.26	C6	C7	1.38
C8	N1	1.43	C7	C8	1.38

Bond Angles

C2	S1	C3	88	C4	C3	C8	119
C1	S2	C2	94	C3	C4	C5	120
C2	N1	C8	113	C4	C5	C6	121
S1	C2	S2	115	C5	C6	C7	119
S1	C2	N1	115	C6	C7	C8	121
S2	C2	N1	129	N1	C8	C3	111
S1	C3	C4	128	N1	C8	C7	129
S1	C3	C8	113	C3	C8	C7	120

Torsion Angles

C1	S2	C2	S1	171
C1	S2	C2	N1	−17

41.8 Phenylthiazolidinedione sodium salt

$C_9H_6NO_2S^-$, Na^+

B.W.Matthews, Acta Cryst., 17, 1413, 1964

$P2_1/a$ $Z = 4$ $R = 0.07$

PTHAZN   LB 9-6-12

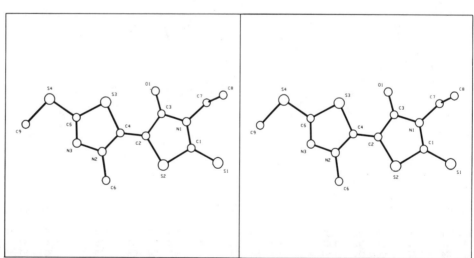

Bond Lengths

S1	C2	1.78	C3	C4	1.51
S1	C3	1.81	C4	C5	1.40
C1	N1	1.32	C4	C9	1.36
C2	N1	1.34	C5	C6	1.40
C1	O1	1.26	C6	C7	1.36
C2	O2	1.23	C7	C8	1.31
C1	C3	1.53	C8	C9	1.42

Bond Angles

C2	S1	C3	91	C1	C3	C4	111
C1	N1	C2	111	C3	C4	C5	120
N1	C1	O1	123	C3	C4	C9	121
N1	C1	C3	119	C5	C4	C9	119
O1	C1	C3	118	C4	C5	C6	119
S1	C2	N1	116	C5	C6	C7	120
S1	C2	O2	120	C6	C7	C8	120
N1	C2	O2	124	C7	C8	C9	121
S1	C3	C1	103	C4	C9	C8	120
S1	C3	C4	114				

Torsion Angles

C3	S1	C2	N1	4	N1	C1	C3	S1	9
C3	S1	C2	O2	−178	N1	C1	C3	C4	−114
C2	S1	C3	C1	−6	O1	C1	C3	S1	−172
C2	S1	C3	C4	114	O1	C1	C3	C4	65
C2	N1	C1	O1	175	S1	C3	C4	C5	−53
C2	N1	C1	C3	−7	S1	C3	C4	C9	132
C1	N1	C2	S1	1	C1	C3	C4	C5	62
C1	N1	C2	O2	−178	C1	C3	C4	C9	−113

41.9   3 - Methyl - 5 - thiomethyl - 2,3 - dihydro - 1,3,4 - thiadiazol - 2 - (1' - ethyl - 4' - thiazolidinylidene - 2' - thione - 5' - one)

$C_9H_{11}N_3OS_4$

3 - Ethyl - 5 - (4 - methylthio) - Δ^2 - 1,3,4 - (thiadiazolin - 5 - ylidene) rhodanine
G.Germain, C.Paternotte, P.Piret, M.van Meerssche,
J. Chim. Phys. Phys.-Chim. Biol., 61, 1059, 1964

$P2_1/c$ $Z = 4$ $R = 0.16$

MSTAZO   LB 9-11-29

Bond Lengths

S1	C1	1.61	C3	N1	1.40
S2	C1	1.71	C7	N1	1.46
S2	C2	1.75	C4	N2	1.35
S3	C4	1.74	C6	N2	1.46
S3	C5	1.73	C5	N3	1.30
S4	C5	1.69	C3	O1	1.21
S4	C9	1.81	C2	C3	1.41
N2	N3	1.38	C2	C4	1.33
C1	N1	1.36	C7	C8	1.55

Bond Angles

C1	S2	C2	92	N2	N3	C5	110
C4	S3	C5	89	S1	C1	S2	122
C5	S4	C9	101	S1	C1	N1	127
C1	N1	C3	116	S2	C1	N1	110
C1	N1	C7	123	S2	C2	C3	111
C3	N1	C7	121	S2	C2	C4	129
N3	N2	C4	117	C3	C2	C4	120
N3	N2	C6	117	N1	C3	O1	122
C4	N2	C6	126	N1	C3	C2	110

(continued)

O1	C3	C2	128
S3	C4	N2	109
S3	C4	C2	123
N2	C4	C2	129
S3	C5	S4	119
S3	C5	N3	116
S4	C5	N3	125
N1	C7	C8	111

Torsion Angles

C9	S4	C5	S3	−179
C9	S4	C5	N3	1
C1	N1	C7	C8	−81
C3	N1	C7	C8	98

41.10   2 - Thio - 3 - ethyl - 5 - (2' - (3' - methylthiazolidinylidine)) - thiazolidine - 2,4 - dione

$C_9H_{12}N_2OS_3$

G.Germain, P.Piret, M.van Meerssche, J.de Kerf, Bull. Soc. Chim. Fr., 1407, 1961

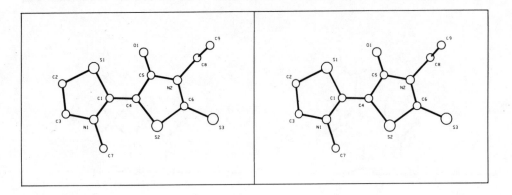

$P2_1/c$ $Z = 4$ $R = 0.17$

SEMTZO   LB 9-12-11

Bond Lengths

S1	C1	1.75	C5	N2	1.41
S1	C2	1.80	C6	N2	1.35
S2	C4	1.74	C8	N2	1.52
S2	C6	1.76	C5	O1	1.24
S3	C6	1.64	C1	C4	1.40
C1	N1	1.37	C2	C3	1.55
C3	N1	1.47	C4	C5	1.40
C7	N1	1.53	C8	C9	1.57

Bond Angles

C1	S1	C2	93	N1	C3	C2	107
C4	S2	C6	93	S2	C4	C1	128
C1	N1	C3	116	S2	C4	C5	109
C1	N1	C7	120	C1	C4	C5	122
C3	N1	C7	119	N2	C5	O1	117
C5	N2	C6	115	N2	C5	C4	113
C5	N2	C8	123	O1	C5	C4	129
C6	N2	C8	122	S2	C6	S3	120
S1	C1	N1	112	S2	C6	N2	109
S1	C1	C4	117	S3	C6	N2	128
N1	C1	C4	124	N2	C8	C9	116
S1	C2	C3	109				

Torsion Angles

C2	S1	C1	N1	14	C8	N2	C5	C4	−175
C2	S1	C1	C4	166	C5	N2	C6	S2	−10
C1	S1	C2	C3	−4	C5	N2	C6	S3	−171
C6	S2	C4	C1	−173	C8	N2	C6	S2	171
C6	S2	C4	C5	−5	C8	N2	C6	S3	10
C4	S2	C6	S3	171	C5	N2	C8	C9	89
C4	S2	C6	N2	8	C6	N2	C8	C9	−92
C3	N1	C1	S1	−22	S1	C1	C4	S2	−175
C3	N1	C1	C4	−171	S1	C1	C4	C5	18
C7	N1	C1	S1	−176	N1	C1	C4	S2	−27
C7	N1	C1	C4	35	N1	C1	C4	C5	166
C1	N1	C3	C2	18	S1	C2	C3	N1	−7
C7	N1	C3	C2	173	S2	C4	C5	N2	1
C6	N2	C5	O1	−171	S2	C4	C5	O1	177
C6	N2	C5	C4	6	C1	C4	C5	N2	170
C8	N2	C5	O1	8	C1	C4	C5	O1	−14

41.11   2 - Thio - 3 - allyl - 5 - (2 - (3'methylthiazolidinylidene)) - thiazolidine - 2,4 - dione

$C_{10}H_{12}N_2OS_3$

G.Germain, P.Piret, M.van Meerssche, Acta Cryst., 15, 373, 1962

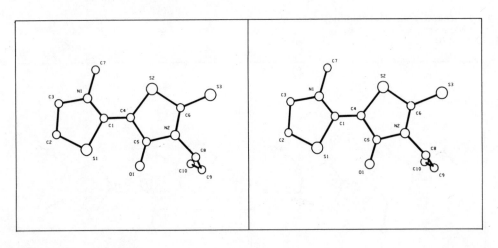

$P2_12_12_1$ $Z = 4$ $R = 0.15$

SALAZO   LB 10-12-25

Bond Lengths

S1	C1	1.79	C6	N2	1.38
S1	C2	1.78	C8	N2	1.48
S2	C4	1.77	C5	O1	1.23
S2	C6	1.71	C1	C4	1.34
S3	C6	1.65	C2	C3	1.53
C1	N1	1.31	C4	C5	1.43
C3	N1	1.49	C8	C9	1.51
C7	N1	1.48	C9	C10	1.33
C5	N2	1.46			

Bond Angles

C1	S1	C2	92	N1	C3	C2	104
C4	S2	C6	94	S2	C4	C1	128
C1	N1	C3	120	S2	C4	C5	109
C1	N1	C7	123	C1	C4	C5	123
C3	N1	C7	116	N2	C5	O1	118
C5	N2	C6	114	N2	C5	C4	112
C5	N2	C8	121	O1	C5	C4	131
C6	N2	C8	125	S2	C6	S3	124
S1	C1	N1	110	S2	C6	N2	112
S1	C1	C4	120	S3	C6	N2	124
N1	C1	C4	130	N2	C8	C9	112
S1	C2	C3	109	C8	C9	C10	126

Torsion Angles

C2	S1	C1	N1	9	C5	N2	C6	S2	2
C2	S1	C1	C4	−173	C5	N2	C6	S3	−179
C1	S1	C2	C3	−19	C8	N2	C6	S2	−180
C6	S2	C4	C1	−180	C8	N2	C6	S3	0
C6	S2	C4	C5	0	C5	N2	C8	C9	89
C4	S2	C6	S3	180	C6	N2	C8	C9	−89
C4	S2	C6	N2	−1	S1	C1	C4	S2	−180
C3	N1	C1	S1	5	S1	C1	C4	C5	0
C3	N1	C1	C4	−173	N1	C1	C4	S2	−2
C7	N1	C1	S1	175	N1	C1	C4	C5	178
C7	N1	C1	C4	−4	S1	C2	C3	N1	23
C1	N1	C3	C2	−18	S2	C4	C5	N2	1
C7	N1	C3	C2	171	S2	C4	C5	O1	176
C6	N2	C5	O1	−178	C1	C4	C5	N2	−179
C6	N2	C5	C4	−2	C1	C4	C5	O1	−4
C8	N2	C5	O1	4	N2	C8	C9	C10	−3
C8	N2	C5	C4	180					

41.12   2 - Benzoylimino - 3 - methylthiazolid - 5 - one $C_{11}H_{10}N_2O_2S$

H.Steeple, Acta Cryst., 14, 847, 1961

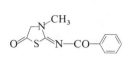

$P2_1/c$ Z = 4 R_{h0l} = 0.15,
R_{0kl} = 0.14

BIMTZO   LB 11-10-6

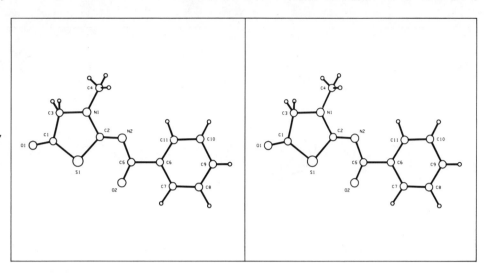

Bond Lengths					
S1	C1	1.77	C1	C3	1.60
S1	C2	1.77	C5	C6	1.54
C2	N1	1.48	C6	C7	1.41
C3	N1	1.53	C6	C11	1.41
C4	N1	1.45	C7	C8	1.39
C2	N2	1.23	C8	C9	1.39
C5	N2	1.34	C9	C10	1.43
C1	O1	1.16	C10	C11	1.37
C5	O2	1.18			

Bond Angles							
C1	S1	C2	97	N2	C5	O2	134
C2	N1	C3	116	N2	C5	C6	111
C2	N1	C4	124	O2	C5	C6	115
C3	N1	C4	120	C5	C6	C7	119
C2	N2	C5	114	C5	C6	C11	124
S1	C1	O1	132	C7	C6	C11	116
S1	C1	C3	109	C6	C7	C8	120
O1	C1	C3	115	C7	C8	C9	121
S1	C2	N1	109	C8	C9	C10	121
S1	C2	N2	130	C9	C10	C11	115
N1	C2	N2	119	C6	C11	C10	126
N1	C3	C1	107				

Torsion Angles							
C2	S1	C1	O1	−171	C5	N2	C2	S1	3
C2	S1	C1	C3	−13	C5	N2	C2	N1	167
C1	S1	C2	N1	13	C2	N2	C5	O2	−3
C1	S1	C2	N2	179	C2	N2	C5	C6	−178
C3	N1	C2	S1	−10	S1	C1	C3	N1	10
C3	N1	C2	N2	−177	O1	C1	C3	N1	171
C4	N1	C2	S1	178	N2	C5	C6	C7	−180
C4	N1	C2	N2	10	N2	C5	C6	C11	3
C2	N1	C3	C1	0	O2	C5	C6	C7	4
C4	N1	C3	C1	173	O2	C5	C6	C11	−173

41.13   **Thiamine hydrochloride monohydrate** $C_{12}H_{18}N_4OS^{2+}$, $2Cl^-$, H_2O

J.Kraut, H.J.Reed, Acta Cryst., 15, 747, 1962

$P2_1/c$ Z = 4   R = 0.08

THIAMC   LB 12-17-4

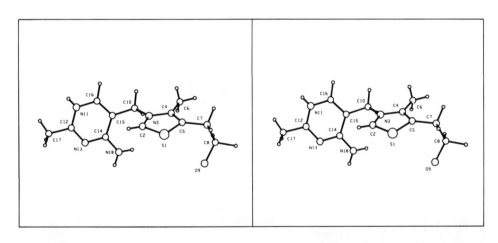

Bond Lengths					
S1	C2	1.67	C8	O9	1.42
S1	C5	1.72	C4	C5	1.35
C2	N3	1.33	C4	C6	1.48
C4	N3	1.40	C5	C7	1.50
C10	N3	1.48	C7	C8	1.52
C12	N11	1.33	C10	C15	1.50
C16	N11	1.36	C12	C17	1.49
C12	N13	1.31	C14	C15	1.43
C14	N13	1.37	C15	C16	1.35
C14	N18	1.32			

Bond Angles							
C2	S1	C5	92	C5	C4	C6	128
C2	N3	C4	113	S1	C5	C4	111
C2	N3	C10	125	S1	C5	C7	121
C4	N3	C10	122	C4	C5	C7	128
C12	N11	C16	121	C5	C7	C8T	111
C12	N13	C14	119	O9	C8	C7	113
S1	C2	N3	112	N3	C10	C15	113
N3	C4	C5	112	C10	C15	C14	113
N3	C4	C6	120	N11	C12	N13	123
				N11	C12	C17	117

N13	C12	C17	120
N13	C14	N18	117
N13	C14	C15	121
N18	C14	C15	123
C10	C15	C14	123
C10	C15	C16	120
C14	C15	C16	117
N11	C16	C15	120

Torsion Angles				
C2	N3	C10	C15	−9
C4	N3	C10	C15	171
S1	C5	C7	C8	103
C4	C5	C7	C8	−71
C5	C7	C8	O9	−54
N3	C10	C15	C14	−76
N3	C10	C15	C16	109

41.14   2,5 - Diphenylthiadiazole

$C_{14}H_{10}N_2S$

Z.V.Zvonkova, A.N.Khvatkina, Kristallografija, 10, 734, 1965

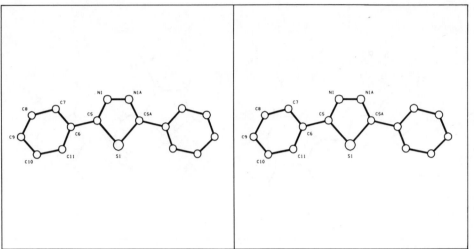

Published value of y(S1) = 0.1315.
The correct value is 0.1351.
C2/c   Z = 4   R = 0.18

DPTHAZ   LB 14-10-36

Bond Lengths

S1	C5	1.76	C6	C11	1.38
N1	N1A	1.19	C7	C8	1.41
C5	N1	1.27	C8	C9	1.39
C5	C6	1.51	C9	C10	1.37
C6	C7	1.38	C10	C11	1.42

Bond Angles

C5	S1	C5A	83		C7	C6	C11	121
S1	C5	N1	112		C6	C7	C8	117
S1	C5	C6	119		C7	C8	C9	125
N1	C5	C6	129		C8	C9	C10	115
C5	C6	C7	118		C9	C10	C11	122
C5	C6	C11	121		C6	C11	C10	120

Torsion Angles

S1	C5	C6	C7	−156
S1	C5	C6	C11	31
N1	C5	C6	C7	16
N1	C5	C6	C11	−156

41.15   (2 - (1 - Methylquinoline)) - (2 - (3 - methylbenzo - thiazole)) methyl - monomethine cyanine iodide

$C_{20}H_{19}N_2S^+$, I^-

J.Effinger, G.Germain, J.Meunier, J.Vanderauwera, M.van Meerssche,
Bull. Soc. Chim. Belges, 69, 387, 1960

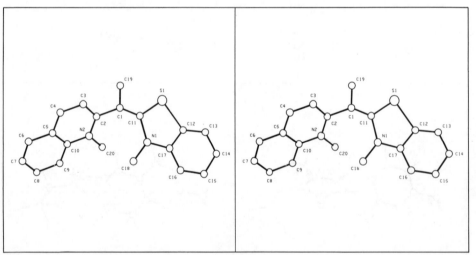

No comparison of bond lengths is
possible since they are not reported
in the paper.
Pbca   Z = 8 R_{0kl} = 0.17,
R_{1kl} = 0.17, R_{h0l} = 0.19, R_{hk0} = 0.27

MQMBTH   LB 20-19-2

Bond Lengths

S1	C11	1.73	C4	C5	1.38
S1	C12	2.09	C5	C6	1.46
C11	N1	1.61	C5	C10	1.34
C17	N1	1.35	C6	C7	1.31
C18	N1	1.49	C7	C8	1.35
C2	N2	1.35	C8	C9	1.47
C10	N2	1.40	C9	C10	1.38
C20	N2	1.34	C12	C13	1.39
C1	C2	1.48	C12	C17	1.46
C1	C11	1.26	C13	C14	1.38
C1	C19	1.28	C14	C15	1.51
C2	C3	1.31	C15	C16	1.43
C3	C4	1.40	C16	C17	1.37

Bond Angles

C11	S1	C12	88		C2	C3	C4	119		S1	C11	C1	123
C11	N1	C17	116		C3	C4	C5	121		N1	C11	C1	125
C11	N1	C18	129		C4	C5	C6	121		S1	C12	C13	126
C17	N1	C18	114		C4	C5	C10	118		S1	C12	C17	108
C2	N2	C10	118		C6	C5	C10	121		C13	C12	C17	126
C2	N2	C20	122		C5	C6	C7	120		C12	C13	C14	117
C10	N2	C20	120		C6	C7	C8	122		C13	C14	C15	120
C2	C1	C11	137		C7	C8	C9	118		C14	C15	C16	120
C2	C1	C19	113		C8	C9	C10	120		C15	C16	C17	121
C11	C1	C19	110		N2	C10	C5	121		N1	C17	C12	115
N2	C2	C1	118		N2	C10	C9	120		N1	C17	C16	128
N2	C2	C3	123		C5	C10	C9	119		C12	C17	C16	117
C1	C2	C3	119		S1	C11	N1	113					

Torsion Angles

C11	C1	C2	N2	−59
C11	C1	C2	C3	124
C19	C1	C2	N2	130
C19	C1	C2	C3	−48
C2	C1	C11	S1	174
C2	C1	C11	N1	−3
C19	C1	C11	S1	−14
C19	C1	C11	N1	169

41.16   2 - p - Methoxyphenyl - 3,4 - dibenzyl - 1,3,4 - thiadiazolidine - 5 - thione

$C_{23}H_{22}N_2OS_2$

I.L.Karle, J.Karle, Acta Cryst., 19, 92, 1965

P-1   Z = 2   R = 0.107

MOBSAZ   LB 23-22-1

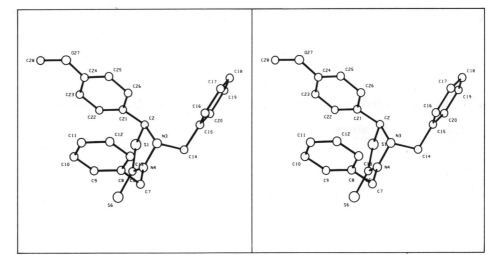

Bond Lengths

S1	C2	1.84	C11	C12	1.41
S1	C5	1.77	C12	C13	1.40
S6	C5	1.65	C14	C15	1.50
N3	N4	1.42	C15	C16	1.39
C2	N3	1.51	C15	C20	1.35
C14	N3	1.47	C16	C17	1.40
C5	N4	1.36	C17	C18	1.35
C7	N4	1.44	C18	C19	1.39
C24	O27	1.35	C19	C20	1.41
C28	O27	1.47	C21	C22	1.38
C2	C21	1.50	C21	C26	1.37
C7	C8	1.47	C22	C23	1.39
C8	C9	1.41	C23	C24	1.36
C8	C13	1.39	C24	C25	1.41
C9	C10	1.40	C25	C26	1.37
C10	C11	1.37			

Bond Angles

C2	S1	C5	90	C11	C12	C13	119
N4	N3	C2	107	C8	C13	C12	117
N4	N3	C14	106	N3	C14	C15	108
C2	N3	C14	117	C14	C15	C16	121
N3	N4	C5	116	C14	C15	C20	120
N3	N4	C7	116	C16	C15	C20	120
C5	N4	C7	127	C15	C16	C17	120
C24	O27	C28	117	C16	C17	C18	121
S1	C2	N3	104	C17	C18	C19	120
S1	C2	C21	113	C18	C19	C20	119
N3	C2	C21	114	C15	C20	C19	121
S1	C5	S6	122	C2	C21	C22	125
S1	C5	N4	111	C2	C21	C26	115
S6	C5	N4	126	C22	C21	C26	121
N4	C7	C8	108	C21	C22	C23	121
C7	C8	C9	117	C22	C23	C24	117
C7	C8	C13	119	O27	C24	C23	123
C9	C8	C13	123	O27	C24	C25	114
C8	C9	C10	119	C23	C24	C25	123
C9	C10	C11	118	C24	C25	C26	119
C10	C11	C12	124	C21	C26	C25	120

Torsion Angles

C5	S1	C2	N3	29	N3	N4	C5	S6	175
C5	S1	C2	C21	-95	C7	N4	C5	S1	167
C2	S1	C5	S6	165	C7	N4	C5	S6	-13
C2	S1	C5	N4	-15	N3	N4	C7	C8	71
C2	N3	N4	C5	27	C5	N4	C7	C8	-100
C2	N3	N4	C7	-145	C28	O27	C24	C23	-2
C14	N3	N4	C5	-98	C28	O27	C24	C25	-180
C14	N3	N4	C7	90	S1	C2	C21	C22	-4
N4	N3	C2	S1	-36	S1	C2	C21	C26	178
N4	N3	C2	C21	87	N3	C2	C21	C22	-122
C14	N3	C2	S1	83	N3	C2	C21	C26	59
C14	N3	C2	C21	-154	N4	C7	C8	C9	74
N4	N3	C14	C15	-176	N4	C7	C8	C13	-105
C2	N3	C14	C15	65	N3	C14	C15	C16	70
N3	N4	C5	S1	-4	N3	C14	C15	C20	-112

42.1   1,3 - Dihydro - 1 - hydroxy - 3 - oxy - 1,2 - benziodoxole

1 - Hydroxy - 1,2 - benziodoxol - 3(1H) - one
E.Shefter, W.Wolf, J. Pharm. Sci., 54, 104, 1965

$C_7H_5IO_3$

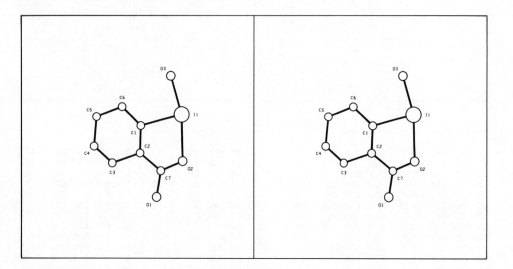

P2$_1$/c   Z = 4   R = 0.137

BENIOX   LB 7-5-18

Bond Lengths

I1	O2	2.30	C1	C6	1.36
I1	O3	2.00	C2	C3	1.53
I1	C1	2.16	C2	C7	1.39
C7	O1	1.32	C3	C4	1.28
C7	O2	1.23	C4	C5	1.47
C1	C2	1.37	C5	C6	1.40

Bond Angles

O2	I1	O3	165	C3	C2	C7	121
O2	I1	C1	77	C2	C3	C4	116
O3	I1	C1	89	C3	C4	C5	123
I1	O2	C7	111	C4	C5	C6	115
I1	C1	C2	106	C1	C6	C5	116
I1	C1	C6	121	O1	C7	O2	122
C2	C1	C6	130	O1	C7	C2	120
C1	C2	C3	109	O2	C7	C2	117
C1	C2	C7	125				

Torsion Angles

O3	I1	O2	C7	−16	I1	C1	C6	C5	−176
C1	I1	O2	C7	0	C2	C1	C6	C5	−21
O2	I1	C1	C2	10	C1	C2	C3	C4	−31
O2	I1	C1	C6	170	C7	C2	C3	C4	173
O3	I1	C1	C2	−174	C1	C2	C7	O1	−168
O3	I1	C1	C6	−14	C1	C2	C7	O2	25
I1	O2	C7	O1	−179	C3	C2	C7	O1	−16
I1	O2	C7	C2	−11	C3	C2	C7	O2	177
I1	C1	C2	C3	−177	C2	C3	C4	C5	35
I1	C1	C2	C7	−22	C3	C4	C5	C6	−28
C6	C1	C2	C3	26	C4	C5	C6	C1	17
C6	C1	C2	C7	−180					

43.1   Alloxan

$C_4H_2N_2O_4$

N.Bolton, Acta Cryst., 17, 147, 1964

P4$_1$2$_1$2   Z = 4   R = 0.092

ALOXAN   LB 4-2-8

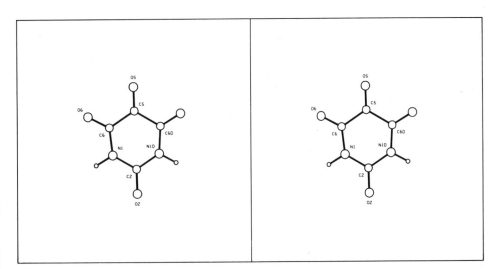

Bond Lengths			Bond Angles			
C2	N1	1.39	C2	N1	C6	126
C6	N1	1.36	N1	C2	N1D	117
C2	O2	1.22	N1	C2	O2	121
C5	O5	1.19	O5	C5	C6	121
C6	O6	1.21	C6	C5	C6D	118
C5	C6	1.52	N1	C6	O6	123
			N1	C6	C5	116
			O6	C6	C5	120

43.2   Potassium violurate dihydrate

$C_4H_2N_3O_4^-$, K^+ , $2H_2O$

H.Gillier, Bull. Soc. Chim. Fr., 2373, 1965

P2$_1$/a   Z = 4   R = 0.18

KVIOLD   LB 4-2-6

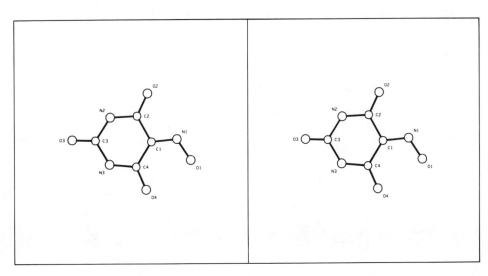

Bond Lengths			Bond Angles			
N1	O1	1.26	O1	N1	C1	119
C1	N1	1.34	C2	N2	C3	126
C2	N2	1.37	C3	N3	C4	126
C3	N2	1.38	N1	C1	C2	114
C3	N3	1.38	N1	C1	C4	127
C4	N3	1.37	C2	C1	C4	119
C2	O2	1.24	N2	C2	O2	119
C3	O3	1.20	N2	C2	C1	117
C4	O4	1.22	O2	C2	C1	124
C1	C2	1.45	N2	C3	N3	115
C1	C4	1.46	N2	C3	O3	121
			N3	C3	O3	124
			N3	C4	O4	119
			N3	C4	C1	117
			O4	C4	C1	124

43.3 Rubidium violurate

$C_4H_2N_3O_4^-$, Rb^+

H.Gillier, Bull. Soc. Chim. Fr., 2373, 1965

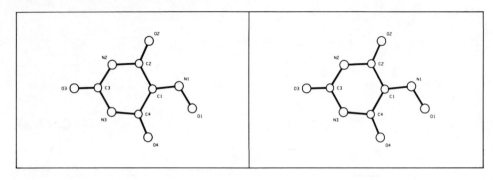

P-1   Z = 2   R = 0.13

RBVIOL   LB 4-2-10

Bond Lengths

N1	O1	1.29	C2	O2	1.23
C1	N1	1.36	C3	O3	1.22
C2	N2	1.37	C4	O4	1.24
C3	N2	1.36	C1	C2	1.44
C3	N3	1.38	C1	C4	1.44
C4	N3	1.38			

Bond Angles

O1	N1	C1	116	C2	C1	C4	120	N2	C3	O3	124
C2	N2	C3	125	N2	C2	O2	117	N3	C3	O3	120
C3	N3	C4	125	N2	C2	C1	117	N3	C4	O4	118
N1	C1	C2	113	O2	C2	C1	126	N3	C4	C1	116
N1	C1	C4	126	N2	C3	N3	117	O4	C4	C1	126

43.4 Ammonium barbiturate

$C_4H_3N_2O_3^-$, H_4N^+

B.M.Craven, Acta Cryst., 17, 282, 1964

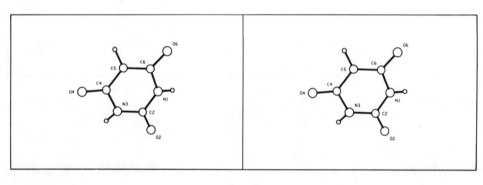

Published value of y(H10) = 0.400.
The correct value is −0.400.
$P2_1/n$ Z = 4   R = 0.15

AMBARB   LB 4-7-18

Bond Lengths

C2	N1	1.36	C4	O4	1.25
C6	N1	1.39	C6	O6	1.23
C2	N3	1.37	C4	C5	1.42
C4	N3	1.39	C5	C6	1.41
C2	O2	1.23			

Bond Angles

C2	N1	C6	126	N3	C2	O2	123	C4	C5	C6	120
C2	N3	C4	125	N3	C4	O4	117	N1	C6	O6	118
N1	C2	N3	115	N3	C4	C5	117	N1	C6	C5	117
N1	C2	O2	121	O4	C4	C5	126	O6	C6	C5	125

43.5 Violuric acid monohydrate, perdeuterated

$C_4D_3N_3O_4$, D_2O

B.M.Craven, Y.Mascarenhas, Acta Cryst., 17, 407, 1964

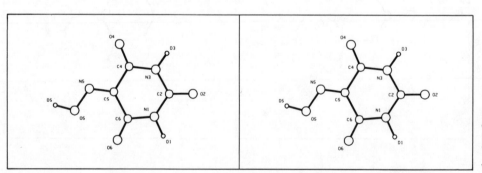

Bond lengths corrected for molecular oscillations are reported in the paper.
$Cmc2_1$ Z = 4   R = 0.059

VIOLMD   LB 4-0-12

Bond Lengths

N5	O5	1.33	C2	O2	1.23
C2	N1	1.36	C4	O4	1.21
C6	N1	1.37	C6	O6	1.18
C2	N3	1.38	C4	C5	1.47
C4	N3	1.38	C5	C6	1.51
C5	N5	1.27			

Bond Angles

C2	N1	C6	128	N3	C2	O2	120	N5	C5	C6	126
C2	N3	C4	126	N3	C4	O4	120	C4	C5	C6	119
O5	N5	C5	118	N3	C4	C5	116	N1	C6	O6	121
N1	C2	N3	116	O4	C4	C5	124	N1	C6	C5	114
N1	C2	O2	124	N5	C5	C4	115	O6	C6	C5	124

43.6 Violuric acid monohydrate, perdeuterated (neutron study) $C_4D_3N_3O_4 , D_2O$

B.M.Craven, W.J.Takei, Acta Cryst., 17, 415, 1964

Cmc2₁   Z = 4   R = 0.076

VIOLMD01   LB 4-0-12

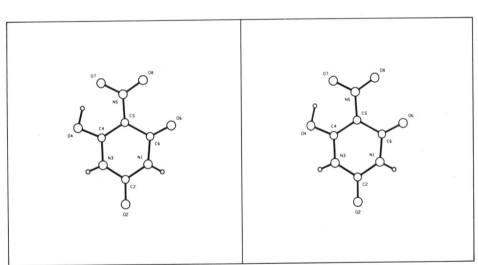

Bond Lengths

N5	O5	1.33	C4	C5	1.47
C2	N1	1.36	C5	C6	1.51
C6	N1	1.37	N1	D1	1.06
C2	N3	1.38	N3	D3	0.97
C4	N3	1.38	O5	D5	1.02
C5	N5	1.27			
C2	O2	1.22	O7	D6	0.97
C4	O4	1.21	O7	D7	0.94
C6	O6	1.18			

Bond Angles

C2	N1	C6	128	N1	C2	N3	116	C4	C5	C6	119
C2	N1	D1	117	N1	C2	O2	124	N1	C6	O6	121
C6	N1	D1	115	N3	C2	O2	120	N1	C6	C5	114
C2	N3	C4	126	N3	C4	O4	120	O6	C6	C5	124
C2	N3	D3	116	N3	C4	C5	116				
C4	N3	D3	118	O4	C4	C5	124	D6	O7	D7	106
O5	N5	C5	118	N5	C5	C4	115				
N5	O5	D5	104	N5	C5	C6	126				

43.7 5 - Nitrobarbituric acid $C_4H_3N_3O_5$

W.Bolton, Acta Cryst., 16, 950, 1963

4-3-9 NO₂

The molecule is in the 5 - nitro - 2,6 - dioxo - 4 - hydroxyl configuration and not the commonly reported trioxo form.

P2₁/c   Z = 4   R = 0.093

NBARBA   LB 4-3-9

Bond Lengths

N5	O7	1.26	C5	N5	1.41
N5	O8	1.22	C2	O2	1.23
C2	N1	1.37	C4	O4	1.30
C6	N1	1.38	C6	O6	1.22
C2	N3	1.36	C4	C5	1.41
C4	N3	1.35	C5	C6	1.45

Bond Angles

C2	N1	C6	127	N3	C4	C5	119
C2	N3	C4	124	O4	C4	C5	125
O7	N5	O8	120	N5	C5	C4	118
O7	N5	C5	119	N5	C5	C6	122
O8	N5	C5	121	C4	C5	C6	120
N1	C2	N3	116	N1	C6	O6	120
N1	C2	O2	123	N1	C6	C5	114
N3	C2	O2	122	O6	C6	C5	126
N3	C4	O4	115				

43.8 5 - Nitrobarbituric acid trihydrate (monoclinic form) $C_4H_3N_3O_5$, $3H_2O$

B.M.Craven, S.Martinez-Carrera, G.A.Jeffrey, Acta Cryst., 17, 891, 1964

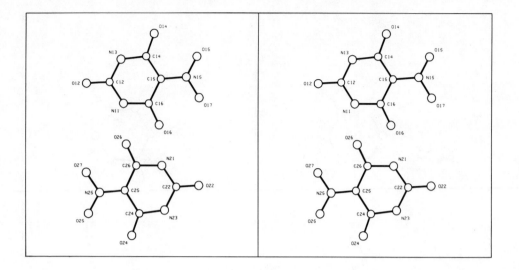

$P2_1/n$ $Z = 8$ $R = 0.129$

NBARBT   LB 4-3-10

Bond Lengths

N15	O15	1.22	N25	O25	1.23
N15	O17	1.29	N25	O27	1.26
C12	N11	1.36	C22	N21	1.36
C16	N11	1.37	C26	N21	1.39
C12	N13	1.35	C22	N23	1.36
C14	N13	1.38	C24	N23	1.38
C15	N15	1.40	C25	N25	1.38
C12	O12	1.25	C22	O22	1.22
C14	O14	1.26	C24	O24	1.23
C16	O16	1.24	C26	O26	1.23
C14	C15	1.44	C24	C25	1.44
C15	C16	1.44	C25	C26	1.43

Bond Angles

C12	N11	C16	125	N13	C14	C15	117	C22	N21	C26	125	N23 C24 C25 116
C12	N13	C14	125	O14	C14	C15	126	C22	N23	C24	125	O24 C24 C25 127
O15	N15	O17	119	N15	C15	C14	119	O25	N25	O27	117	N25 C25 C24 119
O15	N15	C15	123	N15	C15	C16	121	O25	N25	C25	123	N25 C25 C26 120
O17	N15	C15	118	C14	C15	C16	120	O27	N25	C25	120	C24 C25 C26 121
N11	C12	N13	117	N11	C16	O16	117	N21	C22	N23	117	N21 C26 O26 115
N11	C12	O12	122	N11	C16	C15	116	N21	C22	O22	122	N21 C26 C25 116
N13	C12	O12	121	O16	C16	C15	127	N23	C22	O22	121	O26 C26 C25 129
N13	C14	O14	117					N23	C24	O24	117	

43.9 Barbituric acid $C_4H_4N_2O_3$

W.Bolton, Acta Cryst., 16, 166, 1963

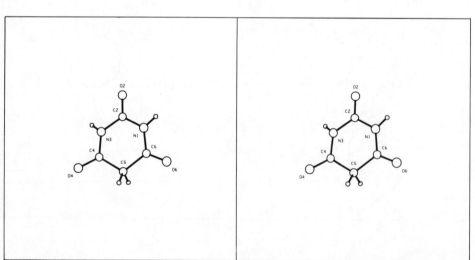

The author attributes the deviation of the molecule from planarity to crystal field forces.
$P2_1/c$ $Z = 4$ $R = 0.102$

BARBAC   LB 4-4-39

Bond Lengths

C2	N1	1.37
C6	N1	1.39
C2	N3	1.35
C4	N3	1.37
C2	O2	1.23
C4	O4	1.20
C6	O6	1.19
C4	C5	1.49
C5	C6	1.47

Bond Angles

C2	N1	C6	128	N3	C4	C5	120
C2	N3	C4	125	O4	C4	C5	121
N1	C2	N3	115	C4	C5	C6	114
N1	C2	O2	124	N1	C6	O6	122
N3	C2	O2	121	N1	C6	C5	116
N3	C4	O4	119	O6	C6	C5	121

Torsion Angles

C6	N1	C2	N3	1	C2	N3	C4	O4	174
C6	N1	C2	O2	−179	C2	N3	C4	C5	−8
C2	N1	C6	O6	−176	N3	C4	C5	C6	16
C2	N1	C6	C5	8	O4	C4	C5	C6	−166
C4	N3	C2	N1	−1	C4	C5	C6	N1	−15
C4	N3	C2	O2	180	C4	C5	C6	O6	169

43.10   Barbituric acid dihydrate

$C_4H_4N_2O_3$, $2H_2O$

G.A.Jeffrey, S.Ghose, J.O.Warwicker, Acta Cryst., 14, 881, 1961

The x and z coordinates of H6 are
interchanged in the paper.
Pnma   Z = 4   R = 0.14

BARBAD   LB 4-4-40

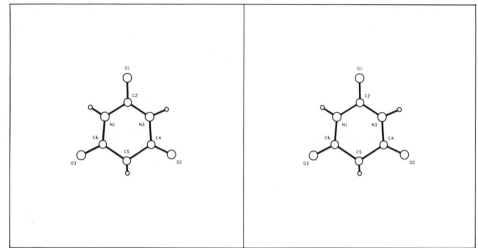

Bond Lengths			Bond Angles						
C2	N1	1.38	C2	N1	C6	125	N3	C4	C5	118
C6	N1	1.37	C2	N3	C4	125	O2	C4	C5	124
C2	N3	1.35	N1	C2	N3	118	C4	C5	C6	116
C4	N3	1.38	N1	C2	O1	120	N1	C6	O3	120
C2	O1	1.21	N3	C2	O1	122	N1	C6	C5	118
C4	O2	1.21	N3	C4	O2	118	O3	C6	C5	122
C6	O3	1.22							
C4	C5	1.51							
C5	C6	1.49							

43.11   Dialuric acid monohydrate

$C_4H_4N_2O_4$, H_2O

5,6 - Dihydroxyuracil
W.Bolton, Acta Cryst., 19, 1051, 1965

The structure was re - examined
by Craven and Sabine, Acta
Cryst.(B), 25, 1970, 1969 using
neutron diffraction. They found that
y(O7) = 0.5407 in Bolton's paper
should be 0.4593. The reported
interatomic distances involving this
atom, however, are correct.
See also Alexander & Pitman, Acta
Cryst., 9, 501, 1956.
$P2_1/n$ Z = 4   R = 0.08

DIALAC   LB 4-4-41

Bond Lengths			Bond Angles						
C2	N1	1.35	C2	N1	C6	123	O4	C4	C5	124
C6	N1	1.35	C2	N3	C4	126	O5	C5	C4	120
C2	N3	1.35	N1	C2	N3	115	O5	C5	C6	121
C4	N3	1.37	N1	C2	O2	123	C4	C5	C6	119
C2	O2	1.22	N3	C2	O2	122	N1	C6	O6	112
C4	O4	1.23	N3	C4	O4	120	N1	C6	C5	121
C5	O5	1.36	N3	C4	C5	116	O6	C6	C5	127
C6	O6	1.31							
C4	C5	1.42							
C5	C6	1.36							

43.12   5,5 - Dihydroxybarbituric acid

$C_4H_4N_2O_5$

C.Singh, Acta Cryst., 19, 759, 1965

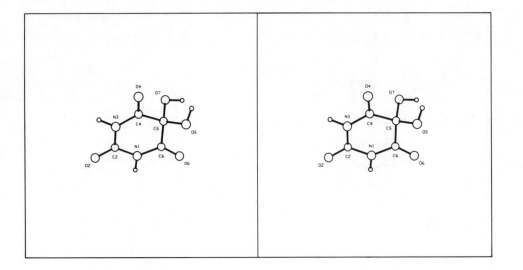

P-1   Z = 2   R = 0.087

ALXANM10   LB 4-4-42

Bond Lengths

C2	N1	1.37
C6	N1	1.38
C2	N3	1.37
C4	N3	1.37
C2	O2	1.22
C4	O4	1.21
C5	O5	1.39
C6	O6	1.21
C5	O7	1.39
C4	C5	1.54
C5	C6	1.54

Bond Angles

C2	N1	C6	127		O5	C5	C4	111
C2	N3	C4	126		O5	C5	C6	107
N1	C2	N3	117		O7	C5	C4	103
N1	C2	O2	121		O7	C5	C6	108
N3	C2	O2	122		C4	C5	C6	114
N3	C4	O4	121		N1	C6	O6	122
N3	C4	C5	117		N1	C6	C5	116
O4	C4	C5	122		O6	C6	C5	122
O5	C5	O7	113					

Torsion Angles

C6	N1	C2	N3	3		N3	C4	C5	C6	−19
C6	N1	C2	O2	−178		O4	C4	C5	O5	43
C2	N1	C6	O6	177		O4	C4	C5	O7	−79
C2	N1	C6	C5	−10		O4	C4	C5	C6	164
C4	N3	C2	N1	−4		O5	C5	C6	N1	141
C4	N3	C2	O2	176		O5	C5	C6	O6	−46
C2	N3	C4	O4	−170		O7	C5	C6	N1	−97
C2	N3	C4	C5	13		O7	C5	C6	O6	77
N3	C4	C5	O5	−140		C4	C5	C6	N1	17
N3	C4	C5	O7	98		C4	C5	C6	O6	−169

43.13   5,5 - Dihydroxybarbituric acid trihydrate

$C_4H_4N_2O_5$, $3H_2O$

D.Mootz, G.A.Jeffrey, Acta Cryst., 19, 717, 1965

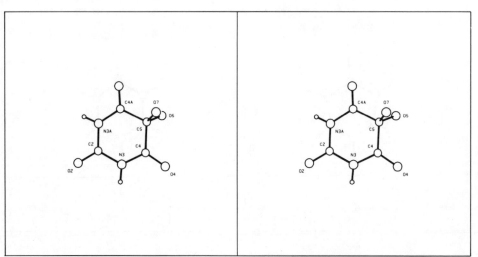

· $3H_2O$

One hydrogen atom of a water molecule and the two hydroxyl hydrogen atoms are disordered.
C2/m   Z = 4   R = 0.097

HBARBT   LB 4-4-43

Bond Lengths

C2	N3	1.37
C4	N3	1.37
C2	O2	1.21
C4	O4	1.22
C5	O5	1.38
C5	O7	1.41
C4	C5	1.53

Bond Angles

C2	N3	C4	125
N3	C2	N3A	118
N3	C2	O2	121
N3	C4	O4	122
N3	C4	C5	118
O4	C4	C5	120
O5	C5	O7	115
O5	C5	C4	109
O7	C5	C4	105
C4	C5	C4A	114

Torsion Angles

C4	N3	C2	N3A	−4
C4	N3	C2	O2	175
C2	N3	C4	O4	−171
C2	N3	C4	C5	12
N3	C4	C5	O5	−140
N3	C4	C5	O7	97
N3	C4	C5	C4A	−18
O4	C4	C5	O5	43
O4	C4	C5	O7	−81
O4	C4	C5	C4A	165

43.14 Alloxantin dihydrate

C.Singh, Acta Cryst., 19, 767, 1965

$C_8H_6N_4O_8$, $2H_2O$

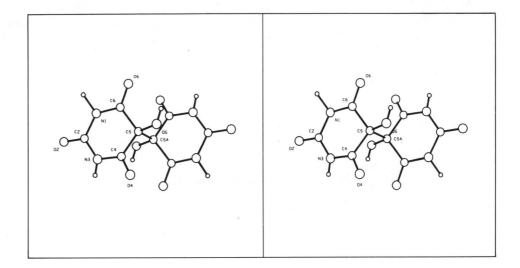

P-1   Z = 1 R_{proj} = 0.046

ALANTD   LB 8-6-18

Bond Lengths

C2	N1	1.38
C6	N1	1.38
C2	N3	1.37
C4	N3	1.39
C2	O2	1.23
C4	O4	1.19

C5	O5	1.40
C6	O6	1.21
C4	C5	1.55
C5	C6	1.52
C5	C5A	1.55

Bond Angles

C2	N1	C6	124
C2	N3	C4	125
N1	C2	N3	118
N1	C2	O2	120
N3	C2	O2	122
N3	C4	O4	123
N3	C4	C5	113
O4	C4	C5	122
O5	C5	C4	107

O5	C5	C6	110
O5	C5	C5A	110
C4	C5	C6	110
C4	C5	C5A	110
C6	C5	C5A	110
N1	C6	O6	122
N1	C6	C5	117
O6	C6	C5	121

Torsion Angles

C6	N1	C2	N3	−2
C6	N1	C2	O2	−178
C2	N1	C6	O6	−167
C2	N1	C6	C5	17
C4	N3	C2	N1	8
C4	N3	C2	O2	−176
C2	N3	C4	O4	163
C2	N3	C4	C5	−28
N3	C4	C5	O5	158

N3	C4	C5	C6	39
O4	C4	C5	O5	−34
O4	C4	C5	C6	−153
O5	C5	C6	N1	−152
O5	C5	C6	O6	32
C4	C5	C6	N1	−35
C4	C5	C6	O6	149
C4	C5	C5A	C4A	−180

43.15 Potassium 5,5 - diethyl barbiturate

J.Berthou, B.Rerat, C.Rerat, Acta Cryst., 18, 768, 1965

$C_8H_{11}N_2O_3{}^-$, K^+

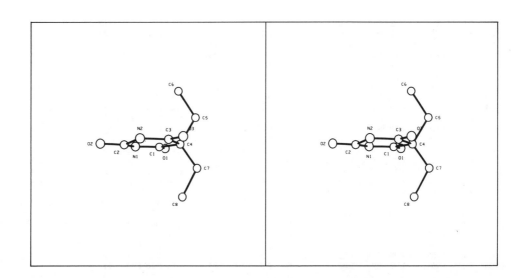

$P2_12_12_1$ Z = 4   R = 0.219

KETBAR   LB 8-11-9

Bond Lengths

C1	N1	1.33
C2	N1	1.44
C2	N2	1.27
C3	N2	1.41
C1	O1	1.15
C2	O2	1.20
C3	O3	1.20

C1	C4	1.58
C3	C4	1.50
C4	C5	1.59
C4	C7	1.46
C5	C6	1.59
C7	C8	1.62

Bond Angles

C1	N1	C2	132
C2	N2	C3	123
N1	C1	O1	126
N1	C1	C4	112
O1	C1	C4	122
N1	C2	N2	116
N1	C2	O2	120
N2	C2	O2	123
N2	C3	O3	117
N2	C3	C4	122

O3	C3	C4	121
C1	C4	C3	113
C1	C4	C5	105
C1	C4	C7	112
C3	C4	C5	105
C3	C4	C7	109
C5	C4	C7	112
C4	C5	C6	114
C4	C7	C8	115

Torsion Angles

C2	N1	C1	O1	179
C2	N1	C1	C4	−1
C1	N1	C2	N2	11
C1	N1	C2	O2	177
C3	N2	C2	N1	−14
C3	N2	C2	O2	−179
C2	N2	C3	O3	−170

C2	N2	C3	C4	9
N1	C1	C4	C3	−5
O1	C1	C4	C3	174
N2	C3	C4	C1	2
O3	C3	C4	C1	−180
C6	C5	C4	C1	63
C8	C7	C4	C3	67

43.16 Sodium - 5,5 - diethyl barbiturate

$C_8H_{11}N_2O_3^-$, Na^+

J.Berthou, C.Cavelier, D.Marek, B.Rerat, C.Rerat, C. R. Acad. Sci., Fr., 255, 1632, 1962

The structure was determined in two dimensions only. Atomic coordinates were not reported in the paper.
See also Berking & Craven, Acta Cryst. (B), 27, 1107, 1971.
$P2_12_12_1$ $Z = 4$ $R_{h0l} = 0.27$,
$R_{0kl} = 0.25$

NAETBA   LB 8-11-15

43.17 5 - (6' - Bromo - 3' - ethyl - 2' - methylbenzimidazolium) barbiturate monohydrate

$C_{14}H_{13}BrN_4O_3$, H_2O

B.W.Matthews, Acta Cryst., 18, 151, 1965

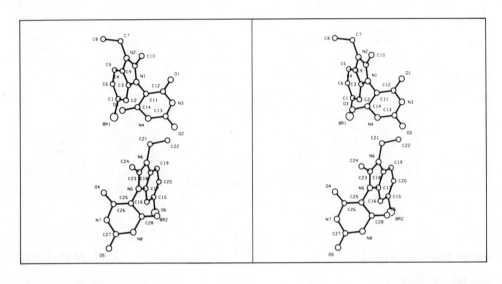

$P2_1/n$ $Z = 8$ $R = 0.173$

BEMBAR   LB 14-13-2

Bond Lengths

Br1	C1	1.89	Br2	C15	1.90
C3	N1	1.38	C17	N5	1.38
C9	N1	1.33	C23	N5	1.39
C11	N1	1.44	C25	N5	1.42
C4	N2	1.41	C18	N6	1.37
C7	N2	1.43	C21	N6	1.48
C9	N2	1.36	C23	N6	1.35
C12	N3	1.38	C26	N7	1.42
C13	N3	1.34	C27	N7	1.35
C13	N4	1.36	C27	N8	1.36
C14	N4	1.42	C28	N8	1.42
C12	O1	1.25	C26	O4	1.25
C13	O2	1.26	C27	O5	1.24
C14	O3	1.22	C28	O6	1.21
C1	C2	1.36	C15	C16	1.38
C1	C6	1.40	C15	C20	1.39
C2	C3	1.40	C16	C17	1.44
C3	C4	1.34	C17	C18	1.37
C4	C5	1.39	C18	C19	1.40
C5	C6	1.37	C19	C20	1.41
C7	C8	1.51	C21	C22	1.50
C9	C10	1.48	C23	C24	1.44
C11	C12	1.40	C25	C26	1.39
C11	C14	1.40	C25	C28	1.40

Bond Angles

C3	N1	C9	107	N1	C11	C14	119		
C3	N1	C11	128	C12	C11	C14	123		
C9	N1	C11	124	N3	C12	O1	120		
C4	N2	C7	124	N3	C12	C11	116		
C4	N2	C9	106	O1	C12	C11	124		
C7	N2	C9	129	N3	C13	N4	117		
C12	N3	C13	125	N3	C13	O2	123		
C13	N4	C14	124	N4	C13	O2	120		
Br1	C1	C2	120	N4	C14	O3	118		
Br1	C1	C6	118	N4	C14	C11	114		
C2	C1	C6	123	O3	C14	C11	128		
C1	C2	C3	115						
N1	C3	C2	130	C17	N5	C23	107		
N1	C3	C4	109	C17	N5	C25	127		
C2	C3	C4	122	C23	N5	C25	125		
N2	C4	C3	108	C18	N6	C21	123		
N2	C4	C5	129	C18	N6	C23	111		
C3	C4	C5	124	C21	N6	C23	125		
C4	C5	C6	115	C26	N7	C27	125		
C1	C6	C5	121	C27	N8	C28	125		
N2	C7	C8	113	Br2	C15	C16	118		
N1	C9	N2	110	Br2	C15	C20	118		
N1	C9	C10	126	C16	C15	C20	125		
N2	C9	C10	124	C15	C16	C17	113		
N1	C11	C12	118	N5	C17	C16	127		

N5	C17	C18	109
C16	C17	C18	124
N6	C18	C17	106
N6	C18	C19	133
C17	C18	C19	122
C18	C19	C20	115
C15	C20	C19	122
N6	C21	C22	112
N5	C23	N6	106
N5	C23	C24	123
N6	C23	C24	131
N5	C25	C26	118
N5	C25	C28	117
C26	C25	C28	125
N7	C26	O4	118
N7	C26	C25	114
O4	C26	C25	128
N7	C27	N8	117
N7	C27	O5	121
N8	C27	O5	122
N8	C28	O6	120
N8	C28	C25	114
O6	C28	C25	126

Torsion Angles

C9	N1	C11	C12	−65
C23	N5	C25	C26	73

44.1   Pyrimidine (at −2 °C)

$C_4H_4N_2$

P.J.Wheatley, Acta Cryst., 13, 80, 1960

Pna2₁   Z = 4   R = 0.087

PRMDIN   LB 4-4-35

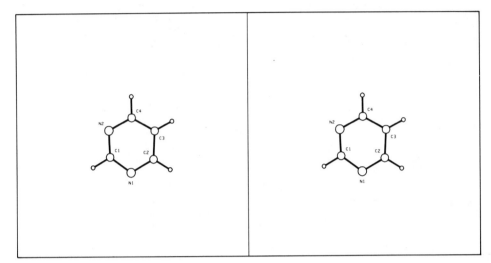

Bond Lengths			Bond Angles			
C1	N1	1.32	C1	N1	C2	115
C2	N1	1.33	C1	N2	C4	115
C1	N2	1.31	N1	C1	N2	128
C4	N2	1.34	N1	C2	C3	122
C2	C3	1.39	C2	C3	C4	116
C3	C4	1.36	N2	C4	C3	123

44.2   Cytosine

$C_4H_5N_3O$

D.L.Barker, R.E.Marsh, Acta Cryst., 17, 1581, 1964

P2₁2₁2₁   Z = 4   R = 0.07

CYTSIN   LB 4-5-20

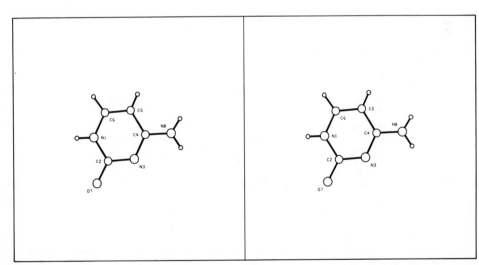

Bond Lengths			Bond Angles			
C2	N1	1.37	C2	N1	C6	123
C6	N1	1.36	C2	N3	C4	120
C2	N3	1.36	N1	C2	N3	118
C4	N3	1.34	N1	C2	O7	120
C4	N8	1.33	N3	C2	O7	122
C2	O7	1.23	N3	C4	N8	118
C4	C5	1.42	N3	C4	C5	122
C5	C6	1.34	N8	C4	C5	120
			C4	C5	C6	117
			N1	C6	C5	120

44.3   Isocytosine

$C_4H_5N_3O$

B.D.Sharma, J.F.McConnell, Acta Cryst., 19, 797, 1965

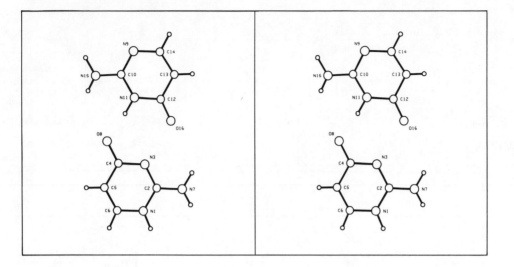

$P2_1/n$ $Z = 8$ $R = 0.061$

ICYTIN   LB 4-5-21

Bond Lengths

C2	N1	1.36	C10	N9	1.33
C6	N1	1.36	C14	N9	1.35
C2	N3	1.33	C10	N11	1.37
C4	N3	1.36	C12	N11	1.38
C2	N7	1.32	C10	N15	1.32
C4	O8	1.25	C12	O16	1.25
C4	C5	1.44	C12	C13	1.42
C5	C6	1.33	C13	C14	1.36

Bond Angles

C2	N1	C6	120	C10	N9	C14	116
C2	N3	C4	120	C10	N11	C12	123
N1	C2	N3	122	N9	C10	N11	122
N1	C2	N7	119	N9	C10	N15	120
N3	C2	N7	119	N11	C10	N15	118
N3	C4	O8	119	N11	C12	O16	119
N3	C4	C5	119	N11	C12	C13	115
O8	C4	C5	122	O16	C12	C13	126
C4	C5	C6	119	C12	C13	C14	118
N1	C6	C5	120	N9	C14	C13	126

44.4   Cytosine monohydrate

$C_4H_5N_3O$, H_2O

G.A.Jeffrey, Y.Kinoshita, Acta Cryst., 16, 20, 1963

See also McClure & Craven, Amer. Cryst. Assoc., Abstr. Papers (Summer Meeting), 25, 1970.
$P2_1/c$ $Z = 4$ $R = 0.11$

CYTOSM   LB 4-5-22

Bond Lengths

C2	N1	1.35
C6	N1	1.35
C2	N3	1.38
C4	N3	1.36
C6	N6	1.33
C2	O2	1.26
C4	C5	1.35
C5	C6	1.43

Bond Angles

C2	N1	C6	119	N3	C4	C5	121
C2	N3	C4	121	C4	C5	C6	117
N1	C2	N3	120	N1	C6	N6	118
N1	C2	O2	122	N1	C6	C5	122
N3	C2	O2	118	N6	C6	C5	120

44.5   Rubidium 5 - fluoro - orotate monohydrate

$C_5H_2FN_2O_4^-$, Rb^+ , H_2O

W.M.Macintyre, M.Zirakzadeh, Acta Cryst., 17, 1305, 1964

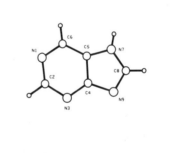

Pbca   Z = 8   R = 0.14

RBFORM   LB 5-2-1

Bond Lengths

F1	C5	1.35	C6	O6	1.22
C2	N1	1.39	C7	O7	1.21
C6	N1	1.37	C7	O8	1.21
C2	N3	1.41	C4	C5	1.35
C4	N3	1.41	C4	C7	1.59
C2	O2	1.22	C5	C6	1.45

Bond Angles

C2	N1	C6	125	N3	C4	C7	115	N1	C6	C5	115
C2	N3	C4	122	C5	C4	C7	128	O6	C6	C5	123
N1	C2	N3	117	F1	C5	C4	121	O7	C7	O8	134
N1	C2	O2	123	F1	C5	C6	115	O7	C7	C4	113
N3	C2	O2	120	C4	C5	C6	124	O8	C7	C4	113
N3	C4	C5	117	N1	C6	O6	122				

44.6   Purine

$C_5H_4N_4$

(i)   D.G.Watson, R.M.Sweet, R.E.Marsh, Acta Cryst., 19, 573, 1965

(ii)   D.G.Watson, R.M.Sweet, R.E.Marsh, Acta Cryst., 19, 573, 1965

(i)

The paper reports two independent investigations. I - Data set and structure by Watson, 327 observed reflexions, R = 0.048. II - Data set and structure by Sweet and Marsh, 586 observed reflexions, R = 0.070.

Pna2₁   Z = 4   R = 0.048

PURINE   LB 5-4-3

(ii)

Pna2₁   Z = 4   R = 0.07

PURINE01   LB 5-4-3

Bond Lengths

		(i)	(ii)
C2	N1	1.35	1.35
C6	N1	1.33	1.32
C2	N3	1.34	1.32
C4	N3	1.34	1.33
C5	N7	1.37	1.37
C8	N7	1.33	1.34
C4	N9	1.38	1.37
C8	N9	1.31	1.31
C4	C5	1.41	1.40
C5	C6	1.39	1.38

Bond Angles

			(i)	(ii)				(i)	(ii)
C2	N1	C6	118	118	N9	C4	C5	110	109
C2	N3	C4	113	113	N7	C5	C4	105	106
C5	N7	C8	106	106	N7	C5	C6	137	136
C4	N9	C8	104	105	C4	C5	C6	118	118
N1	C2	N3	128	128	N1	C6	C5	119	119
N3	C4	N9	127	127	N7	C8	N9	115	114
N3	C4	C5	124	123					

44.7   Purine (independent data set)

$C_5H_4N_4$

For complete entry see 44.6

44.8   N - Methyl uracil

D.W.Green, F.S.Mathews, A.Rich, J. Biol. Chem., 237, 3573, 1962

Atomic coordinates were not given
but bond lengths were reported.
Ibam   Z = 8   R = 0.11

METURA   LB 5-6-20

$C_5H_6N_2O_2$

44.9   Thymine monohydrate

R.Gerdil, Acta Cryst., 14, 333, 1961

$C_5H_6N_2O_2$, H_2O

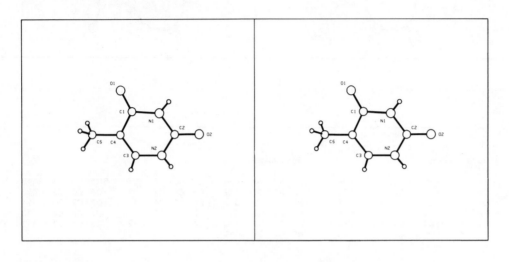

$P2_1/c$ Z = 4   R = 0.078

THYMMH   LB 5-6-22

Bond Lengths

C1	N1	1.39	C2	O2	1.23
C2	N1	1.36	C1	C4	1.45
C2	N2	1.35	C3	C4	1.35
C3	N2	1.38	C4	C5	1.50
C1	O1	1.23			

Bond Angles

C1	N1	C2	126	N1	C2	O2	122
C2	N2	C3	123	N2	C2	O2	123
N1	C1	O1	118	N2	C3	C4	122
N1	C1	C4	116	C1	C4	C3	118
O1	C1	C4	126	C1	C4	C5	119
N1	C2	N2	115	C3	C4	C5	123

44.10   Guanine hydrochloride dihydrate

J.Iball, H.R.Wilson, Proc. R. Soc., A, 288, 418, 1965

$C_5H_6N_5O^+$, Cl^- , $2H_2O$

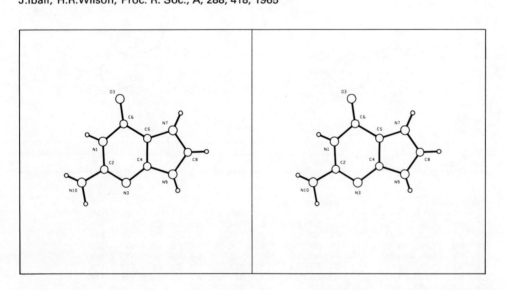

$P2_1/a$ Z = 4   R = 0.073

GUANCD   LB 5-6-11

Bond Lengths

C2	N1	1.37	C4	N9	1.38
C6	N1	1.39	C8	N9	1.34
C2	N3	1.32	C2	N10	1.34
C4	N3	1.34	C6	O3	1.24
C5	N7	1.38	C4	C5	1.38
C8	N7	1.32	C5	C6	1.41

Bond Angles

C2	N1	C6	126	N3	C2	N10	121	C4	C5	C6	120
C2	N3	C4	113	N3	C4	N9	126	N1	C6	O3	120
C5	N7	C8	108	N3	C4	C5	128	N1	C6	C5	111
C4	N9	C8	109	N9	C4	C5	106	O3	C6	C5	129
N1	C2	N3	123	N7	C5	C4	107	N7	C8	N9	110
N1	C2	N10	116	N7	C5	C6	133				

44.11   1 - Methyluracil hydrobromide

$C_5H_7N_2O_2{}^+$, Br^-

H.M.Sobell, K.I.Tomita, Acta Cryst., 17, 122, 1964

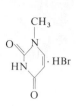

Pnma   Z = 4   R = 0.122

MURHBR   LB 5-7-1

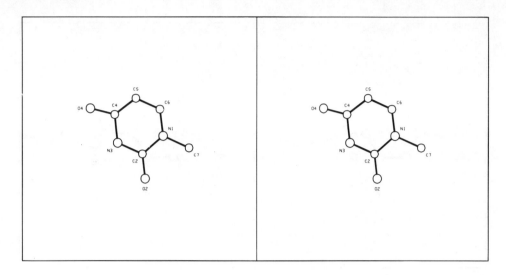

Bond Lengths

C2	N1	1.37	C2	O2	1.23
C6	N1	1.33	C4	O4	1.28
C7	N1	1.47	C4	C5	1.34
C2	N3	1.38	C5	C6	1.35
C4	N3	1.40			

Bond Angles

C2	N1	C6	123	N3	C2	O2	120
C2	N1	C7	117	N3	C4	O4	110
C6	N1	C7	120	N3	C4	C5	120
C2	N3	C4	120	O4	C4	C5	130
N1	C2	N3	116	C4	C5	C6	119
N1	C2	O2	124	N1	C6	C5	121

44.12   N - Methyl cytosine

$C_5H_7N_3O$

F.S.Mathews, A.Rich, Nature, 201, 179, 1964

Atomic coordinates were not reported in the paper.
P-1   Z = 2   R = 0.115

METCYT   LB 5-7-15

44.13   1 - Methylcytosine hydrobromide

$C_5H_8N_3O^+$, Br^-

R.F.Bryan, K.Tomita, Acta Cryst., 15, 1174, 1962

Pnma   Z = 4   R = 0.12

MCYHBR   LB 5-8-7

Bond Lengths

C2	N1	1.36	C4	N7	1.35
C6	N1	1.35	C2	O1	1.22
C8	N1	1.48	C4	C5	1.38
C2	N3	1.34	C5	C6	1.36
C4	N3	1.32			

Bond Angles

C2	N1	C6	114	N3	C2	O1	119
C2	N1	C8	122	N3	C4	N7	123
C6	N1	C8	124	N3	C4	C5	116
C2	N3	C4	127	N7	C4	C5	121
N1	C2	N3	119	C4	C5	C6	116
N1	C2	O1	122	N1	C6	C5	128

44.14 Cytosine - 5 - acetic acid

$C_6H_7N_3O_3$

R.E.Marsh, R.Bierstedt, E.L.Eichhorn, Acta Cryst., 15, 310, 1962

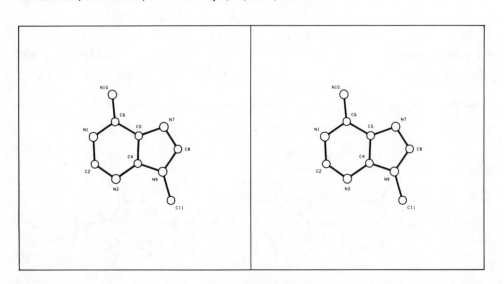

As a result of disorder of the proton on the carboxylic group half of the molecules are uncharged and the other half in the zwitterion form.
P2$_1$/c   Z = 4   R = 0.096

CYACET   LB 6-7-21

Bond Lengths

C2	N1	1.35	C10	O11	1.23
C6	N1	1.36	C10	O12	1.29
C2	N3	1.37	C4	C5	1.43
C4	N3	1.35	C5	C6	1.36
C4	N8	1.32	C5	C9	1.50
C2	O7	1.25	C9	C10	1.52

Bond Angles

C2	N1	C6	122	C4	C5	C6	116
C2	N3	C4	122	C4	C5	C9	122
N1	C2	N3	118	C6	C5	C9	122
N1	C2	O7	121	N1	C6	C5	122
N3	C2	O7	121	C5	C9	C10	114
N3	C4	N8	117	O11	C10	O12	123
N3	C4	C5	121	O11	C10	C9	121
N8	C4	C5	122	O12	C10	C9	116

44.15 9 - Methyladenine

$C_6H_7N_5$

R.F.Stewart, L.H.Jensen, J. Chem. Phys., 40, 2071, 1964

P2$_1$/c   Z = 4   R = 0.091

MEADEN   LB 6-7-25

Bond Lengths

C2	N1	1.35	C4	N9	1.36
C6	N1	1.35	C8	N9	1.35
C2	N3	1.32	C11	N9	1.47
C4	N3	1.34	C6	N10	1.35
C5	N7	1.38	C4	C5	1.36
C8	N7	1.31	C5	C6	1.39

Bond Angles

C2	N1	C6	120	N9	C4	C5	105
C2	N3	C4	112	N7	C5	C4	111
C5	N7	C8	104	N7	C5	C6	132
C4	N9	C8	108	C4	C5	C6	117
C4	N9	C11	124	N1	C6	N10	117
C8	N9	C11	128	N1	C6	C5	117
N1	C2	N3	127	N10	C6	C5	126
N3	C4	N9	129	N7	C8	N9	112
N3	C4	C5	127				

44.16   1 - Methylthymine $C_6H_8N_2O_2$

K.Hoogsteen, Acta Cryst., 16, 28, 1963

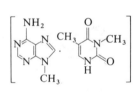

$P2_1/c$ Z = 4   R = 0.072

METHYM   LB 6-8-44

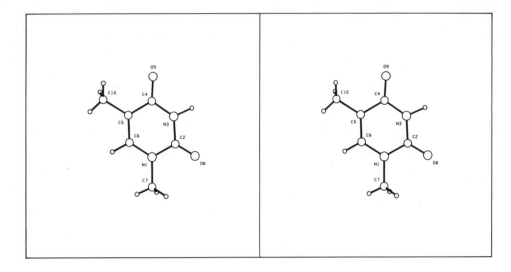

Bond Lengths

C2	N1	1.38	C2	O8	1.21
C6	N1	1.38	C4	O9	1.24
C7	N1	1.47	C4	C5	1.43
C2	N3	1.38	C5	C6	1.35
C4	N3	1.37	C5	C10	1.50

Bond Angles

C2	N1	C6	121	N3	C4	O9	120
C2	N1	C7	118	N3	C4	C5	116
C6	N1	C7	121	O9	C4	C5	124
C2	N3	C4	126	C4	C5	C6	118
N1	C2	N3	115	C4	C5	C10	119
N1	C2	O8	123	C6	C5	C10	122
N3	C2	O8	121	N1	C6	C5	123

44.17   1 - Methylthymine - 9 - methyladenine complex $C_6H_8N_2O_2$, $C_6H_7N_5$

K.Hoogsteen, Acta Cryst., 16, 907, 1963

$P2_1/m$ Z = 2   R = 0.081

MTHMAD   LB 12-15-11

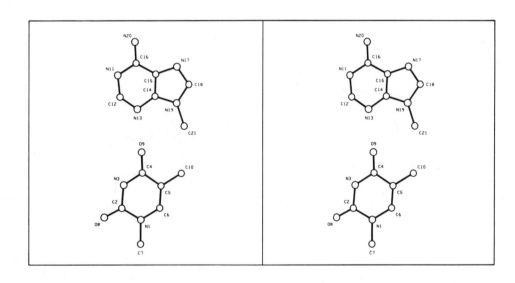

Bond Lengths

C2	N1	1.38	C12	N11	1.36
C6	N1	1.38	C16	N11	1.36
C7	N1	1.45	C12	N13	1.30
C2	N3	1.38	C14	N13	1.35
C4	N3	1.38	C15	N17	1.38
C2	O8	1.21	C18	N17	1.32
C4	O9	1.24	C14	N19	1.39
C4	C5	1.42	C18	N19	1.36
C5	C6	1.33	C21	N19	1.45
C5	C10	1.51	C16	N20	1.33
			C14	C15	1.37
			C15	C16	1.41

Bond Angles

C2	N1	C6	121	N3	C4	C5	116	C12	N11	C16	117	N19	C14	C15	106
C2	N1	C7	119	O9	C4	C5	124	C12	N13	C14	110	N17	C15	C14	111
C6	N1	C7	120	C4	C5	C6	119	C15	N17	C18	104	N17	C15	C16	132
C2	N3	C4	126	C4	C5	C10	117	C14	N19	C18	106	C14	C15	C16	117
N1	C2	N3	115	C6	C5	C10	124	C14	N19	C21	126	N11	C16	N20	119
N1	C2	O8	124	N1	C6	C5	123	C18	N19	C21	128	N11	C16	C15	118
N3	C2	O8	121					N11	C12	N13	131	N20	C16	C15	123
N3	C4	O9	120					N13	C14	N19	127	N17	C18	N19	113
								N13	C14	C15	127				

44.18   9 - Methylguanine hydrobromide

$C_6H_8N_5O^+$, Br^-

H.M.Sobell, K.Tomita, Acta Cryst., 17, 126, 1964

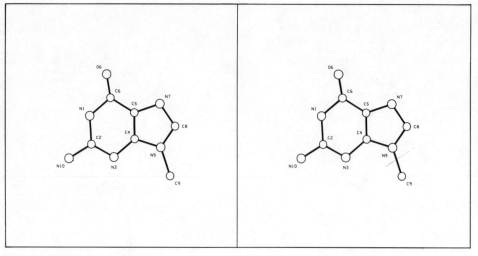

Although the molecule as a whole is planar the torsion angle calculated for N3 C4 C5 C6 is 12°.

P112₁/b   Z = 4   R = 0.077

P112$_1$/b   Z = 4   R = 0.077

MGUHBR   LB 6-8-6

Bond Lengths

C2	N1	1.42	C8	N9	1.28
C6	N1	1.38			(1.40)
C2	N3	1.33	C9	N9	1.49
C4	N3	1.40			(1.41)
C5	N7	1.39	C2	N10	1.33
C8	N7	1.34	C6	O6	1.18
C4	N9	1.39	C4	C5	1.30
			C5	C6	1.43

Bond Angles

C2	N1	C6	127	N3	C4	C5	128
C2	N3	C4	112	N9	C4	C5	108
C5	N7	C8	107	N7	C5	C4	107
C4	N9	C8	107	N7	C5	C6	130
C4	N9	C9	126	C4	C5	C6	122
C8	N9	C9	127	N1	C6	O6	120
N1	C2	N3	121	N1	C6	C5	109
N1	C2	N10	118	O6	C6	C5	131
N3	C2	N10	121	N7	C8	N9	110
N3	C4	N9	123				

44.19   9 - Methyladenine dihydrobromide

$C_6H_9N_5^{2+}$, $2Br^-$

R.F.Bryan, K.Tomita, Acta Cryst., 15, 1179, 1962

Using the published coordinates, the distance between the two bromide ions is 2.21A. Since low accuracy of the light atom positions was reported, the deviation of N10 from the plane of the ring system is probably not significant.

Pna2₁   Z = 4 R_{h0l} = 0.07, R_{hk0} = 0.11

Pna2$_1$ Z = 4 R_{h0l} = 0.07,

MADHBR   LB 6-9-3

Bond Lengths

C2	N1	1.36	C4	N9	1.37
C6	N1	1.39	C8	N9	1.35
C2	N3	1.35	C11	N9	1.48
C4	N3	1.37	C6	N10	1.30
C5	N7	1.37	C4	C5	1.40
C8	N7	1.33	C5	C6	1.38

Bond Angles

C2	N1	C6	124	N9	C4	C5	99
C2	N3	C4	107	N7	C5	C4	111
C5	N7	C8	109	N7	C5	C6	129
C4	N9	C8	116	C4	C5	C6	120
C4	N9	C11	116	N1	C6	N10	123
C8	N9	C11	127	N1	C6	C5	111
N1	C2	N3	127	N10	C6	C5	123
N3	C4	N9	131	N7	C8	N9	104
N3	C4	C5	129				

44.20   Cyclobutane - 1,5 - spiro - 2,4,6 - triketo - hexahydropyrimidine

$C_7H_8N_2O_3$

G.Giacomello, P.Corradini, C.Pedone, Gazz. Chim. Ital., 95, 1100, 1965

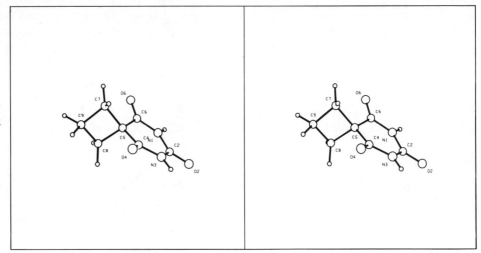

$P2_1/n$ $Z = 4$ $R_{0kl} = 0.174$,
$R_{h0l} = 0.184$, $R_{hk0} = 0.164$

CBUSPY   LB 7-8-10

Bond Lengths

C2	N1	1.36
C6	N1	1.38
C2	N3	1.34
C4	N3	1.38
C2	O2	1.23
C4	O4	1.26
C6	O6	1.20
C4	C5	1.49
C5	C6	1.49
C5	C7	1.58
C5	C8	1.54
C7	C9	1.54
C8	C9	1.52

Bond Angles

C2	N1	C6	125	C4	C5	C8	109
C2	N3	C4	123	C6	C5	C7	116
N1	C2	N3	119	C6	C5	C8	113
N1	C2	O2	123	C7	C5	C8	89
N3	C2	O2	117	N1	C6	O6	122
N3	C4	O4	118	N1	C6	C5	116
N3	C4	C5	118	O6	C6	C5	123
O4	C4	C5	124	C5	C7	C9	88
C4	C5	C6	114	C5	C8	C9	90
C4	C5	C7	112	C7	C9	C8	91

Torsion Angles

C6	N1	C2	N3	−5	N3	C4	C5	C8	108	C4	C5	C7	C9	−103
C6	N1	C2	O2	−177	O4	C4	C5	C6	157	C6	C5	C7	C9	123
C2	N1	C6	O6	168	O4	C4	C5	C7	23	C8	C5	C7	C9	7
C2	N1	C6	C5	−12	O4	C4	C5	C8	−74	C4	C5	C8	C9	105
C4	N3	C2	N1	9	C4	C5	C6	N1	24	C6	C5	C8	C9	−126
C4	N3	C2	O2	−178	C4	C5	C6	O6	−157	C7	C5	C8	C9	−7
C2	N3	C4	O4	−174	C7	C5	C6	N1	157	C5	C7	C9	C8	−7
C2	N3	C4	C5	5	C7	C5	C6	O6	−24	C5	C8	C9	C7	8
N3	C4	C5	C6	−21	C8	C5	C6	N1	−102					
N3	C4	C5	C7	−156	C8	C5	C6	O6	77					

44.21   9 - Ethyladenine - 1 - methyluracil

$C_7H_9N_5$, $C_4H_6N_2O_2$

F.S.Mathews, A.Rich, Acta Cryst., 16, A51, 1963

Atomic coordinates were not reported in the paper.
P-1   Z = 2   No R factor was given.

ETAMEU

44.22   N - Ethylguanine - N - methyl - 5 - bromocytosine

$C_7H_9N_5O$, $C_5H_6BrN_3O$

H.M.Sobell, K.Tomita, A.Rich, Acta Cryst., 16, A79, 1963

Atomic coordinates were not reported in the paper.
$P2_1/c$ Z = 4   R = 0.20

EGUMBC   LB 12-15-1

44.23   2 - (4' - Amino - 5' - aminopyrimidyl) - pent - 2 - ene - 4 - one

$C_9H_{12}N_4O$

J.Silverman, N.F.Yannoni, Acta Cryst., 18, 756, 1965

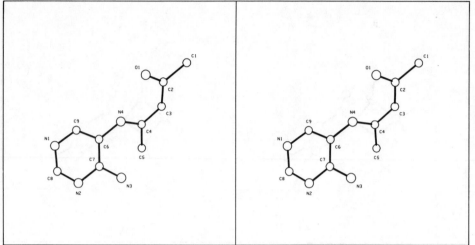

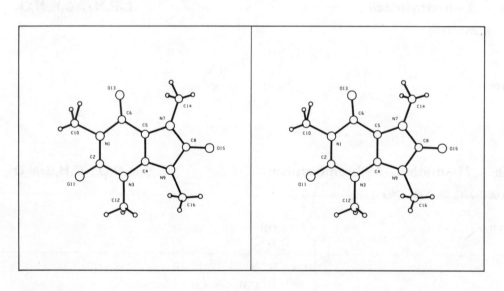

Published value of x(O1) = 0.1173. The correct value is 0.1773 (private communication).

P2₁/c   Z = 4   R = 0.128

AAPYPE   LB 9-12-14

Bond Lengths

C8	N1	1.31	C2	O1	1.26
C9	N1	1.36	C1	C2	1.52
C7	N2	1.34	C2	C3	1.41
C8	N2	1.33	C3	C4	1.37
C7	N3	1.37	C4	C5	1.53
C4	N4	1.37	C6	C7	1.40
C6	N4	1.42	C6	C9	1.37

Bond Angles

C8	N1	C9	116	C3	C4	C5	121
C7	N2	C8	117	N4	C6	C7	123
C4	N4	C6	123	N4	C6	C9	120
O1	C2	C1	117	C7	C6	C9	117
O1	C2	C3	123	N2	C7	N3	117
C1	C2	C3	120	N2	C7	C6	121
C2	C3	C4	125	N3	C7	C6	122
N4	C4	C3	121	N1	C8	N2	127
N4	C4	C5	118	N1	C9	C6	122

44.24   1,3,7,9 - Tetramethyluric acid (form ii)

$C_9H_{12}N_4O_3$

D.J.Sutor, Acta Cryst., 16, 97, 1963

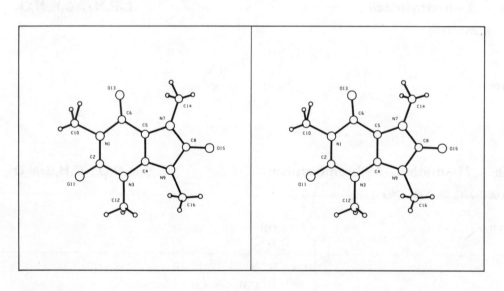

P2₁/a   Z = 4   R = 0.112

TMURIC   LB 9-12-16

Bond Lengths

C2	N1	1.37	C4	N9	1.37
C6	N1	1.41	C8	N9	1.41
C10	N1	1.47	C16	N9	1.48
C2	N3	1.38	C2	O11	1.21
C4	N3	1.36	C6	O13	1.24
C12	N3	1.47	C8	O15	1.23
C5	N7	1.39	C4	C5	1.35
C8	N7	1.35	C5	C6	1.41
C14	N7	1.46			

Bond Angles

C2	N1	C6	126	C4	N9	C8	108	N7	C5	C4	109
C2	N1	C10	116	C4	N9	C16	131	N7	C5	C6	130
C6	N1	C10	118	C8	N9	C16	121	C4	C5	C6	121
C2	N3	C4	118	N1	C2	N3	117	N1	C6	O13	121
C2	N3	C12	117	N1	C2	O11	121	N1	C6	C5	113
C4	N3	C12	124	N3	C2	O11	121	O13	C6	C5	126
C5	N7	C8	108	N3	C4	N9	128	N7	C8	N9	107
C5	N7	C14	129	N3	C4	C5	124	N7	C8	O15	129
C8	N7	C14	123	N9	C4	C5	108	N9	C8	O15	124

44.25   1,3,7,9 - Tetramethyluric acid (form i)

$C_9H_{12}N_4O_3$

P.de Santis, E.Giglio, A.M.Liquori, D.J.Sutor, Nature, 188, 46, 1960

Atomic coordinates were not reported in the paper.
P2$_1$/a   Z = 4   No R factor was given.

TMURIC01   LB 9-12-15

44.26   9 - β - Chloroethyl - 7,8 - dihydro - 9H - imidazo(2,1 - i)purine methiodide

$C_{10}H_{13}ClN_5{}^+$, I$-$

W.M.Macintyre, R.F.Zahrobsky, Z. Kristallogr., 119, 226, 1963

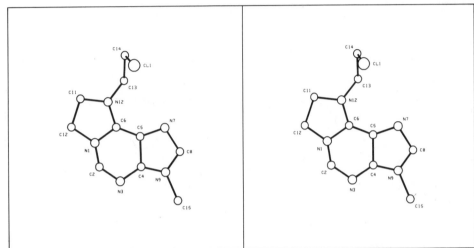

No comparison of bond lengths is possible since they are not reported in the paper.
P2$_1$/c   Z = 4   R = 0.20

CEIMPU   LB 10-13-9

Bond Lengths

Cl1	C14	1.81	C8	N9	1.30
C2	N1	1.25	C15	N9	1.55
C6	N1	1.38	C6	N12	1.40
C12	N1	1.45	C11	N12	1.47
C2	N3	1.31	C13	N12	1.43
C4	N3	1.30	C4	C5	1.56
C5	N7	1.38	C5	C6	1.33
C8	N7	1.43	C11	C12	1.65
C4	N9	1.34	C13	C14	1.59

Bond Angles

C2	N1	C6	116	N3	C4	C5	122
C2	N1	C12	129	N9	C4	C5	100
C6	N1	C12	114	N7	C5	C4	108
C2	N3	C4	112	N7	C5	C6	141
C5	N7	C8	104	C4	C5	C6	109
C4	N9	C8	116	N1	C6	N12	109
C4	N9	C15	125	N1	C6	C5	125
C8	N9	C15	118	N12	C6	C5	126
C6	N12	C11	112	N7	C8	N9	109
C6	N12	C13	126	N12	C11	C12	101
C11	N12	C13	122	N1	C12	C11	101
N1	C2	N3	130	N12	C13	C14	113
N3	C4	N9	133	Cl1	C14	C13	110

Torsion Angles

C6	N1	C2	N3	-20	C15	N9	C4	C5	-171
C12	N1	C2	N3	176	C4	N9	C8	N7	-2
C2	N1	C6	N12	-180	C15	N9	C8	N7	179
C2	N1	C6	C5	9	C11	N12	C6	N1	2
C12	N1	C6	N12	-13	C11	N12	C6	C5	173
C12	N1	C6	C5	176	C6	N12	C11	C12	7
C2	N1	C12	C11	-179	N3	C4	C5	N7	-172
C6	N1	C12	C11	17	N9	C4	C5	C6	21
C4	N3	C2	N1	30	N9	C4	C5	N7	-14
C2	N3	C4	N9	-178	N9	C4	C5	C6	179
C2	N3	C4	C5	-29	N7	C5	C6	N1	-169
C8	N7	C5	C4	13	N7	C5	C6	N12	21
C8	N7	C5	C6	173	C4	C5	C6	N1	-9
C5	N7	C8	N9	-8	C4	C5	C6	N12	-179
C8	N9	C4	N3	164	N12	C11	C12	N1	-14
C8	N9	C4	C5	10	C13	N12	C11	C12	-171
C15	N9	C4	N3	-17					

45.1 Pentaerythritol tetranitrate (refinement of data of Booth and Llewellyn, J. Chem. Soc., 837,1947)

$C_5H_8N_4O_{12}$

J.Trotter, Acta Cryst., 16, 698, 1963

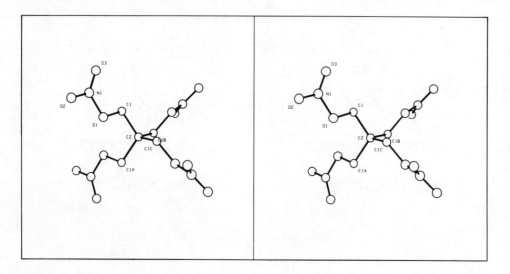

$$O_2N-O-CH_2 \quad CH_2-O-NO_2$$
$$C$$
$$O_2N-O-CH_2 \quad CH_2-O-NO_2$$

P-42$_1$c   Z = 2   R = 0.152

PERYTN10   LB 5-8-20

Bond Lengths			Bond Angles				Torsion Angles			
N1	O1	1.40	O1	N1	O2	112	O2	N1	O1	C1	176
N1	O2	1.20	O1	N1	O3	117	O3	N1	O1	C1	−4
N1	O3	1.22	O2	N1	O3	130	N1	O1	C1	C2	169
C1	O1	1.46	N1	O1	C1	113	O1	C1	C2	C1A	52
C1	C2	1.54	O1	C1	C2	106	O1	C1	C2	C1B	171
			C1	C2	C1A	113	O1	C1	C2	C1C	−67
			C1	C2	C1B	108					

45.2 Calcium arabonate pentahydrate $2C_5H_9O_6^-$, Ca^{2+} , $5H_2O$

S.Furberg, S.Helland, Acta Chem. Scand., 16, 2373, 1962

C2 Z = 2 $R_{h0l} = 0.09$,
$R_{hk0} = 0.09$

CAARAB LB 10-18-6

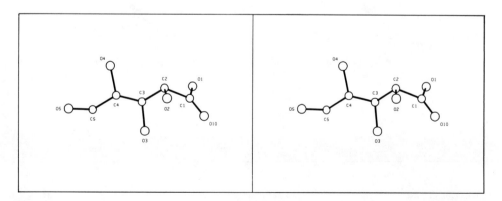

$$Ca^{2+} \left(HO-CH_2-\overset{\overset{OH}{|}}{\underset{\underset{H}{|}}{C}}-\overset{\overset{OH}{|}}{\underset{\underset{H}{|}}{C}}-\overset{\overset{H}{|}}{\underset{\underset{OH}{|}}{C}}-COO^- \right)_2 \cdot 5H_2O$$

Bond Lengths

Ca1	O0	2.47
Ca1	O2	2.45
Ca1	O3	2.52
Ca1	O6	2.44
C1	O0	1.22
C1	O1	1.30
C2	O2	1.39
C3	O3	1.43
C4	O4	1.42
C5	O5	1.41
C1	C2	1.57
C2	C3	1.55
C3	C4	1.55
C4	C5	1.56

Bond Angles

O0	Ca1	O2	65
O0	Ca1	O3	75
O0	Ca1	O6	146
O0	Ca1	O2B	138
O0	Ca1	O0B	82
O0	Ca1	O3B	83
O0	Ca1	O6B	106
O2	Ca1	O3	65
O2	Ca1	O6	91
O2	Ca1	O0B	138

O2	Ca1	O2B	155
O2	Ca1	O3B	122
O2	Ca1	O6B	71
O3	Ca1	O6	73
O3	Ca1	O0B	83
O3	Ca1	O2B	122
O3	Ca1	O3B	151
O3	Ca1	O6B	131
O6	Ca1	O0B	106
O6	Ca1	O2B	71

O6	Ca1	O3B	131
O6	Ca1	O6B	87
Ca1	O0	C1	115
Ca1	O2	C2	107
Ca1	O3	C3	119
O0	C1	O1	125
O0	C1	C2	118
O1	C1	C2	116
O2	C2	C1	109
O2	C2	C3	111

C1	C2	C3	108
O3	C3	C2	104
O3	C3	C4	107
C2	C3	C4	110
O4	C4	C3	112
O4	C4	C5	108
C3	C4	C5	113
O5	C5	C4	114

Torsion Angles

O6	Ca1	O0	C1	16
O0B	Ca1	O0	C1	122
O2B	Ca1	O0	C1	158
O3B	Ca1	O0	C1	−163
O6B	Ca1	O0	C1	−93
Ca1	O0	C1	C2	17
O0	C1	C2	C3	−96
C1	C2	C3	C4	−179
C2	C3	C4	C5	−174
C3	C4	C5	O5	165

45.3 Strontium arabonate pentahydrate $2C_5H_9O_6^-$, Sr^{2+} , $5H_2O$

S.Furberg, S.Helland, Acta Chem. Scand., 16, 2373, 1962

C2 Z = 2 $R_{h0l} = 0.10$,
$R_{hk0} = 0.10$

SRARAB LB 10-18-27

$$Sr^{2+} \left(HO-CH_2-\overset{\overset{OH}{|}}{\underset{\underset{H}{|}}{C}}-\overset{\overset{OH}{|}}{\underset{\underset{H}{|}}{C}}-\overset{\overset{H}{|}}{\underset{\underset{OH}{|}}{C}}-COO^- \right)_2 \cdot 5H_2O$$

Bond Lengths

C1	O1	1.34		C1	O10	1.19
C2	O2	1.36		C1	C2	1.57
C3	O3	1.46		C2	C3	1.57
C4	O4	1.49		C3	C4	1.49
C5	O5	1.45		C4	C5	1.59

Bond Angles

O1	C1	O10	124
O1	C1	C2	113
O10	C1	C2	124
O2	C2	C1	104
O2	C2	C3	114

C1	C2	C3	103
O3	C3	C2	106
O3	C3	C4	105
C2	C3	C4	108
O4	C4	C3	113

O4	C4	C5	105
C3	C4	C5	116
O5	C5	C4	114

Torsion Angles

O1	C1	C2	C3	74
C1	C2	C3	C4	176
C2	C3	C4	C5	−174
C3	C4	C5	O5	165

45.4   Barium ribose - 5 - phosphate pentahydrate $C_5H_9O_8P^{2-}$, Ba^{2+} , $5H_2O$

S.Furberg, A.Mostad, Acta Chem. Scand., 16, 1627, 1962

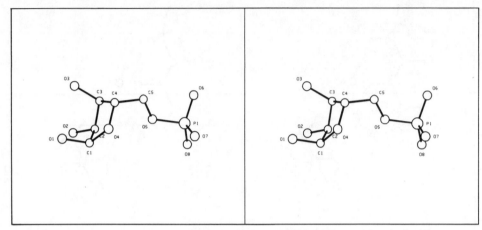

Two of the water molecules (O13, O14) are disordered.

C2   Z = 4 $R_{h0l} = 0.09$, $R_{hk0} = 0.12$

BARIBP   LB 5-9-1

Bond Lengths

P1	O5	1.67		C1	O4	1.48
P1	O6	1.52		C4	O4	1.44
P1	O7	1.51		C5	O5	1.44
P1	O8	1.51		C1	C2	1.48
C1	O1	1.43		C2	C3	1.44
C2	O2	1.47		C3	C4	1.59
C3	O3	1.52		C4	C5	1.45

Bond Angles

O5	P1	O6	103		P1	O5	C5	115		O3	C3	C2	111
O5	P1	O7	108		O1	C1	O4	111		O3	C3	C4	102
O5	P1	O8	104		O1	C1	C2	111		C2	C3	C4	99
O6	P1	O7	119		O4	C1	C2	103		O4	C4	C3	109
O6	P1	O8	117		O2	C2	C1	108		O4	C4	C5	110
O7	P1	O8	106		O2	C2	C3	111		C3	C4	C5	115
C1	O4	C4	107		C1	C2	C3	109		O5	C5	C4	109

Torsion Angles

O6	P1	O5	C5	−60
O7	P1	O5	C5	67
O8	P1	O5	C5	178
C4	O4	C1	C2	23
C1	O4	C4	C3	−1
C1	O4	C4	C5	−128
P1	O5	C5	C4	−166
O4	C1	C2	C3	−39
C1	C2	C3	C4	36
C2	C3	C4	O4	−21
C2	C3	C4	C5	103
O4	C4	C5	O5	67
C3	C4	C5	O5	−56

45.5   2 - Deoxyribose $C_5H_{10}O_4$

S.Furberg, Acta Chem. Scand., 14, 1357, 1960

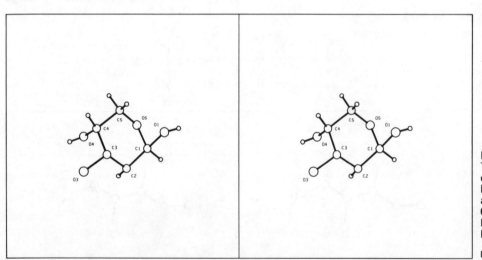

Published value of y(O3) = 0.060. The correct value is −0.060. To obtain agreement between calculated and reported bond lengths the author's origin was shifted by 0.25, 0, 0.

$P2_12_12_1$ Z = 4 $R_{hk0} = 0.10$, $R_{h0l} = 0.10$

DRIBSE   LB 5-10-20

Bond Lengths

C1	O1	1.41		C1	C2	1.50
C3	O3	1.44		C2	C3	1.49
C4	O4	1.40		C3	C4	1.53
C1	O5	1.45		C4	C5	1.53
C5	O5	1.41				

Bond Angles

C1	O5	C5	113		O3	C3	C4	107
O1	C1	O5	91		C2	C3	C4	111
O1	C1	C2	133		O4	C4	C3	109
O5	C1	C2	111		O4	C4	C5	112
C1	C2	C3	107		C3	C4	C5	108
O3	C3	C2	114		O5	C5	C4	109

Torsion Angles

C5	O5	C1	C2	63
C1	O5	C5	C4	−61
O5	C1	C2	C3	−58
C1	C2	C3	C4	57
C2	C3	C4	C5	−57
C3	C4	C5	O5	57

45.6 β - L - Arabinose $C_5H_{10}O_5$

A.Hordvik, Acta Chem. Scand., 15, 16, 1961

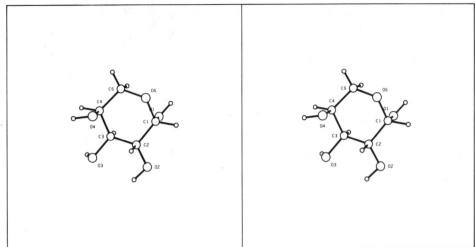

$P2_12_12_1$ $Z = 4$ $R_{0kl} = 0.067$,
$R_{hk0} = 0.055$

ABINOS   LB 5-10-22

Bond Lengths						Bond Angles							Torsion Angles				
C1	O1	1.38	C5	O5	1.44	C1	O5	C5	113	O3	C3	C2	109	C5	O5	C1	C2	−61
C2	O2	1.45	C1	C2	1.52	O1	C1	O5	113	O3	C3	C4	110	C1	O5	C5	C4	61
C3	O3	1.43	C2	C3	1.52	O1	C1	C2	109	C2	C3	C4	110	O5	C1	C2	C3	60
C4	O4	1.43	C3	C4	1.55	O5	C1	C2	109	O4	C4	C3	112	C1	C2	C3	C4	−58
C1	O5	1.42	C4	C5	1.54	O2	C2	C1	107	O4	C4	C5	108	C2	C3	C4	C5	55
						O2	C2	C3	111	C3	C4	C5	107	C3	C4	C5	O5	−56
						C1	C2	C3	109	O5	C5	C4	112					

45.7   **Potassium - β - D - glucuronate dihydrate** $C_6H_9O_7^-$, K^+ , $2H_2O$

G.E.Gurr, Acta Cryst., 16, 690, 1963

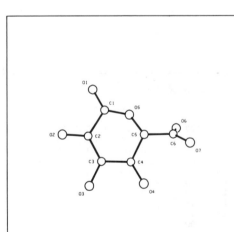

$P2_12_12_1$ $Z = 4$ $R_{0kl} = 0.071$,
$R_{hk0} = 0.095$

KGLUCD   LB 6-9-12

Bond Lengths						Bond Angles							Torsion Angles				
C1	O1	1.41	C6	O7	1.21	C1	O5	C5	110	O4	C4	C3	107	C5	O5	C1	C2	−72
C2	O2	1.38	C1	C2	1.55	O1	C1	O5	108	O4	C4	C5	110	C1	O5	C5	C4	72
C3	O3	1.40	C2	C3	1.56	O1	C1	C2	106	C3	C4	C5	110	O5	C1	C2	C3	60
C4	O4	1.41	C3	C4	1.55	O5	C1	C2	108	O5	C5	C4	107	C1	C2	C3	C4	−51
C1	O5	1.41	C4	C5	1.53	O2	C2	C1	113	O5	C5	C6	110	C2	C3	C4	C5	52
C5	O5	1.45	C5	C6	1.57	O2	C2	C3	108	C4	C5	C6	113	C3	C4	C5	O5	−60
C6	O6	1.24				C1	C2	C3	109	O6	C6	O7	128					
						O3	C3	C2	113	O6	C6	C5	117					
						O3	C3	C4	110	O7	C6	C5	115					
						C2	C3	C4	110									

45.8 Rubidium β - D - glucuronate dihydrate

$C_6H_9O_7^-$, Rb^+ , $2H_2O$

G.E.Gurr, Acta Cryst., 16, 690, 1963

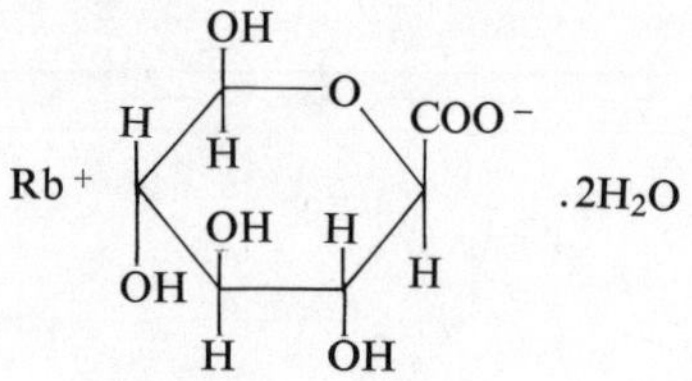

No comparison of bond lengths is possible since they are not reported in the paper. Preliminary unrefined coordinates are reported in the paper. See 45.7 for the structure of the isomorphous potassium salt.
$P2_12_12_1$ $Z = 4$ No R factor was given.

RGLUCD   LB 6-9-29

45.9 Calcium 5 - keto - D - glucuronate dihydrate

$2C_6H_9O_7^-$, Ca^{2+} , $2H_2O$

A.A.Balchin, C.H.Carlisle, Acta Cryst., 19, 103, 1965

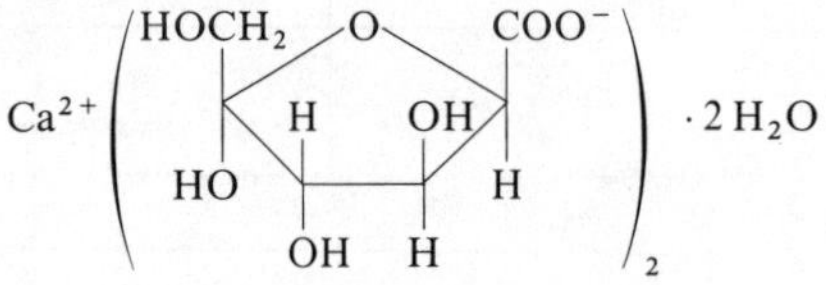

A2   Z = 2   R = 0.12

CAOGUC   LB 12-18-15

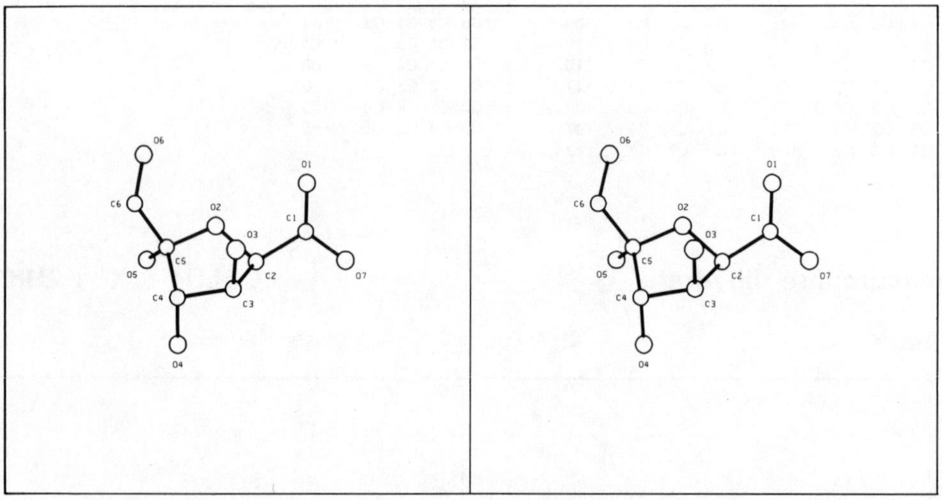

Bond Lengths

C1	O1	1.23
C2	O2	1.45
C5	O2	1.44
C3	O3	1.42
C4	O4	1.41
C5	O5	1.39
C6	O6	1.44
C1	O7	1.28
C1	C2	1.49
C2	C3	1.52
C3	C4	1.51
C4	C5	1.56
C5	C6	1.51

Bond Angles

C2	O2	C5	110	O4	C4	C3	107
O1	C1	O7	125	O4	C4	C5	112
O1	C1	C2	121	C3	C4	C5	104
O7	C1	C2	115	O2	C5	O5	105
O2	C2	C1	110	O2	C5	C4	105
O2	C2	C3	103	O2	C5	C6	109
C1	C2	C3	116	O5	C5	C4	113
O3	C3	C2	108	O5	C5	C6	111
O3	C3	C4	111	C4	C5	C6	113
C2	C3	C4	101	O6	C6	C5	109

Torsion Angles

C5	O2	C2	C3	−31
C2	O2	C5	C4	8
O2	C2	C3	C4	41
C2	C3	C4	C5	−36
C3	C4	C5	O2	19

45.10   Dipotassium - α - glucose - 1 - phosphate dihydrate $C_6H_{11}O_9P^{2-}$, $2K^+$, $2H_2O$

C.A.Beevers, G.H.Maconochie, Acta Cryst., 18, 232, 1965

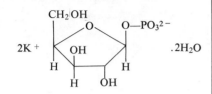

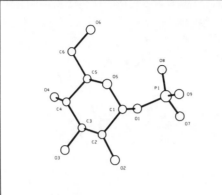 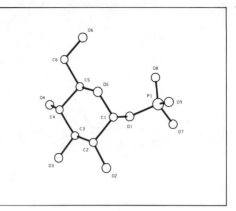

See also Rosenstein, Amer. Cryst. Assoc., Abstr. Papers (Summer Meeting), 92, 1968.

P2₁   Z = 2   R = 0.172

KGLUCP   LB 6-11-9

Bond Lengths

P1	O1	1.59	C1	O5	1.46
P1	O7	1.52	C5	O5	1.48
P1	O8	1.53	C6	O6	1.44
P1	O9	1.48	C1	C2	1.59
C1	O1	1.36	C2	C3	1.55
C2	O2	1.41	C3	C4	1.53
C3	O3	1.42	C4	C5	1.54
C4	O4	1.46	C5	C6	1.57

Bond Angles

O1	P1	O7	104	O2	C2	C3	110
O1	P1	O8	106	C1	C2	C3	106
O1	P1	O9	109	O3	C3	C2	109
O7	P1	O8	112	O3	C3	C4	111
O7	P1	O9	111	C2	C3	C4	111
O8	P1	O9	114	O4	C4	C3	103
P1	O1	C1	124	O4	C4	C5	103
C1	O5	C5	111	C3	C4	C5	106
O1	C1	O5	117	O5	C5	C4	111
O1	C1	C2	113	O5	C5	C6	114
O5	C1	C2	108	C4	C5	C6	107
O2	C2	C1	113	O6	C6	C5	108

Torsion Angles

O7	P1	O1	C1	137	C1	O5	C5	C4	64
O8	P1	O1	C1	−105	O1	C1	C2	C3	−70
O9	P1	O1	C1	19	O5	C1	C2	C3	61
P1	O1	C1	O5	84	C1	C2	C3	C4	−62
P1	O1	C1	C2	−150	C2	C3	C4	C5	61
C5	O5	C1	O1	65	C3	C4	C5	O5	−59
C5	O5	C1	C2	−64				

45.11   α - D - Glucose (neutron study) $C_6H_{12}O_6$

G.M.Brown, H.A.Levy, Science, 147, 1038, 1965

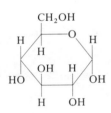

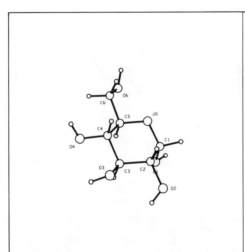 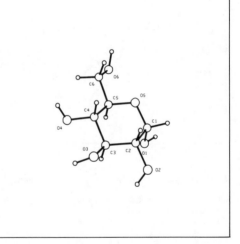

For the X - ray study see McDonald and Beevers, Acta Cryst., 5, 654, 1952.

P2₁2₁2₁   Z = 4   R = 0.061

GLUCSA   LB 6-12-80

Bond Lengths

C1	O1	1.39	O1	H8	0.97
C2	O2	1.42	O2	H9	0.96
C3	O3	1.42	O3	H10	0.97
C4	O4	1.43	O4	H11	0.97
C1	O5	1.43	O6	H12	0.96
C5	O5	1.43	C1	H1	1.10
C6	O6	1.41	C2	H2	1.09
C1	C2	1.53	C3	H3	1.11
C2	C3	1.53	C4	H4	1.10
C3	C4	1.52	C5	H5	1.10
C4	C5	1.53	C6	H6	1.09
C5	C6	1.51	C6	H7	1.10

Bond Angles

C1	O1	H8	108	O2	C2	H2	107	C3	C4	H4	108
C2	O2	H9	112	C1	C2	C3	111	C5	C4	H4	108
C3	O3	H10	112	C1	C2	H2	107	O5	C5	C4	109
C4	O4	H11	107	C3	C2	H2	108	O5	C5	C6	108
C1	O5	C5	114	O3	C3	C2	108	O5	C5	H5	110
C6	O6	H12	108	O3	C3	C4	111	C4	C5	C6	112
O1	C1	O5	112	O3	C3	H3	110	C4	C5	H5	110
O1	C1	C2	109	C2	C3	C4	110	C6	C5	H5	109
O1	C1	H1	112	C2	C3	H3	110	O6	C6	C5	110
O5	C1	C2	110	C4	C3	H3	109	O6	C6	H6	110
O5	C1	H1	105	O4	C4	C3	108	O6	C6	H7	110
C2	C1	H1	109	O4	C4	C5	111	C5	C6	H6	109
O2	C2	C1	111	O4	C4	H4	110	C5	C6	H7	109
O2	C2	C3	112	C3	C4	C5	111	H6	C6	H7	108

Torsion Angles

C5	O5	C1	C2	−61
C1	O5	C5	C4	62
O5	C1	C2	C3	54
C1	C2	C3	C4	−51
C2	C3	C4	C5	53
C3	C4	C5	O5	−57

45.12   β - D - Glucose

C₆H₁₂O₆

W.G.Ferrier, Acta Cryst., 16, 1023, 1963

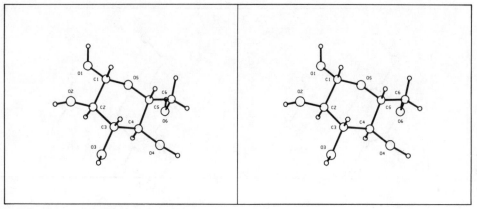

See also Chu & Jeffrey, Acta Cryst. (B), 24, 830, 1968.
P2₁2₁2₁   Z = 4   R = 0.11

GLUCSE   LB 6-12-81

Bond Lengths

C1	O1	1.40	C6	O6	1.43
C2	O2	1.44	C1	C2	1.54
C3	O3	1.45	C2	C3	1.53
C4	O4	1.45	C3	C4	1.52
C1	O5	1.44	C4	C5	1.53
C5	O5	1.46	C5	C6	1.51

Bond Angles

C1	O5	C5	113	C1	C2	C3	110	C3	C4	C5	109
O1	C1	O5	107	O3	C3	C2	107	O5	C5	C4	107
O1	C1	C2	107	O3	C3	C4	109	O5	C5	C6	107
O5	C1	C2	109	C2	C3	C4	111	C4	C5	C6	115
O2	C2	C1	108	O4	C4	C3	111	O6	C6	C5	111
O2	C2	C3	111	O4	C4	C5	108

Torsion Angles

C5	O5	C1	C2	−63
C1	O5	C5	C4	66
O5	C1	C2	C3	54
C1	C2	C3	C4	−52
C2	C3	C4	C5	55
C3	C4	C5	O5	−60

45.13   α - D - Glucose monohydrate

C₆H₁₂O₆ , H₂O

R.C.G.Killean, W.G.Ferrier, D.W.Young, Acta Cryst., 15, 911, 1962

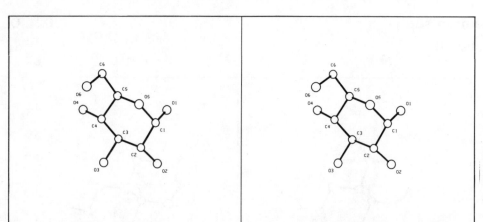

See also Neidle & Rogers, Nature, 225, 376, 1970.
P2₁   Z = 2   R = 0.17

GLUCMH   LB 6-12-82

Bond Lengths

C1	O1	1.38	C6	O6	1.46
C2	O2	1.42	C1	C2	1.55
C3	O3	1.48	C2	C3	1.50
C4	O4	1.42	C3	C4	1.55
C1	O5	1.41	C4	C5	1.49
C5	O5	1.41	C5	C6	1.57

Bond Angles

C1	O5	C5	114	C1	C2	C3	111	C3	C4	C5	110
O1	C1	O5	109	O3	C3	C2	105	O5	C5	C4	112
O1	C1	C2	109	O3	C3	C4	108	O5	C5	C6	105
O5	C1	C2	112	C2	C3	C4	110	C4	C5	C6	115
O2	C2	C1	110	O4	C4	C3	109	O6	C6	C5	110
O2	C2	C3	113	O4	C4	C5	110

Torsion Angles

C5	O5	C1	C2	−54
C1	O5	C5	C4	58
O5	C1	C2	C3	51
C1	C2	C3	C4	−51
C2	C3	C4	C5	54
C3	C4	C5	O5	−56

45.14   Mycosamine hydrochloride (absolute configuration)

C₆H₁₄NO₄⁺ , Cl⁻

α - d - 3 - Amino - 3,6 - dideoxymannopyranose hydrochloride
H.O.Locke, Dissert. Abstr., 23, 88, 1962

Atomic coordinates were not reported in the paper.
P2₁2₁2₁   Z was not reported.
R = 0.073

MYCOSH

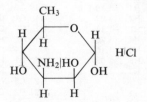

45.15 α - D - Glucosamine hydrobromide $C_6H_{14}NO_5^+$, Br^-

S.S.C.Chu, G.A.Jeffrey, Proc. R. Soc., A, 285, 470, 1965

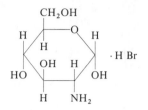

See also Chandrasekharan & Mal-
likarjunan, Z. Kristallogr., 129, 29,
1969.
$P2_1$ Z = 2 R = 0.13

GLUAMB   LB 6-14-7

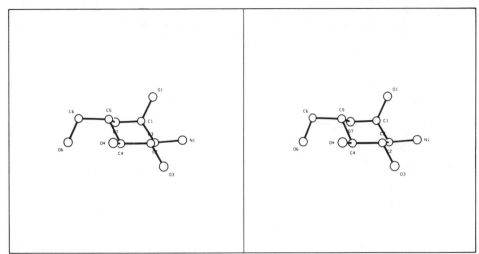

Bond Lengths

C2	N1	1.50	C5	O7	1.49
C1	O1	1.42	C1	C2	1.49
C3	O3	1.40	C2	C3	1.53
C4	O4	1.46	C3	C4	1.52
C6	O6	1.45	C4	C5	1.53
C1	O7	1.40	C5	C6	1.54

Bond Angles

C1	O7	C5	111	C1	C2	C3	112	C3	C4	C5	110
O1	C1	O7	115	O3	C3	C2	110	O7	C5	C4	108
O1	C1	C2	108	O3	C3	C4	113	O7	C5	C6	106
O7	C1	C2	111	C2	C3	C4	108	C4	C5	C6	113
N1	C2	C1	110	O4	C4	C3	112	O6	C6	C5	112
N1	C2	C3	109	O4	C4	C5	109				

Torsion Angles

C5	O7	C1	C2	62
C1	O7	C5	C4	−63
O7	C1	C2	C3	−57
C1	C2	C3	C4	54
C2	C3	C4	C5	−56
C3	C4	C5	O7	61

45.16 α - Methyl - D - galactoside 6 - bromohydrin $C_7H_{13}BrO_5$

J.H.Robertson, B.Sheldrick, Acta Cryst., 19, 820, 1965

$P2_12_12$ Z = 4 R = 0.108

MGALBH   LB 7-13-4

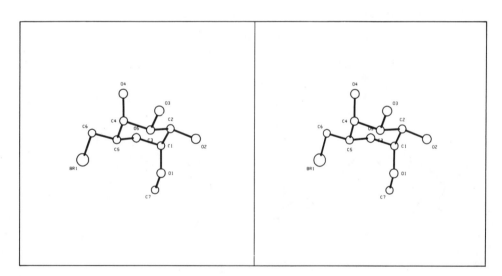

Bond Lengths

Br1	C6	1.97	C5	O5	1.47
C1	O1	1.43	C1	C2	1.51
C7	O1	1.44	C2	C3	1.55
C2	O2	1.45	C3	C4	1.51
C3	O3	1.42	C4	C5	1.52
C4	O4	1.42	C5	C6	1.49
C1	O5	1.42			

Bond Angles

C1	O1	C7	113	O2	C2	C3	107	O4	C4	C5	108
C1	O5	C5	113	C1	C2	C3	111	C3	C4	C5	108
O1	C1	O5	110	O3	C3	C2	110	O5	C5	C4	110
O1	C1	C2	108	O3	C3	C4	109	O5	C5	C6	108
O5	C1	C2	110	C2	C3	C4	109	C4	C5	C6	113
O2	C2	C1	111	O4	C4	C3	114	Br1	C6	C5	111

Torsion Angles

C5	O5	C1	C2	−58
C1	O5	C5	C4	61
O5	C1	C2	C3	55
C1	C2	C3	C4	−56
C2	C3	C4	C5	58
C3	C4	C5	O5	−60

45.17 6 - Sulfo - 6 - deoxy - α - D - glucopyranosyl - (1,1') - D - glycerol rubidium salt

$C_9H_{17}O_{10}S^-$, Rb^+

Y.Okaya, Acta Cryst., 17, 1276, 1964

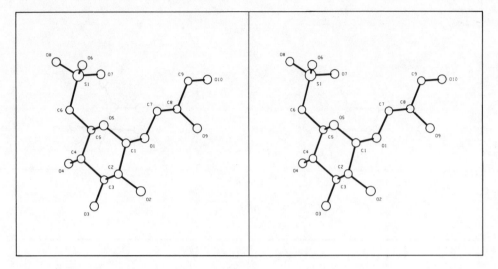

$P2_1$ $Z = 4$ $R = 0.123$

SGLOLR   LB 9-17-5

Bond Lengths

S1	O6	1.47	C5	O5	1.42
S1	O7	1.44	C8	O9	1.44
S1	O8	1.47	C9	O10	1.43
S1	C6	1.77	C1	C2	1.51
C1	O1	1.39	C2	C3	1.55
C7	O1	1.45	C3	C4	1.59
C2	O2	1.37	C4	C5	1.52
C3	O3	1.41	C5	C6	1.51
C4	O4	1.45	C7	C8	1.46
C1	O5	1.42	C8	C9	1.51

Bond Angles

O6	S1	O7	113	O5	C1	C2	113	O5	C5	C4	108
O6	S1	O8	110	O2	C2	C1	111	O5	C5	C6	111
O6	S1	C6	109	O2	C2	C3	109	C4	C5	C6	112
O7	S1	O8	114	C1	C2	C3	110	S1	C6	C5	117
O7	S1	C6	106	O3	C3	C2	109	O1	C7	C8	115
O8	S1	C6	105	O3	C3	C4	109	O9	C8	C7	111
C1	O1	C7	117	C2	C3	C4	106	O9	C8	C9	110
O1	C1	O5	109	O4	C4	C3	109	C7	C8	C9	110
O1	C1	C2	110	O4	C4	C5	111	O10	C9	C8	111
				C3	C4	C5	110				

Torsion Angles

O6	S1	C6	C5	−75
O7	S1	C6	C5	47
O8	S1	C6	C5	168
C5	O5	C1	C2	−58
C1	O5	C5	C4	60
C1	O5	C5	C6	−178
O5	C1	C2	C3	54
C1	C2	C3	C4	−54
C2	C3	C4	C5	59
C3	C4	C5	O5	−60
C3	C4	C5	C6	178
O5	C5	C6	S1	56
C4	C5	C6	S1	176

45.18 Arabinose p - bromophenylhydrazone

$C_{11}H_{15}BrN_2O_4$

S.Furberg, C.S.Petersen, Acta Chem. Scand., 16, 1539, 1962

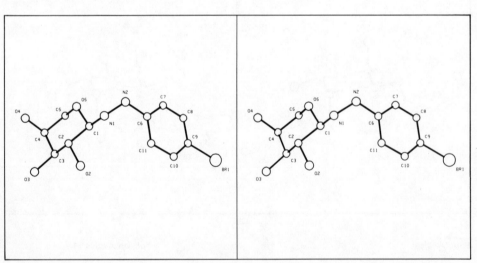

See also Furberg & Petersen, Select. Top. Struct. Chem., 183, 1967.
$P2_1$ $Z = 2$ $R_{hol} = 0.08$, $R_{0kl} = 0.10$

ARABRP   LB 11-15-2

Bond Lengths

Br1	C9	1.91	C2	C3	1.50
N1	N2	1.38	C3	C4	1.54
C1	N1	1.36	C4	C5	1.51
C6	N2	1.42	C6	C7	1.39
C2	O2	1.41	C6	C11	1.44
C3	O3	1.43	C7	C8	1.37
C4	O4	1.46	C8	C9	1.41
C1	O5	1.47	C9	C10	1.37
C5	O5	1.42	C10	C11	1.44
C1	C2	1.49			

Bond Angles

N2	N1	C1	114	O3	C3	C2	110	C7	C6	C11	122
N1	N2	C6	119	O3	C3	C4	111	C6	C7	C8	122
C1	O5	C5	116	C2	C3	C4	113	C7	C8	C9	117
N1	C1	O5	114	O4	C4	C3	109	Br1	C9	C8	116
N1	C1	C2	111	O4	C4	C5	111	Br1	C9	C10	118
O5	C1	C2	106	C3	C4	C5	109	C8	C9	C10	125
O2	C2	C1	107	O5	C5	C4	106	C9	C10	C11	118
O2	C2	C3	108	N2	C6	C7	120	C6	C11	C10	116
C1	C2	C3	108	N2	C6	C11	118				

Torsion Angles

C5	O5	C1	C2	−67
C1	O5	C5	C4	65
O5	C1	C2	C3	59
C1	C2	C3	C4	−58
C2	C3	C4	C5	56
C3	C4	C5	O5	−54
C1	N1	N2	C6	−80
N1	N2	C6	C7	159

45.19 **Ribose p - bromophenylhydrazone**

$C_{11}H_{15}BrN_2O_4$

K.Bjamer, S.Furberg, C.S.Petersen, Acta Chem. Scand., 18, 587, 1964

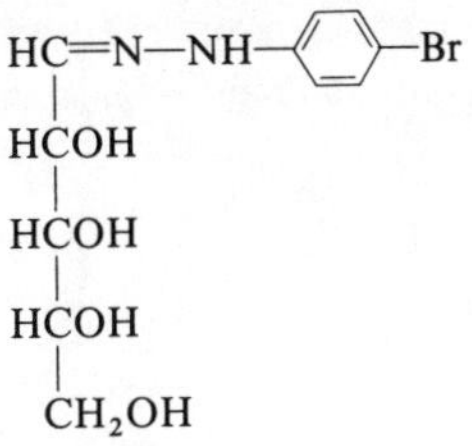

HC=N—NH—⟨⟩—Br

HCOH

HCOH

HCOH

CH₂OH

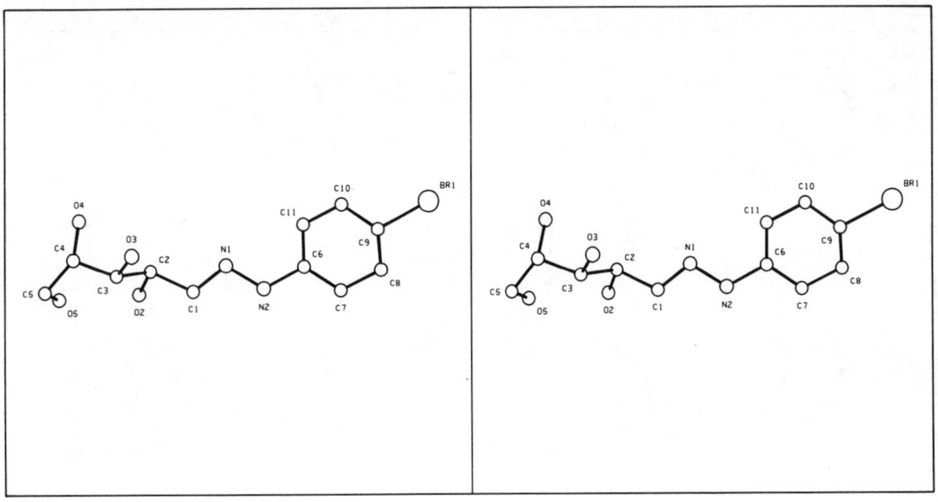

The published coordinates do not refer to the standard origin for space group $P2_12_12_1$. The standard coordinates are $x + 0.25$, y, $z + 0.25$ See also Furberg & Petersen, Select. Top. Struct. Chem., 183, 1967.
$P2_12_12_1$ $Z = 4$ $R_{hk0} = 0.11$,
$R_{0kl} = 0.14$

RIBBRP   LB 11-15-3

Bond Lengths

Br1	C9	1.94		C2	C3	1.55
N1	N2	1.43		C3	C4	1.48
C1	N1	1.32		C4	C5	1.52
C6	N2	1.45		C6	C7	1.37
C2	O2	1.35		C6	C11	1.38
C3	O3	1.43		C7	C8	1.46
C4	O4	1.42		C8	C9	1.35
C5	O5	1.43		C9	C10	1.40
C1	C2	1.58		C10	C11	1.44

Bond Angles

N2	N1	C1	112		O5	C5	C4	109
N1	N2	C6	118		N2	C6	C7	117
N1	C1	C2	119		N2	C6	C11	119
O2	C2	C1	104		C7	C6	C11	124
O2	C2	C3	109		C6	C7	C8	119
C1	C2	C3	112		C7	C8	C9	115
O3	C3	C2	110		Br1	C9	C8	117
O3	C3	C4	106		Br1	C9	C10	116
C2	C3	C4	122		C8	C9	C10	127
O4	C4	C3	104		C9	C10	C11	115
O4	C4	C5	115		C6	C11	C10	119
C3	C4	C5	114					

Torsion Angles

N2	N1	C1	C2	180		O3	C3	C4	O4	89
N1	C1	C2	O2	127		O3	C3	C4	C5	−145
N1	C1	C2	C3	−116		C2	C3	C4	O4	−38
O2	C2	C3	O3	171		C2	C3	C4	C5	89
O2	C2	C3	C4	−65		O4	C4	C5	O5	53
C1	C2	C3	O3	56		C3	C4	C5	O5	−68
C1	C2	C3	C4	−179		C7	C6	N2	N1	−174

CARBOHYDRATES

45.20   2 - O - (p - Bromobenzenesulfonyl) - 1,4 - 3,6 - dianhydro - D - glucitol 5 - nitrate

$C_{12}H_{12}BrNO_8S$

A.Camerman, N.Camerman, J.Trotter, Acta Cryst., 19, 449, 1965

P2$_1$ Z = 4   R = 0.157

BSGLON   LB 12-12-11

Bond Lengths

Br1	C23	1.87	Br2	C35	1.96
S3	O5	1.37	S4	O13	1.41
S3	O6	1.40	S4	O14	1.22
S3	O7	1.57	S4	O15	1.60
S3	C26	1.81	S4	C38	1.75
N21	O10	1.50	N22	O18	1.56
N21	O11	1.19	N22	O19	1.12
N21	O12	1.15	N22	O20	1.18
C29	O7	1.47	C41	O15	1.46
C30	O8	1.46	C42	O16	1.44
C31	O8	1.35	C43	O16	1.51
C32	O9	1.61	C44	O17	1.50
C33	O9	1.49	C45	O17	1.55
C34	O10	1.43	C46	O18	1.38
C23	C24	1.37	C35	C36	1.24
C23	C28	1.37	C35	C40	1.52
C24	C25	1.44	C36	C37	1.41
C25	C26	1.37	C37	C38	1.49
C26	C27	1.49	C38	C39	1.35
C27	C28	1.49	C39	C40	1.39
C29	C30	1.46	C41	C42	1.61
C29	C32	1.61	C41	C44	1.49
C31	C32	1.54	C43	C44	1.60
C31	C34	1.63	C43	C46	1.73
C33	C34	1.59	C45	C46	1.57

Bond Angles

O5	S3	O6	121	O13	S4	O14	118
O5	S3	O7	107	O13	S4	O15	110
O5	S3	C26	107	O13	S4	C38	108
O6	S3	O7	108	O14	S4	O15	107
O6	S3	C26	109	O14	S4	C38	109
O7	S3	C26	104	O15	S4	C38	104
O10	N21	O11	107	O18	N22	O19	113
O10	N21	O12	105	O18	N22	O20	101
O11	N21	O12	147	O19	N22	O20	146
S3	O7	C29	121	S4	O15	C41	117
C30	O8	C31	109	C42	O16	C43	111
C32	O9	C33	109	C44	O17	C45	97
N21	O10	C34	119	N22	O18	C46	107
Br1	C23	C24	120	Br2	C35	C36	120
Br1	C23	C28	118	Br2	C35	C40	111
C24	C23	C28	121	C36	C35	C40	128
C23	C24	C25	126	C35	C36	C37	116
C24	C25	C26	110	C36	C37	C38	118
S3	C26	C25	119	S4	C38	C37	120
S3	C26	C27	110	S4	C38	C39	118
C25	C26	C27	131	C37	C38	C39	121
C26	C27	C28	110	C38	C39	C40	119
C23	C28	C27	122	C35	C40	C39	115
O7	C29	C30	108	O15	C41	C42	101
O7	C29	C32	97	O15	C41	C44	107
C30	C29	C32	103	C42	C41	C44	100
O8	C30	C29	106	O16	C42	C41	106
O8	C31	C32	112	O16	C43	C44	102
O8	C31	C34	112	O16	C43	C46	101
C32	C31	C34	103	C44	C43	C46	98
O9	C32	C29	97	O17	C44	C41	101
O9	C32	C31	100	O17	C44	C43	113
C29	C32	C31	100	C41	C44	C43	108
O9	C33	C34	96	O17	C45	C46	105
O10	C34	C31	111	O18	C46	C43	116
O10	C34	C33	106	O18	C46	C45	109
C31	C34	C33	111	C43	C46	C45	101

Torsion Angles

O11	N21	O10	C34	12	O19	N22	O18	C46	6
O12	N21	O10	C34	−174	O20	N22	O18	C46	178
C31	O8	C30	C29	31	C43	O16	C42	C41	22
C30	O8	C31	C32	−16	C42	O16	C43	C44	−1
C30	O8	C31	C34	98	C42	O16	C43	C46	99
C33	O9	C32	C29	149	C45	O17	C44	C41	155
C33	O9	C32	C31	47	C45	O17	C44	C43	40
C32	O9	C33	C34	−44	C44	O17	C45	C46	−51
N21	O10	C34	C31	66	N22	O18	C46	C43	75
N21	O10	C34	C33	−174	N22	O18	C46	C45	−172
O7	C29	C30	O8	70	O15	C41	C42	O16	76
C32	C29	C30	O8	−32	C44	C41	C42	O16	−34
O7	C29	C32	O9	169	O15	C41	C44	O17	169
O7	C29	C32	C31	−89	O15	C41	C44	C43	−72
C30	C29	C32	O9	−80	C42	C41	C44	O17	−86
C30	C29	C32	C31	22	C42	C41	C44	C43	33
O8	C31	C32	O9	96	O16	C43	C44	O17	89
O8	C31	C32	C29	−4	O16	C43	C44	C41	−22
C34	C31	C32	O9	−25	C46	C43	C44	O17	−14
C34	C31	C32	C29	−124	C46	C43	C44	C41	−125
O8	C31	C34	O10	−2	O16	C43	C46	O18	−4
O8	C31	C34	C33	−120	O16	C43	C46	C45	−121
C32	C31	C34	O10	118	C44	C43	C46	O18	100
C32	C31	C34	C33	0	C44	C43	C46	C45	−17
O9	C33	C34	O10	−94	O17	C45	C46	O18	−79
O9	C33	C34	C31	26	O17	C45	C46	C43	43
C32	C29	O7	S3	−95	C42	C41	O15	S4	149
C30	C29	O7	S3	158	C44	C41	O15	S4	−107
C29	O7	S3	C26	−69	C41	O15	S4	C38	−101
C25	C26	S3	O7	−73	C37	C38	S4	O15	−79

270

45.21 D - β - Glucose p - bromophenylhydrazone

$C_{12}H_{17}BrN_2O_5$

T.Dukefos, A.Mostad, Acta Chem. Scand., 19, 685, 1965

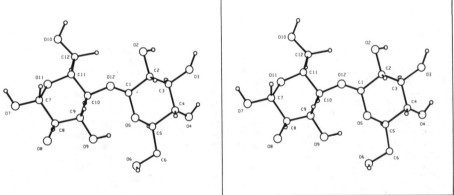

See also Furberg & Petersen, Select.
Top. Struct. Chem., 183, 1967.
$P2_12_12_1$ Z = 4 R_{hk0} = 0.11,
R_{0kl} = 0.11

GLUBRP   LB 12-17-1

Bond Lengths

Br1	C1	1.89	C1	C6	1.43
N1	N2	1.43	C2	C3	1.39
C4	N1	1.43	C3	C4	1.38
C7	N2	1.38	C4	C5	1.41
C8	O8	1.48	C5	C6	1.41
C9	O9	1.43	C7	C8	1.53
C10	O10	1.41	C8	C9	1.53
C7	O11	1.41	C9	C10	1.51
C11	O11	1.42	C10	C11	1.55
C12	O12	1.40	C11	C12	1.53
C1	C2	1.40			

Bond Angles

N2	N1	C4	118	O11	C7	C8	107
N1	N2	C7	113	O8	C8	C7	107
C7	O11	C11	115	O8	C8	C9	108
Br1	C1	C2	120	C7	C8	C9	110
Br1	C1	C6	118	O9	C9	C8	110
C2	C1	C6	121	O9	C9	C10	109
C1	C2	C3	117	C8	C9	C10	110
C2	C3	C4	122	O10	C10	C9	110
N1	C4	C3	120	O10	C10	C11	108
N1	C4	C5	119	C9	C10	C11	112
C3	C4	C5	121	O11	C11	C10	108
C4	C5	C6	117	O11	C11	C12	109
C1	C6	C5	119	C10	C11	C12	115
N2	C7	O11	113	O12	C12	C11	114
N2	C7	C8	110				

Torsion Angles

C4	N1	N2	C7	110	C1	C2	C3	C4	5
N2	N1	C4	C3	163	C2	C3	C4	N1	173
N2	N1	C4	C5	−13	C2	C3	C4	C5	−11
N1	N2	C7	O11	75	N1	C4	C5	C6	−180
N1	N2	C7	C8	−165	C3	C4	C5	C6	4
C11	O11	C7	N2	−172	C4	C5	C6	C1	7
C11	O11	C7	C8	66	N2	C7	C8	C9	177
C7	O11	C11	C10	−62	O11	C7	C8	C9	−59
Br1	C1	C2	C3	175	C7	C8	C9	C10	55
C6	C1	C2	C3	6	C8	C9	C10	C11	−51
Br1	C1	C6	C5	178	C9	C10	C11	O11	53
C2	C1	C6	C5	−12					

45.22 β - Cellobiose

$C_{12}H_{22}O_{11}$

R.A.Jacobson, J.A.Wunderlich, W.N.Lipscomb,
Acta Cryst., 14, 598, 1961

Published value of y(C1) = 0.307.
The correct value is 0.317.
See also Brown, J. Chem. Soc. (A),
927, 1966; Chu & Jeffrey, Acta Cryst.
(B), 24, 830, 1968; Moncrief & Sims,
J. Chem. Soc. (D), 914, 1969.
$P2_1$ Z = 2   R = 0.17

CELLOB   LB 12-22-18

Bond Lengths

C2	O2	1.44
C3	O3	1.47
C4	O4	1.31
C1	O5	1.44
C5	O5	1.39
C6	O6	1.39
C7	O7	1.40
C8	O8	1.43
C9	O9	1.40
C12	O10	1.41
C7	O11	1.36
C11	O11	1.47
C1	O12	1.37
C10	O12	1.46
C1	C2	1.53
C2	C3	1.52
C3	C4	1.50
C4	C5	1.59
C5	C6	1.53
C7	C8	1.53
C8	C9	1.44
C9	C10	1.56
C10	C11	1.49
C11	C12	1.55

Bond Angles

C1	O5	C5	117	O4	C4	C3	117	C7	C8	C9	113
C7	O11	C11	115	O4	C4	C5	114	O9	C9	C8	109
C1	O12	C10	116	C3	C4	C5	110	O9	C9	C10	113
O5	C1	O12	111	O5	C5	C4	114	C8	C9	C10	112
O5	C1	C2	109	O5	C5	C6	113	O12	C10	C9	110
O12	C1	C2	109	C4	C5	C6	115	O12	C10	C11	107
O2	C2	C1	110	O6	C6	C5	111	C9	C10	C11	114
O2	C2	C3	113	O7	C7	O11	113	O11	C11	C10	107
C1	C2	C3	108	O7	C7	C8	112	O11	C11	C12	105
O3	C3	C2	110	O11	C7	C8	110	C10	C11	C12	115
O3	C3	C4	109	O8	C8	C7	111	O10	C12	C11	104
C2	C3	C4	115	O8	C8	C9	108				

Torsion Angles

C5	O5	C1	O12	180	O12	C1	C2	C3	−179
C5	O5	C1	C2	−60	C1	C2	C3	C4	−56
C1	O5	C5	C4	49	C2	C3	C4	C5	44
C11	O11	C7	C8	−63	C3	C4	C5	O5	−39
C7	O11	C11	C10	61	O11	C7	C8	C9	54
C10	O12	C1	O5	−75	C7	C8	C9	C10	−44
C10	O12	C1	C2	165	C8	C9	C10	O12	165
C1	O12	C10	C9	104	C8	C9	C10	C11	45
C1	O12	C10	C11	−132	O12	C10	C11	O11	−171
O5	C1	C2	C3	60	C9	C10	C11	O11	−49

271

45.23   Sucrose (neutron study)

$C_{12}H_{22}O_{11}$

G.M.Brown, H.A.Levy, Science, 141, 921, 1963

Atomic coordinates were not given
but bond lengths were reported.
P2$_1$ Z = 2   R = 0.083

SUCROS   LB 12-22-19

45.24   1 - O - (p - Bromobenzenesulfonyl) - 4,5,7 - tri - O - acetyl - 2,6 - anhydro - 3 - deoxy - D - glucoheptitol

$C_{19}H_{23}BrO_{10}S$

A.Camerman, J.Trotter, Acta Cryst., 18, 197, 1965

P2$_1$2$_1$2   Z = 4   R = 0.090

BACGLO   LB 19-23-4

Bond Lengths

Br1	C13	1.98		C26	O12	1.25
S2	O3	1.38		C13	C14	1.34
S2	O4	1.42		C13	C18	1.39
S2	O5	1.55		C14	C15	1.40
S2	C16	1.78		C15	C16	1.51
C19	O5	1.44		C16	C17	1.39
C20	O6	1.46		C17	C18	1.46
C24	O6	1.44		C19	C20	1.53
C25	O7	1.48		C20	C21	1.57
C26	O7	1.36		C21	C22	1.51
C23	O8	1.48		C22	C23	1.58
C28	O8	1.32		C23	C24	1.48
C22	O9	1.43		C24	C25	1.51
C30	O9	1.41		C26	C27	1.41
C30	O10	1.14		C28	C29	1.59
C28	O11	1.16		C30	C31	1.54

Bond Angles

O3	S2	O4	118		O6	C20	C21	103
O3	S2	O5	107		C19	C20	C21	108
O3	S2	C16	108		C20	C21	C22	108
O4	S2	O5	110		O9	C22	C21	110
O4	S2	C16	109		O9	C22	C23	106
O5	S2	C16	103		C21	C22	C23	106
S2	O5	C19	120		O8	C23	C22	104
C20	O6	C24	110		O8	C23	C24	108
C25	O7	C26	121		C22	C23	C24	108
C23	O8	C28	116		O6	C24	C23	108
C22	O9	C30	114		O6	C24	C25	108
Br1	C13	C14	117		C23	C24	C25	113
Br1	C13	C18	110		O7	C25	C24	106
C14	C13	C18	132		O7	C26	O12	116
C13	C14	C15	118		O7	C26	C27	117
C14	C15	C16	112		O12	C26	C27	127
S2	C16	C15	116		O8	C28	O11	125
S2	C16	C17	116		O8	C28	C29	109
C15	C16	C17	128		O11	C28	C29	125
C16	C17	C18	115		O9	C30	O10	124
C13	C18	C17	113		O9	C30	C31	108
O5	C19	C20	107		O10	C30	C31	129
O6	C20	C19	105					

Torsion Angles

O3	S2	O5	C19	168		C14	C15	C16	S2	177
O4	S2	O5	C19	38		C14	C15	C16	C17	2
C16	S2	O5	C19	−78		S2	C16	C17	C18	−179
O3	S2	C16	C15	−151		C15	C16	C17	C18	−3
O3	S2	C16	C17	25		C16	C17	C18	C13	−1
O4	S2	C16	C15	−21		O5	C19	C20	O6	−88
O4	S2	C16	C17	155		O5	C19	C20	C21	162
O5	S2	C16	C15	95		O6	C20	C21	C22	66
O5	S2	C16	C17	−88		C19	C20	C21	C22	176
S2	O5	C19	C20	−158		C20	C21	C22	O9	−176
C24	O6	C20	C19	178		C20	C21	C22	C23	−62
C24	O6	C20	C21	−69		O9	C22	C23	O8	−68
C20	O6	C24	C23	71		O9	C22	C23	C24	177
C20	O6	C24	C25	−166		C21	C22	C23	O8	174
C26	O7	C25	C24	−158		C21	C22	C23	C24	60
C25	O7	C26	O12	5		O8	C23	C24	O6	−175
C25	O7	C26	C27	−179		O8	C23	C24	C25	66
C28	O8	C23	C22	118		C22	C23	C24	O6	−63
C28	O8	C23	C24	−128		C22	C23	C24	C25	177
C23	O8	C28	O11	12		O6	C24	C25	O7	−68
C23	O8	C28	C29	179		C23	C24	C25	O7	51
C30	O9	C22	C21	−96		C23	C24	O6	C20	71
C30	O9	C22	C23	150		C24	O6	C20	C21	−69
C22	O9	C30	O10	3		O6	C20	C21	C22	66
C22	O9	C30	C31	−175		C20	C21	C22	C23	−62
Br1	C13	C14	C15	179		C21	C22	C23	C24	60
C18	C13	C14	C15	−8		C22	C23	C24	O6	−63
Br1	C13	C18	C17	179		O6	C20	C19	O5	−88
C14	C13	C18	C17	7		C19	O5	S2	C16	−78
C13	C14	C15	C16	3		O5	S2	C16	C17	−88

45.25 Cyclohexa - amylose - potassium acetate complex

$C_{72}H_{120}O_{60}$, $3.8C_2H_3O_2^-$, $3.8K^+$, $19.4H_2O$

A.Hybl, R.E.Rundle, D.E.Williams, J. Amer. Chem. Soc., 87, 2779, 1965

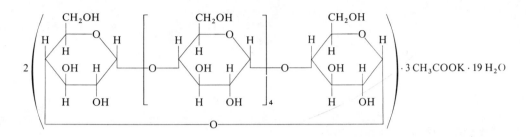

The cyclohexa - amylose molecules form a rigid framework permeated by channels. The channels contain disordered acetate ions and water molecules. The potassium ions statistically occupy three of the four symmetry - equivalent sites in the unit cell.

$P2_12_12$ $Z = 2$ $R = 0.10$

CHAMPA   LB 78-129-1

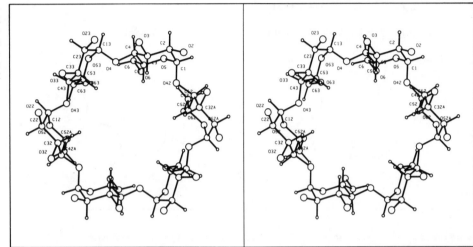

Bond Lengths

C2	O2	1.44	C53	O53	1.40
C3	O3	1.43	C62	O62	1.39
C4	O4	1.41	C63	O63	1.38
C13	O4	1.42	C1	C2	1.53
C1	O5	1.43	C2	C3	1.54
C5	O5	1.45	C3	C4	1.52
C6	O6	1.43	C4	C5	1.55
C22	O22	1.43	C5	C6	1.51
C23	O23	1.41	C12	C22	1.53
C32	O32	1.43	C13	C23	1.51
C33	O33	1.43	C22	C32	1.50
C1	O42	1.40	C23	C33	1.54
C42	O42	1.44	C32	C42A	1.53
C12	O43	1.41	C33	C43	1.51
C43	O43	1.43	C42	C52	1.54
C12	O52	1.42	C43	C53	1.55
C52A	O52	1.45	C52	C62	1.54
C13	O53	1.44	C53	C63	1.53

Bond Angles

C4	O4	C13	119	O5	C5	C4	109	C22	C32	C42A	111
C1	O5	C5	115	O5	C5	C6	107	O33	C33	C23	109
C1	O42	C42	119	C4	C5	C6	111	O33	C33	C43	108
C12	O43	C43	119	O6	C6	C5	112	C23	C33	C43	110
C12	O52	C52A	112	O43	C12	O52	112	O42	C42	C52	108
C13	O53	C53	113	O43	C12	C22	107	O42	C42	C32A	106
O5	C1	O42	111	O52	C12	C22	109	C52	C42	C32A	110
O5	C1	C2	108	O4	C13	O53	111	O43	C43	C33	105
O42	C1	C2	107	O4	C13	C23	108	O43	C43	C53	108
O2	C2	C1	109	O53	C13	C23	110	C33	C43	C53	110
O2	C2	C3	111	O22	C22	C12	110	C42	C52	C62	108
C1	C2	C3	110	O22	C22	C32	112	O53	C53	C43	110
O3	C3	C2	110	C12	C22	C32	109	O53	C53	C63	106
O3	C3	C4	108	O23	C23	C13	110	C43	C53	C63	111
C2	C3	C4	109	O23	C23	C33	113	O62	C62	C52	111
O4	C4	C3	106	C13	C23	C33	109	O63	C63	C53	112
O4	C4	C5	108	O32	C32	C22	111				
C3	C4	C5	110	O32	C32	C42A	107				

Torsion Angles

O53	C13	O4	C4	111
O5	C1	O42	C42	113
O52	C12	O43	C43	111

46.1   2 - Amino - ethanol phosphate

C₂H₈NO₄P

$$C_2H_8NO_4P$$

(i)   J.Kraut, Acta Cryst., 14, 1146, 1961

(ii) W.G.Ferrier, A.R.Lindsay, D.W.Young, Acta Cryst., 15, 616, 1962

$$H_3N^+ - CH_2 - CH_2 - O - PO_3H^-$$

(i)

The structure was confirmed by Ferrier et al., Acta Cryst., 15, 616, 1962. They reported an independent data set but refined the structure to only R = 0.155.
P2₁/c   Z = 4   R = 0.065

AEPHOS   LB 2-8-37

Bond Lengths		
P1	O2	1.49
P1	O3	1.50
P1	O4	1.56
P1	O5	1.59
C7	N8	1.49
C6	O5	1.43
C6	C7	1.52

Bond Angles							
O2	P1	O3	117	O4	P1	O5	106
O2	P1	O4	110	P1	O5	C6	119
O2	P1	O5	104	O5	C6	C7	109
O3	P1	O4	109	N8	C7	C6	111
O3	P1	O5	110				

Torsion Angles				
O2	P1	O5	C6	−179
O3	P1	O5	C6	55
O4	P1	O5	C6	−63
P1	O5	C6	C7	−166
O5	C6	C7	N8	−60

46.2   2 - Amino - ethanol phosphate

$$C_2H_8NO_4P$$

For complete entry see 46.1

46.3   Methyl ethylene phosphate (at −40 °C)

$$C_3H_7O_4P$$

T.A.Steitz, W.N.Lipscomb, J. Amer. Chem. Soc., 87, 2488, 1965

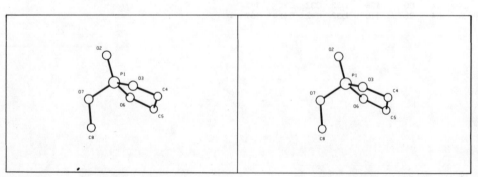

The labelling of atoms in Table 1 and Fig. 1 are contradictory. In Table 1 the set O2, O3, O4, O5, O6, C7, C8 should be replaced by O3, O6, O7, O2, C4, C5, C8. - Published value of y(O5) = 0.2137. The corrrect value is −0.2137.
See also Chiu & Lipscomb, J. Amer. Chem. Soc., 91, 4150, 1969.
Cc   Z = 4   R = 0.10

METPOS   LB 3-7-25

Bond Lengths		
P1	O2	1.44
P1	O3	1.57
P1	O6	1.57
P1	O7	1.57
C4	O3	1.40
C5	O6	1.46
C8	O7	1.42
C4	C5	1.52

Bond Angles							
O2	P1	O3	116	P1	O3	C4	112
O2	P1	O6	117	P1	O6	C5	112
O2	P1	O7	109	P1	O7	C8	119
O3	P1	O6	99	O3	C4	C5	108
O3	P1	O7	106	O6	C5	C4	105
O6	P1	O7	109				

Torsion Angles									
O2	P1	O3	C4	−115	O2	P1	O7	C8	176
O6	P1	O3	C4	11	O3	P1	O7	C8	−58
O7	P1	O3	C4	124	O6	P1	O7	C8	47
O2	P1	O6	C5	127	P1	O3	C4	C5	−20
O3	P1	O6	C5	2	P1	O6	C5	C4	−13
O7	P1	O6	C5	−108	O3	C4	C5	O6	20

46.4 Barium phenyl phosphate sesquihydrate

$C_6H_5O_4P^{2-}$, Ba^{2+} , $1.5H_2O$

G.W.Svetich, C.N.Caughlan, Acta Cryst., 16, A73, 1963

Atomic coordinates were not reported in the paper.
$P2_1/a$ Z = 4   No R factor was given.

BAPPOP   LB 6-5-1

$$Ba^{2+} \left(O{-}\underset{\underset{O}{\|}}{\overset{\overset{O}{\|}}{P}}{-}O{-}\bigcirc \right)^{2-} \cdot 1 \cdot 5\ H_2O$$

46.5 L - α - Glycerophosphorylcholine cadmium chloride trihydrate

$C_8H_{20}NO_6P$, $CdCl_2$, $3H_2O$

M.Sundaralingam, L.H.Jensen, Science, 150, 1035, 1965

Atomic coordinates were not reported in the paper.
$P2_12_12_1$ Z = 4   R = 0.115

GLYCAC   LB 8-20-14

$$\left[\begin{array}{l} CH_2OH \\ | \\ CHOH \qquad O \\ | \qquad\quad \| \\ CH_2{-}O{-}P{-}O{-}CH_2{-}CH_2{-}\overset{+}{N}(CH_3)_3 \cdot CdCl_2 \\ \qquad\quad | \\ \qquad\quad O^- \end{array} \right] \cdot 3\,H_2O$$

46.6 Calcium 1 - naphthylphosphate trihydrate

$2C_{10}H_8O_4P^-$, Ca^{2+} , $3H_2O$

C.-T.Li, C.N.Caughlan, Acta Cryst., 19, 637, 1965

$$Ca^{2+} \left(O{-}\underset{\underset{O^-}{\|}}{\overset{\overset{O}{\|}}{P}}{-}OH \right)_2 \cdot 3\,H_2O$$

P-1   Z = 2   R = 0.097

CANAPO   LB 20-16-4

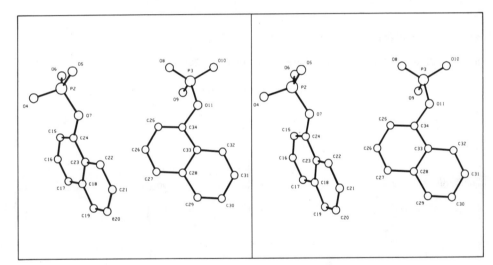

Bond Lengths

P2	O4	1.53	P3	O8	1.47
P2	O5	1.50	P3	O9	1.57
P2	O6	1.49	P3	O10	1.47
P2	O7	1.59	P3	O11	1.59
C24	O7	1.41	C34	O11	1.40
C15	C16	1.35	C25	C26	1.39
C15	C24	1.35	C25	C34	1.32
C16	C17	1.35	C26	C27	1.32
C17	C18	1.40	C27	C28	1.42
C18	C19	1.41	C28	C29	1.48
C18	C23	1.36	C28	C33	1.40
C19	C20	1.32	C29	C30	1.27
C20	C21	1.39	C30	C31	1.36
C21	C22	1.38	C31	C32	1.36
C22	C23	1.41	C32	C33	1.36
C23	C24	1.43	C33	C34	1.44

Bond Angles

O4	P2	O5	108	C19	C18	C23	120	O8	P3	O9	111	C29	C28	C33	115
O4	P2	O6	112	C18	C19	C20	120	O8	P3	O10	117	C28	C29	C30	124
O4	P2	O7	104	C19	C20	C21	122	O8	P3	O11	110	C29	C30	C31	118
O5	P2	O6	117	C20	C21	C22	117	O9	P3	O10	110	C30	C31	C32	122
O5	P2	O7	104	C21	C22	C23	122	O9	P3	O11	105	C31	C32	C33	122
O6	P2	O7	111	C18	C23	C22	118	O10	P3	O11	103	C28	C33	C32	119
P2	O7	C24	125	C18	C23	C24	118	P3	O11	C34	125	C28	C33	C34	114
C16	C15	C24	119	C22	C23	C24	124	C26	C25	C34	117	C32	C33	C34	127
C15	C16	C17	122	O7	C24	C15	126	C25	C26	C27	123	O11	C34	C25	123
C16	C17	C18	120	O7	C24	C23	113	C26	C27	C28	119	O11	C34	C33	112
C17	C18	C19	121	C15	C24	C23	122	C27	C28	C29	124	C25	C34	C33	125
C17	C18	C23	119					C27	C28	C33	121				

46.7 Di - p - chlorophenyl hydrogen phosphate

$C_{12}H_9Cl_2O_4P$

M.Calleri, J.C.Speakman, Acta Cryst., 17, 1097, 1964

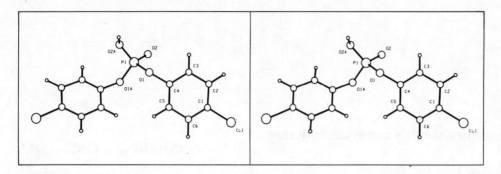

Pnaa   Z = 4   R = 0.111

CLPHOS   LB 12-9-13

Bond Lengths

Cl1	C1	1.73	C1	C6	1.34
P1	O1	1.58	C2	C3	1.42
P1	O2	1.50	C3	C4	1.34
C4	O1	1.42	C4	C5	1.36
C1	C2	1.39	C5	C6	1.40

Bond Angles

O1	P1	O2	110	Cl1	C1	C2	118	O1	C4	C5	118
O1	P1	O1A	108	Cl1	C1	C6	120	C3	C4	C5	122
O1	P1	O2A	107	C2	C1	C6	122	C4	C5	C6	120
O2	P1	O1A	107	C1	C2	C3	117	C1	C6	C5	119
O2	P1	O2A	116	C2	C3	C4	120				
P1	O1	C4	121	O1	C4	C3	120				

Torsion Angles

P1	O1	C4	C3	91

46.8 Triphenyl phosphate

$C_{18}H_{15}O_4P$

For complete entry see 46.9

46.9 Triphenyl phosphate

$C_{18}H_{15}O_4P$

(i)   G.W.Svetich, C.N.Caughlan, Acta Cryst., 19, 645, 1965

(ii) W.O.Davies, E.Stanley, Acta Cryst., 15, 1092, 1962

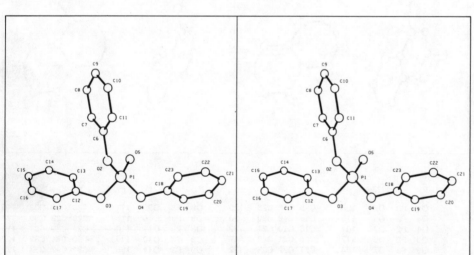

(i)

Also reported by Davies and Stanley, Acta Cryst., 15, 1902, 1962. They solved the structure from two projections   —   R(0kl) = 0.19, R(h0l) = 0.14.

P2₁/a   Z = 4   R = 0.107

TPHEPO01   LB 18-15-24

Bond Lengths

P1	O2	1.60	C12	C13	1.34
P1	O3	1.55	C12	C17	1.36
P1	O4	1.56	C13	C14	1.42
P1	O5	1.43	C14	C15	1.34
C6	O2	1.43	C15	C16	1.35
C12	O3	1.42	C16	C17	1.43
C18	O4	1.38	C18	C19	1.37
C6	C7	1.36	C18	C23	1.39
C6	C11	1.34	C19	C20	1.34
C7	C8	1.39	C20	C21	1.43
C8	C9	1.44	C21	C22	1.38
C9	C10	1.43	C22	C23	1.35
C10	C11	1.38			

Bond Angles

O2	P1	O3	104	C7	C6	C11	122	C14	C15	C16	116
O2	P1	O4	104	C6	C7	C8	122	C15	C16	C17	126
O2	P1	O5	113	C7	C8	C9	117	C12	C17	C16	112
O3	P1	O4	97	C8	C9	C10	118	O4	C18	C19	116
O3	P1	O5	119	C9	C10	C11	120	O4	C18	C23	122
O4	P1	O5	118	C6	C11	C10	120	C19	C18	C23	122
P1	O2	C6	125	O3	C12	C13	119	C18	C19	C20	118
P1	O3	C12	123	O3	C12	C17	114	C19	C20	C21	123
P1	O4	C18	123	C13	C12	C17	127	C20	C21	C22	116
O2	C6	C7	123	C12	C13	C14	116	C21	C22	C23	122
O2	C6	C11	114	C13	C14	C15	123	C18	C23	C22	119

Torsion Angles

P1	O4	C18	C23	87
P1	O2	C6	C11	−130
P1	O3	C12	C13	68

47.1　5 - Fluoro - 2′ - deoxy - β - uridine

C₉H₁₁FN₂O₅

$C_9H_{11}FN_2O_5$

D.R.Harris, W.M.Macintyre, Biophys. J., 4, 203, 1964

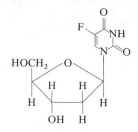

P2₁2₁2₁　Z = 2　R = 0.092

$P2_12_12_1$　Z = 2　R = 0.092

FDOURD　LB 9-11-8

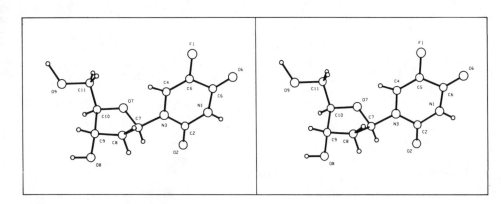

Bond Lengths

F1	C5	1.35	C10	O7	1.45
C2	N1	1.38	C9	O8	1.43
C6	N1	1.37	C11	O9	1.44
C2	N3	1.39	C4	C5	1.33
C4	N3	1.36	C5	C6	1.43
C7	N3	1.48	C7	C8	1.53
C2	O2	1.20	C8	C9	1.53
C6	O6	1.18	C9	C10	1.50
C7	O7	1.44	C10	C11	1.51

Bond Angles

C2	N1	C6	128	F1	C5	C4	121	C7	C8	C9	100
C2	N3	C4	122	F1	C5	C6	117	O8	C9	C8	109
C2	N3	C7	117	C4	C5	C6	123	O8	C9	C10	112
C4	N3	C7	120	N1	C6	O6	125	C8	C9	C10	102
C7	O7	C10	109	N1	C6	C5	113	O7	C10	C9	106
N1	C2	N3	114	O6	C6	C5	123	O7	C10	C11	108
N1	C2	O2	123	N3	C7	O7	107	C9	C10	C11	115
N3	C2	O2	123	N3	C7	C8	114	O9	C11	C10	106
N3	C4	C5	120	O7	C7	C8	105				

Torsion Angles

C10	O7	C7	C8	−19
C7	O7	C10	C9	−7
O7	C7	C8	C9	37
C7	C8	C9	C10	−40
C8	C9	C10	O7	30
C2	N3	C7	O7	−114

47.2　5 - Iodo - 2′ - deoxyuridine

C₉H₁₁IN₂O₅

$C_9H_{11}IN_2O_5$

N.Camerman, J.Trotter, Acta Cryst., 18, 203, 1965

P1　Z = 1　R = 0.054

IDOXUR　LB 9-11-10

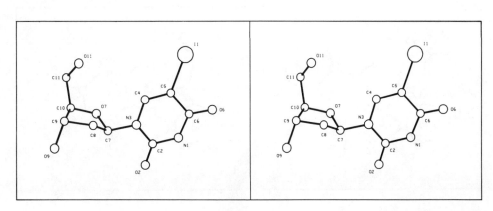

Bond Lengths

I1	C5	2.05	C10	O7	1.42
C2	N1	1.38	C9	O9	1.44
C6	N1	1.36	C11	O11	1.39
C2	N3	1.37	C4	C5	1.34
C4	N3	1.37	C5	C6	1.49
C7	N3	1.49	C7	C8	1.55
C2	O2	1.23	C8	C9	1.56
C6	O6	1.21	C9	C10	1.59
C7	O7	1.42	C10	C11	1.56

Bond Angles

C2	N1	C6	125	I1	C5	C4	123	C7	C8	C9	101
C2	N3	C4	123	I1	C5	C6	119	O9	C9	C8	106
C2	N3	C7	118	C4	C5	C6	118	O9	C9	C10	107
C4	N3	C7	119	N1	C6	O6	121	C8	C9	C10	102
C7	O7	C10	111	N1	C6	C5	116	O7	C10	C9	107
N1	C2	N3	116	O6	C6	C5	122	O7	C10	C11	110
N1	C2	O2	119	N3	C7	O7	109	C9	C10	C11	113
N3	C2	O2	125	N3	C7	C8	114	O11	C11	C10	112
N3	C4	C5	121	O7	C7	C8	105				

Torsion Angles

C10	O7	C7	C8	−28
C7	O7	C10	C9	5
O7	C7	C8	C9	38
C7	C8	C9	C10	−33
C8	C9	C10	O7	19
O7	C7	N3	C2	−111

47.3   D(+) - Barium uridine - 5′ - phosphate hydrate (absolute configuration)

$C_9H_{11}N_2O_9P^{2-}$, Ba^{2+} , $8.9H_2O$

E.Shefter, K.N.Trueblood, Acta Cryst., 18, 1067, 1965

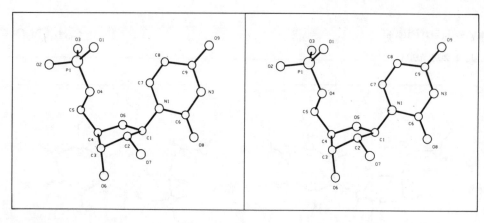

Only seven water molecules were located. In Table 1 atom O2′ should be labelled O5′. The torsion angles reported by the authors about bond C5′ - C4′(relabelled C5 - C4) do not agree with the torsion angles calculated on the basis of the published coordinates.

$C222_1$ Z = 8   R = 0.098

BAURIP   LB 9-11-1

Bond Lengths

P1	O1	1.55	C4	O5	1.46
P1	O2	1.50	C3	O6	1.40
P1	O3	1.52	C2	O7	1.38
P1	O4	1.64	C6	O8	1.22
C1	N1	1.43	C9	O9	1.29
C6	N1	1.39	C1	C2	1.56
C7	N1	1.38	C2	C3	1.53
C6	N3	1.41	C3	C4	1.58
C9	N3	1.40	C4	C5	1.47
C5	O4	1.44	C7	C8	1.30
C1	O5	1.43	C8	C9	1.41

Bond Angles

O1	P1	O2	108	C1	O5	C4	112	O5	C4	C5	110
O1	P1	O3	118	N1	C1	O5	110	C3	C4	C5	117
O1	P1	O4	103	N1	C1	C2	112	O4	C5	C4	105
O2	P1	O3	110	O5	C1	C2	104	N1	C6	N3	112
O2	P1	O4	108	O7	C2	C1	113	N1	C6	O8	124
O3	P1	O4	108	O7	C2	C3	111	N3	C6	O8	124
C1	N1	C6	116	C1	C2	C3	106	N1	C7	C8	122
C1	N1	C7	120	O6	C3	C2	109	C7	C8	C9	120
C6	N1	C7	124	O6	C3	C4	109	N3	C9	O9	118
C6	N3	C9	125	C2	C3	C4	100	N3	C9	C8	116
P1	O4	C5	122	O5	C4	C3	107	O9	C9	C8	125

Torsion Angles

O1	P1	O4	C5	−179
O2	P1	O4	C5	67
O3	P1	O4	C5	−53
P1	O4	C5	C4	176
C4	O5	C1	C2	−16
C1	O5	C4	C3	−5
C1	O5	C4	C5	123
O5	C1	C2	C3	31
C1	C2	C3	C4	−33
C2	C3	C4	O5	24
C2	C3	C4	C5	−100
O5	C4	C5	O4	−67
C3	C4	C5	O4	55
C6	N1	C1	O5	−137

47.4   Cytidine

$C_9H_{13}N_3O_5$

S.Furberg, C.S.Petersen, C.Romming, Acta Cryst., 18, 313, 1965

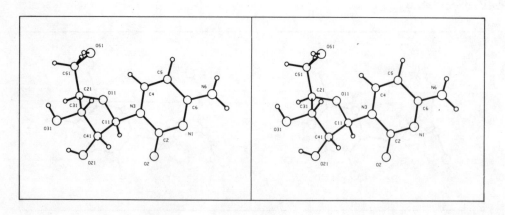

$P2_12_12_1$ Z = 4   R = 0.056

CYTIDI10   LB 9-13-6

Bond Lengths

C2	N1	1.36	C41	O21	1.42
C6	N1	1.33	C31	O31	1.41
C2	N3	1.38	C51	O51	1.40
C4	N3	1.37	C4	C5	1.35
C11	N3	1.50	C5	C6	1.42
C6	N6	1.33	C11	C41	1.53
C2	O2	1.25	C21	C31	1.53
C11	O11	1.41	C21	C51	1.51
C21	O11	1.44	C31	C41	1.51

Bond Angles

C2	N1	C6	119	C4	C5	C6	118	C31	C21	C51	115
C2	N3	C4	121	N1	C6	N6	117	O31	C31	C21	114
C2	N3	C11	117	N1	C6	C5	121	O31	C31	C41	113
C4	N3	C11	122	N6	C6	C5	122	C21	C31	C41	102
C11	O11	C21	110	N3	C11	O11	109	O21	C41	C11	109
N1	C2	N3	120	N3	C11	C41	111	O21	C41	C31	113
N1	C2	O2	121	O11	C11	C41	107	C11	C41	C31	102
N3	C2	O2	119	O11	C21	C31	104	O51	C51	C21	114
N3	C4	C5	120	O11	C21	C51	110				

Torsion Angles

C21	O11	C11	C41	6
C11	O11	C21	C31	18
O11	C11	C41	C31	−28
O11	C21	C31	C41	−35
C21	C31	C41	C11	37
C2	N3	C11	O11	−163

47.5   Cytidine 3' - phosphate

$C_9H_{14}N_3O_8P$

Cytidylic acid b
M.Sundaralingam, L.H.Jensen, J. Molec. Biol., 13, 914, 1965

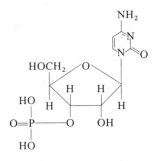

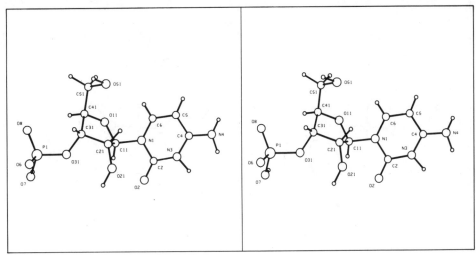

Published bond length for C2' - H2'
(relabelled   C21 -   H4) = 1.999A.
The correct value is 0.999A.
See also Bugg & Marsh, J. Molec.
Biol., 25, 67, 1967.
$P2_12_12$ Z = 4   R = 0.045

CYTIAC   LB 9-14-16

Bond Lengths

P1	O6	1.50		C11	O11	1.42
P1	O7	1.55		C41	O11	1.46
P1	O8	1.48		C21	O21	1.40
P1	O31	1.61		C31	O31	1.43
C2	N1	1.40		C51	O51	1.44
C6	N1	1.35		C4	C5	1.42
C11	N1	1.48		C5	C6	1.35
C2	N3	1.38		C11	C21	1.51
C4	N3	1.34		C21	C31	1.53
C4	N4	1.32		C31	C41	1.54
C2	O2	1.20		C41	C51	1.51

Bond Angles

O6	P1	O7	106		P1	O31	C31	121		O11	C11	C21	106
O6	P1	O8	116		N1	C2	N3	113		O21	C21	C11	115
O6	P1	O31	109		N1	C2	O2	125		O21	C21	C31	118
O7	P1	O8	114		N3	C2	O2	122		C11	C21	C31	101
O7	P1	O31	102		N3	C4	N4	120		O31	C31	C21	108
O8	P1	O31	110		N3	C4	C5	118		O31	C31	C41	110
C2	N1	C6	122		N4	C4	C5	122		C21	C31	C41	102
C2	N1	C11	117		C4	C5	C6	117		O11	C41	C31	105
C6	N1	C11	120		N1	C6	C5	123		O11	C41	C51	110
C2	N3	C4	126		N1	C11	O11	108		C31	C41	C51	116
C11	O11	C41	110		N1	C11	C21	113		O51	C51	C41	114

Torsion Angles

O6	P1	O31	C31	−78
O7	P1	O31	C31	171
O8	P1	O31	C31	50
C41	O11	C11	C21	−20
C11	O11	C41	C31	−6
P1	O31	C31	C21	158
P1	O31	C31	C41	−92
O11	C11	C21	C31	37
C11	C21	C31	O31	77
C11	C21	C31	C41	−39
O31	C31	C41	O11	−87
C21	C31	C41	O11	28
C2	N1	C11	O11	−134

47.6   Calcium thymidylate hexahydrate

$C_{10}H_{13}N_2O_8P^{2-}$, Ca^{2+} , $6H_2O$

K.N.Trueblood, P.Horn, V.Luzzati, Acta Cryst., 14, 965, 1961

$P2_1$ Z = 4   R = 0.141

CATHYM   LB 10-13-7

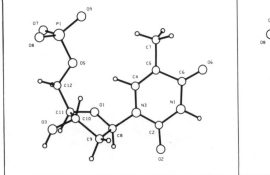

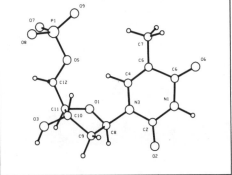

Bond Lengths

P1	O5	1.59
P1	O7	1.49
P1	O8	1.51
P1	O9	1.47
C2	N1	1.38
C6	N1	1.41
C2	N3	1.37
C4	N3	1.37
C8	N3	1.47
C8	O1	1.44
C11	O1	1.44
C2	O2	1.25
C10	O3	1.41
C12	O5	1.47
C6	O6	1.22
C4	C5	1.31
C5	C6	1.45
C5	C7	1.53
C8	C9	1.53
C9	C10	1.55
C10	C11	1.49
C11	C12	1.53

Bond Angles

O5	P1	O7	108
O5	P1	O8	108
O5	P1	O9	102
O7	P1	O8	106
O7	P1	O9	118
O8	P1	O9	114
C2	N1	C6	126
C2	N3	C4	121
C2	N3	C8	118
C4	N3	C8	121
C8	O1	C11	109
P1	O5	C12	119
N1	C2	N3	116
N1	C2	O2	121
N3	C2	O2	123
N3	C4	C5	123
C4	C5	C6	120
C4	C5	C7	125
C6	C5	C7	115

O3	C10	C9	114		N1	C6	O6	118
O3	C10	C11	114		N1	C6	C5	113
C9	C10	C11	102		O6	C6	C5	129
O1	C11	C10	107		N3	C8	O1	107
O1	C11	C12	108		N3	C8	C9	115
C10	C11	C12	117		O1	C8	C9	107
O5	C12	C11	109		C8	C9	C10	103

Torsion Angles

O7	P1	O5	C12	−47		O1	C8	C9	C10	−18
O8	P1	O5	C12	67		C8	C9	C10	C11	31
O9	P1	O5	C12	−172		C9	C10	C11	O1	−35
C11	O1	C8	C9	−4		C9	C10	C11	C12	−155
C8	O1	C11	C10	25		O1	C11	C12	O5	−63
C8	O1	C11	C12	151		C10	C11	C12	O5	57
P1	O5	C12	C11	−156		C2	N3	C8	O1	−137

47.7   Deoxyadenosine monohydrate $C_{10}H_{13}N_5O_3$, H_2O

D.G.Watson, D.J.Sutor, P.Tollin, Acta Cryst., 19, 111, 1965

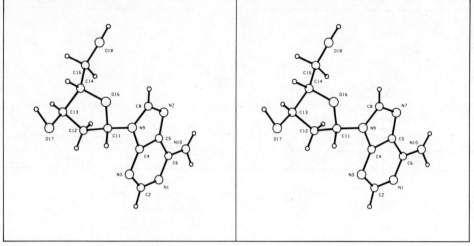

$P2_1$ $Z = 2$ $R = 0.078$

DOXADM   LB 10-13-19

Bond Lengths

C2	N1	1.32	C11	O16	1.41
C6	N1	1.34	C14	O16	1.43
C2	N3	1.33	C13	O17	1.42
C4	N3	1.35	C15	O18	1.44
C5	N7	1.37	C4	C5	1.39
C8	N7	1.31	C5	C6	1.41
C4	N9	1.37	C11	C12	1.51
C8	N9	1.36	C12	C13	1.51
C11	N9	1.47	C13	C14	1.53
C6	N10	1.33	C14	C15	1.51

Bond Angles

C2	N1	C6	120	N9	C4	C5	105	O16	C11	C12	107
C2	N3	C4	111	N7	C5	C4	111	C11	C12	C13	103
C5	N7	C8	104	N7	C5	C6	134	O17	C13	C12	108
C4	N9	C8	107	C4	C5	C6	115	O17	C13	C14	111
C4	N9	C11	123	N1	C6	N10	119	C12	C13	C14	101
C8	N9	C11	130	N1	C6	C5	118	O16	C14	C13	105
C11	O16	C14	110	N10	C6	C5	123	O16	C14	C15	112
N1	C2	N3	129	N7	C8	N9	113	C13	C14	C15	114
N3	C4	N9	128	N9	C11	O16	108	O18	C15	C14	107
N3	C4	C5	127	N9	C11	C12	111				

Torsion Angles

C14	O16	C11	C12	2
C11	O16	C14	C13	20
O16	C11	C12	C13	−24
C11	C12	C13	C14	34
C12	C13	C14	O16	−34
C8	N9	C11	O16	−11

47.8   Adenosine - 5 - bromouridine monohydrate

$C_{10}H_{13}N_5O_4$, $C_9H_{11}BrN_2O_6$, H_2O

A.E.V.Haschemeyer, H.M.Sobell, Acta Cryst., 18, 525, 1965

The water molecules are disordered.
$P22_12_1$ Z = 4   R = 0.138

ADBURM   LB 19-24-2

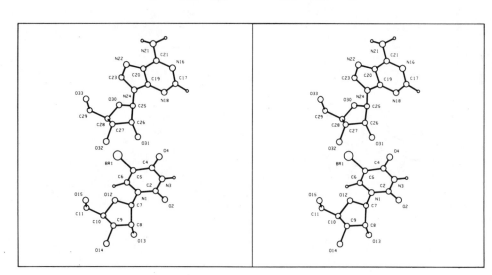

Bond Lengths

Br1	C5	1.88		C17	N16	1.34
C2	N1	1.37		C21	N16	1.30
C6	N1	1.34		C17	N18	1.31
C7	N1	1.54		C19	N18	1.36
C2	N3	1.33		C21	N21	1.39
C4	N3	1.39		C20	N22	1.37
C2	O2	1.25		C23	N22	1.29
C4	O4	1.24		C19	N24	1.34
C7	O12	1.39		C23	N24	1.37
C10	O12	1.50		C25	N24	1.51
C8	O13	1.42		C25	O30	1.32
C9	O14	1.46		C28	O30	1.43
C11	O15	1.52		C26	O31	1.42
C4	C5	1.45		C27	O32	1.39
C5	C6	1.35		C29	O33	1.38
C7	C8	1.58		C19	C20	1.37
C8	C9	1.46		C20	C21	1.39
C9	C10	1.52		C25	C26	1.52
C10	C11	1.50		C26	C27	1.50
				C27	C28	1.52
				C28	C29	1.56

Bond Angles

C2	N1	C6	122		C17	N16	C21	118
C2	N1	C7	117		C17	N18	C19	113
C6	N1	C7	121		C20	N22	C23	105
C2	N3	C4	126		C19	N24	C23	106
C7	O12	C10	109		C23	N24	C25	127
N1	C2	N3	118		C25	O30	C28	111
N1	C2	O2	120		N16	C17	N18	127
N3	C2	O2	122		N18	C19	N24	129
N3	C4	O4	122		N18	C19	C20	124
N3	C4	C5	113		N24	C19	C20	107
O4	C4	C5	125		N22	C20	C19	109
Br1	C5	C4	117		N22	C20	C21	134
Br1	C5	C6	122		C19	C20	C21	117
C4	C5	C6	121		N16	C21	N21	118
N1	C6	C5	120		N16	C21	C20	120
N1	C7	O12	107		N21	C21	C20	122
N1	C7	C8	109		N22	C23	N24	112
O12	C7	C8	109		N24	C25	O30	110
O13	C8	C7	102		N24	C25	C26	108
O13	C8	C9	112		O30	C25	C26	108
C7	C8	C9	99		O31	C26	C25	109
O14	C9	C8	113		O31	C26	C27	109
O14	C9	C10	106		C25	C26	C27	101
C8	C9	C10	107		O32	C27	C26	116
O12	C10	C9	99		O32	C27	C28	113
O12	C10	C11	107		C26	C27	C28	99
C9	C10	C11	119		O30	C28	C27	104
O15	C11	C10	112		O30	C28	C29	106
					C27	C28	C29	116
					O33	C29	C28	110

Torsion Angles

C6	N1	C2	N3	−2		O13	C8	C9	O14	47		C23	N24	C25	O30	12
C6	N1	C2	O2	−178		O13	C8	C9	C10	−68		C23	N24	C25	C26	−105
C7	N1	C2	N3	178		C7	C8	C9	O14	154		C28	O30	C25	N24	−113
C7	N1	C2	O2	3		C7	C8	C9	C10	38		C28	O30	C25	C26	5
C2	N1	C6	C5	1		O14	C9	C10	O12	−162		C25	O30	C28	C27	21
C7	N1	C6	C5	−180		O14	C9	C10	C11	83		C25	O30	C28	C29	143
C2	N1	C7	O12	−161		C8	C9	C10	O12	−41		N18	C19	C20	N22	179
C2	N1	C7	C8	82		C8	C9	C10	C11	−156		N18	C19	C20	C21	−6
C6	N1	C7	O12	20		O12	C10	C11	O15	−75		N24	C19	C20	N22	2
C6	N1	C7	C8	−97		C9	C10	C11	O15	36		N24	C19	C20	C21	178
C4	N3	C2	N1	4								N22	C20	C21	N16	179
C4	N3	C2	O2	179		C21	N16	C17	N18	0		N22	C20	C21	N21	−4
C2	N3	C4	O4	179		C17	N16	C21	N21	−179		C19	C20	C21	N16	5
C2	N3	C4	C5	−3		C17	N16	C21	C20	−2		C19	C20	C21	N21	−178
C10	O12	C7	N1	−121		C19	N18	C17	N16	0		N24	C25	C26	O31	−155
C10	O12	C7	C8	−4		C17	N18	C19	N24	179		N24	C25	C26	C27	91
C7	O12	C10	C9	26		C17	N18	C19	C20	4		O30	C25	C26	O31	86
C7	O12	C10	C11	150		C23	N22	C20	C19	−2		O30	C25	C26	C27	−29
N3	C4	C5	Br1	−178		C23	N22	C20	C21	−176		O31	C26	C27	O32	45
N3	C4	C5	C6	2		C20	N22	C23	N24	1		O31	C26	C27	C28	−76
O4	C4	C5	Br1	0		C23	N24	C19	N18	−178		C25	C26	C27	O32	159
O4	C4	C5	C6	179		C23	N24	C19	C20	−2		C25	C26	C27	C28	38
Br1	C5	C6	N1	179		C25	N24	C19	N18	5		O32	C27	C28	O30	−160
C4	C5	C6	N1	−1		C25	N24	C19	C20	−179		O32	C27	C28	C29	84
N1	C7	C8	O13	−151		C19	N24	C23	N22	1		C26	C27	C28	O30	−37
N1	C7	C8	C9	95		C25	N24	C23	N22	178		C26	C27	C28	C29	−153
O12	C7	C8	O13	93		C19	N24	C25	O30	−171		O30	C28	C29	O33	−74
O12	C7	C8	C9	−21		C19	N24	C25	C26	71		C27	C28	C29	O33	41

47.9 Deoxyguanosine - 5 - bromodeoxycytidine complex $C_{10}H_{13}N_5O_4$, $C_9H_{12}BrN_3O_4$

A.E.V.Haschemeyer, H.M.Sobell, Acta Cryst., 19, 125, 1965

$P2_12_12_1$ Z = 4   R = 0.135

DGUBCY   LB 19-25-1

Bond Lengths

Br1	C5	1.90	C17	N16	1.40
C2	N1	1.37	C22	N16	1.37
C6	N1	1.44	C17	N18	1.35
C7	N1	1.50	C17	N19	1.38
C2	N3	1.33	C20	N19	1.35
C4	N3	1.35	C21	N24	1.34
C4	N4	1.29	C25	N24	1.29
C2	O2	1.35	C20	N26	1.45
C7	O12	1.44	C25	N26	1.43
C10	O12	1.52	C27	N26	1.43
C9	O13	1.42	C22	O23	1.25
C11	O14	1.37	C27	O32	1.42
C11	O15	1.39	C30	O32	1.47
C4	C5	1.47	C29	O33	1.49
C5	C6	1.34	C31	O34	1.43
C7	C8	1.49	C20	C21	1.32
C8	C9	1.56	C21	C22	1.50
C9	C10	1.52	C27	C28	1.43
C10	C11	1.64	C28	C29	1.47
			C29	C30	1.57
			C30	C31	1.57

Bond Angles

C2	N1	C6	121	C17	N16	C22	125
C2	N1	C7	120	C17	N19	C20	110
C6	N1	C7	119	C21	N24	C25	105
C2	N3	C4	122	C20	N26	C25	103
C7	O12	C10	109	C20	N26	C27	131
N1	C2	N3	122	C25	N26	C27	123
N1	C2	O2	116	C27	O32	C30	110
N3	C2	O2	121	N16	C17	N18	118
N3	C4	N4	117	N16	C17	N19	122
N3	C4	C5	115	N18	C17	N19	119
N4	C4	C5	128	N19	C20	N26	121
Br1	C5	C4	118	N19	C20	C21	135
Br1	C5	C6	117	N26	C20	C21	104
C4	C5	C6	125	N24	C21	C20	115
N1	C6	C5	114	N24	C21	C22	130
N1	C7	O12	106	C20	C21	C22	115
N1	C7	C8	111	N16	C22	O23	122
O12	C7	C8	106	N16	C22	C21	112
C7	C8	C9	102	O23	C22	C21	125
O13	C9	C8	107	N24	C25	N26	112
O13	C9	C10	108	N26	C27	O32	108
C8	C9	C10	105	N26	C27	C28	116
O12	C10	C9	104	O32	C27	C28	109
O12	C10	C11	105	C27	C28	C29	105
C9	C10	C11	111	O33	C29	C28	104
O14	C11	O15	123	O33	C29	C30	107
O14	C11	C10	110	C28	C29	C30	105
O15	C11	C10	88	O32	C30	C29	102
				O32	C30	C31	107
				C29	C30	C31	116
				O34	C31	C30	114

Torsion Angles

C6	N1	C2	N3	8	C7	C8	C9	C10	−32	C20	N26	C27	O32	57
C6	N1	C2	O2	−175	O13	C9	C10	O12	−98	C20	N26	C27	C28	−66
C7	N1	C2	N3	−179	O13	C9	C10	C11	149	C25	N26	C27	O32	−149
C7	N1	C2	O2	−3	C8	C9	C10	O12	16	C25	N26	C27	C28	89
C2	N1	C6	C5	−5	C8	C9	C10	C11	−97	C30	O32	C27	N26	−145
C7	N1	C6	C5	−177	O12	C10	C11	O14	−51	C30	O32	C27	C28	−18
C2	N1	C7	O12	−114	O12	C10	C11	O15	73	C27	O32	C30	C29	−2
C2	N1	C7	C8	131	C9	C10	C11	O14	61	C27	O32	C30	C31	120
C6	N1	C7	O12	59	C9	C10	C11	O15	−175	N19	C20	C21	N24	−177
C6	N1	C7	C8	−56						N19	C20	C21	C22	6
C4	N3	C2	N1	−8	C22	N16	C17	N18	−177	N26	C20	C21	N24	−1
C4	N3	C2	O2	176	C22	N16	C17	N19	−9	N26	C20	C21	C22	−178
C2	N3	C4	N4	180	C17	N16	C22	O23	178	N24	C21	C22	N16	177
C2	N3	C4	C5	4	C17	N16	C22	C21	9	N24	C21	C22	O23	9
C10	O12	C7	N1	−147	C20	N19	C17	N16	5	C20	C21	C22	N16	−7
C10	O12	C7	C8	−28	C20	N19	C17	N18	174	C20	C21	C22	O23	−175
C7	O12	C10	C9	7	C17	N19	C20	N26	179	N26	C27	C28	C29	153
C7	O12	C10	C11	124	C17	N19	C20	C21	−5	O32	C27	C28	C29	31
N3	C4	C5	Br1	−180	C25	N24	C21	C20	−2	C27	C28	C29	O33	81
N3	C4	C5	C6	−1	C25	N24	C21	C22	174	C27	C28	C29	C30	−31
N4	C4	C5	Br1	5	C21	N24	C25	N26	5	O33	C29	C30	O32	−90
N4	C4	C5	C6	−176	C25	N26	C20	N19	−179	O33	C29	C30	C31	153
Br1	C5	C6	N1	−180	C25	N26	C20	C21	4	C28	C29	C30	O32	20
C4	C5	C6	N1	1	C27	N26	C20	N19	−21	C28	C29	C30	C31	−96
N1	C7	C8	C9	152	C27	N26	C20	C21	162	O32	C30	C31	O34	−71
O12	C7	C8	C9	37	C20	N26	C25	N24	−6	C29	C30	C31	O34	43
C7	C8	C9	O13	83	C27	N26	C25	N24	−166					

47.10   Adenosine - 5' - phosphate monohydrate

$C_{10}H_{14}N_5O_7P$, H_2O

J.Kraut, L.H.Jensen, Acta Cryst., 16, 79, 1963

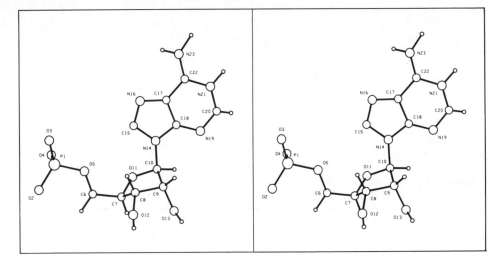

P2$_1$ Z = 2   R = 0.068

ADPOSM   LB 10-14-33

Bond Lengths

P1	O2	1.51	C22	N23	1.31
P1	O3	1.50	C6	O5	1.47
P1	O4	1.57	C7	O11	1.48
P1	O5	1.61	C10	O11	1.44
C10	N14	1.49	C8	O12	1.40
C15	N14	1.40	C9	O13	1.44
C18	N14	1.38	C6	C7	1.53
C15	N16	1.33	C7	C8	1.52
C17	N16	1.36	C8	C9	1.54
C18	N19	1.34	C9	C10	1.51
C20	N19	1.31	C17	C18	1.40
C20	N21	1.37	C17	C22	1.45
C22	N21	1.36			

Bond Angles

O2	P1	O3	118	C7	O11	C10	108	O11	C10	C9	107
O2	P1	O4	110	O5	C6	C7	108	N14	C15	N16	112
O2	P1	O5	109	O11	C7	C6	108	N16	C17	C18	112
O3	P1	O4	107	O11	C7	C8	104	N16	C17	C22	132
O3	P1	O5	106	C6	C7	C8	119	C18	C17	C22	116
O4	P1	O5	106	O12	C8	C7	116	N14	C18	N19	127
C10	N14	C15	129	O12	C8	C9	115	N14	C18	C17	104
C10	N14	C18	124	C7	C8	C9	100	N19	C18	C17	128
C15	N14	C18	107	O13	C9	C8	110	N19	C20	N21	126
C18	N19	C20	112	O13	C9	C10	107	N21	C22	N23	122
C20	N21	C22	123	C8	C9	C10	102	N21	C22	C17	115
P1	O5	C6	115	N14	C10	O11	107	N23	C22	C17	124
				N14	C10	C9	113				

Torsion Angles

O2	P1	O5	C6	50
O3	P1	O5	C6	177
O4	P1	O5	C6	−69
P1	O5	C6	C7	177
C10	O11	C7	C6	150
C10	O11	C7	C8	23
C7	O11	C10	C9	5
O5	C6	C7	O11	−78
O5	C6	C7	C8	40
O11	C7	C8	C9	−40
C6	C7	C8	C9	−160
C7	C8	C9	C10	42
C8	C9	C10	O11	−30
C15	N14	C10	O11	26

48.1 β - Glycine

C₂H₅NO₂

Y.Iitaka, Acta Cryst., 13, 35, 1960

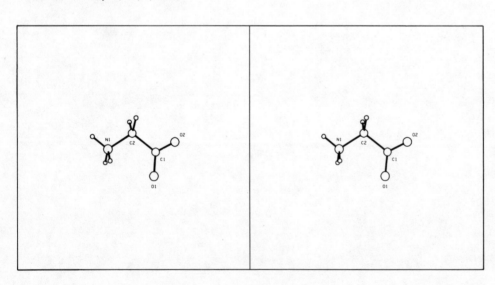

$$H_2N-CH_2-COOH$$

P2₁   Z = 2   R$_{hol}$ = 0.046,
R$_{0kl}$ = 0.043

GLYCIN   LB 2-5-16

Bond Lengths			*Bond Angles*			
C2	N1	1.48	O1	C1	O2	126
C1	O1	1.23	O1	C1	C2	118
C1	O2	1.25	O2	C1	C2	116
C1	C2	1.52	N1	C2	C1	111

Torsion Angles

O1	C1	C2	N1	27
O2	C1	C2	N1	−156

48.2 γ - Glycine

C₂H₅NO₂

Y.Iitaka, Acta Cryst., 14, 1, 1961

$$H_2N-CH_2-COOH$$

See also Marsh, Acta Cryst., 11,
654, 1958.
P3₂   Z = 3   R = 0.108

GLYCIN01   LB 2-5-14

Bond Lengths			*Bond Angles*			
C2	N1	1.49	O1	C1	O2	125
C1	O1	1.25	O1	C1	C2	118
C1	O2	1.24	O2	C1	C2	116
C1	C2	1.53	N1	C2	C1	111

Torsion Angles

O1	C1	C2	N1	−15
O2	C1	C2	N1	168

48.3   Diglycine hydrochloride

$C_2H_5NO_2$, $C_2H_6NO_2{}^+$, Cl^-

T.Hahn, Z. Kristallogr., 113, 26, 1960

$2\ H_2N-CH_2-COOH \cdot HCl$

$P2_12_12_1$ Z = 4   R = 0.13

DGLYHC   LB 4-11-4

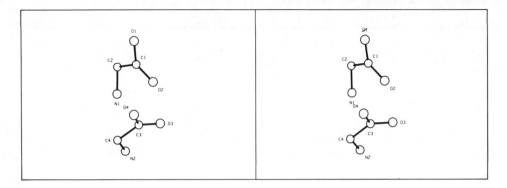

Bond Lengths

C2	N1	1.49	C4	N2	1.50
C1	O1	1.31	C3	O3	1.27
C1	O2	1.22	C3	O4	1.26
C1	C2	1.51	C3	C4	1.50

Bond Angles

O1	C1	O2	125	O3	C3	O4	126
O1	C1	C2	113	O3	C3	C4	117
O2	C1	C2	122	O4	C3	C4	117
N1	C2	C1	110	N2	C4	C3	114

Torsion Angles

O1	C1	C2	N1	−167	O3	C3	C4	N2	1
O2	C1	C2	N1	16	O4	C3	C4	N2	−177

48.4   Taurine

$C_2H_7NO_3S$

β - Alanine sulphonic acid
H.H.Sutherland, D.W.Young, Acta Cryst., 16, 897, 1963

$H_2N-CH_2-CH_2-SO_3H$

See also Okaya, Acta Cryst., 21, 726, 1966.
$P2_1/c$ Z = 4   R = 0.11

TAURIN   LB 2-7-11

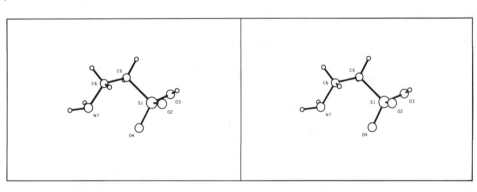

Bond Lengths

S1	O2	1.48	S1	C5	1.81
S1	O3	1.45	C6	N7	1.50
S1	O4	1.46	C5	C6	1.51

Bond Angles

O2	S1	O3	114	O3	S1	C5	107
O2	S1	O4	111	O4	S1	C5	106
O2	S1	C5	106	S1	C5	C6	112
O3	S1	O4	112	N7	C6	C5	113

Torsion Angles

O2	S1	C5	C6	−58
O3	S1	C5	C6	−180
O4	S1	C5	C6	60
S1	C5	C6	N7	−70

48.5 β - Alanine

$C_3H_7NO_2$

P.Jose, L.M.Pant, Acta Cryst., 18, 806, 1965

$H_2N-CH_2-CH_2-COOH$

Pbca   Z = 8   R = 0.157

BALNIN   LB 3-7-17

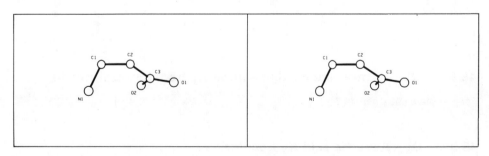

Bond Lengths

C1	N1	1.48
C3	O1	1.29
C3	O2	1.29
C1	C2	1.55
C2	C3	1.55

Bond Angles

N1	C1	C2	108
C1	C2	C3	115
O1	C3	O2	127
O1	C3	C2	116
O2	C3	C2	117

Torsion Angles

N1	C1	C2	C3	84
C1	C2	C3	O1	−170
C1	C2	C3	O2	8

48.6 N - Acetyl glycine (refinement of structure of Carpenter and Donohue, J. Amer. Chem. Soc., 72,2315,1950)

$C_4H_7NO_3$

J.Donohue, R.E.Marsh, Acta Cryst., 15, 941, 1962

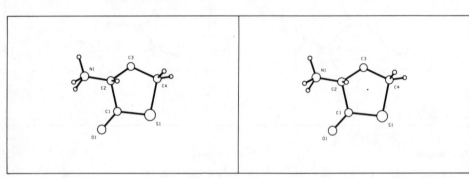

The methyl hydrogen atoms are disordered.
See also Mackay & Mathieson, Tetrahedron Letters, 5069, 1969; Peterson et al., Acta Cryst., 10, 844, 1957.
$P2_1/c$ Z = 4   R = 0.065

ACYGLY   LB 4-7-10

Bond Lengths					Bond Angles					Torsion Angles				
C2	N1	1.44	C3 O3	1.24	C2	N1	C3	120	N1 C2 C1 110	C3	N1	C2	C1	−178
C3	N1	1.33	C1 C2	1.51	O1	C1	O2	125	N1 C3 O3 120	C2	N1	C3	O3	1
C1	O1	1.31	C3 C4	1.49	O1	C1	C2	111	N1 C3 C4 118	C2	N1	C3	C4	−178
C1	O2	1.20			O2	C1	C2	124	O3 C3 C4 122	O1	C1	C2	N1	−177
										O2	C1	C2	N1	4

48.7 DL - Homocysteine thiolactone hydrochloride

$C_4H_8NOS^+$, Cl^-

(i)   S.T.Freer, J.Kraut, Acta Cryst., 19, 992, 1965 (form i)

(ii) S.T.Freer, J.Kraut, Acta Cryst., 19, 992, 1965 (form ii)

(i)
$Pbc2_1$ Z = 4   R = 0.042

HOCYSL   LB 4-8-16

(ii)
Pbca   Z = 8   R = 0.049

HOCYSL01   LB 4-8-17

A third form, a hybrid of forms I and II, was also observed and refined to R = 0.09.

Bond Lengths				Bond Angles					Torsion Angles					
		(i)	(ii)				(i)	(ii)					(i)	(ii)
S1	C1	1.74	1.76	C1	S1	C4	96	94	C4	S1	C1	O1	176	178
S1	C4	1.84	1.81	S1	C1	O1	126	125	C4	S1	C1	C2	−1	−3
C2	N1	1.49	1.49	S1	C1	C2	109	109	C1	S1	C4	C3	−25	−22
C1	O1	1.20	1.20	O1	C1	C2	124	126	S1	C1	C2	N1	148	151
C1	C2	1.56	1.53	N1	C2	C1	109	110	S1	C1	C2	C3	27	27
C2	C3	1.52	1.52	N1	C2	C3	113	114	O1	C1	C2	N1	−29	−29
C3	C4	1.55	1.52	C1	C2	C3	105	107	O1	C1	C2	C3	−150	−153
				C2	C3	C4	107	106	N1	C2	C3	C4	−165	−165
				S1	C4	C3	102	106	C1	C2	C3	C4	−46	−44
									C2	C3	C4	S1	44	41

48.8 DL - Homocysteine thiolactone hydrochloride (form ii)

$C_4H_8NOS^+$, Cl^-

For complete entry see 48.7

48.9 DL - Aspartic acid hydrochloride

$C_4H_8NO_4^+$, Cl^-

B.Dawson, Acta Cryst., 13, 1034, 1960

$$HOOC-CH_2-CH-COOH \cdot HCl$$
$$|$$
$$NH_2$$

Atomic coordinates were not given but bond lengths were reported.
$P2_1/a$ Z = 4 $R_{h0l} = 0.045$, $R_{0kl} = 0.065$, $R_{h1l} = 0.057$

ASPART   LB 4-8-20

48.10   L - Asparagine monohydrate

$C_4H_8N_2O_3$, H_2O

G.Kartha, A.de Vries, Nature, 192, 862, 1961

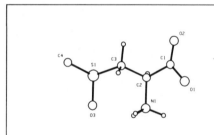

```
      COOH
       |
 H₂NCH            · H₂O
       |
      CH₂
       |
      CONH₂
```

The headings of the orthogonal coordinate table should read x, y, z, not y, z, x, Published value of C1 - O2 = 1.34A. The correct value is 1.24A (private communication).
$P2_12_12_1$ Z = 4   R = 0.074·

ASPARM   LB 4-8-68

Bond Lengths

C2	N1	1.50	C4	O3	1.24
C4	N2	1.33	C1	C2	1.54
C1	O1	1.26	C2	C3	1.51
C1	O2	1.25	C3	C4	1.53

Bond Angles

O1	C1	O2	126	C1	C2	C3	115
O1	C1	C2	116	C2	C3	C4	113
O2	C1	C2	118	N2	C4	O3	123
N1	C2	C1	110	N2	C4	C3	116
N1	C2	C3	111	O3	C4	C3	121

Torsion Angles

O1	C1	C2	N1	−174	N1	C2	C3	C4	73
O1	C1	C2	C3	−48	C1	C2	C3	C4	−53
O2	C1	C2	N1	11	N1	C2	C3	C4	−177
O2	C1	C2	C3	137	C2	C3	C4	O3	3

48.11   (+) - S - Methyl - L - cysteine sulfoxide (absolute configuration)

$C_4H_9NO_3S$

R.Hine, Acta Cryst., 15, 635, 1962

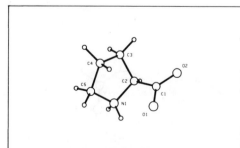

$$H_3C-SO-CH_2-CH-COOH$$
$$|$$
$$NH_2$$

$P2_12_12_1$ Z = 4   R = 0.128

SMECYO   LB 4-9-16

Bond Lengths

S1	O3	1.49	C1	O1	1.24
S1	C3	1.83	C1	O2	1.22
S1	C4	1.81	C1	C2	1.57
C2	N1	1.52	C2	C3	1.49

Bond Angles

O3	S1	C3	104	O2	C1	C2	114
O3	S1	C4	107	N1	C2	C1	111
C3	S1	C4	97	N1	C2	C3	109
O1	C1	O2	131	C1	C2	C3	110
O1	C1	C2	115	S1	C3	C2	115

Torsion Angles

O3	S1	C3	C2	59	O2	C1	C2	N1	170
C4	S1	C3	C2	169	O2	C1	C2	C3	−69
O1	C1	C2	N1	−3	N1	C2	C3	S1	−65
O1	C1	C2	C3	117	C1	C2	C3	S1	173

48.12   L - Proline

$C_5H_9NO_2$

R.L.Kayushina, B.K.Vainshtein, Kristallografija, 10, 833, 1965

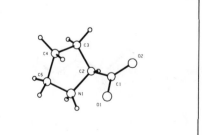

```
      COOH
   N
   H
```

$P2_12_12_1$ Z = 4   R = 0.169

PROLIN   LB 5-9-9

Bond Lengths

C2	N1	1.53	C1	C2	1.53
C5	N1	1.48	C2	C3	1.52
C1	O1	1.28	C3	C4	1.54
C1	O2	1.26	C4	C5	1.53

Bond Angles

C2	N1	C5	107	N1	C2	C3	106
O1	C1	O2	120	C1	C2	C3	112
O1	C1	C2	119	C2	C3	C4	101
O2	C1	C2	121	C3	C4	C5	104
N1	C2	C1	106	N1	C5	C4	105

Torsion Angles

C5	N1	C2	C1	105	O2	C1	C2	C3	−74
C5	N1	C2	C3	−14	N1	C2	C3	C4	34
C2	N1	C5	C4	−12	C1	C2	C3	C4	−82
O1	C1	C2	N1	−7	C2	C3	C4	C5	−41
O1	C1	C2	C3	109	C3	C4	C5	N1	34
O2	C1	C2	N1	171				

48.13   Cucurbitine perchlorate (absolute configuration) $C_5H_{11}N_2O_2^+$, ClO_4^-

Hai-Fu Fan, Cheng-Chung Lin, Acta Phys. Sinica, 21, 253, 1965

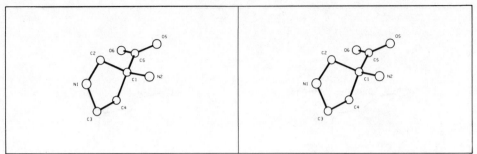

Published values of Cl1 - O2 = 1.48A and Cl2 - O3 = 1.44A are incorrect. The correct values are 1.44 and 1.48A respectively.
$P2_1$ Z = 2   R = 0.26

CRCURB   LB 5-11-9

Bond Lengths						Bond Angles							Torsion Angles								
Cl1	O1	1.43	C1	N2	1.53	O1	Cl1	O2	112	N2	C1	C5	114	C3	N1	C2	C1	−25	N2	C1	C5	O5	−2
Cl1	O2	1.44	C5	O5	1.23	O1	Cl1	O3	114	C2	C1	C4	98	C2	N1	C3	C4	−1	N2	C1	C5	O6	176
Cl1	O3	1.48	C5	O6	1.18	O1	Cl1	O4	108	C2	C1	C5	106	N2	C1	C2	N1	−75	C2	C1	C5	O5	124
Cl1	O4	1.46	C1	C2	1.56	O2	Cl1	O3	108	C4	C1	C5	115	C4	C1	C2	N1	39	C2	C1	C5	O6	−58
			C1	C4	1.54	O2	Cl1	O4	112	N1	C2	C1	106	C5	C1	C2	N1	159	C4	C1	C5	O5	−129
C2	N1	1.49	C1	C5	1.58	O3	Cl1	O4	102	N1	C3	C4	102	N2	C1	C4	C3	77	C4	C1	C5	O6	49
C3	N1	1.53	C3	C4	1.55					C1	C4	C3	107	C2	C1	C4	C3	−41	N1	C3	C4	C1	28
						C2	N1	C3	109	O5	C5	O6	127	C5	C1	C4	C3	−153					
						N2	C1	C2	114	O5	C5	C1	113										
						N2	C1	C4	109	O6	C5	C1	120										

48.14   Betaine hydrobromide $C_5H_{12}NO_2^+$, Br^-

J.Clastre, C. R. Acad. Sci., Fr., 259, 3267, 1964

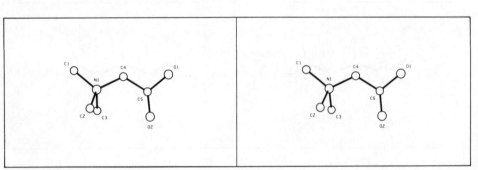

No comparison of bond lengths is possible since they are not reported in the paper.
$P2_1/c$ Z = 4 R_{proj} = 0.15

BETANB   LB 5-12-6

Bond Lengths						Bond Angles								Torsion Angles				
C1	N1	1.51	C5	O1	1.37	C1	N1	C2	98	C3	N1	C4	111	C1	N1	C4	C5	−176
C2	N1	1.70	C5	O2	1.24	C1	N1	C3	117	N1	C4	C5	124	C2	N1	C4	C5	76
C3	N1	1.60	C4	C5	1.45	C1	N1	C4	116	O1	C5	O2	122	C3	N1	C4	C5	−39
C4	N1	1.50				C2	N1	C3	106	O1	C5	C4	111	N1	C4	C5	O1	170
						C2	N1	C4	107	O2	C5	C4	125	N1	C4	C5	O2	−25

48.15   Betaine hydrochloride $C_5H_{12}NO_2^+$, Cl^-

J.Clastre, C. R. Acad. Sci., Fr., 259, 3267, 1964

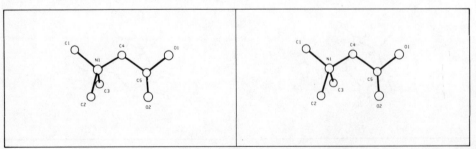

No comparison of bond lengths is possible since they are not reported in the paper.
See also Fischer et al., Acta Cryst. (B), 26, 1392, 1970.
$P2_1/c$ Z = 4 R_{proj} = 0.18

BETANC   LB 5-12-8

Bond Lengths						Bond Angles								Torsion Angles				
C1	N1	1.52	C5	O1	1.40	C1	N1	C2	108	C3	N1	C4	118	C1	N1	C4	C5	−179
C2	N1	1.64	C5	O2	1.17	C1	N1	C3	114	N1	C4	C5	113	C2	N1	C4	C5	64
C3	N1	1.60	C4	C5	1.50	C1	N1	C4	108	O1	C5	O2	123	C3	N1	C4	C5	−49
C4	N1	1.49				C2	N1	C3	100	O1	C5	C4	108	N1	C4	C5	O1	169
						C2	N1	C4	109	O2	C5	C4	129	N1	C4	C5	O2	−19

48.16 L - Histidine hydrochloride monohydrate (refinement of structure of Donohue et al., Acta Cryst., 9,655,1956)

$C_6H_{10}N_3O_2{}^+$, Cl^- , H_2O

J.Donohue, A.Caron, Acta Cryst., 17, 1178, 1964

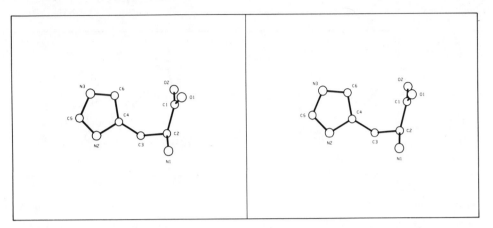

$P2_12_12_1$ $Z = 4$ $R = 0.076$

HISTCM   LB 6-10-14

Bond Lengths

C2	N1	1.50		C1	O2	1.26
C4	N2	1.39		C1	C2	1.53
C5	N2	1.32		C2	C3	1.53
C5	N3	1.31		C3	C4	1.51
C6	N3	1.36		C4	C6	1.36
C1	O1	1.24				

Bond Angles

C4	N2	C5	109		C1	C2	C3	113
C5	N3	C6	110		C2	C3	C4	115
O1	C1	O2	126		N2	C4	C3	122
O1	C1	C2	120		N2	C4	C6	106
O2	C1	C2	114		C3	C4	C6	132
N1	C2	C1	109		N2	C5	N3	109
N1	C2	C3	111		N3	C6	C4	107

Torsion Angles

C5	N2	C4	C3	−179		O2	C1	C2	C3	−56
C5	N2	C4	C6	0		N1	C2	C3	C4	72
C4	N2	C5	N3	−1		C1	C2	C3	C4	−52
C6	N3	C5	N2	2		C2	C3	C4	N2	−121
C5	N3	C6	C4	−2		C2	C3	C4	C6	61
O1	C1	C2	N1	0		N2	C4	C6	N3	1
O1	C1	C2	C3	125		C3	C4	C6	N3	180
O2	C1	C2	N1	180					

L - Cystine dihydrobromide

$C_6H_{14}N_2O_4S_2{}^{2+}$, $2Br^-$

For complete entry see 48.18

48.18 L - Cystine dihydrobromide

$C_6H_{14}N_2O_4S_2{}^{2+}$, $2Br^-$

(i) J.Peterson, L.K.Steinrauf, L.H.Jensen, Acta Cryst., 13, 104, 1960

(ii) N.Ananthakrishnan, R.Srinivasan, Indian J. Pure Appl. Phys., 2, 62, 1964

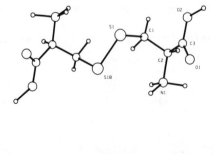

(i)

Also reported by Ananthrakrishnan and Srinivasan, Indian J. Pure Appl. Phys., 2, 62, 1964, who used an alternative method of solution. They obtained an identical structure which, however, was only refined to R(h0l) = 0.164,   R(hk0) = 0.182. Also the hydrogen atoms were not located.
$P2_122_1$ $Z = 2$ $R_{h0l} = 0.071$,
$R_{hk0} = 0.071$

CYSTBR01   LB 6-14-8

(ii)

No comparison of bond lengths is possible since they are not reported in the paper.
$P2_122_1$ $Z = 2$ $R_{h0l} = 0.164$,
$R_{hk0} = 0.182$

CYSTBR   LB 6-14-8

Bond Lengths

S1	S1B	2.02
S1	C1	1.86
C2	N1	1.49
C3	O1	1.21
C3	O2	1.27
C1	C2	1.50
C2	C3	1.51

Bond Angles

S1	C1	C2	112
N1	C2	C1	115
N1	C2	C3	108
C1	C2	C3	114
O1	C3	O2	124
O1	C3	C2	122
O2	C3	C2	114

Torsion Angles

C1	S1	S1B	C1B	−81
S1B	S1	C1	C2	−89
S1	C1	C2	N1	71
S1	C1	C2	C3	−55
N1	C2	C3	O1	1
N1	C2	C3	O2	−179
C1	C2	C3	O1	129
C1	C2	C3	O2	−51

48.19   L - Arginine dihydrate

I.L.Karle, J.Karle, Acta Cryst., 17, 835, 1964

$C_6H_{14}N_4O_2$, $2H_2O$

$$^+(H_2N)_2-C-NH-(CH_2)_3-CH-COO^- \cdot 2H_2O$$
$$|$$
$$NH_2$$

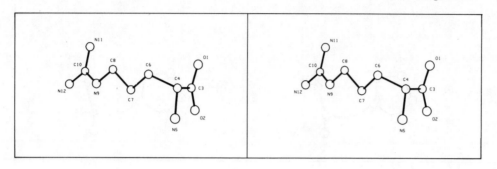

$P2_12_12_1$ $Z = 8$ $R = 0.103$

ARGIND   LB 6-14-27

Bond Lengths

C4	N5	1.48	C3	O2	1.25	
C8	N9	1.47	C3	C4	1.55	
C10	N9	1.35	C4	C6	1.54	
C10	N11	1.34	C6	C7	1.54	
C10	N12	1.32	C7	C8	1.52	
C3	O1	1.26				

Bond Angles

C8	N9	C10	123	C4	C6	C7	114
O1	C3	O2	126	C6	C7	C8	110
O1	C3	C4	115	N9	C8	C7	111
O2	C3	C4	119	N9	C10	N11	121
N5	C4	C3	111	N9	C10	N12	119
N5	C4	C6	111	N11	C10	N12	120
C3	C4	C6	108				

Torsion Angles

C10	N9	C8	C7	−162	O2	C3	C4	C6	−111
C8	N9	C10	N11	8	N5	C4	C6	C7	−62
C8	N9	C10	N12	−172	C3	C4	C6	C7	60
O1	C3	C4	N5	−168	C4	C6	C7	C8	−151
O1	C3	C4	C6	70	C6	C7	C8	N9	−175
O2	C3	C4	N5	11					

48.20   L - Lysine monohydrochloride dihydrate

D.A.Wright, R.E.Marsh, Acta Cryst., 15, 54, 1962

$C_6H_{15}N_2O_2{}^+$, Cl^- , $2H_2O$

$$H_2N-(CH_2)_4-CH-COOH \cdot HCl \cdot 2H_2O$$
$$|$$
$$NH_2$$

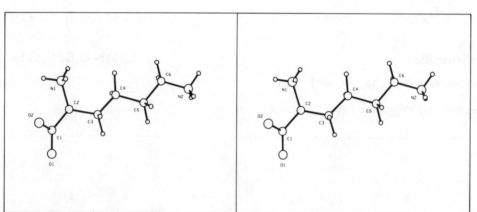

$P2_1$ $Z = 2$ $R = 0.057$

LYSCLH   LB 6-15-5

Bond Lengths

C2	N1	1.48	C2	C3	1.52
C6	N2	1.48	C3	C4	1.52
C1	O1	1.25	C4	C5	1.53
C1	O2	1.25	C5	C6	1.52
C1	C2	1.53			

Bond Angles

O1	C1	O2	125	C1	C2	C3	110
O1	C1	C2	117	C2	C3	C4	115
O2	C1	C2	118	C3	C4	C5	111
N1	C2	C1	110	C4	C5	C6	112
N1	C2	C3	112	N2	C6	C5	111

Torsion Angles

O1	C1	C2	N1	162	C1	C2	C3	C4	−178
O1	C1	C2	C3	−75	C2	C3	C4	C5	−176
O2	C1	C2	N1	−20	C3	C4	C5	C6	−171
O2	C1	C2	C3	103	C4	C5	C6	N2	179
N1	C2	C3	C4	−56					

48.21   L - Phenylalanine hydrochloride

G.V.Gurskaya, B.K.Vainshtein, Kristallografija, 8, 368, 1963

$C_9H_{12}NO_2{}^+$, Cl^-

Atomic coordinates were not reported in the paper. The paper describes the method of obtaining single crystals and the structure solution. For definitive entry see 48.22.

$P2_12_12_1$ $Z = 4$ $R_{hk0} = 0.15$,
$R_{h0l} = 0.20$

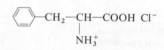

PHALNC   LB 9-12-4

48.22 L - Phenylalanine hydrochloride (refinement) $C_9H_{12}NO_2^+$, Cl^-

G.V.Gurskaya, Kristallografija, 9, 839, 1964

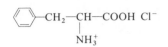

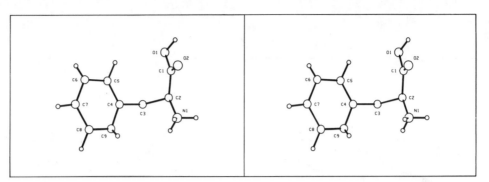

$P2_12_12_1$ Z = 4 R = 0.138

PHALNC01 LB 9-12-4

Bond Lengths

C2	N1	1.48	C4	C9	1.36
C1	O1	1.34	C5	C6	1.38
C1	O2	1.16	C6	C7	1.38
C1	C2	1.50	C7	C8	1.43
C2	C3	1.55			(1.37)
C3	C4	1.57	C8	C9	1.38
C4	C5	1.36			

Bond Angles

O1	C1	O2	124	C1	C2	C3	116	C4	C5	C6	122
O1	C1	C2	109	C2	C3	C4	113	C5	C6	C7	118
O2	C1	C2	127	C3	C4	C5	121	C6	C7	C8	119
N1	C2	C1	106	C3	C4	C9	118	C7	C8	C9	121
N1	C2	C3	112	C5	C4	C9	121	C4	C9	C8	118

Torsion Angles

C9	C4	C5	C6	−2
C5	C4	C9	C8	1
C4	C5	C6	C7	2
C5	C6	C7	C8	−2
C6	C7	C8	C9	1
C7	C8	C9	C4	0
C9	C4	C3	C2	−98

48.23 Cyclo(hexaglycyl) hemihydrate $C_{12}H_{18}N_6O_6$, $0.5H_2O$

I.L.Karle, J.Karle, Acta Cryst., 16, 969, 1963

The structure is totally disordered.
P-1 Z = 2 R = 0.182

CYHEXG LB 12-18-36

$$HN-CH_2-CO-NH-CH_2-CO-NH-CH_2-CO$$
$$CO-CH_2-NH-CO-CH_2-NH-CO-CH_2-NH$$
$$.0 \cdot 5\,H_2O$$

48.24 DL - Glycyl - phenylalanyl - glycine hemihydrate $C_{13}H_{17}N_3O_4$, $0.5H_2O$

R.E.Marsh, J.P.Glusker, Acta Cryst., 14, 1110, 1961

$$H_2N-CH_2-CO-NH-CH-CO-NH-CH_2-COOH \ .0 \cdot 5\,H_2O$$
$$CH_2$$

The water molecules are disordered.
$P2_12_12_1$ Z = 4 R = 0.126

GPAGLM LB 13-17-3

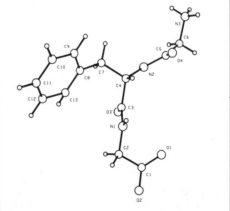

Bond Lengths

C2	N1	1.46
C3	N1	1.34
C4	N2	1.46
C5	N2	1.39
C6	N3	1.46
C1	O1	1.25
C1	O2	1.26
C3	O3	1.23
C5	O4	1.21
C1	C2	1.48
C3	C4	1.55
C4	C7	1.52
C5	C6	1.53
C7	C8	1.50
C8	C9	1.35
C8	C13	1.37
C9	C10	1.42
C10	C11	1.36
C11	C12	1.35
C12	C13	1.44

Bond Angles

C2	N1	C3	120	N2	C4	C3	107	C7	C8	C13	122
C4	N2	C5	118	N2	C4	C7	107	C9	C8	C13	119
O1	C1	O2	122	C3	C4	C7	109	C8	C9	C10	122
O1	C1	C2	120	N2	C5	O4	126	C9	C10	C11	119
O2	C1	C2	117	N2	C5	C6	110	C10	C11	C12	120
N1	C2	C1	115	O4	C5	C6	123	C11	C12	C13	121
N1	C3	O3	124	N3	C6	C5	110	C8	C13	C12	119
N1	C3	C4	114	C4	C7	C8	115				
O3	C3	C4	122	C7	C8	C9	119				

Torsion Angles

C3	N1	C2	C1	84	O2	C1	C2	N1	179
C2	N1	C3	O3	−3	N1	C3	C4	N2	132
C2	N1	C3	C4	180	N1	C3	C4	C7	−112
C5	N2	C4	C3	−126	O3	C3	C4	N2	−46
C5	N2	C4	C7	117	O3	C3	C4	C7	70
C4	N2	C5	O4	−1	N2	C5	C6	N3	128
C4	N2	C5	C6	−175	O4	C5	C6	N3	−47
O1	C1	C2	N1	−5	C9	C8	C7	C4	102

48.25   Tosyl - L - prolyl - L - hydroxyproline monohydrate $C_{17}H_{22}N_2O_6S$, H_2O

J.Fridrichsons, A.McL.Mathieson, Acta Cryst., 15, 569, 1962

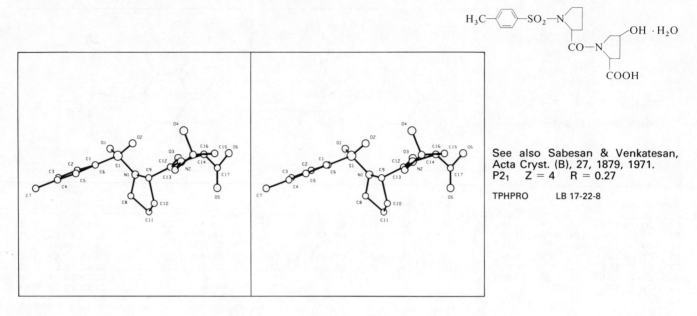

See also Sabesan & Venkatesan,
Acta Cryst. (B), 27, 1879, 1971.
$P2_1$ Z = 4   R = 0.27

TPHPRO   LB 17-22-8

Bond Lengths

S1	N1	1.60	C1	C6	1.38
S1	O1	1.34	C2	C3	1.40
S1	O2	1.39	C3	C4	1.41
S1	C1	1.78	C4	C5	1.37
C8	N1	1.49	C4	C7	1.54
C9	N1	1.50	C5	C6	1.42
C12	N2	1.33	C8	C11	1.56
C13	N2	1.43	C9	C10	1.55
C16	N2	1.44	C9	C12	1.50
C12	O3	1.25	C10	C11	1.56
C14	O4	1.43	C13	C14	1.54
C17	O5	1.19	C14	C15	1.55
C17	O6	1.41	C15	C16	1.53
C1	C2	1.38	C16	C17	1.53

Bond Angles

N1	S1	O1	119	N1	C8	C11	108
N1	S1	O2	86	N1	C9	C10	99
N1	S1	C1	110	N1	C9	C12	110
O1	S1	O2	121	C10	C9	C12	101
O1	S1	C1	106	C9	C10	C11	115
O2	S1	C1	115	C8	C11	C10	95
S1	N1	C8	121	N2	C12	O3	113
S1	N1	C9	116	N2	C12	C9	111
C8	N1	C9	111	O3	C12	C9	133
C12	N2	C13	125	N2	C13	C14	98
C12	N2	C16	115	O4	C14	C13	109
C13	N2	C16	116	O4	C14	C15	109
S1	C1	C2	118	C13	C14	C15	106
S1	C1	C6	120	C14	C15	C16	103
C2	C1	C6	122	N2	C16	C15	104
C1	C2	C3	119	N2	C16	C17	118
C2	C3	C4	120	C15	C16	C17	114
C3	C4	C5	120	O5	C17	O6	125
C3	C4	C7	122	O5	C17	C16	123
C5	C4	C7	118	O6	C17	C16	112
C4	C5	C6	121				
C1	C6	C5	118				

Torsion Angles

S1	N1	C8	C11	−170	N1	C8	C11	C10	32
C9	N1	C8	C11	−29	N1	C9	C10	C11	14
S1	N1	C9	C10	152	C12	C9	C10	C11	−98
S1	N1	C9	C12	−102	N1	C9	C12	N2	157
C8	N1	C9	C10	9	N1	C9	C12	O3	−5
C8	N1	C9	C12	115	C10	C9	C12	N2	−99
C13	N2	C12	O3	179	C10	C9	C12	O3	99
C13	N2	C12	C9	13	C9	C10	C11	C8	−29
C16	N2	C12	O3	−23	N2	C13	C14	O4	83
C16	N2	C12	C9	171	N2	C13	C14	C15	−35
C12	N2	C13	C14	−174	O4	C14	C15	C16	−87
C16	N2	C13	C14	28	C13	C14	C15	C16	31
C12	N2	C16	C15	−170	C14	C15	C16	N2	−14
C12	N2	C16	C17	−42	C14	C15	C16	C17	−143
C13	N2	C16	C15	−10	C2	C1	S1	N1	−107
C13	N2	C16	C17	118	C1	S1	N1	C9	−76

49.1 Porphine

$C_{20}H_{14}N_4$

L.E.Webb, E.B.Fleischer, J. Chem. Phys., 43, 3100, 1965

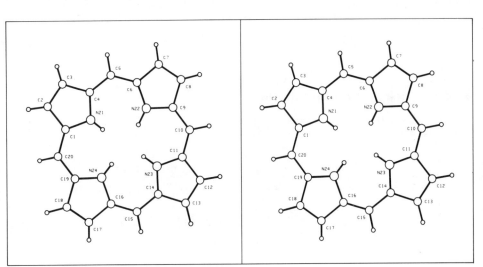

The two hydrogen atoms attached to the nitrogens were treated as four half - atoms. They can be considered to be statistically disordered or involved in the rapid interconversion of N - H tautomers.
$P2_1/a$ Z = 4 R = 0.049

PORPIN   LB 20-14-3

Bond Lengths

C1	N21	1.36	C6	C7	1.44
C4	N21	1.37	C7	C8	1.34
C6	N22	1.37	C8	C9	1.44
C9	N22	1.36	C9	C10	1.39
C11	N23	1.36	C10	C11	1.38
C14	N23	1.37	C11	C12	1.45
C16	N24	1.37	C12	C13	1.34
C19	N24	1.37	C13	C14	1.45
C1	C2	1.44	C14	C15	1.38
C1	C20	1.39	C15	C16	1.38
C2	C3	1.34	C16	C17	1.44
C3	C4	1.45	C17	C18	1.34
C4	C5	1.38	C18	C19	1.44
C5	C6	1.39	C19	C20	1.39

Bond Angles

C1	N21	C4	107	N22	C6	C7	108	N23	C14	C15	125
C6	N22	C9	109	C5	C6	C7	126	C13	C14	C15	126
C11	N23	C14	108	C6	C7	C8	108	C14	C15	C16	127
C16	N24	C19	108	C7	C8	C9	108	N24	C16	C15	126
N21	C1	C2	110	N22	C9	C8	108	N24	C16	C17	108
N21	C1	C20	125	N22	C9	C10	126	C15	C16	C17	126
C2	C1	C20	125	C8	C9	C10	126	C16	C17	C18	108
C1	C2	C3	107	C9	C10	C11	127	C17	C18	C19	107
C2	C3	C4	107	N23	C11	C10	125	N24	C19	C18	109
N21	C4	C3	109	N23	C11	C12	109	N24	C19	C20	125
N21	C4	C5	126	C10	C11	C12	126	C18	C19	C20	126
C3	C4	C5	126	C11	C12	C13	108	C1	C20	C19	126
C4	C5	C6	127	C12	C13	C14	107				
N22	C6	C5	126	N23	C14	C13	109				

49.2 Nickel(ii) 1,8,8,13,13 - pentamethyl - 5 - cyano - trans - corrin chloride water - methanol solvate

$C_{25}H_{30}N_5Ni^+$, Cl^- , xH_2O , yCH_4O

J.D.Dunitz, E.F.Mayer, Proc. R. Soc., A, 288, 324, 1965

Atomic coordinates were not given but bond lengths were reported.
P-1 Z = 2 R = 0.16

NIPCOR   LB 25-30-4

49.3 pseudo - Corrin bromide ethyl acetate - methanol solvate

$C_{30}H_{41}CoN_7O^+$, Br^- , $xC_4H_8O_2$, yCH_4O

B.Kamenar, B.F.Hoskins, C.K.Prout, Proc. R. Soc., A, 288, 331, 1965

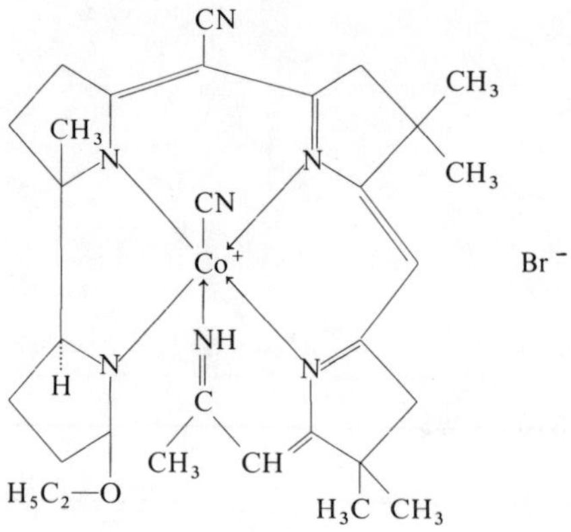

Atomic coordinates were not reported in the paper.
P2$_1$/n   Z = 4   No R factor was given.

PSCORB   LB 30-40-1

49.4 Nickel(ii) etioporphyrin - I

$C_{32}H_{36}N_4Ni$

1,3,5,7 - Tetramethyl - 2,4,6,8 - tetraethyl porphine
E.B.Fleischer, J. Amer. Chem. Soc., 85, 146, 1963

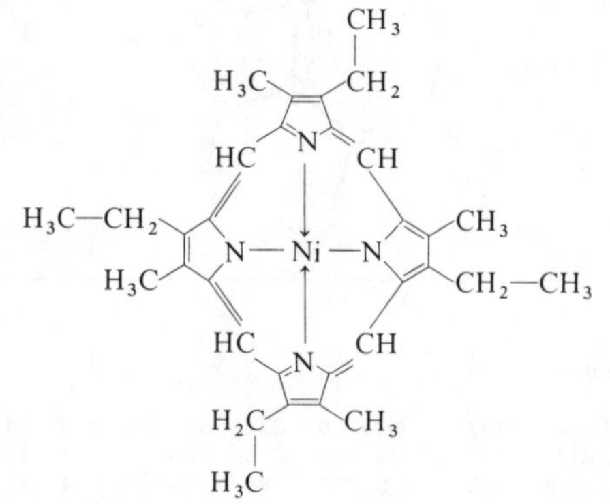

The molecule has statistical symmetry −4m2 with the ethyl groups statistically distributed between two enantiomorphic configurations.
I4$_1$/amd   Z = 4   R = 0.074

NIEPOR   LB 32-36-4

Bond Lengths			Bond Angles			
Ni1	N2	1.96	N2	Ni1	N2D	176
C5	N2	1.40	N2	Ni1	N2R	90
C3	C5	1.41	Ni1	N2	C5	128
C5	C6	1.43	C5	N2	C5A	105
C6	C7	1.55	C5	C3	C5R	118
C6	C6A	1.33	N2	C5	C3	128
			N2	C5	C6	110
			C3	C5	C6	122
			C5	C6	C7	124
			C5	C6	C6A	108
			C7	C6	C6A	128

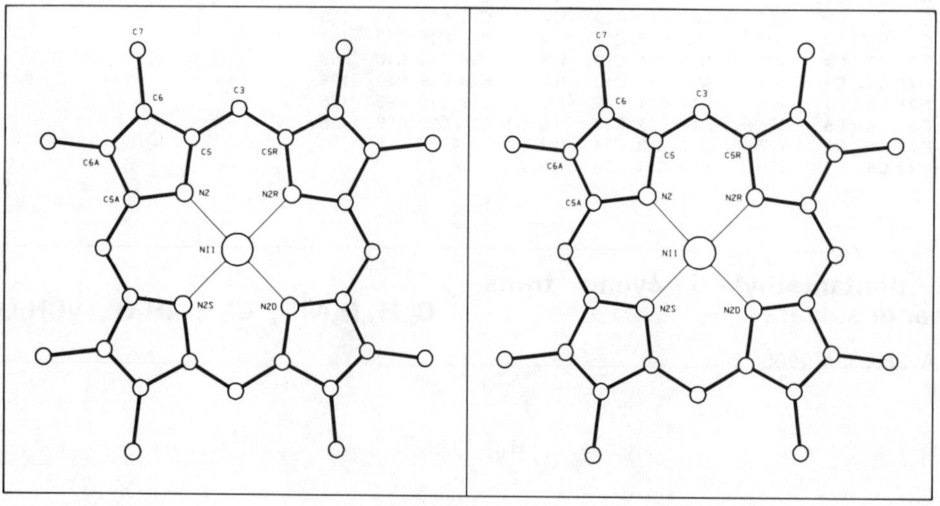

49.5   Chlorohemin (α form)

$C_{34}H_{32}ClFeN_4O_4$

D.F.Koenig, Acta Cryst., 18, 663, 1965

The two vinyl groups per molecule were not located unambiguously. They are either disordered in pairs (P - 1) or non - centrosymmetrically arranged in the cell (P1).
P-1   Z = 2   R = 0.095

CHEMIN   LB 34-32-2

Bond Lengths

Fe1	Cl1	2.22	C7	C8	1.35
Fe1	N1	2.08	C7	C25	1.51
Fe1	N2	2.06	C8	C9	1.44
Fe1	N3	2.05	C8	C26	1.57
Fe1	N4	2.07	C9	C10	1.35
C1	N1	1.39	C10	C11	1.37
C4	N1	1.36	C11	C12	1.45
C6	N2	1.38	C12	C13	1.33
C9	N2	1.41	C12	C29	1.55
C11	N3	1.39	C13	C14	1.46
C14	N3	1.36	C13	C32	1.50
C16	N4	1.37	C14	C15	1.40
C19	N4	1.41	C15	C16	1.40
C28	O1	1.20	C16	C17	1.47
C28	O2	1.24	C17	C18	1.34
C31	O3	1.23	C17	C33	1.57
C31	O4	1.19	C18	C19	1.44
C1	C2	1.46	C18	C35	1.59
C1	C20	1.37	C19	C20	1.36
C2	C3	1.34	C21	C22	1.34
C2	C21	1.55	C26	C27	1.53
C3	C4	1.45	C27	C28	1.47
C3	C23	1.53	C29	C30	1.55
C4	C5	1.40	C30	C31	1.52
C5	C6	1.37	C33	C34	1.34
C6	C7	1.43			

Bond Angles

Cl1	Fe1	N1	105	N1	C1	C2	108	N2	C9	C8	107	C18	C17	C33	132
Cl1	Fe1	N2	103	N1	C1	C20	125	N2	C9	C10	126	C17	C18	C19	112
Cl1	Fe1	N3	102	C2	C1	C20	127	C8	C9	C10	127	C17	C18	C35	124
Cl1	Fe1	N4	104	C1	C2	C3	110	C9	C10	C11	126	C19	C18	C35	124
N1	Fe1	N2	86	C1	C2	C21	119	N3	C11	C10	126	N4	C19	C18	107
N1	Fe1	N3	153	C3	C2	C21	131	N3	C11	C12	108	N4	C19	C20	125
N1	Fe1	N4	88	C2	C3	C4	104	C10	C11	C12	126	C18	C19	C20	129
N2	Fe1	N3	88	C2	C3	C23	133	C11	C12	C13	110	C1	C20	C19	127
N2	Fe1	N4	153	C4	C3	C23	123	C11	C12	C29	121	C2	C21	C22	119
N3	Fe1	N4	86	N1	C4	C3	112	C13	C12	C29	129	C8	C26	C27	109
Fe1	N1	C1	126	N1	C4	C5	124	C12	C13	C14	105	C26	C27	C28	110
Fe1	N1	C4	127	C3	C4	C5	124	C12	C13	C32	129	O1	C28	O2	116
C1	N1	C4	106	C4	C5	C6	126	C14	C13	C32	126	O1	C28	C27	124
Fe1	N2	C6	126	N2	C6	C5	125	N3	C14	C13	111	O2	C28	C27	120
Fe1	N2	C9	126	N2	C6	C7	110	N3	C14	C15	125	C12	C29	C30	110
C6	N2	C9	107	C5	C6	C7	125	C13	C14	C15	123	C29	C30	C31	110
Fe1	N3	C11	127	C6	C7	C8	106	C14	C15	C16	125	O3	C31	O4	124
Fe1	N3	C14	127	C6	C7	C25	126	N4	C16	C15	124	O3	C31	C30	115
C11	N3	C14	106	C8	C7	C25	127	N4	C16	C17	111	O4	C31	C30	121
Fe1	N4	C16	126	C7	C8	C9	110	C15	C16	C17	124	C17	C33	C34	123
Fe1	N4	C19	126	C7	C8	C26	127	C16	C17	C18	104				
C16	N4	C19	106	C9	C8	C26	122	C16	C17	C33	124				

49.6   Nickel(ii) 2,4 - diacetyldeuteroporphyrin - IX - dimethyl ester benzene solvate

$C_{36}H_{36}N_4NiO_6$, $0.5C_6H_6$

T.A.Hamor, W.S.Caughey, J.L.Hoard, J. Amer. Chem. Soc., 87, 2305, 1965

P-1   Z = 2   R = 0.099

NADPOR   LB 36-36-1

Bond Lengths

Ni1	N1	1.98	C4	C25	1.47
Ni1	N2	1.95	C5	C6	1.33
Ni1	N3	1.95	C5	C17	1.45
Ni1	N4	1.96	C5	C27	1.54
C13	N1	1.37	C6	C18	1.44
C14	N1	1.40	C6	C28	1.54
C15	N2	1.38	C7	C8	1.34
C16	N2	1.36	C7	C19	1.44
C17	N3	1.36	C7	C32	1.54
C18	N3	1.38	C8	C20	1.48
C19	N4	1.41	C8	C36	1.53
C20	N4	1.40	C9	C14	1.38
C22	O1	1.21	C9	C15	1.36
C25	O2	1.22	C10	C16	1.41
C30	O3	1.19	C10	C17	1.39
C30	O4	1.31	C11	C18	1.34
C31	O4	1.48	C11	C19	1.40
C34	O5	1.17	C12	C13	1.36
C34	O6	1.32	C12	C20	1.36
C35	O6	1.47	C22	C23	1.51
C1	C2	1.37	C25	C26	1.52
C1	C13	1.43	C28	C29	1.54
C1	C21	1.50	C29	C30	1.49
C2	C14	1.45	C32	C33	1.57
C2	C22	1.50	C33	C34	1.55
C3	C4	1.36			
C3	C15	1.44	C37	C38	1.37
C3	C24	1.50	C37	C39	1.36
C4	C16	1.44	C38	C39A	1.48

Bond Angles

N1	Ni1	N2	91	C34	O6	C35	116	C8	C7	C19	109	N2	C16	C4	112	O2	C25	C26	117
N1	Ni1	N3	179	C2	C1	C13	107	C8	C7	C32	129	N2	C16	C10	125	C4	C25	C26	121
N1	Ni1	N4	89	C2	C1	C21	130	C19	C7	C32	122	C4	C16	C10	123	C6	C28	C29	111
N2	Ni1	N3	90	C13	C1	C21	123	C7	C8	C20	106	N3	C17	C5	111	C28	C29	C30	111
N2	Ni1	N4	178	C1	C2	C14	107	C7	C8	C36	131	N3	C17	C10	126	O3	C30	O4	120
N3	Ni1	N4	90	C1	C2	C22	130	C20	C8	C36	123	C5	C17	C10	122	O3	C30	C29	126
Ni1	N1	C13	127	C14	C2	C22	123	C14	C9	C15	125	N3	C18	C6	111	O4	C30	C29	113
Ni1	N1	C14	127	C4	C3	C15	106	C16	C10	C17	122	N3	C18	C11	127	C7	C32	C33	106
C13	N1	C14	105	C4	C3	C24	132	C18	C11	C19	124	C6	C18	C11	123	C32	C33	C34	111
Ni1	N2	C15	127	C15	C3	C24	122	C13	C12	C20	124	N4	C19	C7	110	O5	C34	O6	125
Ni1	N2	C16	129	C3	C4	C16	106	N1	C13	C1	111	N4	C19	C11	123	O5	C34	C33	125
C15	N2	C16	104	C3	C4	C25	128	N1	C13	C12	126	C7	C19	C11	126	O6	C34	C33	110
Ni1	N3	C17	128	C16	C4	C25	126	C1	C13	C12	122	N4	C20	C8	111				
Ni1	N3	C18	128	C6	C5	C17	106	N1	C14	C2	110	N4	C20	C12	125	C38	C37	C39	129
C17	N3	C18	104	C6	C5	C27	129	N1	C14	C9	124	C8	C20	C12	124	C37	C38	C39A	112
Ni1	N4	C19	128	C17	C5	C27	124	C2	C14	C9	126	O1	C22	C2	123	C37	C39	C38A	119
Ni1	N4	C20	128	C5	C6	C18	107	N2	C15	C3	112	O1	C22	C23	120				
C19	N4	C20	104	C5	C6	C28	128	N2	C15	C9	126	C2	C22	C23	117				
C30	O4	C31	121	C18	C6	C28	125	C3	C15	C9	122	O2	C25	C4	122				

49.7 Methoxy iron(iii) mesoporphyrin - IX dimethyl ester $C_{37}H_{43}FeN_4O_5$

J.L.Hoard, M.J.Hamor, T.A.Hamor, W.S.Caughey, J. Amer. Chem. Soc., 87, 2312, 1965

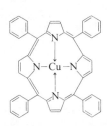

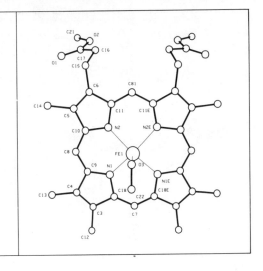

There is disorder in the molecular packing which is attributed to the incomplete sorting of the stereo-chemically similar D - and L - isomers on to their respective sublattices.

I2/m Z = 4 R = 0.119

MFMPOR   LB 37-43-2

Bond Lengths

Fe1	N1	2.07	C4	C9	1.49
Fe1	N2	2.07	C4	C13	1.51
Fe1	O3	1.84	C5	C6	1.37
C9	N1	1.38	C5	C10	1.44
C18	N1	1.41	C5	C14	1.53
C10	N2	1.41	C6	C11	1.46
C11	N2	1.39	C6	C15	1.51
C17	O1	1.23	C7	C18	1.35
C17	O2	1.32	C8	C9	1.39
C21	O2	1.51	C8	C10	1.40
C22	O3	1.37	C11	C81	1.38
C3	C4	1.37	C15	C16	1.56
C3	C12	1.55	C16	C17	1.50
C3	C18	1.47			

Bond Angles

N1	Fe1	N2	87	C10	N2	C11	107	C5	C6	C11	108	N2	C11	C81	128
N1	Fe1	N1E	88	C17	O2	C21	118	C5	C6	C15	127	C6	C11	C81	124
N1	Fe1	N2E	155	Fe1	O3	C22	126	C11	C6	C15	125	C6	C15	C16	112
N1	Fe1	O3	103	C4	C3	C12	127	C18	C7	C18E	128	C15	C16	C17	110
N2	Fe1	N1E	155	C4	C3	C18	112	C9	C8	C10	125	O1	C17	O2	119
N2	Fe1	N2E	88	C12	C3	C18	121	N1	C9	C4	111	O1	C17	C16	129
N2	Fe1	O3	102	C3	C4	C9	103	N1	C9	C8	127	O2	C17	C16	111
Fe1	N1	C9	126	C3	C4	C13	131	C4	C9	C8	122	N1	C18	C3	106
Fe1	N1	C18	125	C9	C4	C13	126	N2	C10	C5	110	N1	C18	C7	125
C9	N1	C18	108	C6	C5	C10	107	N2	C10	C8	124	C3	C18	C7	128
Fe1	N2	C10	127	C6	C5	C14	130	C5	C10	C8	126	C11	C81	C11E	124
Fe1	N2	C11	125	C10	C5	C14	123	N2	C11	C6	109				

49.8 Copper(ii) tetraphenylporphine $C_{44}H_{28}CuN_4$

E.B.Fleischer, C.K.Miller, L.E.Webb, J. Amer. Chem. Soc., 86, 2342, 1964

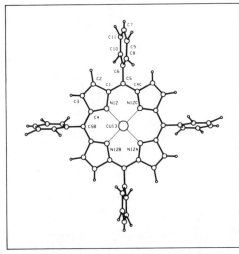

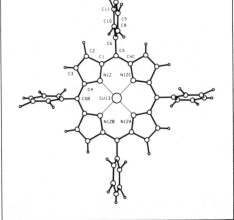

Note that the R - factor refers to all reflexions, including unobserved terms. Compare 49.9.
I-42d Z = 4 R = 0.061

CUTPOR   LB 44-28-2

Bond Lengths

Cu13	N12	1.98	C5	C6	1.49
C1	N12	1.39	C6	C8	1.38
C4	N12	1.38	C6	C10	1.40
C1	C2	1.43	C7	C9	1.39
C1	C5	1.38	C7	C11	1.34
C2	C3	1.34	C8	C9	1.39
C3	C4	1.46	C10	C11	1.41
C4	C5B	1.36			

Bond Angles

N12	Cu13	N12A	177	C1	C2	C3	109	C5	C6	C8	120
N12	Cu13	N12B	90	C2	C3	C4	108	C5	C6	C10	121
Cu13	N12	C1	126	N12	C4	C3	108	C8	C6	C10	119
Cu13	N12	C4	126	N12	C4	C5B	127	C9	C7	C11	121
C1	N12	C4	108	C3	C4	C5B	125	C6	C8	C9	121
N12	C1	C2	108	C1	C5	C6	117	C7	C9	C8	119
N12	C1	C5	126	C1	C5	C4C	123	C6	C10	C11	119
C2	C1	C5	126	C6	C5	C4C	120	C7	C11	C10	121

49.9 Palladium(ii) tetraphenylporphine

$C_{44}H_{28}N_4Pd$

E.B.Fleischer, C.K.Miller, L.E.Webb, J. Amer. Chem. Soc., 86, 2342, 1964

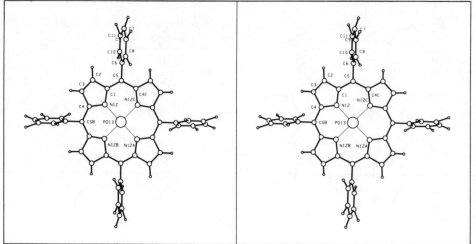

Note that the R - factor refers to observed terms only. If unobserved terms are included then R = 0.161. Compare 49.8.

I-42d   Z = 4   R = 0.051

PDTPOR   LB 44-28-4

Bond Lengths

Pd13	N12	2.01	C5	C6	1.50
C1	N12	1.37	C6	C8	1.38
C4	N12	1.38	C6	C10	1.38
C1	C2	1.44	C7	C9	1.35
C1	C5	1.39	C7	C11	1.42
C2	C3	1.35	C8	C9	1.39
C3	C4	1.43	C10	C11	1.34
C4	C5B	1.41			

Bond Angles

N12	Pd13	N12A	178	C1	C2	C3	108	C5	C6	C8	121
N12	Pd13	N12B	90	C2	C3	C4	107	C5	C6	C10	123
Pd13	N12	C1	126	N12	C4	C3	110	C8	C6	C10	117
Pd13	N12	C4	127	N12	C4	C5B	124	C9	C7	C11	118
C1	N12	C4	106	C3	C4	C5B	125	C6	C8	C9	120
N12	C1	C2	109	C1	C5	C6	119	C7	C9	C8	122
N12	C1	C5	126	C1	C5	C4C	125	C6	C10	C11	124
C2	C1	C5	125	C6	C5	C4C	116	C7	C11	C10	119

49.10 Tetraphenylporphine (tetragonal form)

$C_{44}H_{30}N_4$

M.J.Hamor, T.A.Hamor, J.L.Hoard, J. Amer. Chem. Soc., 86, 1936, 1964

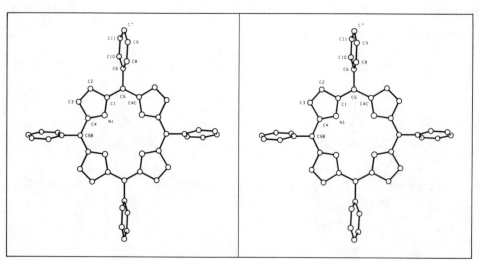

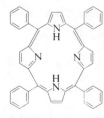

See also Silvers & Tulinsky, J. Amer. Chem. Soc., 89, 3331, 1967.

I-42d   Z = 4   R = 0.108

TPHPOR10   LB 44-30-3

Bond Lengths

C1	N1	1.35	C5	C6	1.51
C4	N1	1.35	C6	C8	1.38
C1	C2	1.44	C6	C10	1.40
C1	C5	1.40	C7	C9	1.39
C2	C3	1.36	C8	C9	1.39
C3	C4	1.43	C10	C11	1.38
C4	C5B	1.41			

Bond Angles

C1	N1	C4	109	N1	C4	C5B	126	C8	C6	C10	119
N1	C1	C2	108	C3	C4	C5B	125	C9	C7	C11	119
N1	C1	C5	126	C1	C5	C6	118	C6	C8	C9	122
C2	C1	C5	125	C1	C5	C4C	125	C7	C9	C8	119
C1	C2	C3	107	C6	C5	C4C	117	C6	C10	C11	118
C2	C3	C4	107	C5	C6	C8	119	C7	C11	C10	123
N1	C4	C3	109	C5	C6	C10	121				

49.11   Aquo zinc tetraphenylporphine

$C_{44}H_{30}N_4OZn$

E.B.Fleischer, C.K.Miller, L.E.Webb, J. Amer. Chem. Soc., 86, 2342, 1964

The authors describe this compound as the dihydrate. However a re - examination by Glick et al., J. Amer. Chem. Soc., 89, 1996, 1967 supports the reformulation of this complex as the monoaquo derivative. They also suggest that the structure studied by Fleischer et al. was a partially disordered arrangement of polar molecules with respect to the tetragonal c - axis.
I4/m   Z = 2   R = 0.131

ZNTPOR   LB 44-28-7

49.12   Aquohydroxy iron(iii) tetraphenylporphine

$C_{44}H_{31}FeN_4O_2$

E.B.Fleischer, C.K.Miller, L.E.Webb, J. Amer. Chem. Soc., 86, 2342, 1964

The data reported in this paper have been fully refined by Hoard et al., J. Amer. Chem. Soc., 89, 1992, 1967. The latter analysis suggests that the material studied was, in fact, the chloro derivative.
I4   Z = 2   R = 0.170

FHTPOR   LB 44-31-1

49.13 Vitamin B₁₂ (wet)

$C_{63}H_{88}CoN_{14}O_{14}P$, $22H_2O$

C.Brink-Shoemaker, D.W.J.Cruickshank, D.C.Hodgkin, M.J.Kamper, D.Pilling,
Proc. R. Soc., A, 278, 1, 1964

$P2_12_12_1$ Z = 4   R = 0.218

VITAMB   LB 63-88-1

22 H₂O

Bond Lengths

Co1	N20	1.80	C9	N21	1.37	C8	C9	1.54
Co1	N21	1.92	C11	N22	1.32	C8	C41	1.49
Co1	N22	1.86	C14	N22	1.52	C9	C10	1.59
Co1	N23	1.87	C16	N23	1.32	C10	C11	1.28
Co1	N31	1.97	C19	N23	1.54	C11	C12	1.58
Co1	C64	1.92	C27	N28	1.39	C12	C13	1.56
P1	O21	1.60	C21	N31	1.47	C12	C46	1.66
P1	O31	1.55	C91	N31	1.32	C12	C47	1.54
P1	O41	1.53	C32	N34	1.34	C13	C14	1.56
P1	O511	1.65	C38	N40	1.48	C13	C48	1.61
C21	N11	1.40	C43	N45	1.26	C14	C15	1.37
C81	N11	1.47	C50	N52	1.42	C15	C16	1.48
C121	N11	1.57	C53	N59	1.27	C15	C53	1.52
C1	N20	1.53	C100	N59	1.48	C16	C17	1.42
C4	N20	1.39	C61	N63	1.50	C17	C18	1.62
C6	N21	1.30	C64	N65	1.11	C17	C54	1.43
			C321	O21	1.47	C17	C55	1.63
			C27	O29	1.39	C18	C19	1.60
			C200	O31	1.49	C18	C60	1.58
			C32	O33	1.22	C26	C27	1.54
			C38	O39	1.16	C30	C31	1.54
			C43	O44	1.22	C31	C32	1.55
			C50	O51	1.26	C37	C38	1.40
			C57	O58	1.30	C41	C42	1.52
			C121	O61	1.46	C42	C43	1.37
			C421	O61	1.47	C48	C49	1.63
			C61	O62	1.10	C49	C50	1.56
			C221	O71	1.44	C51	C101	1.53
			C521	O81	1.59	C51	C411	1.32
			C1	C2	1.58	C51	C611	1.33
			C1	C19	1.51	C55	C56	1.68
			C1	C24	1.55	C56	C57	1.39
			C2	C3	1.53	C60	C61	1.48
			C2	C25	1.58	C7.1	C81	1.36
			C2	C26	1.50	C71	C611	1.48
			C3	C4	1.57	C81	C91	1.42
			C3	C30	1.55	C91	C411	1.48
			C4	C5	1.33	C100	C200	1.48
			C5	C6	1.50	C111	C611	1.55
			C5	C35	1.61	C121	C221	1.56
			C6	C7	1.50	C200	C300	1.56
			C7	C8	1.53	C221	C321	1.52
			C7	C36	1.55	C321	C421	1.70
			C7	C37	1.51	C421	C521	1.42

Bond Angles

N20	Co1	N21	89	Co1	N23	C19	111	C6	C7	C36	118	C16	C17	C54	110	O51	C50	C49	105
N20	Co1	N22	175	C16	N23	C19	110	C6	C7	C37	103	C16	C17	C55	125	C101	C51	C411	122
N20	Co1	N23	84	Co1	N31	C21	117	C8	C7	C36	112	C18	C17	C54	109	C101	C51	C611	116
N20	Co1	N31	96	Co1	N31	C91	135	C8	C7	C37	102	C18	C17	C55	102	C411	C51	C611	122
N20	Co1	C64	87	C21	N31	C91	107	C36	C7	C37	118	C54	C17	C55	108	C17	C55	C56	112
N21	Co1	N22	96	C57	N59	C100	131	C7	C8	C9	99	C17	C18	C19	102	C55	C56	C57	112
N21	Co1	N23	172	P1	O21	C321	114	C7	C8	C41	111	C17	C18	C60	121	N59	C57	O58	118
N21	Co1	N31	88	P1	O31	C200	121	C9	C8	C41	109	C19	C18	C60	109	N59	C57	C56	126
N21	Co1	C64	87	C121	O61	C421	114	N21	C9	C8	112	N23	C19	C1	108	O58	C57	C56	115
N22	Co1	N23	92	N20	C1	C2	101	N21	C9	C10	125	N23	C19	C18	99	C18	C60	C61	106
N22	Co1	N31	87	N20	C1	C19	97	C8	C9	C10	123	C1	C19	C18	127	N63	C61	O62	125
N22	Co1	C64	91	N20	C1	C24	114	C9	C10	C11	121	N11	C21	N31	105	N63	C61	C60	108
N23	Co1	N31	97	C2	C1	C19	118	N22	C11	C10	126	C2	C26	C27	120	O62	C61	C60	126
N23	Co1	C64	89	C2	C1	C24	117	N22	C11	C12	114	N28	C27	O29	125	Co1	C64	N65	176
N31	Co1	C64	174	C19	C1	C24	108	C10	C11	C12	118	N28	C27	C26	112	C81	C71	C611	113
O21	P1	O31	100	C1	C2	C3	102	C11	C12	C13	102	O29	C27	C26	123	N11	C81	C71	129
O21	P1	O41	111	C1	C2	C25	115	C11	C12	C46	104	C3	C30	C31	113	N11	C81	C91	102
O21	P1	O511	108	C1	C2	C26	114	C11	C12	C47	113	C30	C31	C32	106	C71	C81	C91	129
O31	P1	O41	113	C3	C2	C25	109	C13	C12	C46	105	N34	C32	O33	121	N31	C91	C81	114
O31	P1	O511	101	C3	C2	C26	115	C13	C12	C47	116	N34	C32	C31	111	N31	C91	C411	134
O41	P1	O511	122	C25	C2	C26	103	C46	C12	C47	116	O33	C32	C31	128	C81	C91	C411	111
C21	N11	C81	110	C2	C3	C4	100	C12	C13	C14	99	C7	C37	C38	111	N59	C100	C200	113
C21	N11	C121	125	C2	C3	C30	125	C12	C13	C48	113	N40	C38	O39	115	N11	C121	O61	97
C81	N11	C121	119	C4	C3	C30	112	C14	C13	C48	105	N40	C38	C37	132	N11	C121	C221	108
Co1	N20	C1	120	N20	C4	C3	110	N22	C14	C13	111	O39	C38	C37	113	O61	C121	C221	108
Co1	N20	C4	131	N20	C4	C5	125	N22	C14	C15	127	C8	C41	C42	114	O31	C200	C100	108
C1	N20	C4	109	C3	C4	C5	126	C13	C14	C15	122	C41	C42	C43	114	O31	C200	C300	104
Co1	N21	C6	132	C4	C5	C6	120	C14	C15	C16	121	N45	C43	O44	107	C100	C200	C300	108
Co1	N21	C9	121	C4	C5	C35	119	C14	C15	C53	119	N45	C43	C42	122	O71	C221	C121	113
C6	N21	C9	106	C6	C5	C35	119	C16	C15	C53	120	O44	C43	C42	128	O71	C221	C321	113
Co1	N22	C11	131	N21	C6	C5	120	N23	C16	C15	120	C13	C48	C49	117	C121	C221	C321	97
Co1	N22	C14	124	N21	C6	C7	116	N23	C16	C17	116	C48	C49	C50	105	O21	C321	C221	112
C11	N22	C14	105	C5	C6	C7	124	C15	C16	C17	124	N52	C50	O51	126				
Co1	N23	C16	136	C6	C7	C8	101	C16	C17	C18	102	N52	C50	C49	128				

50.1   Bromoemimycin

$C_4H_3BrN_2O_2$

C.Tamura, Bull. Chem. Soc. Jap., 36, 1187, 1963

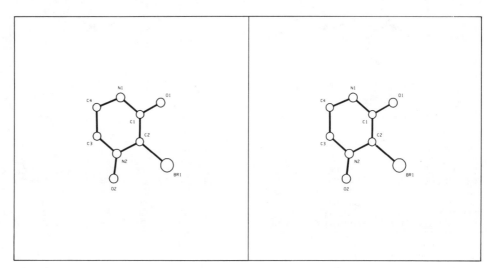

Pna2$_1$ Z = 4   R$_{hk0}$ = 0.123,
R$_{0kl}$ = 0.143

BREMIN

Bond Lengths					
Br1	C2	1.81	C3	N2	1.32
N2	O2	1.24	C1	O1	1.22
C1	N1	1.30	C1	C2	1.34
C4	N1	1.30	C3	C4	1.42
C2	N2	1.32			

Bond Angles							
C1	N1	C4	118	O1	C1	C2	119
O2	N2	C2	124	Br1	C2	N2	113
O2	N2	C3	124	Br1	C2	C1	129
C2	N2	C3	112	N2	C2	C1	118
N1	C1	O1	111	N2	C3	C4	131
N1	C1	C2	129	N1	C4	C3	111

50.2   Benzyl penicillin potassium salt (refinement of data of Pitt, Acta Cryst., 5,770,1952)

$C_{16}H_{17}N_2O_4S^-$, K^+

A.Vaciago, Atti Accad. Nazion. Lincei, R. C., Cl. Sci. Fis. Mat. Nat., 28, 851, 1960

Atomic coordinates were not reported in the paper.
P2$_1$2$_1$2$_1$ Z = 4   R = 0.205

BZPENK   LB 16-17-2

50.3   6 - (N - Benzylformamido)penicillanic acid

$C_{16}H_{18}N_2O_4S$

D.J.Hunt, D.Rogers, Biochem. J., 93, 35C, 1964

Atomic coordinates were not reported in the paper.
C2   Z = 4   R = 0.09

BZFPNA   LB 16-19-3

50.4 Phenoxymethylpenicillin

$C_{16}H_{18}N_2O_5S$

S.Abrahamsson, D.C.Hodgkin, E.N.Maslen, Biochem. J., 86, 514, 1963

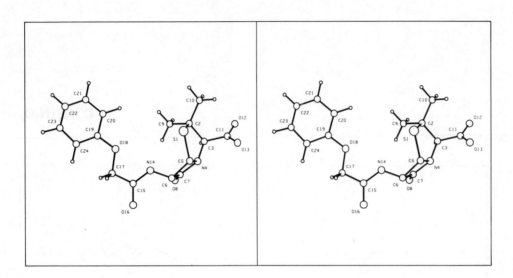

C2   Z = 4   R = 0.13

PMEPEN   LB 16-18-28

Bond Lengths

S1	C2	1.87	C2	C3	1.57
S1	C5	1.82	C2	C9	1.51
C3	N4	1.46	C2	C10	1.58
C5	N4	1.52	C3	C11	1.54
C7	N4	1.45	C5	C6	1.58
C6	N14	1.44	C6	C7	1.55
C15	N14	1.37	C15	C17	1.49
C7	O8	1.21	C19	C20	1.42
C11	O12	1.35	C19	C24	1.44
C11	O13	1.21	C20	C21	1.43
C15	O16	1.29	C21	C22	1.38
C17	O18	1.47	C22	C23	1.37
C19	O18	1.40	C23	C24	1.45

Bond Angles

C2	S1	C5	96		C5	C6	C7	83
C3	N4	C5	120		N4	C7	O8	128
C3	N4	C7	129		N4	C7	C6	96
C5	N4	C7	88		O8	C7	C6	136
C6	N14	C15	125		O12	C11	O13	122
C17	O18	C19	117		O12	C11	C3	115
S1	C2	C3	105		O13	C11	C3	122
S1	C2	C9	109		N14	C15	O16	125
S1	C2	C10	108		N14	C15	C17	120
C3	C2	C9	110		O16	C15	C17	116
C3	C2	C10	113		O18	C17	C15	106
C9	C2	C10	112		O18	C19	C20	112
N4	C3	C2	104		O18	C19	C24	122
N4	C3	C11	114		C20	C19	C24	126
C2	C3	C11	113		C19	C20	C21	115
S1	C5	N4	103		C20	C21	C22	121
S1	C5	C6	122		C21	C22	C23	123
N4	C5	C6	92		C22	C23	C24	121
N14	C6	C5	115		C19	C24	C23	114
N14	C6	C7	115					

Torsion Angles

C5	S1	C2	C3	−24		C15	N14	C6	C7	111		N4	C5	C6	N14	−120
C5	S1	C2	C9	94		C6	N14	C15	O16	−7		N4	C5	C6	C7	−6
C5	S1	C2	C10	−144		C6	N14	C15	C17	170		N14	C6	C7	N4	120
C2	S1	C5	N4	5		C19	O18	C17	C15	161		N14	C6	C7	O8	−59
C2	S1	C5	C6	−96		C17	O18	C19	C20	−168		C5	C6	C7	N4	6
C5	N4	C3	C2	−36		C17	O18	C19	C24	15		C5	C6	C7	O8	−173
C5	N4	C3	C11	88		S1	C2	C3	N4	34		N14	C15	C17	O18	5
C7	N4	C3	C2	79		S1	C2	C3	C11	−89		O16	C15	C17	O18	−177
C7	N4	C3	C11	−157		C9	C2	C3	N4	−83		O18	C19	C20	C21	−179
C3	N4	C5	S1	18		C9	C2	C3	C11	153		C24	C19	C20	C21	−2
C3	N4	C5	C6	141		C10	C2	C3	N4	151		O18	C19	C24	C23	179
C7	N4	C5	S1	−118		C10	C2	C3	C11	27		C20	C19	C24	C23	3
C7	N4	C5	C6	6		N4	C3	C11	O12	156		C19	C20	C21	C22	2
C3	N4	C7	O8	45		N4	C3	C11	O13	−24		C20	C21	C22	C23	−3
C3	N4	C7	C6	−134		C2	C3	C11	O12	−85		C21	C22	C23	C24	3
C5	N4	C7	O8	173		C2	C3	C11	O13	94		C22	C23	C24	C19	−3
C5	N4	C7	C6	−6		S1	C5	C6	N14	−13						
C15	N14	C6	C5	−156		S1	C5	C6	C7	101						

50.5 Cephalosporin C sodium salt dihydrate

$C_{16}H_{20}N_3O_8S^-$, Na^+, $2H_2O$

D.C.Hodgkin, E.N.Maslen, Biochem. J., 79, 393, 1961

No comparison of bond lengths is possible since they are not reported in the paper. The carbon and oxygen atoms of the acetoxy groups were not distinguished by the authors. They have been labelled C13, O14, C113, O114 on the basis of the bond lengths. Published z coordinate for C2(b) (relabelled C102) = 0.2739 and published y coordinate for C15(b) (relabelled C115) = 0.538. The correct values are 0.7379 and 0.638 respectively.

C2   Z = 4   R = 0.264

CEPHNA

Bond Lengths

S1	C2	1.90
S1	C6	1.82
C4	N5	1.46
C6	N5	1.42
C8	N5	1.59
C7	N18	1.53
C19	N18	1.42
C24	N25	1.44
C8	O9	1.15
C10	O11	1.73
C12	O11	1.39
C12	O14	1.29
C15	O16	1.32
C15	O17	1.24
C19	O20	1.42
C26	O27	1.24
C26	O28	1.34
C2	C3	1.40
C3	C4	1.28
C3	C10	1.53
C4	C15	1.60
C6	C7	1.52
C7	C8	1.55
C12	C13	1.50
C19	C21	1.40
C21	C22	1.30
C22	C23	1.56
C23	C24	1.32
C24	C26	1.49
S101	C102	1.92
S101	C106	1.81
C104	N105	1.48
C106	N105	1.47
C108	N105	1.29
C107	N118	1.53
C119	N118	1.38
C124	N125	1.42
C108	O109	1.39
C110	O111	1.37
C112	O111	1.56
C112	O114	1.26
C115	O116	1.40
C115	O117	1.35
C119	O120	1.12
C126	O127	1.27
C126	O128	1.36
C102	C103	1.49
C103	C104	1.35
C103	C110	1.53
C104	C115	1.50
C106	C107	1.54
C107	C108	1.54
C112	C113	1.47
C119	C121	1.62
C121	C122	1.52
C122	C123	1.65
C123	C124	1.52
C124	C126	1.43

Bond Angles

C2	S1	C6	84
C4	N5	C6	108
C4	N5	C8	141
C6	N5	C8	99
C7	N18	C19	119
C10	O11	C12	113
S1	C2	C3	115
C2	C3	C4	129
C2	C3	C10	123
C4	C3	C10	108
N5	C4	C3	125
N5	C4	C15	101
C3	C4	C15	134
S1	C6	N5	123
S1	C6	C7	109
N5	C6	C7	84
N18	C7	C6	130
N18	C7	C8	102
C6	C7	C8	97
C6	C7	C8	92
N5	C8	O9	120
N5	C8	C7	78
O9	C8	C7	162
O11	C10	C3	93
O11	C10	C3	98
O11	C12	O14	108
O11	C12	C13	117
O14	C12	C13	134
O16	C15	O17	130
O16	C15	C4	105
O17	C15	C4	125
N18	C19	O20	126
N18	C19	C21	118
O20	C19	C21	114
C19	C21	C22	115
C21	C22	C23	117
C22	C23	C24	108
N25	C24	C23	119
N25	C24	C26	104
C23	C24	C26	128
O27	C26	O28	114
O27	C26	C24	124
O28	C26	C24	123

C102	S101	C106	96
C104	N105	C106	118
C104	N105	C108	133
C106	N105	C108	106
C107	N118	C119	114
C110	O111	C112	121
S101	C102	C103	118
C102	C103	C104	112
C102	C103	C110	111
C104	C103	C110	137
N105	C104	C103	134
N105	C104	C115	111
C103	C104	C115	114
S101	C106	N105	105
S101	C106	C107	120
N105	C106	C107	78
N118	C107	C106	118
N118	C107	C108	113
C106	C107	C108	92
N105	C108	O109	135
N105	C108	C107	83
O109	C108	C107	141
O111	C110	C103	98
O111	C112	O114	101
O111	C112	C113	114
O114	C112	C113	145
O116	C115	O117	109
O116	C115	C104	129
O117	C115	C104	122
N118	C119	O120	119
N118	C119	C121	103
O120	C119	C121	138
C119	C121	C122	113
C121	C122	C123	108
C122	C123	C124	111
N125	C124	C123	110
N125	C124	C126	108
C123	C124	C126	106
O127	C126	O128	116
O127	C126	C124	131
O128	C126	C124	113

Torsion Angles

C6	S1	C2	C3	47
C2	S1	C6	N5	−66
C2	S1	C6	C7	−162
C6	N5	C4	C3	−11
C6	N5	C4	C15	166
C8	N5	C4	C3	121
C8	N5	C4	C15	−62
C4	N5	C6	S1	54
C4	N5	C6	C7	163
C8	N5	C6	S1	−98
C8	N5	C6	C7	11
C4	N5	C8	O9	32
C4	N5	C8	C7	−146
C6	N5	C8	O9	167
C6	N5	C8	C7	−11
C19	N18	C7	C6	−107
C19	N18	C7	C8	144
C7	N18	C19	O20	5
C7	N18	C19	C21	−163
C12	O11	C10	C3	178
C10	O11	C12	O14	5
C10	O11	C12	C13	−166
S1	C2	C3	C4	−28
S1	C2	C3	C10	156
C2	C3	C4	N5	2
C2	C3	C4	C15	−174
C10	C3	C4	N5	178
C10	C3	C4	C15	2
C2	C3	C10	O11	31
C4	C3	C10	O11	−145
N5	C4	C15	O16	150
N5	C4	C15	O17	−28
C3	C4	C15	O16	−33
C3	C4	C15	O17	149
S1	C6	C7	N18	0
S1	C6	C7	C8	111
N5	C6	C7	N18	−123
N5	C6	C7	C8	−11
N18	C7	C8	N5	144
N18	C7	C8	O9	−30
C6	C7	C8	N5	10
C6	C7	C8	O9	−163
N18	C19	C21	C22	77
O20	C19	C21	C22	−92
C19	C21	C22	C23	−179
C21	C22	C23	C24	−170
C22	C23	C24	N25	95
C22	C23	C24	C26	−48
N25	C24	C26	O27	152
N25	C24	C26	O28	−30
C23	C24	C26	O27	−61
C23	C24	C26	O28	117

C106	S101	C102	C103	52
C102	S101	C106	N105	−61
C102	S101	C106	C107	−146
C106	N105	C104	C103	−21
C106	N105	C104	C115	166
C108	N105	C104	C103	135
C108	N105	C104	C115	−37
C104	N105	C106	S101	53
C104	N105	C106	C107	171
C108	N105	C106	S101	−109
C108	N105	C106	C107	9
C104	N105	C108	O109	6
C104	N105	C108	C107	−167
C106	N105	C108	O109	164
C106	N105	C108	C107	−9
C119	N118	C107	C106	−95
C119	N118	C107	C108	160
C107	N118	C119	O120	−1
C107	N118	C119	C121	−176
C112	O111	C110	C103	−169
C110	O111	C112	O114	−24
C110	O111	C112	C113	158
S101	C102	C103	C104	−25
S101	C102	C103	C110	158
C102	C103	C104	N105	4
C102	C103	C104	C115	177
C110	C103	C104	N105	−180
C110	C103	C104	C115	−7
C102	C103	C110	O111	58
C104	C103	C110	O111	−118
N105	C104	C115	O116	153
N105	C104	C115	O117	−36
C103	C104	C115	O116	−22
C103	C104	C115	O117	149
S101	C106	C107	N118	−23
S101	C106	C107	C108	94
N105	C106	C107	N118	−124
N105	C106	C107	C108	−7
N118	C107	C108	N105	129
N118	C107	C108	O109	−43
C106	C107	C108	N105	8
C106	C107	C108	O109	−164
N118	C119	C121	C122	88
O120	C119	C121	C122	−86
C119	C121	C122	C123	64
C121	C122	C123	C124	175
C122	C123	C124	N125	−169
C122	C123	C124	C126	74
N125	C124	C126	O127	143
N125	C124	C126	O128	−28
C123	C124	C126	O127	−99
C123	C124	C126	O128	90

50.6 5 - Bromogriseofulvin $C_{17}H_{16}BrClO_6$

W.A.C.Brown, G.A.Sim, J. Chem. Soc., 1050, 1963

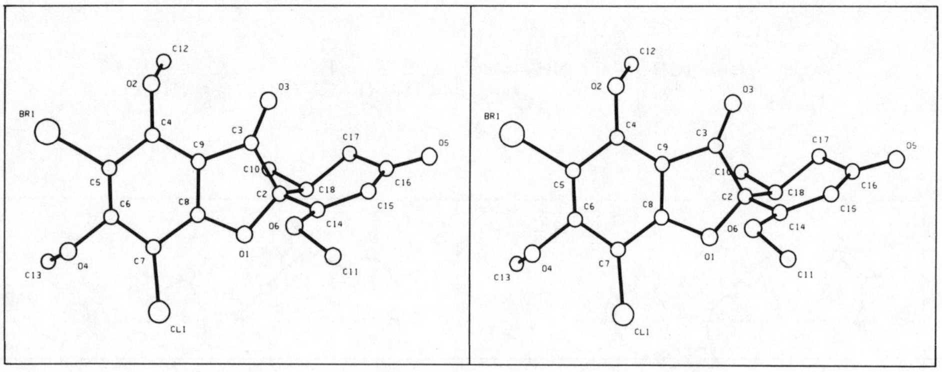

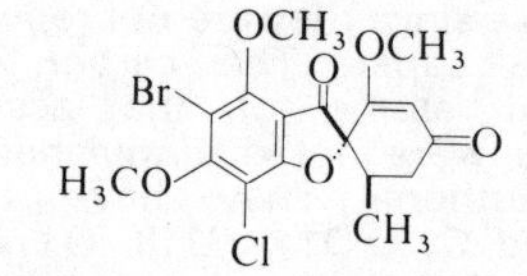

P2$_1$ Z = 2 R = 0.14

BGIFUL LB 17-16-2

Bond Lengths

Br1	C5	1.91
Cl1	C7	1.69
C2	O1	1.44
C8	O1	1.39
C4	O2	1.33
C12	O2	1.38
C3	O3	1.20
C6	O4	1.45
C13	O4	1.43
C16	O5	1.25
C11	O6	1.60
C14	O6	1.33
C2	C3	1.55
C2	C14	1.43
C2	C18	1.47
C3	C9	1.50
C4	C5	1.46
C4	C9	1.44
C5	C6	1.26
C6	C7	1.40
C7	C8	1.48
C8	C9	1.38
C10	C18	1.61
C14	C15	1.42
C15	C16	1.43
C16	C17	1.51
C17	C18	⁻ 1.55

Bond Angles

C2	O1	C8	109	C5	C6	C7	127
C4	O2	C12	117	Cl1	C7	C6	128
C6	O4	C13	115	Cl1	C7	C8	120
C11	O6	C14	115	C6	C7	C8	110
O1	C2	C3	108	O1	C8	C7	123
O1	C2	C14	106	O1	C8	C9	112
O1	C2	C18	113	C7	C8	C9	125
C3	C2	C14	118	C3	C9	C4	132
C3	C2	C18	110	C3	C9	C8	109
C14	C2	C18	103	C4	C9	C8	118
O3	C3	C2	127	O6	C14	C2	107
O3	C3	C9	132	O6	C14	C15	119
C2	C3	C9	102	C2	C14	C15	128
O2	C4	C5	125	C14	C15	C16	117
O2	C4	C9	120	O5	C16	C15	125
C5	C4	C9	114	O5	C16	C17	116
Br1	C5	C4	114	C15	C16	C17	118
Br1	C5	C6	122	C16	C17	C18	108
C4	C5	C6	124	C2	C18	C10	105
O4	C6	C5	125	C2	C18	C17	116
O4	C6	C7	109	C10	C18	C17	107

Torsion Angles

C8	O1	C2	C3	0	C18	C2	C14	C15	41	C4	C5	C6	C7	3
C8	O1	C2	C14	127	O1	C2	C18	C10	71	O4	C6	C7	Cl1	−12
C8	O1	C2	C18	−122	O1	C2	C18	C17	−170	O4	C6	C7	C8	−177
C2	O1	C8	C7	−176	C3	C2	C18	C10	−49	C5	C6	C7	Cl1	171
C2	O1	C8	C9	5	C3	C2	C18	C17	69	C5	C6	C7	C8	6
C12	O2	C4	C5	−120	C14	C2	C18	C10	−176	Cl1	C7	C8	O1	9
C12	O2	C4	C9	74	C14	C2	C18	C17	−57	Cl1	C7	C8	C9	−172
C13	O4	C6	C5	91	O3	C3	C9	C4	2	C6	C7	C8	O1	175
C13	O4	C6	C7	−86	O3	C3	C9	C8	−174	C6	C7	C8	C9	−6
C11	O6	C14	C2	171	C2	C3	C9	C4	−176	O1	C8	C9	C3	−8
C11	O6	C14	C15	−35	C2	C3	C9	C8	8	O1	C8	C9	C4	175
O1	C2	C3	O3	177	O2	C4	C5	Br1	11	C7	C8	C9	C3	172
O1	C2	C3	C9	−5	O2	C4	C5	C6	180	C7	C8	C9	C4	−4
C14	C2	C3	O3	58	C9	C4	C5	Br1	178	O6	C14	C15	C16	−171
C14	C2	C3	C9	−124	C9	C4	C5	C6	−14	C2	C14	C15	C16	−22
C18	C2	C3	O3	−59	O2	C4	C9	C3	5	C14	C15	C16	O5	−171
C18	C2	C3	C9	119	O2	C4	C9	C8	−179	C14	C15	C16	C17	16
O1	C2	C14	O6	−49	C5	C4	C9	C3	−163	O5	C16	C17	C18	154
O1	C2	C14	C15	159	C5	C4	C9	C8	13	C15	C16	C17	C18	−32
C3	C2	C14	O6	71	Br1	C5	C6	O4	−5	C16	C17	C18	C2	57
C3	C2	C14	C15	−81	Br1	C5	C6	C7	171	C16	C17	C18	C10	174
C18	C2	C14	O6	−168	C4	C5	C6	O4	−173					

50.7 7 - Bromo - 4 - hydroxytetracycloxide dimethylformamide solvate $C_{19}H_{14}BrNO_9$, C_3H_7NO

J.H.van den Hende, J. Amer. Chem. Soc., 87, 929, 1965

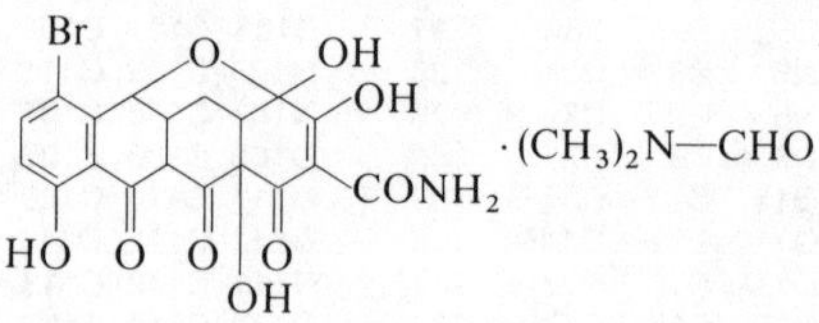

Atomic coordinates were not given
but bond lengths were reported.
P2$_1$ Z = 2 R = 0.13

BHTCYO LB 19-14-4

50.8 7 - Chloro - 4 - hydroxytetracycloxide dimethylformamide solvate $C_{19}H_{14}ClNO_9$, C_3H_7NO

J.H.van den Hende, J. Amer. Chem. Soc., 87, 929, 1965

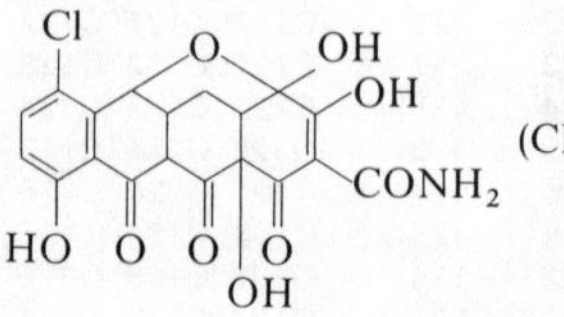

Atomic coordinates were not given
but bond lengths were reported.
P112$_1$ Z = 2 R = 0.11

CHOMFO LB 19-14-7

50.9 Nidulin $C_{20}H_{17}Cl_3O_5$

J.A.S.McMillan, Dissert. Abstr., 25, 868, 1964

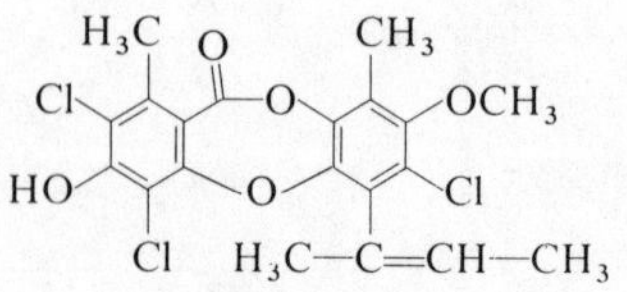

Atomic coordinates were not reported in the paper.
P2$_1$/a Z = 4 R = 0.108

NIDLIN LB 20-17-4

50.10 Aureomycin hydrochloride (refinement of structure of Hirokawa et al., Acta Cryst., 12,811,1959)

$C_{22}H_{24}ClN_2O_8^+$, Cl^-

J.Donohue, J.D.Dunitz, K.N.Trueblood, M.S.Webster, J. Amer. Chem. Soc., 85, 851, 1963

Atomic coordinates were not given but bond lengths were reported.
$P2_12_12_1$ Z = 4 No R factor was given.

AURMYC   LB 22-24-2

50.11 Oxytetracycline hydrochloride

$C_{22}H_{25}N_2O_9^+$, Cl^-

H.Cid-Dresdner, Z. Kristallogr., 121, 170, 1965

$P2_12_12_1$ Z = 4 R = 0.14

TERMYC   LB 22-25-5

Bond Lengths

C13	N2	1.28	C4	C40	1.55
C4	N4	1.47	C5	C40	1.58
C14	N4	1.49	C5	C50	1.51
C15	N4	1.55	C6	C16	1.51
C1	O1	1.26	C6	C50	1.57
C13	O2	1.31	C6	C60	1.52
C3	O3	1.26	C7	C8	1.38
C5	O5	1.44	C7	C60	1.40
C6	O6	1.43	C8	C9	1.40
C10	O10	1.30	C9	C10	1.41
C11	O11	1.26	C10	C100	1.43
C12	O12	1.28	C11	C100	1.43
C120	O13	1.43	C11	C110	1.43
C1	C2	1.41	C12	C110	1.34
C1	C120	1.51	C12	C120	1.53
C2	C3	1.40	C40	C120	1.51
C2	C13	1.45	C50	C110	1.54
C3	C4	1.50	C60	C100	1.45

Bond Angles

C4	N4	C14	119
C4	N4	C15	111
C14	N4	C15	109
O1	C1	C2	123
O1	C1	C120	119
C2	C1	C120	117
C1	C2	C3	121
C1	C2	C13	121
C3	C2	C13	118
O3	C3	C2	123
O3	C3	C4	117
C2	C3	C4	120
N4	C4	C3	110
N4	C4	C40	114
C3	C4	C40	114
O5	C5	C40	104
O5	C5	C50	113
C40	C5	C50	112
O6	C6	C16	109
O6	C6	C50	106
O6	C6	C60	108
C16	C6	C50	113
C16	C6	C60	112
C50	C6	C60	109
C8	C7	C60	119
C7	C8	C9	124
C8	C9	C10	118
O10	C10	C9	120
O10	C10	C100	121
C9	C10	C100	119
O11	C11	C100	121
O11	C11	C110	120
C100	C11	C110	119
O12	C12	C110	125
O12	C12	C120	111
C110	C12	C120	124
N2	C13	O2	117
N2	C13	C2	124
O2	C13	C2	118
C4	C40	C5	110
C4	C40	C120	116
C5	C40	C120	109
C5	C50	C6	114
C5	C50	C110	113
C6	C50	C110	106
C6	C60	C7	124
C6	C60	C100	117
C7	C60	C100	119
C10	C100	C11	120
C10	C100	C60	119
C11	C100	C60	120
C11	C110	C12	119
C11	C110	C50	119
C12	C110	C50	122
O13	C120	C1	107
O13	C120	C12	110
O13	C120	C40	107
C1	C120	C12	112
C1	C120	C40	108
C12	C120	C40	112

Torsion Angles

C14	N4	C4	C3	−62
C14	N4	C4	C40	68
C15	N4	C4	C3	170
C15	N4	C4	C40	−59
O1	C1	C2	C3	165
O1	C1	C2	C13	−16
C120	C1	C2	C3	−19
C120	C1	C2	C13	161
O1	C1	C120	O13	112
O1	C1	C120	C12	−9
O1	C1	C120	C40	−133
C2	C1	C120	O13	−64
C2	C1	C120	C12	175
C2	C1	C120	C40	51
C1	C2	C3	O3	165
C1	C2	C3	C4	−17
C13	C2	C3	O3	−15
C13	C2	C3	C4	163
C1	C2	C13	N2	13
C1	C2	C13	O2	−171
C3	C2	C13	N2	−167
C3	C2	C13	O2	9
O3	C3	C4	N4	−34
O3	C3	C4	C40	−165
C2	C3	C4	N4	147
C2	C3	C4	C40	17
N4	C4	C40	C5	126
N4	C4	C40	C120	−110
C3	C4	C40	C5	−106
C3	C4	C40	C120	18
O5	C5	C40	C4	−49

O5	C5	C40	C120	−177
C50	C5	C40	C4	−171
C50	C5	C40	C120	61
O5	C5	C50	C6	80
O5	C5	C50	C110	−159
C40	C5	C50	C6	−162
C40	C5	C50	C110	−42
O6	C6	C50	C5	68
O6	C6	C50	C110	−56
C16	C6	C50	C5	−51
C16	C6	C50	C110	−176
C60	C6	C50	C5	−176
C60	C6	C50	C110	60
O6	C6	C60	C7	−111
O6	C6	C60	C100	74
C16	C6	C60	C7	10
C16	C6	C60	C100	−166
C50	C6	C60	C7	135
C50	C6	C60	C100	−40
C60	C7	C8	C9	2
C8	C7	C60	C6	178
C8	C7	C60	C100	−6
C7	C8	C9	C10	−3
C8	C9	C10	O10	−175
C8	C9	C10	C100	8
O10	C10	C100	C11	0
O10	C10	C100	C60	171
C9	C10	C100	C11	177
C9	C10	C100	C60	−12
O11	C11	C100	C10	10
O11	C11	C100	C60	−161

C110	C11	C100	C10	−166
C110	C11	C100	C60	23
O11	C11	C110	C12	5
O11	C11	C110	C50	−174
C100	C11	C110	C12	−179
C100	C11	C110	C50	2
O12	C12	C110	C11	−4
O12	C12	C110	C50	175
C120	C12	C110	C11	179
C120	C12	C110	C50	−3
O12	C12	C120	O13	−37
O12	C12	C120	C1	83
O12	C12	C120	C40	−156
C110	C12	C120	O13	141
C110	C12	C120	C1	−99
C110	C12	C120	C40	22
C4	C40	C120	O13	66
C4	C40	C120	C1	−49
C4	C40	C120	C12	−173
C5	C40	C120	O13	−170
C5	C40	C120	C1	75
C5	C40	C120	C12	−49
C5	C50	C110	C11	−168
C5	C50	C110	C12	13
C6	C50	C110	C11	−43
C6	C50	C110	C12	138
C6	C60	C100	C10	−173
C6	C60	C100	C11	−2
C7	C60	C100	C10	11
C7	C60	C100	C11	−178

50.12 Erythromycin A hydroiodide dihydrate (absolute configuration)

$C_{37}H_{68}NO_{13}{}^{+} , I^{-} , 2H_2O$

D.R.Harris, S.G.McGeachin, H.H.Mills, Tetrahedron Letters, 679, 1965

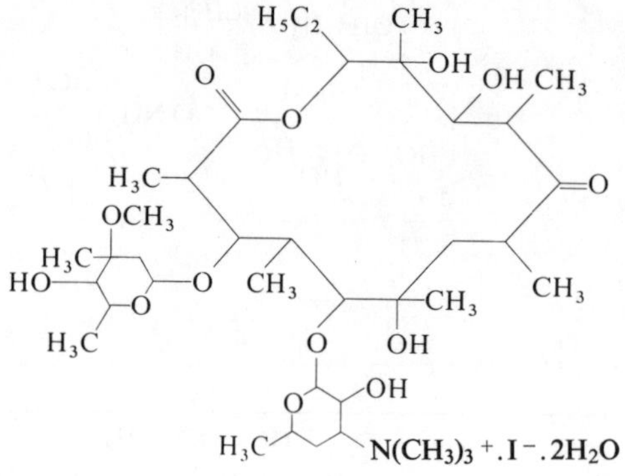

Atomic coordinates were not reported in the paper.
$P2_12_12_1$ $Z = 4$ $R = 0.153$

ERYTMI   LB 37-68-2

50.13 Rifamycin B p - iodoanilide pentahydrate acetone solvate

$C_{45}H_{53}IN_2O_{13} , C_3H_6O , 5H_2O$

M.Brufani, W.Fedeli, G.Giacomello, A.Vaciago, Experientia, 20, 339, 1964

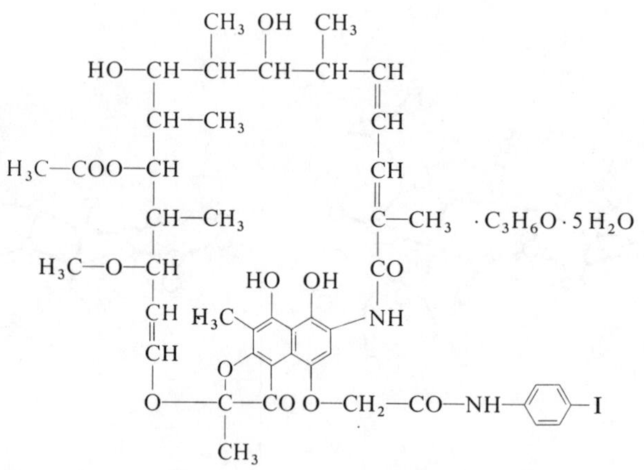

No comparison of bond lengths is possible since they are not reported in the paper. Published value of x(C34) = 0.4738. The correct value is −0.4738.
$P2_12_12_1$ $Z = 4$ $R = 0.202$

RIFIAN   LB 45-53-1

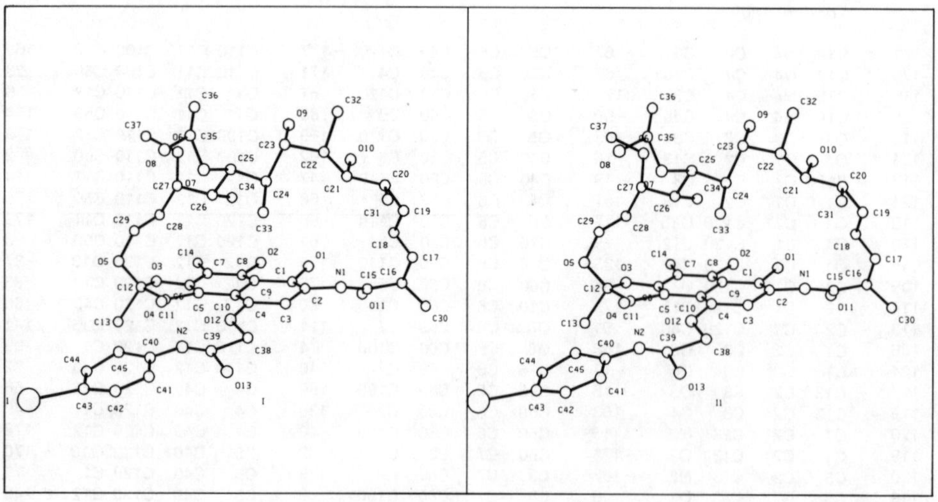

Bond Lengths

I1	C43	2.10	C9	C10	1.33
C2	N1	1.43	C11	C12	1.58
C15	N1	1.46	C12	C13	1.64
C39	N2	1.07	C15	C16	1.48
C40	N2	1.38	C16	C17	1.38
C1	O1	1.44	C16	C30	1.45
C8	O2	1.40	C17	C18	1.33
C6	O3	1.40	C18	C19	1.40
C12	O3	1.42	C19	C20	1.38
C11	O4	1.03	C20	C21	1.55
C12	O5	1.40	C20	C31	1.55
C29	O5	1.41	C21	C22	1.45
C27	O6	1.49	C22	C23	1.56
C37	O6	1.43	C22	C32	1.54
C25	O7	1.72	C23	C24	1.57
C35	O7	1.35	C24	C25	1.62
C35	O8	1.55	C24	C33	1.55
C23	O9	1.48	C25	C26	1.46
C21	O10	1.46	C26	C27	1.46
C15	O11	1.24	C26	C34	1.31
C4	O12	1.22	C27	C28	1.63
C38	O12	1.50	C28	C29	1.28
C39	O13	1.55	C35	C36	1.10
C1	C2	1.32	C38	C39	1.62
C1	C9	1.54	C40	C41	1.42
C2	C3	1.42	C40	C45	1.41
C3	C4	1.45	C41	C42	1.38
C4	C10	1.49	C42	C43	1.39
C5	C6	1.52	C43	C44	1.34
C5	C10	1.47	C44	C45	1.47
C5	C11	1.55			
C6	C7	1.24	C47	O14	1.39
C7	C8	1.43	C46	C47	1.63
C7	C14	1.51	C47	C48	1.75
C8	C9	1.45			

Bond Angles

C2	N1	C15	125	C16	C17	C18	130
C39	N2	C40	142	C17	C18	C19	129
C6	O3	C12	108	C18	C19	C20	134
C12	O5	C29	114	C19	C20	C21	114
C27	O6	C37	114	C19	C20	C31	107
C25	O7	C35	116	C21	C20	C31	116
C4	O12	C38	118	O10	C21	C20	108
O1	C1	C2	127	O10	C21	C22	109
O1	C1	C9	114	C20	C21	C22	116
C2	C1	C9	117	C21	C22	C23	118
N1	C2	C1	125	C21	C22	C32	122
N1	C2	C3	111	C23	C22	C32	104
C1	C2	C3	123	O9	C23	C22	106
C2	C3	C4	120	O9	C23	C24	103
O12	C4	C3	121	C22	C23	C24	112
O12	C4	C10	119	C23	C24	C25	106
C3	C4	C10	114	C23	C24	C33	113
C6	C5	C10	116	C25	C24	C83	119
C6	C5	C11	110	O7	C25	C24	94
C10	C5	C11	141	O7	C25	C26	100
O3	C6	C5	109	C24	C25	C26	120
O3	C6	C7	120	C25	C26	C27	116
C5	C6	C7	128	C25	C26	C34	103
C6	C7	C8	119	C27	C26	C34	113
C6	C7	C14	126	O6	C27	C26	109
C8	C7	C14	114	O6	C27	C28	106
O2	C8	C7	119	C26	C27	C28	114
O2	C8	C9	123	C27	C28	C29	114
C7	C8	C9	117	O5	C29	C28	128
C1	C9	C8	116	O7	C35	O8	97
C1	C9	C10	120	O7	C35	C36	133
C8	C9	C10	121	O8	C35	C36	130
C4	C10	C5	114	O12	C38	C39	97
C4	C10	C9	121	N2	C39	O13	116
C5	C10	C9	121	N2	C39	C38	142
O4	C11	C5	130	O13	C39	C38	101
O4	C11	C12	129	N2	C40	C41	122
C5	C11	C12	97	N2	C40	C45	117
O3	C12	O5	117	C41	C40	C45	121
O3	C12	C11	114	C40	C41	C42	122
O3	C12	C13	103	C41	C42	C43	120
O5	C12	C11	112	I1	C43	C42	122
O5	C12	C13	105	I1	C43	C44	118
C11	C12	C13	103	C42	C43	C44	118
N1	C15	O11	124	C43	C44	C45	126
N1	C15	C16	112	C40	C45	C44	112
O11	C15	C16	124				
C15	C16	C17	128	O14	C47	C46	121
C15	C16	C30	109	O14	C47	C48	108
C17	C16	C30	122	C46	C47	C48	125

Torsion Angles

C15	N1	C2	C1	−21	C10	C5	C6	O3	−177	C18	C19	C20	C31	121
C15	N1	C2	C3	151	C10	C5	C6	C7	−18	C19	C20	C21	O10	−62
C2	N1	C15	O11	−4	C11	C5	C6	O3	7	C19	C20	C21	C22	175
C2	N1	C15	C16	174	C11	C5	C6	C7	166	C31	C20	C21	O10	173
C40	N2	C39	O13	−12	C6	C5	C10	C4	178	C31	C20	C21	C22	49
C40	N2	C39	C38	−179	C6	C5	C10	C9	19	O10	C21	C22	C23	62
C12	O3	C6	C5	0	C11	C5	C10	C4	−8	O10	C21	C22	C32	−69
C12	O3	C6	C7	−162	C11	C5	C10	C9	−167	C20	C21	C22	C23	−176
C6	O3	C12	O5	127	C6	C5	C11	O4	−168	C20	C21	C22	C32	54
C6	O3	C12	C11	−6	C6	C5	C11	C12	−9	C21	C22	C23	O9	−65
C6	O3	C12	C13	−117	C10	C5	C11	O4	18	C32	C22	C23	O9	73
C29	O5	C12	O3	−77	C10	C5	C11	C12	177	C32	C22	C23	C24	−175
C29	O5	C12	C11	57	O3	C6	C7	C8	175	O9	C23	C24	C25	−57
C29	O5	C12	C13	169	C5	C6	C7	C8	18	O9	C23	C24	C33	171
C12	O5	C29	C28	43	C6	C7	C8	C9	−17	C22	C23	C24	C25	−170
C37	O6	C27	C26	−166	C7	C8	C9	C1	−179	C22	C23	C24	C33	58
C37	O6	C27	C28	71	C7	C8	C9	C10	21	C23	C24	C25	O7	−89
C35	O7	C25	C24	115	C1	C9	C10	C4	19	C23	C24	C25	C26	166
C35	O7	C25	C26	−123	C1	C9	C10	C5	177	C33	C24	C25	O7	39
C25	O7	C35	O8	175	C8	C9	C10	C4	179	C33	C24	C25	C26	−65
C25	O7	C35	C36	−3	C8	C9	C10	C5	−23	O7	C25	C26	C27	60
C38	O12	C4	C3	10	O4	C11	C12	O3	168	O7	C25	C26	C34	−176
C38	O12	C4	C10	162	O4	C11	C12	O5	32	C24	C25	C26	C27	161
C4	O12	C38	C39	171	O4	C11	C12	C13	−81	C24	C25	C26	C34	−75
C9	C1	C2	N1	−173	C5	C11	C12	O3	9	C25	C26	C27	O6	62
C9	C1	C2	C3	16	C5	C11	C12	O5	−127	C25	C26	C27	C28	−180
C2	C1	C9	C8	−178	C5	C11	C12	C13	121	C34	C26	C27	O6	−57
C2	C1	C9	C10	−17	N1	C15	C16	C17	−44	C34	C26	C27	C28	61
N1	C2	C3	C4	171	N1	C15	C16	C30	144	O6	C27	C28	C29	−126
C1	C2	C3	C4	−17	O11	C15	C16	C17	134	C26	C27	C28	C29	114
C2	C3	C4	O12	170	O11	C15	C16	C30	−38	C27	C28	C29	O5	−165
C2	C3	C4	C10	17	C15	C16	C17	C18	5	O12	C38	C39	N2	−12
O12	C4	C10	C5	28	C30	C16	C17	C18	176	O12	C38	C39	O13	180
O12	C4	C10	C9	−173	C16	C17	C18	C19	163	C41	C40	N2	C39	16
C3	C4	C10	C5	−178	C17	C18	C19	C20	−173					
C3	C4	C10	C9	−19	C18	C19	C20	C21	−9					

51.1   4 - Bromoestrone

D.A.Norton, G.Kartha, C.T.Lu, Acta Cryst., 16, 89, 1963

$C_{18}H_{21}BrO_2$

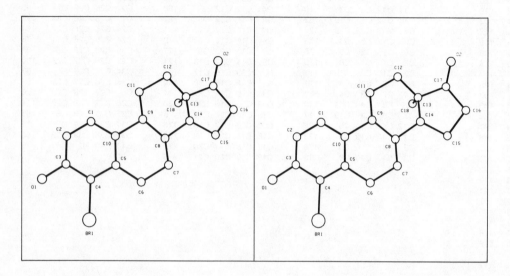

$P2_12_12_1$ Z = 4   R = 0.12

BRESON   LB 18-21-1

Bond Lengths

Br1	C4	1.92
C3	O1	1.37
C17	O2	1.29
C1	C2	1.39
C1	C10	1.42
C2	C3	1.34
C3	C4	1.42
C4	C5	1.43
C5	C6	1.46
C5	C10	1.40
C6	C7	1.56
C7	C8	1.53

C8	C9	1.56
C8	C14	1.50
C9	C10	1.55
C9	C11	1.58
C11	C12	1.61
C12	C13	1.55
C13	C14	1.49
C13	C17	1.53
C13	C18	1.58
C14	C15	1.57
C15	C16	1.56
C16	C17	1.57

Bond Angles

C2	C1	C10	121
C1	C2	C3	121
O1	C3	C2	122
O1	C3	C4	119
C2	C3	C4	119
Br1	C4	C3	119
Br1	C4	C5	119
C3	C4	C5	122
C4	C5	C6	120
C4	C5	C10	116
C6	C5	C10	123
C5	C6	C7	117
C6	C7	C8	108
C7	C8	C9	108
C7	C8	C14	112
C9	C8	C14	106
C8	C9	C10	109
C8	C9	C11	111
C10	C9	C11	109

C1	C10	C5	121
C1	C10	C9	121
C5	C10	C9	118
C9	C11	C12	108
C11	C12	C13	106
C12	C13	C14	108
C12	C13	C17	114
C12	C13	C18	113
C14	C13	C17	103
C14	C13	C18	117
C17	C13	C18	101
C8	C14	C13	112
C8	C14	C15	118
C13	C14	C15	105
C14	C15	C16	102
C15	C16	C17	104
O2	C17	C13	123
O2	C17	C16	129
C13	C17	C16	108

Torsion Angles

C10	C1	C2	C3	2
C2	C1	C10	C5	−1
C2	C1	C10	C9	−176
C1	C2	C3	O1	180
C1	C2	C3	C4	−5
O1	C3	C4	Br1	−2
O1	C3	C4	C5	−178
C2	C3	C4	Br1	−177
C2	C3	C4	C5	7
Br1	C4	C5	C6	6
Br1	C4	C5	C10	178
C3	C4	C5	C6	−178
C3	C4	C5	C10	−6
C4	C5	C6	C7	−176
C10	C5	C6	C7	13
C4	C5	C10	C1	2
C4	C5	C10	C9	178
C6	C5	C10	C1	174
C6	C5	C10	C9	−10
C5	C6	C7	C8	−40
C6	C7	C8	C9	64
C6	C7	C8	C14	−179
C7	C8	C9	C10	−62
C7	C8	C9	C11	177
C14	C8	C9	C10	177
C14	C8	C9	C11	57
C7	C8	C14	C13	180
C7	C8	C14	C15	57
C9	C8	C14	C13	−63

C9	C8	C14	C15	175
C8	C9	C10	C1	−150
C8	C9	C10	C5	35
C11	C9	C10	C1	−28
C11	C9	C10	C5	157
C8	C9	C11	C12	−58
C10	C9	C11	C12	−178
C9	C11	C12	C13	60
C11	C12	C13	C14	−65
C11	C12	C13	C17	−179
C11	C12	C13	C18	66
C12	C13	C14	C8	70
C12	C13	C14	C15	−161
C17	C13	C14	C8	−170
C17	C13	C14	C15	−40
C18	C13	C14	C8	−60
C18	C13	C14	C15	70
C12	C13	C17	O2	−35
C12	C13	C17	C16	140
C14	C13	C17	O2	−152
C14	C13	C17	C16	24
C18	C13	C17	O2	87
C18	C13	C17	C16	−98
C8	C14	C15	C16	167
C13	C14	C15	C16	41
C14	C15	C16	C17	−25
C15	C16	C17	O2	177
C15	C16	C17	C13	2

51.2   4 - Bromoestradiol methanol solvate

$C_{18}H_{23}BrO_2$, CH_4O

D.A.Norton, G.Kartha, C.T.Lu, Acta Cryst., 17, 77, 1964

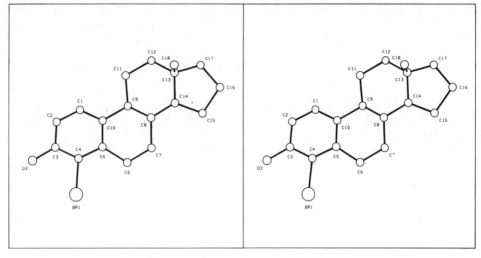

In the publication identical coordinates have been recorded for C17 and O17. The latter atom is incorrect and has been excluded from the calculation.

$P2_12_12_1$ Z = 4   R = 0.13

BESOLM   LB 18-23-1

Bond Lengths

Br1	C4	1.93	
C3	O3	1.36	
C1	C2	1.39	
C1	C10	1.37	
C2	C3	1.40	
C3	C4	1.39	
C4	C5	1.37	
C5	C6	1.52	
C5	C10	1.42	
C6	C7	1.56	
C7	C8	1.54	
C8	C9	1.56	
C8	C14	1.53	

C9	C10	1.54
C9	C11	1.56
C11	C12	1.57
C12	C13	1.54
C13	C14	1.53
C13	C17	1.54
C13	C18	1.55
C14	C15	1.57
C15	C16	1.58
C16	C17	1.57
C19	O19	1.42

Bond Angles

C2	C1	C10	124
C1	C2	C3	118
O3	C3	C2	122
O3	C3	C4	120
C2	C3	C4	117
Br1	C4	C3	116
Br1	C4	C5	119
C3	C4	C5	125
C4	C5	C6	120
C4	C5	C10	117
C6	C5	C10	123
C5	C6	C7	111
C6	C7	C8	110
C7	C8	C9	107
C7	C8	C14	114
C9	C8	C14	106
C8	C9	C10	111
C8	C9	C11	109

C10	C9	C11	112
C1	C10	C5	118
C1	C10	C9	121
C5	C10	C9	120
C9	C11	C12	112
C11	C12	C13	110
C12	C13	C14	109
C12	C13	C17	114
C12	C13	C18	111
C14	C13	C17	99
C14	C13	C18	115
C17	C13	C18	110
C8	C14	C13	112
C8	C14	C15	117
C13	C14	C15	105
C14	C15	C16	102
C15	C16	C17	105
C13	C17	C16	104

Torsion Angles

C10	C1	C2	C3	−1
C2	C1	C10	C5	3
C2	C1	C10	C9	180
C1	C2	C3	C4	2
C2	C3	C4	C5	−5
C3	C4	C5	C6	−176
C3	C4	C5	C10	7
C4	C5	C6	C7	169
C10	C5	C6	C7	−14
C4	C5	C10	C1	−6
C4	C5	C10	C9	178
C6	C5	C10	C1	177
C6	C5	C10	C9	0
C5	C6	C7	C8	48
C6	C7	C8	C9	−70
C6	C7	C8	C14	173
C7	C8	C9	C10	54
C7	C8	C9	C11	178
C14	C8	C9	C10	176
C14	C8	C9	C11	−60
C7	C8	C14	C13	−176
C7	C8	C14	C15	−56

C9	C8	C14	C13	66
C9	C8	C14	C15	−173
C8	C9	C10	C1	163
C8	C9	C10	C5	−21
C11	C9	C10	C1	40
C11	C9	C10	C5	−143
C8	C9	C11	C12	57
C10	C9	C11	C12	−180
C9	C11	C12	C13	−54
C11	C12	C13	C14	55
C11	C12	C13	C17	164
C12	C13	C14	C8	−64
C12	C13	C14	C15	168
C17	C13	C14	C8	177
C17	C13	C14	C15	50
C12	C13	C17	C16	−159
C14	C13	C17	C16	−45
C8	C14	C15	C16	−159
C13	C14	C15	C16	−35
C14	C15	C16	C17	6
C15	C16	C17	C13	24

51.3 2β,3β,14α,22β,25 - Pentahydroxy - Δ^7 - 5β - cholesten - 6 - one $C_{27}H_{44}O_6$

R.Huber, W.Hoppe, Chem. Ber., 98, 2403, 1965

$P2_12_12_1$ Z = 4   R = 0.15

HYCHLO   LB 27-44-10

Bond Lengths

C6	O1	1.25	C9	C11	1.52
C14	O2	1.42	C10	C19	1.55
C2	O3	1.43	C11	C12	1.57
C3	O4	1.42	C12	C13	1.52
C25	O5	1.43	C13	C14	1.56
C22	O6	1.45	C13	C17	1.56
C1	C2	1.49	C13	C18	1.54
C1	C10	1.55	C14	C15	1.51
C2	C3	1.53	C15	C16	1.56
C3	C4	1.53	C16	C17	1.54
C4	C5	1.51	C17	C20	1.56
C5	C6	1.52	C20	C21	1.57
C5	C10	1.53	C20	C22	1.54
C6	C7	1.43	C22	C23	1.51
C7	C8	1.35	C23	C24	1.55
C8	C9	1.52	C24	C25	1.54
C8	C14	1.50	C25	C26	1.57
C9	C10	1.56	C25	C27	1.56

Bond Angles

C2	C1	C10	114	C12	C13	C17	115
O3	C2	C1	111	C12	C13	C18	111
O3	C2	C3	110	C14	C13	C17	99
C1	C2	C3	111	C14	C13	C18	110
O4	C3	C2	110	C17	C13	C18	113
O4	C3	C4	108	O2	C14	C8	105
C2	C3	C4	109	O2	C14	C13	107
C3	C4	C5	112	O2	C14	C15	108
C4	C5	C6	110	C8	C14	C13	113
C4	C5	C10	113	C8	C14	C15	120
C6	C5	C10	111	C13	C14	C15	104
O1	C6	C5	119	C14	C15	C16	103
O1	C6	C7	123	C15	C16	C17	108
C5	C6	C7	118	C13	C17	C16	103
C6	C7	C8	122	C13	C17	C20	116
C7	C8	C9	124	C16	C17	C20	111
C7	C8	C14	122	C17	C20	C21	112
C9	C8	C14	113	C17	C20	C22	109
C8	C9	C10	111	C21	C20	C22	111
C8	C9	C11	114	O6	C22	C20	106
C10	C9	C11	112	O6	C22	C23	112
C1	C10	C5	107	C20	C22	C23	117
C1	C10	C9	112	C22	C23	C24	114
C1	C10	C19	109	C23	C24	C25	114
C5	C10	C9	110	O5	C25	C24	107
C5	C10	C19	108	O5	C25	C26	107
C9	C10	C19	111	O5	C25	C27	107
C9	C11	C12	113	C24	C25	C26	113
C11	C12	C13	109	C24	C25	C27	109
C12	C13	C14	108	C26	C25	C27	114

Torsion Angles

C10	C1	C2	C3	58	C8	C9	C11	C12	48
C2	C1	C10	C5	-55	C10	C9	C11	C12	175
C2	C1	C10	C9	65	C9	C11	C12	C13	-56
C1	C2	C3	C4	-55	C11	C12	C13	C14	61
C2	C3	C4	C5	55	C11	C12	C13	C17	170
C3	C4	C5	C6	179	C12	C13	C14	C8	-60
C3	C4	C5	C10	-57	C12	C13	C14	C15	168
C4	C5	C6	O1	-89	C17	C13	C14	C8	-180
C10	C5	C6	O1	145	C17	C13	C14	C15	49
C10	C5	C6	C7	-38	C12	C13	C17	C16	-156
C4	C5	C10	C1	54	C12	C13	C17	C20	84
C4	C5	C10	C9	-67	C14	C13	C17	C16	-41
C6	C5	C10	C1	178	C14	C13	C17	C20	-162
C6	C5	C10	C9	56	C8	C14	C15	C16	-163
O1	C6	C7	C8	-176	C13	C14	C15	C16	-36
C5	C6	C7	C8	8	C14	C15	C16	C17	10
C6	C7	C8	C9	4	C15	C16	C17	C13	20
C6	C7	C8	C14	-166	C15	C16	C17	C20	145
C7	C8	C9	C10	16	C13	C17	C20	C21	-57
C7	C8	C9	C11	144	C13	C17	C20	C22	179
C14	C8	C9	C10	-174	C16	C17	C20	C21	-173
C14	C8	C9	C11	-46	C16	C17	C20	C22	63
C7	C8	C14	C13	-137	C17	C20	C22	O6	-162
C7	C8	C14	C15	-15	C21	C20	C22	O6	74
C9	C8	C14	C13	52	C21	C20	C22	C23	-51
C9	C8	C14	C15	175	O6	C22	C23	C24	68
C8	C9	C10	C1	-164	C20	C22	C23	C24	-171
C8	C9	C10	C5	-45	C22	C23	C24	C25	-100
C11	C9	C10	C1	68	C23	C24	C25	O5	63
C11	C9	C10	C5	-174					

51.4 22,23 - Dibromo - 12 - methyl - 18 - norergostan - 8,11,13 - trien - 3β - yl acetate

$C_{30}H_{44}Br_2O_2$

T.N.Margulis, C.F.Hammer, R.Stevenson, J. Chem. Soc., 4396, 1964

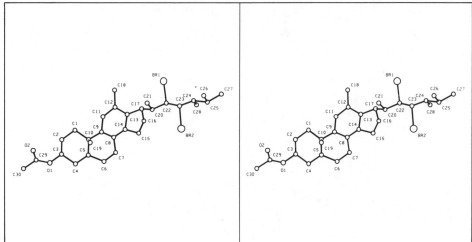

No comparison of bond lengths is possible since they are not reported in the paper.
C2   Z = 4   R = 0.11

NERGAC   LB 30-44-3

Bond Lengths

Br1	C22	2.01
Br2	C23	2.04
C3	O1	1.47
C29	O1	1.51
C29	O2	1.07
C1	C2	1.56
C1	C10	1.54
C2	C3	1.51
C3	C4	1.64
C4	C5	1.57
C5	C6	1.59
C5	C10	1.58
C6	C7	1.60
C7	C8	1.44
C8	C9	1.40
C8	C14	1.34
C9	C10	1.47
C9	C11	1.39
C10	C19	1.57
C11	C12	1.45
C12	C13	1.47
C12	C18	1.53
C13	C14	1.40
C13	C17	1.51
C14	C15	1.66
C15	C16	1.33
C16	C17	1.64
C17	C20	1.46
C20	C21	1.54
C20	C22	1.50
C22	C23	1.50
C23	C24	1.55
C24	C25	1.67
C24	C28	1.48
C25	C26	1.52
C25	C27	1.68
C29	C30	1.72

Bond Angles

C3	O1	C29	109
C2	C1	C10	106
C1	C2	C3	109
O1	C3	C2	103
O1	C3	C4	99
C2	C3	C4	105
C3	C4	C5	102
C4	C5	C6	122
C4	C5	C10	103
C6	C5	C10	108
C5	C6	C7	118
C6	C7	C8	103
C7	C8	C9	124
C7	C8	C14	109
C9	C8	C14	127
C8	C9	C10	133
C8	C9	C11	106
C10	C9	C11	121
C1	C10	C5	112
C1	C10	C9	112
C1	C10	C19	112
C5	C10	C9	105
C5	C10	C19	107
C9	C10	C19	110
C9	C11	C12	131
C11	C12	C13	115
C11	C12	C18	124
C13	C12	C18	119
C12	C13	C14	112
C12	C13	C17	132
C14	C13	C17	116
C8	C14	C13	127
C8	C14	C15	134
C13	C14	C15	99
C14	C15	C16	108
C15	C16	C17	106
C13	C17	C16	96
C13	C17	C20	111
C16	C17	C20	115
C17	C20	C21	116
C17	C20	C22	117
C21	C20	C22	108
Br1	C22	C20	107
Br1	C22	C23	111
C20	C22	C23	122
Br2	C23	C22	102
Br2	C23	C24	103
C22	C23	C24	109
C23	C24	C25	104
C23	C24	C28	124
C25	C24	C28	116
C24	C25	C26	111
C24	C25	C27	103
C26	C25	C27	119
O1	C29	O2	128
O1	C29	C30	100
O2	C29	C30	121

Torsion Angles

C29	O1	C3	C2	92
C29	O1	C3	C4	−160
C3	O1	C29	O2	−27
C3	O1	C29	C30	−171
C10	C1	C2	C3	−62
C2	C1	C10	C5	61
C2	C1	C10	C9	178
C2	C1	C10	C19	−58
C1	C2	C3	O1	172
C1	C2	C3	C4	69
O1	C3	C4	C5	−179
C2	C3	C4	C5	−73
C3	C4	C5	C6	−170
C3	C4	C5	C10	69
C4	C5	C6	C7	177
C10	C5	C6	C7	−64
C4	C5	C10	C1	−67
C4	C5	C10	C9	172
C4	C5	C10	C19	55
C6	C5	C10	C1	162
C6	C5	C10	C9	41
C6	C5	C10	C19	−76
C5	C6	C7	C8	48
C6	C7	C8	C9	−17
C6	C7	C8	C14	163
C7	C8	C9	C10	5
C7	C8	C9	C11	−170
C14	C8	C9	C10	−175
C14	C8	C9	C11	10
C7	C8	C14	C13	179
C7	C8	C14	C15	8
C9	C8	C14	C13	−1
C9	C8	C14	C15	−172
C8	C9	C10	C1	−139
C8	C9	C10	C5	−18
C8	C9	C10	C19	97
C11	C9	C10	C1	35
C11	C9	C10	C5	156
C11	C9	C10	C19	−89
C8	C9	C11	C12	−19

C10	C9	C11	C12	166
C9	C11	C12	C13	17
C9	C11	C12	C18	−177
C11	C12	C13	C14	−4
C11	C12	C13	C17	−178
C18	C12	C13	C14	−170
C18	C12	C13	C17	15
C12	C13	C14	C8	−2
C12	C13	C14	C15	171
C17	C13	C14	C8	173
C17	C13	C14	C15	−14
C12	C13	C17	C16	−155
C12	C13	C17	C20	85
C14	C13	C17	C16	31
C14	C13	C17	C20	−89
C8	C14	C15	C16	159
C13	C14	C15	C16	−14
C14	C15	C16	C17	33
C15	C16	C17	C13	−38
C15	C16	C17	C20	78
C13	C17	C20	C21	−47
C13	C17	C20	C22	−175
C16	C17	C20	C21	−154
C16	C17	C20	C22	77
C17	C20	C22	Br1	65
C17	C20	C22	C23	−165
C21	C20	C22	Br1	−68
C21	C20	C22	C23	62
Br1	C22	C23	Br2	−173
Br1	C22	C23	C24	−64
C20	C22	C23	Br2	59
C20	C22	C23	C24	168
Br2	C23	C24	C25	−79
Br2	C23	C24	C28	57
C22	C23	C24	C25	173
C22	C23	C24	C28	−51
C23	C24	C25	C26	−45
C23	C24	C25	C27	−173
C28	C24	C25	C26	175
C28	C24	C25	C27	46

51.5   Calciferyl 4 - iodo - 3 - nitrobenzoate

$C_{35}H_{46}INO_4$

D.C.Hodgkin, B.M.Rimmer, J.D.Dunitz, K.N.Trueblood, J. Chem. Soc., 4945, 1963

No comparison of bond lengths is possible since they are not reported in the paper.
P2$_1$2$_1$2$_1$ Z = 4   R = 0.154

CALIFI   LB 35-46-1

Bond Lengths

I1	C32	1.95	C13	C14	1.50
N1	O3	1.32	C13	C17	1.62
N1	O4	1.07	C13	C18	1.62
C33	N1	1.55	C14	C15	1.62
C3	O1	1.51	C15	C16	1.56
C35	O1	1.32	C16	C17	1.50
C35	O2	1.22	C17	C20	1.56
C1	C2	1.49	C20	C21	1.55
C1	C10	1.42	C20	C22	1.41
C2	C3	1.56	C22	C23	1.27
C3	C4	1.43	C23	C24	1.41
C4	C5	1.60	C24	C25	1.39
C5	C6	1.30	C24	C28	1.48
C5	C10	1.45	C25	C26	1.54
C6	C7	1.46	C25	C27	1.66
C7	C8	1.43	C29	C30	1.34
C8	C9	1.42	C29	C34	1.58
C8	C14	1.47	C29	C35	1.46
C9	C11	1.64	C30	C31	1.40
C10	C19	1.38	C31	C32	1.26
C11	C12	1.49	C32	C33	1.49
C12	C13	1.46	C33	C34	1.47

Bond Angles

O3	N1	O4	124	C13	C14	C15	104
O3	N1	C33	111	C14	C15	C16	102
O4	N1	C33	123	C15	C16	C17	110
C3	O1	C35	121	C13	C17	C16	104
C2	C1	C10	115	C13	C17	C20	123
C1	C2	C3	108	C16	C17	C20	112
O1	C3	C2	105	C17	C20	C21	109
O1	C3	C4	106	C17	C20	C22	109
C2	C3	C4	113	C21	C20	C22	110
C3	C4	C5	109	C20	C22	C23	134
C4	C5	C6	121	C22	C23	C24	136
C4	C5	C10	116	C23	C24	C25	118
C6	C5	C10	123	C23	C24	C28	116
C5	C6	C7	128	C25	C24	C28	106
C6	C7	C8	123	C24	C25	C26	119
C7	C8	C9	130	C24	C25	C27	119
C7	C8	C14	113	C26	C25	C27	99
C9	C8	C14	114	C30	C29	C34	123
C8	C9	C11	115	C30	C29	C35	133
C1	C10	C5	111	C34	C29	C35	104
C1	C10	C19	128	C29	C30	C31	121
C5	C10	C19	119	C30	C31	C32	129
C9	C11	C12	106	I1	C32	C31	125
C11	C12	C13	121	I1	C32	C33	127
C12	C13	C14	118	C31	C32	C33	108
C12	C13	C17	124	N1	C33	C32	114
C12	C13	C18	107	N1	C33	C34	110
C14	C13	C17	102	C32	C33	C34	136
C14	C13	C18	111	C29	C34	C33	102
C17	C13	C18	103	O1	C35	O2	120
C8	C14	C13	115	O1	C35	C29	106
C8	C14	C15	121	O2	C35	C29	134

Torsion Angles

O3	N1	C33	C32	68	C7	C8	C14	C13	−120
O3	N1	C33	C34	−115	C7	C8	C14	C15	7
O4	N1	C33	C32	−127	C9	C8	C14	C13	54
O4	N1	C33	C34	51	C9	C8	C14	C15	180
C35	O1	C3	C2	76	C8	C9	C11	C12	43
C35	O1	C3	C4	−164	C9	C11	C12	C13	−45
C3	O1	C35	O2	0	C11	C12	C13	C14	50
C3	O1	C35	C29	178	C11	C12	C13	C17	171
C10	C1	C2	C3	−57	C11	C12	C13	C18	−71
C2	C1	C10	C5	54	C12	C13	C14	C8	−50
C2	C1	C10	C19	−111	C12	C13	C14	C15	175
C1	C2	C3	O1	173	C17	C13	C14	C8	177
C1	C2	C3	C4	57	C17	C13	C14	C15	42
O1	C3	C4	C5	−167	C18	C13	C14	C8	68
C2	C3	C4	C5	−52	C18	C13	C14	C15	−67
C3	C4	C5	C6	−131	C12	C13	C17	C16	−160
C3	C4	C5	C10	50	C12	C13	C17	C20	72
C4	C5	C6	C7	−180	C14	C13	C17	C16	−35
C10	C5	C6	C7	−1	C14	C13	C17	C20	−164
C4	C5	C10	C1	−49	C18	C13	C17	C16	80
C4	C5	C10	C19	118	C18	C13	C17	C20	−48
C6	C5	C10	C1	132	C8	C14	C15	C16	−164
C6	C5	C10	C19	−61	C13	C14	C15	C16	−34
C5	C6	C7	C8	167	C14	C15	C16	C17	11
C6	C7	C8	C9	10	C15	C16	C17	C20	149
C6	C7	C8	C14	−179	C13	C17	C20	C21	−49
C7	C8	C9	C11	122	C13	C17	C20	C22	−170
C14	C8	C9	C11	−50					

C16	C17	C20	C21	−174
C16	C17	C20	C22	65
C17	C20	C22	C23	−119
C21	C20	C22	C23	121
C20	C22	C23	C24	175
C22	C23	C24	C25	111
C22	C23	C24	C28	−122
C23	C24	C25	C26	−55
C23	C24	C25	C27	65
C28	C24	C25	C26	173
C28	C24	C25	C27	−66
C34	C29	C30	C31	10
C35	C29	C30	C31	−171
C30	C29	C34	C33	−5
C35	C29	C34	C33	175
C30	C29	C35	O1	−10
C30	C29	C35	O2	168
C34	C29	C35	O1	169
C34	C29	C35	O2	−12
C29	C30	C31	C32	−10
C30	C31	C32	I1	−175
C30	C31	C32	C33	5
I1	C32	C33	N1	−3
I1	C32	C33	C34	−180
C31	C32	C33	N1	176
C31	C32	C33	C34	0
N1	C33	C34	C29	−176
C32	C33	C34	C29	0

51.6 Suprasteryl II 4 - iodo - 3 - nitrobenzoate

$C_{35}H_{46}INO_4$

C.P.Saunderson, Acta Cryst., 19, 187, 1965

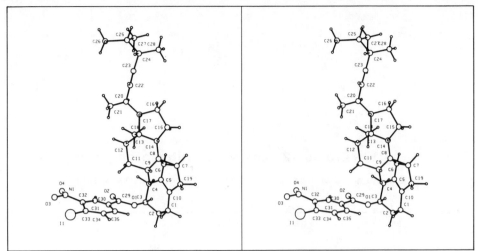

No comparison of bond lengths is possible since they are not reported in the paper.
C2   Z = 4   No R factor was given.

SUPRIN   LB 35-46-5

Bond Lengths

I1	C33	1.82	C12	C13	1.43
N1	O3	1.21	C13	C14	1.53
N1	O4	1.10	C13	C17	1.60
C32	N1	1.58	C13	C18	1.62
C3	O1	1.51	C14	C15	1.43
C29	O1	1.38	C15	C16	1.60
C29	O2	1.40	C16	C17	1.57
C1	C2	1.50	C17	C20	1.52
C1	C10	1.51	C20	C21	1.32
C2	C3	1.48	C20	C22	1.48
C3	C4	1.54	C22	C23	1.35
C4	C5	1.55	C23	C24	1.54
C5	C6	1.33	C24	C25	1.55
C5	C10	1.37	C24	C28	1.58
C6	C7	1.57	C25	C26	1.86
C6	C8	1.57	C25	C27	1.75
C7	C8	1.58	C29	C30	1.48
C7	C19	1.47	C30	C31	1.20
C8	C9	1.39	C30	C35	1.44
C8	C14	1.48	C31	C32	1.61
C9	C11	1.61	C32	C33	1.62
C10	C19	1.42	C33	C34	1.48
C11	C12	1.61	C34	C35	1.31

Bond Angles

O3	N1	O4	121	C17	C13	C18	107
O3	N1	C32	115	C8	C14	C13	113
O4	N1	C32	122	C8	C14	C15	125
C3	O1	C29	114	C13	C14	C15	106
C2	C1	C10	112	C14	C15	C16	106
C1	C2	C3	112	C15	C16	C17	108
O1	C3	C2	106	C13	C17	C16	100
O1	C3	C4	106	C13	C17	C20	123
C2	C3	C4	117	C16	C17	C20	115
C3	C4	C5	109	C7	C19	C10	107
C4	C5	C6	124	C17	C20	C21	118
C4	C5	C10	122	C17	C20	C22	106
C6	C5	C10	114	C21	C20	C22	111
C5	C6	C7	106	C20	C22	C23	122
C5	C6	C8	118	C22	C23	C24	124
C7	C6	C8	60	C23	C24	C25	107
C6	C7	C8	60	C23	C24	C28	118
C6	C7	C19	103	C25	C24	C28	121
C8	C7	C19	120	C24	C25	C26	114
C6	C8	C7	60	C24	C25	C27	103
C6	C8	C9	116	C26	C25	C27	131
C6	C8	C14	122	O1	C29	O2	125
C7	C8	C9	117	O1	C29	C30	108
C7	C8	C14	118	O2	C29	C30	126
C9	C8	C14	114	C29	C30	C31	108
C8	C9	C11	112	C29	C30	C35	124
C1	C10	C5	125	C31	C30	C35	128
C1	C10	C19	126	C30	C31	C32	113
C5	C10	C19	109	N1	C32	C31	114
C9	C11	C12	111	N1	C32	C33	117
C11	C12	C13	110	C31	C32	C33	128
C12	C13	C14	115	I1	C33	C32	130
C12	C13	C17	113	I1	C33	C34	137
C12	C13	C18	106	C32	C33	C34	93
C14	C13	C17	105	C33	C34	C35	142
C14	C13	C18	112	C30	C35	C34	114

Torsion Angles

O3	N1	C32	C31	173	C9	C11	C12	C13	49
O3	N1	C32	C33	−6	C11	C12	C13	C14	−51
O4	N1	C32	C31	10	C11	C12	C13	C17	−171
O4	N1	C32	C33	−170	C11	C12	C13	C18	73
C29	O1	C3	C2	−156	C12	C13	C14	C8	54
C29	O1	C3	C4	79	C12	C13	C14	C15	−165
C3	O1	C29	O2	9	C17	C13	C14	C8	178
C3	O1	C29	C30	−180	C17	C13	C14	C15	−41
C10	C1	C2	C3	−40	C18	C13	C14	C8	−66
C2	C1	C10	C5	12	C18	C13	C14	C15	75
C2	C1	C10	C19	−167	C12	C13	C17	C16	160
C1	C2	C3	O1	−59	C12	C13	C17	C20	−71
C1	C2	C3	C4	59	C14	C13	C17	C16	35
O1	C3	C4	C5	75	C14	C13	C17	C20	163
C2	C3	C4	C5	−43	C18	C13	C17	C16	−84
C3	C4	C5	C6	−164	C18	C13	C17	C20	44
C3	C4	C5	C10	13	C8	C14	C15	C16	163
C4	C5	C6	C7	177	C13	C14	C15	C16	28
C4	C5	C6	C8	112	C14	C15	C16	C17	−5
C10	C5	C6	C7	−1	C15	C16	C17	C13	−18
C10	C5	C6	C8	−65	C15	C16	C17	C20	−151
C4	C5	C10	C1	1	C13	C17	C20	C21	51
C4	C5	C10	C19	180	C13	C17	C20	C22	176
C6	C5	C10	C1	179	C16	C17	C20	C21	172
C6	C5	C10	C19	−3	C16	C17	C20	C22	−63
C5	C6	C7	C8	−114	C17	C20	C22	C23	121
C5	C6	C7	C19	4	C21	C20	C22	C23	−110
C8	C6	C7	C19	117	C20	C22	C23	C24	−175
C5	C6	C8	C7	93	C22	C23	C24	C25	−127
C5	C6	C8	C9	−15	C22	C23	C24	C28	93
C5	C6	C8	C14	−161	C23	C24	C25	C26	70
C7	C6	C8	C9	−108	C23	C24	C25	C27	−78
C7	C6	C8	C14	106	C28	C24	C25	C26	−152
C6	C7	C8	C9	−15	C28	C24	C25	C27	61
C6	C7	C8	C14	−112	O1	C29	C30	C31	180
C19	C7	C8	C6	−88	O1	C29	C30	C35	1
C19	C7	C8	C9	17	O2	C29	C30	C31	−8
C19	C7	C8	C14	159	O2	C29	C30	C35	172
C6	C7	C19	C10	−5	C29	C30	C31	C32	−175
C8	C7	C19	C10	57	C35	C30	C31	C32	4
C6	C8	C9	C11	−95	C29	C30	C35	C34	179
C7	C8	C9	C11	−163	C31	C30	C35	C34	0
C14	C8	C9	C11	54	C30	C31	C32	N1	172
C6	C8	C14	C13	92	C30	C31	C32	C33	−8
C6	C8	C14	C15	−40	N1	C32	C33	I1	5
C7	C8	C14	C13	162	N1	C32	C33	C34	−174
C7	C8	C14	C15	30	C31	C32	C33	I1	−175
C9	C8	C14	C13	−55	C31	C32	C33	C34	6
C9	C8	C14	C15	173	I1	C33	C34	C35	−180
C8	C9	C11	C12	−51	C32	C33	C34	C35	−1
C1	C10	C19	C7	−176	C33	C34	C35	C30	−2
C5	C10	C19	C7	5					

52.1   (+) - 10 - Bromo - 2 - chloro - 2 - nitrosocamphane

C₁₀H₁₅BrClNO

G.Ferguson, C.J.Fritchie, J.M.Robertson, G.A.Sim, J. Chem. Soc., 1976, 1961

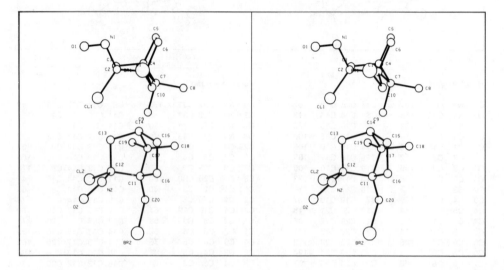

$C_{10}H_{15}BrClNO$

P2₁2₁2₁   Z = 8   R = 0.16

BCNCAM   LB 10-15-1

Bond Lengths

Br1	C10	1.85	Br2	C20	1.89	
Cl1	C2	1.81	Cl2	C12	1.75	
N1	O1	1.16	N2	O2	1.21	
C2	N1	1.52	C12	N2	1.44	
C1	C2	1.55	C11	C12	1.56	
C1	C6	1.59	C11	C16	1.54	
C1	C7	1.58	C11	C17	1.60	
C1	C10	1.53	C11	C20	1.51	
C2	C3	1.56	C12	C13	1.59	
C3	C4	1.54	C13	C14	1.52	
C4	C5	1.58	C14	C15	1.55	
C4	C7	1.52	C14	C17	1.60	
C5	C6	1.55	C15	C16	1.54	
C7	C8	1.54	C17	C18	1.50	
C7	C9	1.61	C17	C19	1.54	

Bond Angles

O1	N1	C2	117	O2	N2	C12	119
C2	C1	C6	108	C12	C11	C16	108
C2	C1	C7	100	C12	C11	C17	103
C2	C1	C10	114	C12	C11	C20	116
C6	C1	C7	97	C16	C11	C17	97
C6	C1	C10	117	C16	C11	C20	117
C7	C1	C10	117	C17	C11	C20	114
Cl1	C2	N1	108	Cl2	C12	N2	111
Cl1	C2	C1	115	Cl2	C12	C11	117
Cl1	C2	C3	109	Cl2	C12	C13	113
N1	C2	C1	110	N2	C12	C11	116
N1	C2	C3	109	N2	C12	C13	96
C2	C3	C4	107	C11	C12	C13	102
C2	C3	C4	100	C12	C13	C14	104
C3	C4	C5	113	C13	C14	C15	112
C3	C4	C7	103	C13	C14	C17	102
C5	C4	C7	100	C15	C14	C17	103
C4	C5	C6	103	C14	C15	C16	98
C1	C6	C5	104	C11	C16	C15	110
C1	C7	C4	95	C11	C17	C14	91
C1	C7	C8	120	C11	C17	C18	114
C1	C7	C9	114	C11	C17	C19	115
C4	C7	C8	119	C14	C17	C18	112
C4	C7	C9	116	C14	C17	C19	113
C8	C7	C9	95	C18	C17	C19	111
Br1	C10	C1	116	Br2	C20	C11	112

Torsion Angles

O1	N1	C2	Cl1	−12	O2	N2	C12	Cl2	14
O1	N1	C2	C1	−137	O2	N2	C12	C11	−122
O1	N1	C2	C3	106	O2	N2	C12	C13	132
C6	C1	C2	Cl1	−166	C16	C11	C12	Cl2	−169
C6	C1	C2	N1	−44	C16	C11	C12	N2	−36
C6	C1	C2	C3	74	C16	C11	C12	C13	68
C7	C1	C2	Cl1	93	C17	C11	C12	Cl2	89
C7	C1	C2	N1	−145	C17	C11	C12	N2	−138
C7	C1	C2	C3	−27	C17	C11	C12	C13	−35
C10	C1	C2	Cl1	−33	C20	C11	C12	Cl2	−36
C10	C1	C2	N1	89	C20	C11	C12	N2	97
C10	C1	C2	C3	−154	C20	C11	C12	C13	−159
C2	C1	C6	C5	−67	C12	C11	C16	C15	−68
C7	C1	C6	C5	36	C17	C11	C16	C15	37
C10	C1	C6	C5	162	C20	C11	C16	C15	159
C2	C1	C7	C4	51	C12	C11	C17	C14	55
C2	C1	C7	C8	179	C12	C11	C17	C18	170
C2	C1	C7	C9	−70	C12	C11	C17	C19	−61
C6	C1	C7	C4	−59	C16	C11	C17	C14	−55
C6	C1	C7	C8	69	C16	C11	C17	C18	59
C6	C1	C7	C9	−180	C16	C11	C17	C19	−172
C10	C1	C7	C4	175	C20	C11	C17	C14	−179
C10	C1	C7	C8	−57	C20	C11	C17	C18	−65
C10	C1	C7	C9	54	C20	C11	C17	C19	65
C2	C1	C10	Br1	−70	C12	C11	C20	Br2	−65
C6	C1	C10	Br1	58	C16	C11	C20	Br2	65
C7	C1	C10	Br1	173	C17	C11	C20	Br2	177
Cl1	C2	C3	C4	−131	Cl2	C12	C13	C14	−128
N1	C2	C3	C4	112	N2	C12	C13	C14	116
C1	C2	C3	C4	−7	C11	C12	C13	C14	−2
C2	C3	C4	C5	−66	C12	C13	C14	C15	−71
C2	C3	C4	C7	41	C12	C13	C14	C17	39
C3	C4	C5	C6	72	C13	C14	C15	C16	70
C7	C4	C5	C6	−37	C17	C14	C15	C16	−38
C3	C4	C7	C1	−57	C13	C14	C17	C11	−57
C3	C4	C7	C8	174	C13	C14	C17	C18	−173
C3	C4	C7	C9	62	C13	C14	C17	C19	61
C5	C4	C7	C1	60	C15	C14	C17	C11	60
C5	C4	C7	C8	−69	C15	C14	C17	C18	−57
C5	C4	C7	C9	179	C15	C14	C17	C19	177
C4	C5	C6	C1	−1	C14	C15	C16	C11	−1

52.2 (−) - 2 - Bromo - 2 - nitrocamphane

$C_{10}H_{16}BrNO_2$

D.A.Brueckner, T.A.Hamor, J.M.Robertson, G.A.Sim, J. Chem. Soc., 799, 1962

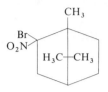

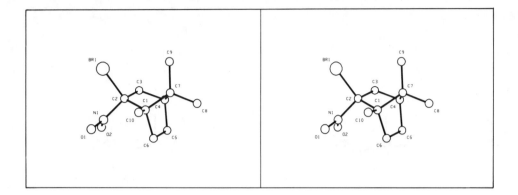

$P2_12_12_1$ Z = 4   R = 0.12

BRONCP   LB 10-16-8

Bond Lengths

Br1	C2	1.96	C2	C3	1.54
N1	O1	1.20	C3	C4	1.47
N1	O2	1.21	C4	C5	1.57
C2	N1	1.54	C4	C7	1.57
C1	C2	1.54	C5	C6	1.59
C1	C6	1.59	C7	C8	1.56
C1	C7	1.57	C7	C9	1.56
C1	C10	1.47			

Bond Angles

O1	N1	O2	124	C1	C2	C3	106
O1	N1	C2	118	C2	C3	C4	102
O2	N1	C2	118	C3	C4	C5	114
C2	C1	C6	105	C3	C4	C7	104
C2	C1	C7	101	C5	C4	C7	101
C2	C1	C10	118	C4	C5	C6	100
C6	C1	C7	98	C1	C6	C5	105
C6	C1	C10	112	C1	C7	C4	93
C7	C1	C10	120	C1	C7	C8	114
Br1	C2	N1	100	C1	C7	C9	114
Br1	C2	C1	116	C4	C7	C8	115
Br1	C2	C3	111	C4	C7	C9	116
N1	C2	C1	111	C8	C7	C9	105
N1	C2	C3	114				

Torsion Angles

O1	N1	C2	Br1	−66	C6	C1	C7	C4	58
O1	N1	C2	C1	57	C6	C1	C7	C8	−62
O1	N1	C2	C3	176	C6	C1	C7	C9	178
O2	N1	C2	Br1	119	C10	C1	C7	C4	179
O2	N1	C2	C1	−118	C10	C1	C7	C8	59
O2	N1	C2	C3	1	C10	C1	C7	C9	−61
C6	C1	C2	Br1	164	Br1	C2	C3	C4	133
C6	C1	C2	N1	51	N1	C2	C3	C4	−115
C6	C1	C2	C3	−73	C1	C2	C3	C4	6
C7	C1	C2	Br1	−95	C2	C3	C4	C5	69
C7	C1	C2	N1	153	C2	C3	C4	C7	−40
C7	C1	C2	C3	29	C3	C4	C5	C6	−71
C10	C1	C2	Br1	38	C7	C4	C5	C6	39
C10	C1	C2	N1	−75	C3	C4	C7	C1	56
C10	C1	C2	C3	162	C3	C4	C7	C8	175
C2	C1	C6	C5	68	C3	C4	C7	C9	−63
C7	C1	C6	C5	−36	C5	C4	C7	C1	−62
C10	C1	C6	C5	−162	C5	C4	C7	C8	57
C2	C1	C7	C4	−50	C5	C4	C7	C9	179
C2	C1	C7	C8	−169	C4	C5	C6	C1	−2
C2	C1	C7	C9	71					

52.3 2,4 - Dibromomenthone

$C_{10}H_{16}Br_2O$

J.A.Wunderlich, W.N.Lipscomb, Tetrahedron, 11, 219, 1960

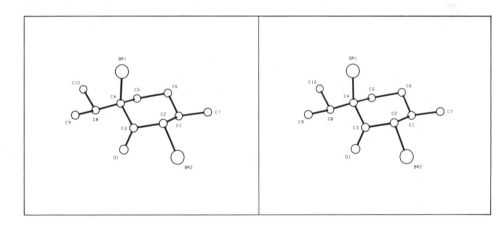

$P2_12_12_1$ Z = 4   R = 0.166

BRMENO

Bond Lengths

Br1	C4	1.98	C3	C4	1.57
Br2	C2	1.95	C4	C5	1.48
C3	O1	1.16	C4	C8	1.40
C1	C2	1.52	C5	C6	1.67
C1	C6	1.50	C8	C9	1.63
C1	C7	1.51	C8	C10	1.58
C2	C3	1.56			

Bond Angles

C2	C1	C6	113	Br1	C4	C5	111
C2	C1	C7	115	Br1	C4	C8	114
C6	C1	C7	111	C3	C4	C5	104
Br2	C2	C1	114	C3	C4	C8	109
Br2	C2	C3	110	C5	C4	C8	112
C1	C2	C3	111	C4	C5	C6	116
O1	C3	C2	121	C1	C6	C5	109
O1	C3	C4	123	C4	C8	C9	112
C2	C3	C4	115	C4	C8	C10	114
Br1	C4	C3	105	C9	C8	C10	107

Torsion Angles

C6	C1	C2	Br2	178	C2	C3	C4	Br1	−59
C6	C1	C2	C3	54	C2	C3	C4	C5	58
C7	C1	C2	Br2	−54	C2	C3	C4	C8	178
C7	C1	C2	C3	−178	Br1	C4	C5	C6	57
C2	C1	C6	C5	−51	C3	C4	C5	C6	−56
C7	C1	C6	C5	179	C8	C4	C5	C6	−174
Br2	C2	C3	O1	−14	Br1	C4	C8	C9	−51
Br2	C2	C3	C4	176	Br1	C4	C8	C10	70
C1	C2	C3	O1	112	C3	C4	C8	C9	67
C1	C2	C3	C4	−58	C3	C4	C8	C10	−172
O1	C3	C4	Br1	131	C5	C4	C8	C9	−179
O1	C3	C4	C5	−112	C5	C4	C8	C10	−58
O1	C3	C4	C8	8	C4	C5	C6	C1	56

52.4 Iridomyrmecin (at −150 °C) $C_{10}H_{16}O_2$

J.F.McConnell, A.McL.Mathieson, B.P.Schoenborn, Acta Cryst., 17, 472, 1964

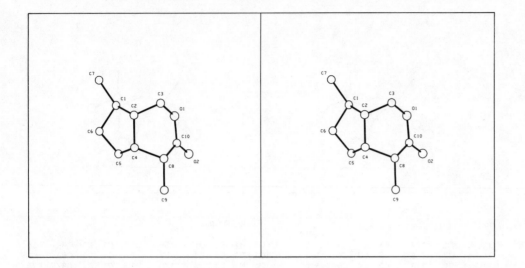

$P2_1$ Z = 2   R = 0.14

IRIDIN   LB 10-16-34

Bond Lengths

C3	O1	1.41	C2	C4	1.56
C10	O1	1.34	C4	C5	1.49
C10	O2	1.32	C4	C8	1.54
C1	C2	1.55	C5	C6	1.52
C1	C6	1.60	C8	C9	1.55
C1	C7	1.53	C8	C10	1.48
C2	C3	1.44			
		(1.50)			

Bond Angles

C3	O1	C10	117		C5	C4	C8	116
C2	C1	C6	102		C4	C5	C6	109
C2	C1	C7	115		C1	C6	C5	102
C6	C1	C7	112		C4	C8	C9	111
C1	C2	C3	112		C4	C8	C10	107
C1	C2	C4	109		C9	C8	C10	110
C3	C2	C4	112		O1	C10	O2	118
O1	C3	C2	111		O1	C10	C8	117
C2	C4	C5	103		O2	C10	C8	125
C2	C4	C8	111					

Torsion Angles

C10	O1	C3	C2	−55		C3	C2	C4	C5	−121
C3	O1	C10	O2	−179		C3	C2	C4	C8	3
C3	O1	C10	C8	2		C2	C4	C5	C6	−27
C6	C1	C2	C3	144		C8	C4	C5	C6	−149
C6	C1	C2	C4	20		C2	C4	C8	C9	−170
C7	C1	C2	C3	−94		C2	C4	C8	C10	−50
C7	C1	C2	C4	141		C5	C4	C8	C9	−53
C2	C1	C6	C5	−35		C5	C4	C8	C10	67
C7	C1	C6	C5	−158		C4	C5	C6	C1	40
C1	C2	C3	O1	−75		C4	C8	C10	O1	50
C4	C2	C3	O1	48		C4	C8	C10	O2	−129
C1	C2	C4	C5	4		C9	C8	C10	O1	170
C1	C2	C4	C8	128		C9	C8	C10	O2	−8

52.5 Isoiridomyrmecin (at −130 °C) $C_{10}H_{16}O_2$

B.P.Schoenborn, J.F.McConnell, Acta Cryst., 15, 779, 1962

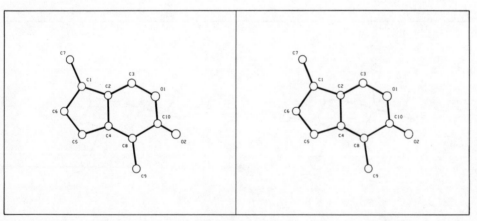

Published value of x(C3) = 0.408.
The correct value is 0.418 (private communication).
$P2_1$ Z = 2   R = 0.14

ISIRIN   LB 10-16-35

Bond Lengths

C3	O1	1.49	C2	C4	1.54
C10	O1	1.36	C4	C5	1.53
C10	O2	1.18	C4	C8	1.54
C1	C2	1.53	C5	C6	1.51
C1	C6	1.54	C8	C9	1.54
C1	C7	1.56	C8	C10	1.57
C2	C3	1.59			(1.51)

Bond Angles

C3	O1	C10	122		C5	C4	C8	113
C2	C1	C6	104		C4	C5	C6	106
C2	C1	C7	119		C1	C6	C5	101
C6	C1	C7	113		C4	C8	C9	113
C1	C2	C3	111		C4	C8	C10	110
C1	C2	C4	107		C9	C8	C10	106
C3	C2	C4	112		O1	C10	O2	124
O1	C3	C2	105		O1	C10	C8	110
C2	C4	C5	104		O2	C10	C8	126
C2	C4	C8	112					

Torsion Angles

C10	O1	C3	C2	−54		C3	C2	C4	C5	118
C3	O1	C10	O2	−175		C3	C2	C4	C8	−4
C3	O1	C10	C8	1		C2	C4	C5	C6	28
C6	C1	C2	C3	−144		C8	C4	C5	C6	149
C6	C1	C2	C4	−21		C2	C4	C8	C9	−168
C7	C1	C2	C3	90		C2	C4	C8	C10	−50
C7	C1	C2	C4	−148		C5	C4	C8	C9	75
C2	C1	C6	C5	38		C5	C4	C8	C10	−166
C7	C1	C6	C5	168		C4	C5	C6	C1	−41
C1	C2	C3	O1	173		C4	C8	C10	O1	54
C4	C2	C3	O1	53		C4	C8	C10	O2	−130
C1	C2	C4	C5	−3		C9	C8	C10	O1	177
C1	C2	C4	C8	−126		C9	C8	C10	O2	−7

52.6 Menthyl trimethylammonium iodide

$C_{13}H_{28}N^+$, I^-

E.J.Gabe, D.F.Grant, Acta Cryst., 15, 1074, 1962

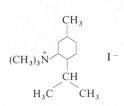

$P2_12_12_1$ $Z = 4$ $R = 0.127$

METMAI   LB 13-28-1

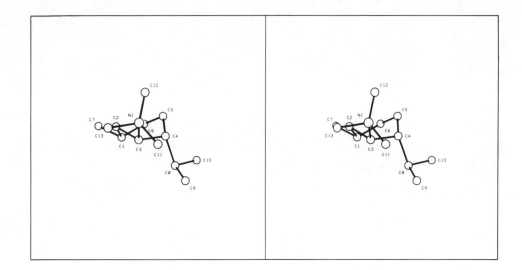

Bond Lengths

C3	N1	1.64	C2	C3	1.53
C11	N1	1.55	C3	C4	1.54
C12	N1	1.47	C4	C5	1.45
C13	N1	1.56	C4	C8	1.63
C1	C2	1.61	C5	C6	1.54
C1	C6	1.52	C8	C9	1.51
C1	C7	1.64	C8	C10	1.60

Bond Angles

C3	N1	C11	99	N1	C3	C4	109
C3	N1	C12	112	C2	C3	C4	115
C3	N1	C13	101	C3	C4	C5	109
C11	N1	C12	124	C3	C4	C8	107
C11	N1	C13	107	C5	C4	C8	117
C12	N1	C13	111	C4	C5	C6	114
C2	C1	C6	110	C1	C6	C5	109
C2	C1	C7	103	C4	C8	C9	105
C6	C1	C7	105	C4	C8	C10	106
C1	C2	C3	102	C9	C8	C10	111
N1	C3	C2	104				

Torsion Angles

C11	N1	C3	C2	164	C2	C3	C4	C5	14
C11	N1	C3	C4	−73	C2	C3	C4	C8	−114
C6	C1	C2	C3	−71	C3	C4	C5	C6	−62
C2	C1	C6	C5	29	C8	C4	C5	C6	60
C1	C2	C3	N1	167	C3	C4	C8	C10	166
C1	C2	C3	C4	48	C5	C4	C8	C10	43
N1	C3	C4	C5	−103	C4	C5	C6	C1	38
N1	C3	C4	C8	130					

52.7 (−) - Menthyl (−) - p - iodobenzenesulfinate (absolute configuration)

$C_{16}H_{23}IO_2S$

E.B.Fleischer, M.Axelrod, M.Green, K.Mislow, J. Amer. Chem. Soc., 86, 3395, 1964

Atomic coordinates were not reported in the paper.
$P112_1$ $Z = 2$ $R = 0.11$

MNIBZS   LB 16-23-1

53.1   Bromonoranisatinone

N.Sakabe, Y.Hirata, A.Furusaki, Y.Tomiie, I.Nitta, Tetrahedron Letters, 4795, 1965

$C_{14}H_{15}BrO_7$

Atomic coordinates were not reported in the paper.
$P2_1$ $Z = 2$ $R = 0.171$

BRANIS   LB 14-15-3

53.2   Caryophyllene chlorohydrin

D.Rogers, M.-ul-Haque, Proc. Chem. Soc., 371, 1963

$C_{14}H_{23}ClO_2$

Atomic coordinates were not reported in the paper.
$P3_1$ $Z = 3$ $R = 0.17$

CARHYD

53.3 α - Bromoisotutinone (at $-150\,^\circ$ C)

M.F.Mackay, A.McL.Mathieson, Acta Cryst., 19, 417, 1965

$C_{15}H_{15}BrO_6$

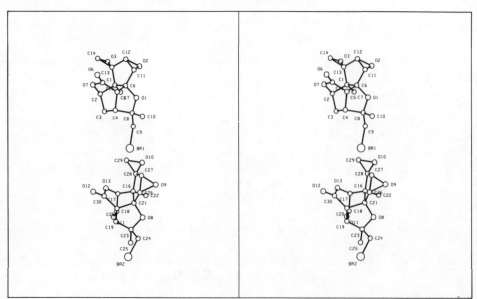

The oxygen atom attached to C3 of molecule A is disordered (75% ketone and 25% hydroxyl). Published x coordinate for C9 of molecule B (relabelled C24) = 0.519. The correct value is 0.516. There are a number of errors in the published bond lengths (private communication).
$P2_12_12_1$ $Z = 8$ $R = 0.16$

BISTON   LB 15-15-4

318

Bond Lengths

Br1	C9	1.98	Br2	C24	1.91
C6	O1	1.41	C21	O8	1.42
C8	O1	1.52	C23	O8	1.46
C11	O2	1.46	C26	O9	1.54
C12	O2	1.40	C27	O9	1.41
C13	O3	1.48	C28	O10	1.40
C14	O3	1.43	C29	O10	1.43
C15	O6	1.17	C18	O11	1.21
C2	O7	1.47	C30	O12	1.20
C15	O7	1.37	C17	O13	1.46
C1	C2	1.56	C30	O13	1.41
C1	C6	1.56	C16	C17	1.57
C1	C7	1.54	C16	C21	1.57
C1	C13	1.56	C16	C22	1.52
C2	C3	1.60	C16	C28	1.55
C3	C4	1.50	C17	C18	1.53
C4	C5	1.54	C18	C19	1.50
C4	C8	1.52	C19	C20	1.56
C5	C6	1.54	C19	C23	1.51
C5	C15	1.47	C20	C21	1.56
C6	C11	1.50	C20	C30	1.49
C8	C9	1.49	C21	C26	1.53
C8	C10	1.50	C23	C24	1.52
C11	C12	1.49	C23	C25	1.51
C12	C13	1.53	C26	C27	1.47
C13	C14	1.47	C27	C28	1.50
			C28	C29	1.48

Bond Angles

C6	O1	C8	109	C5	C6	C11	113	C21	O8	C23	106	C16	C21	C26	107
C11	O2	C12	63	O1	C8	C4	103	C26	O9	C27	60	C20	C21	C26	111
C13	O3	C14	61	O1	C8	C9	105	C28	O10	C29	63	O8	C23	C19	110
C2	O7	C15	114	O1	C8	C10	116	C17	O13	C30	119	O8	C23	C24	107
C2	C1	C6	102	C4	C8	C9	109	C17	C16	C21	110	O8	C23	C25	107
C2	C1	C7	112	C4	C8	C10	113	C17	C16	C22	109	C19	C23	C24	114
C2	C1	C13	109	C9	C8	C10	111	C17	C16	C28	113	C19	C23	C25	115
C6	C1	C7	119	Br1	C9	C8	116	C21	C16	C22	109	C24	C23	C25	103
C6	C1	C13	101	O2	C11	C6	105	C21	C16	C28	107	Br2	C24	C23	120
C7	C1	C13	113	O2	C11	C12	57	C22	C16	C28	108	O9	C26	C21	108
O7	C2	C1	110	C6	C11	C12	103	O13	C17	C16	106	O9	C26	C27	56
O7	C2	C3	108	O2	C12	C11	60	O13	C17	C18	108	C21	C26	C27	107
C1	C2	C3	110	O2	C12	C13	114	C16	C17	C18	103	O9	C27	C26	64
C2	C3	C4	110	C11	C12	C13	112	O11	C18	C17	122	O9	C27	C28	114
C3	C4	C5	109	O3	C13	C1	116	O11	C18	C19	120	C26	C27	C28	113
C3	C4	C8	115	O3	C13	C12	117	C17	C18	C19	117	O10	C28	C16	121
C5	C4	C8	95	O3	C13	C14	58	C18	C19	C20	102	O10	C28	C27	121
C4	C5	C6	101	C1	C13	C12	104	C18	C19	C23	113	O10	C28	C29	60
C4	C5	C15	115	C1	C13	C14	132	C20	C19	C23	96	C16	C28	C27	105
C6	C5	C15	107	C12	C13	C14	122	C19	C20	C21	100	C16	C28	C29	122
O1	C6	C1	108	O3	C14	C13	61	C19	C20	C30	115	C27	C28	C29	124
O1	C6	C5	101	O6	C15	O7	117	C21	C20	C30	120	O10	C29	C28	57
O1	C6	C11	108	O6	C15	C5	130	O8	C21	C16	115	O12	C30	O13	117
C1	C6	C5	114	O7	C15	C5	112	O8	C21	C20	105	O12	C30	C20	137
C1	C6	C11	112					O8	C21	C26	114	O13	C30	C20	106
								C16	C21	C20	104				

Torsion Angles

C8	O1	C6	C1	−104	C6	C1	C13	C14	−133	O1	C8	C9	Br1	176	C28	C16	C17	C18	−169	C20	C19	C23	O8	−37
C8	O1	C6	C5	16	C7	C1	C13	O3	30	C4	C8	C9	Br1	−74	C17	C16	C21	O8	99	C20	C19	C23	C24	−157
C8	O1	C6	C11	135	C7	C1	C13	C12	−101	C10	C8	C9	Br1	50	C17	C16	C21	C20	−16	C20	C19	C23	C25	85
C6	O1	C8	C4	18	C7	C1	C13	C14	99	O2	C11	C12	C13	106	C17	C16	C21	C26	−133	C19	C20	C21	O8	−42
C6	O1	C8	C9	132	O7	C2	C3	C4	−57	C6	C11	C12	O2	−99	C22	C16	C21	O8	−20	C19	C20	C21	C16	80
C6	O1	C8	C10	−106	C1	C2	C3	C4	62	C6	C11	C12	C13	7	C22	C16	C21	C20	−135	C19	C20	C21	C26	−166
C12	O2	C11	C6	96	C2	C3	C4	C5	4	O2	C12	C13	O3	−86	C22	C16	C21	C26	108	C30	C20	C21	O8	−168
C11	O2	C12	C13	−103	C2	C3	C4	C8	−101	O2	C12	C13	C1	43	C28	C16	C21	O8	−137	C30	C20	C21	C16	−47
C14	O3	C13	C1	124	C3	C4	C5	C6	−65	O2	C12	C13	C14	−154	C28	C16	C21	C20	108	C30	C20	C21	C26	68
C14	O3	C13	C12	−112	C3	C4	C5	C15	50	C11	C12	C13	O3	−152	C28	C16	C21	C26	−9	C19	C20	C30	O12	117
C15	O7	C2	C1	−58	C8	C4	C5	C6	53	C11	C12	C13	C1	−23	C17	C16	C28	O10	−86	C19	C20	C30	O13	−62
C15	O7	C2	C3	61	C8	C4	C5	C15	169	C11	C12	C13	C14	140	C17	C16	C28	C27	133	C21	C20	C30	O12	−124
C2	O7	C15	O6	180	C3	C4	C8	O1	70	C1	C13	C14	O3	−98	C17	C16	C28	C29	−15	C21	C20	C30	O13	56
C2	O7	C15	C5	−7	C3	C4	C8	C9	−41	C12	C13	C14	O3	105	C21	C16	C28	O10	152	O8	C21	C26	O9	72
C6	C1	C2	O7	63	C3	C4	C8	C10	−164						C21	C16	C28	C27	12	O8	C21	C26	C27	131
C6	C1	C2	C3	−56	C5	C4	C8	O1	−43	C23	O8	C21	C16	−95	C21	C16	C28	C29	−137	C16	C21	C26	O9	−57
C7	C1	C2	O7	−169	C5	C4	C8	C9	−154	C23	O8	C21	C20	19	C22	C16	C28	O10	35	C16	C21	C26	C27	2
C7	C1	C2	C3	72	C5	C4	C8	C10	83	C23	O8	C21	C26	141	C22	C16	C28	C29	106	C20	C21	C26	O9	−169
C13	C1	C2	O7	−43	C4	C5	C6	O1	−44	C21	O8	C23	C19	12	C22	C16	C28	C27	−106	C20	C21	C26	C27	−110
C13	C1	C2	C3	−162	C4	C5	C6	C1	72	C21	O8	C23	C24	137	O13	C17	C18	O11	115	O8	C23	C24	Br2	170
C2	C1	C6	O1	103	C4	C5	C6	C11	−159	C21	O8	C23	C25	−114	O13	C17	C18	C19	−51	C19	C23	C24	Br2	−67
C2	C1	C6	C5	−9	C15	C5	C6	O1	−166	C27	O9	C26	C21	98	C16	C17	C18	O11	−133	C25	C23	C24	Br2	58
C2	C1	C6	C11	−138	C15	C5	C6	C1	−50	C26	O9	C27	C28	−105	C16	C17	C18	C19	61	O9	C26	C27	C28	106
C7	C1	C6	O1	−21	C15	C5	C6	C11	79	C29	O10	C28	C16	112	O11	C18	C19	C20	−166	C21	C26	C27	O9	−101
C7	C1	C6	C5	−132	C4	C5	C15	O6	120	C29	O10	C28	C27	−114	O11	C18	C19	C23	92	C21	C26	C27	C28	5
C7	C1	C6	C11	98	C4	C5	C15	O7	−51	C30	O13	C17	C16	−59	C17	C18	C19	C20	0	O9	C27	C28	O10	−80
C13	C1	C6	O1	−145	C6	C5	C15	O6	−128	C30	O13	C17	C18	51	C17	C18	C19	C23	−102	O9	C27	C28	C16	60
C13	C1	C6	C5	104	C6	C5	C15	O7	61	C17	O13	C30	O12	−178	C18	C19	C20	C21	−70	O9	C27	C28	C29	−152
C13	C1	C6	C11	−26	O1	C6	C11	O2	73	C17	O13	C30	C20	2	C18	C19	C20	C30	60	C26	C27	C28	O10	−151
C2	C1	C13	O3	−95	O1	C6	C11	C12	131	C21	C16	C17	O13	64	C23	C19	C20	C21	45	C26	C27	C28	C16	−11
C2	C1	C13	C12	134	C1	C6	C11	O2	−46	C21	C16	C17	C18	−49	C23	C19	C20	C30	174	C26	C27	C28	C29	137
C2	C1	C13	C14	−26	C1	C6	C11	C12	12	C22	C16	C17	O13	−176	C18	C19	C23	O8	69	C16	C28	C29	O10	−109
C6	C1	C13	O3	158	C5	C6	C11	O2	−177	C22	C16	C17	C18	70	C18	C19	C23	C24	−51	C27	C28	C29	O10	108
C6	C1	C13	C12	27	C5	C6	C11	C12	−118	C28	C16	C17	O13	−56	C18	C19	C23	C25	−170					

53.4 α - Bromopicrotoxinin (absolute configuration)

B.M.Craven, Acta Cryst., 15, 387, 1962

$C_{15}H_{15}BrO_6$

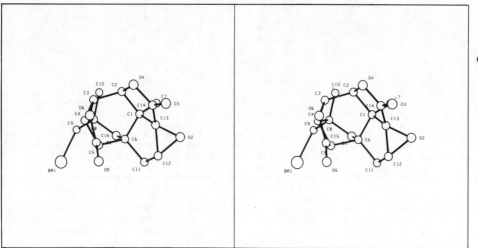

$P2_12_12_1$ Z = 4   R = 0.15

BRPITX   LB 15-15-1

Bond Lengths			Bond Angles					Torsion Angles														
Br1	C9	1.98	C6	O1	C8	107		C1	C6	C11	104		C8	O1	C6	C1	−78		C13	C1	C6	C5	86		C4	C5	C6	C1	66

Bond Lengths
Br1 C9	1.98
C6 O1	1.41
C8 O1	1.49
C12 O2	1.46
C13 O2	1.41
C14 O3	1.21
C2 O4	1.44
C14 O4	1.37
C15 O5	1.24
C3 O6	1.44
C15 O6	1.36
C1 C2	1.56
C1 C6	1.55
C1 C7	1.49
C1 C13	1.50
C2 C3	1.50
C3 C4	1.57
C4 C5	1.53
C4 C8	1.53
C5 C6	1.55
C5 C15	1.48
C6 C11	1.54
C8 C9	1.50
C8 C10	1.54
C11 C12	1.55
C12 C13	1.50
C13 C14	1.50

Bond Angles
C6 O1 C8	107
C12 O2 C13	63
C2 O4 C14	112
C3 O6 C15	106
C2 C1 C6	115
C2 C1 C7	113
C2 C1 C13	102
C6 C1 C7	113
C6 C1 C13	102
C7 C1 C13	110
O4 C2 C1	107
O4 C2 C3	109
C1 C2 C3	114
O6 C3 C2	109
O6 C3 C4	103
C2 C3 C4	114
C3 C4 C5	97
C3 C4 C8	124
C5 C4 C8	102
C4 C5 C6	97
C4 C5 C15	102
C6 C5 C15	118
O1 C6 C1	112
O1 C6 C5	100
O1 C6 C11	115
C1 C6 C5	115

Bond Angles (cont.)
C1 C6 C11	104
C5 C6 C11	112
O1 C8 C4	104
O1 C8 C9	108
O1 C8 C10	112
C4 C8 C9	115
C4 C8 C10	114
C9 C8 C10	104
Br1 C9 C8	116
C6 C11 C12	102
O2 C12 C11	112
O2 C12 C13	57
C11 C12 C13	105
O2 C13 C1	119
O2 C13 C12	60
O2 C13 C14	121
C1 C13 C12	111
C1 C13 C14	109
C12 C13 C14	131
O3 C14 O4	121
O3 C14 C13	130
O4 C14 C13	108
O5 C15 O6	119
O5 C15 C5	130
O6 C15 C5	111

Torsion Angles
C8	O1	C6	C1	−78
C8	O1	C6	C5	45
C8	O1	C6	C11	164
C6	O1	C8	C4	−17
C6	O1	C8	C9	−140
C6	O1	C8	C10	107
C13	O2	C12	C11	94
C12	O2	C13	C1	−99
C12	O2	C13	C14	123
C14	O4	C2	C1	−14
C14	O4	C2	C3	110
C2	O4	C14	O3	−180
C2	O4	C14	C13	6
C15	O6	C3	C2	−85
C15	O6	C3	C4	36
C3	O6	C15	O5	170
C3	O6	C15	C5	−12
C6	C1	C2	O4	125
C6	C1	C2	C3	4
C7	C1	C2	O4	−103
C7	C1	C2	C3	136
C13	C1	C2	O4	16
C13	C1	C2	C3	−105
C2	C1	C6	O1	89
C2	C1	C6	C5	−24
C2	C1	C6	C11	−146
C7	C1	C6	O1	−43
C7	C1	C6	C5	−156
C7	C1	C6	C11	82
C13	C1	C6	O1	−161

C13	C1	C6	C5	86
C13	C1	C6	C11	−37
C2	C1	C13	O2	−155
C2	C1	C13	C12	139
C2	C1	C13	C14	−12
C6	C1	C13	O2	86
C6	C1	C13	C12	20
C6	C1	C13	C14	−131
C7	C1	C13	O2	−35
C7	C1	C13	C12	−101
C7	C1	C13	C14	108
O4	C2	C3	O6	−35
O4	C2	C3	C4	−149
C1	C2	C3	O6	84
C1	C2	C3	C4	−30
O6	C3	C4	C5	−44
O6	C3	C4	C8	−155
C2	C3	C4	C5	73
C2	C3	C4	C8	−37
C3	C4	C5	C6	−85
C3	C4	C5	C15	36
C8	C4	C5	C6	43
C8	C4	C5	C15	164
C3	C4	C8	O1	89
C3	C4	C8	C9	−153
C3	C4	C8	C10	−33
C5	C4	C8	O1	−18
C5	C4	C8	C9	100
C5	C4	C8	C10	−140
C4	C5	C6	O1	−54

C4	C5	C6	C1	66
C4	C5	C6	C11	−176
C15	C5	C6	O1	−162
C15	C5	C6	C1	−42
C15	C5	C6	C11	76
C4	C5	C15	O5	160
C4	C5	C15	O6	−18
C6	C5	C15	O5	−95
C6	C5	C15	O6	87
O1	C6	C11	C12	162
C1	C6	C11	C12	40
C5	C6	C11	C12	−85
O1	C8	C9	Br1	72
C4	C8	C9	Br1	−44
C10	C8	C9	Br1	−169
C6	C11	C12	O2	−88
C6	C11	C12	C13	−28
O2	C12	C13	C1	112
O2	C12	C13	C14	−106
C11	C12	C13	O2	−107
C11	C12	C13	C1	5
C11	C12	C13	C14	147
O2	C13	C14	O3	−27
O2	C13	C14	O4	147
C1	C13	C14	O3	−169
C1	C13	C14	O4	5
C12	C13	C14	O3	49
C12	C13	C14	O4	−138

53.5 2 - Bromo - α - santonin

J.D.M.Asher, G.A.Sim, J. Chem. Soc., 6041, 1965

$C_{15}H_{17}BrO_3$

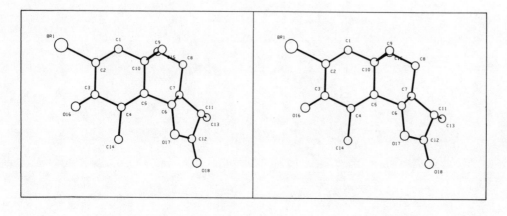

$P2_12_12_1$ Z = 4   R = 0.152

BRSANT   LB 15-17-3

Bond Lengths

Br1	C2	1.92	C5	C6	1.50
C3	O16	1.14	C5	C10	1.56
C6	O17	1.45	C6	C7	1.49
C12	O17	1.37	C7	C8	1.53
C12	O18	1.24	C7	C11	1.52
C1	C2	1.31	C8	C9	1.51
C1	C10	1.42	C9	C10	1.59
C2	C3	1.53	C10	C15	1.58
C3	C4	1.45	C11	C12	1.45
C4	C5	1.32	C11	C13	1.63
C4	C14	1.54			

Bond Angles

C6	O17	C12	106	C6	C7	C8	113
C2	C1	C10	126	C6	C7	C11	99
Br1	C2	C1	124	C8	C7	C11	122
Br1	C2	C3	114	C7	C8	C9	107
C1	C2	C3	121	C8	C9	C10	116
O16	C3	C2	122	C1	C10	C5	113
O16	C3	C4	125	C1	C10	C9	108
C2	C3	C4	113	C1	C10	C15	109
C3	C4	C5	125	C5	C10	C9	109
C3	C4	C14	109	C5	C10	C15	108
C5	C4	C14	126	C9	C10	C15	110
C4	C5	C6	129	C7	C11	C12	102
C4	C5	C10	121	C7	C11	C13	115
C6	C5	C10	110	C12	C11	C13	111
O17	C6	C5	117	O17	C12	O18	116
O17	C6	C7	106	O17	C12	C11	111
C5	C6	C7	109	O18	C12	C11	133

Torsion Angles

C12	O17	C6	C5	145	C4	C5	C10	C9	−123
C12	O17	C6	C7	23	C6	C5	C10	C1	173
C6	O17	C12	O18	−180	C6	C5	C10	C9	53
C6	O17	C12	C11	2	O17	C6	C7	C8	−168
C10	C1	C2	C3	1	O17	C6	C7	C11	−38
C2	C1	C10	C5	0	C5	C6	C7	C8	66
C2	C1	C10	C9	121	C5	C6	C7	C11	−164
C1	C2	C3	C4	0	C6	C7	C8	C9	−59
C2	C3	C4	C5	−2	C11	C7	C8	C9	−176
C3	C4	C5	C6	−171	C6	C7	C11	C12	38
C3	C4	C5	C10	4	C8	C7	C11	C12	161
C4	C5	C6	O17	−6	C7	C8	C9	C10	51
C4	C5	C6	C7	114	C8	C9	C10	C1	−173
C10	C5	C6	O17	178	C8	C9	C10	C5	−50
C10	C5	C6	C7	−62	C7	C11	C12	O17	−26
C4	C5	C10	C1	−3	C7	C11	C12	O18	156

53.6   Shellolic bromolactone monohydrate

$C_{15}H_{17}BrO_5$, H_2O

E.J.Gabe, Acta Cryst., 15, 759, 1962

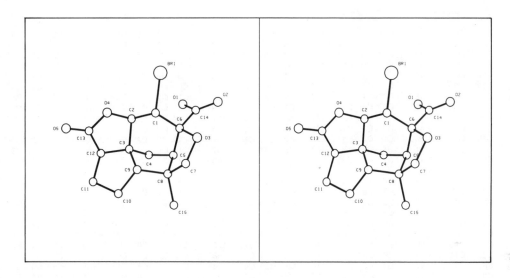

$P2_12_12_1$ Z = 4   R = 0.13

SHELBM   LB 15-17-6

Bond Lengths

Br1	C1	1.94	C3	C12	1.51
C14	O1	1.33	C4	C5	1.53
C14	O2	1.21	C5	C6	1.57
C6	O3	1.40	C5	C8	1.57
C7	O3	1.47	C6	C14	1.53
C2	O4	1.48	C7	C8	1.49
C13	O4	1.32	C8	C9	1.54
C13	O5	1.22	C8	C15	1.58
C1	C2	1.52	C10	C11	1.50
C1	C6	1.53	C11	C12	1.56
C2	C3	1.54	C12	C13	1.53
C3	C4	1.53			
C3	C9	1.58			

Bond Angles

C6	O3	C7	109	C5	C6	C14	110
C2	O4	C13	110	O3	C7	C8	104
Br1	C1	C2	110	C5	C8	C7	106
Br1	C1	C6	115	C5	C8	C9	102
C2	C1	C6	111	C5	C8	C15	111
O4	C2	C1	110	C7	C8	C9	116
O4	C2	C3	102	C7	C8	C15	111
C1	C2	C3	110	C9	C8	C15	111
C2	C3	C4	105	C3	C9	C8	107
C2	C3	C9	116	C3	C9	C10	101
C2	C3	C12	103	C8	C9	C10	120
C4	C3	C9	103	C9	C10	C11	109
C4	C3	C12	126	C10	C11	C12	105
C9	C3	C12	105	C3	C12	C11	108
C3	C4	C5	99	C3	C12	C13	102
C4	C5	C6	116	C11	C12	C13	110
C4	C5	C8	106	O4	C13	O5	121
C6	C5	C8	97	O4	C13	C12	111
O3	C6	C1	110	O5	C13	C12	127
O3	C6	C5	101	O1	C14	O2	123
O3	C6	C14	106	O1	C14	C6	112
C1	C6	C5	116	O2	C14	C6	125
C1	C6	C14	113				

Torsion Angles

C7	O3	C6	C1	78	C9	C3	C12	C11	−23
C7	O3	C6	C5	−45	C9	C3	C12	C13	93
C7	O3	C6	C14	−159	C3	C4	C5	C6	−59
C6	O3	C7	C8	23	C3	C4	C5	C8	48
C13	O4	C2	C1	−142	C4	C5	C6	O3	157
C13	O4	C2	C3	−25	C4	C5	C6	C1	38
C2	O4	C13	O5	−173	C4	C5	C6	C14	−91
C2	O4	C13	C12	7	C8	C5	C6	O3	46
C6	C1	C2	O4	161	C8	C5	C6	C1	−73
C6	C1	C2	C3	49	C8	C5	C6	C14	158
C2	C1	C6	O3	−144	C4	C5	C8	C7	−151
C2	C1	C6	C5	−30	C4	C5	C8	C9	−30
C2	C1	C6	C14	97	C6	C5	C8	C7	−32
O4	C2	C3	C4	166	C6	C5	C8	C9	89
O4	C2	C3	C9	−81	O3	C6	C14	O1	171
O4	C2	C3	C12	33	C1	C6	C14	O1	−68
C1	C2	C3	C4	−77	C5	C6	C14	O1	63
C1	C2	C3	C9	36	O3	C7	C8	C5	8
C1	C2	C3	C12	150	O3	C7	C8	C9	−104
C2	C3	C4	C5	77	C5	C8	C9	C3	1
C9	C3	C4	C5	−45	C5	C8	C9	C10	115
C12	C3	C4	C5	−164	C7	C8	C9	C3	115
C2	C3	C9	C8	−86	C7	C8	C9	C10	−131
C2	C3	C9	C10	147	C3	C9	C10	C11	−34
C4	C3	C9	C8	28	C8	C9	C10	C11	−151
C4	C3	C9	C10	−98	C9	C10	C11	C12	21
C12	C3	C9	C8	161	C10	C11	C12	C3	2
C12	C3	C9	C10	34	C10	C11	C12	C13	−108
C2	C3	C12	C11	−145	C3	C12	C13	O4	15
C2	C3	C12	C13	−29	C3	C12	C13	O5	−165
C4	C3	C12	C11	95	C11	C12	C13	O4	129
C4	C3	C12	C13	−149	C11	C12	C13	O5	−51

53.7 α - Bromoisotutin (absolute configuration)

B.M.Craven, Acta Cryst., 17, 396, 1964

C₁₅H₁₇BrO₆ → $C_{15}H_{17}BrO_6$

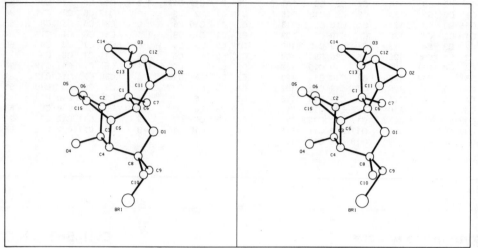

Minus signs have been omitted from the following published coordinates: - x(C12), y(C13), y(C14), y(O1).
P3₁21   Z = 6   R = 0.14

BRITUT   LB 15-15-7

Bond Lengths

Br1	C9	1.97
C6	O1	1.44
C8	O1	1.43
C11	O2	1.47
C12	O2	1.46
C13	O3	1.40
C14	O3	1.46
C3	O4	1.42
C15	O5	1.12
C2	O6	1.44
C15	O6	1.35
C1	C2	1.54
C1	C6	1.46
C1	C7	1.55
C1	C13	1.61
C2	C3	1.53
C3	C4	1.53
C4	C5	1.60
C4	C8	1.53
C5	C6	1.56
C5	C15	1.56
C6	C11	1.51
C8	C9	1.47
C8	C10	1.62
C11	C12	1.47
C12	C13	1.52
C13	C14	1.41
		(1.52)

Bond Angles

C6	O1	C8	110
C11	O2	C12	60
C13	O3	C14	59
C2	O6	C15	114
C2	C1	C6	111
C2	C1	C7	109
C2	C1	C13	109
C6	C1	C7	114
C6	C1	C13	107
C7	C1	C13	106
O6	C2	C1	109
O6	C2	C3	107
C1	C2	C3	110
O4	C3	C2	108
O4	C3	C4	113
C2	C3	C4	111
C3	C4	C5	105
C3	C4	C8	116
C5	C4	C8	98
C4	C5	C6	97
C4	C5	C15	113
C6	C5	C15	112
O1	C6	C1	115
O1	C6	C5	102
O1	C6	C11	110
C1	C6	C5	108

C1	C6	C11	109
C5	C6	C11	112
O1	C8	C4	107
O1	C8	C9	105
O1	C8	C10	106
C4	C8	C9	121
C4	C8	C10	108
C9	C8	C10	109
Br1	C9	C8	111
O2	C11	C6	108
O2	C11	C12	59
C6	C11	C12	107
O2	C12	C11	60
O2	C12	C13	112
C11	C12	C13	111
O3	C13	C1	122
O3	C13	C12	117
O3	C13	C14	63
C1	C13	C12	102
C1	C13	C14	127
C12	C13	C14	123
O3	C14	C13	58
O5	C15	O6	124
O5	C15	C5	125
O6	C15	C5	111

Torsion Angles

C8	O1	C6	C1	−89
C8	O1	C6	C5	28
C8	O1	C6	C11	147
C6	O1	C8	C4	4
C6	O1	C8	C9	133
C6	O1	C8	C10	−112
C12	O2	C11	C6	99
C11	O2	C12	C13	−103
C14	O3	C13	C1	118
C14	O3	C13	C12	−115
C15	O6	C2	C1	−54
C15	O6	C2	C3	64
C2	O6	C15	O5	173
C2	O6	C15	C5	−5
C6	C1	C2	O6	66
C6	C1	C2	C3	−51
C7	C1	C2	O6	−167
C7	C1	C2	C3	76
C13	C1	C2	O6	−51
C13	C1	C2	C3	−168
C2	C1	C6	O1	99
C2	C1	C6	C5	−14
C2	C1	C6	C11	−136
C7	C1	C6	O1	−25
C7	C1	C6	C5	−138
C7	C1	C6	C11	99
C13	C1	C6	O1	−142
C13	C1	C6	C5	104
C13	C1	C6	C11	−18

C2	C1	C13	O3	−89
C2	C1	C13	C12	138
C2	C1	C13	C14	−11
C6	C1	C13	O3	151
C6	C1	C13	C12	18
C6	C1	C13	C14	−131
C7	C1	C13	O3	28
C7	C1	C13	C12	−104
C7	C1	C13	C14	107
O6	C2	C3	O4	56
O6	C2	C3	C4	−68
C1	C2	C3	O4	175
C1	C2	C3	C4	51
O4	C3	C4	C5	−109
O4	C3	C4	C8	144
C2	C3	C4	C5	12
C2	C3	C4	C8	−95
C3	C4	C5	C6	−73
C3	C4	C5	C15	44
C8	C4	C5	C6	46
C8	C4	C5	C15	164
C3	C4	C8	O1	79
C3	C4	C8	C9	−41
C3	C4	C8	C10	−167
C5	C4	C8	O1	−32
C5	C4	C8	C9	−152
C5	C4	C8	C10	81
C4	C5	C6	O1	−46
C4	C5	C6	C1	76

C4	C5	C6	C11	−163
C15	C5	C6	O1	−165
C15	C5	C6	C1	−43
C15	C5	C6	C11	78
C4	C5	C15	O5	130
C4	C5	C15	O6	−52
C6	C5	C15	O5	−121
C6	C5	C15	O6	57
O1	C6	C11	O2	76
O1	C6	C11	C12	138
C1	C6	C11	O2	−52
C1	C6	C11	C12	11
C5	C6	C11	O2	−172
C5	C6	C11	C12	−109
O1	C8	C9	Br1	−171
C4	C8	C9	Br1	−51
C10	C8	C9	Br1	75
O2	C11	C12	C13	104
C6	C11	C12	O2	−102
C6	C11	C12	C13	2
O2	C12	C13	O3	−82
O2	C12	C13	C1	54
O2	C12	C13	C14	−156
C11	C12	C13	O3	−148
C11	C12	C13	C1	−12
C11	C12	C13	C14	139
C1	C13	C14	O3	−111
C12	C13	C14	O3	106

53.8 Isoclovene hydrochloride

J.S.Clunie, J.M.Robertson, J. Chem. Soc., 4382, 1961

C₁₅H₂₅Cl → $C_{15}H_{25}Cl$

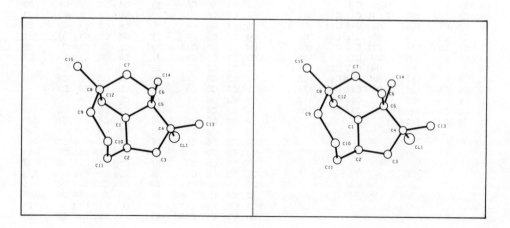

P2₁   Z = 2   R = 0.125

ISOVHC   LB 15-28-8

Bond Lengths

Cl1	C4	1.86	C5	C6	1.58
C1	C2	1.58	C5	C14	1.51
C1	C5	1.57	C6	C7	1.53
C1	C12	1.55	C7	C8	1.58
C2	C3	1.57	C8	C9	1.56
C2	C11	1.55	C8	C12	1.53
C3	C4	1.51	C8	C15	1.57
C4	C5	1.57	C9	C10	1.59
C4	C13	1.57	C10	C11	1.56

Bond Angles

C2	C1	C5	106	C4	C5	C6	108
C2	C1	C12	116	C4	C5	C14	114
C5	C1	C12	113	C6	C5	C14	107
C1	C2	C3	105	C5	C6	C7	113
C1	C2	C11	118	C6	C7	C8	116
C3	C2	C11	112	C7	C8	C9	111
C2	C3	C4	107	C7	C8	C12	111
Cl1	C4	C3	114	C7	C8	C15	107
Cl1	C4	C5	110	C9	C8	C12	112
Cl1	C4	C13	106	C9	C8	C15	107
C3	C4	C5	105	C12	C8	C15	108
C3	C4	C13	114	C8	C9	C10	119
C5	C4	C13	117	C9	C10	C11	116
C1	C5	C4	102	C2	C11	C10	115
C1	C5	C6	114	C1	C12	C8	119
C1	C5	C14	112				

Torsion Angles

C5	C1	C2	C3	−12	C2	C3	C4	C5	34
C5	C1	C2	C11	114	C3	C4	C5	C1	−41
C12	C1	C2	C3	−138	C3	C4	C5	C6	79
C12	C1	C2	C11	−12	C1	C5	C6	C7	−47
C2	C1	C5	C4	32	C4	C5	C6	C7	−159
C2	C1	C5	C6	−85	C5	C6	C7	C8	49
C12	C1	C5	C4	160	C6	C7	C8	C9	78
C12	C1	C5	C6	43	C6	C7	C8	C12	−47
C2	C1	C12	C8	78	C7	C8	C9	C10	−71
C5	C1	C12	C8	−45	C12	C8	C9	C10	53
C1	C2	C3	C4	−14	C7	C8	C12	C1	45
C11	C2	C3	C4	−144	C9	C8	C12	C1	−79
C1	C2	C11	C10	−57	C8	C9	C10	C11	−62
C3	C2	C11	C10	65	C9	C10	C11	C2	83

53.9 Longifolene hydrochloride

$C_{15}H_{25}Cl$

A.F.Cesur, D.F.Grant, Acta Cryst., 18, 55, 1965

$P2_12_12_1$ Z = 4   R = 0.13

LOLENC   LB 15-27-7

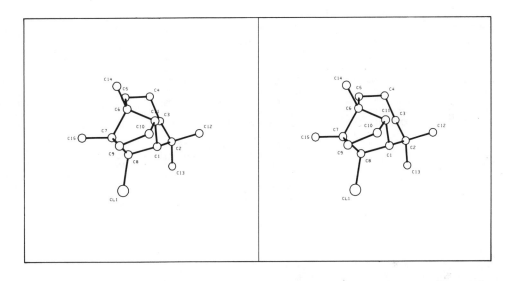

Bond Lengths

Cl1	C8	1.82	C5	C6	1.59
C1	C2	1.54	C6	C7	1.59
C1	C8	1.55	C6	C11	1.55
C1	C11	1.57	C6	C14	1.56
C2	C3	1.55	C7	C8	1.59
C2	C12	1.55	C7	C9	1.51
C2	C13	1.52	C7	C15	1.59
C3	C4	1.50	C9	C10	1.53
C4	C5	1.53	C10	C11	1.51

Bond Angles

C2	C1	C8	113	C7	C6	C14	109
C2	C1	C11	116	C11	C6	C14	112
C8	C1	C11	103	C6	C7	C8	97
C1	C2	C3	116	C6	C7	C9	103
C1	C2	C12	109	C6	C7	C15	116
C1	C2	C13	109	C8	C7	C9	111
C3	C2	C12	109	C8	C7	C15	108
C3	C2	C13	106	C9	C7	C15	120
C12	C2	C13	108	Cl1	C8	C1	112
C2	C3	C4	117	Cl1	C8	C7	111
C3	C4	C5	118	C1	C8	C7	103
C4	C5	C6	116	C7	C9	C10	102
C5	C6	C7	117	C9	C10	C11	107
C5	C6	C11	116	C1	C11	C6	103
C5	C6	C14	108	C1	C11	C10	105
C7	C6	C11	94	C6	C11	C10	100

Torsion Angles

C8	C1	C2	C3	57	C11	C6	C7	C8	−60
C8	C1	C2	C12	179	C11	C6	C7	C9	53
C8	C1	C2	C13	−63	C11	C6	C7	C15	−174
C11	C1	C2	C3	−62	C14	C6	C7	C8	−175
C11	C1	C2	C12	60	C14	C6	C7	C9	−62
C11	C1	C2	C13	178	C14	C6	C7	C15	71
C2	C1	C8	Cl1	103	C5	C6	C11	C1	−68
C2	C1	C8	C7	−138	C5	C6	C11	C10	−175
C11	C1	C8	Cl1	−130	C7	C6	C11	C1	55
C11	C1	C8	C7	−11	C7	C6	C11	C10	−53
C2	C1	C11	C6	97	C14	C6	C11	C1	168
C2	C1	C11	C10	−159	C14	C6	C11	C10	60
C8	C1	C11	C6	−28	C6	C7	C8	Cl1	165
C8	C1	C11	C10	77	C6	C7	C8	C1	45
C1	C2	C3	C4	41	C9	C7	C8	Cl1	58
C12	C2	C3	C4	−82	C9	C7	C8	C1	−62
C13	C2	C3	C4	162	C15	C7	C8	Cl1	−75
C2	C3	C4	C5	−70	C15	C7	C8	C1	165
C3	C4	C5	C6	74	C6	C7	C9	C10	−33
C4	C5	C6	C7	−115	C8	C7	C9	C10	70
C4	C5	C6	C11	−5	C15	C7	C9	C10	−163
C4	C5	C6	C14	122	C7	C9	C10	C11	−2
C5	C6	C7	C8	62	C9	C10	C11	C1	−70
C5	C6	C7	C9	176	C9	C10	C11	C6	36
C5	C6	C7	C15	−52					

53.10 (±) - Cadinene dihydrochloride

$C_{15}H_{26}Cl_2$

N.V.Mani, Z. Kristallogr., 118, 103, 1963

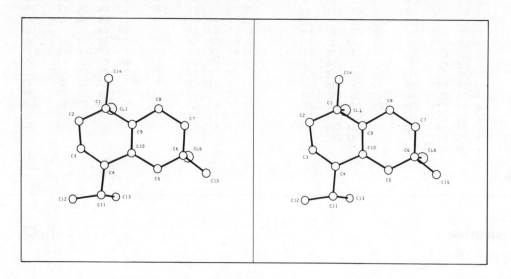

$P2_1/n$ $Z = 4$ $R = 0.144$

CADINC   LB 15-26-4

Bond Lengths

Cl1	C1	1.79	C5	C6	1.53
Cl6	C6	1.79	C5	C10	1.54
C1	C2	1.51	C6	C7	1.54
C1	C9	1.56	C6	C15	1.52
C1	C14	1.53	C7	C8	1.53
C2	C3	1.52	C8	C9	1.57
C3	C4	1.53	C9	C10	1.51
C4	C10	1.55	C11	C12	1.53
C4	C11	1.56	C11	C13	1.55

Bond Angles

Cl1	C1	C2	114	C5	C6	C7	108
Cl1	C1	C9	95	C5	C6	C15	105
Cl1	C1	C14	109	C7	C6	C15	110
C2	C1	C9	119	C6	C7	C8	116
C2	C1	C14	111	C7	C8	C9	116
C9	C1	C14	108	C1	C9	C8	117
C1	C2	C3	101	C1	C9	C10	112
C2	C3	C4	108	C8	C9	C10	113
C3	C4	C10	114	C4	C10	C5	120
C3	C4	C11	107	C4	C10	C9	103
C10	C4	C11	110	C5	C10	C9	109
C6	C5	C10	117	C4	C11	C12	108
Cl6	C6	C5	118	C4	C11	C13	110
Cl6	C6	C7	111	C12	C11	C13	106
Cl6	C6	C15	104				

Torsion Angles

Cl1	C1	C2	C3	53	C10	C4	C11	C12	−147
C9	C1	C2	C3	−58	C10	C4	C11	C13	−32
C14	C1	C2	C3	177	C10	C5	C6	Cl6	−72
Cl1	C1	C9	C8	66	C10	C5	C6	C7	55
Cl1	C1	C9	C10	−66	C10	C5	C6	C15	173
C2	C1	C9	C8	−173	C6	C5	C10	C4	−179
C2	C1	C9	C10	55	C6	C5	C10	C9	−60
C14	C1	C9	C8	−46	Cl6	C6	C7	C8	87
C14	C1	C9	C10	−178	C5	C6	C7	C8	−43
C1	C2	C3	C4	61	C15	C6	C7	C8	−158
C2	C3	C4	C10	−72	C6	C7	C8	C9	40
C2	C3	C4	C11	165	C7	C8	C9	C1	−174
C3	C4	C10	C5	−177	C7	C8	C9	C10	−43
C3	C4	C10	C9	61	C1	C9	C10	C4	−48
C11	C4	C10	C5	−57	C1	C9	C10	C5	−177
C11	C4	C10	C9	−178	C8	C9	C10	C4	178
C3	C4	C11	C12	−22	C8	C9	C10	C5	49
C3	C4	C11	C13	93					

53.11 Bromogeigerin acetate

$C_{17}H_{21}BrO_5$

J.A.Hamilton, A.T.McPhail, G.A.Sim, J. Chem. Soc., 708, 1962

$P2_12_12_1$ $Z = 4$ $R = 0.15$

BGIGAC   LB 17-21-5

Bond Lengths

Br1	C1	1.99	C4	C5	1.31
C3	O1	1.21	C4	C14	1.48
C8	O2	1.45	C5	C6	1.51
C12	O2	1.25	C6	C7	1.51
C12	O3	1.23	C7	C8	1.57
C6	O4	1.47	C7	C11	1.54
C16	O4	1.34	C8	C9	1.53
C16	O5	1.29	C9	C10	1.58
C1	C2	1.57	C10	C15	1.61
C1	C5	1.51	C11	C12	1.54
C1	C10	1.53	C11	C13	1.60
C2	C3	1.47	C16	C17	1.53
C3	C4	1.51			

Bond Angles

C8	O2	C12	114	C5	C6	C7	116
C6	O4	C16	122	C6	C7	C8	116
Br1	C1	C2	105	C6	C7	C11	115
Br1	C1	C5	110	C8	C7	C11	101
Br1	C1	C10	108	O2	C8	C7	101
C2	C1	C5	102	O2	C8	C9	107
C2	C1	C10	117	C7	C8	C9	119
C5	C1	C10	115	C8	C9	C10	112
C1	C2	C3	103	C1	C10	C9	112
O1	C3	C2	128	C1	C10	C15	112
O1	C3	C4	124	C9	C10	C15	107
C2	C3	C4	108	C7	C11	C12	99
C3	C4	C5	108	C7	C11	C13	114
C3	C4	C14	121	C12	C11	C13	115
C5	C4	C14	130	O2	C12	O3	124
C1	C5	C4	114	O2	C12	C11	112
C1	C5	C6	121	O3	C12	C11	124
C4	C5	C6	125	O4	C16	O5	117
O4	C6	C5	112	O4	C16	C17	113
O4	C6	C7	104	O5	C16	C17	129

Torsion Angles

C12	O2	C8	C7	−24	C3	C4	C5	C6	176
C12	O2	C8	C9	101	C1	C5	C6	O4	−36
C8	O2	C12	O3	177	C1	C5	C6	C7	84
C8	O2	C12	C11	1	C4	C5	C6	O4	142
C16	O4	C6	C5	−95	C4	C5	C6	C7	−98
C16	O4	C6	C7	139	O4	C6	C7	C8	65
C6	O4	C16	O5	−5	O4	C6	C7	C11	−177
C5	C1	C2	C3	−21	C5	C6	C7	C8	−59
C10	C1	C2	C3	−147	C5	C6	C7	C11	59
C2	C1	C5	C4	17	C6	C7	C8	O2	161
C2	C1	C5	C6	−165	C6	C7	C8	C9	44
C10	C1	C5	C4	145	C11	C7	C8	O2	36
C10	C1	C5	C6	−37	C11	C7	C8	C9	−81
C2	C1	C10	C9	77	C6	C7	C11	C12	−160
C5	C1	C10	C9	−43	C8	C7	C11	C12	−34
C1	C2	C3	O1	−164	O2	C8	C9	C10	178
C1	C2	C3	C4	19	C7	C8	C9	C10	−69
O1	C3	C4	C5	173	C8	C9	C10	C1	90
C2	C3	C4	C5	−9	C7	C11	C12	O2	23
C3	C4	C5	C1	−6	C7	C11	C12	O3	−153

53.12   Bromoisotenulin (absolute configuration) $C_{17}H_{21}BrO_5$

D.Rogers, M.-ul-Haque, Proc. Chem. Soc., 92, 1963

Atomic coordinates were not reported in the paper.
$P2_1$ $Z = 4$ $R = 0.21$

BITENL   LB 17-21-4

53.13   2 - Bromodihydroisophoto - α - santonic lactone acetate $C_{17}H_{23}BrO_5$

J.D.M.Asher, G.A.Sim, J. Chem. Soc., 1584, 1965

Published value of y(O20) = 0.0056.
The correct value is −0.0056.
$P2_12_12_1$ $Z = 4$ $R = 0.129$

BHSANL   LB 17-23-3

Bond Lengths

Br1	C2	1.98	C4	C5	1.53
C3	O18	1.31	C4	C14	1.48
C6	O19	1.39	C5	C6	1.53
C12	O19	1.37	C6	C7	1.56
C12	O20	1.26	C7	C8	1.53
C10	O21	1.56	C7	C11	1.44
C16	O21	1.34	C8	C9	1.49
C16	O22	1.19	C9	C10	1.59
C1	C2	1.48	C10	C15	1.53
C1	C5	1.57	C11	C12	1.55
C1	C10	1.47	C11	C13	1.51
C2	C3	1.56	C16	C17	1.60
C3	C4	1.49			

Bond Angles

C6	O19	C12	109	C6	C7	C8	113
C10	O21	C16	123	C6	C7	C11	103
C2	C1	C5	107	C8	C7	C11	110
C2	C1	C10	108	C7	C8	C9	115
C5	C1	C10	116	C8	C9	C10	117
Br1	C2	C1	115	O21	C10	C1	109
Br1	C2	C3	106	O21	C10	C9	106
C1	C2	C3	104	O21	C10	C15	97
O18	C3	C2	129	C1	C10	C9	111
O18	C3	C4	122	C1	C10	C15	121
C2	C3	C4	109	C9	C10	C15	111
C3	C4	C5	101	C7	C11	C12	100
C3	C4	C14	115	C7	C11	C13	119
C5	C4	C14	120	C12	C11	C13	111
C1	C5	C4	105	O19	C12	O20	117
C1	C5	C6	121	O19	C12	C11	109
C4	C5	C6	112	O20	C12	C11	133
O19	C6	C5	111	O21	C16	O22	129
O19	C6	C7	102	O21	C16	C17	109
C5	C6	C7	115	O22	C16	C17	122

Torsion Angles

C12	O19	C6	C5	151	C2	C3	C4	C5	−35
C12	O19	C6	C7	28	C3	C4	C5	C1	35
C6	O19	C12	O20	−179	C3	C4	C5	C6	169
C6	O19	C12	C11	−7	C1	C5	C6	O19	−157
C16	O21	C10	C1	−61	C1	C5	C6	C7	−42
C16	O21	C10	C9	58	C4	C5	C6	O19	78
C10	O21	C16	O22	−8	C4	C5	C6	C7	−168
C5	C1	C2	C3	2	O19	C6	C7	C8	−159
C10	C1	C2	C3	−124	O19	C6	C7	C11	−41
C2	C1	C5	C4	−23	C5	C6	C7	C8	81
C2	C1	C5	C6	−152	C5	C6	C7	C11	−161
C10	C1	C5	C4	98	C6	C7	C8	C9	−72
C10	C1	C5	C6	−31	C11	C7	C8	C9	173
C2	C1	C10	O21	−44	C6	C7	C11	C12	35
C2	C1	C10	C9	−160	C8	C7	C11	C12	155
C5	C1	C10	O21	−165	C7	C8	C9	C10	63
C5	C1	C10	C9	79	C8	C9	C10	O21	164
C1	C2	C3	O18	−153	C8	C9	C10	C1	−78
C1	C2	C3	C4	21	C7	C11	C12	O19	−19
O18	C3	C4	C5	140	C7	C11	C12	O20	151

53.14 Fumagillin tetrahydroalcohol - ab - mono - p - bromobenzenesulfonate

$C_{22}H_{33}BrO_6S$

N.J.McCorkindale, J.G.Sime, Proc. Chem. Soc., 331, 1961

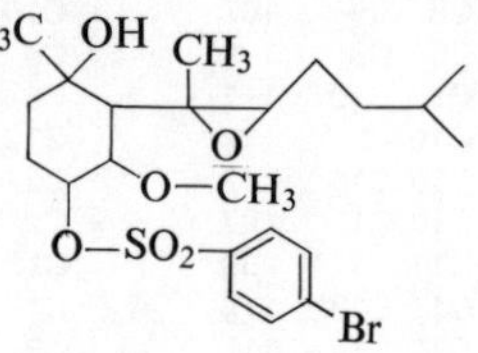

Atomic coordinates were not reported in the paper.
$P2_1$ $Z = 4$ $R = 0.21$

FUMAGI

53.15 Patchouli alcohol diester of chromic acid

$C_{30}H_{50}CrO_4$

M.Dobler, J.D.Dunitz, B.Gubler, H.P.Weber, G.Buchi, J.O.Padilla, Proc. Chem. Soc., 383, 1963

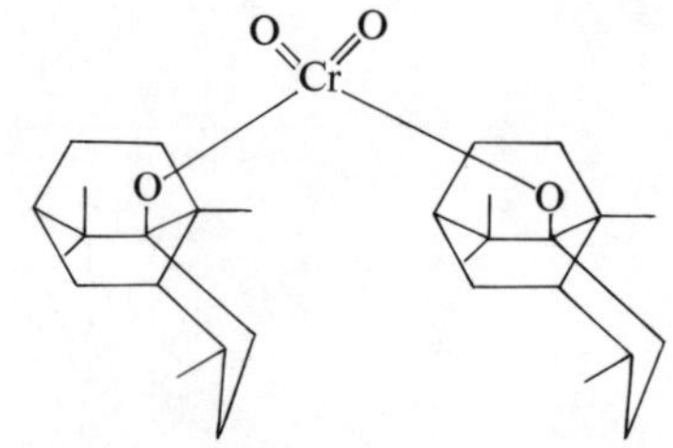

Atomic coordinates were not reported in the paper.
$P2_12_12_1$ $Z = 4$ $R = 0.21$

PATDIE

54.1   Bromo - epoxynorcafestanone

$C_{19}H_{27}BrO_2$

A.I.Scott, G.A.Sim, G.Ferguson, D.W.Young, F.McCapra,
J. Amer. Chem. Soc., 84, 3197, 1962

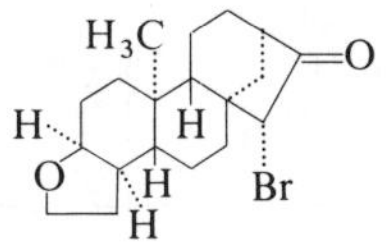

Atomic coordinates were not
reported in the paper.
$P2_12_12_1$ Z = 4   R = 0.21

BREPOX   LB 19-27-2

54.2   Dibromo - rosololactone

$C_{20}H_{30}Br_2O_3$

A.I.Scott, S.A.Sutherland, D.W.Young, L.Gugielmetti, D.Arigone, G.A.Sim,
Proc. Chem. Soc., 19, 1964

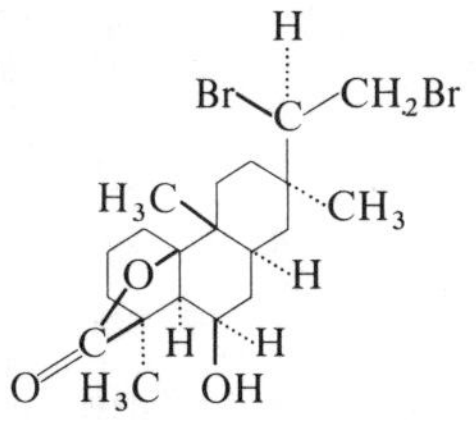

Atomic coordinates were not
reported in the paper.
$P2_12_12_1$ Z = 4   R = 0.19

BRROLA   LB 20-30-3

54.3   Clerodin bromolactone (absolute configuration)

$C_{24}H_{33}BrO_8$

I.C.Paul, G.A.Sim, T.A.Hamor, J.M.Robertson, J. Chem. Soc., 4133, 1962

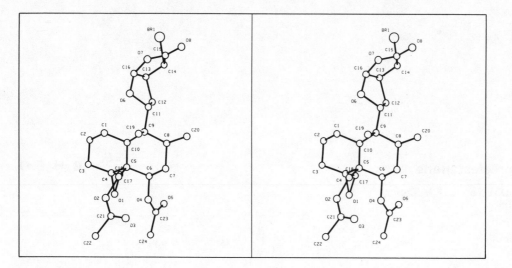

$P2_12_12_1$ Z = 4   R = 0.16

CLINBL   LB 24-33-1

Bond Lengths

Br1	C14	2.06
C4	O1	1.50
C17	O1	1.47
C18	O2	1.54
C21	O2	1.33
C21	O3	1.15
C6	O4	1.45
C23	O4	1.38
C23	O5	1.16
C11	O6	1.47
C16	O6	1.39
C15	O7	1.32
C16	O7	1.45
C15	O8	1.27
C1	C2	1.59
C1	C10	1.58
C2	C3	1.54
C3	C4	1.63
C4	C5	1.62
C4	C17	1.47
C5	C6	1.57
C5	C10	1.53
C5	C18	1.61
C6	C7	1.47
C7	C8	1.55
C8	C9	1.60
C8	C20	1.62
C9	C10	1.53
C9	C11	1.59
C9	C19	1.61
C11	C12	1.53
C12	C13	1.63
C13	C14	1.40
C13	C16	1.50
C14	C15	1.47
C21	C22	1.57
C23	C24	1.49

Bond Angles

C4	O1	C17	59
C18	O2	C21	112
C6	O4	C23	119
C11	O6	C16	103
C15	O7	C16	109
C2	C1	C10	110
C1	C2	C3	108
C2	C3	C4	106
O1	C4	C3	120
O1	C4	C5	115
O1	C4	C17	59
C3	C4	C5	112
C3	C4	C17	123
C5	C4	C17	119
C4	C5	C6	112
C4	C5	C10	104
C4	C5	C18	112
C6	C5	C10	110
C6	C5	C18	109
C10	C5	C18	110
O4	C6	C5	106
O4	C6	C7	106
C5	C6	C7	113
C6	C7	C8	108
C7	C8	C9	111
C7	C8	C20	103
C9	C8	C20	115
C8	C9	C10	109
C8	C9	C11	103
C8	C9	C19	112
C10	C9	C11	113
C10	C9	C19	111
C11	C9	C19	108
C1	C10	C5	110
C1	C10	C9	113
C5	C10	C9	115
O6	C11	C9	109
O6	C11	C12	108
C9	C11	C12	118
C11	C12	C13	97
C12	C13	C14	108
C12	C13	C16	105
C14	C13	C16	107
Br1	C14	C13	109
Br1	C14	C15	96
C13	C14	C15	107
O7	C15	O8	120
O7	C15	C14	111
O8	C15	C14	128
O6	C16	O7	110
O6	C16	C13	111
O7	C16	C13	106
O1	C17	C4	61
O2	C18	C5	106
O2	C21	O3	128
O2	C21	C22	109
O3	C21	C22	123
O4	C23	O5	120
O4	C23	C24	109
O5	C23	C24	132

Torsion Angles

C17	O1	C4	C3	112
C17	O1	C4	C5	-110
C21	O2	C18	C5	133
C18	O2	C21	O3	-13
C23	O4	C6	C5	131
C23	O4	C6	C7	-109
C6	O4	C23	O5	6
C16	O6	C11	C9	-172
C16	O6	C11	C12	-42
C11	O6	C16	O7	-87
C11	O6	C16	C13	30
C16	O7	C15	O8	-166
C16	O7	C15	C14	5
C15	O7	C16	O6	118
C15	O7	C16	C13	-2
C10	C1	C2	C3	63
C2	C1	C10	C5	-64
C2	C1	C10	C9	166
C1	C2	C3	C4	-60
C2	C3	C4	O1	-158
C2	C3	C4	C5	63
C2	C3	C4	C17	-87
O1	C4	C5	C6	38
O1	C4	C5	C10	156
O1	C4	C5	C18	-85
C3	C4	C5	C6	179
C3	C4	C5	C10	-63
C3	C4	C5	C18	56
C17	C4	C5	C6	-29
C17	C4	C5	C10	89
C17	C4	C5	C18	-152
C3	C4	C17	O1	-108
C5	C4	C17	O1	103
C4	C5	C6	O4	-73
C4	C5	C6	C7	171
C10	C5	C6	O4	172
C10	C5	C6	C7	57
C18	C5	C6	O4	52
C18	C5	C6	C7	-64
C4	C5	C10	C1	62
C4	C5	C10	C9	-170
C6	C5	C10	C1	-179
C6	C5	C10	C9	-50
C18	C5	C10	C1	-59
C18	C5	C10	C9	70
C4	C5	C18	O2	30
C6	C5	C18	O2	-94
C10	C5	C18	O2	146
O4	C6	C7	C8	-178
C5	C6	C7	C8	-62
C6	C7	C8	C9	61
C7	C8	C9	C10	-55
C7	C8	C9	C11	-176
C8	C9	C10	C1	178
C8	C9	C10	C5	51
C11	C9	C10	C1	-68
C11	C9	C10	C5	165
C8	C9	C11	O6	-172
C8	C9	C11	C12	64
C10	C9	C11	O6	71
C10	C9	C11	C12	-53
O6	C11	C12	C13	35
C9	C11	C12	C13	159
C11	C12	C13	C14	98
C11	C12	C13	C16	-16
C12	C13	C14	C15	-106
C16	C13	C14	C15	6
C12	C13	C16	O6	-8
C12	C13	C16	O7	111
C14	C13	C16	O6	-122
C14	C13	C16	O7	-3
C13	C14	C15	O7	-7
C13	C14	C15	O8	163

54.4 Methyl gibberellate di - p - bromobenzoate

$C_{34}H_{30}Br_2O_8$

J.A.Hartsuck, W.N.Lipscomb, J. Amer. Chem. Soc., 85, 3414, 1963

C2   Z = 4   R = 0.13

MGIBBZ   LB 34-30-1

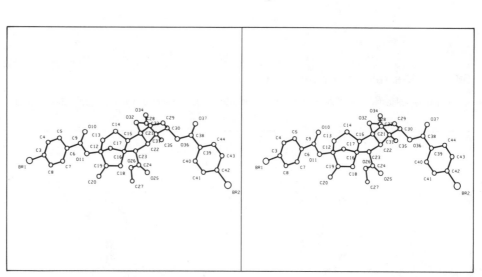

Bond Lengths

Br1	C3	1.90		C14	C15	1.55
Br2	C42	1.83		C15	C16	1.57
C9	O10	1.23		C15	C21	1.51
C9	O11	1.36		C16	C17	1.56
C12	O11	1.42		C16	C18	1.57
C24	O25	1.18		C16	C23	1.50
C24	O26	1.29		C18	C19	1.46
C27	O26	1.49		C19	C20	1.33
C21	O32	1.55		C21	C22	1.52
C33	O32	1.42		C21	C28	1.51
C33	O34	1.15		C22	C23	1.59
C30	O36	1.46		C22	C31	1.54
C38	O36	1.37		C23	C24	1.55
C38	O37	1.21		C28	C29	1.35
C3	C4	1.34		C29	C30	1.42
C3	C8	1.41		C30	C31	1.56
C4	C5	1.43		C31	C33	1.52
C5	C6	1.40		C31	C35	1.51
C6	C7	1.34		C38	C39	1.48
C6	C9	1.51		C39	C40	1.39
C7	C8	1.46		C39	C44	1.45
C12	C13	1.59		C40	C41	1.38
C12	C17	1.55		C41	C42	1.42
C12	C19	1.52		C42	C43	1.43
C13	C14	1.53		C43	C44	1.38

Bond Angles

C9	O11	C12	121	
C24	O26	C27	118	
C21	O32	C33	107	
C30	O36	C38	119	
Br1	C3	C4	122	
Br1	C3	C8	117	
C4	C3	C8	121	
C3	C4	C5	122	
C4	C5	C6	117	
C5	C6	C7	123	
C5	C6	C9	114	
C7	C6	C9	123	
C6	C7	C8	119	
C3	C8	C7	118	
O10	C9	O11	122	
O10	C9	C6	126	
O11	C9	C6	112	
O11	C12	C13	112	
O11	C12	C17	118	
O11	C12	C19	110	
C13	C12	C17	107	
C17	C12	C19	101	
C12	C13	C14	116	
C13	C14	C15	111	
C14	C15	C16	113	
C14	C15	C21	117	
C16	C15	C21	106	
C15	C16	C17	111	
C15	C16	C18	109	
C15	C16	C23	105	
C17	C16	C18	97	
C17	C16	C23	116	
C18	C16	C23	118	
C12	C17	C16	102	
C16	C18	C19	108	
C12	C19	C18	108	
C12	C19	C20	124	
C18	C19	C20	127	
O32	C21	C15	109	
O32	C21	C22	101	

O32	C21	C28	105	
C15	C21	C22	105	
C15	C21	C28	122	
C22	C21	C28	112	
C21	C22	C23	101	
C21	C22	C31	99	
C23	C22	C31	117	
C16	C23	C22	107	
C16	C23	C24	112	
C22	C23	C24	113	
O25	C24	O26	125	
O25	C24	C23	125	
O26	C24	C23	111	
C21	C28	C29	118	
C28	C29	C30	123	
O36	C30	C29	114	
O36	C30	C31	105	
C29	C30	C31	115	
C22	C31	C30	107	
C22	C31	C33	102	
C22	C31	C35	115	
C30	C31	C33	111	
C30	C31	C35	112	
C33	C31	C35	109	
O32	C33	O34	118	
O32	C33	C31	108	
O34	C33	C31	134	
O36	C38	O37	125	
O36	C38	C39	113	
O37	C38	C39	122	
C38	C39	C40	121	
C38	C39	C44	118	
C40	C39	C44	120	
C39	C40	C41	121	
C40	C41	C42	121	
Br2	C42	C41	122	
Br2	C42	C43	120	
C41	C42	C43	118	
C42	C43	C44	122	
C39	C44	C43	118	

Torsion Angles

C12	O11	C9	O10	−12	
C12	O11	C9	C6	171	
C9	O11	C12	C13	70	
C9	O11	C12	C17	−55	
C9	O11	C12	C19	−170	
C27	O26	C24	O25	4	
C27	O26	C24	C23	−175	
C33	O32	C21	C15	−140	
C33	O32	C21	C22	−30	
C33	O32	C21	C28	87	
C21	O32	C33	O34	−172	
C21	O32	C33	C31	1	
C38	O36	C30	C29	−87	
C38	O36	C30	C31	147	
C30	O36	C38	O37	−9	
C30	O36	C38	C39	166	
C7	C6	C9	O10	177	
C7	C6	C9	O11	−5	
O11	C12	C13	C14	−146	
C17	C12	C13	C14	−15	
C19	C12	C13	C14	93	
O11	C12	C17	C16	−164	
C13	C12	C17	C16	69	
C19	C12	C17	C16	−45	
O11	C12	C19	C18	150	
O11	C12	C19	C20	−22	
C13	C12	C19	C18	−88	
C13	C12	C19	C20	100	
C17	C12	C19	C18	24	
C17	C12	C19	C20	−147	
C12	C13	C14	C15	−42	

C13	C14	C15	C16	44	
C13	C14	C15	C21	168	
C14	C15	C16	C17	11	
C14	C15	C16	C18	−95	
C14	C15	C16	C23	137	
C21	C15	C16	C17	−119	
C21	C15	C16	C18	135	
C21	C15	C16	C23	7	
C14	C15	C21	O32	−49	
C14	C15	C21	C22	−157	
C14	C15	C21	C28	74	
C16	C15	C21	O32	78	
C16	C15	C21	C22	−29	
C16	C15	C21	C28	−159	
C15	C16	C17	C12	−68	
C18	C16	C17	C12	46	
C23	C16	C17	C12	172	
C15	C16	C18	C19	83	
C17	C16	C18	C19	−32	
C23	C16	C18	C19	−156	
C15	C16	C23	C22	17	
C15	C16	C23	C24	142	
C17	C16	C23	C22	141	
C17	C16	C23	C24	−95	
C18	C16	C23	C22	−105	
C18	C16	C23	C24	19	
C16	C18	C19	C12	5	
C16	C18	C19	C20	176	
O32	C21	C22	C23	−75	
O32	C21	C22	C31	45	
C15	C21	C22	C23	39	

C15	C21	C22	C31	158	
C28	C21	C22	C23	174	
C28	C21	C22	C31	−66	
O32	C21	C28	C29	−74	
C15	C21	C28	C29	161	
C22	C21	C28	C29	34	
C21	C22	C23	C16	−35	
C21	C22	C23	C24	−159	
C31	C22	C23	C16	−141	
C31	C22	C23	C24	95	
C21	C22	C31	C30	71	
C21	C22	C31	C33	−45	
C23	C22	C31	C30	178	
C23	C22	C31	C33	62	
C16	C23	C24	O25	−96	
C16	C23	C24	O26	83	
C22	C23	C24	O25	25	
C22	C23	C24	O26	−156	
C21	C28	C29	C30	−4	
C28	C29	C30	O36	−109	
C28	C29	C30	C31	11	
O36	C30	C31	C22	78	
O36	C30	C31	C33	−172	
C29	C30	C31	C22	−47	
C29	C30	C31	C33	63	
C22	C31	C33	O32	28	
C22	C31	C33	O34	−161	
C30	C31	C33	O32	−86	
C30	C31	C33	O34	86	
O36	C38	C39	C40	13	
O37	C38	C39	C40	−173	

56.1 Cedrelone iodoacetate

$C_{28}H_{31}IO_6$

I.J.Grant, J.A.Hamilton, T.A.Hamor, J.M.Robertson, G.A.Sim, J. Chem. Soc., 2506, 1963

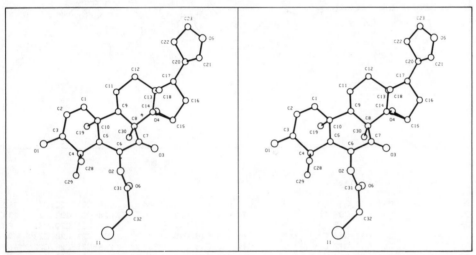

Published value of x(C15) = 0.0235.
The correct value is 0.235.
P2$_1$2$_1$2$_1$ Z = 4   R = 0.17

CEDRIA   LB 28-31-4

Bond Lengths			Bond Angles							Torsion Angles													
I1	C32	2.05	C6	O2	C31	115	C5	C10	C9	110	C31	O2	C6	C5	125	C5	C6	C7	O3	163	C17	C13	C14	O4	−41
C3	O1	1.29	C14	O4	C15	66	C5	C10	C19	105	C31	O2	C6	C7	−70	C5	C6	C7	C8	−32	C17	C13	C14	C8	−171
C6	O2	1.40	C21	O5	C23	114	C9	C10	C19	110	C6	O2	C31	O6	−10	O3	C7	C8	C9	−141	C17	C13	C14	C15	18
C31	O2	1.30	C2	C1	C10	122	C9	C11	C12	103	C6	O2	C31	C32	180	O3	C7	C8	C14	−29	C12	C13	C17	C16	−164
C7	O3	1.11	C1	C2	C3	118	C11	C12	C13	111	C15	O4	C14	C8	−118	C6	C7	C8	C9	54	C12	C13	C17	C20	76
C14	O4	1.48	O1	C3	C2	122	C12	C13	C14	113	C15	O4	C14	C13	104	C6	C7	C8	C14	165	C14	C13	C17	C16	−37
C15	O4	1.45	O1	C3	C4	115	C12	C13	C17	115	C14	O4	C15	C16	−86	C7	C8	C9	C10	−67	C14	C13	C17	C20	−158
C21	O5	1.22	C2	C3	C4	120	C12	C13	C18	102	C23	O5	C21	C20	20	C7	C8	C9	C11	165	O4	C14	C15	C16	104
C23	O5	1.32	C3	C4	C5	106	C14	C13	C17	108	C21	O5	C23	C22	7	C14	C8	C9	C10	178	C8	C14	C15	O4	93
C31	O6	1.21	C3	C4	C28	105	C14	C13	C18	109	C10	C1	C2	C3	4	C14	C8	C9	C11	51	C8	C14	C15	C16	−163
C1	C2	1.29	C3	C4	C29	115	C17	C13	C18	111	C2	C1	C10	C5	−45	C7	C8	C14	O4	132	C13	C14	C15	O4	−96
C1	C10	1.50	C5	C4	C28	114	O4	C14	C8	110	C2	C1	C10	C9	−165	C7	C8	C14	C13	−99	C13	C14	C15	C16	8
C2	C3	1.37	C5	C4	C29	111	O4	C14	C13	106	C1	C2	C3	O1	−158	C7	C8	C14	C15	71	O4	C15	C16	C17	24
C3	C4	1.54	C28	C4	C29	107	O4	C14	C15	56	C1	C2	C3	C4	41	C9	C8	C14	O4	−116	C14	C15	C16	C17	−34
C4	C5	1.51	C4	C5	C6	123	C8	C14	C13	125	O1	C3	C4	C5	164	C9	C8	C14	C13	12	C15	C16	C17	C13	45
C4	C28	1.55	C4	C5	C10	120	C8	C14	C15	124	C2	C3	C4	C5	−34	C9	C8	C14	C15	−178	C15	C16	C17	C20	172
C4	C29	1.65	C6	C5	C10	117	C13	C14	C15	111	C3	C4	C5	C6	172	C8	C9	C10	C1	162	C13	C17	C20	C21	75
C5	C6	1.45	O2	C6	C5	113	O4	C15	C14	58	C3	C4	C5	C10	−13	C8	C9	C10	C5	45	C13	C17	C20	C22	−56
C5	C10	1.52	O2	C6	C7	118	O4	C15	C16	105	C4	C5	C6	O2	−12	C11	C9	C10	C1	−71	C16	C17	C20	C21	−38
C6	C7	1.47	C5	C6	C7	128	C14	C15	C16	94	C4	C5	C6	C7	−34	C11	C9	C10	C5	172	C16	C17	C20	C22	−169
C7	C8	1.53	O3	C7	C6	124	C15	C16	C17	111	C10	C5	C6	O2	173	C8	C9	C11	C12	−81	C17	C20	C21	O5	−173
C8	C9	1.52	O3	C7	C8	126	C13	C17	C16	98	C10	C5	C6	C7	10	C10	C9	C11	C12	148	C22	C20	C21	O5	−33
C8	C14	1.56	C6	C7	C8	108	C13	C17	C20	120	C4	C5	C10	C1	48	C9	C11	C12	C13	44	C17	C20	C22	C23	−174
C8	C30	1.45	C7	C8	C9	105	C16	C17	C20	112	C4	C5	C10	C9	172	C11	C12	C13	C14	9	C21	C20	C22	C23	38
C9	C10	1.52	C7	C8	C14	109	C17	C20	C21	135	C6	C5	C10	C1	−137	C11	C12	C13	C17	133	C20	C22	C23	O5	−29
C9	C11	1.59	C7	C8	C30	111	C17	C20	C22	120	C6	C5	C10	C9	−13	C12	C13	C14	O4	87	O2	C31	C32	I1	112
C10	C19	1.68	C9	C8	C14	104	C21	C20	C22	93	O2	C6	C7	O3	0	C12	C13	C14	C8	−43	O6	C31	C32	I1	−58
C11	C12	1.62	C9	C8	C30	117	O5	C21	C20	110	O2	C6	C7	C8	166	C12	C13	C14	C15	146					
C12	C13	1.62	C14	C8	C30	111	C20	C22	C23	108															
C13	C14	1.45	C8	C9	C10	118	O5	C23	C22	100															
C13	C17	1.51	C8	C9	C11	110	O2	C31	O6	117															
C13	C18	1.79	C10	C9	C11	110	O2	C31	C32	119															
C14	C15	1.60	C1	C10	C5	104	O6	C31	C32	124															
C15	C16	1.58	C1	C10	C9	115	I1	C32	C31	110															
C16	C17	1.47	C1	C10	C19	112																			
C17	C20	1.58																							
C20	C21	1.36																							
C20	C22	1.46																							
C22	C23	1.31																							
C31	C32	1.65																							

56.2 Epilimonol iodoacetate

$C_{28}H_{33}IO_9$

S.Arnott, A.W.Davie, J.M.Robertson, G.A.Sim, D.G.Watson, J. Chem. Soc., 4183, 1961

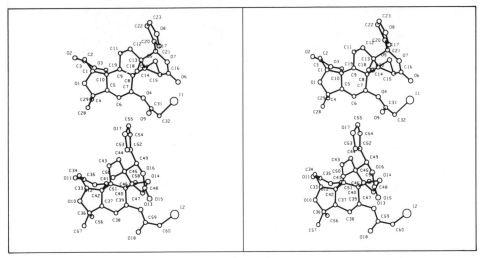

Published bond length for C7'- O4'(relabelled C39 - O13) = 1.66A. The correct value is 1.46A (private communication).

P2₁   Z = 4   R = 0.181

EPOLIA   LB 28-33-3

Bond Lengths

I1	C32	2.21	I2	C60	2.03
C1	O1	1.45	C33	O10	1.51
C4	O1	1.49	C36	O10	1.45
C3	O2	1.25	C35	O11	1.28
C3	O3	1.41	C35	O12	1.24
C19	O3	1.37	C51	O12	1.54
C7	O4	1.51	C39	O13	1.48
C31	O4	1.37	C59	O13	1.30
C14	O5	1.56	C46	O14	1.53
C15	O5	1.55	C47	O14	1.45
C16	O6	1.23	C48	O15	1.35
C16	O7	1.28	C48	O16	1.34
C17	O7	1.49	C49	O16	1.40
C21	O8	1.48	C53	O17	1.37
C23	O8	1.35	C55	O17	1.46
C31	O9	1.28	C59	O18	1.22
C1	C2	1.42	C33	C34	1.66
C1	C10	1.54	C33	C42	1.48
C2	C3	1.52	C34	C35	1.53
C4	C5	1.57	C36	C37	1.52
C4	C28	1.53	C36	C56	1.51
C4	C29	1.64	C36	C57	1.48
C5	C6	1.44	C37	C38	1.55
C5	C10	1.55	C37	C42	1.50
C6	C7	1.53	C38	C39	1.61
C7	C8	1.56	C39	C40	1.61
C8	C9	1.49	C40	C41	1.47
C8	C14	1.68	C40	C46	1.49
C8	C30	1.46	C40	C58	1.65
C9	C10	1.68	C41	C42	1.55
C9	C11	1.52	C41	C43	1.66
C10	C19	1.43	C42	C51	1.58
C11	C12	1.58	C43	C44	1.55
C12	C13	1.46	C44	C45	1.54
C13	C14	1.42	C45	C46	1.56
C13	C17	1.63	C45	C49	1.57
C13	C18	1.51	C45	C50	1.48
C14	C15	1.60	C46	C47	1.54
C15	C16	1.50	C47	C48	1.45
C17	C20	1.43	C49	C52	1.54
C20	C21	1.17	C52	C53	1.36
C20	C22	1.50	C52	C54	1.38
C22	C23	1.28	C54	C55	1.18
C31	C32	1.37	C59	C60	1.48

Bond Angles

C1	O1	C4	114	O5	C14	C15	59	C39	C40	C41	107
C3	O3	C19	114	C8	C14	C13	123	C39	C40	C46	109
C7	O4	C31	124	C8	C14	C15	114	C39	C40	C58	102
C14	O5	C15	62	C13	C14	C15	121	C41	C40	C46	109
C16	O7	C17	123	O5	C15	C14	60	C41	C40	C58	118
C21	O8	C23	104	O5	C15	C16	118	C46	C40	C58	110
O1	C1	C2	104	C14	C15	C16	110	C40	C41	C42	117
O1	C1	C10	102	O6	C16	O7	126	C40	C41	C43	110
C2	C1	C10	121	O6	C16	C15	112	C42	C41	C43	112
C1	C2	C3	105	O7	C16	C15	121	C33	C42	C37	96
O2	C3	O3	112	O7	C17	C13	109	C33	C42	C41	112
O2	C3	C2	125	O7	C17	C20	113	C33	C42	C51	111
O3	C3	C2	123	C13	C17	C20	117	C37	C42	C41	105
O1	C4	C5	99	O3	C19	C10	122	C37	C42	C51	122
O1	C4	C28	105	C17	C20	C21	115	C41	C42	C51	111
O1	C4	C29	114	C17	C20	C22	134	C41	C43	C44	110
C5	C4	C28	111	C21	C20	C22	111	C43	C44	C45	114
C5	C4	C29	114	O8	C21	C20	109	C44	C45	C46	108
C28	C4	C29	113	C20	C22	C23	103	C44	C45	C49	108
C4	C5	C6	120	O8	C23	C22	113	C44	C45	C50	113
C4	C5	C10	103	O4	C31	O9	116	C46	C45	C49	108
C6	C5	C10	117	O4	C31	C32	120	C46	C45	C50	112
C5	C6	C7	107	O9	C31	C32	123	C49	C45	C50	108
O4	C7	C6	104	I1	C32	C31	110	O14	C46	C40	113
O4	C7	C8	106					O14	C46	C45	112
C6	C7	C8	113	C33	O10	C36	111	O14	C46	C47	57
C7	C8	C9	106	C35	O12	C51	116	C40	C46	C45	119
C7	C8	C14	113	C39	O13	C59	119	C40	C46	C47	127
C7	C8	C30	113	C46	O14	C47	62	C45	C46	C47	111
C9	C8	C14	102	C48	O16	C49	116	O14	C47	C46	61
C9	C8	C30	118	C53	O17	C55	104	O14	C47	C48	110
C14	C8	C30	105	O10	C33	C34	100	C46	C47	C48	115
C8	C9	C10	113	O10	C33	C42	106	O15	C48	O16	115
C8	C9	C11	115	C34	C33	C42	117	O15	C48	C47	119
C10	C9	C11	113	C33	C34	C35	102	O16	C48	C47	126
C1	C10	C5	100	O11	C35	O12	119	O16	C49	C45	113
C1	C10	C9	113	O11	C35	C34	115	O16	C49	C52	107
C1	C10	C19	108	O12	C35	C34	126	C45	C49	C52	112
C5	C10	C9	98	O10	C36	C37	99	O12	C51	C42	111
C5	C10	C19	118	O10	C36	C56	109	C49	C52	C53	125
C9	C10	C19	119	O10	C36	C57	112	C49	C52	C54	127
C9	C11	C12	110	C37	C36	C56	114	C53	C52	C54	107
C11	C12	C13	115	C37	C36	C57	112	O17	C53	C52	107
C12	C13	C14	114	C56	C36	C57	111	C52	C54	C55	112
C12	C13	C17	108	C36	C37	C38	116	O17	C55	C54	109
C12	C13	C18	114	C36	C37	C42	112	O13	C59	O18	125
C14	C13	C17	109	C38	C37	C42	112	O13	C59	C60	111
C14	C13	C18	104	C37	C38	C39	103	O18	C59	C60	123
C17	C13	C18	108	O13	C39	C38	110	I2	C60	C59	112
O5	C14	C8	105	O13	C39	C40	109				
O5	C14	C13	114	C38	C39	C40	120				

Torsion Angles

C4	O1	C1	C2	147
C4	O1	C1	C10	20
C1	O1	C4	C5	9
C1	O1	C4	C28	124
C1	O1	C4	C29	−112
C19	O3	C3	O2	170
C19	O3	C3	C2	−18
C3	O3	C19	C10	43
C31	O4	C7	C6	−107
C31	O4	C7	C8	135
C7	O4	C31	O9	−6
C7	O4	C31	C32	164
C15	O5	C14	C8	−109
C15	O5	C14	C13	113
C14	O5	C15	C16	−98
C17	O7	C16	O6	178
C17	O7	C16	C15	11
C16	O7	C17	C13	33
C16	O7	C17	C20	165
C23	O8	C21	C20	−1
C21	O8	C23	C22	4
O1	C1	C2	C3	−64
C10	C1	C2	C3	50
O1	C1	C10	C5	−40
O1	C1	C10	C9	−143
O1	C1	C10	C19	84
C2	C1	C10	C5	−156
C2	C1	C10	C9	102
C2	C1	C10	C19	−32
C1	C2	C3	O2	146
C1	C2	C3	O3	−25
O1	C4	C5	C6	−167
O1	C4	C5	C10	−34
C28	C4	C5	C6	83
C28	C4	C5	C10	−144
C29	C4	C5	C6	−45
C29	C4	C5	C10	87
C4	C5	C6	C7	−169
C10	C5	C6	C7	65
C4	C5	C10	C1	47
C4	C5	C10	C9	162
C4	C5	C10	C19	−70
C6	C5	C10	C1	−179
C6	C5	C10	C9	−64
C6	C5	C10	C19	64
C5	C6	C7	O4	−171
C5	C6	C7	C8	−57
O4	C7	C8	C9	171
O4	C7	C8	C14	−79
O4	C7	C8	C30	40
C6	C7	C8	C9	58
C6	C7	C8	C14	169
C6	C7	C8	C30	−73
C7	C8	C9	C10	−63
C7	C8	C9	C11	167
C14	C8	C9	C10	180
C14	C8	C9	C11	49

continued

56.2 Epilimonol iodoacetate

continued

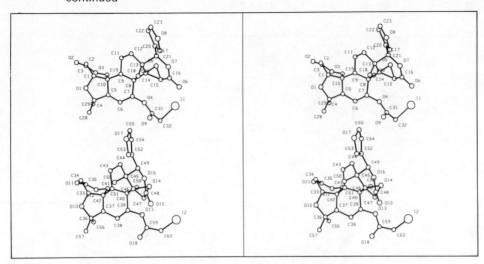

C30	C8	C9	C10	65
C30	C8	C9	C11	-66
C7	C8	C14	O5	121
C7	C8	C14	C13	-106
C7	C8	C14	C15	59
C9	C8	C14	O5	-126
C9	C8	C14	C13	7
C9	C8	C14	C15	173
C30	C8	C14	O5	-2
C30	C8	C14	C13	131
C30	C8	C14	C15	-64
C8	C9	C10	C1	166
C8	C9	C10	C5	62
C8	C9	C10	C19	-66
C11	C9	C10	C1	-62
C11	C9	C10	C5	-166
C11	C9	C10	C19	66
C8	C9	C11	C12	-69
C10	C9	C11	C12	161
C1	C10	C19	O3	-20
C5	C10	C19	O3	93
C9	C10	C19	O3	-150
C9	C11	C12	C13	26
C11	C12	C13	C14	25
C11	C12	C13	C17	147
C11	C12	C13	C18	-93
C12	C13	C14	O5	84
C12	C13	C14	C8	-45
C12	C13	C14	C15	151
C17	C13	C14	O5	-37
C17	C13	C14	C8	-166
C17	C13	C14	C15	30
C18	C13	C14	O5	-152
C18	C13	C14	C8	79
C18	C13	C14	C15	-85
C12	C13	C17	O7	-176
C12	C13	C17	C20	55
C14	C13	C17	O7	-51
C14	C13	C17	C20	179
C18	C13	C17	O7	61
C18	C13	C17	C20	-69
O5	C14	C15	C16	111
C8	C14	C15	O5	94
C8	C14	C15	C16	-155
C13	C14	C15	O5	-100
C13	C14	C15	C16	11
O5	C15	C16	O6	-137
O5	C15	C16	O7	31
C14	C15	C16	O6	157
C14	C15	C16	O7	-35
O7	C17	C20	C21	-23
O7	C17	C20	C22	159
C13	C17	C20	C21	105
C13	C17	C20	C22	-73
C17	C20	C21	O8	-180
C22	C20	C21	O8	-2
C17	C20	C22	C23	-178
C21	C20	C22	C23	4
C20	C22	C23	O8	-4
O4	C31	C32	I1	64
O9	C31	C32	I1	-127
C36	O10	C33	C34	147
C36	O10	C33	C42	24
C33	O10	C36	C37	2
C33	O10	C36	C56	-117
C33	O10	C36	C57	119
C51	O12	C35	O11	168
C51	O12	C35	C34	-19
C35	O12	C51	C42	56
C59	O13	C39	C38	-78
C59	O13	C39	C40	148
C39	O13	C59	O18	2
C39	O13	C59	C60	174
C47	O14	C46	C40	-120
C47	O14	C46	C45	102
C46	O14	C47	C48	-109
C49	O16	C48	O15	-172
C49	O16	C48	C47	10
C48	O16	C49	C45	36
C48	O16	C49	C52	160
C55	O17	C53	C52	-4
C53	O17	C55	C54	8
O10	C33	C34	C35	-62
C42	C33	C34	C35	52
O10	C33	C42	C37	-38
O10	C33	C42	C41	-146
O10	C33	C42	C51	90
C34	C33	C42	C37	-148
C34	C33	C42	C41	104
C34	C33	C42	C51	-20
C33	C34	C35	O11	141
C33	C34	C35	O12	-32
O10	C36	C37	C38	-159
O10	C36	C37	C42	-28
C56	C36	C37	C38	-44
C56	C36	C37	C42	87
C57	C36	C37	C38	83
C57	C36	C37	C42	-146
C42	C37	C38	C39	61
C36	C37	C42	C33	42
C36	C37	C42	C41	156
C36	C37	C42	C51	-77
C38	C37	C42	C33	175
C38	C37	C42	C41	-71
C38	C37	C42	C51	56
C37	C38	C39	O13	-174
C37	C38	C39	C40	-46
O13	C39	C40	C41	169
O13	C39	C40	C46	-73
O13	C39	C40	C58	44
C38	C39	C40	C41	40
C38	C39	C40	C46	159
C38	C39	C40	C58	-85
C39	C40	C41	C42	-48
C39	C40	C41	C43	-178
C46	C40	C41	C42	-166
C46	C40	C41	C43	64
C58	C40	C41	C42	67
C58	C40	C41	C43	-63
C39	C40	C46	O14	86
C39	C40	C46	C45	-139
C39	C40	C46	C47	22
C41	C40	C46	O14	-156
C41	C40	C46	C45	-22
C41	C40	C46	C47	139
C58	C40	C46	O14	-25
C58	C40	C46	C45	110
C58	C40	C46	C47	-89
C40	C41	C42	C33	166
C40	C41	C42	C37	64
C40	C41	C42	C51	-70
C43	C41	C42	C33	-65
C43	C41	C42	C37	-167
C43	C41	C42	C51	59
C40	C41	C43	C44	-45
C42	C41	C43	C44	-177
C33	C42	C51	O12	-32
C37	C42	C51	O12	79
C41	C42	C51	O12	-157
C41	C43	C44	C45	-17
C43	C44	C45	C46	56
C43	C44	C45	C49	172
C43	C44	C45	C50	-68
C44	C45	C46	O14	97
C44	C45	C46	C40	-38
C44	C45	C46	C47	158
C49	C45	C46	O14	-19
C49	C45	C46	C40	-154
C49	C45	C46	C47	42
C50	C45	C46	O14	-138
C50	C45	C46	C40	87
C50	C45	C46	C47	-77
C44	C45	C49	O16	-179
C44	C45	C49	C52	61
C46	C45	C49	O16	-62
C46	C45	C49	C52	177
C50	C45	C49	O16	59
C50	C45	C49	C52	-62
O14	C46	C47	C48	100
C40	C46	C47	O14	95
C40	C46	C47	C48	-165
C45	C46	C47	O14	-103
C45	C46	C47	C48	-3
O14	C47	C48	O15	-139
O14	C47	C48	O16	39
C46	C47	C48	O15	154
C46	C47	C48	O16	-28
O16	C49	C52	C53	-21
O16	C49	C52	C54	144
C45	C49	C52	C53	103
C45	C49	C52	C54	-92
C49	C52	C53	O17	167
C54	C52	C53	O17	0
C49	C52	C54	C55	-162
C53	C52	C54	C55	6
C52	C54	C55	O17	-8
O13	C59	C60	I2	76
O18	C59	C60	I2	-111

56.3 Dihydrogedun - 3β - yl iodoacetate

$C_{30}H_{39}IO_8$

S.A.Sutherland, G.A.Sim, J.M.Robertson, Proc. Chem. Soc., 222, 1962

Atomic coordinates were not reported in the paper.
P2₁2₁2₁   Z = 4   R = 0.22

DHGDIA   LB 30-39-2

56.4 Eupteleogenin iodoacetate

$C_{31}H_{43}IO_5$

M.Nishikawa, K.Kamiya, T.Murata, Y.Tomiie, I.Nitta, Tetrahedron Letters, 3223, 1965

Atomic coordinates were not given
but bond lengths were reported.
$P2_1$ $Z = 2$ $R = 0.22$

EUPTIA   LB 31-43-1

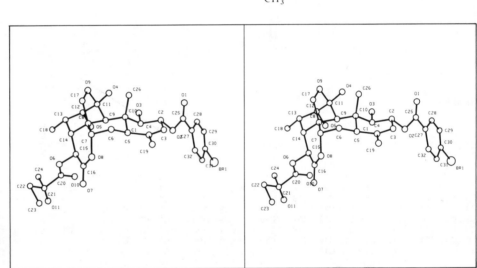

56.5 Glaucarubin p - bromobenzoate

$C_{32}H_{39}BrO_{11}$

G.Kartha, D.J.Haas, J. Amer. Chem. Soc., 86, 3630, 1964

$P2_1$ $Z = 2$ $R = 0.14$

GLINBB   LB 32-39-1

Bond Lengths

Br1	C30	1.94
C25	O1	1.11
C2	O2	1.44
C25	O2	1.38
C1	O3	1.41
C11	O4	1.41
C12	O5	1.41
C15	O6	1.44
C20	O6	1.30
C16	O7	1.20
C7	O8	1.48
C16	O8	1.34
C11	O9	1.46
C17	O9	1.41
C20	O10	1.21
C21	O11	1.36
C1	C2	1.54
C1	C10	1.56
C2	C3	1.53
C3	C4	1.31
C4	C5	1.54
C4	C19	1.47
C5	C6	1.56
C5	C10	1.56
C6	C7	1.51
C7	C8	1.45
C8	C9	1.56
C8	C14	1.60
C8	C17	1.55
C9	C10	1.54
C9	C11	1.51
C10	C26	1.54
C11	C12	1.50
C12	C13	1.54
C13	C14	1.56
C13	C18	1.61
C14	C15	1.48
C15	C16	1.47
C20	C21	1.56
C21	C22	1.24
C21	C24	1.57
C22	C23	1.66
C25	C27	1.46
C27	C28	1.40
C27	C32	1.43
C28	C29	1.39
C29	C30	1.28
C30	C31	1.44
C31	C32	1.36

Bond Angles

C2	O2	C25	116
C15	O6	C20	118
C7	O8	C16	124
C11	O9	C17	106
O3	C1	C2	107
O3	C1	C10	111
C2	C1	C10	111
O2	C2	C1	106
O2	C2	C3	108
C1	C2	C3	111
C2	C3	C4	123
C3	C4	C5	121
C3	C4	C19	122
C5	C4	C19	117
C6	C5	C10	109
C5	C6	C7	108
O8	C7	C6	104
O8	C7	C8	113
C6	C7	C8	114
C7	C8	C9	119
C7	C8	C14	110
C7	C8	C17	112
C9	C8	C14	109
C9	C8	C17	99
C14	C8	C17	106
C8	C9	C10	115
C8	C9	C11	99
C10	C9	C11	120
C1	C10	C5	102
C1	C10	C9	109
C1	C10	C26	111
C5	C10	C9	108
C5	C10	C26	112
C9	C10	C26	114
O4	C11	O9	105
O4	C11	C9	119
O4	C11	C12	107
O9	C11	C9	106
O9	C11	C12	108
C9	C11	C12	110
O5	C12	C11	108
O5	C12	C13	112
C11	C12	C13	111
C12	C13	C14	111
C12	C13	C18	108
C14	C13	C18	115
C8	C14	C13	110
C13	C14	C15	119
O6	C15	C14	109
O6	C15	C16	106
C14	C15	C16	115

Torsion Angles

O7	C16	O8		116
O7	C16	C15		123
O8	C16	C15		121
O9	C17	C8		109
O6	C20	O10		124
O6	C20	C21		116
O10	C20	C21		120
O11	C21	C20		113
O11	C21	C22		131
O11	C21	C24		81
C20	C21	C22		116
C20	C21	C24		96
C22	C21	C24		100
C21	C22	C23		84
O1	C25	O2		121
O1	C25	C27		130
O2	C25	C27		109
C25	C27	C28		118
C25	C27	C32		126
C28	C27	C32		116
C27	C28	C29		122
C28	C29	C30		118
Br1	C30	C29		120
Br1	C30	C31		113
C29	C30	C31		127
C30	C31	C32		113
C27	C32	C31		124

C25	O2	C2	C1	110
C25	O2	C2	C3	-132
C2	O2	C25	O1	10
C2	O2	C25	C27	-172
C20	O6	C15	C14	137
C20	O6	C15	C16	-99
C15	O6	C20	O10	-5
C15	O6	C20	C21	170
C16	O8	C7	C6	-147
C16	O8	C7	C8	-22
C7	O8	C16	O7	-172
C7	O8	C16	C15	8
C17	O9	C11	C9	-27
C17	O9	C11	C12	92
C11	O9	C17	C8	-1
C10	C1	C2	O2	169
C10	C1	C2	C3	52
C2	C1	C10	C5	-67
C2	C1	C10	C9	179
O2	C2	C3	C4	-134
C1	C2	C3	C4	-18
C2	C3	C4	C5	5
C3	C4	C5	C6	-152
C3	C4	C5	C10	-25
C4	C5	C6	C7	-162
C10	C5	C6	C7	68
C4	C5	C10	C1	53

C4	C5	C10	C9	168
C6	C5	C10	C1	-177
C6	C5	C10	C9	-62
C5	C6	C7	O8	70
C5	C6	C7	C8	-54
O8	C7	C8	C9	-81
O8	C7	C8	C14	47
O8	C7	C8	C17	164
C6	C7	C8	C9	38
C6	C7	C8	C14	166
C6	C7	C8	C17	-77
C7	C8	C9	C10	-34
C7	C8	C9	C11	-162
C14	C8	C9	C10	-162
C14	C8	C9	C11	70
C17	C8	C9	C10	88
C17	C8	C9	C11	-41
C7	C8	C14	C13	168
C7	C8	C14	C15	-60
C9	C8	C14	C13	-59
C9	C8	C14	C15	73
C17	C8	C14	C13	47
C17	C8	C14	C15	179
C7	C8	C17	O9	154
C9	C8	C17	O9	27
C14	C8	C17	O9	-86
C8	C9	C10	C1	154

C8	C9	C10	C5	44
C11	C9	C10	C1	-89
C11	C9	C10	C5	161
C8	C9	C11	O9	43
C8	C9	C11	C12	-74
C10	C9	C11	O9	-81
C10	C9	C11	C12	161
O9	C11	C12	C13	-50
C9	C11	C12	C13	66
C11	C12	C13	C14	-48
C12	C13	C14	C8	45
C12	C13	C14	C15	-81
C8	C14	C15	O6	164
C8	C14	C15	C16	46
C13	C14	C15	O6	-69
C13	C14	C15	C16	173
O6	C15	C16	O7	38
O6	C15	C16	O8	-142
C14	C15	C16	O7	159
C14	C15	C16	O8	-22
O6	C20	C21	C22	5
O10	C20	C21	C22	180
C20	C21	C22	C23	-90
O1	C25	C27	C28	-22
O2	C25	C27	C28	160

56.6 Methylmicromerol bromoacetate

C₃₃H₅₁BrO₄ → $C_{33}H_{51}BrO_4$

G.H.Stout, K.L.Stevens, J. Org. Chem., 28, 1259, 1963

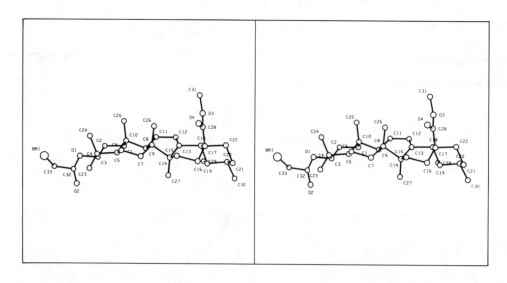

No comparison of bond lengths is possible since they are not reported in the paper.
$P2_12_12_1$ Z = 4   R = 0.161

MEMICB

Bond Lengths

Br1	C33	1.95	C9	C10	1.73
C3	O1	1.54	C9	C11	1.66
C32	O1	1.21	C10	C25	1.57
C32	O2	1.20	C11	C12	1.67
C28	O3	1.17	C12	C13	1.20
C31	O3	1.42	C13	C14	1.69
C28	O4	1.29	C13	C18	1.80
C1	C2	1.71	C14	C15	1.51
C1	C10	1.40	C14	C27	1.52
C2	C3	1.36	C15	C16	1.64
C3	C4	1.86	C16	C17	1.48
C4	C5	1.65	C17	C18	1.48
C4	C23	1.42	C17	C22	1.63
C4	C24	1.53	C17	C28	1.45
C5	C6	1.64	C18	C19	1.69
C5	C10	1.61	C19	C20	1.60
C6	C7	1.56	C19	C29	1.60
C7	C8	1.52	C20	C21	1.69
C8	C9	1.64	C20	C30	1.57
C8	C14	1.72	C21	C22	1.54
C8	C26	1.48	C32	C33	1.67

Bond Angles

C3	O1	C32	114	C8	C9	C10	113	C16	C17	C28	127
C28	O3	C31	133	C8	C9	C11	113	C18	C17	C22	105
C2	C1	C10	110	C10	C9	C11	101	C18	C17	C28	96
e1	C2	C3	104	C1	C10	C5	115	C22	C17	C28	94
O1	C3	C2	108	C1	C10	C9	102	C13	C18	C17	114
O1	C3	C4	95	C1	C10	C25	117	C13	C18	C19	101
C2	C3	C4	122	C5	C10	C9	95	C17	C18	C19	112
C3	C4	C5	96	C5	C10	C25	113	C18	C19	C20	102
C3	C4	C23	112	C9	C10	C25	113	C18	C19	C29	110
C3	C4	C24	108	C9	C11	C12	107	C20	C19	C29	103
C5	C4	C23	115	C11	C12	C13	116	C19	C20	C21	106
C5	C4	C24	107	C12	C13	C14	140	C19	C20	C30	108
C23	C4	C24	117	C12	C13	C18	115	C20	C21	C22	105
C4	C5	C6	108	C14	C13	C18	104	C17	C22	C21	108
C4	C5	C10	115	C8	C14	C13	95	O3	C28	O4	105
C6	C5	C10	119	C8	C14	C15	102	O3	C28	C17	144
C5	C6	C7	104	C8	C14	C27	117	O4	C28	C17	111
C6	C7	C8	112	C13	C14	C15	117	O1	C32	O2	139
C7	C8	C9	107	C13	C14	C27	103	O1	C32	C33	112
C7	C8	C14	100	C15	C14	C27	120	O2	C32	C33	110
C7	C8	C26	116	C14	C15	C16	111	Br1	C33	C32	105
C9	C8	C14	100	C15	C16	C17	102				
C9	C8	C26	116	C16	C17	C18	118				
C14	C8	C26	116	C16	C17	C22	113				

Torsion Angles

C32	O1	C3	C2	129	C14	C8	C9	C10	169	C15	C16	C17	C18	−69
C32	O1	C3	C4	−106	C14	C8	C9	C11	−77	C15	C16	C17	C22	168
C3	O1	C32	O2	7	C7	C8	C14	C13	172	C15	C16	C17	C28	54
C3	O1	C32	C33	−176	C7	C8	C14	C15	−69	C16	C17	C18	C13	55
C31	O3	C28	O4	4	C9	C8	C14	C13	63	C16	C17	C18	C19	−59
C31	O3	C28	C17	178	C9	C8	C14	C15	−178	C22	C17	C18	C13	−178
C10	C1	C2	C3	−60	C8	C9	C10	C1	−177	C22	C17	C18	C19	67
C2	C1	C10	C5	60	C8	C9	C10	C5	−60	C28	C17	C18	C13	−83
C2	C1	C10	C9	161	C11	C9	C10	C1	62	C28	C17	C18	C19	163
C1	C2	C3	O1	171	C11	C9	C10	C5	179	C16	C17	C22	C21	61
C1	C2	C3	C4	63	C8	C9	C11	C12	40	C18	C17	C22	C21	−69
O1	C3	C4	C5	−173	C10	C9	C11	C12	161	C28	C17	C22	C21	−166
C2	C3	C4	C5	−59	C9	C11	C12	C13	2	C16	C17	C28	O3	−152
C3	C4	C5	C6	−178	C11	C12	C13	C14	−2	C16	C17	C28	O4	21
C3	C4	C5	C10	46	C11	C12	C13	C18	−179	C18	C17	C28	O3	−20
C4	C5	C6	C7	159	C12	C13	C14	C8	−34	C18	C17	C28	O4	153
C10	C5	C6	C7	−67	C12	C13	C14	C15	−140	C22	C17	C28	O3	85
C4	C5	C10	C1	−61	C12	C13	C18	C17	146	C22	C17	C28	O4	−102
C4	C5	C10	C9	−166	C12	C13	C18	C19	−94	C13	C18	C19	C20	170
C6	C5	C10	C1	168	C14	C13	C18	C17	−32	C17	C18	C19	C20	−68
C6	C5	C10	C9	63	C14	C13	C18	C19	89	C18	C19	C20	C21	63
C5	C6	C7	C8	61	C8	C14	C15	C16	−160	C19	C20	C21	C22	−69
C6	C7	C8	C9	−64	C13	C14	C15	C16	−58	C20	C21	C22	C17	68
C6	C7	C8	C14	−167	C14	C15	C16	C17	68	O1	C32	C33	Br1	−60
C7	C8	C9	C10	66						O2	C32	C33	Br1	118
C7	C8	C9	C11	179										

56.7 Phytolaccagenin 2 - oxazoline derivative

C₃₃H₅₁NO₆ → $C_{33}H_{51}NO_6$

G.H.Stout, B.M.Malofsky, V.F.Stout, J. Amer. Chem. Soc., 86, 957, 1964

Atomic coordinates were not reported in the paper.
$P2_12_12_1$ Z = 4   R = 0.145

PHYTOZ   LB 33-51-2

56.8 Simarolide 4 - iodo - 3 - nitrobenzoate acetone solvate (absolute configuration)

$C_{34}H_{38}INO_{12}$, C_3H_6O

W.A.C.Brown, G.A.Sim, Proc. Chem. Soc., 293, 1964

Atomic coordinates were not reported in the paper.
P2$_1$2$_1$2$_1$ Z = 4   R = 0.21

SMINIB   LB 34-38-1

56.9 Methyl melaleucate iodoacetate (absolute configuration)

$C_{34}H_{51}IO_6$

S.R.Hall, E.N.Maslen, Acta Cryst., 18, 265, 1965

P2$_1$2$_1$2$_1$ Z = 4   R = 0.079

MELALI   LB 34-51-1

Bond Lengths

I1	C32	2.06	C8	C26	1.56
C3	O1	1.56	C9	C10	1.50
C31	O1	1.29	C9	C11	1.55
C31	O2	1.19	C10	C25	1.59
C27	O3	1.25	C11	C12	1.53
C34	O3	1.49	C12	C13	1.53
C27	O4	1.24	C13	C14	1.54
C28	O5	1.24	C13	C18	1.53
C28	O6	1.30	C14	C15	1.56
C33	O6	1.47	C14	C27	1.56
C1	C2	1.53	C15	C16	1.51
C1	C10	1.57	C16	C17	1.58
C2	C3	1.46	C17	C18	1.54
C3	C4	1.52	C17	C22	1.49
C4	C5	1.65	C17	C28	1.54
C4	C23	1.48	C18	C19	1.54
C4	C24	1.55	C19	C20	1.51
C5	C6	1.54	C19	C21	1.55
C5	C10	1.59	C20	C29	1.30
C6	C7	1.47	C20	C30	1.44
C7	C8	1.53	C21	C22	1.46
C8	C9	1.53	C31	C32	1.49
C8	C14	1.66			

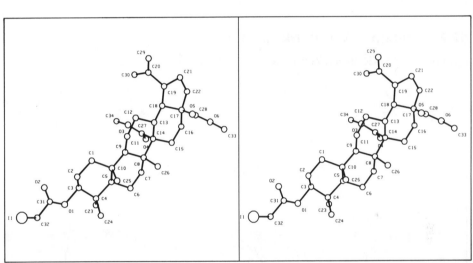

Bond Angles

C3	O1	C31	116	C8	C9	C10	119	C18	C17	C22	100
C27	O3	C34	118	C8	C9	C11	110	C18	C17	C28	115
C28	O6	C33	118	C10	C9	C11	114	C22	C17	C28	108
C2	C1	C10	113	C1	C10	C5	107	C13	C18	C17	110
C1	C2	C3	111	C1	C10	C9	113	C13	C18	C19	120
O1	C3	C2	108	C1	C10	C25	106	C17	C18	C19	104
O1	C3	C4	101	C5	C10	C9	107	C18	C19	C20	121
C2	C3	C4	120	C5	C10	C25	107	C18	C19	C21	101
C3	C4	C5	102	C9	C10	C25	116	C20	C19	C21	110
C3	C4	C23	112	C9	C11	C12	112	C19	C20	C29	122
C3	C4	C24	115	C11	C12	C13	111	C19	C20	C30	119
C5	C4	C23	109	C12	C13	C14	114	C29	C20	C30	123
C5	C4	C24	109	C12	C13	C18	113	C19	C21	C22	108
C23	C4	C24	109	C14	C13	C18	108	C17	C22	C21	106
C4	C5	C6	115	C8	C14	C13	110	O3	C27	O4	125
C4	C5	C10	120	C8	C14	C15	112	O3	C27	C14	114
C6	C5	C10	112	C8	C14	C27	108	O4	C27	C14	122
C5	C6	C7	111	C13	C14	C15	109	O5	C28	O6	122
C6	C7	C8	113	C13	C14	C27	113	O5	C28	C17	124
C7	C8	C9	111	C15	C14	C27	105	O6	C28	C17	114
C7	C8	C14	109	C14	C15	C16	116	O1	C31	O2	130
C7	C8	C26	107	C15	C16	C17	109	O1	C31	C32	109
C9	C8	C14	109	C16	C17	C18	110	O2	C31	C32	119
C9	C8	C26	114	C16	C17	C22	117	I1	C32	C31	115
C14	C8	C26	107	C16	C17	C28	106				

Torsion Angles

C31	O1	C3	C2	98	C7	C8	C14	C27	52	C14 C15 C16 C17	50
C31	O1	C3	C4	−135	C9	C8	C14	C13	54	C15 C16 C17 C18	−53
C3	O1	C31	O2	−11	C9	C8	C14	C15	176	C15 C16 C17 C22	−167
C3	O1	C31	C32	−174	C9	C8	C14	C27	−69	C15 C16 C17 C28	72
C34	O3	C27	O4	−2	C8	C9	C10	C1	−166	C16 C17 C18 C13	62
C34	O3	C27	C14	−175	C8	C9	C10	C5	−48	C16 C17 C18 C19	−169
C33	O6	C28	O5	0	C11	C9	C10	C1	61	C22 C17 C18 C13	−174
C33	O6	C28	C17	−175	C11	C9	C10	C5	179	C22 C17 C18 C19	−45
C10	C1	C2	C3	−56	C8	C9	C11	C12	61	C28 C17 C18 C13	−58
C2	C1	C10	C5	49	C10	C9	C11	C12	−163	C28 C17 C18 C19	71
C2	C1	C10	C9	167	C9	C11	C12	C13	−57	C16 C17 C22 C21	161
C1	C2	C3	O1	177	C11	C12	C13	C14	54	C18 C17 C22 C21	41
C1	C2	C3	C4	63	C11	C12	C13	C18	178	C28 C17 C22 C21	−80
O1	C3	C4	C5	−171	C12	C13	C14	C8	−52	C16 C17 C28 O5	−130
C2	C3	C4	C5	−53	C12	C13	C14	C15	−176	C16 C17 C28 O6	46
C3	C4	C5	C6	−176	C12	C13	C14	C27	68	C18 C17 C28 O5	−8
C3	C4	C5	C10	46	C18	C13	C14	C8	−179	C18 C17 C28 O6	168
C4	C5	C6	C7	159	C18	C13	C14	C15	58	C22 C17 C28 O5	103
C10	C5	C6	C7	−60	C18	C13	C14	C27	−58	C22 C17 C28 O6	−81
C4	C5	C10	C1	−47	C12	C13	C18	C17	169	C13 C18 C19 C20	−85
C4	C5	C10	C9	−169	C12	C13	C18	C19	49	C13 C18 C19 C21	154
C6	C5	C10	C1	174	C14	C13	C18	C17	−64	C17 C18 C19 C20	152
C6	C5	C10	C9	53	C14	C13	C18	C19	176	C17 C18 C19 C21	31
C5	C6	C7	C8	58	C8	C14	C15	C16	−176	C18 C19 C20 C29	162
C6	C7	C8	C9	−50	C13	C14	C15	C16	−54	C21 C19 C20 C29	−81
C6	C7	C8	C14	−170	C27	C14	C15	C16	67	C20 C19 C21 C22	−6
C7	C8	C9	C10	48	C8	C14	C27	O3	80	C20 C19 C21 C22	−135
C7	C8	C9	C11	−178	C8	C14	C27	O4	−94	C19 C21 C22 C17	−22
C14	C8	C9	C10	168	C13	C14	C27	O3	−42	O1 C31 C32 I1	81
C14	C8	C9	C11	−58	C13	C14	C27	O4	144	O2 C31 C32 I1	−84
C7	C8	C14	C13	175	C15	C14	C27	O3	−161		
C7	C8	C14	C15	−63	C15	C14	C27	O4	26		

57.1 $\Delta^{12,14}$ - cis - β - Ionylidene - trans - γ - crotonic acid

$C_{17}H_{24}O_2$

B.Koch, C.H.MacGillavry, Acta Cryst., 16, A48, 1963

Atomic coordinates were not reported in the paper.
P1   Z = 2   No R factor was given.

IONCRT   LB 17-24-2

57.2 Vitamin A acid (triclinic form)

$C_{20}H_{28}O_2$

C.H.Stam, C.H.MacGillavry, Acta Cryst., 16, 62, 1963

P-1   Z = 2   R = 0.13

VITAAC   LB 20-28-11

Bond Lengths

C20	O1	1.33	C9	C10	1.47
C20	O2	1.20	C10	C11	1.37
C1	C3	1.52	C11	C12	1.45
C2	C3	1.55	C12	C13	1.57
C3	C4	1.55	C12	C14	1.35
C3	C9	1.56	C14	C15	1.44
C4	C5	1.45	C15	C16	1.36
C5	C6	1.53	C16	C17	1.45
C6	C7	1.54	C17	C18	1.53
C7	C8	1.52	C17	C19	1.34
C7	C9	1.36	C19	C20	1.45

Bond Angles

C1	C3	C2	112	C9	C10	C11	125
C1	C3	C4	111	C10	C11	C12	125
C1	C3	C9	110	C11	C12	C13	118
C2	C3	C4	103	C11	C12	C14	118
C2	C3	C9	111	C13	C12	C14	123
C4	C3	C9	110	C12	C14	C15	124
C3	C4	C5	115	C14	C15	C16	122
C4	C5	C6	112	C15	C16	C17	125
C5	C6	C7	112	C16	C17	C18	118
C6	C7	C8	112	C16	C17	C19	118
C6	C7	C9	123	C18	C17	C19	124
C8	C7	C9	125	C17	C19	C20	125
C3	C9	C7	123	O1	C20	O2	120
C3	C9	C10	113	O1	C20	C19	112
C7	C9	C10	124	O2	C20	C19	128

Torsion Angles

C9	C3	C4	C5	−42	C9	C10	C11	C12	−179
C4	C3	C9	C7	13	C10	C11	C12	C13	−3
C4	C3	C9	C10	−167	C10	C11	C12	C14	173
C3	C4	C5	C6	59	C11	C12	C14	C15	−176
C4	C5	C6	C7	−45	C13	C12	C14	C15	0
C5	C6	C7	C8	−167	C12	C14	C15	C16	178
C5	C6	C7	C9	17	C14	C15	C16	C17	179
C6	C7	C9	C3	−2	C15	C16	C17	C18	5
C6	C7	C9	C10	177	C15	C16	C17	C19	−176
C8	C7	C9	C3	−177	C16	C17	C19	C20	−177
C8	C7	C9	C10	2	C18	C17	C19	C20	1
C3	C9	C10	C11	−140	C17	C19	C20	O1	171
C7	C9	C10	C11	40					

57.3 15,15′ - Dehydro - β - carotene

$C_{40}H_{54}$

W.G.Sly, Acta Cryst., 17, 511, 1964

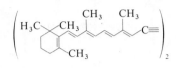

P2₁/c   Z = 2   R = 0.096

DCAROT   LB 40-54-1

Bond Lengths

C1	C2	1.53
C1	C6	1.54
C1	C17	1.54
C1	C18	1.54
C2	C3	1.50
C3	C4	1.52
C4	C5	1.50
C5	C6	1.34
C5	C16	1.52
C6	C7	1.48
C7	C8	1.34
C8	C9	1.46
C9	C10	1.35
C9	C19	1.51
C10	C11	1.46
C11	C12	1.34
C12	C13	1.45
C13	C14	1.35
C13	C20	1.50
C14	C15	1.43
C15	C15B	1.20

Bond Angles

C2	C1	C6	111	C5	C6	C7	123
C2	C1	C17	111	C6	C7	C8	126
C2	C1	C18	107	C7	C8	C9	125
C6	C1	C17	110	C8	C9	C10	119
C6	C1	C18	111	C8	C9	C19	118
C17	C1	C18	107	C10	C9	C19	123
C1	C2	C3	113	C9	C10	C11	125
C2	C3	C4	111	C10	C11	C12	124
C3	C4	C5	113	C11	C12	C13	126
C4	C5	C6	123	C12	C13	C14	119
C4	C5	C16	113	C12	C13	C20	120
C6	C5	C16	124	C14	C13	C20	121
C1	C6	C5	123	C13	C14	C15	124
C1	C6	C7	115	C14	C15	C15B	180

Torsion Angles

C6	C1	C2	C3	42	C6	C7	C8	C9	178
C2	C1	C6	C5	−9	C7	C8	C9	C10	−171
C2	C1	C6	C7	170	C7	C8	C9	C19	7
C1	C2	C3	C4	−60	C8	C9	C10	C11	173
C2	C3	C4	C5	44	C19	C9	C10	C11	−4
C3	C4	C5	C6	−12	C9	C10	C11	C12	−179
C3	C4	C5	C16	169	C10	C11	C12	C13	176
C4	C5	C6	C1	−6	C11	C12	C13	C14	180
C4	C5	C6	C7	175	C11	C12	C13	C20	−3
C16	C5	C6	C1	173	C12	C13	C14	C15	178
C16	C5	C6	C7	−6	C20	C13	C14	C15	1
C1	C6	C7	C8	132	C13	C14	C15	C15B	180
C5	C6	C7	C8	−49	C14	C15	C15B	C14B	−178

57.4 β - Carotene

$C_{40}H_{56}$

C.Sterling, Acta Cryst., 17, 1224, 1964

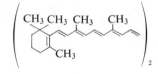

P2₁/c   Z = 2   R = 0.19

CARTEN   LB 40-56-2

Bond Lengths

C1	C2	1.63
C1	C6	1.49
C1	C100	1.50
C1	C101	1.63
C2	C3	1.41
C3	C4	1.42
C4	C5	1.63
C5	C6	1.29
C5	C50	1.46
C6	C7	1.55
C7	C8	1.31
C8	C9	1.52
C9	C10	1.37
C9	C90	1.58
C10	C11	1.47
C11	C12	1.35
C12	C13	1.55
C13	C14	1.37
C13	C130	1.53
C14	C15	1.52
C15	C15B	1.35

Bond Angles

C2	C1	C6	109	C5	C6	C7	122
C2	C1	C100	112	C6	C7	C8	121
C2	C1	C101	100	C7	C8	C9	124
C6	C1	C100	113	C8	C9	C10	117
C6	C1	C101	112	C8	C9	C90	116
C100	C1	C101	111	C10	C9	C90	126
C1	C2	C3	119	C9	C10	C11	121
C2	C3	C4	122	C10	C11	C12	113
C3	C4	C5	113	C11	C12	C13	120
C4	C5	C6	122	C12	C13	C14	114
C4	C5	C50	109	C12	C13	C130	118
C6	C5	C50	130	C14	C13	C130	128
C1	C6	C5	128	C13	C14	C15	121
C1	C6	C7	110	C14	C15	C15B	113

Torsion Angles

C6	C1	C2	C3	−21	C6	C7	C8	C9	174
C2	C1	C6	C5	−1	C7	C8	C9	C10	174
C2	C1	C6	C7	−179	C7	C8	C9	C90	3
C1	C2	C3	C4	35	C8	C9	C10	C11	−177
C2	C3	C4	C5	−26	C90	C9	C10	C11	−7
C3	C4	C5	C6	3	C9	C10	C11	C12	178
C3	C4	C5	C50	−177	C10	C11	C12	C13	−176
C4	C5	C6	C1	9	C11	C12	C13	C14	−179
C4	C5	C6	C7	−173	C11	C12	C13	C130	4
C50	C5	C6	C1	−171	C12	C13	C14	C15	−2
C50	C5	C6	C7	7	C130	C13	C14	C15	−2
C1	C6	C7	C8	−143	C13	C14	C15	C15B	−179
C5	C6	C7	C8	39	C14	C15	C15B	C14B	−180

57.5   7,7 - Dihydro - β - carotene

C.Sterling, Acta Cryst., 17, 500, 1964

$C_{40}H_{58}$

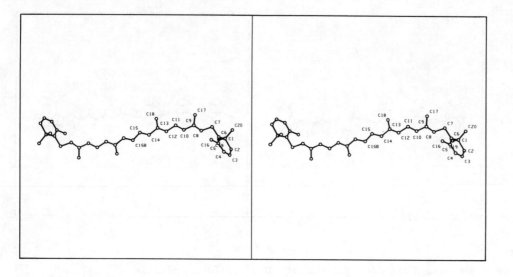

P2₁/c   Z = 2   R = 0.17

HCAROT   LB 40-58-1

Bond Lengths

C1	C2	1.65
C1	C6	1.51
C1	C19	1.44
C1	C20	1.53
C2	C3	1.44
C3	C4	1.43
C4	C5	1.35
C5	C6	1.42
C5	C16	1.51
C6	C7	1.60
C7	C8	1.57
C8	C9	1.33
C9	C10	1.49
C9	C17	1.55
C10	C11	1.38
C11	C12	1.48
C12	C13	1.38
G13	C14	1.49
C13	C18	1.53
C14	C15	1.40
C15	C15B	1.44

Bond Angles

C2	C1	C6	111
C2	C1	C19	105
C2	C1	C20	109
C6	C1	C19	107
C6	C1	C20	107
C19	C1	C20	117
C1	C2	C3	114
C2	C3	C4	127
C3	C4	C5	121
C4	C5	C6	119
C4	C5	C16	123
C6	C5	C16	118
C1	C6	C5	127
C1	C6	C7	112

C5	C6	C7	121
C6	C7	C8	106
C7	C8	C9	124
C8	C9	C10	117
C8	C9	C17	124
C10	C9	C17	119
C9	C10	C11	122
C10	C11	C12	117
C11	C12	C13	123
C12	C13	C14	116
C12	C13	C18	124
C14	C13	C18	120
C13	C14	C15	122
C14	C15	C15B	111

Torsion Angles

C6	C1	C2	C3	−4
C2	C1	C6	C5	8
C2	C1	C6	C7	−175
C1	C2	C3	C4	−3
C2	C3	C4	C5	7
C3	C4	C5	C6	−3
C3	C4	C5	C16	174
C4	C5	C6	C1	−5
C4	C5	C6	C7	178
C16	C5	C6	C1	178
C16	C5	C6	C7	1
C1	C6	C7	C8	119
C5	C6	C7	C8	−64

C6	C7	C8	C9	145
C7	C8	C9	C10	176
C7	C8	C9	C17	−2
C8	C9	C10	C11	175
C17	C9	C10	C11	−7
C9	C10	C11	C12	−173
C10	C11	C12	C13	178
C11	C12	C13	C14	180
C11	C12	C13	C18	−6
C12	C13	C14	C15	176
C18	C13	C14	C15	1
C13	C14	C15	C15B	177
C14	C15	C15B	C14B	−180

58.1 Fescue alkaloid hydrochloride

$C_8H_{16}N_2O^{2+}$, $2Cl^-$

J.A.S.McMillan, Dissert. Abstr., 25, 868, 1964

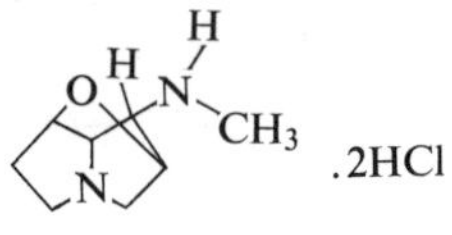

Atomic coordinates were not reported in the paper.
P2₁2₁2₁   Z = 4   R = 0.065

FESCUE   LB 8-16-22

58.2 Nicotine dihydroiodide

$C_{10}H_{16}N_2^{2+}$, $2I^-$

C.H.Koo, H.S.Kim, Daehan Hwahak Hwoejee, 9, 134, 1965

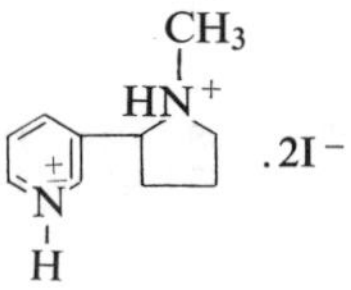

P2₁2₁2₁   Z = 4   R = 0.16

NICOTI

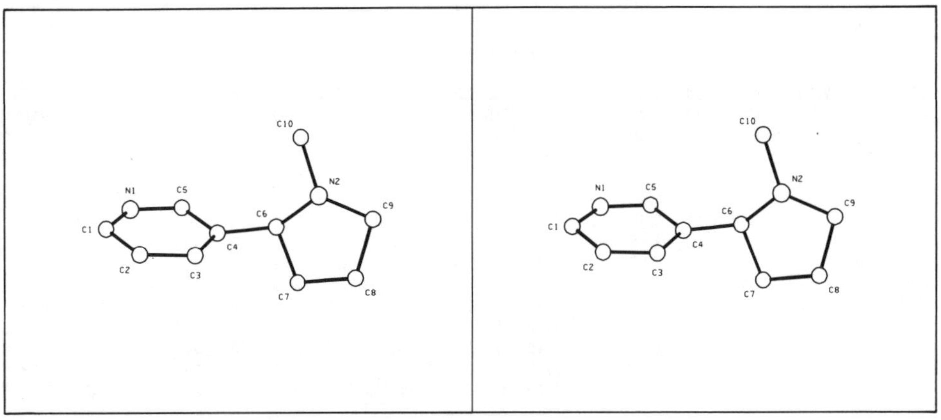

Bond Lengths

C1	N1	1.34		C3	C4	1.41		
C5	N1	1.36		C4	C5	1.37		
C6	N2	1.49		C4	C6	1.52		
C9	N2	1.48		C6	C7	1.54		
C10	N2	1.49		C7	C8	1.55		
C1	C2	1.40		C8	C9	1.58		
C2	C3	1.40						

Bond Angles

C1	N1	C5	123		C5	C4	C6	124
C6	N2	C9	115		N1	C5	C4	125
C6	N2	C10	106		N2	C6	C4	133
C9	N2	C10	131		N2	C6	C7	107
N1	C1	C2	114		C4	C6	C7	107
C1	C2	C3	122		C6	C7	C8	103
C2	C3	C4	122		C7	C8	C9	113
C3	C4	C5	112		N2	C9	C8	99
C3	C4	C6	122					

Torsion Angles

C9	N2	C6	C4	151		C3	C4	C6	N2	−60
C9	N2	C6	C7	17		C3	C4	C6	C7	75
C10	N2	C6	C4	−55		N2	C6	C7	C8	−6
C10	N2	C6	C7	170		C4	C6	C7	C8	−153
C6	N2	C9	C8	−18		C6	C7	C8	C9	−5
C10	N2	C9	C8	−164		C7	C8	C9	N2	14

58.3 Bromoanhydrotetrodoic lactone hydrobromide

$C_{11}H_{15}BrN_3O_7^-$, Br

Y.Tomiie, A.Furusaki, K.Kasami, N.Yasuoka, K.Miyake, M.Haisa, I.Nitta,
Tetrahedron Letters 2101, 1963

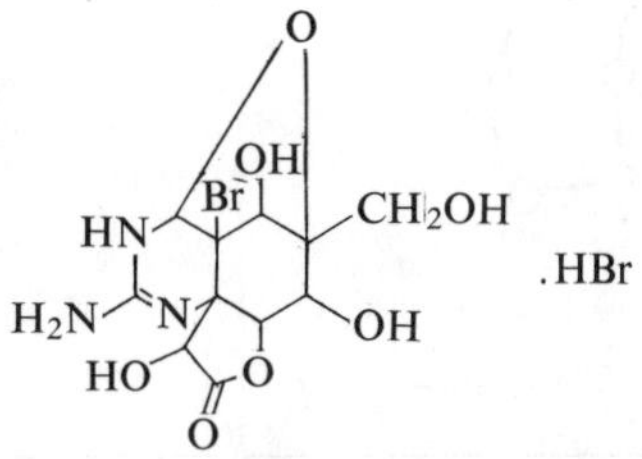

Atomic coordinates were not reported in the paper.
See also Furusaki et al., Bull. Chem. Soc. Jap., 43, 3325, 1970.
P2₁2₁2₁   Z = 4   R = 0.154

BATETB

58.4   Casimidine dihydrochloride

S.Raman, J.M. Reddy, W.N. Lipscomb
Acta Cryst., 16, 364, 1963

$C_{12}H_{23}N_3O_5$, $2Cl^-$

$P2_12_12_1$ $Z = 4$ $R = 0.12$

CASDIN   LB 12-23-2

Bond Lengths

C7	N15	1.40		C13	O21	1.46
C8	N15	1.39		C14	O22	1.43
C9	N15	1.41		C4	C5	1.49
C6	N16	1.40		C4	C6	1.51
C8	N16	1.35		C6	C7	1.34
C3	N17	1.53		C9	C14	1.48
C5	N17	1.52		C10	C11	1.48
C9	O18	1.43		C11	C12	1.58
C11	O18	1.46		C12	C13	1.58
C10	O19	1.41		C13	C14	1.53
C12	O20	1.36				

Bond Angles

C7	N15	C8	108		O18	C9	C14	111
C7	N15	C9	128		O19	C10	C11	113
C8	N15	C9	124		O18	C11	C10	109
C6	N16	C8	113		O18	C11	C12	109
C3	N17	C5	113		C10	C11	C12	114
C9	O18	C11	115		O20	C12	C11	111
C5	C4	C6	116		O20	C12	C13	109
N17	C5	C4	112		C11	C12	C13	110
N16	C6	C4	120		O21	C13	C12	103
N16	C6	C7	104		O21	C13	C14	112
C4	C6	C7	136		C12	C13	C14	110
N15	C7	C6	111		O22	C14	C9	112
N15	C8	N16	105		O22	C14	C13	105
N15	C9	O18	104		C9	C14	C13	113
N15	C9	C14	112					

Torsion Angles

C8	N15	C7	C6	2		C9	O18	C11	C12	58
C9	N15	C7	C6	-171		C6	C4	C5	N17	65
C7	N15	C8	N16	2		C5	C4	C6	N16	48
C9	N15	C8	N16	175		C5	C4	C6	C7	-143
C7	N15	C9	O18	-137		N16	C6	C7	N15	-4
C7	N15	C9	C14	103		C4	C6	C7	N15	-175
C8	N15	C9	O18	51		N15	C9	C14	C13	172
C8	N15	C9	C14	-69		O18	C9	C14	C13	56
C8	N16	C6	C4	178		O19	C10	C11	O18	-69
C8	N16	C6	C7	6		O19	C10	C11	C12	53
C6	N16	C8	N15	-5		O18	C11	C12	C13	-52
C3	N17	C5	C4	179		C10	C11	C12	C13	-174
C11	O18	C9	N15	180		C11	C12	C13	C14	50
C11	O18	C9	C14	-60		C12	C13	C14	C9	-52
C9	O18	C11	C10	-177					

58.5   Securine hydrobromide dihydrate

S.Imado, M.Shiro, Z.Horii
Chem. Pharm. Bull., Jap. 13, 643, 1965

$C_{13}H_{16}NO_2^+$, Br^-, $2H_2O$

$P112_1$ $Z = 2$ $R_{hk0} = 0.135$,
$R_{hk1} = 0.105$, $R_{hk2} = 0.105$,
$R_{hk3} = 0.106$, $R_{hk4} = 0.090$,
$R_{hk5} = 0.115$

SECINB   LB 13-16-4

Bond Lengths

C1	N1	1.48	C5	C8	1.62
C5	N1	1.54	C6	C7	1.49
C6	N1	1.53	C6	C11	1.46
C13	O1	1.19	C7	C8	1.47
C8	O2	1.40	C8	C9	1.54
C13	O2	1.37	C9	C10	1.44
C1	C2	1.54	C9	C12	1.32
C2	C3	1.63	C10	C11	1.40
C3	C4	1.54	C12	C13	1.49
C4	C5	1.52			

Bond Angles

C1	N1	C5	115	O2	C8	C5	107
C1	N1	C6	112	O2	C8	C7	123
C5	N1	C6	103	O2	C8	C9	104
C8	O2	C13	110	C5	C8	C7	104
N1	C1	C2	109	C5	C8	C9	109
C1	C2	C3	112	C7	C8	C9	109
C2	C3	C4	109	C8	C9	C10	115
C3	C4	C5	110	C8	C9	C12	109
N1	C5	C4	111	C10	C9	C12	135
N1	C5	C8	103	C9	C10	C11	120
C4	C5	C8	115	C6	C11	C10	117
N1	C6	C7	103	C9	C12	C13	107
N1	C6	C11	113	O1	C13	O2	122
C7	C6	C11	115	O1	C13	C12	129
C6	C7	C8	99	O2	C13	C12	109

Torsion Angles

C5	N1	C1	C2	−60	C4	C5	C8	O2	33
C6	N1	C1	C2	−177	C4	C5	C8	C7	−99
C1	N1	C5	C4	12	C4	C5	C8	C9	145
C1	N1	C5	C8	−111	N1	C6	C7	C8	55
C6	N1	C5	C4	134	C11	C6	C7	C8	−69
C6	N1	C5	C8	11	N1	C6	C11	C10	−79
C1	N1	C6	C7	84	C7	C6	C11	C10	38
C1	N1	C6	C11	−151	C6	C7	C8	O2	−168
C5	N1	C6	C7	−40	C6	C7	C8	C5	−46
C5	N1	C6	C11	84	C6	C7	C8	C9	70
C13	O2	C8	C5	120	O2	C8	C9	C10	−180
C13	O2	C8	C7	−120	O2	C8	C9	C12	−3
C13	O2	C8	C9	5	C5	C8	C9	C10	66
C8	O2	C13	O1	−179	C5	C8	C9	C12	−117
C8	O2	C13	C12	−5	C7	C8	C9	C10	−46
N1	C1	C2	C3	45	C7	C8	C9	C12	130
C1	C2	C3	C4	12	C8	C9	C10	C11	11
C2	C3	C4	C5	−61	C12	C9	C10	C11	−164
C3	C4	C5	N1	50	C8	C9	C12	C13	0
C3	C4	C5	C8	166	C10	C9	C12	C13	176
N1	C5	C8	O2	154	C9	C10	C11	C6	−7
N1	C5	C8	C7	22	C9	C12	C13	O1	176
N1	C5	C8	C9	−94	C9	C12	C13	O2	3

58.6 Dihydro - β - erythroidine hydrobromide (absolute configuration)

$C_{16}H_{22}NO_3^+$, Br^-

A.W.Hanson, Acta Cryst., 16, 939, 1963

$P2_12_12_1$ Z = 4   R = 0.13

HERINB   LB 16-22-2

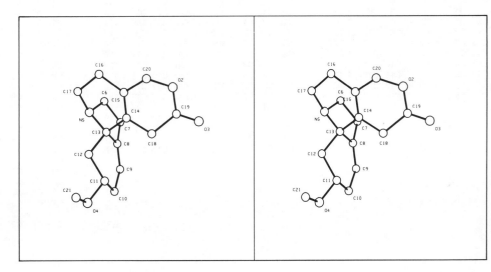

Bond Lengths

C6	N5	1.50	C9	C10	1.51
C13	N5	1.48	C10	C11	1.57
C17	N5	1.52	C11	C12	1.52
C19	O2	1.33	C12	C13	1.59
C20	O2	1.43	C13	C14	1.50
C19	O3	1.21	C14	C15	1.30
C11	O4	1.45	C14	C18	1.51
C21	O4	1.47	C15	C16	1.56
C6	C7	1.49	C15	C20	1.52
C7	C8	1.52	C16	C17	1.51
C8	C9	1.35	C18	C19	1.54
C8	C13	1.53			

Bond Angles

C6	N5	C13	106	N5	C13	C14	110
C6	N5	C17	116	C8	C13	C12	111
C13	N5	C17	113	C8	C13	C14	113
C19	O2	C20	120	C12	C13	C14	113
C11	O4	C21	115	C13	C14	C15	124
N5	C6	C7	107	C13	C14	C18	119
C6	C7	C8	103	C15	C14	C18	118
C7	C8	C9	129	C14	C15	C16	124
C7	C8	C13	108	C14	C15	C20	120
C9	C8	C13	123	C16	C15	C20	116
C8	C9	C10	125	C15	C16	C17	111
C9	C10	C11	112	N5	C17	C16	111
O4	C11	C10	106	C14	C18	C19	111
O4	C11	C12	108	O2	C19	O3	120
C10	C11	C12	115	O2	C19	C18	118
C11	C12	C13	109	O3	C19	C18	123
N5	C13	C8	98	O2	C20	C15	110
N5	C13	C12	110				

Torsion Angles

C13	N5	C6	C7	33	C9	C10	C11	O4	153
C17	N5	C6	C7	158	C9	C10	C11	C12	33
C6	N5	C13	C8	−41	O4	C11	C12	C13	−176
C6	N5	C13	C12	−157	C10	C11	C12	C13	−57
C6	N5	C13	C14	77	C11	C12	C13	N5	157
C17	N5	C13	C8	−169	C11	C12	C13	C8	49
C17	N5	C13	C12	75	C11	C12	C13	C14	−79
C17	N5	C13	C14	−50	N5	C13	C14	C15	21
C6	N5	C17	C16	−60	N5	C13	C14	C18	−162
C13	N5	C17	C16	62	C8	C13	C14	C15	130
C20	O2	C19	O3	−172	C8	C13	C14	C18	−53
C20	O2	C19	C18	9	C12	C13	C14	C15	−102
C19	O2	C20	C15	−43	C12	C13	C14	C18	75
C21	O4	C11	C10	176	C13	C14	C15	C16	−2
C21	O4	C11	C12	−60	C13	C14	C15	C20	178
N5	C6	C7	C8	−8	C18	C14	C15	C16	−179
C6	C7	C8	C9	154	C18	C14	C15	C20	1
C6	C7	C8	C13	−18	C13	C14	C18	C19	148
C7	C8	C9	C10	−174	C15	C14	C18	C19	−35
C13	C8	C9	C10	−3	C14	C15	C16	C17	11
C7	C8	C13	N5	37	C20	C15	C16	C17	−169
C7	C8	C13	C12	151	C14	C15	C20	O2	38
C7	C8	C13	C14	−80	C16	C15	C20	O2	−142
C9	C8	C13	N5	−136	C15	C16	C17	N5	−39
C9	C8	C13	C12	−21	C14	C18	C19	O2	31
C9	C8	C13	C14	108	C14	C18	C19	O3	−149
C8	C9	C10	C11	−1					

58.7   L - Cocaine hydrochloride

$C_{17}H_{22}NO_4^+$, Cl^-

E.J.Gabe, W.H.Barnes, Acta Cryst., 16, 796, 1963

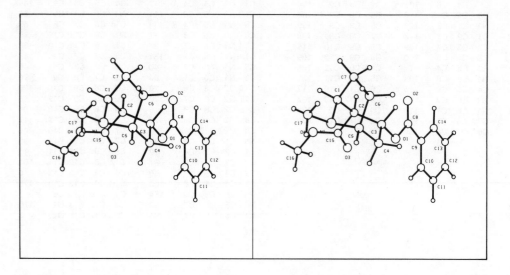

$P2_12_12_1$ Z = 4   R = 0.10

COCHCL   LB 17-22-3

Bond Lengths

C1	N1	1.50	
C5	N1	1.49	
C17	N1	1.48	
C3	O1	1.38	
C8	O1	1.39	
C8	O2	1.17	
C15	O3	1.25	
C15	O4	1.29	
C16	O4	1.43	
C1	C2	1.55	
C1	C7	1.56	
C2	C3	1.56	
C2	C15	1.51	
C3	C4	1.52	
C4	C5	1.55	
C5	C6	1.53	
C6	C7	1.56	
C8	C9	1.49	
C9	C10	1.38	
C9	C14	1.41	
C10	C11	1.38	
C11	C12	1.37	
C12	C13	1.36	
C13	C14	1.38	

Bond Angles

C1	N1	C5	104
C1	N1	C17	112
C5	N1	C17	112
C3	O1	C8	117
C15	O4	C16	118
N1	C1	C2	109
N1	C1	C7	101
C2	C1	C7	112
C1	C2	C3	109
C1	C2	C15	109
C3	C2	C15	115
O1	C3	C2	115
O1	C3	C4	108
C2	C3	C4	113
C3	C4	C5	110
N1	C5	C4	108
N1	C5	C6	102
C4	C5	C6	112
C5	C6	C7	106
C1	C7	C6	104
O1	C8	O2	123
O1	C8	C9	112
O2	C8	C9	125
C8	C9	C10	124
C8	C9	C14	116
C10	C9	C14	120
C9	C10	C11	120
C10	C11	C12	120
C11	C12	C13	121
C12	C13	C14	121
C9	C14	C13	119
O3	C15	O4	121
O3	C15	C2	122
O4	C15	C2	116

Torsion Angles

C5	N1	C1	C2	72
C5	N1	C1	C7	−47
C17	N1	C1	C2	−166
C17	N1	C1	C7	75
C1	N1	C5	C4	−72
C1	N1	C5	C6	46
C17	N1	C5	C4	166
C17	N1	C5	C6	−75
C8	O1	C3	C2	77
C8	O1	C3	C4	−157
C3	O1	C8	O2	1
C3	O1	C8	C9	179
C16	O4	C15	O3	8
C16	O4	C15	C2	−178
N1	C1	C2	C3	−59
N1	C1	C2	C15	67
C7	C1	C2	C3	52
C7	C1	C2	C15	178
N1	C1	C7	C6	28
C2	C1	C7	C6	−88
C1	C2	C3	O1	172
C1	C2	C3	C4	47
C15	C2	C3	O1	49
C15	C2	C3	C4	−76

C1	C2	C15	O3	−169
C1	C2	C15	O4	17
C3	C2	C15	O3	−46
C3	C2	C15	O4	140
O1	C3	C4	C5	−176
C2	C3	C4	C5	−48
C3	C4	C5	N1	61
C3	C4	C5	C6	−50
N1	C5	C6	C7	−27
C4	C5	C6	C7	89
C5	C6	C7	C1	−1
O1	C8	C9	C10	3
O1	C8	C9	C14	−178
O2	C8	C9	C10	−179
O2	C8	C9	C14	0
C8	C9	C10	C11	−180
C14	C9	C10	C11	1
C8	C9	C14	C13	180
C10	C9	C14	C13	−1
C9	C10	C11	C12	1
C10	C11	C12	C13	−2
C11	C12	C13	C14	2
C12	C13	C14	C9	0

58.8 Sporidesmin - methylene dibromide adduct (at −150 °C) C₁₈H₂₀ClN₃O₆S₂ , 0.65CH₂Br₂

58.8 **Sporidesmin - methylene dibromide adduct (at $-150\,^\circ$C)** $\quad$ $C_{18}H_{20}ClN_3O_6S_2$, $0.65CH_2Br_2$

J.Fridrichsons, A.McL.Mathieson, Acta Cryst., 18, 1043, 1965

$P2_12_12_1$ $\quad$ Z = 4 $\quad$ R = 0.144

SPORMB $\quad$ LB 19-20-1

0·65 CH₂ Br₂

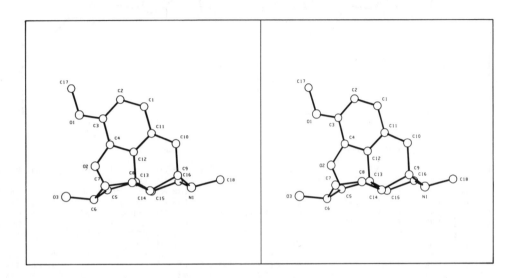

Bond Lengths

Br1	C19	1.87		C7	O4	1.45
Br2	C19	1.93		C10	O5	1.34
				C17	O5	1.41
Cl1	C12	1.76		C11	O6	1.37
S1	S2	2.09		C18	O6	1.45
S1	C1	1.91		C1	C2	1.46
S2	C4	1.90		C1	C15	1.50
C1	N1	1.53		C3	C7	1.56
C5	N1	1.33		C4	C5	1.58
C14	N1	1.47		C4	C6	1.56
C2	N2	1.39		C6	C7	1.45
C3	N2	1.49		C7	C8	1.40
C4	N2	1.35		C8	C9	1.38
C3	N3	1.48		C8	C13	1.43
C9	N3	1.41		C9	C10	1.43
C16	N3	1.48		C10	C11	1.39
C2	O1	1.20		C11	C12	1.37
C5	O2	1.27		C12	C13	1.43
C6	O3	1.45				

Bond Angles

Br1	C19	Br2	112		N2	C4	C6	106
					C5	C4	C6	117
S2	S1	C1	98		N1	C5	O2	123
S1	S2	C4	97		N1	C5	C4	113
C1	N1	C5	116		O2	C5	C4	124
C1	N1	C14	121		O3	C6	C4	109
C5	N1	C14	121		O3	C6	C7	111
C2	N2	C3	124		C4	C6	C7	105
C2	N2	C4	121		O4	C7	C3	110
C3	N2	C4	112		O4	C7	C6	106
C3	N3	C9	106		O4	C7	C8	115
C3	N3	C16	116		C3	C7	C6	105
C9	N3	C16	119		C3	C7	C8	104
C10	O5	C17	116		C6	C7	C8	115
C11	O6	C18	118		C7	C8	C9	111
S1	C1	N1	107		C7	C8	C13	129
S1	C1	C2	106		C9	C8	C13	120
S1	C1	C15	105		N3	C9	C8	111
N1	C1	C2	112		N3	C9	C10	127
N1	C1	C15	113		C8	C9	C10	122
C2	C1	C15	112		O5	C10	C9	121
N2	C2	O1	124		O5	C10	C11	121
N2	C2	C1	111		C9	C10	C11	118
O1	C2	C1	124		O6	C11	C10	120
N2	C3	N3	112		O6	C11	C12	119
N2	C3	C7	104		C10	C11	C12	121
N3	C3	C7	104		Cl1	C12	C11	121
S2	C4	N2	116		Cl1	C12	C13	117
S2	C4	C5	98		C11	C12	C13	122
S2	C4	C6	109		C8	C13	C12	117
N2	C4	C5	111					

Torsion Angles

C1	S1	S2	C4	−9		C16	N3	C3	N2	−96		C5	C4	C6	C7	−153
S2	S1	C1	N1	−54		C16	N3	C3	C7	152		O3	C6	C7	O4	151
S2	S1	C1	C2	66		C3	N3	C9	C8	−10		O3	C6	C7	C3	−93
S2	S1	C1	C15	−175		C3	N3	C9	C10	168		O3	C6	C7	C8	21
S1	S2	C4	N2	−48		C16	N3	C9	C8	−143		C4	C6	C7	O4	−92
S1	S2	C4	C5	70		C16	N3	C9	C10	34		C4	C6	C7	C3	25
S1	S2	C4	C6	−167		C17	O5	C10	C9	69		C4	C6	C7	C8	139
C5	N1	C1	S1	66		C17	O5	C10	C11	−109		O4	C7	C8	C9	134
C5	N1	C1	C2	−50		C18	O6	C11	C10	102		O4	C7	C8	C13	−50
C5	N1	C1	C15	−178		C18	O6	C11	C12	−75		C3	C7	C8	C9	13
C14	N1	C1	S1	−100		S1	C1	C2	N2	−76		C3	C7	C8	C13	−171
C14	N1	C1	C2	144		S1	C1	C2	O1	99		C6	C7	C8	C9	−101
C14	N1	C1	C15	16		N1	C1	C2	N2	74		C6	C7	C8	C13	74
C1	N1	C5	O2	−171		N1	C1	C2	O1	−143		C7	C8	C9	N3	−3
C1	N1	C5	C4	8		C15	C1	C2	N2	170		C7	C8	C9	C10	179
C14	N1	C5	O2	−5		C15	C1	C2	O1	−15		C13	C8	C9	N3	−179
C14	N1	C5	C4	174		N2	C3	C7	O4	100		C13	C8	C9	C10	3
C3	N2	C2	O1	−6		N2	C3	C7	C6	−14		C7	C8	C13	C12	−179
C3	N2	C2	C1	169		N2	C3	C7	C8	−136		C9	C8	C13	C12	−4
C4	N2	C2	O1	−166		N3	C3	C7	O4	−143		N3	C9	C10	O5	4
C4	N2	C2	C1	9		N3	C3	C7	C6	103		N3	C9	C10	C11	−177
C2	N2	C3	N3	83		N3	C3	C7	C8	−19		C8	C9	C10	O5	−179
C2	N2	C3	C7	−165		S2	C4	C5	N1	−83		C8	C9	C10	C11	0
C4	N2	C3	N3	−116		S2	C4	C5	O2	97		O5	C10	C11	O6	−2
C4	N2	C3	C7	−4		N2	C4	C5	N1	39		O5	C10	C11	C12	175
C2	N2	C4	S2	60		N2	C4	C5	O2	−141		C9	C10	C11	O6	179
C2	N2	C4	C5	−50		C6	C4	C5	N1	162		C9	C10	C11	C12	−3
C2	N2	C4	C6	−179		C6	C4	C5	O2	−19		O6	C11	C12	Cl1	0
C3	N2	C4	S2	−102		S2	C4	C6	O3	−143		O6	C11	C12	C13	−179
C3	N2	C4	C5	147		S2	C4	C6	C7	98		C10	C11	C12	Cl1	−177
C3	N2	C4	C6	19		N2	C4	C6	O3	91		C10	C11	C12	C13	3
C9	N3	C3	N2	129		N2	C4	C6	C7	−28		Cl1	C12	C13	C8	−179
C9	N3	C3	C7	17		C5	C4	C6	O3	−34		C11	C12	C13	C8	1

58.9 Codeine hydrobromide dihydrate (absolute configuration)

$C_{18}H_{22}NO_3^+$, Br^- , $2H_2O$

G.Kartha, F.R.Ahmed, W.H.Barnes, Acta Cryst., 15, 326, 1962

$P2_12_12_1$ Z = 4   R = 0.126

CODHBH   LB 18-22-3

Bond Lengths

C9	N1	1.52
C16	N1	1.47
C18	N1	1.51
C3	O1	1.40
C17	O1	1.44
C4	O2	1.37
C5	O2	1.47
C6	O3	1.43
C1	C2	1.40
C1	C11	1.39
C2	C3	1.37
C3	C4	1.39
C4	C12	1.37
C5	C6	1.52
C5	C13	1.53
C6	C7	1.53
C7	C8	1.32
C8	C14	1.50
C9	C10	1.54
C9	C14	1.56
C10	C11	1.50
C11	C12	1.40
C12	C13	1.50
C13	C14	1.56
C13	C15	1.53
C15	C16	1.53

Bond Angles

C9	N1	C16	114	N1	C9	C10	113
C9	N1	C18	113	N1	C9	C14	105
C16	N1	C18	110	C10	C9	C14	114
C3	O1	C17	117	C9	C10	C11	115
C4	O2	C5	108	C1	C11	C10	126
C2	C1	C11	123	C1	C11	C12	115
C1	C2	C3	120	C10	C11	C12	119
O1	C3	C2	127	C4	C12	C11	123
O1	C3	C4	115	C4	C12	C13	109
C2	C3	C4	118	C11	C12	C13	127
O2	C4	C3	127	C5	C13	C12	101
O2	C4	C12	112	C5	C13	C14	117
C3	C4	C12	121	C5	C13	C15	112
O2	C5	C6	111	C12	C13	C14	105
O2	C5	C13	105	C12	C13	C15	112
C6	C5	C13	113	C14	C13	C15	108
O3	C6	C5	113	C8	C14	C9	112
O3	C6	C7	111	C8	C14	C13	108
C5	C6	C7	114	C9	C14	C13	108
C6	C7	C8	120	C13	C15	C16	113
C7	C8	C14	121	N1	C16	C15	111

Torsion Angles

C16	N1	C9	C10	−61	C3	C4	C12	C11	6	C9	C10	C11	C1	172
C16	N1	C9	C14	64	C3	C4	C12	C13	178	C9	C10	C11	C12	0
C18	N1	C9	C10	66	O2	C5	C6	O3	40	C1	C11	C12	C4	−7
C18	N1	C9	C14	−169	O2	C5	C6	C7	−88	C1	C11	C12	C13	−177
C9	N1	C16	C15	−57	C13	C5	C6	O3	157	C10	C11	C12	C4	166
C18	N1	C16	C15	175	C13	C5	C6	C7	30	C10	C11	C12	C13	−4
C17	O1	C3	C2	−1	O2	C5	C13	C12	21	C4	C12	C13	C5	−15
C17	O1	C3	C4	179	O2	C5	C13	C14	135	C4	C12	C13	C14	−137
C5	O2	C4	C3	−163	O2	C5	C13	C15	−99	C4	C12	C13	C15	105
C5	O2	C4	C12	11	C6	C5	C13	C12	−101	C11	C12	C13	C5	156
C4	O2	C5	C6	102	C6	C5	C13	C14	13	C11	C12	C13	C14	34
C4	O2	C5	C13	−20	C6	C5	C13	C15	140	C11	C12	C13	C15	−84
C11	C1	C2	C3	3	O3	C6	C7	C8	−170	C5	C13	C14	C8	−48
C2	C1	C11	C10	−170	C5	C6	C7	C8	−41	C5	C13	C14	C9	−170
C2	C1	C11	C12	2	C6	C7	C8	C14	3	C12	C13	C14	C8	63
C1	C2	C3	O1	176	C7	C8	C14	C9	159	C12	C13	C14	C9	−58
C1	C2	C3	C4	−4	C7	C8	C14	C13	40	C15	C13	C14	C8	−176
O1	C3	C4	O2	−6	N1	C9	C10	C11	91	C15	C13	C14	C9	62
O1	C3	C4	C12	179	C14	C9	C10	C11	−29	C5	C13	C15	C16	175
C2	C3	C4	O2	174	N1	C9	C14	C8	176	C12	C13	C15	C16	61
C2	C3	C4	C12	−1	N1	C9	C14	C13	−65	C14	C13	C15	C16	−55
O2	C4	C12	C11	−169	C10	C9	C14	C8	−59	C13	C15	C16	N1	52
O2	C4	C12	C13	3	C10	C9	C14	C13	60					

58.10 Galanthamine methiodide (absolute configuration)

$C_{18}H_{24}NO_3^+$, I^-

D.J.Williams, D.Rogers, Proc. Chem. Soc., 357, 1964

Atomic coordinates were not reported in the paper.
$P2_12_12_1$ Z = 4   R = 0.14

GALAMI   LB 18-24-9

58.11 Jacobine bromohydrin ethanol solvate (at −150 °C, absolute configuration)

$C_{18}H_{26}BrNO_6$, $0.5C_2H_6O$

J.Fridrichsons, A.McL.Mathieson, D.J.Sutor, Acta Cryst., 16, 1075, 1963

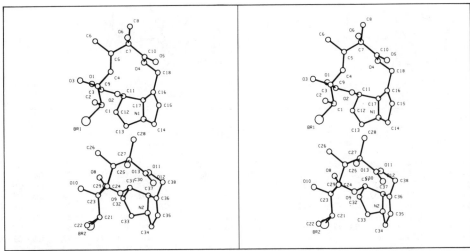

P2₁ Z = 4 R = 0.27

JACBRH   LB 18-26-2

Bond Lengths

Br1	C1	1.98	Br2	C21	2.00
C13	N1	1.47	C33	N2	1.46
C14	N1	1.51	C34	N2	1.47
C17	N1	1.52	C37	N2	1.49
C9	O1	1.23	C29	O8	1.20
C9	O2	1.33	C29	O9	1.32
C11	O2	1.42	C31	O9	1.44
C3	O3	1.43	C23	O10	1.43
C10	O4	1.24	C30	O11	1.28
C18	O4	1.39	C38	O11	1.44
C10	O5	1.23	C30	O12	1.19
C7	O6	1.36	C27	O13	1.45
C1	C2	1.52	C21	C22	1.50
C1	C3	1.60	C21	C23	1.61
C3	C4	1.57	C23	C24	1.60
C3	C9	1.58	C23	C29	1.48
C4	C5	1.60	C24	C25	1.56
C5	C6	1.55	C25	C26	1.56
C5	C7	1.55	C25	C27	1.53
C7	C8	1.54	C27	C28	1.51
C7	C10	1.58	C27	C30	1.62
C11	C12	1.53	C31	C32	1.54
C11	C17	1.61	C31	C37	1.58
C12	C13	1.55	C32	C33	1.54
C14	C15	1.55	C34	C35	1.53
C15	C16	1.32	C35	C36	1.31
C16	C17	1.53	C36	C37	1.50
C16	C18	1.55	C36	C38	1.50
C19	O7	1.43			
C19	C20	1.54			

Bond Angles

C13	N1	C14	118	C33	N2	C34	113
C13	N1	C17	109	C33	N2	C37	111
C14	N1	C17	113	C34	N2	C37	109
C9	O2	C11	116	C29	O9	C31	123
C10	O4	C18	115	C30	O11	C38	120
Br1	C1	C2	109	Br2	C21	C22	103
Br1	C1	C3	101	Br2	C21	C23	108
C2	C1	C3	103	C22	C21	C23	108
O3	C3	C1	111	O10	C23	C21	114
O3	C3	C4	111	O10	C23	C24	103
O3	C3	C9	112	O10	C23	C29	103
C1	C3	C4	106	C21	C23	C24	112
C1	C3	C9	105	C21	C23	C29	116
C4	C3	C9	111	C24	C23	C29	106
C3	C4	C5	113	C23	C24	C25	115
C4	C5	C6	120	C24	C25	C26	108
C4	C5	C7	107	C24	C25	C27	114
C6	C5	C7	115	C26	C25	C27	103
O6	C7	C5	105	O13	C27	C25	113
O6	C7	C8	105	O13	C27	C28	114
O6	C7	C10	115	O13	C27	C30	102
C5	C7	C8	110	C25	C27	C28	112
C5	C7	C10	110	C25	C27	C30	104
C8	C7	C10	112	C28	C27	C30	112
O1	C9	O2	130	O8	C29	O9	114
O1	C9	C3	121	O8	C29	C23	135
O2	C9	C3	106	O9	C29	C23	108
O4	C10	O5	122	O11	C30	O12	126
O4	C10	C7	113	O11	C30	C27	115
O5	C10	C7	125	O12	C30	C27	119
O2	C11	C12	110	O9	C31	C32	105
O2	C11	C17	113	O9	C31	C37	109
C12	C11	C17	102	C32	C31	C37	101
C11	C12	C13	99	C31	C32	C33	108
N1	C13	C12	106	N2	C33	C32	105
N1	C14	C15	98	N2	C34	C35	103
C14	C15	C16	118	C34	C35	C36	113
C15	C16	C17	108	C35	C36	C37	110
C15	C16	C18	130	C35	C36	C38	130
C17	C16	C18	122	C37	C36	C38	120
N1	C17	C11	101	N2	C37	C31	107
N1	C17	C16	104	N2	C37	C36	105
C11	C17	C16	112	C31	C37	C36	118
O4	C18	C16	110	O11	C38	C36	110
O7	C19	C20	107				

Torsion Angles

C14	N1	C13	C12	147	C34	N2	C33	C32	132
C17	N1	C13	C12	18	C37	N2	C33	C32	9
C13	N1	C14	C15	−124	C33	N2	C34	C35	−133
C17	N1	C14	C15	4	C37	N2	C34	C35	−9
C13	N1	C17	C11	11	C33	N2	C37	C31	10
C13	N1	C17	C16	128	C33	N2	C37	C36	136
C14	N1	C17	C11	−121	C34	N2	C37	C31	−115
C14	N1	C17	C16	−5	C34	N2	C37	C36	11
C11	O2	C9	O1	−16	C31	O9	C29	O8	14
C11	O2	C9	C3	−175	C31	O9	C29	C23	178
C9	O2	C11	C12	−70	C29	O9	C31	C32	−86
C9	O2	C11	C17	176	C29	O9	C31	C37	167
C18	O4	C10	O5	−8	C38	O11	C30	O12	−4
C18	O4	C10	C7	175	C38	O11	C30	C27	176
C10	O4	C18	C16	101	C30	O11	C38	C36	104
C2	C1	C3	C4	71	C22	C21	C23	C24	73
C2	C1	C3	C9	−171	C22	C21	C23	C29	−164
C1	C3	C4	C5	168	C21	C23	C24	C25	155
C4	C3	C9	O1	−107	C29	C23	C24	C25	27
C1	C3	C9	O1	138	C21	C23	C29	O8	116
C1	C3	C9	O2	−60	C21	C23	C29	O9	−44
C4	C3	C9	O1	−107	C24	C23	C29	O8	−118
C4	C3	C9	O2	54	C24	C23	C29	O9	82
C3	C4	C5	C7	−161	C23	C24	C25	C27	−153
C4	C5	C7	C10	56	C24	C25	C27	C30	63
C5	C7	C10	O4	58	C25	C27	C30	O11	59
C5	C7	C10	O5	−120	C25	C27	C30	O12	−122
O2	C11	C12	C13	−74	O9	C31	C32	C33	−83
C17	C11	C12	C13	46	C37	C31	C32	C33	30
O2	C11	C17	N1	81	O9	C31	C37	N2	86
O2	C11	C17	C16	−29	O9	C31	C37	C36	−31
C12	C11	C17	N1	−36	C32	C31	C37	N2	−24
C12	C11	C17	C16	−146	C32	C31	C37	C36	−141
C11	C12	C13	N1	−40	C31	C32	C33	N2	−25
N1	C14	C15	C16	−2	N2	C34	C35	C36	4
C14	C15	C16	C17	−1	C34	C35	C36	C37	2
C14	C15	C16	C18	−170	C34	C35	C36	C38	−171
C15	C16	C17	N1	3	C35	C36	C37	N2	−8
C15	C16	C17	C11	112	C35	C36	C37	C31	110
C18	C16	C17	N1	173	C38	C36	C37	N2	166
C18	C16	C17	C11	−78	C38	C36	C37	C31	−76
C15	C16	C18	O4	−113	C35	C36	C38	O11	−110
C17	C16	C18	O4	79	C37	C36	C38	O11	77

58.12 Samandarine hydrobromide methanolate

$C_{19}H_{32}NO_2{}^+$, CH_4O , Br^-

G.Weitz, E.Wolfel, Acta Cryst., 15, 484, 1962

Published value of y(O3) = 0.398. The correct value is 0.298. There are errors in the published coordinates of the methanol residue (private communication).
$P2_1$ Z = 4   R = 0.18

SAMHBM   LB 19-32-1

Bond Lengths

C2	N1	1.54
C3	N1	1.45
C16	O1	1.37
C1	O2	1.48
C3	O2	1.38
C1	C2	1.62
C1	C10	1.51
C3	C4	1.65
C4	C5	1.49
C5	C6	1.60
C5	C10	1.50
C6	C7	1.63
C7	C8	1.52
C8	C9	1.58
C8	C14	1.46
C9	C10	1.51
C9	C11	1.60
C10	C19	1.62
C11	C12	1.59
C12	C13	1.56
C13	C14	1.56
C13	C17	1.57
C13	C18	1.60
C14	C15	1.55
C15	C16	1.57
C16	C17	1.82

Bond Angles

C2	N1	C3	107		C1	C10	C9	110
C1	O2	C3	107		C1	C10	C19	107
O2	C1	C2	96		C5	C10	C9	110
O2	C1	C10	111		C5	C10	C19	109
C2	C1	C10	118		C9	C10	C19	111
N1	C2	C1	102		C9	C11	C12	109
N1	C3	O2	102		C11	C12	C13	111
N1	C3	C4	111		C12	C13	C14	107
O2	C3	C4	108		C12	C13	C17	108
C3	C4	C5	113		C12	C13	C18	111
C4	C5	C6	112		C14	C13	C17	105
C4	C5	C10	115		C14	C13	C18	112
C6	C5	C10	114		C17	C13	C18	113
C5	C6	C7	107		C8	C14	C13	113
C6	C7	C8	109		C8	C14	C15	119
C7	C8	C9	108		C13	C14	C15	104
C7	C8	C14	109		C14	C15	C16	106
C9	C8	C14	111		O1	C16	C15	116
C8	C9	C10	114		O1	C16	C17	110
C8	C9	C11	112		C15	C16	C17	105
C10	C9	C11	112		C13	C17	C16	96
C1	C10	C5	109					

Torsion Angles

C3	N1	C2	C1	0		C4	C5	C10	C9	77		C8	C9	C11	C12	−50
C2	N1	C3	O2	29		C4	C5	C10	C19	−161		C10	C9	C11	C12	179
C2	N1	C3	C4	−85		C6	C5	C10	C1	−174		C9	C11	C12	C13	55
C3	O2	C1	C2	49		C6	C5	C10	C9	−54		C11	C12	C13	C14	−60
C3	O2	C1	C10	−75		C6	C5	C10	C19	69		C11	C12	C13	C17	−172
C1	O2	C3	N1	−51		C5	C6	C7	C8	−60		C11	C12	C13	C18	63
C1	O2	C3	C4	66		C6	C7	C8	C9	61		C12	C13	C14	C8	63
O2	C1	C2	N1	−27		C6	C7	C8	C14	−179		C12	C13	C14	C15	−166
C10	C1	C2	N1	90		C7	C8	C9	C10	−59		C17	C13	C14	C8	178
O2	C1	C10	C5	60		C7	C8	C9	C11	172		C17	C13	C14	C15	−51
O2	C1	C10	C9	−61		C14	C8	C9	C10	−178		C18	C13	C14	C8	−59
C2	C1	C10	C5	−50		C14	C8	C9	C11	53		C18	C13	C14	C15	72
C2	C1	C10	C9	−171		C7	C8	C14	C13	−178		C12	C13	C17	C16	156
C2	C1	C10	C19	68		C7	C8	C14	C15	60		C14	C13	C17	C16	42
N1	C3	C4	C5	60		C9	C8	C14	C13	−60		C18	C13	C17	C16	−80
O2	C3	C4	C5	−51		C9	C8	C14	C15	178		C8	C14	C15	C16	161
C3	C4	C5	C6	171		C8	C9	C10	C1	175		C13	C14	C15	C16	34
C3	C4	C5	C10	39		C8	C9	C10	C5	54		C14	C15	C16	O1	−129
C4	C5	C6	C7	−76		C8	C9	C10	C19	−67		C14	C15	C16	C17	−7
C10	C5	C6	C7	57		C11	C9	C10	C1	−56		O1	C16	C17	C13	104
C4	C5	C10	C1	−44		C11	C9	C10	C5	−176		C15	C16	C17	C13	−22
						C11	C9	C10	C19	62					

58.13 Bulbocapnine methiodide (absolute configuration)

$C_{20}H_{22}NO_4{}^+$, I^-

T.Ashida, R.Pepinsky, Y.Okaya, Acta Cryst., 16, A48, 1963

Atomic coordinates were not reported in the paper.
$P2_1$ Z = 2   R = 0.125

BLBCPI

58.14 Alkaloid C (from Alstonia Muellerian)

$C_{20}H_{22}N_2O_3$

C.E.Nordman, K.Nakatsu, J. Amer. Chem. Soc., 85, 353, 1963

Atomic coordinates were not reported in the paper.
$P2_1$ Z = 2   R = 0.06

ALKCAM   LB 22-20-10

58.15 Cleavamine methiodide (absolute configuration)

$C_{20}H_{27}N_2^+$, I^-

N.Camerman, J.Trotter, Acta Cryst., 17, 384, 1964

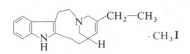

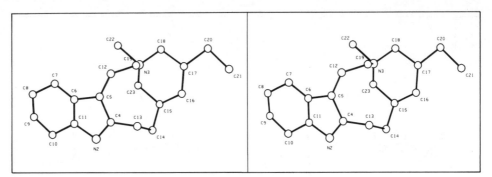

$P2_12_12_1$ $Z = 4$ $R = 0.084$

CLVAMI   LB 20-27-5

Bond Lengths

C4	N2	1.30	C8	C9	1.33
C11	N2	1.45	C9	C10	1.41
C18	N3	1.47	C10	C11	1.53
C19	N3	1.61	C12	C19	1.55
C22	N3	1.66	C13	C14	1.61
C23	N3	1.29	C14	C15	1.60
C4	C5	1.54	C15	C16	1.49
C4	C13	1.47	C15	C23	1.60
C5	C6	1.52	C16	C17	1.48
C5	C12	1.43	C17	C18	1.59
C6	C7	1.34	C17	C20	1.61
C6	C11	1.40	C20	C21	1.60
C7	C8	1.48			

Bond Angles

C4	N2	C11	100	C9	C10	C11	108
C18	N3	C19	102	N2	C11	C6	117
C18	N3	C22	103	N2	C11	C10	120
C18	N3	C23	118	C6	C11	C10	123
C19	N3	C22	102	C5	C12	C19	115
C19	N3	C23	118	C4	C13	C14	112
C22	N3	C23	112	C13	C14	C15	113
N2	C4	C5	119	C14	C15	C16	110
N2	C4	C13	126	C14	C15	C23	112
C5	C4	C13	114	C16	C15	C23	113
C4	C5	C6	98	C15	C16	C17	119
C4	C5	C12	133	C16	C17	C18	120
C6	C5	C12	128	C16	C17	C20	130
C5	C6	C7	132	C18	C17	C20	111
C5	C6	C11	105	N3	C18	C17	108
C7	C6	C11	124	N3	C19	C12	124
C6	C7	C8	116	C17	C20	C21	102
C7	C8	C9	120	N3	C23	C15	119
C8	C9	C10	130				

Torsion Angles

C19	N3	C18	C17	76	C13	C14	C15	C16	82
C22	N3	C18	C17	−178	C13	C14	C15	C23	−45
C23	N3	C18	C17	−55	C14	C15	C16	C17	−142
C18	N3	C19	C12	164	C23	C15	C16	C17	−15
C22	N3	C19	C12	57	C14	C15	C23	N3	113
C23	N3	C19	C12	−65	C16	C15	C23	N3	−13
C18	N3	C23	C15	51	C15	C16	C17	C18	8
C19	N3	C23	C15	−72	C15	C16	C17	C20	−173
C22	N3	C23	C15	170	C16	C17	C18	N3	23
C13	C4	C5	C12	9	C20	C17	C18	N3	−155
C5	C4	C13	C14	−123	C16	C17	C20	C21	2
C4	C5	C12	C19	41	C18	C17	C20	C21	−179
C5	C12	C19	N3	46	N2	C4	C5	C12	−179
C4	C13	C14	C15	84	N2	C4	C13	C14	66

58.16 Ibogaine hydrobromide

$C_{20}H_{27}N_2O^+$, Br^-

G.Arai, J.Coppola, G.A.Jeffrey, Acta Cryst., 13, 553, 1960

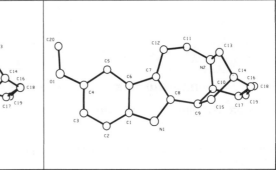

$P2_12_12_1$ $Z = 4$ $R = 0.17$

IBGHBR   LB 20-27-1

Bond Lengths

C1	N1	1.41
C8	N1	1.40
C10	N2	1.58
C11	N2	1.50
C13	N2	1.51
C4	O1	1.38
C20	O1	1.45
C1	C2	1.39
C1	C6	1.39
C2	C3	1.35
C3	C4	1.42
C4	C5	1.45
C5	C6	1.48
C6	C7	1.51
C7	C8	1.40
C7	C12	1.47
C8	C9	1.49
C9	C10	1.52
C9	C15	1.66
C10	C17	1.47
C11	C12	1.55
C13	C14	1.57
C14	C15	1.59
C14	C16	1.52
C16	C17	1.50
C17	C18	1.55
C18	C19	1.39

Bond Angles

C1	N1	C8	111	N1	C8	C9	120
C10	N2	C11	118	C7	C8	C9	131
C10	N2	C13	113	C8	C9	C10	124
C11	N2	C13	111	C8	C9	C15	104
C4	O1	C20	119	C10	C9	C15	108
N1	C1	C2	135	N2	C10	C9	106
N1	C1	C6	106	N2	C10	C17	110
C2	C1	C6	117	C9	C10	C17	113
C1	C2	C3	123	N2	C11	C12	119
C2	C3	C4	119	C7	C12	C11	114
O1	C4	C3	115	N2	C13	C14	108
O1	C4	C5	123	C13	C14	C15	105
C3	C4	C5	123	C13	C14	C16	107
C4	C5	C6	113	C15	C14	C16	109
C1	C6	C5	123	C9	C15	C14	108
C1	C6	C7	123	C14	C16	C17	117
C5	C6	C7	128	C10	C17	C16	107
C6	C7	C8	105	C10	C17	C18	121
C6	C7	C12	124	C16	C17	C18	105
C8	C7	C12	131	C17	C18	C19	109
N1	C8	C7	109				

Torsion Angles

C8	N1	C1	C2	180	C2	C3	C4	O1	−178	C8	C9	C10	C17	178
C8	N1	C1	C6	2	C2	C3	C4	C5	6	C15	C9	C10	N2	−64
C1	N1	C8	C7	−5	O1	C4	C5	C6	179	C15	C9	C10	C17	57
C1	N1	C8	C9	−179	C4	C5	C6	C1	−6	C8	C9	C15	C14	−126
C11	N2	C10	C9	−75	C4	C5	C6	C1	4	C10	C9	C15	C14	7
C11	N2	C10	C17	162	C4	C5	C6	C7	177	N2	C10	C17	C16	50
C13	N2	C10	C9	58	C1	C6	C7	C8	−5	N2	C10	C17	C18	−70
C13	N2	C10	C17	−65	C1	C6	C7	C12	−178	C9	C10	C17	C16	−68
C10	N2	C11	C12	80	C5	C6	C7	C8	−179	C9	C10	C17	C18	172
C13	N2	C11	C12	−54	C5	C6	C7	C12	8	N2	C11	C12	C7	−57
C10	N2	C13	C14	9	C6	C7	C8	N1	6	N2	C13	C14	C15	−67
C11	N2	C13	C14	146	C6	C7	C8	C9	179	N2	C13	C14	C16	48
C20	O1	C4	C3	−170	C12	C7	C8	N1	178	C13	C14	C15	C9	58
C20	O1	C4	C5	6	C12	C7	C8	C9	−9	C16	C14	C15	C9	−56
N1	C1	C2	C3	−176	C6	C7	C12	C11	−152	C13	C14	C16	C17	−65
C6	C1	C2	C3	2	C8	C7	C12	C11	36	C15	C14	C16	C17	48
N1	C1	C6	C5	176	N1	C8	C9	C10	139	C14	C16	C17	C10	12
N1	C1	C6	C7	2	N1	C8	C9	C15	−97	C14	C16	C17	C18	141
C2	C1	C6	C5	−2	C7	C8	C9	C10	−33	C10	C17	C18	C19	−65
C2	C1	C6	C7	−176	C7	C8	C9	C15	90	C16	C17	C18	C19	174
C1	C2	C3	C4	−3	C8	C9	C10	N2	58					

58.17   Hunterburnine β - methiodide

$C_{20}H_{27}N_2O_2^+$, I^-

J.D.M.Asher, J.M.Robertson, G.A.Sim, J. Chem. Soc., 6355, 1965

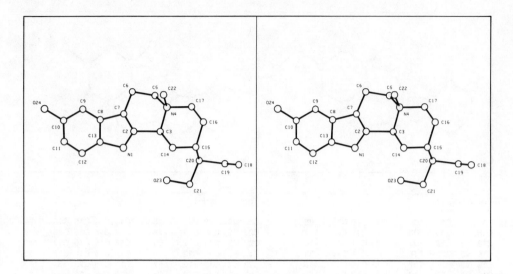

$P2_12_12_1$ $Z = 4$ $R = 0.154$

HUNTMI   LB 20-27-6

Bond Lengths

C2	N1	1.29	C8	C9	1.29
C13	N1	1.49	C8	C13	1.50
C3	N4	1.51	C9	C10	1.43
C5	N4	1.54	C10	C11	1.35
C17	N4	1.57	C11	C12	1.38
C22	N4	1.63	C12	C13	1.35
C21	O23	1.51	C14	C15	1.53
C10	O24	1.45	C15	C16	1.56
C2	C3	1.66	C15	C20	1.60
C2	C7	1.28	C16	C17	1.37
C3	C14	1.65	C18	C19	1.21
C5	C6	1.51	C19	C20	1.63
C6	C7	1.57	C20	C21	1.56
C7	C8	1.54			

Bond Angles

C2	N1	C13	107	C8	C9	C10	116
C3	N4	C5	109	O24	C10	C9	114
C3	N4	C17	107	O24	C10	C11	126
C3	N4	C22	111	C9	C10	C11	120
C5	N4	C17	112	C10	C11	C12	127
C5	N4	C22	113	C11	C12	C13	110
C17	N4	C22	105	N1	C13	C8	104
N1	C2	C3	122	N1	C13	C12	132
N1	C2	C7	119	C8	C13	C12	124
C3	C2	C7	119	C3	C14	C15	101
N4	C3	C2	106	C14	C15	C16	108
N4	C3	C14	115	C14	C15	C20	116
C2	C3	C14	112	C16	C15	C20	115
N4	C5	C6	111	C15	C16	C17	120
C5	C6	C7	106	N4	C17	C16	114
C2	C7	C6	130	C18	C19	C20	128
C2	C7	C8	106	C15	C20	C19	106
C6	C7	C8	124	C15	C20	C21	115
C7	C8	C9	136	C19	C20	C21	106
C7	C8	C13	103	O23	C21	C20	105
C9	C8	C13	121				

Torsion Angles

C5	N4	C3	C2	−56	C3	C14	C15	C16	58
C5	N4	C3	C14	179	C3	C14	C15	C20	−73
C17	N4	C3	C2	−178	C14	C15	C16	C17	−59
C17	N4	C3	C14	58	C20	C15	C16	C17	73
C3	N4	C5	C6	74	C14	C15	C20	C19	−163
C17	N4	C5	C6	−168	C14	C15	C20	C21	−46
C3	N4	C17	C16	−45	C16	C15	C20	C19	69
C5	N4	C17	C16	−165	C16	C15	C20	C21	−174
C7	C2	C3	N4	21	C15	C16	C17	N4	49
C7	C2	C3	C14	148	C18	C19	C20	C15	27
C3	C2	C7	C6	3	C18	C19	C20	C21	−95
N4	C3	C14	C15	−66	C15	C20	C21	O23	80
C2	C3	C14	C15	172	C19	C20	C21	O23	−164
N4	C5	C6	C7	−44	N1	C2	C7	C6	175
C5	C6	C7	C2	8	N1	C2	C3	N4	−150

58.18   Hunterburnine α - methiodide

$C_{20}H_{27}N_2O_2^+$, I^-

C.C.Scott, G.A.Sim, J.M.Robertson, Proc. Chem. Soc., 355, 1962

Atomic coordinates were not reported in the paper.
$P2_12_12_1$ $Z = 4$ $R = 0.20$

HUNTMJ

58.19 (+) - Hetisine hydrobromide (absolute configuration) $C_{20}H_{28}NO_3^+$, Br^-

M.Przybylska, Acta Cryst., 16, 871, 1963

$P2_1$ Z = 2 R = 0.11

HETHBR LB 20-28-1

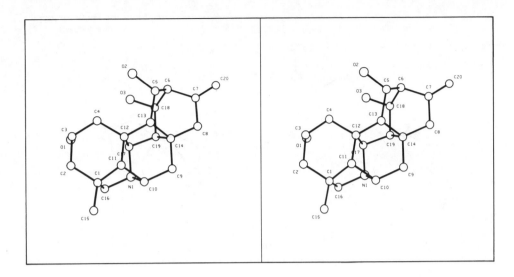

Bond Lengths

C10	N1	1.50
C16	N1	1.50
C17	N1	1.52
C3	O1	1.42
C5	O2	1.41
C18	O3	1.44
C1	C2	1.55
C1	C11	1.48
C1	C15	1.52
C1	C16	1.53
C2	C3	1.54
C3	C4	1.51
C4	C12	1.58
C5	C6	1.51
C5	C13	1.56
C6	C7	1.51
C6	C18	1.51
C7	C8	1.53
C7	C20	1.32
C8	C14	1.51
C9	C10	1.52
C9	C14	1.52
C10	C11	1.57
C11	C12	1.55
C12	C13	1.53
C12	C17	1.56
C13	C14	1.55
C14	C19	1.54
C17	C19	1.53
C18	C19	1.56

Bond Angles

C10	N1	C16	102	C1	C11	C10	100
C10	N1	C17	103	C1	C11	C12	117
C16	N1	C17	110	C10	C11	C12	100
C2	C1	C11	110	C4	C12	C11	106
C2	C1	C15	107	C4	C12	C13	118
C2	C1	C16	113	C4	C12	C17	115
C11	C1	C15	114	C11	C12	C13	109
C11	C1	C16	102	C11	C12	C17	101
C15	C1	C16	110	C13	C12	C17	106
C1	C2	C3	116	C5	C13	C12	120
O1	C3	C2	109	C5	C13	C14	105
O1	C3	C4	112	C12	C13	C14	101
C2	C3	C4	111	C8	C14	C9	110
C3	C4	C12	117	C8	C14	C13	115
O2	C5	C6	110	C8	C14	C19	114
O2	C5	C13	116	C9	C14	C13	110
C6	C5	C13	111	C9	C14	C19	108
C5	C6	C7	108	C13	C14	C19	100
C5	C6	C18	112	N1	C16	C1	104
C7	C6	C18	107	N1	C17	C12	103
C6	C7	C8	110	N1	C17	C19	106
C6	C7	C20	126	C12	C17	C19	104
C8	C7	C20	123	C14	C19	C17	102
C7	C8	C14	109	C14	C19	C18	109
C10	C9	C14	112	C17	C19	C18	111
N1	C10	C9	109				
N1	C10	C11	91				
C9	C10	C11	118				

Torsion Angles

C16	N1	C10	C9	−177	O2	C5	C13	C12	36	C4	C12	C13	C14	−159
C16	N1	C10	C11	−56	O2	C5	C13	C14	149	C11	C12	C13	C5	−165
C17	N1	C10	C9	−62	C6	C5	C13	C12	−90	C11	C12	C13	C14	80
C17	N1	C10	C11	58	C6	C5	C13	C14	22	C17	C12	C13	C5	87
C10	N1	C16	C1	35	C5	C6	C7	C8	52	C17	C12	C13	C14	−28
C17	N1	C16	C1	−74	C5	C6	C7	C20	−132	C4	C12	C17	N1	−119
C10	N1	C17	C12	−34	C18	C6	C7	C8	−68	C4	C12	C17	C19	130
C10	N1	C17	C19	75	C18	C6	C7	C20	108	C11	C12	C17	N1	−6
C16	N1	C17	C12	74	C5	C6	C18	O3	71	C11	C12	C17	C19	−117
C16	N1	C17	C19	−177	C5	C6	C18	C19	−56	C13	C12	C17	N1	108
C11	C1	C2	C3	48	C7	C6	C18	O3	−172	C13	C12	C17	C19	−3
C15	C1	C2	C3	172	C7	C6	C18	C19	61	C5	C13	C14	C8	44
C16	C1	C2	C3	−66	C6	C7	C8	C14	11	C5	C13	C14	C9	169
C2	C1	C11	C10	−161	C20	C7	C8	C14	−165	C5	C13	C14	C19	−78
C2	C1	C11	C12	−54	C7	C8	C14	C9	171	C12	C13	C14	C8	170
C15	C1	C11	C10	79	C7	C8	C14	C13	−64	C12	C13	C14	C9	−65
C15	C1	C11	C12	−174	C7	C8	C14	C19	50	C12	C13	C14	C19	48
C16	C1	C11	C10	−40	C14	C9	C10	N1	57	C8	C14	C19	C17	−173
C16	C1	C11	C12	67	C14	C9	C10	C11	−46	C8	C14	C19	C18	−56
C2	C1	C16	N1	123	C10	C9	C14	C8	178	C9	C14	C19	C17	65
C11	C1	C16	N1	4	C10	C9	C14	C13	50	C9	C14	C19	C18	−178
C15	C1	C16	N1	−118	C10	C9	C14	C19	−58	C13	C14	C19	C17	−50
C1	C2	C3	O1	77	N1	C10	C11	C1	60	C13	C14	C19	C18	67
C1	C2	C3	C4	−46	N1	C10	C11	C12	−60	N1	C17	C19	C14	−76
O1	C3	C4	C12	−72	C9	C10	C11	C1	172	N1	C17	C19	C18	168
C2	C3	C4	C12	50	C9	C10	C11	C12	52	C12	C17	C19	C14	32
C3	C4	C12	C11	−52	C1	C11	C12	C4	55	C12	C17	C19	C18	−83
C3	C4	C12	C13	−174	C1	C11	C12	C13	−177	O3	C18	C19	C14	−128
C3	C4	C12	C17	59	C1	C11	C12	C17	−66	O3	C18	C19	C17	−17
O2	C5	C6	C7	158	C10	C11	C12	C4	162	C6	C18	C19	C14	−2
O2	C5	C6	C18	−86	C10	C11	C12	C13	−71	C6	C18	C19	C17	109
C13	C5	C6	C7	−72	C10	C11	C12	C17	41					
C13	C5	C6	C18	45	C4	C12	C13	C5	−44					

58.20 (−)-N-Methyl gelsemicine hydroiodide (absolute configuration) C₂₁H₂₉N₂O₄⁺, I⁻

$C_{21}H_{29}N_2O_4^+$, I^-

M.Przybylska, Acta Cryst., 15, 301, 1962

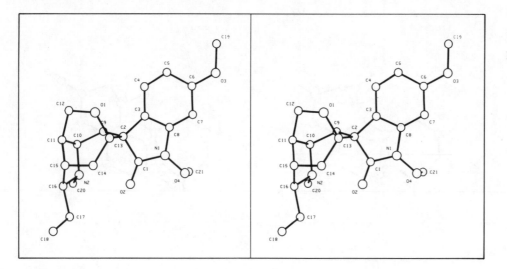

C2   Z = 4   R = 0.16

MEGELI   LB 21-29-8

Bond Lengths

N1	O4	1.34
C1	N1	1.40
C8	N1	1.40
C10	N2	1.54
C16	N2	1.47
C20	N2	1.57
C12	O1	1.46
C13	O1	1.41
C1	O2	1.21
C6	O3	1.38
C19	O3	1.40
C21	O4	1.36
C1	C2	1.51
C2	C3	1.47
C2	C9	1.57
C2	C13	1.56
C3	C4	1.43
C3	C8	1.37
C4	C5	1.33
C5	C6	1.44
C6	C7	1.39
C7	C8	1.33
C9	C10	1.54
C10	C11	1.64
C11	C12	1.57
C11	C15	1.47
C13	C14	1.55
C14	C15	1.50
C15	C16	1.58
C16	C17	1.51
C17	C18	1.46

Bond Angles

O4	N1	C1	124		C5	C6	C7	119
O4	N1	C8	122		C6	C7	C8	116
C1	N1	C8	113		N1	C8	C3	104
C10	N2	C16	107		C3	C8	C7	130
C10	N2	C20	109		C2	C9	C10	118
C16	N2	C20	118		N2	C10	C9	111
C12	O1	C13	115		N2	C10	C11	101
C6	O3	C19	118		C9	C10	C11	113
N1	O4	C21	105		C10	C11	C12	113
N1	C1	O2	125		C10	C11	C15	109
N1	C1	C2	106		C12	C11	C15	117
O2	C1	C2	128		O1	C12	C11	110
C1	C2	C3	100		O1	C13	C2	111
C1	C2	C9	108		O1	C13	C14	113
C1	C2	C13	113		C13	C14	C15	113
C3	C2	C9	114		C11	C15	C14	109
C3	C2	C13	109		C11	C15	C16	97
C9	C2	C13	112		C14	C15	C16	111
C2	C3	C4	131		N2	C16	C15	107
C2	C3	C8	115		N2	C16	C17	110
C4	C3	C8	114		C15	C16	C17	119
C3	C4	C5	121		C16	C17	C18	113
C4	C5	C6	121					
O3	C6	C5	125					
O3	C6	C7	116					

Torsion Angles

C1	N1	O4	C21	86	O2	C1	C2	C9	−58	C5	C6	C7	C8	−1
C8	N1	O4	C21	−83	O2	C1	C2	C13	68	C6	C7	C8	N1	177
O4	N1	C1	O2	5	C1	C2	C3	C4	170	C6	C7	C8	C3	2
O4	N1	C1	C2	175	C1	C2	C3	C8	−9	C2	C9	C10	N2	−64
C8	N1	C1	O2	175	C9	C2	C3	C4	55	C2	C9	C10	C11	49
C8	N1	C1	C2	−15	C9	C2	C3	C8	−125	N2	C10	C11	C12	151
O4	N1	C8	C3	179	C13	C2	C3	C4	−71	N2	C10	C11	C15	20
O4	N1	C8	C7	3	C13	C2	C3	C8	109	C9	C10	C11	C12	32
C1	N1	C8	C3	9	C1	C2	C9	C10	89	C9	C10	C11	C15	−99
C1	N1	C8	C7	−167	C3	C2	C9	C10	−160	C10	C11	C12	O1	−81
C16	N2	C10	C9	129	C13	C2	C9	C10	−36	C15	C11	C12	O1	46
C16	N2	C10	C11	9	C1	C2	C13	O1	179	C10	C11	C15	C14	77
C20	N2	C10	C9	−103	C1	C2	C13	C14	−47	C10	C11	C15	C16	−38
C20	N2	C10	C11	138	C3	C2	C13	O1	69	C12	C11	C15	C14	−51
C10	N2	C16	C15	−34	C3	C2	C13	C14	−158	C12	C11	C15	C16	−166
C10	N2	C16	C17	−165	C9	C2	C13	O1	−58	O1	C13	C14	C15	49
C20	N2	C16	C15	−157	C9	C2	C13	C14	76	C2	C13	C14	C15	−84
C20	N2	C16	C17	72	C2	C3	C4	C5	−177	C13	C14	C15	C11	4
C13	O1	C12	C11	10	C8	C3	C4	C5	2	C13	C14	C15	C16	110
C12	O1	C13	C2	81	C2	C3	C8	N1	1	C11	C15	C16	N2	44
C12	O1	C13	C14	−56	C4	C3	C8	N1	−178	C11	C15	C16	C17	170
C19	O3	C6	C5	10	C4	C3	C8	C7	−3	C14	C15	C16	N2	−69
C19	O3	C6	C7	−174	C3	C4	C5	C6	−1	C14	C15	C16	C17	56
N1	C1	C2	C3	13	C4	C5	C6	O3	176	N2	C16	C17	C18	−179
N1	C1	C2	C9	133	C4	C5	C6	C7	0	C15	C16	C17	C18	57
N1	C1	C2	C13	−102	O3	C6	C7	C8	−177					
O2	C1	C2	C3	−177										

58.21 Thelepogine methiodide (at −150°C, absolute configuration) C₂₁H₃₄NO⁺, I⁻

$C_{21}H_{34}NO^+$, I^-

J.Fridrichsons, A.McL.Mathieson, Acta Cryst., 16, 206, 1963

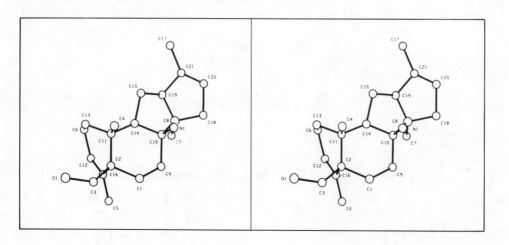

P2₁   Z = 2   R = 0.11

TELPOM   LB 21-34-1

Bond Lengths

C7	N1	1.51
C10	N1	1.48
C18	N1	1.51
C19	N1	1.50
C3	O1	1.41
C1	C2	1.58
C1	C9	1.53
C2	C3	1.49
C2	C11	1.56
C2	C16	1.57
C4	C11	1.53
C5	C16	1.47
C6	C12	1.56
C6	C13	1.53
C8	C10	1.52
C9	C10	1.57
C10	C14	1.52
C11	C13	1.52
C11	C14	1.51
C12	C16	1.39
C14	C15	1.52
C15	C19	1.56
C17	C21	1.50
C18	C20	1.57
C19	C21	1.51
C20	C21	1.31

Bond Angles

C7	N1	C10	112	C2	C11	C13	106
C7	N1	C18	107	C2	C11	C14	109
C7	N1	C19	106	C4	C11	C13	113
C10	N1	C18	117	C4	C11	C14	109
C10	N1	C19	108	C13	C11	C14	114
C18	N1	C19	106	C6	C12	C16	120
C2	C1	C9	116	C6	C13	C11	113
C1	C2	C3	103	C10	C14	C11	121
C1	C2	C11	111	C10	C14	C15	99
C1	C2	C16	107	C11	C14	C15	120
C3	C2	C11	117	C14	C15	C19	99
C3	C2	C16	107	C2	C16	C5	121
C11	C2	C16	110	C2	C16	C12	125
C1	C9	C10	108	C5	C16	C12	114
N1	C10	C8	113	N1	C18	C20	102
N1	C10	C9	114	N1	C19	C15	103
N1	C10	C14	100	N1	C19	C21	108
C8	C10	C9	108	C15	C19	C21	108
C8	C10	C14	113	C18	C20	C21	114
C9	C10	C14	109	C17	C21	C19	115
C2	C11	C4	105	C17	C21	C20	134
				C19	C21	C20	108

Torsion Angles

C7	N1	C10	C8	155	C1	C2	C11	C4	−71	C9	C10	C14	C15	−172
C7	N1	C10	C9	32	C1	C2	C11	C13	169	C2	C11	C13	C6	−70
C7	N1	C10	C14	−84	C1	C2	C11	C14	45	C4	C11	C13	C6	176
C18	N1	C10	C8	31	C3	C2	C11	C4	47	C14	C11	C13	C6	51
C18	N1	C10	C9	−93	C3	C2	C11	C13	−73	C2	C11	C14	C10	−50
C18	N1	C10	C14	151	C3	C2	C11	C14	163	C2	C11	C14	C15	−174
C19	N1	C10	C8	−88	C16	C2	C11	C4	170	C4	C11	C14	C10	64
C19	N1	C10	C9	148	C16	C2	C11	C13	50	C4	C11	C14	C15	−60
C19	N1	C10	C14	32	C16	C2	C11	C14	−74	C13	C11	C14	C10	−169
C7	N1	C18	C20	126	C1	C2	C16	C5	40	C13	C11	C14	C15	67
C10	N1	C18	C20	−107	C1	C2	C16	C12	−141	C6	C12	C16	C2	2
C19	N1	C18	C20	13	C3	C2	C16	C5	−71	C6	C12	C16	C5	−178
C7	N1	C19	C15	121	C3	C2	C16	C12	109	C10	C14	C15	C19	52
C7	N1	C19	C21	−125	C11	C2	C16	C5	161	C11	C14	C15	C19	−174
C10	N1	C19	C15	1	C11	C2	C16	C12	−20	C14	C15	C19	N1	−33
C10	N1	C19	C21	115	C13	C6	C12	C16	−16	C14	C15	C19	C21	−147
C18	N1	C19	C15	−125	C1	C9	C10	N1	−163	N1	C18	C20	C21	−12
C18	N1	C19	C21	−11	C1	C9	C10	C8	70	N1	C19	C21	C17	−160
C9	C1	C2	C3	179	C1	C9	C10	C14	−53	N1	C19	C21	C20	4
C9	C1	C2	C11	−54	N1	C10	C14	C11	174	C15	C19	C21	C17	−49
C9	C1	C2	C16	66	N1	C10	C14	C15	−52	C15	C19	C21	C20	115
C2	C1	C9	C10	57	C8	C10	C14	C11	−66	C18	C20	C21	C17	165
C1	C2	C3	O1	−173	C8	C10	C14	C15	68	C18	C20	C21	C19	5
C11	C2	C3	O1	65	C9	C10	C14	C11	54					
C16	C2	C3	O1	−59										

58.22 Jamine

$C_{21}H_{35}N_3$

I.L.Karle, J.Karle, Acta Cryst., 17, 1356, 1964

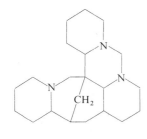

P-1   Z = 2   R = 0.169

JAMINE   LB 21-35-1

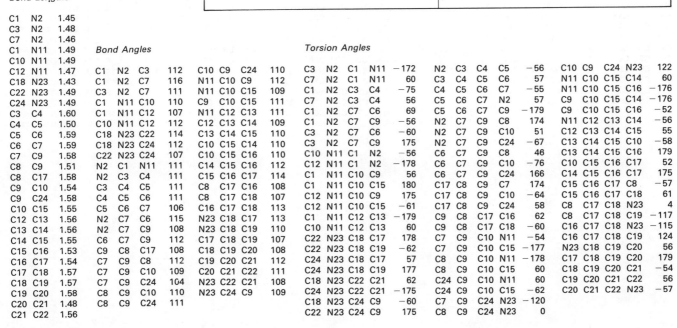

Bond Lengths

C1	N2	1.45
C3	N2	1.48
C7	N2	1.46
C1	N11	1.49
C10	N11	1.49
C12	N11	1.47
C18	N23	1.43
C22	N23	1.49
C24	N23	1.49
C3	C4	1.60
C4	C5	1.50
C5	C6	1.59
C6	C7	1.59
C7	C9	1.58
C8	C9	1.51
C8	C17	1.58
C9	C10	1.54
C9	C24	1.58
C10	C15	1.55
C12	C13	1.56
C13	C14	1.56
C14	C15	1.55
C15	C16	1.53
C16	C17	1.54
C17	C18	1.57
C18	C19	1.58
C19	C20	1.58
C20	C21	1.48
C21	C22	1.56

Bond Angles

C1	N2	C3	112	C10	C9	C24	110
C1	N2	C7	116	N11	C10	C9	112
C3	N2	C7	111	N11	C10	C15	109
C1	N11	C10	110	C9	C10	C15	111
C1	N11	C12	107	N11	C12	C13	111
C10	N11	C12	112	C12	C13	C14	109
C18	N23	C22	114	C13	C14	C15	110
C18	N23	C24	112	C10	C15	C14	110
C22	N23	C24	107	C10	C15	C16	111
N2	C1	N11	111	C14	C15	C16	112
N2	C3	C4	111	C15	C16	C17	114
C3	C4	C5	111	C8	C17	C16	108
C4	C5	C6	111	C8	C17	C18	107
C5	C6	C7	106	C16	C17	C18	113
N2	C7	C6	115	N23	C18	C17	113
N2	C7	C9	108	N23	C18	C19	110
C6	C7	C9	112	C17	C18	C19	107
C9	C8	C17	108	C18	C19	C20	108
C7	C9	C8	112	C19	C20	C21	112
C7	C9	C10	109	C20	C21	C22	111
C7	C9	C24	104	N23	C22	C21	108
C8	C9	C10	110	N23	C24	C9	109
C8	C9	C24	111				

Torsion Angles

C3	N2	C1	N11	−172	N2	C3	C4	C5	−56	C10	C9	C24	N23	122
C7	N2	C1	N11	60	C3	C4	C5	C6	57	N11	C10	C15	C14	60
C1	N2	C3	C4	−75	C4	C5	C6	C7	−55	N11	C10	C15	C16	−176
C7	N2	C3	C4	56	C5	C6	C7	N2	57	C9	C10	C15	C14	−176
C1	N2	C7	C6	69	C5	C6	C7	C9	−179	C9	C10	C15	C16	−52
C1	N2	C7	C9	−56	N2	C7	C9	C8	174	N11	C12	C13	C14	−56
C3	N2	C7	C6	−60	N2	C7	C9	C10	51	C12	C13	C14	C15	55
C3	N2	C7	C9	175	N2	C7	C9	C24	−67	C13	C14	C15	C10	−58
C10	N11	C1	N2	−56	C6	C7	C9	C8	46	C13	C14	C15	C16	179
C12	N11	C1	N2	−178	C6	C7	C9	C10	−76	C10	C15	C16	C17	52
C1	N11	C10	C9	56	C6	C7	C9	C24	166	C14	C15	C16	C17	175
C1	N11	C10	C15	180	C17	C8	C9	C7	174	C15	C16	C17	C8	−57
C12	N11	C10	C9	175	C17	C8	C9	C10	−64	C15	C16	C17	C18	61
C12	N11	C10	C15	−61	C17	C8	C9	C24	58	C8	C17	C18	N23	4
C1	N11	C12	C13	−179	C9	C8	C17	C16	62	C8	C17	C18	C19	−117
C10	N11	C12	C13	60	C9	C8	C17	C18	−60	C16	C17	C18	N23	−115
C22	N23	C18	C17	178	C7	C9	C10	N11	−54	C16	C17	C18	C19	124
C22	N23	C18	C19	−62	C7	C9	C10	C15	−177	N23	C18	C19	C20	56
C24	N23	C18	C17	57	C8	C9	C10	N11	−178	C17	C18	C19	C20	179
C24	N23	C18	C19	177	C8	C9	C10	C15	60	C18	C19	C20	C21	−54
C18	N23	C22	C21	62	C24	C9	C10	N11	60	C19	C20	C21	C22	56
C24	N23	C22	C21	−175	C24	C9	C10	C15	−62	C20	C21	C22	N23	−57
C18	N23	C24	C9	−60	C7	C9	C24	N23	−120					
C22	N23	C24	C9	175	C8	C9	C24	N23	0					

58.23 Macusine - A iodide

A.T.McPhail, J.M.Robertson, G.A.Sim, J. Chem. Soc., 1832, 1963

$C_{22}H_{27}N_2O_3{}^+$, I^-

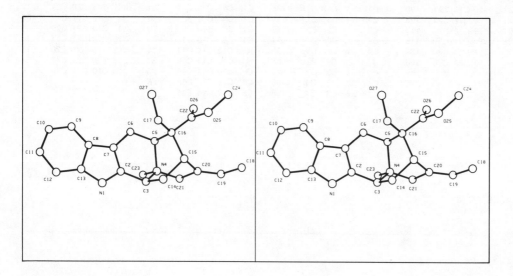

$P2_12_12_1$ Z = 4   R = 0.14

MACUSI   LB 22-27-3

Bond Lengths

C2	N1	1.32	C7	C8	1.44
C13	N1	1.35	C8	C9	1.41
C3	N4	1.46	C8	C13	1.50
C5	N4	1.66	C9	C10	1.27
C21	N4	1.36	C10	C11	1.50
C23	N4	1.50	C11	C12	1.38
C22	O25	1.33	C12	C13	1.39
C24	O25	1.43	C14	C15	1.60
C22	O26	1.16	C15	C16	1.66
C17	O27	1.40	C15	C20	1.50
C2	C3	1.50	C16	C17	1.49
C2	C7	1.42	C16	C22	1.42
C3	C14	1.63	C18	C19	1.55
C5	C6	1.45	C19	C20	1.31
C5	C16	1.61	C20	C21	1.55
C6	C7	1.44			

Bond Angles

C2	N1	C13	113		C9	C10	C11	122
C3	N4	C5	103		C10	C11	C12	120
C3	N4	C21	113		C11	C12	C13	119
C3	N4	C23	115		N1	C13	C8	105
C5	N4	C21	112		N1	C13	C12	137
C5	N4	C23	102		C8	C13	C12	118
C21	N4	C23	111		C3	C14	C15	104
C22	O25	C24	120		C14	C15	C16	111
N1	C2	C3	126		C14	C15	C20	108
N1	C2	C7	111		C16	C15	C20	107
C3	C2	C7	123		C5	C16	C15	108
N4	C3	C2	112		C5	C16	C17	115
N4	C3	C14	114		C5	C16	C22	115
C2	C3	C14	112		C15	C16	C17	104
N4	C5	C6	114		C15	C16	C22	104
N4	C5	C16	108		C17	C16	C22	110
C6	C5	C16	117		O27	C17	C16	109
C5	C6	C7	113		C18	C19	C20	127
C2	C7	C6	122		C15	C20	C19	127
C2	C7	C8	104		C15	C20	C21	110
C6	C7	C8	134		C19	C20	C21	123
C7	C8	C9	133		N4	C21	C20	114
C7	C8	C13	107		O25	C22	O26	120
C9	C8	C13	120		O25	C22	C16	114
C8	C9	C10	120		O26	C22	C16	125

Torsion Angles

C13	N1	C2	C3	−179		C3	C2	C7	C6	−5		C11	C12	C13	N1	178
C13	N1	C2	C7	1		C3	C2	C7	C8	−178		C11	C12	C13	C8	−4
C2	N1	C13	C8	−3		N4	C3	C14	C15	13		C3	C14	C15	C16	55
C2	N1	C13	C12	175		C2	C3	C14	C15	−115		C3	C14	C15	C20	−63
C5	N4	C3	C2	54		N4	C5	C6	C7	39		C14	C15	C16	C5	−59
C5	N4	C3	C14	−73		C16	C5	C6	C7	−88		C14	C15	C16	C17	63
C21	N4	C3	C2	176		N4	C5	C16	C15	−2		C14	C15	C16	C22	178
C21	N4	C3	C14	48		N4	C5	C16	C17	−117		C20	C15	C16	C5	59
C23	N4	C3	C2	−55		N4	C5	C16	C22	113		C20	C15	C16	C17	−179
C23	N4	C3	C14	177		C6	C5	C16	C15	128		C20	C15	C16	C22	−64
C3	N4	C5	C6	−66		C6	C5	C16	C17	13		C14	C15	C20	C19	−128
C3	N4	C5	C16	66		C6	C5	C16	C22	−116		C14	C15	C20	C21	56
C21	N4	C5	C6	172		C5	C6	C7	C2	−4		C16	C15	C20	C19	112
C21	N4	C5	C16	−57		C5	C6	C7	C8	167		C16	C15	C20	C21	−64
C23	N4	C5	C6	53		C2	C7	C8	C9	−178		C5	C16	C17	O27	−77
C23	N4	C5	C16	−175		C2	C7	C8	C13	−3		C15	C16	C17	O27	166
C3	N4	C21	C20	−60		C6	C7	C8	C9	9		C22	C16	C17	O27	55
C5	N4	C21	C20	56		C6	C7	C8	C13	−175		C5	C16	C22	O25	−172
C23	N4	C21	C20	169		C7	C8	C9	C10	174		C5	C16	C22	O26	12
C24	O25	C22	O26	3		C13	C8	C9	C10	0		C15	C16	C22	O25	−55
C24	O25	C22	C16	−173		C7	C8	C13	N1	3		C15	C16	C22	O26	130
N1	C2	C3	N4	155		C7	C8	C13	C12	−175		C17	C16	C22	O25	56
N1	C2	C3	C14	−77		C9	C8	C13	N1	179		C17	C16	C22	O26	−120
C7	C2	C3	N4	−26		C9	C8	C13	C12	1		C18	C19	C20	C15	6
C7	C2	C3	C14	103		C8	C9	C10	C11	3		C18	C19	C20	C21	−178
N1	C2	C7	C6	175		C9	C10	C11	C12	−7		C15	C20	C21	N4	5
N1	C2	C7	C8	1		C10	C11	C12	C13	7		C19	C20	C21	N4	−171

58.24 Akuammidine methiodide monohydrate

$C_{22}H_{27}N_2O_3^+$, I^- , H_2O

S.J.Silvers, A.Tulinsky, Acta Cryst., 16, 579, 1963

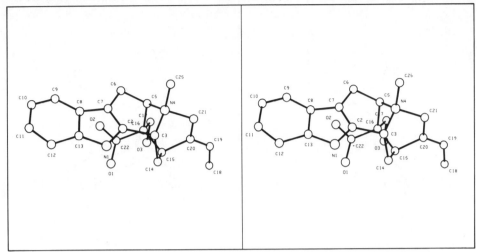

The methyl ester side chain is disordered.

$P2_12_12_1$ Z = 4   R = 0.095

AKUAMI   LB 22-27-5

Bond Lengths

C2	N1	1.35
C13	N1	1.39
C3	N4	1.52
C5	N4	1.51
C21	N4	1.57
C25	N4	1.56
C22	O1	1.26
C22	O2	1.27
C17	O3	1.45
C2	C3	1.57
C2	C7	1.40
C3	C14	1.55
C5	C6	1.55
C5	C16	1.58
C6	C7	1.43
C7	C8	1.47
C8	C9	1.43
C8	C13	1.44
C9	C10	1.30
C10	C11	1.40
C11	C12	1.36
C12	C13	1.49
C14	C15	1.58
C15	C16	1.54
C15	C20	1.60
C16	C17	1.47
C16	C22	1.52
C18	C19	1.45
C19	C20	1.34
C20	C21	1.45

Bond Angles

C2	N1	C13	105
C3	N4	C5	113
C3	N4	C21	105
C3	N4	C25	108
C5	N4	C21	112
C21	N4	C25	114
C5	N4	C25	103
N1	C2	C3	121
N1	C2	C7	115
C3	C2	C7	124
N4	C3	C2	105
N4	C3	C14	108
C2	C3	C14	111
N4	C5	C6	107
N4	C5	C16	107
C6	C5	C16	115
C5	C6	C7	110
C2	C7	C6	124
C2	C7	C8	103
C6	C7	C8	133
C7	C8	C9	134
C7	C8	C13	106
C8	C9	C13	119
C8	C9	C10	120
C9	C10	C11	120

C10	C11	C12	126
C11	C12	C13	114
N1	C13	C8	110
N1	C13	C12	131
C8	C13	C12	119
C3	C14	C15	110
C14	C15	C16	112
C14	C15	C20	102
C16	C15	C20	106
C5	C16	C15	112
C5	C16	C17	104
C5	C16	C22	116
C15	C16	C17	109
C15	C16	C22	110
C17	C16	C22	107
O3	C17	C16	109
C18	C19	C20	128
C15	C20	C19	126
C15	C20	C21	112
C19	C20	C21	122
N4	C21	C20	110
O1	C22	O2	123
O1	C22	C16	119
O2	C22	C16	118

Torsion Angles

C13	N1	C2	C3	−173
C13	N1	C2	C7	−2
C2	N1	C13	C8	−3
C2	N1	C13	C12	−174
C5	N4	C3	C2	−49
C5	N4	C3	C14	70
C21	N4	C3	C2	−171
C21	N4	C3	C14	−52
C25	N4	C3	C2	79
C25	N4	C3	C14	−162
C3	N4	C5	C6	70
C3	N4	C5	C16	−54
C21	N4	C5	C6	−171
C21	N4	C5	C16	65
C25	N4	C5	C6	−54
C25	N4	C5	C16	−179
C3	N4	C21	C20	73
C5	N4	C21	C20	−50
C25	N4	C21	C20	−173
N1	C2	C3	N4	−171
N1	C2	C3	C14	72
C7	C2	C3	N4	18
C7	C2	C3	C14	−99
N1	C2	C7	C6	−179
N1	C2	C7	C8	6
C3	C2	C7	C6	−8
C3	C2	C7	C8	177

N4	C3	C14	C15	−16
C2	C3	C14	C15	99
N4	C5	C6	C7	−54
C16	C5	C6	C7	65
N4	C5	C16	C15	−11
N4	C5	C16	C17	−128
N4	C5	C16	C22	116
C6	C5	C16	C15	−130
C6	C5	C16	C17	113
C6	C5	C16	C22	−4
C5	C6	C7	C2	26
C5	C6	C7	C8	−161
C2	C7	C8	C9	−177
C2	C7	C8	C13	−7
C6	C7	C8	C9	9
C6	C7	C8	C13	179
C7	C8	C9	C10	−178
C13	C8	C9	C10	13
C7	C8	C13	N1	7
C7	C8	C13	C12	179
C9	C8	C13	N1	178
C9	C8	C13	C12	−9
C8	C9	C10	C11	−11
C9	C10	C11	C12	7
C10	C11	C12	C13	−3
C11	C12	C13	N1	175
C11	C12	C13	C8	4

C3	C14	C15	C16	−44
C3	C14	C15	C20	69
C14	C15	C16	C5	60
C14	C15	C16	C17	174
C14	C15	C16	C22	−69
C20	C15	C16	C5	−50
C20	C15	C16	C17	64
C20	C15	C16	C22	−180
C14	C15	C20	C19	124
C14	C15	C20	C21	−49
C16	C15	C20	C19	−119
C16	C15	C20	C21	68
C5	C16	C17	O3	−177
C15	C16	C17	O3	64
C22	C16	C17	O3	−55
C5	C16	C22	O1	−119
C5	C16	C22	O2	61
C15	C16	C22	O1	8
C15	C16	C22	O2	−171
C17	C16	C22	O1	126
C17	C16	C22	O2	−53
C18	C19	C20	C15	4
C18	C19	C20	C21	176
C15	C20	C21	N4	−17
C19	C20	C21	N4	170

58.25 Corymine hydrobromide monohydrate (absolute configuration)

$C_{22}H_{27}N_2O_4^+$, Br^- , H_2O

C.W.L.Bevan, M.B.Patel, A.H.Rees, D.R.Harris, M.L.Marshak, H.H.Mills, Chem. and Industry, 603, 1965

Atomic coordinates were not reported in the paper.

$P2_12_12_1$ Z = 4   R = 0.083

CORYBH   LB 22-27-1

58.26   Chimonanthine dihydrobromide

$C_{22}H_{28}N_4^{2+}$, $2Br^-$

I.J.Grant, T.A.Hamor, J.M.Robertson, G.A.Sim, J. Chem. Soc., 5678, 1965

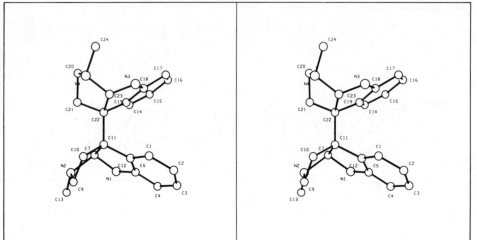

The space group could be the enantiomorphous $P4_32_12$.
$P4_12_12$ $Z = 8$ $R = 0.149$

CHANHB   LB 22-28-5

Bond Lengths

C5	N1	1.38	C7	C11	1.54
C7	N1	1.51	C9	C10	1.49
C7	N2	1.55	C10	C11	1.58
C9	N2	1.57	C11	C12	1.52
C13	N2	1.40	C11	C22	1.58
C18	N3	1.49	C14	C15	1.38
C19	N3	1.36	C14	C23	1.36
C19	N4	1.48	C15	C16	1.46
C20	N4	1.45	C16	C17	1.34
C24	N4	1.55	C17	C18	1.45
C1	C2	1.41	C18	C23	1.34
C1	C12	1.42	C19	C22	1.51
C2	C3	1.44	C20	C21	1.53
C3	C4	1.36	C21	C22	1.53
C4	C5	1.36	C22	C23	1.52
C5	C12	1.35			

Bond Angles

C5	N1	C7	109	C12	C11	C22	115
C7	N2	C9	101	C1	C12	C5	123
C7	N2	C13	119	C1	C12	C11	128
C9	N2	C13	117	C5	C12	C11	109
C18	N3	C19	100	C15	C14	C23	120
C19	N4	C20	97	C14	C15	C16	119
C19	N4	C24	110	C15	C16	C17	123
C20	N4	C24	114	C16	C17	C18	114
C2	C1	C12	116	N3	C18	C17	123
C1	C2	C3	119	N3	C18	C23	113
C2	C3	C4	121	C17	C18	C23	124
C3	C4	C5	120	N3	C19	N4	121
N1	C5	C4	125	N3	C19	C22	117
N1	C5	C12	113	N4	C19	C22	111
C4	C5	C12	121	N4	C20	C21	106
N1	C7	N2	111	C20	C21	C22	99
N1	C7	C11	104	C11	C22	C19	124
N2	C7	C11	108	C11	C22	C21	109
N2	C9	C10	106	C11	C22	C23	109
C9	C10	C11	103	C19	C22	C21	103
C7	C11	C10	105	C19	C22	C23	96
C7	C11	C12	104	C21	C22	C23	115
C7	C11	C22	112	C14	C23	C18	121
C10	C11	C12	109	C14	C23	C22	129
C10	C11	C22	110	C18	C23	C22	110

Torsion Angles

C7	N1	C5	C12	0	C7	C11	C22	C19	173
C5	N1	C7	N2	−114	C7	C11	C22	C21	52
C5	N1	C7	C11	3	C7	C11	C22	C23	−75
C9	N2	C7	N1	91	C10	C11	C22	C19	56
C9	N2	C7	C11	−22	C10	C11	C22	C21	−65
C7	N2	C9	C10	39	C10	C11	C22	C23	168
C19	N3	C18	C23	−9	C12	C11	C22	C19	−68
C18	N3	C19	N4	−120	C12	C11	C22	C21	171
C18	N3	C19	C22	19	C12	C11	C22	C23	44
C20	N4	C19	N3	109	N3	C18	C23	C22	−4
C20	N4	C19	C22	−33	N3	C19	C22	C11	98
C19	N4	C20	C21	49	N3	C19	C22	C21	−138
N1	C5	C12	C11	−3	N3	C19	C22	C23	−21
N1	C7	C11	C10	−119	N4	C19	C22	C11	−119
N1	C7	C11	C12	−4	N4	C19	C22	C21	5
N1	C7	C11	C22	122	N4	C19	C22	C23	122
N2	C7	C11	C10	−1	N4	C20	C21	C22	−48
N2	C7	C11	C12	114	C20	C21	C22	C11	157
N2	C7	C11	C22	−120	C20	C21	C22	C19	24
N2	C9	C10	C11	−40	C20	C21	C22	C23	−79
C9	C10	C11	C7	25	C11	C22	C23	C18	−116
C9	C10	C11	C12	−86	C19	C22	C23	C18	13
C9	C10	C11	C22	146	C21	C22	C23	C18	121
C7	C11	C12	C5	4	N3	C18	C23	C14	173
C10	C11	C12	C5	116	N1	C5	C12	C1	179
C22	C11	C12	C5	−119					

58.27   Calycanthine dihydrobromide dihydrate

$C_{22}H_{28}N_4^{2+}$, $2Br-$, $2H_2O$

T.A.Hamor, J.M.Robertson, J. Chem. Soc., 194, 1962

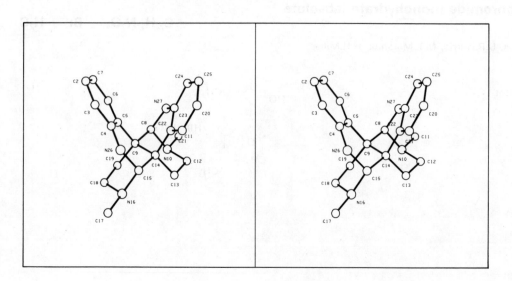

$P2_12_12_1$ $Z = 4$ $R = 0.096$

CANTBR   LB 22-28-6

Bond Lengths

C8	N10	1.53
C11	N10	1.49
C12	N10	1.50
C15	N16	1.56
C17	N16	1.49
C18	N16	1.43
C4	N26	1.38
C15	N26	1.44
C8	N27	1.44
C23	N27	1.44
C2	C3	1.40
C2	C7	1.34
C3	C4	1.40
C4	C5	1.43
C5	C6	1.36
C5	C9	1.54
C6	C7	1.43
C8	C9	1.56
C9	C14	1.54
C9	C19	1.55
C12	C13	1.52
C13	C14	1.57
C14	C15	1.57
C14	C22	1.52
C18	C19	1.51
C20	C21	1.41
C20	C25	1.37
C21	C22	1.39
C22	C23	1.37
C23	C24	1.40
C24	C25	1.40

Bond Angles

C8	N10	C11	109		C8	C9	C19	113
C8	N10	C12	111		C14	C9	C19	112
C11	N10	C12	111		N10	C12	C13	110
C15	N16	C17	110		C12	C13	C14	111
C15	N16	C18	113		C9	C14	C13	111
C17	N16	C18	111		C9	C14	C15	106
C4	N26	C15	123		C9	C14	C22	108
C8	N27	C23	119		C13	C14	C15	113
C3	C2	C7	119		C13	C14	C22	110
C2	C3	C4	122		C15	C14	C22	108
N26	C4	C3	120		N16	C15	N26	110
N26	C4	C5	121		N16	C15	C14	107
C3	C4	C5	119		N26	C15	C14	110
C4	C5	C6	118		N16	C18	C19	113
C4	C5	C9	118		C9	C19	C18	113
C6	C5	C9	123		C21	C20	C25	121
C5	C6	C7	122		C20	C21	C22	119
C2	C7	C6	120		C14	C22	C21	122
N10	C8	N27	110		C14	C22	C23	119
N10	C8	C9	110		C21	C22	C23	119
N27	C8	C9	111		N27	C23	C22	122
C5	C9	C8	110		N27	C23	C24	116
C5	C9	C14	109		C22	C23	C24	122
C5	C9	C19	107		C23	C24	C25	118
C8	C9	C14	106		C20	C25	C24	120

Torsion Angles

C11	N10	C8	N27	−63		C9	C5	C6	C7	−176		C12	C13	C14	C15	176
C11	N10	C8	C9	174		C4	C5	C9	C8	−148		C12	C13	C14	C22	−63
C12	N10	C8	N27	59		C4	C5	C9	C14	−32		C9	C14	C15	N16	61
C12	N10	C8	C9	−63		C4	C5	C9	C19	89		C9	C14	C15	N26	−58
C8	N10	C12	C13	58		C6	C5	C9	C8	32		C13	C14	C15	N16	−61
C11	N10	C12	C13	179		C6	C5	C9	C14	147		C13	C14	C15	N26	179
C17	N16	C15	N26	−68		C6	C5	C9	C19	−92		C22	C14	C15	N16	177
C17	N16	C15	C14	172		C5	C6	C7	C2	−3		C22	C14	C15	N26	57
C18	N16	C15	N26	57		N10	C8	C9	C5	178		C9	C14	C22	C21	148
C18	N16	C15	C14	−63		N10	C8	C9	C14	61		C9	C14	C22	C23	−32
C15	N16	C18	C19	57		N10	C8	C9	C19	−62		C13	C14	C22	C21	−91
C17	N16	C18	C19	−179		N27	C8	C9	C5	57		C13	C14	C22	C23	90
C15	N26	C4	C3	−174		N27	C8	C9	C14	−60		C15	C14	C22	C21	33
C15	N26	C4	C5	6		N27	C8	C9	C19	177		C15	C14	C22	C23	−146
C4	N26	C15	N16	−93		C5	C9	C14	C13	−176		N16	C18	C19	C9	−50
C4	N26	C15	C14	26		C5	C9	C14	C15	61		C25	C20	C21	C22	3
C23	N27	C8	N10	−98		C5	C9	C14	C22	−55		C21	C20	C25	C24	−5
C23	N27	C8	C9	24		C8	C9	C14	C13	−58		C20	C21	C22	C14	−179
C8	N27	C23	C22	10		C8	C9	C14	C15	178		C20	C21	C22	C23	1
C8	N27	C23	C24	−173		C8	C9	C14	C22	63		C14	C22	C23	N27	−6
C7	C2	C3	C4	0		C19	C9	C14	C13	66		C14	C22	C23	C24	177
C3	C2	C7	C6	1		C19	C9	C14	C15	−57		C21	C22	C23	N27	174
C2	C3	C4	N26	−180		C19	C9	C14	C22	−173		C21	C22	C23	C24	−2
C2	C3	C4	C5	1		C5	C9	C19	C18	−67		N27	C23	C24	C25	−176
N26	C4	C5	C6	178		C8	C9	C19	C18	171		C22	C23	C24	C25	0
N26	C4	C5	C9	−2		C14	C9	C19	C18	52		C23	C24	C25	C20	3
C3	C4	C5	C6	−2		N10	C12	C13	C14	−54						
C3	C4	C5	C9	177		C12	C13	C14	C9	57						
C4	C5	C6	C7	3												

58.28   Echitamine iodide

$C_{22}H_{29}N_2O_4{}^+$, I^-

H.Manohar, S.Ramaseshan, Z. Kristallogr., 117, 273, 1962

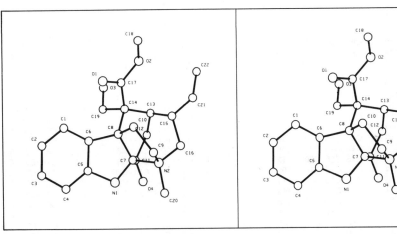

No comparison of bond lengths is possible since they are not reported in the paper.

$P2_12_12_1$ Z = 4   R = 0.145

ECHITI   LB 22-29-6

Bond Lengths

C5	N1	1.49
C7	N1	1.48
C7	N2	1.51
C9	N2	1.48
C16	N2	1.50
C20	N2	1.52
C17	O1	1.30
C17	O2	1.45
C18	O2	1.42
C19	O3	1.43
C11	O4	1.36
C1	C2	1.38
C1	C6	1.39
C2	C3	1.42
C3	C4	1.38
C4	C5	1.41
C5	C6	1.45
C6	C8	1.55
C7	C8	1.55
C7	C11	1.55
C8	C10	1.53
C8	C14	1.56
C9	C10	1.55
C11	C12	1.58
C12	C13	1.56
C13	C14	1.56
C13	C15	1.52
C14	C17	1.50
C14	C19	1.54
C15	C16	1.52
C15	C21	1.36
C21	C22	1.54

Bond Angles

C5	N1	C7	109		O4	C11	C7	122
C7	N2	C9	105		O4	C11	C12	111
C7	N2	C16	113		C7	C11	C12	114
C7	N2	C20	99		C11	C12	C13	110
C9	N2	C16	108		C12	C13	C14	109
C9	N2	C20	122		C12	C13	C15	118
C16	N2	C20	109		C14	C13	C15	107
C17	O2	C18	104		C8	C14	C13	110
C2	C1	C6	116		C8	C14	C17	110
C1	C2	C3	127		C8	C14	C19	104
C2	C3	C4	119		C13	C14	C17	117
C3	C4	C5	114		C13	C14	C19	110
N1	C5	C4	120		C17	C14	C19	104
N1	C5	C6	112		C13	C15	C16	114
C4	C5	C6	128		C13	C15	C21	126
C1	C6	C5	116		C16	C15	C21	113
C1	C6	C8	141		N2	C16	C15	113
C5	C6	C8	102		O1	C17	O2	126
N1	C7	N2	108		O1	C17	C14	118
N1	C7	C8	101		O2	C17	C14	116
N1	C7	C11	109		O3	C19	C14	114
N2	C7	C8	108		C15	C21	C22	126
N2	C7	C11	115					
C8	C7	C11	114					
C6	C8	C7	111					
C6	C8	C10	111					
C7	C8	C10	102					
C7	C8	C14	112					
C10	C8	C14	101					
N2	C9	C10	102					
C8	C10	C9	109					

Torsion Angles

C7	N1	C5	C6	−18		N2	C7	C8	C10	−13		C12	C13	C14	C8	70
C5	N1	C7	N2	133		N2	C7	C8	C14	94		C12	C13	C14	C17	−163
C5	N1	C7	C8	20		C11	C7	C8	C6	101		C12	C13	C14	C19	−45
C5	N1	C7	C11	−101		C11	C7	C8	C10	−143		C15	C13	C14	C8	−60
C9	N2	C7	N1	−76		C11	C7	C8	C14	−35		C15	C13	C14	C17	67
C9	N2	C7	C8	33		N1	C7	C11	C12	165		C15	C13	C14	C19	−174
C9	N2	C7	C11	162		N2	C7	C11	C12	−73		C12	C13	C15	C16	−24
C16	N2	C7	N1	167		C8	C7	C11	C12	52		C12	C13	C15	C21	124
C16	N2	C7	C8	−85		C6	C8	C10	C9	107		C14	C13	C15	C16	99
C16	N2	C7	C11	44		C7	C8	C10	C9	−10		C14	C13	C15	C21	−112
C7	N2	C9	C10	−38		C14	C8	C10	C9	−126		C8	C14	C17	O1	−30
C16	N2	C9	C10	84		C6	C8	C14	C13	−155		C8	C14	C17	O2	146
C7	N2	C16	C15	51		C6	C8	C14	C17	74		C13	C14	C17	O1	−158
C9	N2	C16	C15	−65		C6	C8	C14	C19	−38		C13	C14	C17	O2	18
C18	O2	C17	O1	14		C7	C8	C14	C13	−23		C19	C14	C17	O1	81
C18	O2	C17	C14	−162		C7	C8	C14	C17	−154		C19	C14	C17	O2	−103
N1	C5	C6	C8	7		C10	C8	C14	C13	85		C8	C14	C19	O3	173
C5	C6	C8	C7	6		C10	C8	C14	C17	−46		C13	C14	C19	O3	−69
C5	C6	C8	C10	−106		C10	C8	C14	C19	−157		C17	C14	C19	O3	57
N1	C7	C8	C6	−16		N2	C9	C10	C8	30		C13	C15	C16	N2	−65
N1	C7	C8	C10	100		C7	C11	C12	C13	−7		C21	C15	C16	N2	142
N1	C7	C8	C14	−152		C11	C12	C13	C14	−52		C13	C15	C21	C22	−2
N2	C7	C8	C6	−129		C11	C12	C13	C15	71		C16	C15	C21	C22	148
											C1	C6	C5	N1	180

58.29   Echitamine bromide methanol solvate

J.A.Hamilton, T.A.Hamor, J.M.Robertson, G.A.Sim, J. Chem. Soc., 5061, 1962

$C_{22}H_{29}N_2O_4^+ , CH_4O , Br^-$

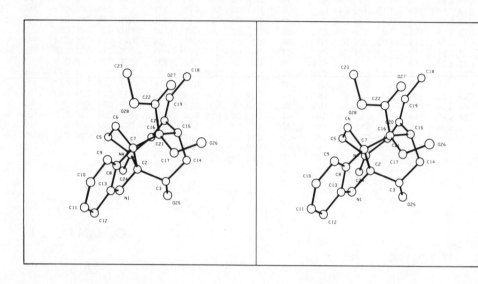

$. Br^-. CH_3OH$

$P2_12_12_1$ $Z = 4$ $R = 0.134$

ECHBME   LB 22-29-1

Bond Lengths

C2	N1	1.43	C7	C16	1.55
C13	N1	1.38	C8	C9	1.39
C2	N4	1.54	C8	C13	1.43
C5	N4	1.56	C9	C10	1.42
C21	N4	1.54	C10	C11	1.37
C24	N4	1.54	C11	C12	1.42
C3	O25	1.38	C12	C13	1.46
C17	O26	1.41	C14	C15	1.50
C22	O27	1.22	C15	C16	1.59
C22	O28	1.32	C15	C20	1.52
C23	O28	1.52	C16	C17	1.58
C2	C3	1.62	C16	C22	1.55
C2	C7	1.57	C18	C19	1.51
C3	C14	1.54	C19	C20	1.37
C5	C6	1.56	C20	C21	1.48
C6	C7	1.55			
C7	C8	1.56	C29	O30	1.37

Bond Angles

C2	N1	C13	108		C9	C8	C13	122
C2	N4	C5	104		C8	C9	C10	117
C2	N4	C21	115		C9	C10	C11	121
C2	N4	C24	115		C10	C11	C12	125
C5	N4	C21	110		C11	C12	C13	114
C5	N4	C24	106		N1	C13	C8	114
C21	N4	C24	106		N1	C13	C12	126
C22	O28	C23	116		C8	C13	C12	120
N1	C2	N4	109		C3	C14	C15	116
N1	C2	C3	110		C14	C15	C16	110
N1	C2	C7	107		C14	C15	C20	108
N4	C2	C3	111		C16	C15	C20	112
N4	C2	C7	104		C7	C16	C15	109
C3	C2	C7	116		C7	C16	C17	111
O25	C3	C2	111		C7	C16	C22	113
O25	C3	C14	112		C15	C16	C17	108
C2	C3	C14	112		C15	C16	C22	108
N4	C5	C6	101		C17	C16	C22	108
C5	C6	C7	107		O26	C17	C16	112
C2	C7	C6	106		C18	C19	C20	126
C2	C7	C8	102		C15	C20	C19	126
C2	C7	C16	113		C15	C20	C21	120
C6	C7	C8	110		C19	C20	C21	111
C6	C7	C16	109		N4	C21	C20	115
C8	C7	C16	116		O27	C22	O28	126
C7	C8	C9	133		O27	C22	C16	124
C7	C8	C13	105		O28	C22	C16	109

Torsion Angles

C13	N1	C2	N4	−133		N4	C2	C7	C16	−101		C14	C15	C16	C7	−70
C13	N1	C2	C3	105		C3	C2	C7	C6	141		C14	C15	C16	C17	51
C13	N1	C2	C7	−21		C3	C2	C7	C8	−105		C14	C15	C16	C22	167
C2	N1	C13	C8	16		C3	C2	C7	C16	21		C20	C15	C16	C7	51
C5	N4	C2	N1	75		C2	C3	C14	C15	10		C20	C15	C16	C17	171
C5	N4	C2	C3	−163		N4	C5	C6	C7	−30		C20	C15	C16	C22	−72
C5	N4	C2	C7	−38		C5	C6	C7	C2	7		C14	C15	C20	C19	−128
C21	N4	C2	N1	−164		C5	C6	C7	C8	−102		C14	C15	C20	C21	31
C21	N4	C2	C3	−43		C5	C6	C7	C16	129		C16	C15	C20	C19	110
C21	N4	C2	C7	82		C2	C7	C8	C13	−9		C16	C15	C20	C21	−90
C2	N4	C5	C6	42		C6	C7	C8	C13	103		C7	C16	C17	O26	171
C21	N4	C5	C6	−81		C16	C7	C8	C13	−132		C15	C16	C17	O26	51
C2	N4	C21	C20	−45		C2	C7	C16	C15	34		C22	C16	C17	O26	−65
C5	N4	C21	C20	72		C2	C7	C16	C17	−85		C7	C16	C22	O27	−145
C23	O28	C22	O27	9		C2	C7	C16	C22	154		C7	C16	C22	O28	46
C23	O28	C22	C16	178		C6	C7	C16	C15	−84		C15	C16	C22	O27	−25
N1	C2	C3	C14	−167		C6	C7	C16	C17	157		C15	C16	C22	O28	166
N4	C2	C3	C14	72		C6	C7	C16	C22	36		C17	C16	C22	O27	92
C7	C2	C3	C14	−45		C8	C7	C16	C15	151		C17	C16	C22	O28	−77
N1	C2	C7	C6	−96		C8	C7	C16	C17	32		C18	C19	C20	C15	−7
N1	C2	C7	C8	18		C8	C7	C16	C22	−89		C18	C19	C20	C21	−168
N1	C2	C7	C16	144		C7	C8	C13	N1	−3		C15	C20	C21	N4	56
N4	C2	C7	C6	19		C3	C14	C15	C16	46		C19	C20	C21	N4	−142
N4	C2	C7	C8	134		C3	C14	C15	C20	−77		C9	C8	C13	N1	176

58.30 N(a) - Acetyl - 7 - ethyl - 5 - desethyl - aspidospermidine N(b) - methiodide (absolute configuration)

$C_{22}H_{31}N_2O^+ , I^-$

A.Camerman, N.Camerman, J.Trotter, Acta Cryst., 19, 314, 1965

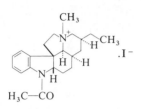

$P2_12_12_1$ Z = 4   R = 0.066

AEASPM   LB 22-31-2

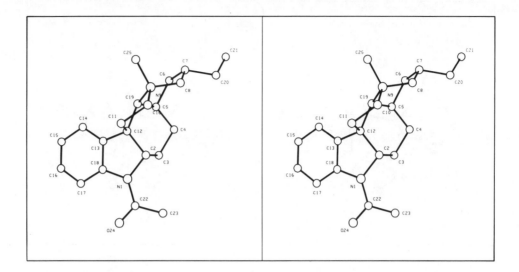

Bond Lengths

C2	N1	1.51	C7	C8	1.55
C18	N1	1.43	C7	C20	1.64
C22	N1	1.37	C10	C11	1.60
C8	N9	1.51	C11	C12	1.56
C10	N9	1.56	C12	C13	1.49
C19	N9	1.58	C12	C19	1.58
C25	N9	1.54	C13	C14	1.39
C22	O24	1.24	C13	C18	1.42
C2	C3	1.56	C14	C15	1.44
C2	C12	1.54	C15	C16	1.36
C3	C4	1.57	C16	C17	1.40
C4	C5	1.52	C17	C18	1.40
C5	C6	1.56	C20	C21	1.56
C5	C19	1.56	C22	C23	1.50
C6	C7	1.50			

Bond Angles

C2	N1	C18	108
C2	N1	C22	125
C18	N1	C22	124
C8	N9	C10	104
C8	N9	C19	115
C8	N9	C25	111
C10	N9	C19	108
C10	N9	C25	110
C19	N9	C25	108
N1	C2	C3	108
N1	C2	C12	102
C3	C2	C12	114
C2	C3	C4	109
C3	C4	C5	109
C4	C5	C6	113
C4	C5	C19	116
C6	C5	C19	109
C5	C6	C7	114
C6	C7	C8	116
C6	C7	C20	113
C8	C7	C20	102
N9	C8	C7	110
N9	C10	C11	100
C10	C11	C12	104
C2	C12	C11	114
C2	C12	C13	102
C2	C12	C19	115
C11	C12	C13	110
C11	C12	C19	102
C13	C12	C19	114
C12	C13	C14	129
C12	C13	C18	109
C14	C13	C18	122
C13	C14	C15	117
C14	C15	C16	120
C15	C16	C17	123
C16	C17	C18	117
N1	C18	C13	108
N1	C18	C17	131
C13	C18	C17	121
N9	C19	C5	112
N9	C19	C12	105
C5	C19	C12	116
C7	C20	C21	110
N1	C22	O24	119
N1	C22	C23	118
O24	C22	C23	122

Torsion Angles

C18	N1	C2	C3	−93	C4	C5	C6	C7	−71
C18	N1	C2	C12	28	C19	C5	C6	C7	59
C22	N1	C2	C3	67	C4	C5	C19	N9	85
C22	N1	C2	C12	−172	C4	C5	C19	C12	−36
C2	N1	C18	C13	−12	C6	C5	C19	N9	−44
C22	N1	C18	C13	−172	C6	C5	C19	C12	−164
C2	N1	C22	O24	−162	C5	C6	C7	C8	−16
C18	N1	C22	O24	−5	C5	C6	C7	C20	102
C10	N9	C8	C7	173	C6	C7	C8	N9	−40
C19	N9	C8	C7	55	C20	C7	C8	N9	−163
C8	N9	C10	C11	−148	C6	C7	C20	C21	74
C19	N9	C10	C11	−25	C8	C7	C20	C21	−161
C8	N9	C19	C5	−12	N9	C10	C11	C12	43
C8	N9	C19	C12	115	C10	C11	C12	C2	80
C10	N9	C19	C5	−128	C10	C11	C12	C13	−166
C10	N9	C19	C12	−1	C10	C11	C12	C19	−44
N1	C2	C3	C4	171	C2	C12	C13	C18	27
C12	C2	C3	C4	59	C11	C12	C13	C18	−94
N1	C2	C12	C11	87	C19	C12	C13	C18	151
N1	C2	C12	C13	−32	C2	C12	C19	N9	−96
N1	C2	C12	C19	−157	C2	C12	C19	C5	28
C3	C2	C12	C11	−158	C11	C12	C19	N9	27
C3	C2	C12	C13	84	C11	C12	C19	C5	152
C3	C2	C12	C19	−41	C13	C12	C19	N9	147
C2	C3	C4	C5	−64	C13	C12	C19	C5	−89
C3	C4	C5	C6	180	C12	C13	C18	N1	−10
C3	C4	C5	C19	54	C14	C13	C18	N1	179

58.31 Heteratisine hydrobromide monohydrate

$C_{22}H_{34}NO_5^+$, Br^- , H_2O

M.Przybylska, Acta Cryst., 18, 536, 1965

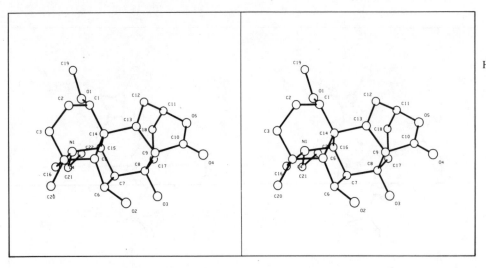

P2₁   Z = 2   R = 0.12

HATBRM   LB 22-34-3

Bond Lengths

C15	N1	1.52
C16	N1	1.54
C21	N1	1.56
C1	O1	1.41
C19	O1	1.49
C6	O2	1.47
C8	O3	1.39
C10	O4	1.19
C10	O5	1.37
C11	O5	1.48
C1	C2	1.55
C1	C14	1.55
C2	C3	1.51
C3	C4	1.58
C4	C5	1.49
C4	C16	1.55
C4	C20	1.59
C5	C6	1.62
C5	C14	1.60
C6	C7	1.56
C7	C8	1.57
C7	C15	1.57
C8	C9	1.60
C8	C17	1.59
C9	C10	1.50
C9	C13	1.58
C11	C12	1.56
C11	C18	1.54
C12	C13	1.58
C13	C14	1.63
C14	C15	1.58
C17	C18	1.56
C21	C22	1.59

Bond Angles

C15	N1	C16	118
C15	N1	C21	111
C16	N1	C21	104
C1	O1	C19	113
C10	O5	C11	119
O1	C1	C2	121
O1	C1	C14	105
C2	C1	C14	111
C1	C2	C3	118
C2	C3	C4	113
C3	C4	C5	112
C3	C4	C16	112
C3	C4	C20	104
C5	C4	C16	113
C5	C4	C20	111
C16	C4	C20	105
C4	C5	C6	104
C4	C5	C14	107
C6	C5	C14	103
O2	C6	C5	110
O2	C6	C7	112
C5	C6	C7	106
C6	C7	C8	114
C6	C7	C15	103
C8	C7	C15	109
O3	C8	C7	108
O3	C8	C9	109
O3	C8	C17	103
C7	C8	C9	110
C7	C8	C17	115
C9	C8	C17	112
C8	C9	C10	109
C8	C9	C13	113
C10	C9	C13	111
O4	C10	O5	120
O4	C10	C9	122
O5	C10	C9	118
O5	C11	C12	107
O5	C11	C18	111
C12	C11	C18	116
C11	C12	C13	114
C9	C13	C12	111
C9	C13	C14	113
C12	C13	C14	111
C1	C14	C5	115
C1	C14	C13	104
C1	C14	C15	116
C5	C14	C13	111
C5	C14	C15	101
C13	C14	C15	109
N1	C15	C7	111
N1	C15	C14	107
C7	C15	C14	102
N1	C16	C4	112
C8	C17	C18	120
C11	C18	C17	116
N1	C21	C22	109

Torsion Angles

C16	N1	C15	C7	58
C16	N1	C15	C14	−52
C21	N1	C15	C7	−63
C21	N1	C15	C14	−173
C15	N1	C16	C4	36
C21	N1	C16	C4	160
C15	N1	C21	C22	−56
C16	N1	C21	C22	176
C19	O1	C1	C2	67
C19	O1	C1	C14	−167
C11	O5	C10	O4	−179
C11	O5	C10	C9	−1
C10	O5	C11	C12	52
C10	O5	C11	C18	−75
O1	C1	C2	C3	77
C14	C1	C2	C3	−47
O1	C1	C14	C5	−129
O1	C1	C14	C13	109
O1	C1	C14	C15	−11
C2	C1	C14	C5	3
C2	C1	C14	C13	−118
C2	C1	C14	C15	122
C1	C2	C3	C4	34
C2	C3	C4	C5	25
C2	C3	C4	C16	−103
C3	C4	C5	C6	−174
C3	C4	C5	C14	−65
C16	C4	C5	C6	−46

C6	C7	C8	C9	−49
C6	C7	C8	C17	−176
C15	C7	C8	C9	65
C15	C7	C8	C17	−62
C6	C7	C15	N1	−69
C6	C7	C15	C14	45
C8	C7	C15	N1	171
C8	C7	C15	C14	−76
C7	C8	C9	C10	−170
C7	C8	C9	C13	−46
C17	C8	C9	C10	−42
C17	C8	C9	C13	83
C7	C8	C17	C18	85
C9	C8	C17	C18	−41
C8	C9	C10	O4	−103
C16	C4	C5	C14	63
C3	C4	C16	N1	86
C5	C4	C16	N1	−41
C4	C5	C6	C7	105
C14	C5	C6	C7	−7
C4	C5	C14	C1	50
C4	C5	C14	C13	169
C4	C5	C14	C15	−76
C6	C5	C14	C1	160
C6	C5	C14	C13	−82
C6	C5	C14	C15	34
C5	C6	C7	C8	94
C5	C6	C7	C15	−23

C8	C9	C10	O5	79
C13	C9	C10	O4	131
C13	C9	C10	O5	−47
C8	C9	C13	C12	−85
C8	C9	C13	C14	40
C10	C9	C13	C12	39
C10	C9	C13	C14	164
O5	C11	C12	C13	−54
C18	C11	C12	C13	70
O5	C11	C18	C17	36
C12	C11	C18	C17	−86
C11	C12	C13	C9	10
C11	C12	C13	C14	−116
C9	C13	C14	C1	−178
C9	C13	C14	C5	57
C9	C13	C14	C15	−53
C12	C13	C14	C1	−53
C12	C13	C14	C15	−177
C12	C13	C14	C15	72
C1	C14	C15	N1	−58
C1	C14	C15	C7	−175
C5	C14	C15	N1	68
C5	C14	C15	C7	−49
C13	C14	C15	N1	−175
C13	C14	C15	C7	68
C8	C17	C18	C11	46

58.32 Himbacine hydrobromide monohydrate (at −150 °C, absolute configuration)

$C_{22}H_{36}NO_2^+$, Br^- , H_2O

J.Fridrichsons, A.McL.Mathieson, Acta Cryst., 15, 119, 1962

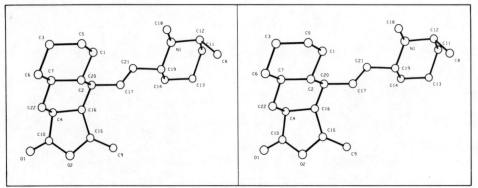

P2₁2₁2₁   Z = 4 R_{0kl} = 0.104,
R_{1kl} = 0.148, R_{2kl} = 0.160,
R_{3kl} = 0.209, R_{4kl} = 0.234

HIMBHM   LB 22–36–1

Bond Lengths

C12	N1	1.53	C4	C22	1.55
C18	N1	1.45	C6	C7	1.53
C19	N1	1.48	C7	C22	1.47
C10	O1	1.22	C8	C12	1.53
C10	O2	1.38	C9	C15	1.53
C15	O2	1.48	C11	C12	1.58
C1	C2	1.50	C11	C13	1.56
C2	C7	1.53	C13	C14	1.55
C2	C20	1.56	C14	C19	1.54
C3	C5	1.54	C15	C16	1.57
C3	C6	1.53	C16	C20	1.52
C4	C10	1.50	C17	C20	1.51
C4	C16	1.56	C17	C21	1.33
			C19	C21	1.53

Bond Angles

C12	N1	C18	102	N1	C12	C8	117
C12	N1	C19	115	N1	C12	C11	100
C18	N1	C19	114	C8	C12	C11	113
C10	O2	C15	110	C11	C13	C14	111
C2	C1	C5	106	C13	C14	C19	101
C1	C2	C7	114	O2	C15	C9	104
C7	C2	C20	110	O2	C15	C16	103
C5	C3	C6	112	C9	C15	C16	113
C10	C4	C16	102	C4	C16	C15	100
C10	C4	C22	110	C4	C16	C20	111
C16	C4	C22	114	C15	C16	C20	117
C1	C5	C3	114	C20	C17	C21	126
C3	C6	C7	109	N1	C19	C14	114
C2	C7	C6	111	N1	C19	C21	108
C2	C7	C22	110	C14	C19	C21	109
C6	C7	C22	110	C2	C20	C16	115
O1	C10	O2	121	C2	C20	C17	115
O1	C10	C4	129	C16	C20	C17	109
O2	C10	C4	109	C17	C21	C19	125
C12	C11	C13	111	C4	C22	C7	112

Torsion Angles

C19	N1	C12	C11	60	C22	C4	C16	C15	81
C12	N1	C19	C14	−65	C22	C4	C16	C20	−44
C12	N1	C19	C21	174	C10	C4	C22	C7	165
C15	O2	C10	O1	−179	C16	C4	C22	C7	52
C15	O2	C10	C4	−7	C3	C6	C7	C22	178
C10	O2	C15	C16	−18	C2	C7	C22	C4	−59
C5	C1	C2	C7	58	C6	C7	C22	C4	178
C5	C1	C2	C20	178	C12	C11	C13	C14	−60
C2	C1	C5	C3	−54	C11	C13	C14	C19	−60
C1	C2	C7	C6	−62	C13	C14	C19	N1	58
C1	C2	C7	C22	176	C13	C14	C19	C21	179
C20	C2	C7	C6	−178	O2	C15	C16	C4	34
C20	C2	C7	C22	60	O2	C15	C16	C20	155
C1	C2	C20	C16	−176	C4	C16	C20	C2	46
C1	C2	C20	C17	56	C15	C16	C20	C17	176
C7	C2	C20	C16	−54	C15	C16	C20	C2	−69
C7	C2	C20	C17	179	C15	C16	C20	C17	62
C6	C3	C5	C1	54	C21	C17	C20	C2	−120
C5	C3	C6	C7	−53	C21	C17	C20	C16	109
C16	C4	C10	O1	−159	C20	C17	C21	C19	−178
C16	C4	C10	O2	29	N1	C19	C21	C17	−128
C22	C4	C10	O1	80	C14	C19	C21	C17	109
C22	C4	C10	O2	−92					
C10	C4	C16	C15	−37					
C10	C4	C16	C20	−162					

58.33   Mitragynine hydroiodide

$C_{23}H_{31}N_2O_4^+$, I⁻

D.E.Zacharias, R.D.Rosenstein, G.A.Jeffrey, Acta Cryst., 18, 1039, 1965

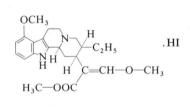

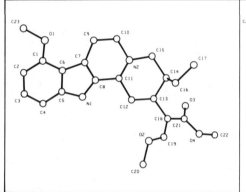

$P2_12_12_1$ Z = 4   R = 0.12

MITGHI   LB 23-31-4

Bond Lengths

C5	N1	1.38	C4	C5	1.40
C8	N1	1.36	C5	C6	1.41
C10	N2	1.51	C6	C7	1.45
C11	N2	1.49	C7	C8	1.33
C15	N2	1.55	C7	C9	1.45
C1	O1	1.35	C8	C11	1.57
C23	O1	1.50	C9	C10	1.54
C19	O2	1.29	C11	C12	1.54
C20	O2	1.45	C12	C13	1.52
C21	O3	1.23	C13	C14	1.64
C21	O4	1.33	C13	C18	1.51
C22	O4	1.44	C14	C15	1.58
C1	C2	1.36	C14	C16	1.57
C1	C6	1.41	C16	C17	1.54
C2	C3	1.39	C18	C19	1.34
C3	C4	1.41	C18	C21	1.40

Bond Angles

C5	N1	C8	107	N1	C8	C11	122
C10	N2	C11	112	C7	C8	C11	122
C10	N2	C15	109	C7	C9	C10	110
C11	N2	C15	108	N2	C10	C9	112
C1	O1	C23	118	N2	C11	C8	106
C19	O2	C20	118	N2	C11	C12	109
C21	O4	C22	120	C8	C11	C12	113
O1	C1	C2	125	C11	C12	C13	113
O1	C1	C6	115	C12	C13	C14	108
C2	C1	C6	120	C12	C13	C18	120
C1	C2	C3	120	C14	C13	C18	110
C2	C3	C4	124	C13	C14	C15	111
C3	C4	C5	114	C13	C14	C16	112
N1	C5	C4	130	C15	C14	C16	110
N1	C5	C6	107	N2	C15	C14	111
C4	C5	C6	124	C14	C16	C17	110
C1	C6	C5	119	C13	C18	C19	123
C1	C6	C7	133	C13	C18	C21	118
C5	C6	C7	108	C19	C18	C21	119
C6	C7	C8	104	O2	C19	C18	129
C6	C7	C9	129	O3	C21	O4	119
C8	C7	C9	127	O3	C21	C18	123
N1	C8	C7	114	O4	C21	C18	118

Torsion Angles

C8	N1	C5	C4	−179	C5	C6	C7	C9	173
C8	N1	C5	C6	0	C6	C7	C8	N1	7
C5	N1	C8	C7	−5	C6	C7	C8	C11	174
C5	N1	C8	C11	−172	C9	C7	C8	N1	−172
C11	N2	C10	C9	65	C9	C7	C8	C11	−5
C15	N2	C10	C9	−176	C6	C7	C9	C10	−168
C10	N2	C11	C8	−54	C8	C7	C9	C10	11
C10	N2	C11	C12	−176	N1	C8	C11	N2	−168
C15	N2	C11	C8	−173	N1	C8	C11	C12	−48
C15	N2	C11	C12	64	C7	C8	C11	N2	26
C10	N2	C15	C14	178	C7	C8	C11	C12	146
C11	N2	C15	C14	−60	C7	C9	C10	N2	−39
C23	O1	C1	C2	−6	N2	C11	C12	C13	−66
C23	O1	C1	C6	179	C8	C11	C12	C13	176
C20	O2	C19	C18	159	C11	C12	C13	C14	56
C22	O4	C21	O3	−4	C11	C12	C13	C18	−178
C22	O4	C21	C18	177	C12	C13	C14	C15	−50
O1	C1	C2	C3	−175	C12	C13	C14	C16	77
C6	C1	C2	C3	0	C18	C13	C14	C15	178
O1	C1	C6	C5	174	C18	C13	C14	C16	−55
O1	C1	C6	C7	−6	C12	C13	C18	C19	−13
C2	C1	C6	C5	−1	C12	C13	C18	C21	162
C2	C1	C6	C7	179	C14	C13	C18	C19	112
C1	C2	C3	C4	−1	C14	C13	C18	C21	−72
C2	C3	C4	C5	3	C13	C14	C15	N2	53
C3	C4	C5	N1	175	C16	C14	C15	N2	−74
C3	C4	C5	C6	−4	C13	C14	C16	C17	163
N1	C5	C6	C1	−177	C15	C14	C16	C17	−71
N1	C5	C6	C7	3	C13	C18	C19	O2	−5
C4	C5	C6	C1	3	C21	C18	C19	O2	180
C4	C5	C6	C7	−177	C13	C18	C21	O3	−14
C1	C6	C7	C8	174	C13	C18	C21	O4	166
C1	C6	C7	C9	−7	C19	C18	C21	O3	162
C5	C6	C7	C8	−6	C19	C18	C21	O4	−19

58.34 (−) - Aspidospermine N(b) - methiodide

$C_{23}H_{33}N_2O_2^+$, I^-

J.F.D.Mills, S.C.Nyburg, J. Chem. Soc., 1458, 1960

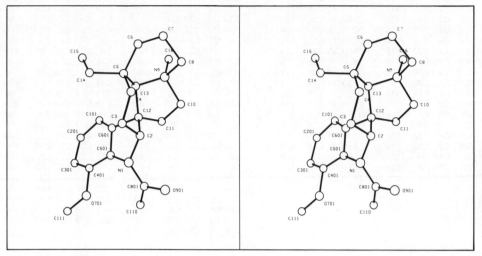

No comparison of bond lengths is possible since they are not reported in the paper.
See also Craven & Zacharias, Experientia, 24, 770, 1968.
$P2_12_12_1$ Z = 4   R = 0.209

ASPERM

Bond Lengths

C2	N1	1.51
C501	N1	1.51
C801	N1	1.39
C8	N9	1.57
C10	N9	1.61
C13	N9	1.56
C16	N9	1.60
C111	O701	1.50
C401	O701	1.50
C801	O901	1.35
C2	C3	1.50
C2	C12	1.52
C3	C4	1.57
C4	C5	1.57
C5	C6	1.59
C5	C13	1.50
C5	C14	1.72
C6	C7	1.27
C7	C8	1.69
C10	C11	1.53
C11	C12	1.67
C12	C13	1.56
C12	C601	1.61
C14	C15	1.43
C101	C201	1.39
C101	C601	1.41
C110	C801	1.48
C201	C301	1.37
C301	C401	1.40
C401	C501	1.38
C501	C601	1.40

Bond Angles

C2	N1	C501	107
C2	N1	C801	121
C501	N1	C801	121
C8	N9	C10	103
C8	N9	C13	120
C8	N9	C16	104
C10	N9	C13	106
C10	N9	C16	107
C13	N9	C16	115
C111	O701	C401	110
N1	C2	C3	110
N1	C2	C12	103
C3	C2	C12	109
C2	C3	C4	111
C3	C4	C5	107
C4	C5	C6	102
C4	C5	C13	110
C4	C5	C14	109
C6	C5	C13	110
C6	C5	C14	116
C13	C5	C14	110
C5	C6	C7	133
C6	C7	C8	106
N9	C8	C7	112
N9	C10	C11	103
C10	C11	C12	92

C2	C12	C11	116
C2	C12	C13	118
C2	C12	C601	100
C11	C12	C13	105
C11	C12	C601	109
C13	C12	C601	107
N9	C13	C5	112
N9	C13	C12	101
C5	C13	C12	120
C5	C14	C15	112
C201	C101	C601	108
C101	C201	C301	141
C201	C301	C401	96
O701	C401	C301	116
O701	C401	C501	112
C301	C401	C501	129
N1	C501	C401	128
N1	C501	C601	108
C401	C501	C601	118
C12	C601	C101	133
C12	C601	C501	106
C101	C601	C501	114
N1	C801	O901	117
N1	C801	C110	120
O901	C801	C110	122

Torsion Angles

C501	N1	C2	C3	89
C501	N1	C2	C12	−28
C801	N1	C2	C3	−126
C801	N1	C2	C12	117
C2	N1	C501	C601	6
C801	N1	C501	C601	−140
C2	N1	C801	O901	28
C501	N1	C801	O901	168
C10	N9	C8	C7	−161
C13	N9	C8	C7	−44
C8	N9	C10	C11	163
C13	N9	C10	C11	36
C8	N9	C13	C5	13
C8	N9	C13	C12	−116
C10	N9	C13	C5	129
C10	N9	C13	C12	0
N1	C2	C3	C4	−172
C12	C2	C3	C4	−59
N1	C2	C12	C11	−81
N1	C2	C12	C13	152
N1	C2	C12	C601	36
C3	C2	C12	C11	162
C3	C2	C12	C13	35
C3	C2	C12	C601	−81
C2	C3	C4	C5	71
C3	C4	C5	C6	−171
C3	C4	C5	C13	−54
C3	C4	C5	C14	66
C4	C5	C6	C7	62

C13	C5	C6	C7	−54
C14	C5	C6	C7	−180
C4	C5	C13	N9	−83
C4	C5	C13	C12	34
C6	C5	C13	N9	28
C6	C5	C13	C12	145
C14	C5	C13	N9	157
C14	C5	C13	C12	−86
C4	C5	C14	C15	−180
C6	C5	C14	C15	66
C13	C5	C14	C15	−59
C5	C6	C7	C8	22
C6	C7	C8	N9	26
N9	C10	C11	C12	−51
C10	C11	C12	C2	−79
C10	C11	C12	C13	54
C10	C11	C12	C601	169
C2	C12	C13	N9	98
C2	C12	C13	C5	−24
C11	C12	C13	N9	−33
C11	C12	C13	C5	−156
C601	C12	C13	N9	−150
C601	C12	C13	C5	87
C2	C12	C601	C501	−35
C11	C12	C601	C501	88
C13	C12	C601	C501	−158
N1	C501	C601	C12	18
C111	O701	C401	C501	−165
C101	C601	C501	N1	172

58.35 7β - Acetoxy - 7H - yohimbine methiodide

$C_{24}H_{31}N_2O_5^+$, I^-

N.Finch, C.W.Gemenden, I.H.-C.Hsu, A.Kerr, G.A.Sim, W.I.Taylor, J. Amer. Chem. Soc., 87, 2229, 1965

Atomic coordinates were not reported in the paper.
$P2_12_12_1$ Z = 4   R = 0.17

AOYHIM   LB 24-31-2

58.36 (+) - Demethanolaconinone hydroiodide trihydrate (absolute configuration)

M.Przybylska, Acta Cryst., 14, 429, 1961

$C_{24}H_{36}NO_8^+$, I^- , $3H_2O$

P2₁2₁2₁   Z = 4   R = 0.19

DMAHIT   LB 24-36-7

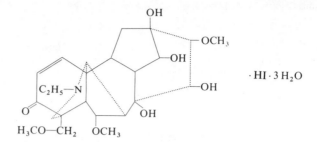

·HI·3H₂O

Bond Lengths

C2	N1	1.57	C4	C15	1.58		
C14	N1	1.54	C5	C6	1.56		
C22	N1	1.52	C5	C14	1.51		
C10	O1	1.41	C5	C18	1.49		
C20	O1	1.38	C6	C7	1.55		
C15	O2	1.39	C6	C19	1.58		
C21	O2	1.39	C7	C8	1.55		
C24	O3	1.39	C7	C12	1.52		
C25	O3	1.37	C8	C9	1.51		
C16	O4	1.22	C9	C10	1.49		
C8	O5	1.37	C9	C19	1.51		
C9	O6	1.46	C10	C11	1.51		
C11	O7	1.47	C10	C11	1.51		
C12	O8	1.45	C11	C12	1.54		
C2	C3	1.53	C12	C13	1.57		
C3	C4	1.54	C13	C14	1.56		
C3	C16	1.56	C13	C15	1.58		
C3	C24	1.58	C16	C17	1.45		
C4	C5	1.58	C17	C18	1.38		
			C22	C23	1.49		

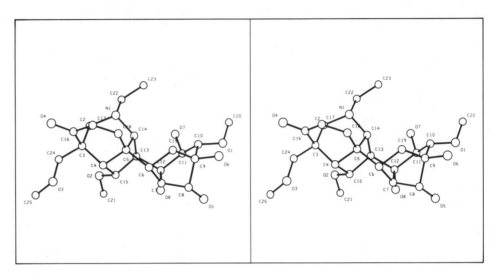

Bond Angles

C2	N1	C14	113	
C2	N1	C22	107	
C14	N1	C22	118	
C10	O1	C20	116	
C15	O2	C21	114	
C24	O3	C25	110	
N1	C2	C3	111	
C2	C3	C4	113	
C2	C3	C16	108	
C2	C3	C24	107	
C4	C3	C16	110	
C4	C3	C24	112	
C16	C3	C24	108	
C3	C4	C5	108	
C3	C4	C15	114	
C5	C4	C15	99	
C4	C5	C6	116	
C4	C5	C14	101	
C4	C5	C18	111	
C6	C5	C14	108	
C6	C5	C18	105	
C14	C5	C18	118	
C5	C6	C7	115	
C5	C6	C19	113	
C7	C6	C19	101	
C6	C7	C8	103	
C6	C7	C12	116	
C8	C7	C12	111	
O5	C8	C7	115	
O5	C8	C9	116	
C7	C8	C9	97	
O6	C9	C8	111	
O6	C9	C10	108	

O6	C9	C19	106	
C8	C9	C10	111	
C8	C9	C19	103	
C10	C9	C19	117	
O1	C10	C9	111	
O1	C10	C11	112	
C9	C10	C11	114	
O7	C11	C10	113	
O7	C11	C12	110	
C10	C11	C12	118	
O8	C12	C7	105	
O8	C12	C11	109	
O8	C12	C13	105	
C7	C12	C11	113	
C7	C12	C13	110	
C11	C12	C13	113	
C12	C13	C14	106	
C12	C13	C15	107	
C14	C13	C15	102	
N1	C14	C5	110	
N1	C14	C13	113	
C5	C14	C13	104	
O2	C15	C4	110	
O2	C15	C13	111	
C4	C15	C13	108	
O4	C16	C3	122	
O4	C16	C17	119	
C3	C16	C17	120	
C16	C17	C18	118	
C5	C18	C17	125	
C6	C19	C9	106	
N1	C22	C23	111	
O3	C24	C3	109	

Torsion Angles

C14	N1	C2	C3	40
C22	N1	C2	C3	173
C2	N1	C14	C5	−57
C2	N1	C14	C13	59
C22	N1	C14	C5	176
C22	N1	C14	C13	−67
C2	N1	C22	C23	170
C14	N1	C22	C23	−60
C20	O1	C10	C9	−149
C20	O1	C10	C11	82
C21	O2	C15	C4	−148
C21	O2	C15	C13	93
C25	O3	C24	C3	−171
N1	C2	C3	C4	−44
N1	C2	C3	C16	78
N1	C2	C3	C24	−167
C2	C3	C4	C5	62
C2	C3	C4	C15	−47
C16	C3	C4	C5	−58
C16	C3	C4	C15	−167
C24	C3	C4	C5	−178
C24	C3	C4	C15	73
C2	C3	C16	O4	86
C2	C3	C16	C17	−89
C4	C3	C16	O4	−151
C4	C3	C16	C17	35
C24	C3	C16	O4	−29
C24	C3	C16	C17	157
C2	C3	C24	O3	170
C4	C3	C24	O3	46
C16	C3	C24	O3	−75
C3	C4	C5	C6	172

C3	C4	C5	C14	−73
C3	C4	C5	C18	52
C15	C4	C5	C6	−69
C15	C4	C5	C14	47
C15	C4	C5	C18	172
C3	C4	C15	O2	−33
C3	C4	C15	C13	88
C5	C4	C15	O2	−147
C5	C4	C15	C13	−26
C4	C5	C6	C7	63
C4	C5	C6	C19	179
C14	C5	C6	C7	−48
C14	C5	C6	C19	67
C18	C5	C6	C7	−174
C18	C5	C6	C19	−59
C4	C5	C14	N1	70
C4	C5	C14	C13	−52
C6	C5	C14	N1	−169
C6	C5	C14	C13	70
C18	C5	C14	N1	−50
C18	C5	C14	C13	−172
C4	C5	C18	C17	−22
C6	C5	C18	C17	−147
C14	C5	C18	C17	93
C5	C6	C7	C8	154
C5	C6	C7	C12	33
C19	C6	C7	C8	32
C19	C6	C7	C12	−89
C5	C6	C19	C9	−125
C7	C6	C19	C9	−1
C6	C7	C8	C9	−52
C12	C7	C8	C9	73

C6	C7	C12	C11	89
C6	C7	C12	C13	−39
C8	C7	C12	C11	−28
C8	C7	C12	C13	−156
C7	C8	C9	C10	−76
C7	C8	C9	C19	51
C8	C9	C10	O1	−95
C8	C9	C10	C11	33
C19	C9	C10	O1	147
C19	C9	C10	C11	−85
C8	C9	C19	C6	−31
C10	C9	C19	C6	91
O1	C10	C11	C12	144
C9	C10	C11	C12	17
C10	C11	C12	C7	−18
C10	C11	C12	C13	108
C7	C12	C13	C14	60
C7	C12	C13	C15	−47
C11	C12	C13	C14	−68
C11	C12	C13	C15	−175
C12	C13	C14	N1	163
C12	C13	C14	C5	−78
C15	C13	C14	N1	−86
C15	C13	C14	C5	34
C12	C13	C15	O2	−132
C12	C13	C15	C4	107
C14	C13	C15	O2	117
C14	C13	C15	C4	−4
O4	C16	C17	C18	−177
C3	C16	C17	C18	−2
C16	C17	C18	C5	−5

58.37 (+)-Des-(oxymethylene)-lycoctonine hydroiodide monohydrate (absolute configuration)

$C_{24}H_{40}NO_6^+$, I^-, H_2O

M.Przybylska, Acta Cryst., 14, 424, 1961

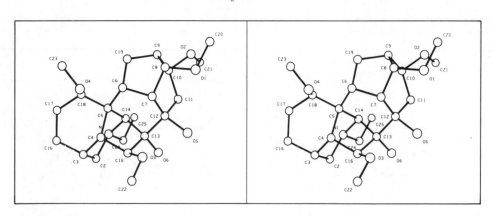

·HI·H₂O

$P2_1$ $Z = 4$ $R_{h0l} = 0.20$,
$R_{hk0} = 0.16$, $R_{0kl} = 0.11$

OMLYHI   LB 24-40-1

Bond Lengths

C2	N1	1.51	C5	C6	1.53
C14	N1	1.51	C5	C14	1.57
C24	N1	1.49	C5	C18	1.50
C8	O1	1.46	C6	C7	1.56
C20	O1	1.45	C6	C19	1.52
C10	O2	1.44	C7	C8	1.50
C21	O2	1.46	C7	C12	1.49
C15	O3	1.46	C8	C9	1.53
C22	O3	1.39	C9	C10	1.55
C18	O4	1.38	C9	C19	1.54
C23	O4	1.40	C10	C11	1.57
C12	O5	1.45	C11	C12	1.56
C13	O6	1.46	C12	C13	1.57
C2	C3	1.53	C13	C14	1.55
C3	C4	1.48	C13	C15	1.53
C3	C16	1.54	C16	C17	1.53
C4	C5	1.57	C17	C18	1.51
C4	C15	1.53	C24	C25	1.55

Bond Angles

C2	N1	C14	117	C10	C9	C19	118
C2	N1	C24	111	O2	C10	C9	103
C14	N1	C24	109	O2	C10	C11	110
C8	O1	C20	113	C9	C10	C11	109
C10	O2	C21	111	C10	C11	C12	121
C15	O3	C22	113	O5	C12	C7	114
C18	O4	C23	114	O5	C12	C11	102
N1	C2	C3	112	O5	C12	C13	107
C2	C3	C4	111	C7	C12	C11	112
C2	C3	C16	128	C7	C12	C13	113
C4	C3	C16	99	C11	C12	C13	107
C3	C4	C5	115	O6	C13	C12	110
C3	C4	C15	105	O6	C13	C14	106
C5	C4	C15	104	O6	C13	C15	114
C4	C5	C6	114	C12	C13	C14	108
C4	C5	C14	99	C12	C13	C15	112
C4	C5	C18	100	C14	C13	C15	107
C6	C5	C14	113	N1	C14	C5	107
C6	C5	C18	97	N1	C14	C13	115
C14	C5	C18	135	C5	C14	C13	96
C5	C6	C7	117	O3	C15	C4	117
C5	C6	C19	115	O3	C15	C13	111
C7	C6	C19	102	C4	C15	C13	104
C6	C7	C8	99	C3	C16	C17	112
C6	C7	C12	113	C16	C17	C18	113
C8	C7	C12	113	O4	C18	C5	97
O1	C8	C7	110	O4	C18	C17	109
O1	C8	C9	115	C5	C18	C17	120
C7	C8	C9	105	C6	C19	C9	110
C8	C9	C10	114	N1	C24	C25	115
C8	C9	C19	91				

Torsion Angles

C14	N1	C2	C3	45	C5	C4	C15	O3	106	C8	C7	C12	C11	−25
C24	N1	C2	C3	170	C5	C4	C15	C13	−16	C8	C7	C12	C13	−146
C2	N1	C14	C5	−60	C4	C5	C6	C7	65	O1	C8	C9	C10	55
C2	N1	C14	C13	45	C4	C5	C6	C19	−175	O1	C8	C9	C19	177
C24	N1	C14	C5	173	C14	C5	C6	C7	−47	C7	C8	C9	C10	−66
C24	N1	C14	C13	−82	C14	C5	C6	C19	73	C7	C8	C9	C19	56
C2	N1	C24	C25	175	C18	C5	C6	C7	169	C8	C9	C10	O2	−98
C14	N1	C24	C25	−55	C18	C5	C6	C19	−71	C8	C9	C10	C11	18
C20	O1	C8	C7	−172	C4	C5	C14	N1	66	C19	C9	C10	O2	157
C20	O1	C8	C9	70	C4	C5	C14	C13	−52	C19	C9	C10	C11	−87
C21	O2	C10	C9	−169	C6	C5	C14	N1	−174	C8	C9	C19	C6	−42
C21	O2	C10	C11	75	C6	C5	C14	C13	68	C10	C9	C19	C6	76
C22	O3	C15	C4	79	C18	C5	C14	N1	−48	O2	C10	C11	C12	140
C22	O3	C15	C13	−162	C18	C5	C14	C13	−166	C9	C10	C11	C12	28
C23	O4	C18	C5	155	C4	C5	C18	O4	72	C10	C11	C12	C7	−25
C23	O4	C18	C17	−79	C4	C5	C18	C17	−45	C10	C11	C12	C13	100
N1	C2	C3	C4	−40	C6	C5	C18	O4	−43	C7	C12	C13	C14	66
N1	C2	C3	C16	80	C6	C5	C18	C17	−160	C7	C12	C13	C15	−52
C2	C3	C4	C5	58	C14	C5	C18	O4	−175	C11	C12	C13	C14	−59
C2	C3	C4	C15	−56	C14	C5	C18	C17	69	C11	C12	C13	C15	−176
C16	C3	C4	C5	−78	C5	C6	C7	C8	147	C12	C13	C14	N1	172
C16	C3	C4	C15	168	C5	C6	C7	C12	27	C12	C13	C14	C5	−76
C2	C3	C16	C17	−63	C19	C6	C7	C8	20	C15	C13	C14	N1	−67
C4	C3	C16	C17	62	C19	C6	C7	C12	−100	C15	C13	C14	C5	44
C3	C4	C5	C6	170	C5	C6	C19	C9	−113	C12	C13	C15	O3	−27
C3	C4	C5	C14	−70	C7	C6	C19	C9	15	C12	C13	C15	C4	100
C3	C4	C5	C18	68	C6	C7	C8	O1	−174	C14	C13	C15	O3	−145
C15	C4	C5	C6	−76	C6	C7	C8	C9	−50	C14	C13	C15	C4	−18
C15	C4	C5	C14	44	C12	C7	C8	O1	−55	C3	C16	C17	C18	−47
C15	C4	C5	C18	−177	C12	C7	C8	C9	69	C16	C17	C18	O4	−70
C3	C4	C15	O3	−133	C6	C7	C12	C11	86	C16	C17	C18	C5	40
C3	C4	C15	C13	105	C6	C7	C12	C13	−35				

58.38 O-Methyl-lythrine hydrobromide methanol solvate

$C_{27}H_{32}NO_5^+$, CH_4O, Br^-

D.E.Zacharias, G.A.Jeffrey, B.Douglas, J.A.Weisbach, J.L.Kirkpatrick, J.P.Ferris, C.B.Boyce,
R.C.Briner, Experientia, 21, 247, 1965

Atomic coordinates were not reported in the paper.
$P2_12_12_1$ $Z = 4$ $R = 0.22$

MLYTBM   LB 27-32-1

58.39 Cevine hydroiodide

W.T.Eeles, Tetrahedron Letters, 24, 1960

Atomic coordinates were not reported in the paper.
P2₁ Z = 2 No R factor was given.

CEVINI

$C_{27}H_{44}NO_8^+ , I^- , 2H_2O$

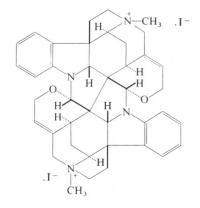

.HI.2H₂O

58.40 Caracurine - II dimethiodide

A.T.McPhail, G.A.Sim, J. Chem. Soc., 1663, 1965

$C_{40}H_{44}N_4O_2^{2+} , 2I^-$

Published y coordinate for C19'(relabelled C43) = 0.3991. The correct value is 0.3391.
P2₁2₁2₁ Z = 4 R = 0.181

CARAMI LB 40-44-1

Bond Lengths

C2	N1	1.50		C12	C13	1.43
C13	N1	1.28		C14	C15	1.73
C41	N1	1.50		C15	C16	1.64
C3	N4	1.31		C15	C20	1.50
C5	N4	1.49		C16	C17	1.45
C21	N4	1.39		C16	C40	1.63
C22	N4	1.53		C18	C19	1.53
C17	N25	1.44		C19	C20	1.24
C26	N25	1.44		C20	C21	1.63
C37	N25	1.36		C26	C31	1.30
C27	N28	1.49		C26	C40	1.52
C29	N28	1.44		C27	C31	1.51
C45	N28	1.53		C27	C38	1.60
C46	N28	1.51		C29	C30	1.57
C17	O23	1.47		C30	C31	1.77
C18	O23	1.32		C31	C32	1.58
C41	O47	1.38		C32	C33	1.37
C42	O47	1.39		C32	C37	1.33
C2	C7	1.48		C33	C34	1.44
C2	C16	1.65		C34	C35	1.30
C3	C7	1.69		C35	C36	1.21
C3	C14	1.59		C36	C37	1.49
C5	C6	1.28		C38	C39	1.52
C6	C7	1.70		C39	C40	1.63
C7	C8	1.48		C39	C44	1.43
C8	C9	1.52		C40	C41	1.51
C8	C13	1.35		C42	C43	1.40
C9	C10	1.33		C43	C44	1.43
C10	C11	1.33		C44	C45	1.34
C11	C12	1.42				

Bond Angles

C2	N1	C13	105		C9	C8	C13	119		C26	C31	C30	114
C2	N1	C41	107		C8	C9	C10	116		C26	C31	C32	105
C13	N1	C41	122		C9	C10	C11	122		C27	C31	C30	94
C3	N4	C5	102		C10	C11	C12	127		C27	C31	C32	109
C3	N4	C21	123		C11	C12	C13	112		C30	C31	C32	99
C3	N4	C22	96		N1	C13	C8	114		C31	C32	C33	140
C5	N4	C21	118		N1	C13	C12	123		C31	C32	C37	99
C5	N4	C22	108		C8	C13	C12	123		C33	C32	C37	120
C21	N4	C22	108		C3	C14	C15	99		C32	C33	C34	117
C17	N25	C26	114		C14	C15	C16	108		C33	C34	C35	117
C17	N25	C37	121		C14	C15	C20	112		C34	C35	C36	129
C26	N25	C37	100		C16	C15	C20	115		C35	C36	C37	115
C27	N28	C29	102		C2	C16	C15	110		N25	C37	C32	118
C27	N28	C45	117		C2	C16	C17	112		N25	C37	C36	122
C27	N28	C46	114		C2	C16	C40	105		C32	C37	C36	118
C29	N28	C45	103		C15	C16	C17	106		C27	C38	C39	109
C29	N28	C46	104		C15	C16	C40	120		C38	C39	C40	103
C45	N28	C46	114		C17	C16	C40	104		C38	C39	C44	107
C17	O23	C18	107		N25	C17	O23	106		C40	C39	C44	112
C41	O47	C42	116		N25	C17	C16	102		C16	C40	C26	104
N1	C2	C7	108		O23	C17	C16	120		C16	C40	C39	109
N1	C2	C16	102		O23	C18	C19	137		C16	C40	C41	97
C7	C2	C16	124		C18	C19	C20	101		C26	C40	C39	118
N4	C3	C7	116		C15	C20	C19	141		C26	C40	C41	124
N4	C3	C14	120		C15	C20	C21	103		C39	C40	C41	103
C7	C3	C14	101		C19	C20	C21	101		N1	C41	O47	116
N4	C5	C6	117		N4	C21	C20	103		N1	C41	C40	106
C5	C6	C7	106		N25	C26	C31	111		O47	C41	C40	120
C2	C7	C3	118		N25	C26	C40	103		O47	C42	C43	121
C2	C7	C6	111		C31	C26	C40	117		C42	C43	C44	122
C2	C7	C8	99		N28	C27	C31	116		C39	C44	C43	120
C3	C7	C6	88		N28	C27	C38	108		C39	C44	C45	127
C3	C7	C8	125		C31	C27	C38	103		C43	C44	C45	109
C6	C7	C8	116		N28	C29	C30	113		N28	C45	C44	107
C7	C8	C9	130		C29	C30	C31	96					
C7	C8	C13	111		C26	C31	C27	130					

Torsion Angles

C13	N1	C2	C7	−19
C13	N1	C2	C16	−151
C41	N1	C2	C7	112
C41	N1	C2	C16	−20
C2	N1	C13	C8	13
C41	N1	C13	C8	−108
C2	N1	C41	O47	−91
C2	N1	C41	C40	45
C13	N1	C41	O47	29
C13	N1	C41	C40	166
C5	N4	C3	C7	−13
C5	N4	C3	C14	−134
C21	N4	C3	C7	122
C21	N4	C3	C14	1
C3	N4	C5	C6	−12
C21	N4	C5	C6	−150
C3	N4	C21	C20	−54
C5	N4	C21	C20	75
C26	N25	C17	O23	−89
C26	N25	C17	C16	37
C37	N25	C17	O23	30
C37	N25	C17	C16	156
C17	N25	C26	C31	104
C17	N25	C26	C40	−22
C37	N25	C26	C31	−27
C37	N25	C26	C40	−152
C17	N25	C37	C32	−105
C26	N25	C37	C32	20
C29	N28	C27	C31	−11
C29	N28	C27	C38	−126
C45	N28	C27	C31	101
C45	N28	C27	C38	−14
C27	N28	C29	C30	−21
C45	N28	C29	C30	−143
C27	N28	C45	C44	−38
C29	N28	C45	C44	73
C18	O23	C17	N25	−162
C18	O23	C17	C16	84
C17	O23	C18	C19	−9
C42	O47	C41	N1	−140

continued

58.40   Caracurine - II dimethiodide

continued

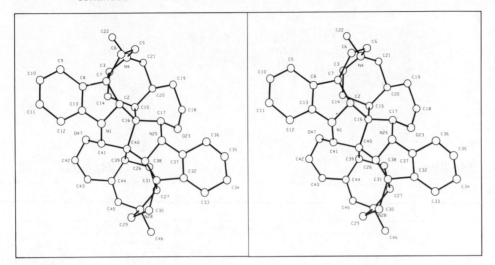

C31	C26	C40	C39	−2
C31	C26	C40	C41	128
N28	C27	C31	C26	−94
N28	C27	C31	C30	33
N28	C27	C31	C32	134
C38	C27	C31	C26	24
C38	C27	C31	C30	150
C38	C27	C31	C32	−108
N28	C27	C38	C39	59
C31	C27	C38	C39	−65
N28	C29	C30	C31	39
C29	C30	C31	C26	99
C29	C30	C31	C27	−39
C29	C30	C31	C32	−149
C26	C31	C32	C37	−10
C27	C31	C32	C37	134
C30	C31	C32	C37	−129
C31	C32	C37	N25	−7
C27	C38	C39	C40	69
C27	C38	C39	C44	−49
C38	C39	C40	C16	83
C38	C39	C40	C26	−36
C38	C39	C40	C41	−175
C44	C39	C40	C16	−163
C44	C39	C40	C26	79
C44	C39	C40	C41	−60
C38	C39	C44	C43	−165
C38	C39	C44	C45	−10
C40	C39	C44	C43	83
C40	C39	C44	C45	−122
C16	C40	C41	N1	−47
C16	C40	C41	O47	87
C26	C40	C41	N1	66
C26	C40	C41	O47	−161
C39	C40	C41	N1	−159
C39	C40	C41	O47	−25
O47	C42	C43	C44	6
C42	C43	C44	C39	−27
C42	C43	C44	C45	174
C39	C44	C45	N28	55
C43	C44	C45	N28	−148
C9	C8	C13	N1	176
C33	C32	C37	N25	178

C42	O47	C41	C40	90	
C41	O47	C42	C43	−55	
N1	C2	C7	C3	−122	
N1	C2	C7	C6	139	
N1	C2	C7	C8	16	
C16	C2	C7	C3	−3	
C16	C2	C7	C6	−102	
C16	C2	C7	C8	135	
N1	C2	C16	C15	122	
N1	C2	C16	C17	−120	
N1	C2	C16	C40	−8	
C7	C2	C16	C15	1	
C7	C2	C16	C17	118	
C7	C2	C16	C40	−130	
N4	C3	C7	C2	−88	
N4	C3	C7	C6	26	
N4	C3	C7	C8	146	
C14	C3	C7	C2	43	

C14	C3	C7	C6	156
C14	C3	C7	C8	−83
N4	C3	C14	C15	51
C7	C3	C14	C15	−77
N4	C5	C6	C7	30
C5	C6	C7	C2	90
C5	C6	C7	C3	−30
C5	C6	C7	C8	−158
C2	C7	C8	C13	−9
C3	C7	C8	C13	125
C6	C7	C8	C13	−128
C7	C8	C13	N1	−2
C3	C14	C15	C16	80
C3	C14	C15	C20	−46
C14	C15	C16	C2	−37
C14	C15	C16	C17	−158
C14	C15	C16	C40	84
C20	C15	C16	C2	88

C20	C15	C16	C17	−34
C20	C15	C16	C40	−151
C14	C15	C20	C19	166
C14	C15	C20	C21	1
C16	C15	C20	C19	44
C16	C15	C20	C21	−122
C2	C16	C17	N25	79
C2	C16	C17	O23	−165
C15	C16	C17	N25	−162
C15	C16	C17	O23	−45
C40	C16	C17	N25	−34
C40	C16	C17	O23	83
C2	C16	C40	C26	−95
C2	C16	C40	C39	139
C2	C16	C40	C41	32
C15	C16	C40	C26	141
C15	C16	C40	C39	14
C15	C16	C40	C41	−92

C17	C16	C40	C26	23
C17	C16	C40	C39	−104
C17	C16	C40	C41	150
O23	C18	C19	C20	−50
C18	C19	C20	C15	19
C18	C19	C20	C21	−174
C15	C20	C21	N4	49
C19	C20	C21	N4	−122
N25	C26	C31	C27	−110
N25	C26	C31	C30	132
N25	C26	C31	C32	24
C40	C26	C31	C27	8
C40	C26	C31	C30	−111
C40	C26	C31	C32	141
N25	C26	C40	C16	−1
N25	C26	C40	C39	120
N25	C26	C40	C41	−110
C31	C26	C40	C16	−123

58.41   Calebassin - C iodide hydrate

$C_{40}H_{48}N_4O_2^{2+}$, $2I^-$, xH_2O

M.Fehlmann, H.Koyama, A.Niggli, Helv. Chim. Acta, 48, 303, 1965

The structure was determined in
two dimensions only. Atomic
coordinates were not reported in
the paper.
$P2_12_12_1$ $Z = 4$ $R = 0.20$

CALBIH

$.2I^- . xH_2O$

58.42   Villalstonine methanol solvate

$C_{41}H_{48}N_4O_4$, CH_4O

C.E.Nordman, S.K.Kumra, J. Amer. Chem. Soc., 87, 2059, 1965

Atomic   coordinates   were   not
reported in the paper.
$P2_1$ $Z = 4$ $R = 0.059$

VILALM   LB 41-48-1

CH_3OH

59.1 Histamine dihydrochloride

$C_5H_{11}N_3^{2+}$, $2Cl^-$

C.Rerat, Bull. Soc. Fr. Mineral. Cristallogr., 85, 153, 1962

$$CH_2-CH_2-NH_2 \cdot 2\,HCl$$
$$HN\quad N$$

P2₁   Z = 2   R = 0.22

HISAHC   LB 5-11-11

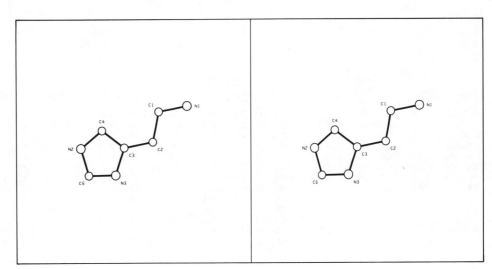

Bond Lengths			Bond Angles			
C1	N1	1.53	C4	N2	C5	113
C4	N2	1.39	C3	N3	C5	109
C5	N2	1.40	N1	C1	C2	107
C3	N3	1.42	C1	C2	C3	109
C5	N3	1.38	N3	C3	C2	119
C1	C2	1.55	N3	C3	C4	108
C2	C3	1.51	C2	C3	C4	132
C3	C4	1.42	N2	C4	C3	104
			N2	C5	N3	105

Torsion Angles

N1	C1	C2	C3	−175
C1	C2	C3	C4	27

59.2 Choline chloride

$C_5H_{14}NO^+$, Cl^-

M.E.Senko, D.H.Templeton, Acta Cryst., 13, 281, 1960

$$((H_3C)_3N-CH_2-CH_2-OH)^+\ Cl^-$$

See also Hjortas & Sorum, Acta Cryst. (B), 27, 1320, 1971.
P2₁2₁2₁   Z = 4   R = 0.11

CHOCHL   LB 5-14-5

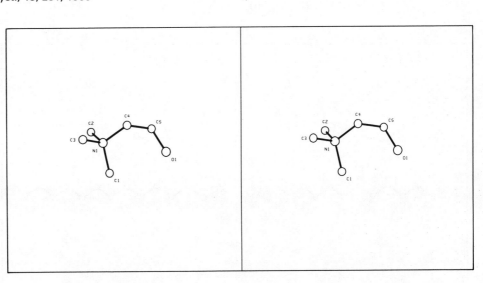

Bond Lengths			Bond Angles			
C1	N1	1.54	C1	N1	C2	111
C2	N1	1.52	C1	N1	C3	108
C3	N1	1.50	C1	N1	C4	112
C4	N1	1.59	C2	N1	C3	108
C5	O1	1.39	C2	N1	C4	117
C4	C5	1.56	C3	N1	C4	100
			N1	C4	C5	111
			O1	C5	C4	112

Torsion Angles

C1	N1	C4	C5	57
N1	C4	C5	O1	−84

59.3 Jacobine bromodilactone (at −150 °C)

A.McL.Mathieson, J.C.Taylor, Acta Cryst., 16, 524, 1963

$C_{10}H_{13}BrO_4$

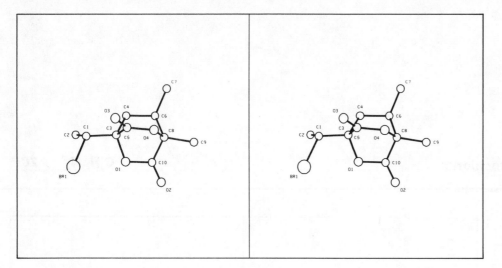

P2₁   Z = 2   R = 0.12

JACBRL   LB 10-13-6

Bond Lengths

Br1	C1	1.99	C1	C3	1.57	
C3	O1	1.49	C3	C4	1.53	
C10	O1	1.40	C3	C5	1.51	
C10	O2	1.20	C4	C6	1.56	
C5	O3	1.19	C6	C7	1.53	
C5	O4	1.36	C6	C8	1.55	
C8	O4	1.40	C8	C9	1.56	
C1	C2	1.52	C8	C10	1.51	

Bond Angles

C3	O1	C10	111	O4	C5	C3	110
C5	O4	C8	116	C4	C6	C7	114
Br1	C1	C2	116	C4	C6	C8	110
Br1	C1	C3	106	C7	C6	C8	113
C2	C1	C3	119	O4	C8	C6	107
O1	C3	C1	106	O4	C8	C9	104
O1	C3	C4	107	O4	C8	C10	111
O1	C3	C5	109	C6	C8	C9	121
C1	C3	C4	108	C6	C8	C10	104
C1	C3	C5	116	C9	C8	C10	110
C4	C3	C5	110	O1	C10	O2	117
C3	C4	C6	105	O1	C10	C8	112
O3	C5	O4	121	O2	C10	C8	131
O3	C5	C3	128				

Torsion Angles

C10	O1	C3	C1	175	C5	C3	C4	C6	53
C10	O1	C3	C4	60	O1	C3	C5	O3	−131
C10	O1	C3	C5	−59	O1	C3	C5	O4	54
C3	O1	C10	O2	−175	C1	C3	C5	O3	−12
C3	O1	C10	C8	8	C1	C3	C5	O4	174
C8	O4	C5	O3	−172	C4	C3	C5	O3	112
C8	O4	C5	C3	3	C4	C3	C5	O4	−63
C5	O4	C8	C6	58	C3	C4	C6	C7	−121
C5	O4	C8	C10	−55	C3	C4	C6	C8	6
Br1	C1	C3	O1	57	C4	C6	C8	O4	−62
Br1	C1	C3	C4	171	C4	C6	C8	C10	55
Br1	C1	C3	C5	−64	C7	C6	C8	O4	66
C2	C1	C3	O1	−77	C7	C6	C8	C10	−176
C2	C1	C3	C4	38	O4	C8	C10	O1	49
C2	C1	C3	C5	162	O4	C8	C10	O2	−128
O1	C3	C4	C6	−65	C6	C8	C10	O1	−66
C1	C3	C4	C6	−179	C6	C8	C10	O2	118

59.4 Spermine phosphate hexahydrate

Y.Iitaka, Y.Huse, Acta Cryst., 18, 110, 1965

$C_{10}H_{30}N_4^{4+}$, $2HO_4P^{2-}$, $6H_2O$

$$[H_3N^+–(CH_2)_3–NH_2^+–(CH_2)_4–NH_2^+–(CH_2)_3–NH_3^+](HPO_4^{2-})_2 \cdot 6H_2O$$

P2₁/a   Z = 2   R = 0.127

SPINPH   LB 10-32-3

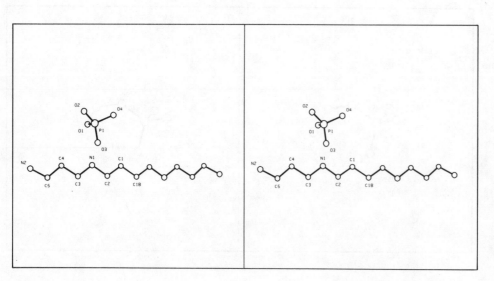

Bond Lengths

P1	O1	1.52
P1	O2	1.52
P1	O3	1.53
P1	O4	1.59
C2	N1	1.49
C3	N1	1.51
C5	N2	1.50
C1	C2	1.50
C1	C1B	1.54
C3	C4	1.52
C4	C5	1.51

Bond Angles

O1	P1	O2	113
O1	P1	O3	110
O1	P1	O4	108
O2	P1	O3	112
O2	P1	O4	108
O3	P1	O4	105
C2	N1	C3	111
C2	C1	C1B	111
N1	C2	C1	112
N1	C3	C4	112
C3	C4	C5	109
N2	C5	C4	112

Torsion Angles

C3	N1	C2	C1	176
C2	N1	C3	C4	−177
C1B	C1	C2	N1	177
C2	C1	C1B	C2B	−180
N1	C3	C4	C5	−180
C3	C4	C5	N2	−175

59.5 Rubrofusarin

$C_{15}H_{12}O_5$

G.H.Stout, L.H.Jensen, Acta Cryst., 15, 451, 1962

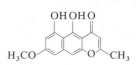

P2$_1$/c   Z = 4   R = 0.114

RUBFUS   LB 15-12-9

Bond Lengths

C2	O1	1.37	C4	C9	1.40
C20	O1	1.42	C5	C6	1.42
C6	O8	1.39	C5	C12	1.41
C12	O13	1.36	C6	C7	1.39
C10	O14	1.37	C9	C10	1.39
C15	O14	1.37	C10	C11	1.41
C17	O18	1.25	C11	C12	1.39
C2	C3	1.38	C11	C17	1.44
C2	C7	1.40	C15	C16	1.32
C3	C4	1.43	C15	C19	1.55
C4	C5	1.46	C16	C17	1.48

Bond Angles

C2	O1	C20	118	C6	C5	C12	126	C12 C11 C17	121
C10	O14	C15	118	O8	C6	C5	120	O13 C12 C5	119
O1	C2	C3	124	O8	C6	C7	117	O13 C12 C11	119
O1	C2	C7	113	C5	C6	C7	123	C5 C12 C11	122
C3	C2	C7	123	C2	C7	C6	118	O14 C15 C16	126
C2	C3	C4	119	C4	C9	C10	119	O14 C15 C19	110
C3	C4	C5	120	O14	C10	C9	116	C16 C15 C17	124
C3	C4	C9	120	O14	C10	C11	121	C15 C16 C17	119
C5	C4	C9	120	C9	C10	C11	123	O18 C17 C11	121
C4	C5	C6	117	C10	C11	C12	118	O18 C17 C16	123
C4	C5	C12	118	C10	C11	C17	120	C11 C17 C16	116

59.6 Aflatoxin G$_1$ bromothiophen solvate

$C_{17}H_{12}O_7$, $0.5C_4H_3BrS$

K.K.Cheung, G.A.Sim, Nature, 201, 1185, 1964

Atomic coordinates were not reported in the paper.
P2$_1$ Z = 2   No R factor was given.

AFOXBT   LB 38-27-1

59.7 Aflatoxin G$_1$ bromobenzene solvate

$C_{17}H_{12}O_7$, $0.5C_6H_5Br$

K.K.Cheung, G.A.Sim, Nature, 201, 1185, 1964

Atomic coordinates were not reported in the paper.
P2$_1$ Z = 2   R = 0.19

AFOXBB   LB 17-12-4

59.8 Aflatoxin G$_1$ benzene solvate

$C_{17}H_{12}O_7$, $0.5C_6H_6$

K.K.Cheung, G.A.Sim, Nature, 201, 1185, 1964

Atomic coordinates were not reported in the paper.
P2$_1$ Z = 2   No R factor was given.

AFOXBZ   LB 17-12-5

59.9   3,4,8 - Trihydroxy - 2 - methoxy - 1 - (3 - methyl - 2 - butenyl) - xanthone

$C_{19}H_{18}O_6$

G.H.Stout, V.F.Stout, M.J.Welsh, Tetrahedron, 19, 667, 1963

Atomic coordinates were not given
but bond lengths were reported.
$P2_1/c$ Z = 4   R = 0.082

THMXAO

59.10   Bromo - bruceol

$C_{19}H_{19}BrO_5$

A.M.Duffield, P.R.Jefferies, E.N.Maslen, A.I.M.Rae, Tetrahedron, 19, 593, 1963

$C222_1$ Z = 8   R = 0.156

BBRUOL

Bond Lengths

Br25	C7	1.85
C2	O1	1.31
C6	O1	1.38
C10	O11	1.31
C12	O11	1.47
C8	O17	1.38
C16	O17	1.44
C2	O20	1.22
C13	O22	1.43
C2	C3	1.45
C3	C4	1.42
C4	C5	1.38
C5	C6	1.38
C5	C10	1.43
C6	C7	1.46
C7	C8	1.38
C8	C9	1.40
C9	C10	1.40
C9	C14	1.76
C12	C13	1.65
C12	C18	1.50
C12	C21	1.48
C13	C14	1.53
C14	C15	1.74
C15	C16	1.60
C15	C19	1.32
C16	C23	1.50
C16	C24	1.70
C18	C19	1.46

Bond Angles

C2	O1	C6	122
C10	O11	C12	118
C8	O17	C16	120
O1	C2	O20	121
O1	C2	C3	119
O20	C2	C3	118
C2	C3	C4	117
C3	C4	C5	121
C4	C5	C6	119
C4	C5	C10	121
C6	C5	C10	119
O1	C6	C5	121
O1	C6	C7	116
C5	C6	C7	121
Br25	C7	C6	120
Br25	C7	C8	123
C6	C7	C8	117
O17	C8	C7	122
O17	C8	C9	116
C7	C8	C9	122
C8	C9	C10	120
C8	C9	C14	117
C10	C9	C14	122
O11	C10	C5	118

O11	C10	C9	123
C5	C10	C9	119
O11	C12	C13	110
O11	C12	C18	112
O11	C12	C21	108
C13	C12	C18	103
C13	C12	C21	112
C18	C12	C21	111
O22	C13	C12	114
O22	C13	C14	106
C12	C13	C14	112
C9	C14	C13	106
C9	C14	C15	86
C13	C14	C15	107
C14	C15	C16	101
C14	C15	C19	105
C16	C15	C19	122
O17	C16	C15	113
O17	C16	C23	108
O17	C16	C24	105
C15	C16	C23	116
C15	C16	C24	100
C23	C16	C24	113
C12	C18	C19	116
C15	C19	C18	121

Torsion Angles

C6	O1	C2	O20	−178
C6	O1	C2	C3	16
C2	O1	C6	C5	−14
C2	O1	C6	C7	−177
C12	O11	C10	C5	157
C12	O11	C10	C9	−18
C10	O11	C12	C13	54
C10	O11	C12	C18	−60
C10	O11	C12	C21	177
C16	O17	C8	C7	−140
C16	O17	C8	C9	37
C8	O17	C16	C15	−15
C8	O17	C16	C23	−145
C8	O17	C16	C24	94
O1	C2	C3	C4	−10
O20	C2	C3	C4	−176
C2	C3	C4	C5	1
C3	C4	C5	C6	2
C3	C4	C5	C10	170
C4	C5	C6	O1	4
C4	C5	C6	C7	167
C10	C5	C6	O1	−164
C10	C5	C6	C7	−2
C4	C5	C10	O11	25
C4	C5	C10	C9	−160
C6	C5	C10	O11	−166
C6	C5	C10	C9	9
O1	C6	C7	Br25	−15
O1	C6	C7	C8	164
C5	C6	C7	Br25	−178
C5	C6	C7	C8	1
Br25	C7	C8	O17	−11
Br25	C7	C8	C9	172
C6	C7	C8	O17	169
C6	C7	C8	C9	−7
O17	C8	C9	C10	−162
O17	C8	C9	C14	10

C7	C8	C9	C10	14
C7	C8	C9	C14	−173
C8	C9	C10	O11	160
C8	C9	C10	C5	−15
C14	C9	C10	O11	−12
C14	C9	C10	C5	173
C8	C9	C14	C13	−171
C8	C9	C14	C15	−64
C10	C9	C14	C13	1
C10	C9	C14	C15	108
O11	C12	C13	O22	58
O11	C12	C13	C14	−63
C18	C12	C13	O22	177
C18	C12	C13	C14	57
C21	C12	C13	O22	−63
C21	C12	C13	C14	177
O11	C12	C18	C19	66
C13	C12	C18	C19	−53
C21	C12	C18	C19	−173
O22	C13	C14	C9	−92
O22	C13	C14	C15	177
C12	C13	C14	C9	33
C12	C13	C14	C15	−58
C9	C14	C15	C16	77
C9	C14	C15	C19	−51
C13	C14	C15	C16	−178
C13	C14	C15	C19	54
C14	C15	C16	O17	−50
C14	C15	C16	C23	76
C14	C15	C16	C24	−161
C19	C15	C16	O17	66
C19	C15	C16	C23	−168
C19	C15	C16	C24	−46
C13	C14	C15	C18	−57
C16	C15	C19	C18	−170
C12	C18	C19	C15	63

59.11 Bromomiroestrol (type I)

$C_{20}H_{21}BrO_6$

N.E.Taylor, D.C.Hodgkin, J.S.Rollett, J. Chem. Soc., 3685, 1960

$P2_1$ Z = 2   R = 0.198

BOMESL   LB 20-21-1

Bond Lengths

Br1	C2	1.90	C8	C14	1.60	
C3	O3	1.36	C9	C10	1.49	
C5	O6	1.47	C9	C11	1.57	
C7	O6	1.50	C11	C12	1.64	
C14	O14	1.36	C11	C20	1.38	
C15	O15	1.18	C11	C21	1.42	
C17	O17	1.42	C12	C13	1.37	
C18	O18	1.45	C12	C19	1.70	
C1	C2	1.35	C13	C14	1.47	
C1	C10	1.35	C13	C18	1.56	
C2	C3	1.33	C14	C15	1.60	
C3	C4	1.45	C15	C16	1.44	
C4	C5	1.36	C16	C17	1.50	
C5	C10	1.42	C17	C18	1.36	
C7	C8	1.31	C17	C19	1.62	
C8	C9	1.47				

Bond Angles

C5	O6	C7	103	C20	C11	C21	101
C2	C1	C10	121	C11	C12	C13	116
Br1	C2	C1	117	C11	C12	C19	109
Br1	C2	C3	122	C13	C12	C19	97
C1	C2	C3	121	C12	C13	C14	131
O3	C3	C2	115	C12	C13	C18	101
O3	C3	C4	123	C14	C13	C18	112
C2	C3	C4	122	O14	C14	C8	112
C3	C4	C5	115	O14	C14	C13	120
O6	C5	C4	109	O14	C14	C15	110
O6	C5	C10	130	C8	C14	C13	102
C4	C5	C10	121	C8	C14	C15	104
O6	C7	C8	132	C13	C14	C15	108
C7	C8	C9	116	O15	C15	C14	114
C7	C8	C14	128	O15	C15	C16	127
C9	C8	C14	116	C14	C15	C16	119
C8	C9	C10	117	C15	C16	C17	116
C8	C9	C11	110	O17	C17	C16	105
C10	C9	C11	117	O17	C17	C18	118
C1	C10	C5	120	O17	C17	C19	111
C1	C10	C9	127	C16	C17	C18	108
C5	C10	C9	113	C16	C17	C19	107
C9	C11	C12	109	C18	C17	C19	106
C9	C11	C20	119	O18	C18	C13	111
C9	C11	C21	104	O18	C18	C17	117
C12	C11	C20	109	C13	C18	C17	100
C12	C11	C21	115	C12	C19	C17	97

Torsion Angles

C7	O6	C5	C4	162	C9	C11	C12	C19	−100
C7	O6	C5	C10	−21	C20	C11	C12	C13	−123
C5	O6	C7	C8	24	C20	C11	C12	C19	129
C10	C1	C2	Br1	177	C21	C11	C12	C13	125
C10	C1	C2	C3	0	C21	C11	C12	C19	17
C2	C1	C10	C5	1	C11	C12	C13	C14	−37
C2	C1	C10	C9	−176	C11	C12	C13	C18	−170
Br1	C2	C3	O3	2	C19	C12	C13	C14	78
Br1	C2	C3	C4	−177	C19	C12	C13	C18	−54
C1	C2	C3	O3	178	C11	C12	C19	C17	151
C1	C2	C3	C4	−1	C13	C12	C19	C17	30
O3	C3	C4	C5	−179	C12	C13	C14	O14	135
C2	C3	C4	C5	0	C12	C13	C14	C8	11
C3	C4	C5	O6	179	C12	C13	C14	C15	−98
C3	C4	C5	C10	2	C18	C13	C14	O14	−95
O6	C5	C10	C1	−179	C18	C13	C14	C8	140
O6	C5	C10	C9	−1	C18	C13	C14	C15	31
C4	C5	C10	C1	−2	C12	C13	C18	O18	−60
C4	C5	C10	C9	175	C12	C13	C18	C17	64
O6	C7	C8	C9	−2	C14	C13	C18	O18	157
O6	C7	C8	C14	178	C14	C13	C18	C17	−79
C7	C8	C9	C10	−25	O14	C14	C15	O15	−31
C7	C8	C9	C11	111	O14	C14	C15	C16	146
C14	C8	C9	C10	154	C8	C14	C15	O15	89
C14	C8	C9	C11	−70	C8	C14	C15	C16	−94
C7	C8	C14	O14	94	C13	C14	C15	O15	−164
C7	C8	C14	C13	−136	C13	C14	C15	C16	13
C7	C8	C14	C15	−24	O15	C15	C16	C17	161
C9	C8	C14	O14	−85	C14	C15	C16	C17	−15
C9	C8	C14	C13	45	C15	C16	C17	O17	−161
C9	C8	C14	C15	156	C15	C16	C17	C18	−34
C8	C9	C10	C1	−156	C15	C16	C17	C19	80
C8	C9	C10	C5	26	O17	C17	C18	O18	−45
C11	C9	C10	C1	71	O17	C17	C18	C13	−165
C11	C9	C10	C5	−107	C16	C17	C18	O18	−164
C8	C9	C11	C12	37	C16	C17	C18	C13	76
C8	C9	C11	C20	163	C19	C17	C18	O18	81
C8	C9	C11	C21	−86	C19	C17	C18	C13	−38
C10	C9	C11	C12	174	O17	C17	C19	C12	138
C10	C9	C11	C20	−61	C16	C17	C19	C12	−107
C10	C9	C11	C21	50	C18	C17	C19	C12	8
C9	C11	C12	C13	9					

59.12 N - p - Iodobenzyl - 3 - caprylamido - 1,2,5,6 - tetrahydropyridin - 2,5,6 - trione

$C_{20}H_{23}IN_2O_4$

G.Ferguson, D.R.Pollard, J.M.Robertson, D.M.Hawley, G.O.P.Doherty, N.B.Haynes, D.W.Mathieson, W.B.Whalley, T.H.Simpson, Chem. Communic., 640, 1965

Atomic coordinates were not reported in the paper.
Pbca   Z = 8   R = 0.13

IBCAPT   LB 20-23-5

59.13 Atrovenetin orange trimethyl ether ferrichloride

$C_{22}H_{25}O_6^+$, Cl_4Fe^-

I.C.Paul, G.A.Sim, J. Chem. Soc., 1097, 1965

Published value of z(Cl2) = 0.8856.
The correct value is 0.8556.
$P2_1$ Z = 4   R = 0.214

ATRVND10   LB 22-25-6

Bond Lengths

C9	O10	1.47	C111	O101	1.35
C11	O10	1.34	C910	O101	1.52
C3	O21	1.42	C310	O211	1.32
C4	O22	1.36	C410	O221	1.28
C5	O23	1.49	C241	O231	1.54
C24	O23	1.50	C510	O231	1.30
C6	O25	1.26	C261	O251	1.47
C26	O25	1.33	C610	O251	1.44
C7	O27	1.34	C281	O271	1.40
C28	O27	1.50	C710	O271	1.32
C1	C2	1.28	C110	C121	1.37
C1	C12	1.44	C110	C201	1.55
C1	C20	1.60	C110	C210	1.35
C2	C3	1.32	C111	C121	1.47
C3	C14	1.32	C111	C161	1.31
C4	C5	1.48	C121	C131	1.44
C4	C14	1.40	C131	C141	1.39
C5	C6	1.46	C131	C151	1.43
C6	C15	1.27	C141	C310	1.46
C7	C15	1.40	C141	C410	1.47
C7	C16	1.35	C151	C610	1.45
C8	C9	1.62	C151	C710	1.40
C8	C16	1.51	C161	C710	1.48
C8	C17	1.53	C161	C810	1.48
C8	C18	1.37	C171	C810	1.50
C9	C19	1.35	C181	C810	1.62
C11	C12	1.32	C191	C910	1.57
C11	C16	1.48	C210	C310	1.46
C12	C13	1.42	C410	C510	1.40
C13	C14	1.48	C510	C610	1.31
C13	C15	1.37	C810	C910	1.68
Fe1	Cl1	2.19	Fe11	Cl11	2.17
Fe1	Cl2	2.19	Fe11	Cl21	2.11
Fe1	Cl3	2.19	Fe11	Cl31	2.25
Fe1	Cl4	2.09	Fe11	Cl41	2.13

Bond Angles

C9	O10	C11	116	C111	O101	C910	102
C5	O23	C24	115	C241	O231	C510	104
C6	O25	C26	123	C261	O251	C610	92
C7	O27	C28	120	C281	O271	C710	115
C2	C1	C12	124	C121	C110	C201	117
C2	C1	C20	120	C121	C110	C210	125
C12	C1	C20	116	C201	C110	C210	117
C1	C2	C3	119	C101	C111	C121	117
O21	C3	C2	116	O101	C111	C161	114
O21	C3	C14	120	C121	C111	C161	129
C2	C3	C14	124	C110	C121	C111	130
O22	C4	C5	118	C110	C121	C131	116
O22	C4	C14	121	C111	C121	C131	114
C5	C4	C14	121	C121	C131	C141	120
O23	C5	C4	114	C121	C131	C151	122
O23	C5	C6	127	C141	C131	C151	117
C4	C5	C6	118	C131	C141	C310	123
O25	C6	C5	107	C131	C141	C410	121
O25	C6	C15	134	C310	C141	C410	116
C5	C6	C15	118	C131	C151	C610	119
O27	C7	C15	123	C131	C151	C710	117
O27	C7	C16	114	C610	C151	C710	124
C15	C7	C16	123	C111	C161	C710	114
C9	C8	C16	103	C111	C161	C810	116
C9	C8	C17	89	C710	C161	C810	130
C9	C8	C18	117	C110	C210	C310	121
C16	C8	C17	106	O211	C310	C141	128
C16	C8	C18	120	O211	C310	C210	119
C17	C8	C18	117	C141	C310	C210	113
O10	C9	C8	100	O221	C410	C141	121
O10	C9	C19	116	O221	C410	C510	120
C8	C9	C19	121	C141	C410	C510	118
O10	C11	C12	129	O231	C510	C410	117
O10	C11	C16	109	O231	C510	C610	123
C12	C11	C16	121	C410	C510	C610	120
C1	C12	C11	125	O251	C610	C151	115
C1	C12	C13	118	O251	C610	C510	122
C11	C12	C13	116	C151	C610	C510	123
C12	C13	C14	113	O271	C710	C151	123
C12	C13	C15	126	O271	C710	C161	114
C14	C13	C15	121	C151	C710	C161	123
C3	C14	C4	124	C161	C810	C171	115
C3	C14	C13	122	C161	C810	C181	115
C4	C14	C13	115	C161	C810	C910	90
C6	C15	C7	119	C171	C810	C181	89
C6	C15	C13	126	C171	C810	C910	138
C7	C15	C13	115	C181	C810	C910	111
C7	C16	C8	134	O101	C910	C191	110
C7	C16	C11	118	O101	C910	C810	103
C8	C16	C11	108	C191	C910	C810	109
Cl1	Fe1	Cl2	105	Cl11	Fe11	Cl21	111
Cl1	Fe1	Cl3	111	Cl11	Fe11	Cl31	106
Cl1	Fe1	Cl4	107	Cl11	Fe11	Cl41	109
Cl2	Fe1	Cl3	110	Cl21	Fe11	Cl31	111
Cl2	Fe1	Cl4	115	Cl21	Fe11	Cl41	114
Cl3	Fe1	Cl4	109	Cl31	Fe11	Cl41	106

Torsion Angles

C11	O10	C9	C8	−18
C11	O10	C9	C19	−150
C9	O10	C11	C16	8
C16	C8	C9	O10	20
C16	C8	C9	C19	149
C9	C8	C16	C11	−17
O10	C11	C16	C8	7
C7	C16	C11	O10	180
C16	C7	O27	C28	−108
C15	C6	O25	C26	59
C6	C5	O23	C24	−64
C910	O101	C111	C161	18
C111	O101	C910	C191	−149
C111	O101	C910	C810	−34
O101	C111	C161	C810	10
C111	C161	C810	C910	−28
C161	C810	C910	O101	35
C161	C810	C910	C191	151
C710	C161	C111	O101	−176
C161	C710	O271	C281	116
C151	C610	O251	C261	−128
C610	C510	O231	C241	85

59.14 N(1') - Carboxy - biotin di(p - bromoanilide) $C_{23}H_{24}Br_2N_4O_3S$

C.Bonnemere, J.A.Hamilton, L.K.Steinrauf, J.Knappe, Biochemistry, 4, 240, 1965

$P2_12_12_1$ Z = 4   R = 0.165

CBIOTB   LB 23-24-2

Bond Lengths

Br1	C1	1.99	C3	C4	1.38	
Br2	C21	1.90	C4	C5	1.39	
S1	C10	1.85	C5	C6	1.33	
S1	C11	1.74	C9	C11	1.47	
C4	N1	1.43	C9	C12	1.54	
C7	N1	1.35	C10	C12	1.49	
C7	N2	1.39	C10	C13	1.41	
C8	N2	1.41	C13	C14	1.67	
C9	N2	1.50	C14	C15	1.53	
C8	N3	1.38			(1.46)	
C12	N3	1.52	C15	C16	1.51	
C17	N4	1.32	C16	C17	1.59	
C18	N4	1.45	C18	C19	1.45	
C7	O1	1.16	C18	C23	1.36	
C8	O2	1.16	C19	C20	1.39	
C17	O3	1.20	C20	C21	1.35	
C1	C2	1.28	C21	C22	1.36	
C1	C6	1.40	C22	C23	1.45	
C2	C3	1.47				

Bond Angles

C10	S1	C11	91	C11	C9	C12	110
C4	N1	C7	125	S1	C10	C12	103
C7	N2	C8	126	S1	C10	C13	108
C7	N2	C9	121	C12	C10	C13	124
C8	N2	C9	113	S1	C11	C9	108
C8	N3	C12	111	N3	C12	C9	105
C17	N4	C18	122	N3	C12	C10	111
Br1	C1	C2	113	C9	C12	C10	111
Br1	C1	C6	115	C10	C13	C14	108
C2	C1	C6	132	C13	C14	C15	113
C1	C2	C3	110	C14	C15	C16	110
C2	C3	C4	122	C15	C16	C17	110
N1	C4	C3	115	N4	C17	O3	128
N1	C4	C5	125	N4	C17	C16	110
C3	C4	C5	120	O3	C17	C16	121
C4	C5	C6	120	N4	C18	C19	121
C1	C6	C5	116	N4	C18	C23	116
N1	C7	N2	113	C19	C18	C23	122
N1	C7	O1	128	C18	C19	C20	116
N2	C7	O1	119	C19	C20	C21	122
N2	C8	N3	108	Br2	C21	C20	122
N2	C8	O2	128	Br2	C21	C22	115
N3	C8	O2	124	C20	C21	C22	124
N2	C9	C11	110	C21	C22	C23	117
N2	C9	C12	102	C18	C23	C22	119

Torsion Angles

C11	S1	C10	C12	37	C8	N3	C12	C10	−121	S1	C10	C12	C9	−28
C11	S1	C10	C13	170	C18	N4	C17	O3	3	C13	C10	C12	N3	−34
C10	S1	C11	C9	−37	C18	N4	C17	C16	−175	C13	C10	C12	C9	−150
C7	N1	C4	C3	−170	C17	N4	C18	C19	−37	S1	C10	C13	C14	178
C7	N1	C4	C5	18	C17	N4	C18	C23	155	C12	C10	C13	C14	−62
C4	N1	C7	N2	180	Br1	C1	C2	C3	175	C10	C13	C14	C15	−166
C4	N1	C7	O1	5	C6	C1	C2	C3	−7	C13	C14	C15	C16	63
C8	N2	C7	N1	−11	Br1	C1	C6	C5	−175	C14	C15	C16	C17	154
C8	N2	C7	O1	164	C2	C1	C6	C5	7	C15	C16	C17	N4	−159
C9	N2	C7	N1	176	C1	C2	C3	C4	6	C15	C16	C17	O3	22
C9	N2	C7	O1	−9	C2	C3	C4	N1	−179	N4	C18	C19	C20	−172
C7	N2	C8	N3	−174	C2	C3	C4	C5	−7	C23	C18	C19	C20	−5
C7	N2	C8	O2	9	N1	C4	C5	C6	179	N4	C18	C23	C22	174
C9	N2	C8	N3	0	C3	C4	C5	C6	6	C19	C18	C23	C22	6
C9	N2	C8	O2	−178	C4	C5	C6	C1	−6	C18	C19	C20	C21	−1
C7	N2	C9	C11	−70	N2	C9	C11	S1	−86	C19	C20	C21	Br2	−175
C7	N2	C9	C12	173	C12	C9	C11	S1	25	C19	C20	C21	C22	6
C8	N2	C9	C11	116	N2	C9	C12	N3	0	Br2	C21	C22	C23	177
C8	N2	C9	C12	0	N2	C9	C12	C10	120	C20	C21	C22	C23	−5
C12	N3	C8	N2	2	C11	C9	C12	N3	−116	C21	C22	C23	C18	−2
C12	N3	C8	O2	178	C11	C9	C12	C10	4					
C8	N3	C12	C9	−1	S1	C10	C12	N3	88					

59.15 Glauconic acid m - iodobenzoate $C_{25}H_{23}IO_8$

G.Ferguson, G.A.Sim, J.M.Robertson, Proc. Chem. Soc., 385, 1962

Atomic coordinates were not reported in the paper.
$P22_12_1$ Z = 4   R = 0.196

GLACIB

59.16 Byssochlamic acid bis(p - bromophenylhydrazide) $C_{30}H_{30}Br_2N_4O_4$

I.C.Paul, G.A.Sim, T.A.Hamor, J.M.Robertson, J. Chem. Soc., 5502, 1963

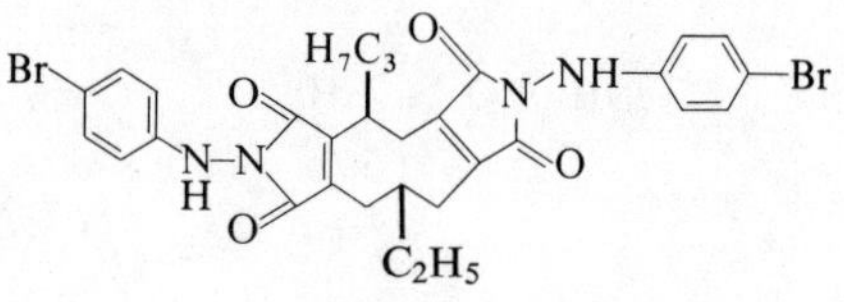

P4₁2₁2 Z = 8 R = 0.17

BYSSHY LB 30-30-2

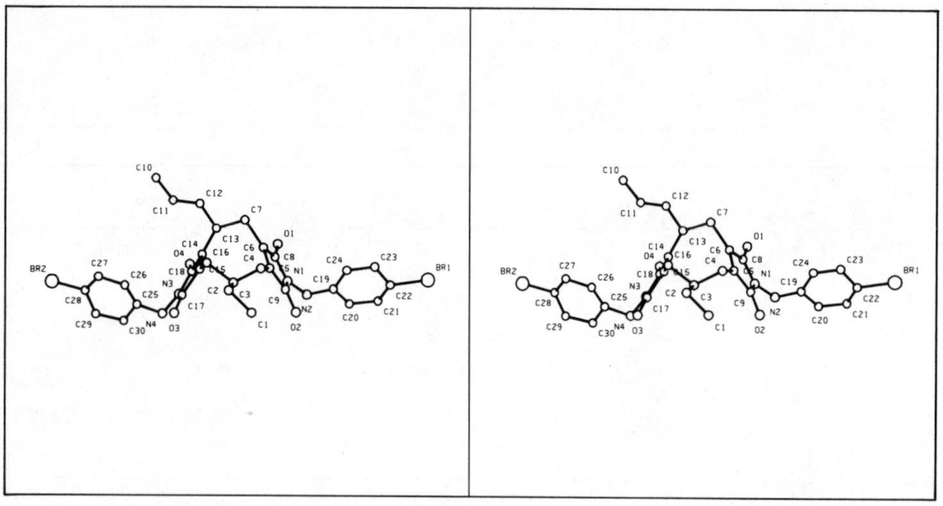

Bond Lengths

Br1	C22	1.89	C6	C8	1.45
Br2	C28	1.82	C7	C13	1.67
N1	N2	1.50	C10	C11	1.36
N3	N4	1.43	C11	C12	1.57
C8	N1	1.34	C12	C13	1.45
C9	N1	1.32	C13	C14	1.44
C19	N2	1.40	C14	C15	1.36
C17	N3	1.40	C14	C18	1.46
C18	N3	1.37	C15	C16	1.55
C25	N4	1.37	C15	C17	1.51
C8	O1	1.16	C19	C20	1.42
C9	O2	1.30	C19	C24	1.33
C17	O3	1.36	C20	C21	1.42
C18	O4	1.14	C21	C22	1.46
C1	C2	1.55	C22	C23	1.38
C2	C3	1.53	C23	C24	1.39
C3	C4	1.45	C25	C26	1.27
C3	C16	1.63	C25	C30	1.38
C4	C5	1.57	C26	C27	1.42
C5	C6	1.46	C27	C28	1.36
C5	C9	1.44	C28	C29	1.39
C6	C7	1.59	C29	C30	1.50

Bond Angles

N2	N1	C8	122	O1	C8	C6	128	N2	C19	C20	105
N2	N1	C9	123	N1	C9	O2	128	N2	C19	C24	139
C8	N1	C9	113	N1	C9	C5	111	C20	C19	C24	114
N1	N2	C19	109	O2	C9	C5	121	C19	C20	C21	121
N4	N3	C17	123	C10	C11	C12	125	C20	C21	C22	116
N4	N3	C18	124	C11	C12	C13	117	Br1	C22	C21	123
C17	N3	C18	113	C7	C13	C12	98	Br1	C22	C23	113
N3	N4	C25	114	C7	C13	C14	122	C21	C22	C23	123
C1	C2	C3	115	C12	C13	C14	113	C22	C23	C24	112
C2	C3	C4	110	C13	C14	C15	126	C19	C24	C23	131
C2	C3	C16	107	C13	C14	C18	124	N4	C25	C26	128
C4	C3	C16	114	C15	C14	C18	109	N4	C25	C30	112
C3	C4	C5	113	C14	C15	C16	135	C26	C25	C30	119
C4	C5	C6	130	C14	C15	C17	107	C25	C26	C27	126
C4	C5	C9	129	C16	C15	C17	116	C26	C27	C28	117
C6	C5	C9	101	C3	C16	C15	111	Br2	C28	C27	122
C5	C6	C7	124	N3	C17	O3	137	Br2	C28	C29	117
C5	C6	C8	109	N3	C17	C15	104	C27	C28	C29	120
C7	C6	C8	127	O3	C17	C15	120	C28	C29	C30	118
C6	C7	C13	103	N3	C18	O4	129	C25	C30	C29	118
N1	C8	O1	126	N3	C18	C14	105				
N1	C8	C6	105	O4	C18	C14	123				

Torsion Angles

C8	N1	N2	C19	99	C4	C5	C9	N1	179
C9	N1	N2	C19	−65	C6	C5	C9	N1	1
N2	N1	C8	C6	−166	C5	C6	C7	C13	−108
C9	N1	C8	C6	−1	C8	C6	C7	C13	70
N2	N1	C9	C5	165	C5	C6	C8	N1	2
C8	N1	C9	C5	0	C7	C6	C8	N1	−177
N1	N2	C19	C24	−20	C6	C7	C13	C12	174
C17	N3	N4	C25	90	C6	C7	C13	C14	51
C18	N3	N4	C25	−86	C10	C11	C12	C13	−177
N4	N3	C17	C15	−176	C11	C12	C13	C7	172
C18	N3	C17	C15	0	C11	C12	C13	C14	−57
N4	N3	C18	C14	169	C7	C13	C14	C15	32
C17	N3	C18	C14	−7	C7	C13	C14	C18	−136
N3	N4	C25	C26	−14	C12	C13	C14	C15	−84
C1	C2	C3	C4	−61	C12	C13	C14	C18	107
C1	C2	C3	C16	175	C13	C14	C15	C16	12
C2	C3	C4	C5	165	C13	C14	C15	C17	178
C16	C3	C4	C5	−74	C18	C14	C15	C16	−178
C2	C3	C16	C15	−147	C18	C14	C15	C17	−12
C4	C3	C16	C15	91	C13	C14	C18	N3	−178
C3	C4	C5	C6	87	C15	C14	C18	N3	12
C3	C4	C5	C9	−90	C14	C15	C16	C3	−112
C4	C5	C6	C7	−1	C17	C15	C16	C3	83
C4	C5	C6	C8	−179	C14	C15	C17	N3	8
C9	C5	C6	C7	177	C16	C15	C17	N3	177
C9	C5	C6	C8	−2					

59.17 Harunganin

C₃₀H₃₆O₄

$C_{30}H_{36}O_4$

R.A.Alden, G.H.Stout, J.Kraut, D.F.High, Acta Cryst., 17, 109, 1964

One methyl group defined by C23,
C24 in the publication is disordered.

C2/c   Z = 8   R = 0.094

HUNGIN

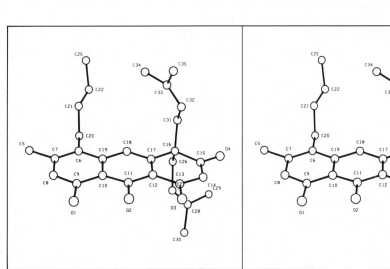

Bond Lengths

C9	O1	1.36
C11	O2	1.35
C13	O3	1.28
C15	O4	1.33
C5	C7	1.52
C6	C7	1.39
C6	C19	1.43
C6	C20	1.51
C7	C8	1.42
C8	C9	1.35
C9	C10	1.41
C10	C11	1.41
C10	C19	1.43
C11	C12	1.40
C12	C13	1.45
C12	C17	1.42
C13	C14	1.41
C14	C15	1.34
C15	C16	1.51
C16	C17	1.52
C16	C26	1.56
C16	C31	1.57
C17	C18	1.38
C18	C19	1.44
C20	C21	1.55
C21	C22	1.27
C22	C25	1.52
C26	C27	1.51
C27	C28	1.32
C28	C29	1.51
C28	C30	1.49
C31	C32	1.47
C32	C33	1.37
C33	C34	1.53
C33	C35	1.49

Bond Angles

C7	C6	C19	118
C7	C6	C20	120
C19	C6	C20	121
C5	C7	C6	122
C5	C7	C8	118
C6	C7	C8	121
C7	C8	C9	121
O1	C9	C8	116
O1	C9	C10	122
C8	C9	C10	121
C9	C10	C11	124
C9	C10	C19	118
C11	C10	C19	118
O2	C11	C10	117
O2	C11	C12	120
C10	C11	C12	123
C11	C12	C13	120
C11	C12	C17	119
C13	C12	C17	120
O3	C13	C12	120
O3	C13	C14	120
C12	C13	C14	120
C13	C14	C15	121
O4	C15	C14	124
O4	C15	C16	111
C14	C15	C16	125
C15	C16	C17	112
C15	C16	C26	108
C15	C16	C31	107
C17	C16	C26	111
C17	C16	C31	109
C26	C16	C31	109
C12	C17	C16	121
C12	C17	C18	120
C16	C17	C18	119
C17	C18	C19	121
C6	C19	C10	121
C6	C19	C18	120
C10	C19	C18	119
C6	C20	C21	111
C20	C21	C22	127
C21	C22	C25	122
C16	C26	C27	114
C26	C27	C28	128
C27	C28	C29	124
C27	C28	C30	122
C29	C28	C30	114
C16	C31	C32	112
C31	C32	C33	128
C32	C33	C34	121
C32	C33	C35	122
C34	C33	C35	117

Torsion Angles

C19	C6	C7	C5	178	C11	C10	C19	C6	−179	C15	C16	C17	C12	3
C19	C6	C7	C8	−3	C11	C10	C19	C18	3	C15	C16	C17	C18	−177
C20	C6	C7	C5	−1	O2	C11	C12	C13	2	C26	C16	C17	C12	124
C20	C6	C7	C8	178	O2	C11	C12	C17	−179	C26	C16	C17	C18	−57
C7	C6	C19	C10	2	C10	C11	C12	C13	−178	C31	C16	C17	C12	−115
C7	C6	C19	C18	−180	C10	C11	C12	C17	2	C31	C16	C17	C18	64
C20	C6	C19	C10	−179	C11	C12	C13	O3	−2	C15	C16	C26	C27	59
C20	C6	C19	C18	0	C11	C12	C13	C14	177	C17	C16	C26	C27	−64
C7	C6	C20	C21	89	C17	C12	C13	O3	178	C31	C16	C26	C27	175
C19	C6	C20	C21	−91	C17	C12	C13	C14	−2	C15	C16	C31	C32	−60
C5	C7	C8	C9	−179	C11	C12	C17	C16	−180	C17	C16	C31	C32	62
C6	C7	C8	C9	1	C11	C12	C17	C18	1	C26	C16	C31	C32	−177
C7	C8	C9	O1	−180	C13	C12	C17	C16	0	C12	C17	C18	C19	−2
C7	C8	C9	C10	1	C13	C12	C17	C18	−180	C16	C17	C18	C19	179
O1	C9	C10	C11	−2	O3	C13	C14	C15	−179	C17	C18	C19	C6	−179
O1	C9	C10	C19	179	C12	C13	C14	C15	2	C17	C18	C19	C10	0
C8	C9	C10	C11	177	C13	C14	C15	O4	−180	C6	C20	C21	C22	147
C8	C9	C10	C19	−2	C13	C14	C15	C16	1	C20	C21	C22	C25	177
C9	C10	C11	O2	−2	O4	C15	C16	C17	177	C16	C26	C27	C28	−123
C9	C10	C11	C12	178	O4	C15	C16	C26	55	C26	C27	C28	C29	3
C19	C10	C11	O2	177	O4	C15	C16	C31	−63	C26	C27	C28	C30	−177
C19	C10	C11	C12	−3	C14	C15	C16	C17	−4	C16	C31	C32	C33	−128
C9	C10	C19	C6	0	C14	C15	C16	C26	−126	C31	C32	C33	C34	−2
C9	C10	C19	C18	−178	C14	C15	C16	C31	116	C31	C32	C33	C35	−179

59.18 Substance B iodoacetate from Cedrela odorata

C₃₀H₃₈ClIO₈

$C_{30}H_{38}ClIO_8$

S.A.Adeoye, D.A.Bekoe, Chem. Communic., 301, 1965

Atomic coordinates were not
reported in the paper.
P2₁2₁2₁   Z = 4   R = 0.183

SUBIAC   LB 30-38-1

59.19   Morellin p - bromobenzenesulfonyl ester

$C_{39}H_{39}BrO_9S$

G.Kartha, G.N.Ramachandran, H.B.Bhat, P.M.Nair, V.K.V.Raghavan, K.Venkataraman,
Tetrahedron Letters, 459, 1963

Atomic coordinates were not given
but bond lengths were reported.
$P2_12_12_1$ Z = 4   R = 0.124

MORELB

59.20   Prostaglandin F_{2-1} methyl ester tri - p - bromobenzoate

$C_{42}H_{47}Br_3O_8$

S.Abrahamsson, Acta Cryst., 16, 409, 1963

$P2_12_12_1$ Z = 4   R = 0.11

BBPROM   LB 42-47-1

C10	C11	C12	C8	47
C10	C11	C12	C20	175
C28	C11	C12	C8	161
C28	C11	C12	C20	−72
C10	C11	C28	C29	−116
C12	C11	C28	C29	133
C8	C12	C20	C21	−145
C11	C12	C20	C21	98
O3	C13	C14	C15	169
O3	C13	C14	C19	−4
O4	C13	C14	C15	−13
O4	C13	C14	C19	174
C13	C14	C15	C16	173
C19	C14	C15	C16	−13
C13	C14	C19	C18	174
C15	C14	C19	C18	1
C14	C15	C16	C17	16
C15	C16	C17	Br2	173
C15	C16	C17	C18	−8
Br2	C17	C18	C19	178
C16	C17	C18	C19	−2
C17	C18	C19	C14	6
C12	C20	C21	C22	−170
C20	C21	C22	C23	−173
C21	C22	C23	C24	−173
C22	C23	C24	C25	−173
C23	C24	C25	C26	−173
C24	C25	C26	O5	24
C24	C25	C26	O6	−169
C11	C28	C29	C30	175
C28	C29	C30	O8	−132
C28	C29	C30	C38	111
O8	C30	C38	C39	173
C29	C30	C38	C39	−69
O7	C31	C32	C33	6
O7	C31	C32	C37	179
O8	C31	C32	C33	180
O8	C31	C32	C37	−7
C31	C32	C33	C34	−176
C37	C32	C33	C34	4
C31	C32	C37	C36	178
C33	C32	C37	C36	−8
C32	C33	C34	C35	−9
C33	C34	C35	Br3	−179
C33	C34	C35	C36	7
Br3	C35	C36	C37	180
C34	C35	C36	C37	−6
C35	C36	C37	C32	7
C30	C38	C39	C40	−180
C38	C39	C40	C41	175
C39	C40	C41	C42	180

Bond Lengths

Br1	C1	1.88
Br2	C17	1.88
Br3	C35	1.90
C7	O1	1.18
C7	O2	1.37
C8	O2	1.41
C10	O3	1.47
C13	O3	1.32
C13	O4	1.13
C26	O5	1.10
C26	O6	1.44
C27	O6	1.49
C31	O7	1.19
C30	O8	1.49
C31	O8	1.34
C1	C2	1.34
C1	C6	1.40
C2	C3	1.33
C3	C4	1.37
C4	C5	1.35
C4	C7	1.55
C5	C6	1.41
C8	C9	1.50
C8	C12	1.50
C9	C10	1.59
C10	C11	1.57
C11	C12	1.57
C11	C28	1.58
C12	C20	1.50
C13	C14	1.52
C14	C15	1.36
C14	C19	1.34
C15	C16	1.35
C16	C17	1.43
C17	C18	1.42
C18	C19	1.42
C20	C21	1.57
C21	C22	1.50
C22	C23	1.53
C23	C24	1.56
C24	C25	1.59
C25	C26	1.54
C28	C29	1.36
C29	C30	1.48
C30	C38	1.54
C31	C32	1.45
C32	C33	1.37
C32	C37	1.33
C33	C34	1.44
C34	C35	1.33
C35	C36	1.39
C36	C37	1.36
C38	C39	1.52
C39	C40	1.58
C40	C41	1.47
C41	C42	1.51

Bond Angles

C7	O2	C8	116
C10	O3	C13	114
C26	O6	C27	117
C30	O8	C31	116
Br1	C1	C2	123
Br1	C1	C6	118
C2	C1	C6	118
C1	C2	C3	122
C2	C3	C4	120
C3	C4	C5	122
C3	C4	C7	119
C5	C4	C7	119
C4	C5	C6	118
C1	C6	C5	120
O1	C7	O2	124
O1	C7	C4	122
O2	C7	C4	113
O2	C8	C9	112
O2	C8	C12	108
C9	C8	C12	111
C8	C9	C10	104
O3	C10	C9	108
O3	C10	C11	106
C9	C10	C11	102
C10	C11	C12	101
C10	C11	C28	105
C12	C11	C28	116
C8	C12	C11	99
C8	C12	C20	118
C11	C12	C20	116
O3	C13	O4	125
O3	C13	C14	112
O4	C13	C14	123
C13	C14	C15	119
C13	C14	C19	121
C15	C14	C19	120
C14	C15	C16	128
C15	C16	C17	110
Br2	C17	C16	118
Br2	C17	C18	117
C16	C17	C18	124
C17	C18	C19	117
C14	C19	C18	120
C12	C20	C21	113
C20	C21	C22	110
C21	C22	C23	113
C22	C23	C24	112
C23	C24	C25	108
C24	C25	C26	103
O5	C26	O6	118
O5	C26	C25	137
O6	C26	C25	104
C11	C28	C29	116
C28	C29	C30	121
O8	C30	C29	108
O8	C30	C38	104
C29	C30	C38	116
O7	C31	O8	122
O7	C31	C32	127
O8	C31	C32	110
C31	C32	C33	118
C31	C32	C37	130
C33	C32	C37	112
C32	C33	C34	125
C33	C34	C35	114
Br3	C35	C34	118
Br3	C35	C36	119
C34	C35	C36	124
C35	C36	C37	116
C32	C37	C36	128
C30	C38	C39	112
C38	C39	C40	113
C39	C40	C41	113
C40	C41	C42	115

Torsion Angles

C8	O2	C7	O1	7
C8	O2	C7	C4	−178
C7	O2	C8	C9	76
C7	O2	C8	C12	−162
C13	O3	C10	C9	83
C13	O3	C10	C11	−168
C10	O3	C13	O4	−3
C10	O3	C13	C14	176
C27	O6	C26	O5	−9
C27	O6	C26	C25	−179
C31	O8	C30	C29	73
C31	O8	C30	C38	−163
C30	O8	C31	O7	7
C30	O8	C31	C32	−167
Br1	C1	C2	C3	−172
C6	C1	C2	C3	12
Br1	C1	C6	C5	177
C2	C1	C6	C5	−7
C1	C2	C3	C4	−12
C2	C3	C4	C5	6
C2	C3	C4	C7	−173
C3	C4	C5	C6	−1
C7	C4	C5	C6	179
C3	C4	C7	O1	−7
C3	C4	C7	O2	178
C5	C4	C7	O1	173
C5	C4	C7	O2	−2
C4	C5	C6	C1	2
O2	C8	C9	C10	132
C12	C8	C9	C10	12
O2	C8	C12	C11	−160
O2	C8	C12	C20	74
C9	C8	C12	C11	−37
C9	C8	C12	C20	−163
C8	C9	C10	O3	130
C8	C9	C10	C11	19
O3	C10	C11	C12	−154
O3	C10	C11	C28	85
C9	C10	C11	C12	−41
C9	C10	C11	C28	−162

60.1 Carbon tetrabromide - p - xylene complex

CBr₄ , C₈H₁₀

F.J.Strieter, D.H.Templeton, J. Chem. Phys., 37, 161, 1962

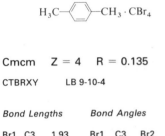

H₃C—⟨benzene ring⟩—CH₃ · CBr₄

Cmcm   Z = 4   R = 0.135

CTBRXY   LB 9-10-4

Bond Lengths			Bond Angles			
Br1	C3	1.93	Br1	C3	Br2	109
Br2	C3	1.89	Br1	C3	Br1C	108
			Br2	C3	Br2J	111
C4	C5	1.40				
C4	C4B	1.38	C5	C4	C4B	121
C5	C6	1.49	C4	C5	C6	122
			C4	C5	C4J	115

Torsion Angles

C4B	C4	C5	C6	−175
C4B	C4	C5	C4J	18
C5	C4	C4B	C5B	−20

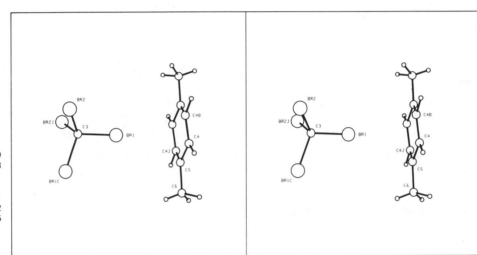

60.2 1,3 - Iodoform - sulfur

CHI₃ , 3S₈

T.Bjorvatten, Acta Chem. Scand., 16, 749, 1962

```
    I
    |
 I—C—H   .3S₈
    |
    I
```

R3m   Z = 3   R = 0.050

IFOSUL

Bond Lengths			Bond Angles			
I1	C1	2.10	I1	C1	I1A	116
S1	S2	2.11	S2	S1	S2C	102
S2	S3	2.04	S1	S2	S3	106
S3	S4	2.02	S2	S3	S4	108
S4	S5	1.99	S3	S4	S5	111
			S4	S5	S4C	110

Torsion Angles

S2C	S1	S2	S3	−102
S1	S2	S3	S4	101
S2	S3	S4	S5	−98
S3	S4	S5	S4C	95

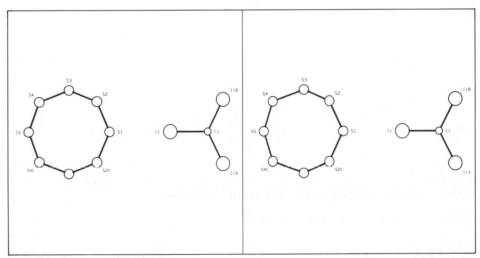

60.3   1,3 - Iodoform - quinoline

T.Bjorvatten, O.Hassel, Acta Chem. Scand., 16, 249, 1962

CHI_3 , $3C_9H_7N$

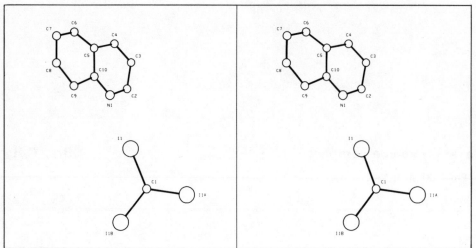

. CHI_3

No comparison of bond lengths is possible since they are not reported in the paper.

R3   Z = 3   R = 0.065

IFOQUI

Bond Lengths

I1	C1	2.12	C5	C6	1.42
			C5	C10	1.45
C2	N1	1.28	C6	C7	1.17
C10	N1	1.31	C7	C8	1.32
C2	C3	1.48	C8	C9	1.44
C3	C4	1.39	C9	C10	1.47
C4	C5	1.45			

Bond Angles

I1	C1	I1A	113	C4	C5	C6	137	C8	C9	C10	112
				C4	C5	C10	109	N1	C10	C5	128
C2	N1	C10	120	C6	C5	C10	113	N1	C10	C9	115
N1	C2	C3	124	C5	C6	C7	136	C5	C10	C9	117
C2	C3	C4	113	C6	C7	C8	110				
C3	C4	C5	126	C7	C8	C9	132				

60.4   Iodoform - 1,4 - diselenane

T.Bjorvatten, Acta Chem. Scand., 17, 2292, 1963

$2CHI_3$, $C_4H_8Se_2$

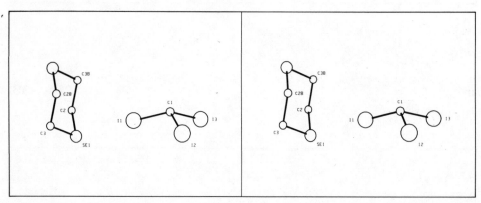

$2I-C-H$ · (diselenane ring with Se, Se)
with I, I above and below

$P2_1/c$ Z = 2 $R_{h0l} = 0.105,$
$R_{hk0} = 0.081, R_{0kl} = 0.072$

IFODSE   LB 6-10-27

Bond Lengths

I1	C1	2.05	Se1	C2	1.94
I2	C1	2.13	Se1	C3	1.89
I3	C1	2.25	C2	C3B	1.71

Bond Angles

I1	C1	I2	117	C2	Se1	C3	100
I1	C1	I3	111	Se1	C2	C3B	111
I2	C1	I3	109	Se1	C3	C2B	111

Torsion Angles

C3	Se1	C2	C3B	62
C2	Se1	C3	C2B	−62
Se1	C2	C3B	Se1B	−69

60.5   Urea - sodium chloride monohydrate

J.H.Palm, C.H.MacGillavry, Acta Cryst., 16, 963, 1963

CH_4N_2O , Na^+ , Cl^- , H_2O

No comparison of bond lengths is possible since they are not reported in the paper.

I2   Z = 4 $R_{h0l} = 0.138,$
$R_{0kl} = 0.145$

NCUREA   LB 1-4-11

Bond Lengths

C1	N1	1.27
C1	N2	1.23
C1	O3	1.29

Bond Angles

N1	C1	N2	118
N1	C1	O3	119
N2	C1	O3	122

$[O{=}C(NH_2) \cdot NaCl] \cdot H_2O$

60.6　Urea - ammonium bromide

CH_4N_2O , H_4N^+ , Br^-

C.G.C.Catesby, Acta Cryst., 16, 392, 1963

$P2_1$　$Z = 2$　$R = 0.12$

URAMBR　　LB 1-8-1

Bond Lengths			Bond Angles			
C1	N1	1.38	N1	C1	N2	121
C1	N2	1.33	N1	C1	O1	122
C1	O1	1.24	N2	C1	O1	117

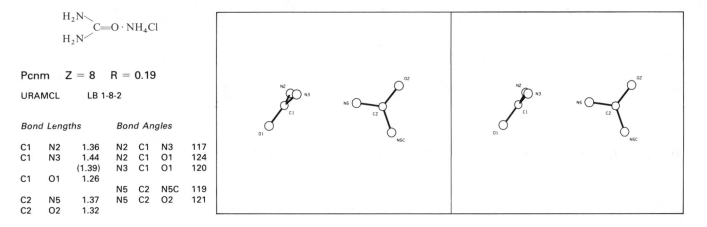

60.7　Urea - ammonium chloride

CH_4N_2O , H_4N^+ , Cl^-

A.Rimsky, Bull. Soc. Fr. Mineral. Cristallogr., 83, 187, 1960

Pcnm　$Z = 8$　$R = 0.19$

URAMCL　　LB 1-8-2

Bond Lengths			Bond Angles			
C1	N2	1.36	N2	C1	N3	117
C1	N3	1.44	N2	C1	O1	124
		(1.39)	N3	C1	O1	120
C1	O1	1.26				
			N5	C2	N5C	119
C2	N5	1.37	N5	C2	O2	121
C2	O2	1.32				

60.8　Methanol - bromine complex

$2CH_4O$, Br_2

P.Groth, O.Hassel, Acta Chem. Scand., 18, 402, 1964

No comparison of bond lengths is possible since they are not reported in the paper. Published value of z(C3) = 0.343. The correct value is 0.243.
$P2_1/c$　$Z = 8$　$R_{hk0} = 0.089$, $R_{h0l} = 0.116$

METHOB　　LB 2-8-10

Bond Lengths					
Br1	Br2	2.25	C2	O2	1.22
Br3	Br4	2.32	C3	O3	1.57
C1	O1	1.52	C4	O4	1.58

$2(CH_3OH) \cdot Br_2$

60.9　Methanol - sodium iodide

$3CH_4O$, Na^+ , I^-

P.Piret, C.Mesureur, J. Chim. Phys. Phys.-Chim. Biol., 62, 287, 1965

No comparison of bond lengths is possible since they are not reported in the paper.
$P6_3/m$　$Z = 2$　$R_{hk0} = 0.099$, $R_{hk1} = 0.075$

NAIMOL　　LB 3-12-17

Bond Lengths		
C1	O1	1.37

$NaI \cdot 3CH_3OH$

60.10　Guanidinium chloride - N,N - dimethylacetamide complex

$3CH_6N_3^+$, C_4H_9NO , $3Cl^-$

D.J.Haas, D.R.Harris, H.H.Mills, Acta Cryst., 18, 623, 1965

The N,N - dimethylacetamide molecules are disordered.
I2/a　$Z = 8$　$R = 0.16$

GUCDMA　　LB 7-27-1

Bond Lengths								
C1	N1	1.34	C2	N4	1.31	C3	N7	1.38
C1	N2	1.33	C2	N5	1.34	C3	N8	1.32
C1	N3	1.35	C2	N6	1.35	C3	N9	1.30

Bond Angles											
N1	C1	N2	120	N4	C2	N5	121	N7	C3	N8	119
N1	C1	N3	121	N4	C2	N6	120	N7	C3	N9	119
N2	C1	N3	119	N5	C2	N6	119	N8	C3	N9	121

60.11 Oxalyl bromide - 1,4 - dioxan complex

$C_2Br_2O_2$, $C_4H_8O_2$

E.Damm, O.Hassel, C.Romming, Acta Chem. Scand., 19, 1159, 1965

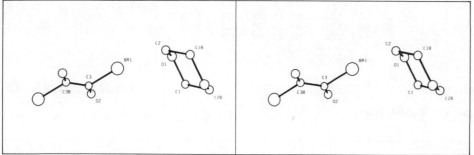

$P2_1/c$ $Z = 2$ No R factor was given.

OXBDOC   LB 6-8-12

Bond Lengths

Br1	C3	1.96	C1	O1	1.54
C3	O2	1.12	C2	O1	1.39
C3	C3B	1.50	C1	C2B	1.62

Bond Angles

Br1	C3	O2	118	C1	O1	C2	117
Br1	C3	C3B	108	O1	C1	C2B	108
O2	C3	C3B	133	O1	C2	C1B	118

Torsion Angles

Br1	C3	C3B	Br1B	−180	C2	O1	C1	C2B	−44
Br1	C3	C3B	O2B	−6	C1	O1	C2	C1B	48
O2	C3	C3B	Br1B	6	O1	C1	C2B	O1B	44
O2	C3	C3B	O2B	−180				

60.12 Oxalyl chloride - 1,4 - dioxan complex

$C_2Cl_2O_2$, $C_4H_8O_2$

E.Damm, O.Hassel, C.Romming, Acta Chem. Scand., 19, 1159, 1965

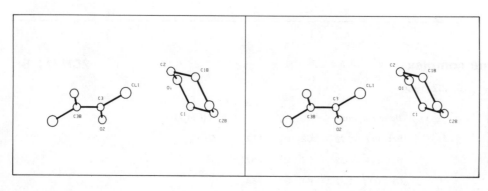

No comparison of bond lengths is possible since they are not reported in the paper.
$P2_1/c$ $Z = 2$ No R factor was given.

OXCDOC   LB 6-8-27

Bond Lengths

Cl1	C3	1.73	C1	O1	1.48
C3	O2	1.15	C2	O1	1.46
C3	C3B	1.58	C1	C2B	1.49

Bond Angles

Cl1	C3	O2	123	C1	O1	C2	120
Cl1	C3	C3B	109	O1	C1	C2B	113
O2	C3	C3B	125	O1	C2	C1B	112

Torsion Angles

Cl1	C3	C3B	Cl1B	−180	C2	O1	C1	C2B	−45
Cl1	C3	C3B	O2B	17	C1	O1	C2	C1B	44
O2	C3	C3B	Cl1B	−17	O1	C1	C2B	O1B	41
O2	C3	C3B	O2B	−180				

60.13 Acetone - sodium iodide

$3C_3H_6O$, Na^+ , I^-

P.Piret, Y.Gobillon, M.van Meerssche, Bull. Soc. Chim. Fr., 205, 1963

$P6_3$ $Z = 2$ $R_{hk0} = 0.151$,
$R_{hk1} = 0.097$

NAIACE   LB 9-18-10

Bond Lengths

C3	O1	1.24
C1	C3	1.57
C2	C3	1.54

Bond Angles

O1	C3	C1	118
O1	C3	C2	120
C1	C3	C2	122

$NaI \cdot 3 CH_3\!-\!CO\!-\!CH_3$

60.14 N - Methylacetamide - sodium perchlorate complex

$2C_3H_7NO$, Na^+ , ClO_4^-

D.J.Haas, Thesis, New York, 1965

Atomic coordinates were not reported in the paper.
$P2_1/a$ $Z = 4$ No R factor was given.

MAANAC

$$2\left(CH_3\!-\!C\!\!\begin{array}{c}\nearrow O \\ \searrow NHCH_3\end{array} \right) \cdot NaClO_4$$

60.15   Tri(dimethylformamide) - sodium iodide

$3C_3H_7NO$, Na^+ , I^-

Y.Gobillon, P.Piret, M.van Meerssche, Bull. Soc. Chim. Fr., 551, 1962

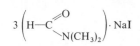

P-62c   Z = 2   R = 0.092

NAIDMF   LB 9-21-5

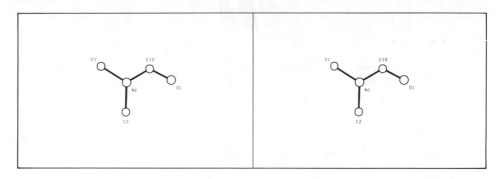

Bond Lengths			Bond Angles				Torsion Angles			
C1	N1	1.53	C1	N1	C2	120	C1	N1	C10	O1	−180
C2	N1	1.45	C1	N1	C10	119	C2	N1	C10	O1	0
C10	N1	1.34	C2	N1	C10	121				
C10	O1	1.23	N1	C10	O1	124				

60.16   N - Methylacetamide - lithium chloride complex

$4C_3H_7NO$, Li^+ , Cl^-

D.J.Haas, Nature, 201, 64, 1964

The structure is totally disordered.

$LiCl·4(H_3C—CO—NH—CH_3)$

$I4_1/a$ Z = 4   R = 0.18

LICMAC   LB 12-28-6

60.17   N - Methylacetamide - potassium iodide - potassium tri - iodide complex

$6C_3H_7NO$, $2K^+$, I^- , I_3^-

K.Toman, J.Honzl, J.Jecny, Acta Cryst., 18, 673, 1965

$KI · KI_3 · 6(CH_3—CO—NH—CH_3)$

P-31c   Z = 2   R = 0.126

KIMACA   LB 18-42-5

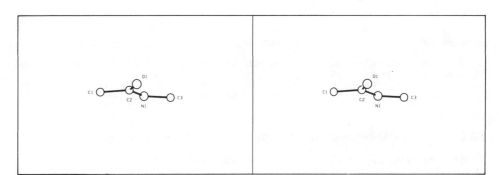

Bond Lengths			Bond Angles				Torsion Angles			
I1	I3	2.95	I3	I1	I3I	180	C3	N1	C2	O1	1
							C3	N1	C2	C1	−175
C2	N1	1.28	C2	N1	C3	120				
C3	N1	1.39	N1	C2	O1	126				
C2	O1	1.26	N1	C2	C1	113				
C1	C2	1.55	O1	C2	C1	120				

60.18   1,4 - Dioxan - dinitrogen tetroxide complex

$C_4H_8O_2$, N_2O_4

P.Groth, O.Hassel, Acta Chem. Scand., 19, 120, 1965

The dioxan molecule is disordered.

$· N_2O_4$

P-1   Z = 1   R = 0.11

NODIOX   LB 4-8-71

60.19   1,4 - Dioxan sulphuric acid

C$_4$H$_8$O$_2$, H$_2$O$_4$S

O.Hassel, C.Romming, Acta Chem. Scand., 14, 398, 1960

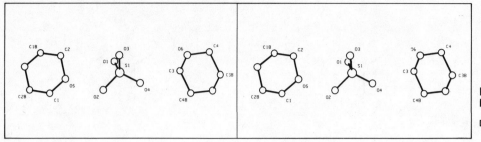

· H$_2$SO$_4$

P2$_1$/c   Z = 4   R$_{hk0}$ = 0.09,
R$_{h0l}$ = 0.12, R$_{0kl}$ = 0.09

DOXSUL   LB 4-10-40

Bond Lengths

S1	O1	1.41	C1	O5	1.44	C3	O6	1.42
S1	O2	1.51	C2	O5	1.47	C4	O6	1.41
S1	O3	1.52	C1	C2B	1.53	C3	C4B	1.59
S1	O4	1.44						

Bond Angles

O1	S1	O2	109	C1	O5	C2	114
O1	S1	O3	105	O5	C1	C2B	111
O1	S1	O4	118	O5	C2	C1B	106
O2	S1	O3	108				
O2	S1	O4	108	C3	O6	C4	119
O3	S1	O4	108	O6	C3	C4B	109
				O6	C4	C3B	110

Torsion Angles

C2	O5	C1	C2B	61
C1	O5	C2	C1B	−58
O5	C1	C2B	O5B	−56
C4	O6	C3	C4B	53
C3	O6	C4	C3B	−53
O6	C3	C4B	O6B	−48

60.20   1,4 - Dioxan - di - iodoacetylene complex

C$_4$H$_8$O$_2$, C$_2$I$_2$

P.Gagnaux, B.P.Susz, Helv. Chim. Acta, 43, 948, 1960

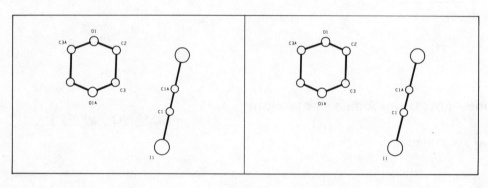

. I—C≡C—I

P-1   Z = 1   R = 0.25

DOXIAC

Bond Lengths

I1	C1	1.89	C2	O1	1.36
C1	C1A	1.22	C3A	O1	1.45
			C2	C3	1.55

Bond Angles

I1	C1	C1A	179
C2	O1	C3A	105
O1	C2	C3	107

Torsion Angles

I1	C1	C1A	I1A	−179
C3A	O1	C2	C3	66
C2	O1	C3A	C2A	−66
O1	C2	C3	O1A	−67

60.21   1,4 - Dithiane - iodoform

C$_4$H$_8$S$_2$, CHI$_3$

T.Bjorvatten, O.Hassel, Acta Chem. Scand., 15, 1429, 1961

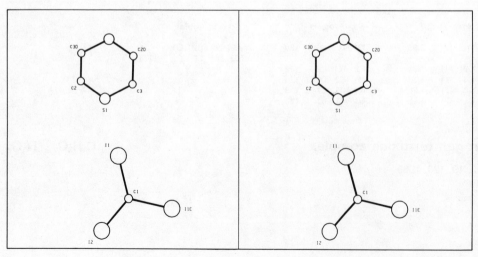

· CHI$_3$

P2$_1$/m   Z = 2   R$_{0kl}$ = 0.094,
R$_{h0l}$ = 0.108, R$_{hk0}$ = 0.123

DTHIOF   LB 5-9-7

Bond Lengths

I1	C1	2.20
I2	C1	2.03
S1	C2	1.75
S1	C3	1.80
C2	C3D	1.44

Bond Angles

I1	C1	I2	113
I1	C1	I1E	107
C2	S1	C3	104
S1	C2	C3D	117
S1	C3	C2D	114

Torsion Angles

C3	S1	C2	C3D	−53
C2	S1	C3	C2D	51
S1	C2	C3D	S1D	58

60.22   1,4 - Diselenane - tetraiodoethylene complex

$C_4H_8Se_2$, C_2I_4

T.Dahl, O.Hassel, Acta Chem. Scand., 19, 2000, 1965

Atomic coordinates were not reported in the paper.
P2$_1$/c   Z = 2 R_{0kl} = 0.055,
R_{h0l} = 0.077

DISTIE   LB 6-8-36

60.23   Morpholine - β - iodophenylacetylene complex

C_4H_9NO , C_8H_5I

R.H.Baughman, J. Org. Chem., 29, 964, 1964

The structure was determined in two dimensions only. Atomic coordinates were not reported in the paper.
P2$_1$/c   Z = 2   R = 0.18

MORIPA

60.24   Diethylether - bromodichloromethane complex (form ii)

$C_4H_{10}O$, $CHBrCl_2$

P.Andersen, T.Thurmann-Moe, Acta Chem. Scand., 18, 433, 1964

$(C_2H_5)_2O \cdot HCBrCl_2$

No comparison of bond lengths is possible since they are not reported in the paper.
Pna2$_1$ Z = 4   R = 0.17

ETHBME   LB 5-11-4

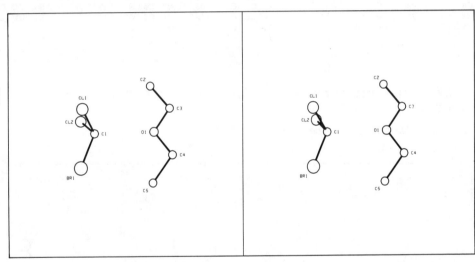

Bond Lengths			Bond Angles				Torsion Angles			
Br1	C1	1.84	Br1	C1	Cl1	108	C4	O1	C3	C2	−179
Cl1	C1	1.89	Br1	C1	Cl2	108	C3	O1	C4	C5	177
Cl2	C1	1.89	Cl1	C1	Cl2	107				
C3	O1	1.41	C3	O1	C4	104				
C4	O1	1.51	O1	C3	C2	103				
C2	C3	1.57	O1	C4	C5	104				
C4	C5	1.68								

60.25   Magnesium oxybromide - diethylether complex

$4C_4H_{10}O$, Br_6Mg_4O

G.Stucky, R.E.Rundle, J. Amer. Chem. Soc., 86, 4821, 1964

$[Mg_4Br_6O] \cdot 4\,O(C_2H_5)_2$

The structure is totally disordered.
P-42$_1$c   Z = 8   R = 0.09

MBODET   LB 16-40-3

60.26   L - Cysteine ethyl ester hydrochloride - urea complex $C_5H_{12}NOS^+$, $CH_4N_2O_2$, Cl^-

D.J.Haas, Acta Cryst., 19, 860, 1965

$$\left(CH_3-CH_2-OOC-\overset{\overset{\displaystyle NH_2}{|}}{CH}-CH_2\dot{-}SH\cdot HCl \right)\cdot CO(NH_2)_2$$

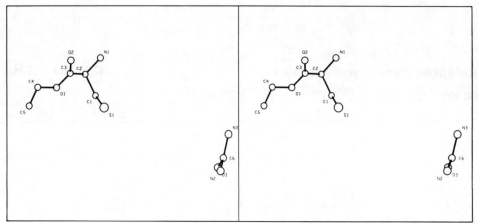

No comparison of bond lengths is possible since they are not reported in the paper.
$P2_1$ Z = 2   R = 0.092

ECYSCU   LB 6-16-10

Bond Lengths

S1	C1	1.77	C2 C3	1.50
C2	N1	1.50	C4 C5	1.28
C3	O1	1.31		
C4	O1	1.49	C6 N2	1.32
C3	O2	1.23	C6 N3	1.37
C1	C2	1.57	C6 O3	1.32

Bond Angles

C3	O1	C4	117	O2	C3	C2	123
S1	C1	C2	117	O1	C4	C5	112
N1	C2	C1	109				
N1	C2	C3	108	N2	C6	N3	123
C1	C2	C3	112	N2	C6	O3	119
O1	C3	O2	127	N3	C6	O3	118
O1	C3	C2	109				

Torsion Angles

C4	O1	C3	O2	8	N1	C2	C3	O1	180
C4	O1	C3	C2	−172	N1	C2	C3	O2	0
C3	O1	C4	C5	−156	C1	C2	C3	O1	−60
S1	C1	C2	N1	75	C1	C2	C3	O2	120
S1	C1	C2	C3	−45					

60.27   Hexabromobenzene - 1,2,4,5 - tetrabromobenzene complex C_6Br_6 , $C_6H_2Br_4$

G.Gafner, F.H.Herbstein, J. Chem. Soc., 5290, 1964

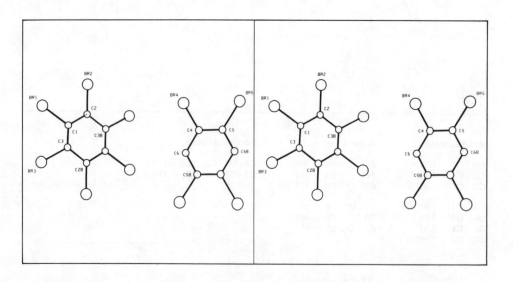

$P2_1/a$ Z = 2   R = 0.14

HBTBBZ   LB 12-2-1

Bond Lengths

Br1	C1	1.93	Br4 C4	1.88
Br2	C2	1.80	Br5 C5	1.85
Br3	C3	1.90	C4 C5	1.39
C1	C2	1.47	C4 C6	1.48
C1	C3	1.33	C5 C6B	1.40
C2	C3B	1.43		

Bond Angles

Br1	C1	C2	116	Br4	C4	C5	122
Br1	C1	C3	119	Br4	C4	C6	117
C2	C1	C3	125	C5	C4	C6	121
Br2	C2	C1	122	Br5	C5	C4	122
Br2	C2	C3B	126	Br5	C5	C6B	117
C1	C2	C3B	111	C4	C5	C6B	120
Br3	C3	C1	122	C4	C6	C5B	118
Br3	C3	C2B	114				
C1	C3	C2B	124				

60.28 Chloranil - hexamethylbenzene complex (refinement of data of Harding and Wallwork, Acta Cryst., 8,787,1955)

$C_6Cl_4O_2$, $C_{12}H_{18}$

N.D.Jones, R.E.Marsh, Acta Cryst., 15, 809, 1962

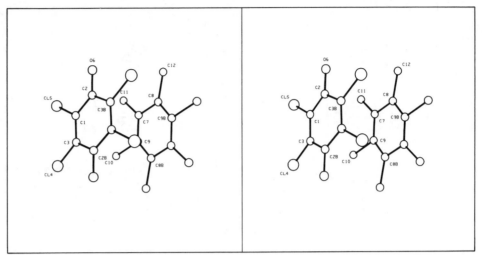

No comparison of bond lengths is possible since they are not reported in the paper.

P2$_1$/c   Z = 2   R = 0.14

CLAHMB   LB 18-18-19

Bond·Lengths

Cl4	C3	1.70	C7	C8	1.41
Cl5	C1	1.83	C7	C9	1.38
C2	O6	1.33	C7	C11	1.47
C1	C2	1.44	C8	C12	1.55
C1	C3	1.34	C8	C9B	1.40
C2	C3B	1.40	C9	C10	1.71

Bond Angles

Cl5	C1	C2	118	C8	C7	C9	115
Cl5	C1	C3	116	C8	C7	C11	119
C2	C1	C3	125	C9	C7	C11	127
O6	C2	C1	121	C7	C8	C12	125
O6	C2	C3B	119	C7	C8	C9B	115
C1	C2	C3B	120	C12	C8	C9B	120
Cl4	C3	C1	126	C7	C9	C10	114
Cl4	C3	C2B	119	C7	C9	C8B	130
C1	C3	C2B	115	C10	C9	C8B	115

60.29 Chloranil - bis(8 - hydroxyquinolinato) palladium(ii)

$C_6Cl_4O_2$, $C_{18}H_{12}N_2O_2Pd$

B.Kamenar, C.K.Prout, J.D.Wright, J. Chem. Soc., 4851, 1965

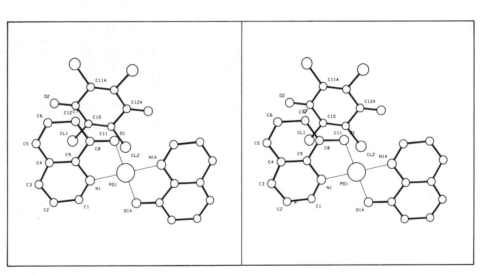

The published bond lengths and angles at N1 are incorrect (private communication).

P-1   Z = 1   R = 0.107

CLAQPD   LB 24-12-4

Bond Lengths

Pd1	N1	1.99	C6	C7	1.45
Pd1	O1	1.98	C7	C8	1.38
C1	N1	1.35	C8	C9	1.45
C9	N1	1.38			
C8	O1	1.31	Cl1	C10	1.72
C1	C2	1.42	Cl2	C11	1.67
C2	C3	1.36	C12	O2	1.22
C3	C4	1.46	C10	C11	1.32
C4	C5	1.33	C10	C12	1.43
C4	C9	1.42	C11	C12A	1.56
C5	C6	1.40			

Bond Angles

N1	Pd1	N1A	180	C3	C4	C5	125	Cl1	C10	C11	121
N1	Pd1	O1	85	C3	C4	C9	115	Cl1	C10	C12	115
N1	Pd1	O1A	95	C5	C4	C9	120	C11	C10	C12	124
O1	Pd1	N1A	95	C4	C5	C6	122	Cl2	C11	C10	125
O1	Pd1	O1A	180	C5	C6	C7	119	Cl2	C11	C12A	115
Pd1	N1	C1	131	C6	C7	C8	121	C10	C11	C12A	120
Pd1	N1	C9	110	O1	C8	C7	124	O2	C12	C10	124
C1	N1	C9	119	O1	C8	C9	119	O2	C12	C11A	120
Pd1	O1	C8	110	C7	C8	C9	116	C10	C12	C11A	116
N1	C1	C2	121	N1	C9	C4	123				
C1	C2	C3	120	N1	C9	C8	114				
C2	C3	C4	121	C4	C9	C8	122				

60.30 Benzotrifuroxan - 13,14 - dithiatricyclo(8,2,1,1^{4,7})tetradeca - 4,6,10,12 - tetraene

$C_6N_6O_6$, $C_{12}H_{12}S_2$

B.Kamenar, C.K.Prout, J. Chem. Soc., 4838, 1965

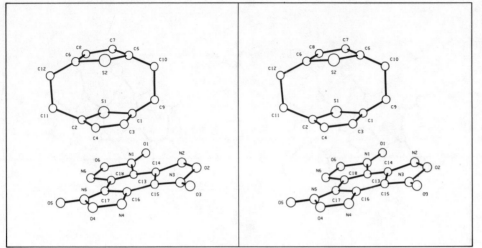

P-1   Z = 2   R = 0.137

BOXTET   LB 18-12-32

Bond Lengths

S1	C1	1.77	N3	O2	1.54
S1	C2	1.72	N3	O3	1.14
S2	C5	1.81	N4	O4	1.37
S2	C6	1.79	N5	O4	1.49
C1	C3	1.39	N5	O5	1.23
C1	C9	1.40	N6	O6	1.39
C2	C4	1.34	C13	N1	1.42
C2	C11	1.57	C14	N2	1.45
C3	C4	1.39	C15	N3	1.41
C5	C7	1.41	C16	N4	1.30
		(1.49)	C17	N5	1.25
C5	C10	1.39	C18	N6	1.49
C6	C8	1.42	C13	C14	1.42
C6	C12	1.51	C13	C18	1.28
C7	C8	1.39	C14	C15	1.40
C9	C10	1.62			(1.35)
C11	C12	1.57	C15	C16	1.51
					(1.56)
N1	O1	1.26	C16	C17	1.40
N1	O6	1.52	C17	C18	1.47
N2	O2	1.34			

Bond Angles

C1	S1	C2	93		O2	N3	C15	101
C5	S2	C6	97		O3	N3	C15	137
S1	C1	C3	106		O4	N4	C16	103
S1	C1	C9	117		O4	N5	O5	117
C3	C1	C9	136		O4	N5	C17	107
S1	C2	C4	110		O5	N5	C17	137
S1	C2	C11	118		O6	N6	C18	99
C4	C2	C11	128		N2	O2	N3	114
C1	C3	C4	115		N4	O4	N5	108
C2	C4	C3	114		N1	O6	N6	112
S2	C5	C7	103		N1	C13	C14	125
S2	C5	C10	118		N1	C13	C18	109
C7	C5	C10	135		C14	C13	C18	124
S2	C6	C8	104		N2	C14	C13	132
S2	C6	C12	119		N2	C14	C15	112
C8	C6	C12	136		C13	C14	C15	116
C5	C7	C8	117		N3	C15	C14	110
C6	C8	C7	117		N3	C15	C16	130
C1	C9	C10	112		C14	C15	C16	119
C5	C10	C9	113		N4	C16	C15	125
C2	C11	C12	113		N4	C16	C17	115
C6	C12	C11	109		C15	C16	C17	120
					N5	C16	C17	107
O1	N1	O6	123		N5	C17	C18	138
O1	N1	C13	134		C16	C17	C18	115
O6	N1	C13	103		N6	C18	C13	116
O2	N2	C14	103		N6	C18	C17	119
O2	N3	O3	121		C13	C18	C17	124

Torsion Angles

C2	S1	C1	C3	9		O2	N3	C15	C14	0
C2	S1	C1	C9	-160		O2	N3	C15	C16	-168
C1	S1	C2	C4	-9		O3	N3	C15	C14	168
C1	S1	C2	C11	151		O3	N3	C15	C16	0
C6	S2	C5	C7	13		C16	N4	O4	N5	8
C6	S2	C5	C10	-148		O4	N4	C16	C15	-179
C5	S2	C6	C8	-9		O4	N4	C16	C17	-9
C5	S2	C6	C12	158		O5	N5	O4	N4	-5
S1	C1	C3	C4	-7		O4	N5	C17	C16	-1
C9	C1	C3	C4	158		O4	N5	C17	C18	-177
S1	C1	C9	C10	83		O5	N5	C17	C16	178
C3	C1	C9	C10	-81		O5	N5	C17	C18	2
S1	C2	C4	C3	7		C18	N6	O6	N1	2
C11	C2	C4	C3	-151		O6	N6	C18	C13	-8
S1	C2	C11	C12	-76		O6	N6	C18	C17	176
C4	C2	C11	C12	80		N1	C13	C14	N2	-12
C1	C3	C4	C2	1		N1	C13	C14	C15	176
S2	C5	C7	C8	-13		C18	C13	C14	N2	-171
C10	C5	C7	C8	143		C18	C13	C14	C15	17
S2	C5	C10	C9	76		N1	C13	C18	N6	10
C7	C5	C10	C9	-78		N1	C13	C18	C17	-174
S2	C6	C8	C7	3		C14	C13	C18	N6	172
C12	C6	C8	C7	-161		C14	C13	C18	C17	-12
C8	C6	C12	C11	79		N2	C14	C15	N3	2
C5	C7	C8	C6	7		N2	C14	C15	C16	171
C1	C9	C10	C5	-37		C13	C14	C15	N3	175
C2	C11	C12	C6	34		C13	C14	C15	C16	-15
						N3	C15	C16	N4	-13
O1	N1	O6	N6	-177		N3	C15	C16	C17	178
C13	N1	O6	N6	3		C14	C15	C16	N4	-180
O1	N1	C13	C14	11		C14	C15	C16	C17	11
O1	N1	C13	C18	173		N4	C16	C17	N5	7
O6	N1	C13	C14	-169		N4	C16	C17	C18	-176
O6	N1	C13	C18	-7		C15	C16	C17	N5	177
C14	N2	O2	N3	2		C15	C16	C17	C18	-6
O2	N2	C14	C13	-174		N5	C17	C18	N6	-2
O2	N2	C14	C15	-2		N5	C17	C18	C13	-177
O3	N3	O2	N2	-172		C16	C17	C18	N6	-178
C15	N3	O2	N2	-1		C16	C17	C18	C13	6

60.31　Picryl azide - bis(8 - hydroxyquinolinato) copper(ii)　　$2C_6H_2N_6O_6$, $C_{18}H_{12}CuN_2O_2$

A.S.Bailey, C.K.Prout, J. Chem. Soc., 4867, 1965

A2/a　Z = 4　R = 0.134

PAZQCU　　LB 30-16-4

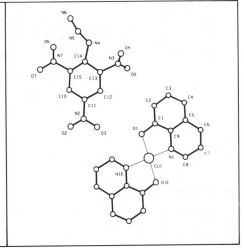

Bond Lengths

Cu1	N1	1.96	N4	N5	1.24
Cu1	O1	1.95	N5	N6	1.12
C8	N1	1.31	N2	O2	1.19
C9	N1	1.41	N2	O3	1.22
C1	O1	1.35	N3	O4	1.16
C1	C2	1.39	N3	O5	1.21
C1	C9	1.38	N7	O6	1.18
C2	C3	1.42	N7	O7	1.21
C3	C4	1.41	C11	N2	1.46
C4	C5	1.39	C13	N3	1.52
C5	C6	1.43	C14	N4	1.44
C5	C9	1.43	C15	N7	1.51
C6	C7	1.37	C10	C11	1.41
C7	C8	1.44	C10	C15	1.40
			C11	C12	1.37
			C12	C13	1.40
			C13	C14	1.39
			C14	C15	1.36

Bond Angles

N1	Cu1	N1E	178	O2	N2	O3	122
N1	Cu1	O1	85	O2	N2	C11	119
N1	Cu1	O1E	95	O3	N2	C11	118
O1	Cu1	N1E	95	O4	N3	O5	128
O1	Cu1	O1E	174	O4	N3	C13	117
Cu1	N1	C8	130	O5	N3	C13	114
Cu1	N1	C9	110	N5	N4	C14	119
C8	N1	C9	120	N4	N5	N6	168
Cu1	O1	C1	110	O6	N7	O7	122
O1	C1	C2	124	O6	N7	C15	120
O1	C1	C9	120	O7	N7	C15	118
C2	C1	C9	116	C11	C10	C15	117
C1	C2	C3	122	N2	C11	C10	118
C2	C3	C4	121	N2	C11	C12	120
C3	C4	C5	117	C10	C11	C12	122
C4	C5	C6	124	C11	C12	C13	117
C4	C5	C9	121	N3	C13	C12	114
C6	C5	C9	115	N3	C13	C14	122
C5	C6	C7	121	C12	C13	C14	124
C6	C7	C8	120	N4	C14	C13	112
N1	C8	C7	121	N4	C14	C15	132
N1	C9	C1	115	C13	C14	C15	116
N1	C9	C5	122	N7	C15	C10	114
C1	C9	C5	123	N7	C15	C14	121
				C10	C15	C14	124

Torsion Angles

N1E	Cu1	N1	C8	86	C1	C2	C3	C4	−4	N5	N4	C14	C15	31
N1E	Cu1	N1	C9	−92	C2	C3	C4	C5	8	O6	N7	C15	C10	−155
O1	Cu1	N1	C8	179	C3	C4	C5	C6	180	O6	N7	C15	C14	19
O1	Cu1	N1	C9	1	C3	C4	C5	C9	−7	O7	N7	C15	C10	22
O1E	Cu1	N1	C8	−6	C4	C5	C6	C7	175	O7	N7	C15	C14	−164
O1E	Cu1	N1	C9	175	C9	C5	C6	C7	2	C15	C10	C11	N2	−176
N1	Cu1	O1	C1	−2	C4	C5	C9	N1	−177	C15	C10	C11	C12	−1
N1E	Cu1	O1	C1	176	C4	C5	C9	C1	2	C11	C10	C15	N7	172
O1E	Cu1	O1	C1	−93	C6	C5	C9	N1	−3	C11	C10	C15	C14	−2
Cu1	N1	C8	C7	−176	C6	C5	C9	C1	176	N2	C11	C12	C13	179
C9	N1	C8	C7	2	C5	C6	C7	C8	2	C10	C11	C12	C13	4
Cu1	N1	C9	C1	0	C6	C7	C8	N1	−4	C11	C12	C13	N3	175
Cu1	N1	C9	C5	180						C11	C12	C13	C14	−4
C8	N1	C9	C1	−178	O2	N2	C11	C10	−13	N3	C13	C14	N4	7
C8	N1	C9	C5	1	O2	N2	C11	C12	171	N3	C13	C14	C15	−177
Cu1	O1	C1	C2	180	O3	N2	C11	C10	173	C12	C13	C14	N4	−174
Cu1	O1	C1	C9	3	O3	N2	C11	C12	−2	C12	C13	C14	C15	2
O1	C1	C2	C3	−177	O4	N3	C13	C12	−125	N4	C14	C15	N7	2
C9	C1	C2	C3	0	O4	N3	C13	C14	55	N4	C14	C15	C10	176
O1	C1	C9	N1	−2	O5	N3	C13	C12	57	C13	C14	C15	N7	−172
O1	C1	C9	C5	179	O5	N3	C13	C14	−124	C13	C14	C15	C10	1
C2	C1	C9	N1	−179	C14	N4	N5	N6	−178					
C2	C1	C9	C5	1	N5	N4	C14	C13	−154					

60.32 Benzene - dialuminium bromide complex

C_6H_6 , Al_2Br_6

D.D.Eley, J.H.Taylor, S.C.Wallwork, J. Chem. Soc., 3867, 1961

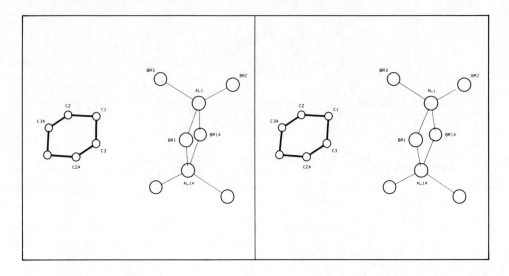

P-1   Z = 1   R = 0.21

ALBROB   LB 6-6-5

Bond Lengths

Al1	Br1	2.36	C1	C2	1.62
Al1	Br2	1.93	C1	C3	1.55
Al1	Br3	2.38	C2	C3A	1.20
Al1	Br1A	2.50			

Bond Angles

Br1	Al1	Br2	119	C2	C1	C3	104
Br1	Al1	Br3	107	C1	C2	C3A	132
Br1	Al1	Br1A	92	C1	C3	C2A	123
Br2	Al1	Br3	122				
Br2	Al1	Br1A	112				
Br3	Al1	Br1A	100				
Al1	Br1	Al1A	88				

Torsion Angles

Br2	Al1	Br1	Al1A	−116
Br3	Al1	Br1	Al1A	101
Br1A	Al1	Br1	Al1A	0
Br1	Al1	Br1A	Al1A	0
Br2	Al1	Br1A	Al1A	122
Br3	Al1	Br1A	Al1A	−108
C3	C1	C2	C3A	10
C2	C1	C3	C2A	−9
C1	C2	C3A	C1A	−12

60.33 Cyclohexane - 1,4 - dione - mercuric chloride

$(C_6H_8O_2)_n$, $(Cl_2Hg)_n$

P.Groth, O.Hassel, Acta Chem. Scand., 18, 1327, 1964

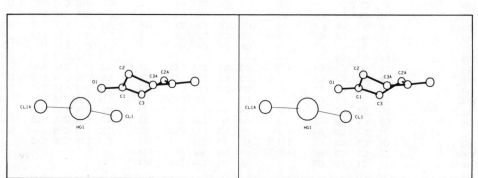

C2/c   Z = 4 $R_{0kl} = 0.042$, $R_{h0l} = 0.103$, $R_{hk0} = 0.082$

CHEXHG   LB 6-8-24

Bond Lengths

Hg1	Cl1	2.30
C1	O1	1.27
C1	C2	1.47
C1	C3	1.45
C2	C3A	1.53

Bond Angles

Cl1	Hg1	Cl1A	173
O1	C1	C2	122
O1	C1	C3	119
C2	C1	C3	117
C1	C2	C3A	111
C1	C3	C2A	111

Torsion Angles

O1	C1	C2	C3A	155
C3	C1	C2	C3A	−37
O1	C1	C3	C2A	151
C2	C1	C3	C2A	−17
C1	C2	C3A	C1A	55

60.34   Cyclohexane - 1,4 - dione - di - iodoacetylene

$C_6H_8O_2$, C_2I_2

P.Groth, O.Hassel, Acta Chem. Scand., 19, 1733, 1965

The cyclohexane - 1,4 - dione molecule is disordered.
$P2_1/c$ Z = 2   R = 0.082

CHXIAC   LB 8-8-27

Bond Lengths			Bond Angles			
I1	C3	1.98	I1	C3	C3B	175
C3	C3B	1.17				

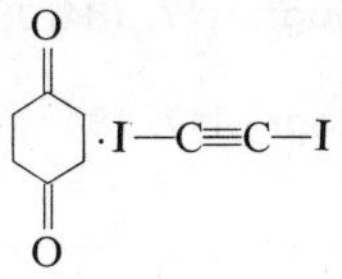

60.35   Benzamide - hydrogen tri - iodide complex

$2C_7H_7NO$, HI_3

J.M.Reddy, K.Knox, M.B.Robin, J. Chem. Phys., 40, 1082, 1964

The benzamide residue is disordered.
P-1   Z = 4 R_{hk0} = 0.084,
R_{h0l} = 0.124, R_{0kl} = 0.086

BZAMTI   LB 14-15-4

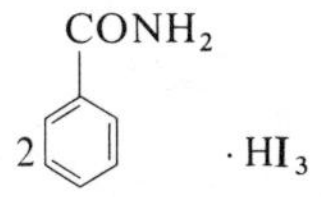

60.36   2,6 - Lutidine - urea complex

C_7H_9N , CH_4N_2O

J.D.Lee, S.C.Wallwork, Acta Cryst., 19, 311, 1965

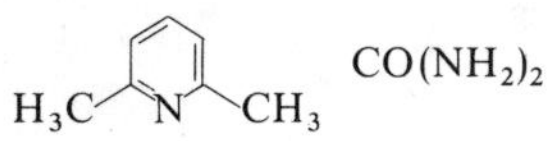

C2/c   Z = 4 R_{hk0} = 0.09,
R_{h0l} = 0.08

LUTDUR   LB 8-13-4

Bond Lengths			Bond Angles			
C1	N1	1.38	C1	N1	C1A	120
C1	C2	1.41	N1	C1	C2	121
C1	C4	1.53	N1	C1	C4	118
C2	C3	1.39	C2	C1	C4	121
			C1	C2	C3	119
C5	N2	1.25	C2	C3	C2A	120
C5	O1	1.27				
			N2	C5	N2A	126
			N2	C5	O1	117

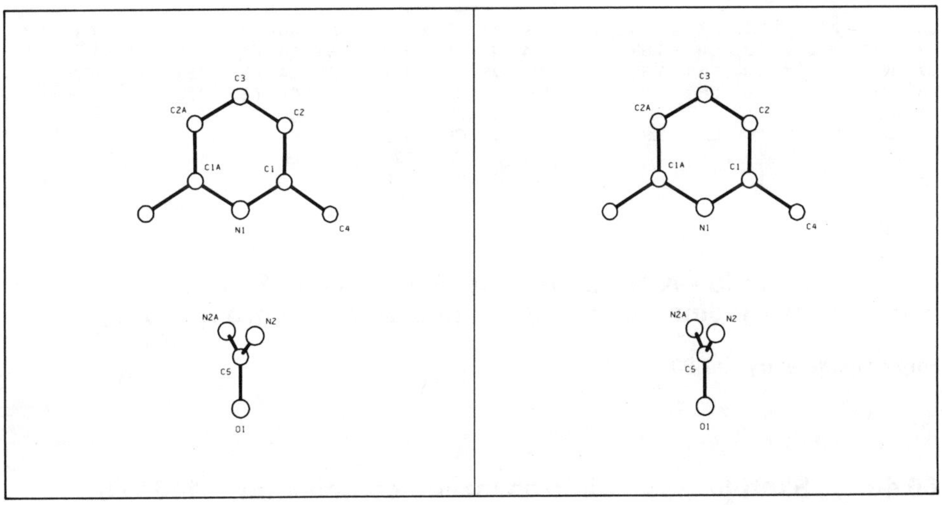

60.37   Indole - s - trinitrobenzene complex

C_8H_7N , $C_6H_3N_3O_6$

A.W.Hanson, Acta Cryst., 17, 559, 1964

The structure is totally disordered.
$P2_1/a$ Z = 4   R = 0.19

INTNIB   LB 14-10-37

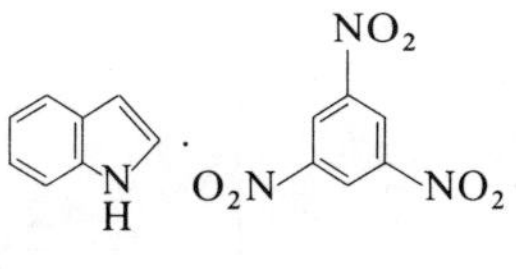

60.38   p - Iodo - N,N - dimethylaniline - hydrochloride - hydroiodide - iodine - complex

$2C_8H_{11}IN^+$, Cl^- , I_3^-

(i)   R.Allmann, Z. Kristallogr., 117, 184, 1962 (refined as space group no. 15)

(ii)   R.Allmann, Z. Kristallogr., 117, 184, 1962 (refined as space group no. 9)

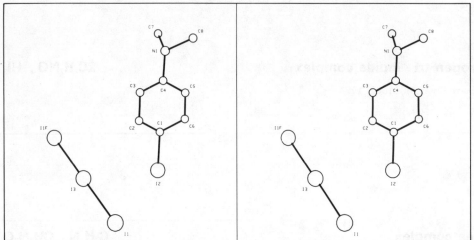

(i)

C2/c   Z = 4   R = 0.152

IDMEAN   LB 16-22-4

(ii)

Atomic coordinates were not reported in the paper.
Cc   Z = 4   R = 0.145

IDMEAN01   LB 16-22-4

Bond Lengths

I2	C1	2.15	C2	C3	1.45
C4	N1	1.49	C3	C4	1.33
C7	N1	1.63	C4	C5	1.37
C8	N1	1.67	C5	C6	1.41
C1	C2	1.30			
C1	C6	1.49	I1	I3	2.91

Bond Angles

C4	N1	C7	110		N1	C4	C3	118
C4	N1	C8	119		N1	C4	C5	117
C7	N1	C8	112		C3	C4	C5	125
I2	C1	C2	120		C4	C5	C6	122
I2	C1	C6	114		C1	C6	C5	111
C2	C1	C6	125					
C1	C2	C3	120		I1	I3	I1F	180
C2	C3	C4	116					

Torsion Angles

C3	C4	N1	C7	−88

60.39   p - Iodo - N,N - dimethylaniline - hydrochloride - hydroiodide - iodine - complex (refined as space group no. 9)

$2C_8H_{11}IN^+$, Cl^- , I_3^-

For complete entry see 60.38

60.40   Skatole - s - trinitrobenzene complex (at −140 ° C)

C_9H_9N , $C_6H_3N_3O_6$

A.W.Hanson, Acta Cryst., 17, 559, 1964

P2₁/a   Z = 4   R = 0.13

SKTNIB   LB 15-12-7

Bond Lengths

N7	O10	1.22		C18	N25	1.38
N7	O11	1.20		C22	N25	1.40
N8	O12	1.23		C16	C17	1.39
N8	O13	1.21		C16	C21	1.42
N9	O14	1.22		C17	C18	1.40
N9	O15	1.21		C18	C19	1.39
C1	N7	1.48		C19	C20	1.37
C3	N8	1.46		C19	C23	1.49
C5	N9	1.49		C20	C21	1.37
C1	C2	1.38		C22	C23	1.34
C1	C6	1.40		C23	C24	1.50
C2	C3	1.38				
C3	C4	1.39				
C4	C5	1.38				
C5	C6	1.38				

Bond Angles

O10	N7	O11	125		C18	N25	C22	108
O10	N7	C1	118		C17	C16	C21	121
O11	N7	C1	117		C16	C17	C18	115
O12	N8	O13	123		N25	C18	C17	129
O12	N8	C3	117		N25	C18	C19	109
O13	N8	C3	120		C17	C18	C19	122
O14	N9	O15	125		C18	C19	C20	123
O14	N9	C5	117		C18	C19	C23	106
O15	N9	C5	118		C20	C19	C23	131
N7	C1	C2	119		C19	C20	C21	116
N7	C1	C6	118		C16	C21	C20	122
C2	C1	C6	123		N25	C22	C23	111
C1	C2	C3	118		C19	C23	C22	106
N8	C3	C2	120		C19	C23	C24	126
N8	C3	C4	117		C22	C23	C24	128
C2	C3	C4	123					
C3	C4	C5	117					
N9	C5	C4	118					
N9	C5	C6	118					
C4	C5	C6	124					
C1	C6	C5	116					

Torsion Angles

O10	N7	C1	C2	−180		C22	N25	C18	C17	180
O10	N7	C1	C6	−1		C22	N25	C18	C19	0
O11	N7	C1	C2	2		C18	N25	C22	C23	1
O11	N7	C1	C6	−179		C21	C16	C17	C18	1
O12	N8	C3	C2	−13		C17	C16	C21	C20	−1
O12	N8	C3	C4	167		C16	C17	C18	N25	180
O13	N8	C3	C2	165		C16	C17	C18	C19	0
O13	N8	C3	C4	−14		N25	C18	C19	C20	179
O14	N9	C5	C4	−3		N25	C18	C19	C23	0
O14	N9	C5	C6	177		C17	C18	C19	C20	−1
O15	N9	C5	C4	174		C17	C18	C19	C23	179
O15	N9	C5	C6	−6		C18	C19	C20	C21	1
N7	C1	C2	C3	179		C23	C19	C20	C21	−180
C6	C1	C2	C3	0		C18	C19	C23	C22	1
N7	C1	C6	C5	−180		C18	C19	C23	C24	179
C2	C1	C6	C5	−1		C20	C19	C23	C22	−179
C1	C2	C3	N8	−178		C20	C19	C23	C24	−1
C1	C2	C3	C4	1		C19	C20	C21	C16	0
N8	C3	C4	C5	178		N25	C22	C23	C19	−1
C2	C3	C4	C5	−1		N25	C22	C23	C24	−179
C3	C4	C5	N9	180						
C3	C4	C5	C6	0						
N9	C5	C6	C1	−179						
C4	C5	C6	C1	1						

60.41   1,3,7,9 - Tetramethyluric acid - pyrene complex $C_9H_{12}N_4O_3$, $C_{16}H_{10}$

A.Damiani, P.de Santis, E.Giglio, A.M.Liquori, R.Puliti, A.Ripamonti,
Acta Cryst., 19, 340, 1965

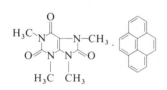

Pc   Z = 2   R = 0.174

MURPYR   LB 25-22-2

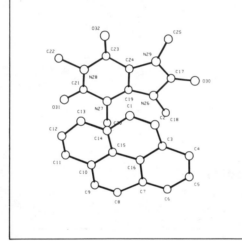
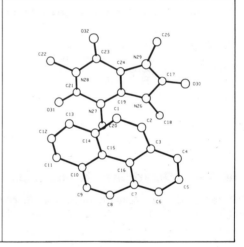

Bond Lengths

C1	C2	1.27		C17	N26	1.44
C1	C14	1.41		C18	N26	1.47
C2	C3	1.45		C19	N26	1.35
C3	C4	1.47		C19	N27	1.35
C3	C16	1.39		C20	N27	1.50
C4	C5	1.37		C21	N27	1.45
C5	C6	1.41		C21	N28	1.34
C6	C7	1.36		C22	N28	1.46
C7	C8	1.51		C23	N28	1.42
C7	C16	1.52		C17	N29	1.36
C8	C9	1.27		C24	N29	1.42
C9	C10	1.40		C25	N29	1.45
C10	C11	1.43		C17	O30	1.22
C10	C15	1.38		C21	O31	1.25
C11	C12	1.26		C23	O32	1.24
C12	C13	1.33		C19	C24	1.40
C13	C14	1.37		C23	C24	1.42
C14	C15	1.42				
C15	C16	1.44				

Bond Angles

C2	C1	C14	120					
C1	C2	C3	126					
C2	C3	C4	130					
C2	C3	C16	114					
C4	C3	C16	116					
C3	C4	C5	117					
C4	C5	C6	128					
C5	C6	C7	117					
C6	C7	C8	128					
C6	C7	C16	117					
C8	C7	C16	115					
C7	C8	C9	127					
C8	C9	C10	116					
C9	C10	C11	121					
C9	C10	C15	123					
C11	C10	C15	116					
C10	C11	C12	120					
C11	C12	C13	129					
C12	C13	C14	114					
C1	C14	C13	118					
C1	C14	C15	120					
C13	C14	C15	122					
C10	C15	C14	119					
C10	C15	C16	124					
C14	C15	C16	117					
C3	C16	C7	124					
C3	C16	C15	122					
C7	C16	C15	114					
C17	N26	C18	115					
C17	N26	C19	111					
C18	N26	C19	133					
C19	N27	C20	124					
C19	N27	C21	115					
C20	N27	C21	121					
C21	N28	C22	116					
C21	N28	C23	130					

Torsion Angles

C22	N28	C23	113		C14	C1	C2	C3	10		C11	C10	C15	C14	4	
C17	N29	C24	106		C2	C1	C14	C13	177		C11	C10	C15	C16	180	
C17	N29	C25	121		C2	C1	C14	C15	−6		C10	C11	C12	C13	6	
C24	N29	C25	133		C1	C2	C3	C4	176		C11	C12	C13	C14	−5	
N26	C17	N29	107		C1	C2	C3	C16	−10		C12	C13	C14	C1	−180	
N26	C17	O30	123		C2	C3	C4	C5	174		C12	C13	C14	C15	3	
N29	C17	O30	130		C16	C3	C4	C5	0		C1	C14	C15	C10	−180	
N26	C19	N27	131		C2	C3	C16	C7	−177		C1	C14	C15	C16	4	
N26	C19	C24	104		C2	C3	C16	C15	7		C13	C14	C15	C10	−3	
N27	C19	C24	125		C4	C3	C16	C7	−3		C13	C14	C15	C16	−179	
N27	C21	N28	118		C4	C3	C16	C15	−178		C10	C15	C16	C3	179	
N27	C21	O31	116		C3	C4	C5	C6	5		C10	C15	C16	C7	3	
N28	C21	O31	126		C4	C5	C6	C7	−6		C14	C15	C16	C3	−5	
N28	C23	O32	125		C5	C6	C7	C8	−178		C14	C15	C16	C7	179	
N28	C23	C24	110		C5	C6	C7	C16	3							
O32	C23	C24	125		C6	C7	C8	C9	−177		C18	N26	C17	N29	176	
N29	C24	C19	112		C16	C7	C8	C9	3		C18	N26	C17	O30	−9	
N29	C24	C23	126		C6	C7	C16	C3	1		C19	N26	C17	N29	2	
C19	C24	C23	122		C6	C7	C16	C15	177		C19	N26	C17	O30	178	
					C8	C7	C16	C3	−178		C17	N26	C19	N27	−176	
					C8	C7	C16	C15	−2		C18	N26	C19	N27	12	
					C7	C8	C9	C10	−3		C18	N26	C19	C24	−174	
					C8	C9	C10	C11	180		C20	N27	C19	N26	−4	
					C8	C9	C10	C15	4		C20	N27	C19	C24	−177	
					C9	C10	C11	C12	179		C21	N27	C19	N26	178	
					C15	C10	C11	C12	−5		C21	N27	C19	C24	5	
					C9	C10	C15	C14	180		C19	N27	C21	N28	−5	
					C9	C10	C15	C16	−4							

C19	N27	C21	O31	179
C20	N27	C21	N28	177
C20	N27	C21	O31	1
C22	N28	C21	N27	−178
C22	N28	C21	O31	−3
C23	N28	C21	N27	5
C23	N28	C21	O31	−179
C21	N28	C23	O32	180
C21	N28	C23	C24	−4
C22	N28	C23	O32	3
C22	N28	C23	C24	179
C24	N29	C17	N26	−1
C24	N29	C17	O30	−176
C25	N29	C17	N26	−178
C25	N29	C17	O30	7
C17	N29	C24	C19	0
C17	N29	C24	C23	−178
C25	N29	C24	C19	176
C25	N29	C24	C23	−2
N26	C19	C24	N29	1
N26	C19	C24	C23	180
N27	C19	C24	N29	176
N27	C19	C24	C23	−6
N28	C23	C24	N29	−177
N28	C23	C24	C19	4
O32	C23	C24	N29	−2
O32	C23	C24	C19	180

60.42 1,3,7,9 - Tetramethyluric acid - coronene complex

$2C_9H_{12}N_4O_3$, $C_{24}H_{12}$

A.Damiani, P.de Santis, E.Giglio, A.M.Liquori, R.Puliti, A.Ripamonti,
Acta Cryst., 16, A57, 1963

Atomic coordinates were not
reported in the paper.
P1 Z = 1 No R factor was given.

TMUCOR   LB 42-36-1

60.43 Azulene - s - trinitrobenzene complex

$C_{10}H_8$, $C_6H_3N_3O_6$

A.W.Hanson, Acta Cryst., 19, 19, 1965

The structure is totally disordered.
P2₁/a Z = 4 R = 0.060

AZUNBZ   LB 16-11-4

60.44 Azulene - s - trinitrobenzene complex

$C_{10}H_8$, $C_6H_3N_3O_6$

D.S.Brown, S.C.Wallwork, Acta Cryst., 19, 149, 1965

The structure is totally disordered.
Atomic coordinates were not
reported in the paper.
P2₁/c Z = 4 R = 0.19

AZUNBZ01   LB 16-11-4

60.45 Dipyridine - iodine heptaiodide

$C_{10}H_{10}IN_2^+$, I_3^- , $2I_2$

O.Hassel, H.Hope, Acta Chem. Scand., 15, 407, 1961

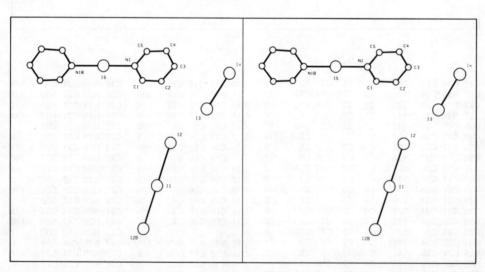

P2₁/c   Z = 2 R_{0kl} = 0.07,
R_{h0l} = 0.11

PYRIDI

Bond Lengths

I1	I2	2.93	C5	N1	1.32
			C1	C2	1.39
I3	I4	2.74	C2	C3	1.43
			C3	C4	1.38
I5	N1	2.16	C4	C5	1.36
C1	N1	1.34			

Bond Angles

I2	I1	I2B	180	N1	C1	C2	125
				C1	C2	C3	117
N1	I5	N1B	180	C2	C3	C4	118
I5	N1	C1	121	C3	C4	C5	119
I5	N1	C5	123	N1	C5	C4	126
C1	N1	C5	116				

Torsion Angles

N1B	I5	N1	C1	90

60.46   Mesitaldehyde - perchloric acid complex

$2C_{10}H_{12}O$, $HClO_4$

C.D.Fisher, L.H.Jensen, W.M.Schubert, J. Amer. Chem. Soc., 87, 33, 1965

The hydrogen atoms of the P - Me
groups are disordered.
$P2_1/m$ Z = 2   R = 0.08

MESPCL   LB 20-25-1

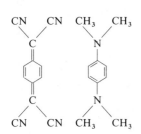

60.47   7,7,8,8 - Tetracyanoquinodimethan - N,N,N',N' - tetramethyl - p - phenylenediamine complex

$C_{10}H_{16}N_2$, $C_{12}H_4N_4$

A.W.Hanson, Acta Cryst., 19, 610, 1965

C2/m   Z = 2   R = 0.083

QMEPHE   LB 22-20-12

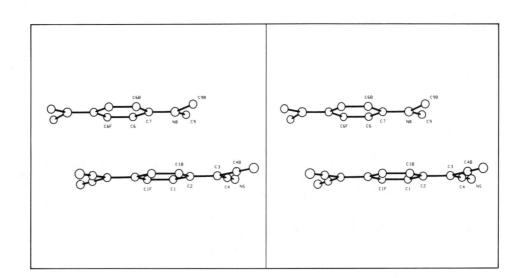

Bond Lengths

C4	N5	1.16	C7	N8	1.36
C1	C2	1.41	C9	N8	1.47
C1	C1F	1.37	C6	C7	1.42
C2	C3	1.41	C6	C6F	1.37
C3	C4	1.41			

Bond Angles

C2	C1	C1F	121	C7	N8	C9	121
C1	C2	C3	121	C9	N8	C9B	117
C1	C2	C1B	118	C7	C6	C6F	121
C2	C3	C4B	122	N8	C7	C6	121
C4	C3	C4B	116	C6	C7	C6B	117
N5	C4	C3	179				

Torsion Angles

C1F	C1	C2	C3	−179	C9	N8	C7	C6	5
C1F	C1	C2	C1B	1	C9	N8	C7	C6B	−175
C2	C1	C1F	C2D	−1	C9B	N8	C7	C6	175
C1	C2	C3	C4	1	C9B	N8	C7	C6B	−5
C1	C2	C3	C4B	178	C6F	C6	C7	N8	180
C1B	C2	C3	C4	−178	C6F	C6	C7	C6B	0
C1B	C2	C3	C4B	−1	C7	C6	C6F	C7D	0
C2	C3	C4	N5	−180					
C4B	C3	C4	N5	6					

60.48   Anthracene - s - trinitrobenzene $C_{14}H_{10}$, $C_6H_3N_3O_6$

(i)   D.S.Brown, S.C.Wallwork, A.Wilson, Acta Cryst., 17, 168, 1964

(ii)   D.S.Brown, S.C.Wallwork, A.Wilson, Acta Cryst., 17, 168, 1964 (at −100°C)

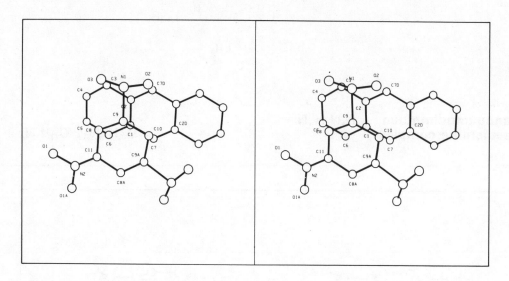

(i)

C2/c   Z = 4   R = 0.180

ANCTNB   LB 20-13-8

(ii)

C2/c   Z = 4   R = 0.162

ANCTNB01   LB 20-13-8

Bond Lengths

		(i)	(ii)			(i)	(ii)
C1	C2	1.52	1.44	N1	O2	1.17	1.22
C1	C6	1.39	1.43	N1	O3	1.14	1.19
C1	C7	1.46	1.41	N2	O1	1.27	1.22
C2	C3	1.49	1.44	C9	N1	1.75	1.52
C2	C7D	1.28	1.39	C11	N2	1.28	1.46
C3	C4	1.37	1.37	C8	C9	1.33	1.36
C4	C5	1.45	1.42	C8	C11	1.45	1.39
C5	C6	1.42	1.39	C9	C10	1.43	1.40

Bond Angles

			(i)	(ii)				(i)	(ii)				(i)	(ii)
C2	C1	C6	122	120	O2	N1	O3	152	128					
C2	C1	C7	117	119	O2	N1	C9	98	116					
C6	C1	C7	122	121	O3	N1	C9	110	116					
C1	C2	C3	116	118	O1	N2	O1A	110	124					
C1	C2	C7D	120	120	O1	N2	C11	125	118					
C3	C2	C7D	124	122	C9	C8	C11	117	116					
C2	C3	C4	119	122	N1	C9	C8	113	117					
C3	C4	C5	125	120	N1	C9	C10	119	117					
C4	C5	C6	118	120	C8	C9	C10	128	125					
C1	C6	C5	121	120	C9	C10	C9A	111	114					
C1	C7	C2D	123	120	N2	C11	C8	120	118					
					C8	C11	C8A	120	124					

Torsion Angles

				(i)	(ii)
C6	C1	C2	C3	−4	3
C6	C1	C2	C7D	−177	−179
C7	C1	C2	C3	177	−179
C7	C1	C2	C7D	4	−1
C2	C1	C6	C5	2	−2
C7	C1	C6	C5	180	−180
C2	C1	C7	C2D	−4	1
C6	C1	C7	C2D	177	179
C1	C2	C3	C4	2	−2
C7D	C2	C3	C4	175	180
C1	C2	C7D	C1D	−5	1
C3	C2	C7D	C1D	−177	179
C2	C3	C4	C5	2	0
C3	C4	C5	C6	−5	1
C4	C5	C6	C1	3	0
O2	N1	C9	C8	−175	−174
O2	N1	C9	C10	3	4
O3	N1	C9	C8	8	9
O3	N1	C9	C10	−173	−173
O1	N2	C11	C8	1	0
O1	N2	C11	C8A	−179	−180
O1A	N2	C11	C8	−179	−180
O1A	N2	C11	C8A	1	0
C11	C8	C9	N1	180	178
C11	C8	C9	C10	2	0
C9	C8	C11	N2	179	−180
C9	C8	C11	C8A	−1	0
N1	C9	C10	C9A	−179	−178
C8	C9	C10	C9A	−1	0

60.49   Anthracene - s - trinitrobenzene (at − 100 ° C) $C_{14}H_{10}$, $C_6H_3N_3O_6$

For complete entry see 60.48

60.50   Anthracene - pyromellitic dianhydride complex $C_{14}H_{10}$, $C_{10}H_2O_6$

J.C.A.Boeyens, F.H.Herbstein, J. Phys. Chem., 69, 2160, 1965

No comparison of bond lengths is possible since they are not reported in the paper.

P-1   Z = 1   R = 0.185

ANTPML   LB 24-12-6

Bond Lengths

C6	C7	1.56	C4	O6	1.22
C6	C12	1.41	C4	O7	1.49
C7	C8	1.42	C5A	O7	1.35
C7	C12A	1.44	C5	O8	1.32
C8	C9	1.62	C1	C2	1.50
C9	C10	1.43	C1	C3	1.45
C10	C11	1.35	C2	C4	1.46
C11	C12A	1.55	C2	C3A	1.48
			C3	C5	1.44

Bond Angles

C7	C6	C12	122	C6	C12	C7A	116	C1	C3	C5	132
C6	C7	C8	120	C6	C12	C11A	121	C1	C3	C2A	111
C6	C7	C12A	121					C5	C3	C2A	111
C8	C7	C12A	115	C4	O7	C5A	107	O6	C4	O7	118
C7	C8	C9	116	C2	C1	C3	120	O6	C4	C2	127
C8	C9	C10	117	C1	C2	C4	133	O7	C4	C2	111
C9	C10	C11	119	C1	C2	C3A	126	O8	C5	O7A	117
C10	C11	C12A	120	C4	C2	C3A	101	O8	C5	C3	133

60.51   Benzyl sulfide - iodine $C_{14}H_{14}S$, I_2

C.Romming, Acta Chem. Scand., 14, 2145, 1960

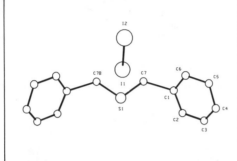

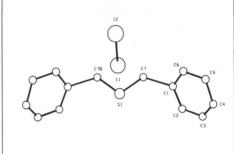

Pnma   Z = 4 R_{hk0} = 0.104,
R_{0kl} = 0.138, R_{h0l} = 0.105

BENZSI   LB 14-14-26

Bond Lengths

I1	I2	2.82	C1	C7	1.80
			C2	C3	1.36
S1	C7	1.82	C3	C4	1.23
C1	C2	1.48	C4	C5	1.50
C1	C6	1.30	C5	C6	1.41

Bond Angles

C7	S1	C7B	92	C2	C3	C4	123
C2	C1	C6	129	C3	C4	C5	130
C2	C1	C7	117	C4	C5	C6	109
C6	C1	C7	114	C1	C6	C5	120
C1	C2	C3	109	S1	C7	C1	113

Torsion Angles

C7B	S1	C7	C1	−180
S1	C7	C1	C6	−96

60.52   Perylene - fluoranil complex $C_{20}H_{12}$, $C_6F_4O_2$

A.W.Hanson, Acta Cryst., 16, 1147, 1963

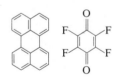

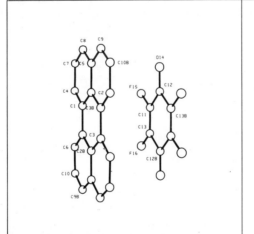

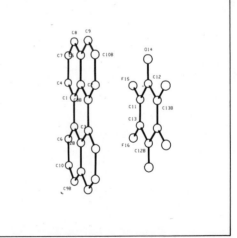

$P2_1/n$ Z = 2   R = 0.11

PERFAN   LB 26-12-1

Bond Lengths

C1	C2	1.43	C7	C8	1.36
C1	C3	1.47	C9	C10B	1.36
C1	C4	1.38			
C2	C5	1.43	F15	C11	1.33
C2	C3B	1.43	F16	C13	1.33
C3	C6	1.38	C12	O14	1.20
C4	C7	1.42	C11	C12	1.48
C5	C8	1.41	C11	C13	1.32
C5	C9	1.41	C12	C13B	1.50
C6	C10	1.40			

Bond Angles

C2	C1	C3	119	C1	C4	C7	122	F15	C11	C12	115
C2	C1	C4	118	C2	C5	C8	119	F15	C11	C13	122
C3	C1	C4	123	C2	C5	C9	119	C12	C11	C13	123
C1	C2	C5	119	C8	C5	C9	121	O14	C12	C11	123
C1	C2	C3B	122	C3	C6	C10	122	O14	C12	C13B	123
C5	C2	C3B	119	C4	C7	C8	120	C11	C12	C13B	114
C1	C3	C6	122	C5	C8	C7	121	F16	C13	C11	122
C1	C3	C2B	119	C5	C9	C10B	121	F16	C13	C12B	115
C6	C3	C2B	119	C6	C10	C9B	120	C11	C13	C12B	123

60.53 Perylene - pyromellitic dianhydride complex

$C_{20}H_{12}$, $C_{10}H_2O_6$

J.C.A.Boeyens, F.H.Herbstein, J. Phys. Chem., 69, 2160, 1965

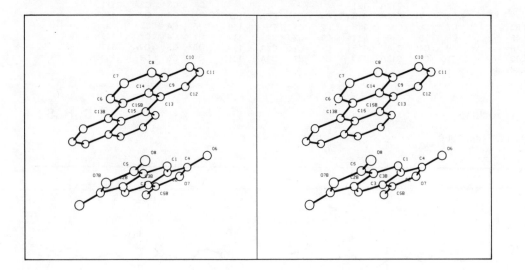

$P2_1/n$ $Z = 2$ $R = 0.14$

PERPML   LB 30-14-3

Bond Lengths

C6	C7	1.38	C10	C11	1.36	C4	O6	1.23
C6	C15	1.38	C11	C12	1.41	C4	O7	1.36
C7	C8	1.37	C12	C13	1.39	C5B	O7	1.41
C8	C9	1.44	C13	C14	1.42	C5	O8	1.18
C9	C10	1.37	C13	C15B	1.49	C1	C2	1.39
C9	C14	1.44	C14	C15	1.41	C1	C3	1.39
						C2	C4	1.46
						C2	C3B	1.38
						C3	C5	1.46

Bond Angles

C7	C6	C15	122	C14	C13	C15B	118	C1	C2	C3B	124
C6	C7	C8	120	C9	C14	C13	119	C4	C2	C3B	108
C7	C8	C9	120	C9	C14	C15	118	C1	C3	C5	131
C8	C9	C10	121	C13	C14	C15	123	C1	C3	C2B	122
C8	C9	C14	119	C6	C15	C14	121	C5	C3	C2B	107
C10	C9	C14	120	C6	C15	C13B	120	O6	C4	O7	122
C9	C10	C11	121	C14	C15	C13B	119	O6	C4	C2	130
C10	C11	C12	121					O7	C4	C2	109
C11	C12	C13	120	C4	O7	C5B	109	O8	C5	O7B	122
C12	C13	C14	119	C2	C1	C3	114	O8	C5	C3	131
C12	C13	C15B	123	C1	C2	C4	129				

61.1 Ethylene oxide hydrate

C_2H_4O , $7.2H_2O$

R.K.McMullan, G.A.Jeffrey, J. Chem. Phys., 42, 2725, 1965

The structure is totally disordered.
Pm3n   Z was not reported.
R = 0.081

ETHYLO   LB 2-4-41

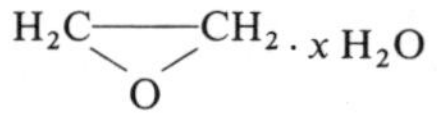

H_2C———$CH_2 \cdot x\,H_2O$
O

61.2 Tetrahydrofuran hydrogen sulfide hydrate

$8C_4H_8O$, $7.33H_2S$, $136H_2O$

T.C.W.Mak, R.K.McMullan, J. Chem. Phys., 42, 2732, 1965

The structure is totally disordered.
Fd3m   Z = 8   R = 0.116

THFHSH   LB 4-8-91

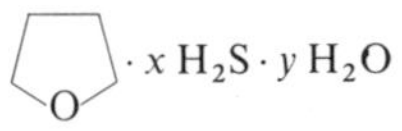

$\cdot x\,H_2S \cdot y\,H_2O$
O

61.3 Hexamethylenetetramine hexahydrate

$C_6H_{12}N_4$, $6H_2O$

T.C.W.Mak, J. Chem. Phys., 43, 2799, 1965

The atomic coordinates have not
been processed, details of the
molecular geometry are presented
in the paper.
R3m   Z = 1   R = 0.096

HXMTHH   LB 6-12-42

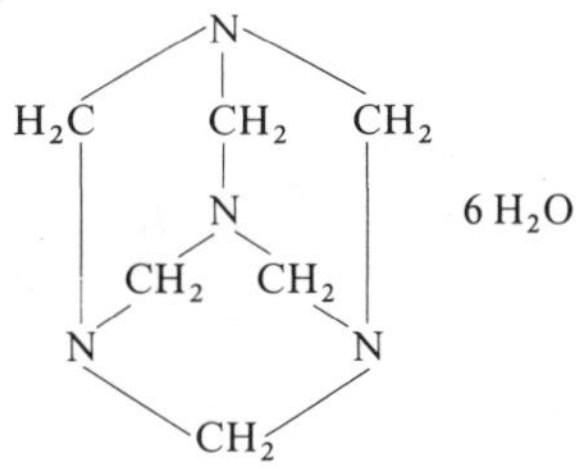

N
H_2C CH_2 CH_2
N $6\,H_2O$
CH_2 CH_2
N N
CH_2

61.4 Tri - n - butyl sulfonium fluoride hydrate (cubic form)

$C_{12}H_{27}S^+$, F^- , $20H_2O$

G.A.Jeffrey, R.K.McMullan, J. Chem. Phys., 37, 2231, 1962

The atomic coordinates have not
been processed, details of the
molecular geometry are presented
in the paper.
Pm3n   Z = 2   R = 0.158

TBUTSF   LB 12-27-3

$(C_4H_9)_3S^+$ $F^- \cdot 20\,H_2O$

61.5 Tri - n - butyl sulfonium fluoride hydrate (monoclinic form)

$C_{12}H_{27}S^+$, F^- , $23H_2O$

P.T.Beurskens, G.A.Jeffrey, J. Chem. Phys., 40, 2800, 1964

The atomic coordinates have not
been processed, details of the
molecular geometry are presented
in the paper.
P2$_1$/m   Z = 4   R = 0.13

TBUTSF01   LB 12-27-5

$(C_4H_9)_3\,S^+\,F^- \cdot 23\,H_2O$

61.6 Tetra - n - butyl ammonium fluoride hydrate

$C_{16}H_{36}N^+$, F^- , $32.8H_2O$

R.K.McMullan, M.Bonamico, G.A.Jeffrey, J. Chem. Phys., 39, 3295, 1963

The atomic coordinates have not been processed, details of the molecular geometry are presented in the paper.

P4$_2$/m   Z = 5   R = 0.12

TBUAMF   LB 16-36-7

$[(C_4H_9)_4N]^+ . F^- . 32 \cdot 8H_2O$

61.7 Tetra - n - butyl ammonium benzoate hydrate

$C_{16}H_{36}N^+$, $C_7H_5O_2^-$, $39.5H_2O$

M.Bonamico, G.A.Jeffrey, R.K.McMullan, J. Chem. Phys., 37, 2219, 1962

The atomic coordinates have not been processed, details of the molecular geometry are presented in the paper.

P4$_2$/mnm   Z = 4   R = 0.175

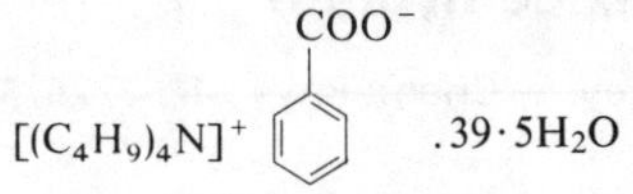

BUABZO   LB 23-41-1

$[(C_4H_9)_4N]^+$ $.39 \cdot 5H_2O$

61.8 Tetra iso - amyl ammonium fluoride hydrate

$C_{20}H_{44}N^+$, F^- , $38H_2O$

D.Feil, G.A.Jeffrey, J. Chem. Phys., 35, 1863, 1961

The atomic coordinates have not been processed, details of the molecular geometry are presented in the paper.

Pbmm   Z = 2   R = 0.135

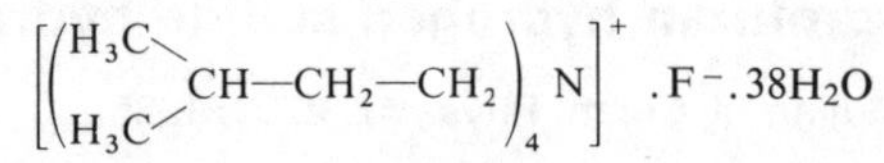

TAAMFH   LB 20-44-2

$$\left[\left(\begin{matrix} H_3C \\ H_3C \end{matrix} CH-CH_2-CH_2 \right)_4 N \right]^+ . F^- . 38H_2O$$

62.1   Octachloro - 1,2 - dicarbaclovododecaborane $C_2H_4B_{10}Cl_8$

J.A.Potenza, W.N.Lipscomb, Inorg. Chem., 3, 1673, 1964

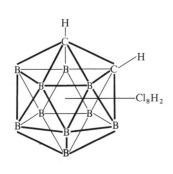

See also Pawley, Acta Cryst., 20, 631, 1966.

Pbna   Z = 8   R = 0.11

OCLCDB   LB 2-4-6

Bond Lengths

B3	B4	1.85
B3	B7	1.74
B3	B8	1.70
B3	C1	1.77
B3	C2	1.71
B4	B5	1.77
B4	B8	1.83
B4	B9	1.75
B4	Cl4	1.72
B4	C1	1.75
B5	B6	1.87
B5	B9	1.77
B5	B10	1.75
B5	Cl5	1.77
B5	C1	1.71
B6	B10	1.79
B6	B11	1.76
B6	C1	1.75
B6	C2	1.70
B7	B8	1.74
B7	B11	1.81
B7	B12	1.74
B7	Cl7	1.77
B7	C2	1.66
B8	B9	1.81
B8	B12	1.80
B8	Cl8	1.78
B9	B10	1.82
B9	B12	1.82
B9	Cl9	1.77
B10	B11	1.79
B10	B12	1.80
B10	Cl10	1.78
B11	B12	1.77
B11	Cl11	1.74
B11	C2	1.68
B12	Cl12	1.79
C1	C2	1.67

Bond Angles

B4	B3	B7	110	B6	B5	Cl5	117	Cl7	B7	C2	122	B5	B10	B9	59	B7	B12	B11	62
B4	B3	B8	62	B6	B5	C1	58	B3	B8	B4	63	B5	B10	B11	110	B7	B12	Cl12	124
B4	B3	C1	58	B9	B5	B10	62	B3	B8	B7	61	B5	B10	B12	108	B8	B12	B9	60
B4	B3	C2	104	B9	B5	Cl5	128	B3	B8	B9	109	B5	B10	Cl10	122	B8	B12	B10	108
B7	B3	B8	61	B9	B5	C1	105	B3	B8	B12	108	B6	B10	B9	110	B8	B12	B11	109
B7	B3	C1	105	B10	B5	Cl5	126	B3	B8	Cl8	122	B6	B10	B11	59	B8	B12	Cl12	121
B7	B3	C2	58	B10	B5	C1	104	B4	B8	B7	110	B6	B10	B12	107	B9	B12	B10	60
B8	B3	C1	106	Cl5	B5	C1	118	B4	B8	B9	58	B6	B10	Cl10	122	B9	B12	B11	109
B8	B3	C2	105	B5	B6	B10	57	B4	B8	B12	107	B9	B10	B11	109	B9	B12	Cl12	118
C1	B3	C2	57	B5	B6	B11	106	B4	B8	Cl8	117	B9	B10	B12	60	B10	B12	B11	60
B3	B4	B5	107	B5	B6	C1	56	B7	B8	B9	108	B9	B10	Cl10	121	B10	B12	Cl12	121
B3	B4	B8	55	B5	B6	C2	102	B7	B8	B12	59	B11	B10	B12	59	B11	B12	Cl12	123
B3	B4	B9	105	B10	B6	B11	61	B7	B8	Cl8	126	B11	B10	Cl10	121	B3	C1	B4	64
B3	B4	Cl4	119	B10	B6	C1	101	B9	B8	B12	61	B12	B10	Cl10	121	B3	C1	B5	113
B3	B4	C1	59	B10	B6	C2	102	B9	B8	Cl8	118	B6	B11	B7	108	B3	C1	B6	113
B5	B4	B8	107	B11	B6	C1	105	B12	B8	Cl8	124	B6	B11	B10	61	B3	C1	C2	60
B5	B4	B9	60	B11	B6	C2	58	B4	B9	B5	60	B6	B11	B12	110	B4	C1	B5	61
B5	B4	Cl4	122	C1	B6	C2	58	B4	B9	B8	62	B6	B11	Cl11	122	B4	C1	B6	116
B5	B4	C1	58	B3	B7	B8	59	B4	B9	B10	108	B6	B11	C2	59	B4	C1	C2	111
B8	B4	B9	61	B3	B7	B11	109	B4	B9	B12	109	B7	B11	B10	107	B5	C1	B6	65
B8	B4	Cl4	128	B3	B7	B12	108	B4	B9	Cl9	119	B7	B11	B12	58	B5	C1	C2	110
B8	B4	C1	101	B3	B7	Cl7	119	B5	B9	B8	108	B7	B11	Cl11	119	B6	C1	C2	60
B9	B4	Cl4	130	B3	B7	C2	60	B5	B9	B10	59	B7	B11	C2	57	B3	C2	B6	118
B9	B4	C1	104	B8	B7	B11	110	B5	B9	B12	106	B10	B11	B12	61	B3	C2	B7	62
Cl4	B4	C1	119	B8	B7	B12	62	B5	B9	Cl9	119	B10	B11	Cl11	127	B3	C2	B11	117
B4	B5	B6	110	B8	B7	Cl7	124	B8	B9	B10	107	B10	B11	C2	103	B3	C2	C1	63
B4	B5	B9	60	B8	B7	C2	105	B8	B9	B12	59	B12	B11	Cl11	123	B6	C2	B7	118
B4	B5	B10	110	B11	B7	B12	60	B8	B9	Cl9	125	B12	B11	C2	102	B6	C2	B11	63
B4	B5	Cl5	120	B11	B7	Cl7	121	B10	B9	B12	59	Cl11	B11	C2	124	B6	C2	C1	62
B4	B5	C1	60	B11	B7	C2	58	B10	B9	Cl9	121	B7	B12	B8	59	B7	C2	B11	66
B6	B5	B9	109	B12	B7	Cl7	126	B12	B9	Cl9	125	B7	B12	B9	108	B7	C2	C1	113
B6	B5	B10	59	B12	B7	C2	104	B5	B10	B6	64	B7	B12	B10	109	B11	C2	C1	113

62.2   Dimethylsulfoxide - boron trifluoride

$C_2H_6BF_3OS$

E.L.McGandy, Dissert. Abstr., 22, 754, 1961

$(CH_3)_2SO \rightarrow BF_3$

Atomic coordinates were not given
but bond lengths were reported.
$P2_1/c$ Z = 4   No R factor was
given.

DMSBTF

62.3   Carbon monoxide - borane - monomethylamine complex

$C_2H_7BNO^-$, CH_6N^+

R.W.Parry, C.E.Nordman, J.C.Carter, G.Terhaar, Adv. Chem. Ser., 302, 1964

Atomic coordinates were not given
but bond lengths were reported.
$Pna2_1$ Z = 4   No R factor was
given.

$[CH_3—NH—CO—BH_3]^-$ $[CH_3NH_3]^+$

COBMAM

62.4   2,3 - Dicarbahexaborane(8)

$C_2H_8B_4$

F.P.Boer, W.E.Streib, W.N.Lipscomb, Inorg. Chem., 3, 1666, 1964

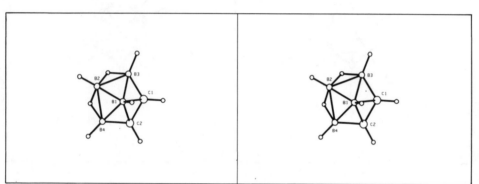

There are errors in the published
bond lengths.
See also Pawley, Acta Cryst., 20,
631, 1966.
$P2_1/n$ Z = 4   R = 0.081

CAHBOR   LB 2-8-2

Bond Lengths						Bond Angles																	
B1	B2	1.71	B2	B3	1.78	B2	B1	B3	61	B3	B1	C2	90	B3	B2	B4	100	B2	B4	C2	104	B4	C2	C1	116
B1	B3	1.78	B2	B4	1.80	B2	B1	B4	62	B4	B1	C1	89	B1	B3	B2	58	B1	C1	B3	66	B2	H7	B3	88
B1	B4	1.76	B3	C1	1.51	B2	B1	C1	97	B4	B1	C2	50	B1	B3	C1	64	B1	C1	C2	66	B2	H8	B4	88
B1	C1	1.75	B4	C2	1.49	B2	B1	C2	97	C1	B1	C2	48	B2	B3	C1	103	B3	C1	C2	116			
B1	C2	1.75	C1	C2	1.42	B3	B1	B4	102	B1	B2	B3	61	B1	B4	B2	58	B1	C2	B4	65			
						B3	B1	C1	51	B1	B2	B4	60	B1	B4	C2	64	B1	C2	C1	66			

62.5   Acetonitrile - tridecahydrononaborane

$C_2H_{16}B_9N$

F.E.Wang, P.G.Simpson, W.N.Lipscomb, J. Chem. Phys., 35, 1335, 1961

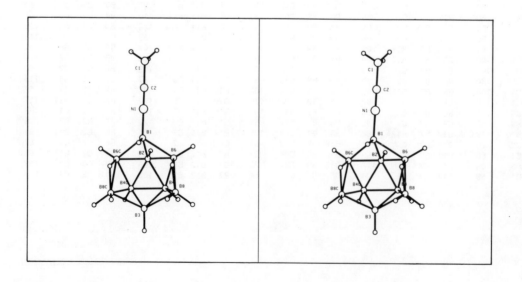

$P2_1/m$ Z = 2   R = 0.14

ACNDNB   LB 2-16-1

Bond Lengths

B1	B2	1.74		B4	B6	1.78
B1	B6	1.87		B4	B8	1.72
B1	N1	1.50		B4	B4C	1.83
B2	B4	1.76		B6	B8	1.85
B2	B6	1.75		C2	N1	1.13
B3	B4	1.76		C1	C2	1.43
B3	B8	1.87				

Bond Angles

B2	B1	B6	58	B6	B2	B6C	118	B3	B4	B6	110	B2	B6	B8	107
B2	B1	N1	110	B4	B3	B8	56	B3	B4	B8	65	B4	B6	B8	56
B6	B1	B6C	107	B4	B3	B4C	62	B3	B4	B4C	59	B3	B8	B4	59
B6	B1	N1	116	B4	B3	B8C	112	B6	B4	B8	64	B3	B8	B6	103
B1	B2	B4	115	B8	B3	B4C	112	B6	B4	B4C	109	B4	B8	B6	60
B1	B2	B6	65	B8	B3	B8C	125	B8	B4	B4C	116	B1	N1	C2	180
B4	B2	B6	61	B2	B4	B3	104	B1	B6	B2	57	N1	C2	C1	180
B4	B2	B4C	62	B2	B4	B6	59	B1	B6	B4	107	B6	H9	B8	92
B4	B2	B6C	114	B2	B4	B8	112	B1	B6	B8	115				
B6	B2	B4C	114	B2	B4	B4C	59	B2	B6	B4	60				

62.6   1 - Ethyldecaborane

$C_2H_{18}B_{10}$

A.Perloff, Acta Cryst., 17, 332, 1964

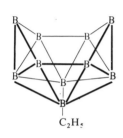

C_2H_5

$P2_12_12_1$ $Z = 4$ $R = 0.095$

EDABOR   LB 2-18-1

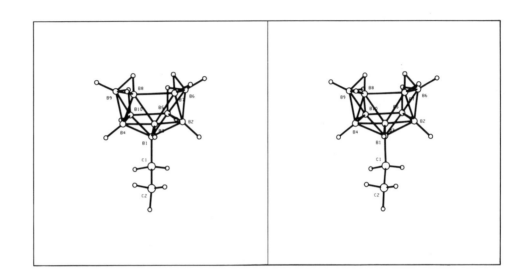

Bond Lengths

B1	B2	1.80
B1	B3	1.77
B1	B4	1.78
B1	B5	1.78
B1	B10	1.76
B1	C1	1.59
B2	B3	1.79
B2	B5	1.79
B2	B6	1.70
B2	B7	1.79
B3	B4	1.76
B3	B7	1.76
B3	B8	1.74
B4	B8	1.78
B4	B9	1.72
B4	B10	1.78
B5	B6	1.77
B5	B10	1.96
B6	B7	1.79
B7	B8	1.99
B8	B9	1.77
B9	B10	1.79
C1	C2	1.55

Bond Angles

B2	B1	B3	60	B3	B2	B6	110	B3	B4	B9	110	B3	B8	B4	60
B2	B1	B4	114	B3	B2	B7	59	B3	B4	B10	106	B3	B8	B7	56
B2	B1	B5	60	B5	B2	B6	61	B8	B4	B9	61	B3	B8	B9	109
B2	B1	B10	115	B5	B2	B7	105	B8	B4	B10	105	B4	B8	B7	107
B2	B1	C1	118	B6	B2	B7	62	B9	B4	B10	62	B4	B8	B9	58
B3	B1	B4	60	B1	B3	B2	61	B1	B5	B2	61	B7	B8	B9	117
B3	B1	B5	106	B1	B3	B4	60	B1	B5	B6	109	B4	B9	B8	61
B3	B1	B10	106	B1	B3	B7	109	B1	B5	B10	56	B4	B9	B10	61
B3	B1	C1	129	B1	B3	B8	109	B2	B5	B6	57	B8	B9	B10	105
B4	B1	B5	115	B2	B3	B4	115	B2	B5	B10	107	B1	B10	B4	60
B4	B1	B10	60	B2	B3	B7	61	B6	B5	B10	117	B1	B10	B5	57
B4	B1	C1	120	B2	B3	B8	118	B2	B6	B5	62	B1	B10	B9	109
B5	B1	B10	67	B4	B3	B7	118	B2	B6	B7	62	B4	B10	B5	107
B5	B1	C1	116	B4	B3	B8	61	B5	B6	B7	106	B4	B10	B9	58
B10	B1	C1	116	B7	B3	B8	69	B2	B7	B3	61	B5	B10	B9	116
B1	B2	B3	59	B1	B4	B3	60	B2	B7	B6	57	B1	C1	C2	112
B1	B2	B5	59	B1	B4	B8	107	B2	B7	B8	106	B6	H11	B7	90
B1	B2	B6	112	B1	B4	B9	112	B3	B7	B6	108	B5	H12	B6	81
B1	B2	B7	106	B1	B4	B10	59	B3	B7	B8	55	B9	H13	B10	93
B3	B2	B5	105	B3	B4	B8	59	B6	B7	B8	116	B8	H14	B9	87

Torsion Angles

C2	C1	B1	B3	7

62.7   **Trimethylamine triborane**

$C_3H_{16}B_3N$

H.G.Norment, Acta Cryst., 14, 1216, 1961

$$(CH_3)_3 N \cdot B_3H_7$$

The structure is totally disordered.
R3m $Z = 3$ $R = 0.11$

TMATBO   LB 3-16-1

62.8 Dimethylamino - boron dichloride dimer

$C_4H_{12}B_2Cl_4N_2$

H.Hess, Z. Kristallogr., 118, 361, 1963

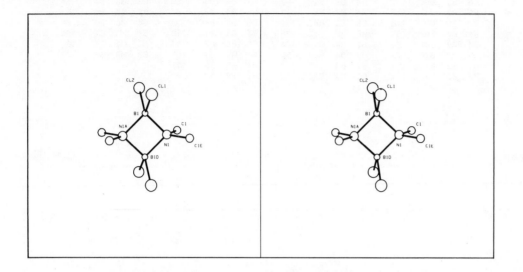

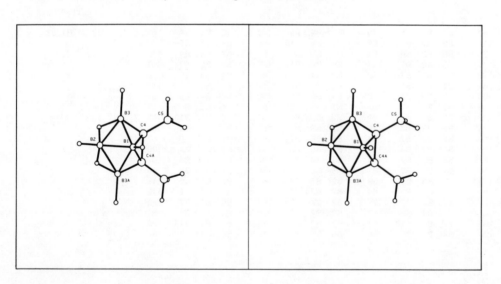

C2/m   Z = 2   R = 0.15

DMNBCL   LB 4-12-4

Bond Lengths			Bond Angles				Torsion Angles			
B1	Cl1	1.83	Cl1	B1	Cl2	107	Cl1	B1	N1	B1D	118
B1	Cl2	1.83	Cl1	B1	N1	114	Cl1	B1	N1	C1	−126
B1	N1	1.59	Cl2	B1	N1	114	Cl1	B1	N1	C1E	1
C1	N1	1.50	N1	B1	N1A	93	Cl2	B1	N1	B1D	−119
			B1	N1	B1D	87	Cl2	B1	N1	C1	−2
			B1	N1	C1	115	Cl2	B1	N1	C1E	125
			B1	N1	C1E	115	N1A	B1	N1	B1D	0
			C1	N1	C1E	108	N1A	B1	N1	C1	116
							N1A	B1	N1	C1E	−116

62.9 2,3 - Dimethyl - 2,3 - dicarbahexaborane

$C_4H_{12}B_4$

F.P.Boer, W.E.Streib, W.N.Lipscomb, Inorg. Chem., 3, 1666, 1964

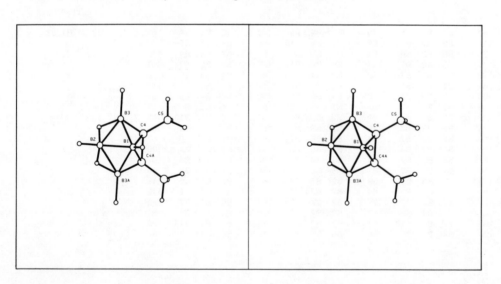

P2₁mn   Z = 2   R = 0.078

MCHBOR   LB 4-12-6

Bond Lengths			Bond Angles							
B1	B2	1.70	B2	B1	B3	62	B1	B3	C4	64
B1	B3	1.77	B2	B1	C4	98	B2	B3	C4	105
B1	C4	1.76	B3	B1	B3A	101	B1	C4	B3	65
B2	B3	1.78	B3	B1	C4	51	B1	C4	C5	128
B3	C4	1.52	B3	B1	C4A	90	B1	C4	C4A	66
C4	C5	1.51	C4	B1	B3A	90	B3	C4	C5	122
C4	C4A	1.43	C4	B1	C4A	48	B3	C4	C4A	115
			B1	B2	B3	61	C5	C4	C4A	121
			B3	B2	B3A	100	B2	H9	B3	84
			B1	B3	B2	57				

62.10   1,2 - bis(Bromomethyl) - 1,2 - dicarbaclovododecaborane

$C_4H_{14}B_{10}Br_2$

D.Voet, W.N.Lipscomb, Inorg. Chem., 3, 1679, 1964

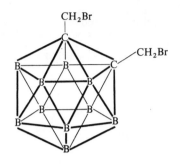

No comparison of bond lengths is possible since they are not reported in the paper.
See also Pawley, Acta Cryst., 20, 631, 1966.
$P2_12_12_1$ Z = 4   R = 0.132

BRMCDB   LB 4-14-1

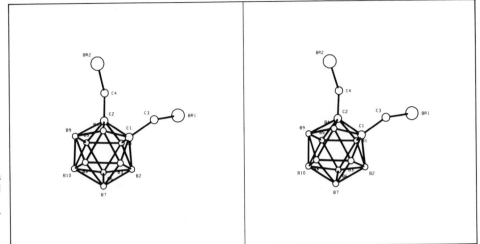

Bond Lengths

B1	B2	1.73
B1	B5	1.85
B1	B6	1.77
B1	C1	1.68
B1	C2	1.75
B2	B3	1.80
B2	B6	1.77
B2	B7	1.81
B2	C1	1.70
B3	B4	1.76
B3	B7	1.68
B3	B8	1.73
B3	C1	1.69
B4	B8	1.72
B4	B9	1.75
B4	C1	1.71
B4	C2	1.72
B5	B6	1.76
B5	B9	1.77
B5	B10	1.81
B5	C2	1.77
B6	B7	1.79
B6	B10	1.84
B7	B8	1.76
B7	B10	1.82
B8	B9	1.71
B8	B10	1.73
B9	B10	1.69
B9	C2	1.77
Br1	C3	1.97
Br2	C4	1.94
C1	C2	1.63
C1	C3	1.56
C2	C4	1.48

Bond Angles

B2	B1	B5	108	B3	B4	C2	105	B3	B7	B10	107	B8	B10	B9	60
B2	B1	B6	61	B8	B4	B9	59	B6	B7	B8	106	B1	C1	B2	62
B2	B1	C1	60	B8	B4	C1	105	B6	B7	B10	61	B1	C1	B3	115
B2	B1	C2	107	B8	B4	C2	107	B8	B7	B10	58	B1	C1	B4	116
B5	B1	B6	58	B9	B4	C1	105	B3	B8	B4	61	B1	C1	C2	64
B5	B1	C1	103	B9	B4	C2	61	B3	B8	B7	58	B1	C1	C3	121
B5	B1	C2	59	C1	B4	C2	57	B3	B8	B9	109	B2	C1	B3	64
B6	B1	C1	103	B1	B5	B6	59	B3	B8	B10	110	B2	C1	B4	117
B6	B1	C2	103	B1	B5	B9	107	B4	B8	B7	108	B2	C1	C2	114
C1	B1	C2	57	B1	B5	B10	108	B4	B8	B9	61	B2	C1	C3	122
B1	B2	B3	107	B1	B5	C2	58	B4	B8	B10	110	B3	C1	B4	62
B1	B2	B6	61	B6	B5	B9	106	B7	B8	B9	109	B3	C1	C2	112
B1	B2	B7	108	B6	B5	B10	62	B7	B8	B10	63	B3	C1	C3	117
B1	B2	C1	59	B6	B5	C2	103	B9	B8	B10	59	B4	C1	C2	62
B3	B2	B6	103	B9	B5	B10	56	B4	B9	B5	109	B4	C1	C3	111
B3	B2	B7	56	B9	B5	C2	60	B4	B9	B8	60	C2	C1	C3	117
B3	B2	C1	58	B10	B5	C2	104	B4	B9	B10	110	B1	C2	B4	112
B6	B2	B7	60	B1	B6	B2	58	B4	B9	C2	58	B1	C2	B5	64
B6	B2	C1	102	B1	B6	B5	63	B5	B9	B8	111	B1	C2	B9	111
B7	B2	C1	101	B1	B6	B7	108	B5	B9	B10	63	B1	C2	C1	59
B2	B3	B4	109	B1	B6	B10	110	B5	B9	C2	60	B1	C2	C4	115
B2	B3	B7	63	B2	B6	B5	111	B8	B9	B10	61	B4	C2	B5	111
B2	B3	B8	111	B2	B6	B7	61	B8	B9	C2	106	B4	C2	B9	60
B2	B3	C1	58	B2	B6	B10	110	B10	B9	C2	109	B4	C2	C1	61
B4	B3	B7	110	B5	B6	B7	109	B5	B10	B6	58	B4	C2	C4	125
B4	B3	B8	59	B5	B6	B10	60	B5	B10	B7	105	B5	C2	B9	60
B4	B3	C1	59	B7	B6	B10	60	B5	B10	B8	108	B5	C2	C1	109
B7	B3	B8	62	B2	B7	B3	62	B5	B10	B9	61	B5	C2	C4	115
B7	B3	C1	107	B2	B7	B6	59	B6	B10	B7	59	B9	C2	C1	107
B8	B3	C1	105	B2	B7	B8	110	B6	B10	B8	105	B9	C2	C4	122
B3	B4	B8	60	B2	B7	B10	109	B6	B10	B9	105	C1	C2	C4	125
B3	B4	B9	106	B3	B7	B6	108	B7	B10	B8	59	Br1	C3	C1	115
B3	B4	C1	58	B3	B7	B8	60	B7	B10	B9	106	Br2	C4	C2	116

Torsion Angles

C2	C1	C3	Br1	−91
C1	C2	C4	Br2	−88

62.11   Dimethylaminoborine dimer

$C_4H_{16}B_2N_2$

P.J.Schapiro, Dissert. Abstr., 22, 2607, 1962

Atomic coordinates were not given but bond lengths were reported.
C2/m   Z = 2   R = 0.21

DMABDI   LB 4-16-7

62.12   bis(o - Dodecacarborane)   C₄H₂₂B₂₀

$C_4H_{22}B_{20}$

L.H.Hall, A.Perloff, F.A.Maver, S.Block, J. Chem. Phys., 43, 3911, 1965

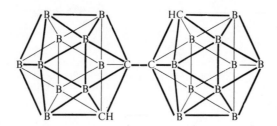

One C atom and one B atom could not be distinguished in the analysis. They have been relabelled as X1 and X2.

$P2_1/n$ $Z = 2$ $R = 0.064$

DOCBOR   LB 4-22-2

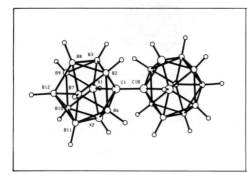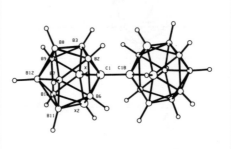

Bond Lengths

B2	B3	1.78	B8	B9	1.77
B2	B6	1.77	B8	B12	1.78
B2	B7	1.77	B9	B10	1.78
B2	B8	1.78	B9	B12	1.78
B2	C1	1.72	B9	X1	1.73
B3	B8	1.76	B10	B11	1.78
B3	B9	1.76	B10	B12	1.77
B3	X1	1.74	B10	X1	1.73
B3	C1	1.73	B10	X2	1.73
B6	B7	1.76	B11	B12	1.78
B6	B11	1.77	B11	X2	1.72
B6	X2	1.74	X1	X2	1.71
B6	C1	1.71	X1	C1	1.69
B7	B8	1.78	X2	C1	1.69
B7	B11	1.78	C1	C1B	1.52
B7	B12	1.77			

Bond Angles

B3	B2	B6	108	B7	B6	X2	106	B3	B9	B8	60	B7	B11	B12	60
B3	B2	B7	107	B7	B6	C1	106	B3	B9	B10	108	B7	B11	X2	106
B3	B2	B8	59	B11	B6	X2	59	B3	B9	B12	108	B10	B11	B12	60
B3	B2	C1	59	B11	B6	C1	106	B3	B9	X1	60	B10	B11	X2	59
B6	B2	B7	59	X2	B6	C1	59	B8	B9	B10	108	B12	B11	X2	106
B6	B2	B8	108	B2	B7	B6	60	B8	B9	B12	60	B7	B12	B8	60
B6	B2	C1	59	B2	B7	B8	60	B8	B9	X1	107	B7	B12	B9	108
B7	B2	B8	60	B2	B7	B11	108	B10	B9	B12	60	B7	B12	B10	108
B7	B2	C1	105	B2	B7	B12	108	B10	B9	X1	59	B7	B12	B11	60
B8	B2	C1	105	B6	B7	B8	108	B12	B9	X1	106	B8	B12	B9	60
B2	B3	B8	60	B6	B7	B11	60	B9	B10	B11	108	B8	B12	B10	108
B2	B3	B9	109	B6	B7	B12	108	B9	B10	B12	60	B8	B12	B11	108
B2	B3	X1	106	B8	B7	B11	108	B9	B10	X1	59	B9	B12	B10	60
B2	B3	C1	59	B8	B7	B12	60	B9	B10	X2	106	B9	B12	B11	108
B8	B3	B9	60	B11	B7	B12	60	B11	B10	B12	60	B10	B12	B11	60
B8	B3	X1	106	B2	B8	B3	60	B11	B10	X1	106	B3	X1	B9	61
B8	B3	C1	105	B2	B8	B7	60	B11	B10	X2	59	B3	X1	B10	111
B9	B3	X1	59	B2	B8	B9	108	B12	B10	X1	106	B3	X1	X2	109
B9	B3	C1	105	B2	B8	B12	108	B12	B10	X2	106	B3	X1	C1	60
X1	B3	C1	58	B3	B8	B7	108	X1	B10	X2	59	B9	X1	B10	62
B2	B6	B7	60	B3	B8	B9	60	B6	B11	B7	59	B9	X1	X2	110
B2	B6	B11	109	B3	B8	B12	108	B6	B11	B10	108	B9	X1	C1	109
B2	B6	X2	107	B7	B8	B9	108	B6	B11	B12	107	B10	X1	X2	60
B2	B6	C1	59	B7	B8	B12	60	B6	B11	X2	60	B10	X1	C1	109
B7	B6	B11	61	B9	B8	B12	60	B7	B11	B10	108	X2	X1	C1	60

(continued)

B6	X2	B10	112
B6	X2	B11	62
B6	X2	X1	109
B6	X2	C1	60
B10	X2	B11	62
B10	X2	X1	60
B10	X2	C1	109
B11	X2	X1	110
B11	X2	C1	109
X1	X2	C1	60
B2	C1	B3	62
B2	C1	B6	62
B2	C1	X1	112
B2	C1	X2	112
B2	C1	C1B	123
B3	C1	B6	113
B3	C1	X1	61
B3	C1	X2	111
B3	C1	C1B	120
B6	C1	X1	111
B6	C1	X2	61
B6	C1	C1B	120
X1	C1	X2	61
X1	C1	C1B	117
X2	C1	C1B	117

Torsion Angles

B2	C1	C1B	B2B	180

62.13   3 - Ethylamine - 5,6 - μ - ethyl - amino - octaborane(12)   C₄H₂₄B₈N₂

$C_4H_{24}B_8N_2$

Ethylammonium - ethylimmonium undecahydro - octaborane
R.Lewin, P.G.Simpson, W.N.Lipscomb, J. Chem. Phys., 39, 1532, 1963

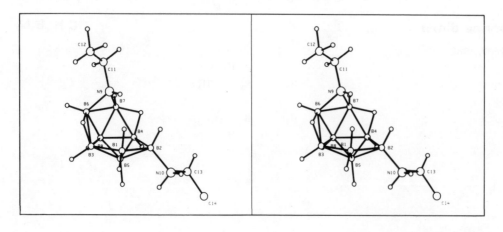

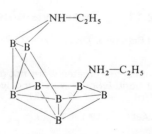

$P2_1/a$ $Z = 4$ $R = 0.13$

EMOBOR   LB 4-24-1

Bond Lengths

B1	B2	1.92
B1	B3	1.90
B1	B5	1.73
B2	B4	1.92
B2	B5	1.71
B2	N10	1.58
B3	B5	1.74
B3	B6	1.83
B3	B8	1.79
B4	B5	1.77
B4	B7	1.84
B4	B8	1.81
B5	B8	1.81
B6	B7	1.99
B6	B8	1.79
B6	N9	1.57
B7	B8	1.81
B7	N9	1.57
C11	N9	1.49
C13	N10	1.50
C11	C12	1.51
C13	C14	1.51

Bond Angles

B2	B1	B3	107	B2	B4	B7	117	B3	B6	B8	59	B4	B8	B6	115
B2	B1	B5	56	B2	B4	B8	110	B3	B6	N9	116	B4	B8	B7	61
B3	B1	B5	57	B5	B4	B7	107	B7	B6	B8	57	B5	B8	B6	107
B1	B2	B4	104	B5	B4	B8	61	B7	B6	N9	51	B5	B8	B7	107
B1	B2	B5	56	B7	B4	B8	59	B8	B6	N9	102	B6	B8	B7	67
B1	B2	N10	119	B1	B5	B2	68	B4	B7	B6	105	B6	N9	B7	78
B4	B2	B5	58	B1	B5	B3	66	B4	B7	B8	59	B6	N9	C11	117
B4	B2	N10	117	B1	B5	B4	120	B4	B7	N9	118	B7	N9	C11	119
B5	B2	N10	111	B1	B5	B8	117	B6	B7	N9	51	B2	N10	C13	116
B1	B3	B5	56	B2	B5	B3	125	B8	B7	N9	101	N9	C11	C12	110
B1	B3	B6	115	B2	B5	B4	67	B3	B8	B4	109	N10	C13	C14	112
B1	B3	B8	110	B2	B5	B8	120	B3	B8	B5	58	B3	H10	B6	85
B5	B3	B6	109	B3	B5	B4	113	B3	B8	B6	61	B4	H11	B7	86
B5	B3	B8	62	B3	B5	B8	60	B3	B8	B7	114				
B6	B3	B8	59	B4	B5	B8	61	B4	B8	B5	58				
B2	B4	B5	55	B3	B6	B7	104								

Torsion Angles

B6	N9	C11	C12	74
B5	B2	N10	C13	105
B2	N10	C13	C14	−176

62.14   bis(Dimethylsulfide) - dodecahydrodecaborane $C_4H_{24}B_{10}S_2$

D.E.Sands, A.Zalkin, Acta Cryst., 15, 410, 1962

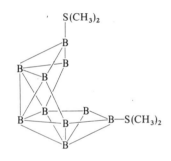

No comparison of bond lengths is possible since they are not reported in the paper. The published bond lengths are incorrect (private communication).
P2₁/c   Z = 4   R = 0.17

DMSBOR   LB 4-24-2

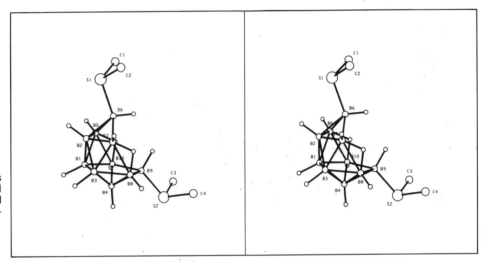

Bond Lengths

B1	B2	1.74
B1	B3	1.82
B1	B4	1.77
B1	B5	1.75
B1	B10	1.77
B2	B3	1.73
B2	B5	1.70
B2	B6	1.74
B2	B7	1.77
B3	B4	1.77
B3	B7	1.79
B3	B8	1.79
B4	B8	1.76
B4	B9	1.75
B4	B10	1.76
B5	B6	1.84
B5	B10	1.92
B6	B7	1.88
B6	S1	1.93
B7	B8	1.89
B8	B9	1.86
B9	B10	1.86
B9	S2	1.92
S1	C1	1.81
S1	C2	1.84
S2	C3	1.82
S2	C4	1.83

Bond Angles

B2	B1	B3	58	B1	B3	B4	59	B1	B5	B10	58	B7	B8	B9	112
B2	B1	B4	105	B1	B3	B7	110	B2	B5	B6	59	B4	B9	B8	58
B2	B1	B5	58	B1	B3	B8	108	B2	B5	B10	105	B4	B9	B10	58
B2	B1	B10	110	B2	B3	B4	105	B6	B5	B10	112	B4	B9	S2	109
B3	B1	B4	59	B2	B3	B7	60	B2	B6	B5	57	B8	B9	B10	106
B3	B1	B5	108	B2	B3	B8	109	B2	B6	B7	58	B8	B9	S2	117
B3	B1	B10	109	B4	B3	B7	110	B2	B6	S1	107	B10	B9	S2	117
B4	B1	B5	110	B7	B3	B8	64	B5	B6	B7	105	B1	B10	B4	60
B4	B1	B10	59	B1	B4	B3	62	B5	B6	S1	114	B1	B10	B5	56
B5	B1	B10	66	B1	B4	B8	112	B7	B6	S1	116	B1	B10	B9	109
B1	B2	B3	63	B1	B4	B9	113	B2	B7	B3	58	B4	B10	B5	104
B1	B2	B5	61	B1	B4	B10	60	B2	B7	B6	57	B4	B10	B9	58
B1	B2	B6	115	B3	B4	B8	61	B2	B7	B8	103	B5	B10	B9	109
B1	B2	B7	114	B3	B4	B9	114	B3	B7	B6	107	B6	S1	C1	102
B3	B2	B5	114	B3	B4	B10	112	B3	B7	B8	58	B6	S1	C2	103
B3	B2	B6	116	B8	B4	B9	64	B6	B7	B8	109	C1	S1	C2	104
B3	B2	B7	61	B8	B4	B10	115	B3	B8	B4	60	B9	S2	C3	102
B5	B2	B6	64	B9	B4	B10	64	B3	B8	B7	58	B9	S2	C4	102
B5	B2	B7	117	B1	B5	B2	60	B3	B8	B9	108	C3	S2	C4	101
B6	B2	B7	65	B1	B5	B6	110	B4	B8	B9	58	B7	H11	B8	109
B1	B3	B2	59									B5	H12	B10	107

Torsion Angles

C1	S1	B6	B5	−78
C3	S2	B9	B10	66

62.15   Dimethylaminoborine trimer

L.M.Trefonas, F.S.Mathews, W.N.Lipscomb, Acta Cryst., 14, 273, 1961

$C_6H_{24}B_3N_3$

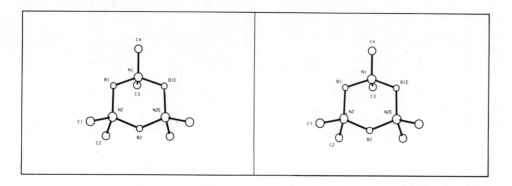

Pnma   Z = 4   R = 0.19

DMABTR   LB 6-24-1

Bond Lengths

B1	N1	1.56
B1	N2	1.57
B2	N2	1.62
C3	N1	1.48
C4	N1	1.43
C1	N2	1.56
C2	N2	1.47

Bond Angles

N1	B1	N2	115	B1	N2	B2	114
N2	B2	N2E	110	B1	N2	C1	109
B1	N1	B1E	112	B1	N2	C2	117
B1	N1	C3	114	B2	N2	C1	101
B1	N1	C4	109	B2	N2	C2	109
C3	N1	C4	100	C1	N2	C2	106

Torsion Angles

N2	B1	N1	B1E	−50
N1	B1	N2	B2	50
N2E	B2	N2	B1	−46

62.16   Dimethylphosphinoborine tetramer

P.Goldstein, R.A.Jacobson, J. Amer. Chem. Soc., 84, 2457, 1962

$C_8H_{32}B_4P_4$

Atomic coordinates were not given
but bond lengths were reported.
Cc   Z = 4   R = 0.18

DMPHSB   LB 8-32-1

62.17   Hexaethyl borazine

M.A.Viswamitra, S.N.Vaidya, Z. Kristallogr., 121, 472, 1965

$C_{12}H_{30}B_3N_3$

No comparison of bond lengths is
possible since they are not reported
in the paper. The B and N atoms
could not be distinguished in the
analysis. They have been relabelled
as X.
P-1   Z = 1   R = 0.188

HETBOR   LB 12-30-6

Bond Lengths

X1	X2	1.42
X1	X3	1.42
X1	C4	1.53
X2	X3A	1.43
X2	C5	1.48
X3	C6	1.49
C4	C7	1.54
C5	C8	1.54
C6	C9	1.54

Bond Angles

X2	X1	X3	120
X2	X1	C4	122
X3	X1	C4	117
X1	X2	X3A	122
X1	X2	C5	120
X1	X3	X2A	118
X1	X3	C6	119
X1	C4	C7	107
X2	C5	C8	111
X3	C6	C9	113

Torsion Angles

X3	X1	X2	X3A	−6	X3	X1	C4	C7	95
X3	X1	X2	C5	176	X1	X2	X3A	X1A	6
C4	X1	X2	X3A	180	X1	X2	X3A	C6A	−178
C4	X1	X2	C5	2	C5	X2	X3A	X1A	−176
X2	X1	X3	X2A	6	C5	X2	X3A	C6A	0
X2	X1	X3	C6	−178	X1	X2	C5	C8	−90
C4	X1	X3	X2A	−180	X3A	X2	C5	C8	92
C4	X1	X3	C6	−3	X1	X3	C6	C9	95
X2	X1	C4	C7	−91	X2A	X3	C6	C9	−89

62.18 Rubidium tetraphenylborate

$C_{24}H_{20}B^-$, Rb^+

Ya.Ozol, S.Vimba, A.Ievins, Kristallografija, 7, 362, 1962

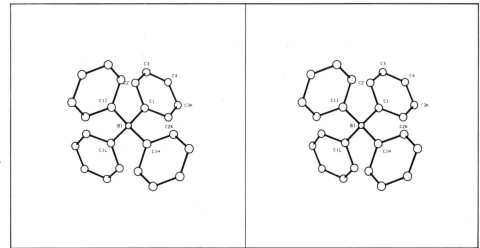

I-42m   Z = 2 $R_{hk0} = 0.11$,
$R_{h0l} = 0.20$

RBPBOR   LB 24-20-11

Bond Lengths		
B1	C1	1.52
C1	C2	1.43
C2	C3	1.41
C3	C4	1.41

Bond Angles			
C1	B1	C1H	109
C1	B1	C1L	110
B1	C1	C2	120
C2	C1	C2K	119
C1	C2	C3	119
C2	C3	C4	120
C3	C4	C3K	120

Torsion Angles				
C1H	B1	C1	C2	−149
C1H	B1	C1	C2K	29
C1I	B1	C1	C2	−29
C1I	B1	C1	C2K	149
C1L	B1	C1	C2	91
C1L	B1	C1	C2K	−91

63.1   Cyclotetra(methylenedichlorosilicon)   C₄H₈Cl₈Si₄

E.Krahe, Thesis, Munster, 1965

Atomic coordinates were not
reported in the paper.
P1   Z = 1   No R factor was given.

CTMCSI

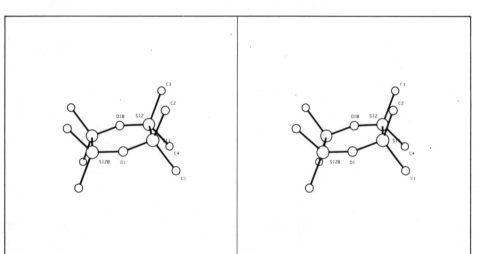

63.2   bis - Tetramethyl - disilanilene - dioxide   C₈H₂₄O₂Si₄

T.Takano, N.Kasai, M.Kakudo, Bull. Chem. Soc. Jap., 36, 585, 1963

P2₁/c   Z = 2   R₀ₖₗ = 0.201,
Rₕₒₗ = 0.135

MESILO   LB 8-24-42

Bond Lengths			Bond Angles								Torsion Angles				
Si1	Si2	2.35	Si2	Si1	O1	108	Si1	Si2	O1B	109	O1	Si1	Si2	O1B	6
Si1	O1	1.61	Si2	Si1	C1	112	Si1	Si2	C3	110	Si2	Si1	O1	Si2B	−10
Si1	C1	1.85	Si2	Si1	C2	112	Si1	Si2	C4	107					
Si1	C2	1.89	O1	Si1	C1	106	C3	Si2	O1B	111					
Si2	O1B	1.61	O1	Si1	C2	110	C3	Si2	C4	107					
Si2	C3	1.85	C1	Si1	C2	109	Si1	O1	Si2B	143					
Si2	C4	1.92													

63.3   Octa - (methylsilsesquioxane)

$C_8H_{24}O_{12}Si_8$

K.Larsson, Ark. Kemi, 16, 203, 1960

$(CH_3SiO_{1.5})_8$

R-3   Z = 3   R = 0.17

OCMSIO   LB 8-24-48

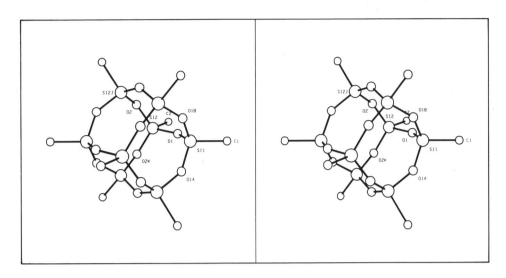

Bond Lengths

Si1	O1	1.62
Si1	C1	1.87
Si2	O1	1.60
Si2	O2	1.60
Si2	O2K	1.62
Si2	C2	1.92

Bond Angles

O1	Si1	O1A	111
O1	Si1	C1	108
O1	Si2	O2	113
O1	Si2	O2K	108
O1	Si2	C2	97
O2	Si2	O2K	113
O2	Si2	C2	115
Si1	O1	Si2	146
Si2	O2	Si2J	144

Torsion Angles

O1A	Si1	O1	Si2	65
O1B	Si1	O1	Si2	−58
O2	Si2	O1	Si1	58
O2K	Si2	O1	Si1	−67
O1	Si2	O2	Si2J	−57
O2K	Si2	O2	Si2J	66
O1	Si2	O2K	Si2K	66
O2	Si2	O2K	Si2K	−59

63.4   Octamethylcyclotetrasilazane

$C_8H_{28}N_4Si_4$

G.S.Smith, L.E.Alexander, Acta Cryst., 16, 1015, 1963

```
        CH₃    CH₃
         |      |
         |  H   |
  H₃C—Si—N—Si—CH₃
         |      |
        HN     NH
         |      |
  H₃C—Si—N—Si—CH₃
         |  H   |
         |      |
        CH₃    CH₃
```

The structure is a 1:1 - mixture of the 'chair' and 'cradle' conformations of the 8 - membered ring. In Table 4, under the heading 'cradle', the bond labelled Si(3) - N(3*) should read Si(4) - N(3*).

P2/c   Z = 4   R = 0.079

OTETSI   LB 8-28-3

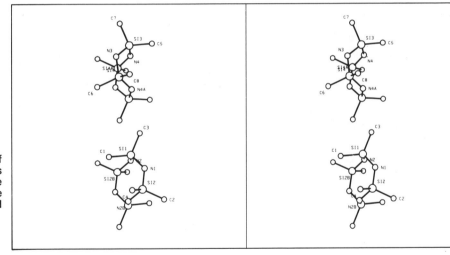

Bond Lengths

Si1	N1	1.73		Si3	N3	1.71
Si1	N2	1.74		Si3	N4	1.74
Si1	C1	1.88		Si3	C5	1.92
Si1	C3	1.87		Si3	C7	1.87
Si2	N1	1.73		Si4	N3	1.75
Si2	N2B	1.73		Si4	N4A	1.69
Si2	C2	1.85		Si4	C6	1.87
Si2	C4	1.90		Si4	C8	1.87

Bond Angles

N1	Si1	N2	112		N3	Si3	N4	110
N1	Si1	C1	110		N3	Si3	C5	112
N1	Si1	C3	106		N3	Si3	C7	106
N2	Si1	C1	108		N4	Si3	C5	106
N2	Si1	C3	106		N4	Si3	C7	111
C1	Si1	C3	114		C5	Si3	C7	111
N1	Si2	N2B	111		N3	Si4	N4A	110
N1	Si2	C2	107		N3	Si4	C6	107
N1	Si2	C4	113		N3	Si4	C8	111
C2	Si2	N2B	114		C6	Si4	N4A	112
C2	Si2	C4	109		C6	Si4	C8	109
Si1	N1	Si2	132		Si3	N3	Si4	130
Si1	N2	Si2B	132		Si3	N4	Si4A	133

Torsion Angles

N2	Si1	N1	Si2	−82
N1	Si1	N2	Si2B	99
N2B	Si2	N1	Si1	30
N1	Si2	N2B	Si1B	55
N4	Si3	N3	Si4	71
N3	Si3	N4	Si4A	28
N4A	Si4	N3	Si3	−30
N3	Si4	N4A	Si3A	−69

63.5 Tetramethyl - NN' - bis(trimethylsilyl) cyclodisilazane

$C_{10}H_{30}N_2Si_4$

P.J.Wheatley, J. Chem. Soc., 1721, 1962

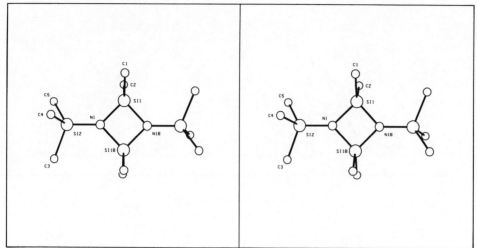

$(CH_3)_3Si-N-Si(CH_3)_2$
$(CH_3)_2Si-N-Si(CH_3)_3$

$P2_1/n$ $Z = 2$ $R_{0kl} = 0.116,$
$R_{hk0} = 0.113$

MSILAZ   LB 10-30-4

Bond Lengths

Si1	N1	1.73	Si2	N1	1.71
Si1	N1B	1.72	Si2	C3	1.88
Si1	C1	1.86	Si2	C4	1.90
Si1	C2	1.86	Si2	C5	1.88

Bond Angles

N1	Si1	N1B	88	N1	Si2	C3	111	
N1	Si1	C1	112	N1	Si2	C4	112	
N1	Si1	C2	117	N1	Si2	C5	114	
C1	Si1	N1B	114	C3	Si2	C4	106	
C1	Si1	C2	108	C3	Si2	C5	106	

C4	Si2	C5	106
Si1	N1	Si2	135
Si1	N1	Si1B	92
Si2	N1	Si1B	133

Torsion Angles

N1B	Si1	N1	Si1B	0
C3	Si2	N1	Si1	157

63.6 2,6 - Di - p - bromophenyl - 1,1 - dimethyl - 1 - sila - 2,4,6 - triazacyclohexane - 3,5 - dione acetone solvate

$C_{16}H_{15}Br_2N_3O_2Si$, C_3H_6O

J.J.Daly, W.Fink, J. Chem. Soc., 4958, 1964

The structure was determined in two dimensions only. Atomic coordinates were not reported in the paper.
$P2_1/a$ $Z = 4$ $R_{hk0} = 0.087$

SILCHO   LB 16-15-3

63.7 (−) - α - Naphthylphenylmethylsilylfluoride (absolute configuration)

$C_{17}H_{15}FSi$

T.Ashida, R.Pepinsky, Y.Okaya, Acta Cryst., 16, A48, 1963

Atomic coordinates were not reported in the paper.
See also Okaya & Ashida, Acta Cryst., 20, 461, 1966.
$P2_12_12_1$ Z was not reported.
R = 0.125

MNPMSF   LB 17-15-7

63.8 Triphenyl trimethyl disiloxane

$C_{21}H_{24}OSi_2$

H.Kandler, E.Wolfel, Acta Cryst., 16, A74, 1963

Atomic coordinates were not reported in the paper.
P-3   Z = 2   R = 0.19

PMSILX

63.9 1,1,4,4 - Tetramethyl - 2,3,5,6 - tetraphenyl - 1,4 - disilicocyclohexa - 2,5 - diene

$C_{32}H_{32}Si_2$

N.G.Bokii, Yu.T.Struchkov, Zh. Strukt. Khim., 6, 571, 1965

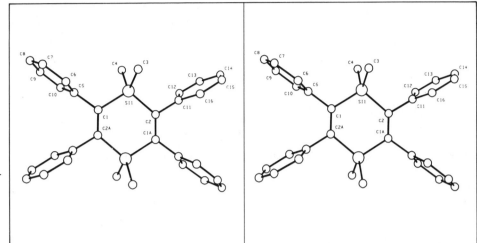

See also Vol'pin et al., J. Organ-ometal. Chem., 8, 87, 1967.
P-1   Z = 1   R = 0.161

MDSICH   LB 32-32-3

Bond Lengths

Si1	C1	1.88	C7	C8	1.42
Si1	C2	1.91	C8	C9	1.32
Si1	C3	1.82	C9	C10	1.38
Si1	C4	1.95	C11	C12	1.42
C1	C5	1.53	C11	C16	1.44
C1	C2A	1.29	C12	C13	1.39
C2	C11	1.53	C13	C14	1.47
C5	C6	1.31	C14	C15	1.35
C5	C10	1.49	C15	C16	1.43
C6	C7	1.46			

Bond Angles

C1	Si1	C2	110	Si1	C2	C1A	126	C2	C11	C12	119
C1	Si1	C3	111	C11	C2	C1A	122	C2	C11	C16	122
C1	Si1	C4	108	C1	C5	C6	123	C12	C11	C16	119
C2	Si1	C3	107	C1	C5	C10	117	C11	C12	C13	120
C2	Si1	C4	112	C6	C5	C10	120	C12	C13	C14	118
C3	Si1	C4	110	C5	C6	C7	119	C13	C14	C15	125
Si1	C1	C5	114	C6	C7	C8	121	C14	C15	C16	116
Si1	C1	C2A	123	C7	C8	C9	118	C11	C16	C15	122
C5	C1	C2A	122	C8	C9	C10	124				
Si1	C2	C11	112	C5	C10	C9	118				

Torsion Angles

C2	Si1	C1	C2A	13
C1	Si1	C2	C1A	−13
Si1	C1	C2A	Si1A	−15
Si1	C1	C2A	C11A	175
C6	C5	C1	Si1	−88
C12	C11	C2	Si1	−82

64.1   Potassium - O,O - dimethyl - phosphordithioate

$C_2H_6O_2PS_2^-$, K^+

P.Coppens, C.H.MacGillavry, S.G.Hovenkamp, H.Douwes, Acta Cryst., 15, 765, 1962

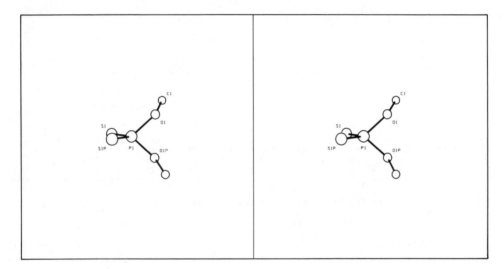

$K [S_2P(OCH_3)_2]$

Fddd   Z = 16   R = 0.16

KDMPDS   LB 2-6-28

Bond Lengths			Bond Angles			
P1	S1	1.96	S1	P1	S1P	118
P1	O1	1.64	S1	P1	O1	119
C1	O1	1.58	S1	P1	O1P	105
			O1	P1	O1P	86
			P1	O1	C1	111

Torsion Angles				
S1	P1	O1	C1	−17
S1P	P1	O1	C1	−152
O1P	P1	O1	C1	88

64.2   Methyl metadithiophosphonate

$C_2H_6P_2S_4$

J.J.Daly, J. Chem. Soc., 4065, 1964

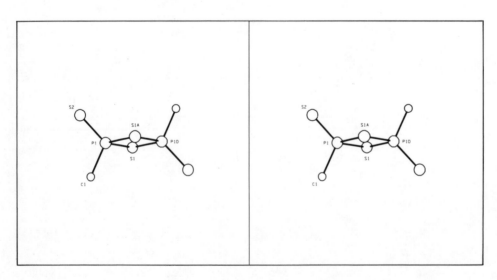

I2/m   Z = 2   R = 0.081

MMETPS   LB 2-6-52

Bond Lengths			Bond Angles			
P1	S1	2.14	S1	P1	S2	117
P1	S2	1.94	S1	P1	S1A	95
P1	C1	1.83	S1	P1	C1	107
			S2	P1	C1	112
			P1	S1	P1D	85

Torsion Angles				
S2	P1	S1	P1D	123
S1A	P1	S1	P1D	0
C1	P1	S1	P1D	−110

64.3   Tetra(trifluoromethyl)cyclotetraphosphine

$C_4F_{12}P_4$

G.J.Palenik, J.Donohue, Acta Cryst., 15, 564, 1962

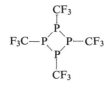

P4$_2$/nmc   Z = 2   R = 0.08

TFCYPH

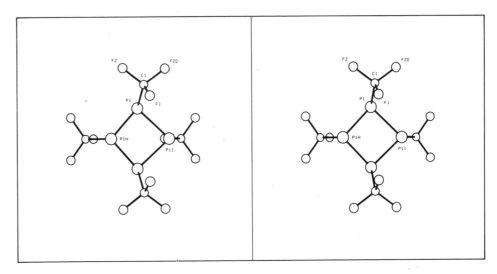

Bond Lengths   *Bond Angles*

F1	C1	1.32	F1	C1	F2	106
F2	C1	1.31	F1	C1	P1	118
P1	P1H	2.21	F2	C1	F2D	108
P1	C1	1.87	F2	C1	P1	110

Torsion Angles

P1H	P1	C1	F1	43
P1I	P1	P1H	P1A	−34

64.4   pentakis - (Trifluoromethyl) - cyclopentaphosphine (at −100 °C)

$C_5F_{15}P_5$

C.J.Spencer, W.N.Lipscomb, Acta Cryst., 14, 250, 1961

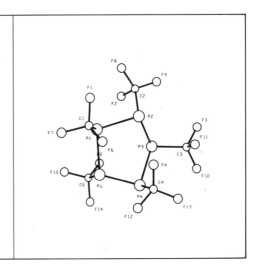

P2$_1$/n   Z = 4   R = 0.18

TFMCPP

Bond Lengths

F1	C1	1.34
F2	C2	1.37
F3	C3	1.35
F4	C4	1.37
F5	C5	1.31
F6	C1	1.33
F7	C1	1.40
F8	C2	1.37
F9	C2	1.28
F10	C3	1.33
F11	C3	1.39
F12	C4	1.34
F13	C4	1.31
F14	C5	1.32
F15	C5	1.37
P1	P2	2.23
P1	P5	2.22
P1	C1	1.87
P2	P3	2.25
P2	C2	1.92
P3	P4	2.21
P3	C3	1.89
P4	P5	2.20
P4	C4	1.92
P5	C5	1.92

Bond Angles

P2	P1	P5	103	F1	C1	F6	108	F10	C3	F11	109
P2	P1	C1	94	F1	C1	F7	104	F10	C3	P3	111
P5	P1	C1	96	F1	C1	P1	111	F11	C3	P3	116
P1	P2	P3	94	F6	C1	F7	105	F4	C4	F12	106
P1	P2	C2	95	F6	C1	P1	120	F4	C4	F13	108
P2	P3	C2	95	F7	C1	P1	108	F4	C4	P4	115
P2	P3	P4	103	F2	C2	F8	105	F12	C4	F13	109
P2	P3	C3	99	F2	C2	F9	109	F12	C4	P4	108
P4	P3	C3	101	F2	C2	P2	115	F13	C4	P4	110
P3	P4	P5	98	F8	C2	F9	112	F5	C5	F14	108
P3	P4	C4	108	F8	C2	P2	107	F5	C5	F15	107
P5	P4	C4	97	F9	C2	P2	110	F5	C5	P5	116
P1	P5	P4	108	F3	C3	F10	107	F14	C5	F15	107
P1	P5	C5	97	F3	C3	F11	105	F14	C5	P5	110
P4	P5	C5	96	F3	C3	P3	109	F15	C5	P5	108

Torsion Angles

P5	P1	P2	P3	44	P3	P2	C2	F2	51
P5	P1	P2	C2	139	P2	P3	P4	P5	48
C1	P1	P2	P3	140	P2	P3	P4	C4	−52
C1	P1	P2	C2	−124	C3	P3	P4	P5	150
P2	P1	P5	P4	−17	C3	P3	P4	C4	50
P2	P1	P5	C5	−116	P2	P3	C3	F3	−83
C1	P1	P5	P4	−113	P4	P3	C3	F3	172
C1	P1	P5	C5	149	P3	P4	P5	P1	−18
P2	P1	C1	F1	66	P3	P4	P5	C5	81
P5	P1	C1	F1	170	C4	P4	P5	P1	91
P1	P2	P3	P4	−58	C4	P4	P5	C5	−170
P1	P2	P3	C3	−161	P3	P4	C4	F4	37
C2	P2	P3	P4	−153	P5	P4	C4	F4	−63
C2	P2	P3	C3	104	P1	P5	C5	F5	51
P1	P2	C2	F2	−43	P4	P5	C5	F5	−59

64.5 Cyclohexane - 1a,3a,5a - thiophosphonic acid ester

$C_6H_9O_3PS$

P.Andersen, K.E.Hjortaas, Acta Chem. Scand., 14, 829, 1960

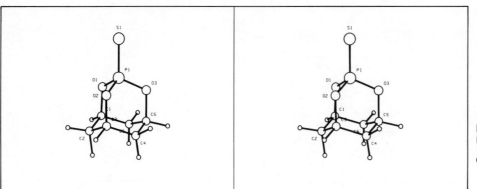

Pna2$_1$ Z = 4 R_{hk0} = 0.09, R_{h0l} = 0.07

CHEXPS   LB 6-9-26

Bond Lengths

P1	S1	1.90	C1	C2	1.55
P1	O1	1.60	C1	C6	1.56
P1	O2	1.59	C2	C3	1.48
P1	O3	1.56	C3	C4	1.54
C1	O1	1.47	C4	C5	1.42
C3	O2	1.48	C5	C6	1.56
C5	O3	1.52			

Bond Angles

S1	P1	O1	113	C2	C1	C6	111
S1	P1	O2	114	C1	C2	C3	108
S1	P1	O3	114	O2	C3	C2	110
O1	P1	O2	105	O2	C3	C4	109
O1	P1	O3	103	C2	C3	C4	112
O2	P1	O3	106	C3	C4	C5	111
P1	O1	C1	114	O3	C5	C4	111
P1	O2	C3	112	O3	C5	C6	104
P1	O3	C5	114	C4	C5	C6	112
O1	C1	C2	111	C1	C6	C5	110
O1	C1	C6	105				

Torsion Angles

O2	P1	O1	C1	−51	O1	C1	C2	C3	−60
O3	P1	O1	C1	59	C6	C1	C2	C3	57
O1	P1	O2	C3	55	O1	C1	C6	C5	67
O3	P1	O2	C3	−54	C2	C1	C6	C5	−54
O1	P1	O3	C5	−59	C1	C2	C3	O2	63
O2	P1	O3	C5	51	C1	C2	C3	C4	−59
P1	O1	C1	C2	56	O2	C3	C4	C5	−62
P1	O1	C1	C6	−64	C2	C3	C4	C5	61
P1	O2	C3	C2	−64	C3	C4	C5	O3	59
P1	O2	C3	C4	59	C3	C4	C5	C6	−57
P1	O3	C5	C4	−57	O3	C5	C6	C1	−65
P1	O3	C5	C6	64	C4	C5	C6	C1	55

64.6 Triethylphosphine selenide

$C_6H_{15}PSe$

M.van Meerssche, A.Leonard, Bull. Soc. Chim. Belges, 69, 45, 1960

The structure is isomorphous with
$SP(C_2H_5)_3$. The carbon atoms are
disordered.
P6$_3$mc   Z = 2   R = 0.072

PHOSSE   LB 6-15-24

$$H_5C_2$$
$$H_5C_2—P \rightarrow Se$$
$$H_5C_2$$

64.7 Carbon disulfide - triethylscarphane

$C_7H_{15}PS_2$

T.N.Margulis, D.H.Templeton, J. Chem. Phys., 36, 2311, 1962

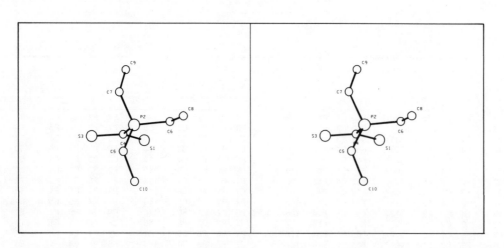

$$(CH_3CH_2)_3P^+—C \overset{S^-}{\underset{S}{\diagdown}}$$

P2$_1$/c   Z = 2   R = 0.093

CSTEPH   LB 7-15-11

Bond Lengths

P2	C4	1.79	S3	C4	1.68
P2	C5	1.77	C5	C10	1.56
P2	C6	1.81	C6	C8	1.54
P2	C7	1.81	C7	C9	1.56
S1	C4	1.69			

Bond Angles

C4	P2	C5	108	P2	C4	S1	119
C4	P2	C6	112	P2	C4	S3	113
C4	P2	C7	110	S1	C4	S3	128
C5	P2	C6	110	P2	C5	C10	114
C5	P2	C7	108	P2	C6	C8	114
C6	P2	C7	109	P2	C7	C9	112

Torsion Angles

C5	P2	C4	S1	−118	C4	P2	C6	C8	−173
C6	P2	C4	S1	4	C5	P2	C6	C8	−53
C7	P2	C4	S1	125	C7	P2	C6	C8	65
C4	P2	C5	C10	60	C4	P2	C7	C9	−58
C6	P2	C5	C10	−62	C5	P2	C7	C9	−176
C7	P2	C5	C10	180	C6	P2	C7	C9	65

64.8 Tetraethyl diphosphine disulfide

$C_8H_{20}P_2S_2$

S.N.Dutta, M.M.Woolfson, Acta Cryst., 14, 178, 1961

Published value of z(C4) = 0.1734.
The correct value is −0.1734.
P-1   Z = 1   R = 0.149

TEDPDS   LB 8-20-40

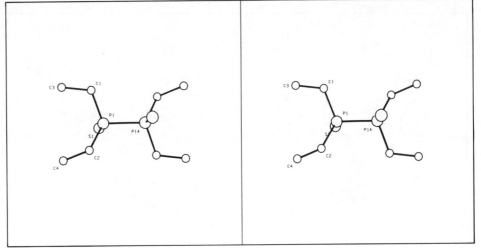

Bond Lengths			Bond Angles				Torsion Angles			
P1	P1A	2.21	S1	P1	C1	115	C3	C1	P1	P1A −171
P1	S1	1.94	S1	P1	C2	116	C4	C2	P1	P1A −162
P1	C1	1.84	C1	P1	C2	107				
P1	C2	1.82	P1	C1	C3	113				
C1	C3	1.51	P1	C2	C4	113				
C2	C4	1.51								

64.9 Octamethylcyclotetraphosphonitrile (at 140 °K)

$C_8H_{24}N_4P_4$

M.W.Dougill, J. Chem. Soc., 5471, 1961

I4₁/a   Z = 4   R = 0.06

MTETPN   LB 8-24-37

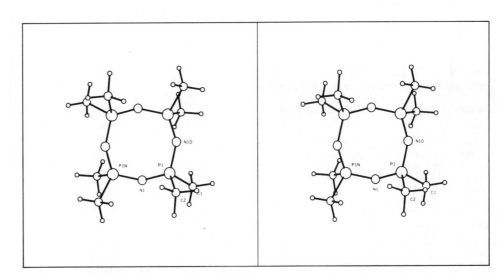

Bond Lengths			Bond Angles				Torsion Angles			
P1	N1	1.59	N1	P1	N1O	120	N1O	P1	N1	P1N −54
P1	N1O	1.60	N1	P1	C1	105	N1	P1	N1O	P1O −31
P1	C1	1.80	N1	P1	C2	113				
P1	C2	1.81	C1	P1	N1O	110				
			C1	P1	C2	104				
			P1	N1	P1N	132				

64.10   2,2 - Diphenyl - 4,4,6,6 - tetrachloro - cyclotriphosphazatriene

$C_{12}H_{10}Cl_4N_3P_3$

N.V.Mani, F.R.Ahmed, W.H.Barnes, Acta Cryst., 19, 693, 1965

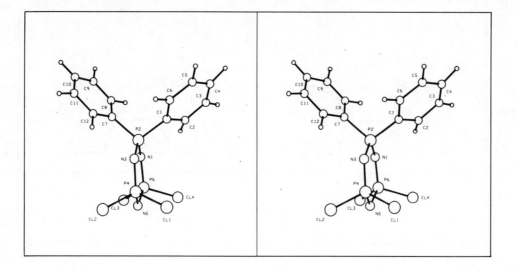

$P2_1/n$ $Z = 4$ $R = 0.048$

PCLPAZ   LB 12-10-33

Bond Lengths

Cl1	P4	1.99	C1	C2	1.38
Cl2	P4	2.00	C1	C6	1.37
Cl3	P6	1.99	C2	C3	1.40
Cl4	P6	2.01	C3	C4	1.35
P2	N1	1.62	C4	C5	1.37
P2	N3	1.61	C5	C6	1.39
P2	C1	1.79	C7	C8	1.40
P2	C7	1.78	C7	C12	1.38
P4	N3	1.55	C8	C9	1.37
P4	N5	1.58	C9	C10	1.38
P6	N1	1.55	C10	C11	1.35
P6	N5	1.58	C11	C12	1.39

Bond Angles

N1	P2	N3	115	Cl3	P6	N1	109	C3	C4	C5	120
N1	P2	C1	108	Cl3	P6	N5	108	C4	C5	C6	120
N1	P2	C7	111	Cl4	P6	N1	111	C1	C6	C5	120
N3	P2	C1	110	Cl4	P6	N5	107	P2	C7	C8	120
N3	P2	C7	108	N1	P6	N5	120	P2	C7	C12	122
C1	P2	C7	104	P2	N1	P6	122	C8	C7	C12	119
Cl1	P4	Cl2	100	P2	N3	P4	122	C7	C8	C9	120
Cl1	P4	N3	110	P4	N5	P6	119	C8	C9	C10	120
Cl1	P4	N5	109	P2	C1	C2	121	C9	C10	C11	119
Cl2	P4	N3	110	P2	C1	C6	119	C10	C11	C12	121
Cl2	P4	N5	107	C2	C1	C6	120	C7	C12	C11	120
N3	P4	N5	120	C1	C2	C3	119				
Cl3	P6	Cl4	100	C2	C3	C4	121				

Torsion Angles

N3	P2	N1	P6	−9
N1	P2	N3	P4	5
N5	P4	N3	P2	−7
N3	P4	N5	P6	12
N5	P6	N1	P2	15
N1	P6	N5	P4	−16
N1	P2	C1	C2	1
N1	P2	C7	C8	−52

64.11   9,10 - Dihydro - 9 - hydroxy - 9 - phosphaphenanthrene - 9 - oxide

$C_{13}H_{11}O_2P$

P.J.Wheatley, J. Chem. Soc., 3733, 1962

The published atomic coordinates result in two symmetry - related molecules becoming interleaved.
$B2_1/c$ $Z = 8$ $R_{0kl} = 0.110$,
$R_{hk0} = 0.126$

HOPPHO   LB 13-11-13

64.12   1,2 - Dimethyl - 1,2 - diphenyldiphosphine disulfide (meso form)

$C_{14}H_{16}P_2S_2$

P.J.Wheatley, J. Chem. Soc., 523, 1960

The structure was determined in two dimensions only. Atomic coordinates were not reported in the paper.
Pbca $Z = 4$ $R = 0.13$

MPPHOS   LB 14-16-22

64.13   octakis(Dimethylamino) cyclotetraphosphazatetraene

$C_{16}H_{48}N_{12}P_4$

G.J.Bullen, J. Chem. Soc., 3193, 1962

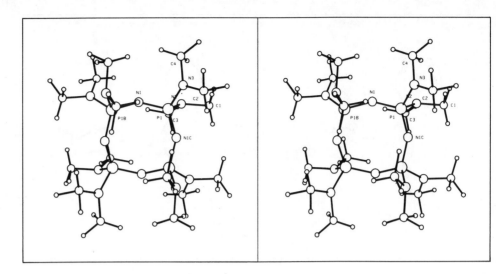

P-4   Z = 2   R = 0.084

PHONMA   LB 16-48-6

Bond Lengths			Bond Angles										Torsion Angles										
P1	N1	1.58	N1	P1	N2	103	P1	N2	C1	115		N2	P1	N1	P1B	160		N1	P1	N3	C2	142
P1	N2	1.69	N1	P1	N3	112	P1	N2	C3	119		N3	P1	N1	P1B	−89		N2	P1	N3	C2	−108
P1	N3	1.67	N1	P1	N1C	120	C1	N2	C3	116		N1C	P1	N1	P1B	32		N1C	P1	N3	C2	11
P1	N1C	1.58	N2	P1	N3	104	P1	N3	C2	125		N1	P1	N2	C1	173		N1	P1	N1C	P1C	52
C1	N2	1.46	N2	P1	N1C	114	P1	N3	C4	118		N3	P1	N2	C1	56		N2	P1	N1C	P1C	−71
C3	N2	1.45	N3	P1	N1C	103	C2	N3	C4	116		N1C	P1	N2	C1	−56		N3	P1	N1C	P1C	178
C2	N3	1.42	P1	N1	P1B	133																
C4	N3	1.48																				

64.14   (+) - Methyl - n - propyl - phenyl - benzyl - phosphonium bromide (absolute configuration)

$C_{17}H_{22}BrP$

A.F.Peerdeman, J.P.C.Holst, L.Horner, H.Winkler, Tetrahedron Letters, 811, 1965

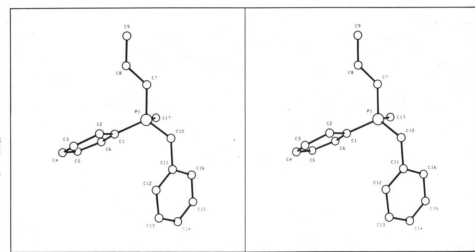

No comparison of bond lengths is possible since they are not reported in the paper.
$P2_12_12_1$ Z = 4   No R factor was given.

MPBPBR   LB 17-22-2

Bond Lengths						Bond Angles												Torsion Angles				
P1	C1	1.76	C7	C8	1.50	C1	P1	C7	111	C1	C2	C3	122	C10	C11	C16	115	C1	P1	C7	C8	−52
P1	C7	1.81	C8	C9	1.52	C1	P1	C10	112	C2	C3	C4	116	C12	C11	C16	122	C10	P1	C7	C8	−173
P1	C10	1.82	C10	C11	1.54	C1	P1	C17	111	C3	C4	C5	120	C11	C12	C13	122	C1	P1	C10	C11	58
P1	C17	1.75	C11	C12	1.37	C7	P1	C10	103	C4	C5	C6	124	C12	C13	C14	115	C7	P1	C10	C11	177
C1	C2	1.44	C11	C16	1.41	C7	P1	C17	107	C1	C6	C5	119	C13	C14	C15	126	P1	C7	C8	C9	180
C1	C6	1.40	C12	C13	1.39	C10	P1	C17	112	P1	C7	C8	117	C14	C15	C16	120	P1	C10	C11	C12	−85
C2	C3	1.39	C13	C14	1.37	P1	C1	C2	119	C7	C8	C9	118	C11	C16	C15	116	C10	P1	C1	C2	64
C3	C4	1.41	C14	C15	1.35	P1	C1	C6	123	P1	C10	C11	113									
C4	C5	1.37	C15	C16	1.40	C2	C1	C6	117	C10	C11	C12	123									
C5	C6	1.34																				

64.15   Triphenyl phosphorus

J.J.Daly, J. Chem. Soc., 3799, 1964

C₁₈H₁₅P

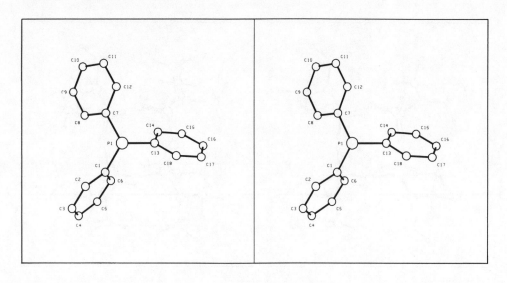

P2₁/n   Z = 4   R = 0.101

PTRPHE   LB 18-15-26

Bond Lengths

P1	C1	1.82	C8	C9	1.40
P1	C7	1.83	C9	C10	1.40
P1	C13	1.83	C10	C11	1.39
C1	C2	1.41	C11	C12	1.40
C1	C6	1.40	C13	C14	1.41
C2	C3	1.39	C13	C18	1.39
C3	C4	1.38	C14	C15	1.40
C4	C5	1.40	C15	C16	1.39
C5	C6	1.40	C16	C17	1.41
C7	C8	1.40	C17	C18	1.41
C7	C12	1.41			

Bond Angles

C1	P1	C7	104	C4	C5	C6	120	C7	C12	C11	120
C1	P1	C13	103	C1	C6	C5	120	P1	C13	C14	123
C7	P1	C13	102	P1	C7	C8	124	P1	C13	C18	116
P1	C1	C2	116	P1	C7	C12	116	C14	C13	C18	121
P1	C1	C6	125	C8	C7	C12	120	C13	C14	C15	119
C2	C1	C6	119	C7	C8	C9	120	C14	C15	C16	121
C1	C2	C3	120	C8	C9	C10	121	C15	C16	C17	120
C2	C3	C4	121	C9	C10	C11	120	C16	C17	C18	119
C3	C4	C5	120	C10	C11	C12	120	C13	C18	C17	120

Torsion Angles

C7	P1	C1	C2	−103
C1	P1	C7	C8	9
C7	P1	C13	C14	−26

64.16   Benzoyl (triphenylphosphoranylidene)methyl chloride

F.S.Stephens, J. Chem. Soc., 5658, 1965

C₂₆H₂₀ClOP

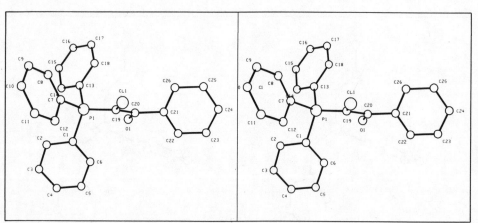

Isomorphous with the bromide compound.
P2₁/a   Z = 4   R = 0.167

BOPOMC   LB 26-20-5

Bond Lengths

Cl1	C19	1.76	C10	C11	1.37
P1	C1	1.82	C11	C12	1.39
P1	C7	1.80	C13	C14	1.38
P1	C13	1.80	C13	C18	1.40
P1	C19	1.74	C14	C15	1.47
C20	O1	1.30	C15	C16	1.37
C1	C2	1.43	C16	C17	1.36
C1	C6	1.39	C17	C18	1.42
C2	C3	1.42	C19	C20	1.36
C3	C4	1.38	C20	C21	1.49
C4	C5	1.37	C21	C22	1.34
C5	C6	1.44	C21	C26	1.39
C7	C8	1.35	C22	C23	1.42
C7	C12	1.44	C23	C24	1.38
C8	C9	1.39	C24	C25	1.36
C9	C10	1.43	C25	C26	1.42

Bond Angles

C1	P1	C7	105	P1	C7	C12	118	Cl1	C19	P1	118
C1	P1	C13	109	C8	C7	C12	119	Cl1	C19	C20	121
C1	P1	C19	113	C7	C8	C9	123	P1	C19	C20	120
C7	P1	C13	106	C8	C9	C10	119	O1	C20	C19	117
C7	P1	C19	110	C9	C10	C11	119	O1	C20	C21	117
C13	P1	C19	112	C10	C11	C12	122	C19	C20	C21	126
P1	C1	C2	117	C7	C12	C11	118	C20	C21	C22	119
P1	C1	C6	120	P1	C13	C14	122	C20	C21	C26	119
C2	C1	C6	123	P1	C13	C18	117	C22	C21	C26	122
C1	C2	C3	117	C14	C13	C18	121	C21	C22	C23	120
C2	C3	C4	119	C13	C14	C15	118	C22	C23	C24	119
C3	C4	C5	124	C14	C15	C16	121	C23	C24	C25	121
C4	C5	C6	119	C15	C16	C17	121	C24	C25	C26	121
C1	C6	C5	118	C16	C17	C18	120	C21	C26	C25	118
P1	C7	C8	123	C13	C18	C17	120				

Torsion Angles

C19	P1	C1	C6	−12
C19	P1	C7	C12	−71
C19	P1	C13	C18	−30
C1	P1	C19	C20	70
P1	C19	C20	C21	175
C19	C20	C21	C26	−61

64.17   Benzoyl (triphenylphosphoranylidene)methyl iodide   C₂₆H₂₀IOP

F.S.Stephens, J. Chem. Soc., 5640, 1965

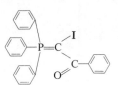

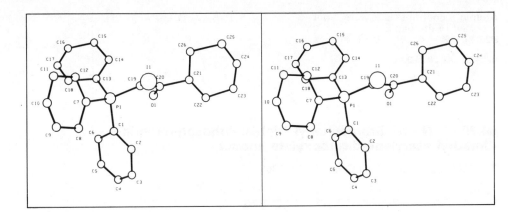

P2₁/c   Z = 4   R = 0.157

BOPOMI   LB 26-20-11

Bond Lengths

I1	C19	2.19	
P1	C1	1.82	
P1	C7	1.77	
P1	C13	1.77	
P1	C19	1.71	
C20	O1	1.28	
C1	C2	1.39	
C1	C6	1.35	
C2	C3	1.42	
C3	C4	1.31	
C4	C5	1.34	
C5	C6	1.48	
C7	C8	1.38	
C7	C12	1.37	
C8	C9	1.50	
C9	C10	1.24	

C10	C11	1.31
C11	C12	1.46
C13	C14	1.45
C13	C18	1.50
C14	C15	1.50
C15	C16	1.48
C16	C17	1.26
C17	C18	1.34
C19	C20	1.35
C20	C21	1.57
C21	C22	1.31
C21	C26	1.47
C22	C23	1.48
C23	C24	1.33
C24	C25	1.29
C25	C26	1.62

Bond Angles

C1	P1	C7	107
C1	P1	C13	106
C1	P1	C19	110
C7	P1	C13	107
C7	P1	C19	115
C13	P1	C19	112
P1	C1	C2	118
P1	C1	C6	121
C2	C1	C6	120
C1	C2	C3	118
C2	C3	C4	120
C3	C4	C5	126
C4	C5	C6	114
C1	C6	C5	121
P1	C7	C8	121

P1	C7	C12	117
C8	C7	C12	122
C7	C8	C9	112
C8	C9	C10	121
C9	C10	C11	131
C10	C11	C12	111
C7	C12	C11	123
P1	C13	C14	127
P1	C13	C18	117
C14	C13	C18	116
C13	C14	C15	119
C14	C15	C16	115
C15	C16	C17	123
C16	C17	C18	126
C13	C18	C17	120

I1	C19	P1	116
I1	C19	C20	120
P1	C19	C20	120
O1	C20	C19	115
O1	C20	C21	117
C19	C20	C21	128
C20	C21	C22	118
C20	C21	C26	105
C22	C21	C26	137
C21	C22	C23	111
C22	C23	C24	115
C23	C24	C25	137
C24	C25	C26	113
C21	C26	C25	106

Torsion Angles

C19	P1	C1	C2	40
C19	P1	C7	C12	71
C19	P1	C13	C14	15
C1	P1	C19	C20	49
P1	C19	C20	C21	−171
C19	C20	C21	C26	−58

64.18   p-Tolyl triphenylphosphoranylidenemethyl sulfone   C₂₆H₂₃O₂PS

P.J.Wheatley, J. Chem. Soc., 5785, 1965

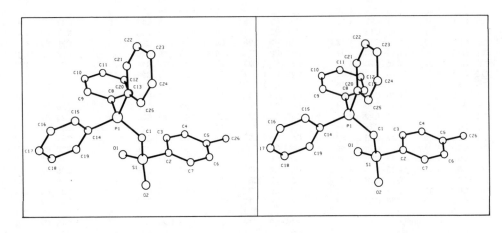

C2/c   Z = 8   R = 0.164

TOLPSO   LB 26-23-2

Bond Lengths

P1	C1	1.71	
P1	C8	1.83	
P1	C14	1.78	
P1	C20	1.81	
S1	O1	1.47	
S1	O2	1.45	
S1	C1	1.69	
S1	C2	1.77	
C2	C3	1.42	
C2	C7	1.39	
C3	C4	1.35	
C4	C5	1.41	
C5	C6	1.35	
C5	C26	1.53	
C6	C7	1.37	
C8	C9	1.42	
C8	C13	1.34	

C9	C10	1.39
C10	C11	1.36
C11	C12	1.36
C12	C13	1.44
C14	C15	1.43
C14	C19	1.40
C15	C16	1.36
C16	C17	1.43
C17	C18	1.34
C18	C19	1.43
C20	C21	1.40
C20	C25	1.40
C21	C22	1.40
C22	C23	1.39
C23	C24	1.41
C24	C25	1.38

Bond Angles

C1	P1	C8	113
C1	P1	C14	118
C1	P1	C20	105
C8	P1	C14	106
C8	P1	C20	107
C14	P1	C20	107
O1	S1	O2	117
O1	S1	C1	110
O1	S1	C2	107
O2	S1	C1	111
O2	S1	C2	105
C1	S1	C2	107
P1	C1	S1	124
S1	C2	C3	119
S1	C2	C7	122
C3	C2	C7	119

C2	C3	C4	119
C3	C4	C5	122
C4	C5	C6	119
C4	C5	C26	120
C6	C5	C26	121
C5	C6	C7	122
C2	C7	C6	120
P1	C8	C9	119
P1	C8	C13	119
C9	C8	C13	123
C8	C9	C10	117
C9	C10	C11	122
C10	C11	C12	120
C11	C12	C13	120
C8	C13	C12	118
P1	C14	C15	121

P1	C14	C19	121
C15	C14	C19	118
C14	C15	C16	119
C15	C16	C17	122
C16	C17	C18	121
C17	C18	C19	119
C14	C19	C18	121
P1	C20	C21	121
P1	C20	C25	119
C21	C20	C25	120
C20	C21	C22	119
C21	C22	C23	121
C22	C23	C24	119
C23	C24	C25	120
C20	C25	C24	120

Torsion Angles

C2	S1	C1	P1	124
C1	S1	C2	C3	−96
C8	P1	C1	S1	−55
C1	P1	C8	C13	−35
C1	P1	C14	C19	−59
C1	P1	C20	C25	−45

64.19   bis(Diphenylphosphino)ethylamine ethyl iodide

$C_{28}H_{30}NP_2^+$, I^-

D.S.Payne, J.A.A.Mokuolu, J.C.Speakman, Chem. Communic., 599, 1965

Atomic coordinates were not reported in the paper.
P2$2_1 2_1$ Z = 4   R = 0.13

DPEAEI   LB 28-30-1

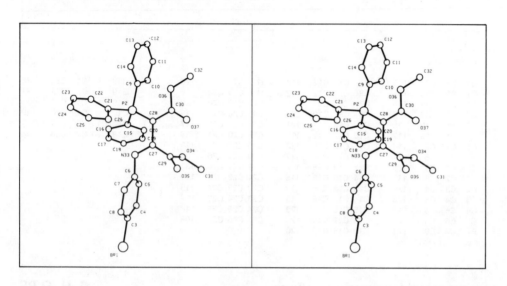

64.20   N - p - Bromophenyl triphenylphosphine imide - dimethyl acetylene dicarboxylate adduct

$C_{30}H_{25}BrNO_4P$

T.C.W.Mak, J.Trotter, Acta Cryst., 18, 81, 1965

P2$_1$/c   Z = 4   R = 0.21

POSACE   LB 30-25-2

Bond Lengths

Br1	C3	1.95	C9	C14	1.43	
P2	C9	1.82	C10	C11	1.36	
P2	C15	1.81	C11	C12	1.45	
P2	C21	1.87	C12	C13	1.41	
P2	C28	1.70	C13	C14	1.42	
C6	N33	1.39	C15	C16	1.41	
C27	N33	1.32	C15	C20	1.42	
C29	O34	1.38	C16	C17	1.42	
C31	O34	1.47	C17	C18	1.35	
C29	O35	1.29	C18	C19	1.46	
C30	O36	1.35	C19	C20	1.38	
C32	O36	1.50	C21	C22	1.42	
C30	O37	1.20	C21	C26	1.43	
C3	C4	1.36	C22	C23	1.33	
C3	C8	1.35	C23	C24	1.45	
C4	C5	1.44	C24	C25	1.41	
C5	C6	1.32	C25	C26	1.41	
C6	C7	1.44	C27	C28	1.48	
C7	C8	1.42	C27	C29	1.34	
C9	C10	1.45	C28	C30	1.47	

Bond Angles

C9	P2	C15	106	P2	C15	C20	117
C9	P2	C21	106	C16	C15	C20	119
C9	P2	C28	112	C15	C16	C17	115
C15	P2	C21	110	C16	C17	C18	126
C15	P2	C28	108	C17	C18	C19	118
C21	P2	C28	114	C18	C19	C20	117
C6	N33	C27	120	C15	C20	C19	124
C29	O34	C31	120	P2	C21	C22	119
C30	O36	C32	115	P2	C21	C26	117
Br1	C3	C4	117	C22	C21	C26	124
Br1	C3	C8	119	C21	C22	C23	117
C4	C3	C8	125	C22	C23	C24	125
C3	C4	C5	114	C23	C24	C25	115
C4	C5	C6	123	C24	C25	C26	125
N33	C6	C5	119	C21	C26	C25	114
N33	C6	C7	117	N33	C27	C28	118
C5	C6	C7	122	N33	C27	C29	120
C6	C7	C8	115	C28	C27	C29	122
C3	C8	C7	121	P2	C28	C27	117
P2	C9	C10	121	P2	C28	C30	128
P2	C9	C14	116	C27	C28	C30	115
C10	C9	C14	123	O34	C29	O35	114
C9	C10	C11	122	O34	C29	C27	117
C10	C11	C12	116	O35	C29	C27	129
C11	C12	C13	123	O36	C30	O37	123
C12	C13	C14	121	O36	C30	C28	112
C9	C14	C13	115	O37	C30	C28	125
P2	C15	C16	123				

Torsion Angles

C15	P2	C9	C10	−35	N33	C6	C7	C8	168
C15	P2	C9	C14	146	C5	C6	C7	C8	4
C21	P2	C9	C10	−153	C6	C7	C8	C3	1
C21	P2	C9	C14	29	P2	C9	C10	C11	−175
C28	P2	C9	C10	83	C14	C9	C10	C11	4
C28	P2	C9	C14	−96	P2	C9	C14	C13	172
C9	P2	C15	C16	−99	C10	C9	C14	C13	−7
C9	P2	C15	C20	78	C9	C10	C11	C12	−2
C21	P2	C15	C16	16	C10	C11	C12	C13	3
C21	P2	C15	C20	−167	C11	C12	C13	C14	−6
C28	P2	C15	C16	141	C12	C13	C14	C9	8
C28	P2	C15	C20	−42	P2	C15	C16	C17	175
C9	P2	C21	C22	53	C20	C15	C16	C17	−2
C9	P2	C21	C26	−130	P2	C15	C20	C19	−173
C15	P2	C21	C22	−61	C16	C15	C20	C19	4
C15	P2	C21	C26	116	C15	C16	C17	C18	2
C28	P2	C21	C22	177	C16	C17	C18	C19	−4
C28	P2	C21	C26	−6	C17	C18	C19	C20	6
C9	P2	C28	C27	−164	C18	C19	C20	C15	−6
C9	P2	C28	C30	15	P2	C21	C22	C23	180
C15	P2	C28	C27	−47	C26	C21	C22	C23	3
C15	P2	C28	C30	132	P2	C21	C26	C25	179
C21	P2	C28	C27	76	C22	C21	C26	C25	−4
C21	P2	C28	C30	−106	C21	C22	C23	C24	−1
C27	N33	C6	C5	−83	C22	C23	C24	C25	0
C27	N33	C6	C7	113	C23	C24	C25	C26	−1
C6	N33	C27	C28	169	C24	C25	C26	C21	3
C6	N33	C27	C29	−4	N33	C27	C28	P2	−16
C31	O34	C29	O35	−1	N33	C27	C28	C30	166
C31	O34	C29	C27	−180	C29	C27	C28	P2	158
C32	O36	C30	O37	0	C29	C27	C28	C30	−21
C32	O36	C30	C28	−177	N33	C27	C29	O34	103
Br1	C3	C4	C5	178	N33	C27	C29	O35	−75
C8	C3	C4	C5	0	C28	C27	C29	O34	−70
Br1	C3	C8	C7	179	C28	C27	C29	O35	112
C4	C3	C8	C7	−2	P2	C28	C30	O36	−178
C3	C4	C5	C6	6	P2	C28	C30	O37	−178
C4	C5	C6	N33	−172	C27	C28	C30	O36	179
C4	C5	C6	C7	−8	C27	C28	C30	O37	1

64.21   Pentaphenyl phosphorus

P.J.Wheatley, J. Chem. Soc., 2206, 1964

$C_{30}H_{25}P$

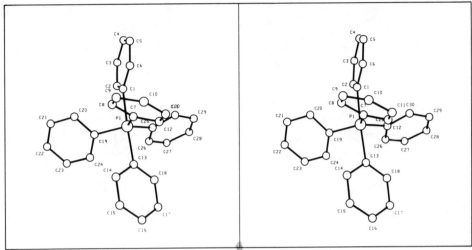

Published value of C28 -
C29 = 1.536A. The correct value is
1.356A.
Cc   Z = 4   R = 0.087.

PHENYP   LB 30-25-5

Bond Lengths

P1	C1	1.99		C13	C18	1.39
P1	C7	1.87		C14	C15	1.39
P1	C13	1.99		C15	C16	1.41
P1	C19	1.85		C16	C17	1.34
P1	C25	1.83		C17	C18	1.40
C1	C2	1.39		C19	C20	1.41
C1	C6	1.40		C19	C24	1.38
C2	C3	1.40		C20	C21	1.39
C3	C4	1.39		C21	C22	1.38
C4	C5	1.37		C22	C23	1.39
C5	C6	1.41		C23	C24	1.39
C7	C8	1.38		C25	C26	1.40
C7	C12	1.39		C25	C30	1.39
C8	C9	1.40		C26	C27	1.39
C9	C10	1.39		C27	C28	1.41
C10	C11	1.41		C28	C29	1.36
C11	C12	1.37		C29	C30	1.39
C13	C14	1.40				

Bond Angles

C1	P1	C7	93		C1	C6	C5	121
C1	P1	C13	177		P1	C7	C8	121
C1	P1	C19	92		P1	C7	C12	120
C1	P1	C25	86		C8	C7	C12	120
C7	P1	C13	87		C7	C8	C9	120
C7	P1	C19	120		C8	C9	C10	120
C7	P1	C25	123		C9	C10	C11	119
C13	P1	C19	91		C10	C11	C12	120
C13	P1	C25	91		C7	C12	C11	121
C19	P1	C25	118		P1	C13	C14	117
P1	C1	C2	116		P1	C13	C18	125
P1	C1	C6	125		C14	C13	C18	117
C2	C1	C6	118		C13	C14	C15	122
C1	C2	C3	121		C14	C15	C16	119
C2	C3	C4	121		C15	C16	C17	120
C3	C4	C5	119		C16	C17	C18	121
C4	C5	C6	121		C13	C18	C17	121

P1	C19	C20	119
P1	C19	C24	121
C20	C19	C24	119
C19	C20	C21	119
C20	C21	C22	121
C21	C22	C23	120
C22	C23	C24	120
C19	C24	C23	121
P1	C25	C26	121
P1	C25	C30	121
C26	C25	C30	118
C25	C26	C27	122
C26	C27	C28	119
C27	C28	C29	119
C28	C29	C30	122
C25	C30	C29	120

Torsion Angles

C7	P1	C1	C6	14
C1	P1	C7	C8	67
C1	P1	C13	C18	−36
C1	P1	C19	C20	−39
C1	P1	C25	C26	−109

64.22 Phosphobenzene pentamer

C₃₀H₂₅P₅

J.J.Daly, J. Chem. Soc., 6147, 1964

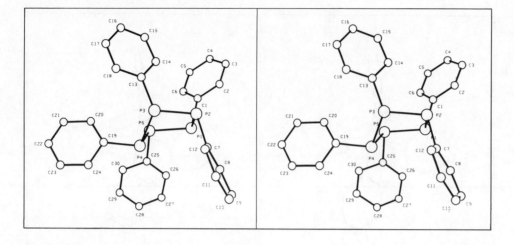

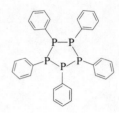

P2₁/n   Z = 4   R = 0.105

PHOSBZ   LB 30-25-6

Bond Lengths

P1	P2	2.19
P1	P5	2.22
P1	C1	1.85
P2	P3	2.22
P2	C7	1.86
P3	P4	2.18
P3	C13	1.87
P4	P5	2.22
P4	C19	1.85
P5	C25	1.81
C1	C2	1.40
C1	C6	1.39
C2	C3	1.44
C3	C4	1.39
C4	C5	1.37
C5	C6	1.44
C7	C8	1.41
C7	C12	1.42
C8	C9	1.44
C9	C10	1.38
C10	C11	1.39
C11	C12	1.44
C13	C14	1.39
C13	C18	1.40
C14	C15	1.43
C15	C16	1.37
C16	C17	1.41
C17	C18	1.39
C19	C20	1.40
C19	C24	1.42
C20	C21	1.43
C21	C22	1.40
C22	C23	1.37
C23	C24	1.43
C25	C26	1.39
C25	C30	1.41
C26	C27	1.43
C27	C28	1.36
C28	C29	1.40
C29	C30	1.41

Bond Angles

P2	P1	P5	103
P2	P1	C1	102
P5	P1	C1	101
P1	P2	P3	107
P1	P2	C7	101
P3	P2	C7	97
P2	P3	P4	94
P2	P3	C13	104
P4	P3	C13	111
P3	P4	P5	100
P3	P4	C19	106
P5	P4	C19	100
P1	P5	P4	95
P1	P5	C25	102
P4	P5	C25	96
P1	C1	C2	119
P1	C1	C6	122
C2	C1	C6	119
C1	C2	C3	120
C2	C3	C4	119
C3	C4	C5	124
C4	C5	C6	116
C1	C6	C5	122
P2	C7	C8	124
P2	C7	C12	117
C8	C7	C12	119
C7	C8	C9	121
C8	C9	C10	119
C9	C10	C11	121
C10	C11	C12	122
C7	C12	C11	118
P3	C13	C14	124
P3	C13	C18	115
C14	C13	C18	121
C13	C14	C15	118
C14	C15	C16	121
C15	C16	C17	119
C16	C17	C18	121
C13	C18	C17	119
P4	C19	C20	125
P4	C19	C24	116
C20	C19	C24	119
C19	C20	C21	120
C20	C21	C22	121
C21	C22	C23	119
C22	C23	C24	122
C19	C24	C23	119
P5	C25	C26	126
P5	C25	C30	116
C26	C25	C30	118
C25	C26	C27	121
C26	C27	C28	121
C27	C28	C29	119
C28	C29	C30	122
C25	C30	C29	120

Torsion Angles

P5	P1	P2	P3	2
P2	P1	P5	P4	−37
P1	P2	P3	P4	34
P2	P3	P4	P5	−58
P3	P4	P5	P1	61
P5	P1	C1	C6	−30
P1	P2	C7	C8	26
P2	P3	C13	C14	3
P3	P4	C19	C24	−119
P4	P5	C25	C26	−109

64.23 Phosphobenzene hexamer (trigonal form)

C₃₆H₃₀P₆

J.J.Daly, J. Chem. Soc., 4789, 1965

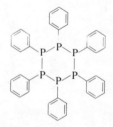

See also Daly, J. Chem. Soc. (A), 428, 1966.

P-3c1   Z = 2   R = 0.072

POBENZ   LB 36-30-19

Bond Lengths

P1	P1G	2.24
P1	C1	1.84
C1	C2	1.41
C1	C6	1.40
C2	C3	1.42
C3	C4	1.44
C4	C5	1.37
C5	C6	1.40

Bond Angles

P1	C1	C2	123
P1	C1	C6	115
C2	C1	C6	122
C1	C2	C3	119
C2	C3	C4	118
C3	C4	C5	123
C4	C5	C6	119
C1	C6	C5	120

Torsion Angles

P1H	P1	P1G	P1B	−85
P1H	P1	P1G	C1G	177
C1	P1	P1G	P1B	174
C1	P1	P1G	C1G	76
P1G	P1	C1	C2	57
P1G	P1	C1	C6	−125
P1H	P1	C1	C2	−39
P1H	P1	C1	C6	139
P1	C1	C2	C3	−179
C6	C1	C2	C3	3
P1	C1	C6	C5	179
C2	C1	C6	C5	−3
C1	C2	C3	C4	−1
C2	C3	C4	C5	−1
C3	C4	C5	C6	1
C4	C5	C6	C1	0

65.1 Di - iodomethylarsine (at 5 °C)

CH$_3$AsI$_2$

N.Camerman, J.Trotter, Acta Cryst., 16, 922, 1963

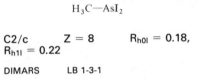

C2/c   Z = 8   R$_{h0l}$ = 0.18, R$_{h1l}$ = 0.22

DIMARS   LB 1-3-1

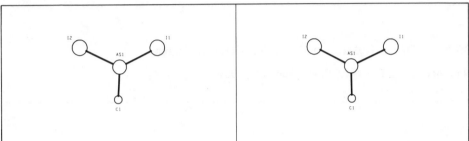

Bond Lengths			Bond Angles			
As1	I1	2.54	I1	As1	I2	104
As1	I2	2.54	I1	As1	C1	90
As1	C1	2.07	I2	As1	C1	90

65.2 Cacodylic acid

C$_2$H$_7$AsO$_2$

J.Trotter, T.Zobel, J. Chem. Soc., 4466, 1965

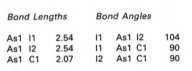

P-1   Z = 2   R = 0.149

CADYLA   LB 2-7-1

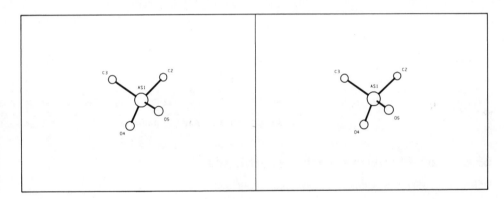

Bond Lengths			Bond Angles			
As1	O4	1.63	O4	As1	O5	109
As1	O5	1.61	O4	As1	C2	115
As1	C2	1.94	O4	As1	C3	109
As1	C3	1.89	O5	As1	C2	108
			O5	As1	C3	106
			C2	As1	C3	110

65.3 Cyanodimethylarsine

C$_3$H$_6$AsN

N.Camerman, J.Trotter, Canad. J. Chem., 41, 460, 1963

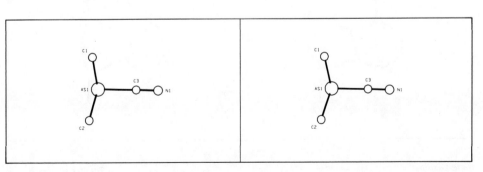

P-1   Z = 4   R$_{0kl}$ = 0.147, R$_{h0l}$ = 0.173, R$_{hk0}$ = 0.140

CNMARS   LB 3-6-10

Bond Lengths			Bond Angles				Torsion Angles				
As1	C1	1.93	C1	As1	C2	105	C1	As1	C3	N1	55
As1	C2	1.93	C1	As1	C3	89	C2	As1	C3	N1	−48
As1	C3	2.01	C2	As1	C3	92					
C3	N1	1.16	As1	C3	N1	180					

65.4   Tetramethylarsonium bromide

$C_4H_{12}As^+$, Br^-

E.Collins, D.J.Sutor, F.G.Mann, J. Chem. Soc., 4051, 1963

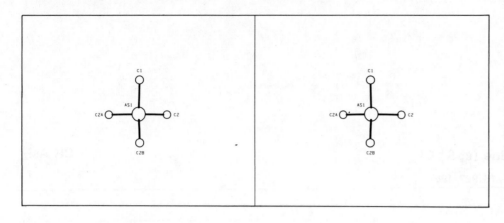

$P6_3mc$ $Z = 2$ $R_{hki0} = 0.042$, $R_{0k\bar{k}l} = 0.091$

TMARSB   LB 4-12-2

Bond Lengths		Bond Angles			
As1 C1	1.90	C1	As1	C2	107
As1 C2	1.85	C1	As1	C2A	107
As1 C2A	1.85	C2	As1	C2A	112
As1 C2B	1.85				

65.5   Dimethylarsino dimethyldithioarsinate

$C_4H_{12}As_2S_2$

N.Camerman, J.Trotter, J. Chem. Soc., 219, 1964

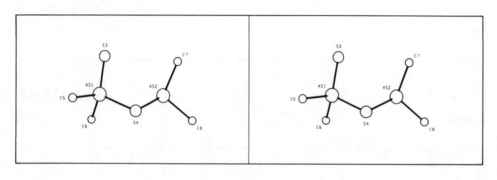

$P-1$ $Z = 2$ $R = 0.091$

DMSARS   LB 4-12-3

Bond Lengths				Bond Angles								Torsion Angles			
As1 S3	2.07	As2 S4	2.28	S3	As1	S4	113	C5	As1	C6	108	S3	As1	S4	As2	−43
As1 S4	2.21	As2 C7	2.01	S3	As1	C5	116	S4	As2	C7	99	C5	As1	S4	As2	−167
As1 C5	1.95	As2 C8	1.97	S3	As1	C6	112	S4	As2	C8	96	C6	As1	S4	As2	81
As1 C6	1.96			S4	As1	C5	101	C7	As2	C8	99	C7	As2	S4	As1	100
				S4	As1	C6	106	As1	S4	As2	96	C8	As2	S4	As1	−160

65.6   o - Phenylenediarsine oxychloride

$C_6H_4As_2Cl_2O$

W.R.Cullen, J.Trotter, Canad. J. Chem., 40, 1113, 1962

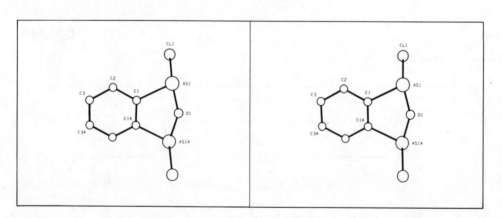

$C2/c$ $Z = 4$ $R_{h0l} = 0.16$, $R_{hk0} = 0.16$

PHASOC   LB 6-4-1

Bond Lengths		Bond Angles								Torsion Angles									
As1 Cl1	2.21	Cl1	As1	O1	104	As1	C1	C1A	118	Cl1	As1	O1	As1A	−94	C1A	C1	C2	C3	1
As1 O1	1.69	Cl1	As1	C1	97	C2	C1	C1A	120	C1	As1	O1	As1A	0	As1	C1	C1A	As1A	0
As1 C1	2.00	O1	As1	C1	76	C1	C2	C3	120	Cl1	As1	C1	C2	−77	As1	C1	C1A	C2A	180
C1 C2	1.39	As1	O1	As1A	152	C2	C3	C3A	120	Cl1	As1	C1	C1A	102	C2	C1	C1A	As1A	180
C1 C1A	1.41	As1	C1	C2	122					O1	As1	C1	C2	−180	C2	C1	C1A	C2A	−1
C2 C3	1.39									O1	As1	C1	C1A	0	C1	C2	C3	C3A	−1
C3 C3A	1.41									As1	C1	C2	C3	−180	C2	C3	C3A	C2A	1

65.7　Phenylarsonic acid

$C_6H_7AsO_3$

(i)　A.Shimada, Bull. Chem. Soc. Jap., 33, 301, 1960

(ii)　Yu.T.Struchkov, Izvest. Akad. Nauk S. S. S. R., Ser. Khim., 1962, 1960

(i)

P2$_1$2$_1$2$_1$　　Z = 4　　R_{hk0} = 0.180,
R_{0kl} = 0.140, R_{h0l} = 0.156

ARSACP　　LB 6-7-1

(ii)

P2$_1$2$_1$2$_1$　　Z = 4　　R_{h0l} = 0.096,
R_{hk0} = 0.136

ARSACP01　　LB 6-8-1

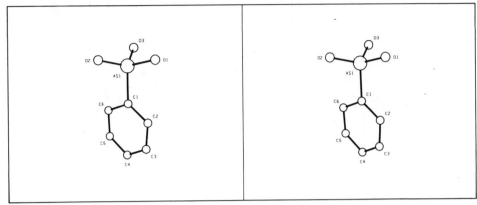

Bond Lengths

	(i)	(ii)
As1 O1	1.73	1.75
As1 O2	1.62	1.65
As1 O3	1.72	1.74
As1 C1	1.91	1.97
C1 C2	1.43	1.40
C1 C6	1.41	1.39
C2 C3	1.41	1.40
C3 C4	1.35	1.39
C4 C5	1.39	1.39
C5 C6	1.43	1.40

Bond Angles

	(i)	(ii)		(i)	(ii)
O1 As1 O2	114	117	As1 C1 C6	113	120
O1 As1 O3	106	106	C2 C1 C6	123	120
O1 As1 C1	107	109	C1 C2 C3	118	120
O2 As1 O3	115	107	C2 C3 C4	122	120
O2 As1 C1	106	104	C3 C4 C5	121	120
O3 As1 C1	110	115	C4 C5 C6	122	120
As1 C1 C2	125	120	C1 C6 C5	115	120

Torsion Angles

	(i)	(ii)
O1 As1 C1 C2	−1	−1

65.8　Phenylarsonic acid

$C_6H_7AsO_3$

For complete entry see 65.7

65.9　m - Aminobenzene arsonic acid

$C_6H_8AsNO_3$

A.Shimada, Bull. Chem. Soc. Jap., 35, 1600, 1962

B2$_1$/a　　Z = 8　　R_{hk0} = 0.100,
R_{0kl} = 0.118, R_{h0l} = 0.116

AMBARS　　LB 6-8-1

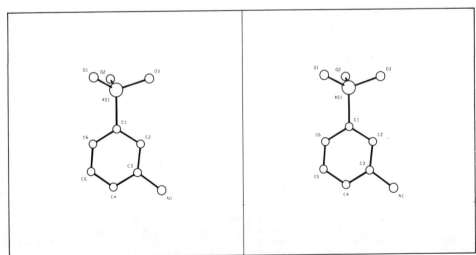

Bond Lengths

As1 O1	1.73	C1 C6	1.41
As1 O2	1.78	C2 C3	1.41
As1 O3	1.78	C3 C4	1.40
As1 C1	1.91	C4 C5	1.38
C3 N1	1.49	C5 C6	1.35
C1 C2	1.41		

Bond Angles

O1 As1 O2	114	C2 C1 C6	118
O1 As1 O3	109	C1 C2 C3	115
O1 As1 C1	108	N1 C3 C2	119
O2 As1 O3	107	N1 C3 C4	115
O2 As1 C1	113	C2 C3 C4	126
O3 As1 C1	106	C3 C4 C5	116
As1 C1 C2	122	C4 C5 C6	119
As1 C1 C6	121	C1 C6 C5	125

Torsion Angles

O3 As1 C1 C2	−22

65.10 Arsenious xanthate

$C_9H_{15}AsO_3S_6$

G.Carrai, G.Gottardi, Z. Kristallogr., 113, 373, 1960

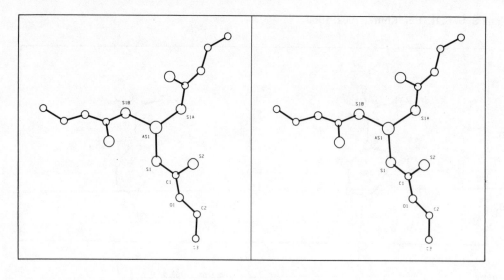

$$\left(H_5C_2-O-C \begin{array}{c} S \\ \\ S \end{array} \right)_3 As$$

R-3   Z = 6   R = 0.146

ASXANT   LB 9-15-1

Bond Lengths			Bond Angles				Torsion Angles				
As1	S1	2.28	S1	As1	S1A	92	S1A	As1	S1	C1	99
S1	C1	1.66	As1	S1	C1	91	S1B	As1	S1	C1	−170
S2	C1	1.67	C1	O1	C2	122	As1	S1	C1	S2	−13
C1	O1	1.31	S1	C1	S2	130	As1	S1	C1	O1	174
C2	O1	1.45	S1	C1	O1	112	C2	O1	C1	S1	179
C2	C3	1.49	S2	C1	O1	118	C2	O1	C1	S2	5
			O1	C2	C3	110	C1	O1	C2	C3	175

65.11   10 - Chloro - 5,10 - dihydrophenarsazine

$C_{12}H_9AsClN$

A.Camerman, J.Trotter, J. Chem. Soc., 730, 1965

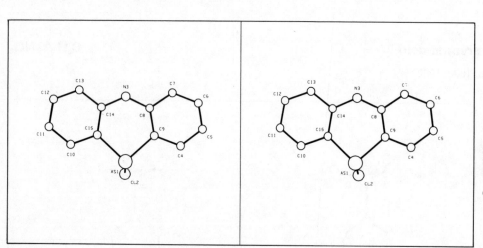

See also Fukuyo et al., Bull. Chem. Soc. Jap., 39, 1614, 1966.
$P2_12_12_1$ Z = 4   R = 0.056

COPHAZ   LB 12-9-2

Bond Lengths						Bond Angles							Torsion Angles									
As1	Cl2	2.30	C7	C8	1.42	Cl2	As1	C9	96	As1	C9	C8	122	Cl2	As1	C9	C4	−92	C6	C7	C8	N3	177
As1	C9	1.92	C8	C9	1.42	Cl2	As1	C15	97	C4	C9	C8	121	Cl2	As1	C9	C8	86	C6	C7	C8	C9	−4
As1	C15	1.91	C10	C11	1.39	C9	As1	C15	97	C11	C10	C15	122	C15	As1	C9	C4	171	N3	C8	C9	As1	8
C8	N3	1.37	C10	C15	1.41	C8	N3	C14	128	C10	C11	C12	119	C15	As1	C9	C8	−12	N3	C8	C9	C4	−175
C14	N3	1.37	C11	C12	1.40	C5	C4	C9	120	C11	C12	C13	120	Cl2	As1	C15	C10	92	C7	C8	C9	As1	−172
C4	C5	1.39	C12	C13	1.39	C4	C5	C6	120	C12	C13	C14	122	Cl2	As1	C15	C14	−88	C7	C8	C9	C4	6
C4	C9	1.39	C13	C14	1.41	C5	C6	C7	120	N3	C14	C13	118	C9	As1	C15	C10	−171	C15	C10	C11	C12	−1
C5	C6	1.40	C14	C15	1.42	C6	C7	C8	121	N3	C14	C15	123	C9	As1	C15	C14	8	C11	C10	C15	As1	180
C6	C7	1.42				N3	C8	C7	118	C13	C14	C15	118	C14	N3	C8	C7	−176	C11	C10	C15	C14	0
						N3	C8	C9	125	As1	C15	C10	117	C14	N3	C8	C9	4	C10	C11	C12	C13	1
						C7	C8	C9	117	As1	C15	C14	124	C8	N3	C14	C13	171	C11	C12	C13	C14	−1
						As1	C9	C4	117	C10	C15	C14	119	C8	N3	C14	C15	−9	C12	C13	C14	N3	−179
														C9	C4	C5	C6	−1	C12	C13	C14	C15	0
														C5	C4	C9	As1	174	N3	C14	C15	As1	0
														C5	C4	C9	C8	−3	N3	C14	C15	C10	180
														C4	C5	C6	C7	3	C13	C14	C15	As1	−179
														C5	C6	C7	C8	−1	C13	C14	C15	C10	0

65.12 Bromodiphenylarsine

$C_{12}H_{10}AsBr$

J.Trotter, J. Chem. Soc., 2567, 1962

$P2_1/a$ $Z = 4$ $R_{h0l} = 0.138$,
$R_{0kl} = 0.118$

BROPAR   LB 12-10-7

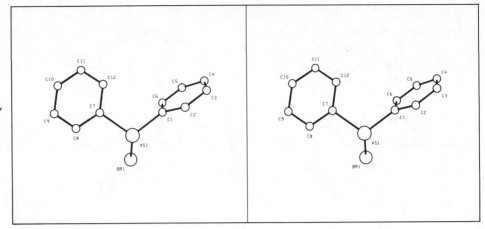

Bond Lengths

As1	Br1	2.40	C5	C6	1.36
As1	C1	1.96	C7	C8	1.41
As1	C7	2.03	C7	C12	1.43
C1	C2	1.41	C8	C9	1.36
C1	C6	1.37	C9	C10	1.41
C2	C3	1.39	C10	C11	1.42
C3	C4	1.37	C11	C12	1.36
C4	C5	1.41			

Bond Angles

Br1	As1	C1	95	C2	C3	C4	119	C7	C8	C9	115
Br1	As1	C7	95	C3	C4	C5	119	C8	C9	C10	116
C1	As1	C7	106	C4	C5	C6	124	C9	C10	C11	129
As1	C1	C2	119	C1	C6	C5	117	C10	C11	C12	115
As1	C1	C6	119	As1	C7	C8	113	C7	C12	C11	116
C2	C1	C6	121	As1	C7	C12	118				
C1	C2	C3	120	C8	C7	C12	129				

Torsion Angles

C7	As1	C1	C6	−54

65.13 Chlorodiphenylarsine

$C_{12}H_{10}AsCl$

J.Trotter, Canad. J. Chem., 40, 1590, 1962

$P2_1/a$ $Z = 4$ $R_{h0l} = 0.148$,
$R_{0kl} = 0.158$

CLPARS   LB 12-10-8

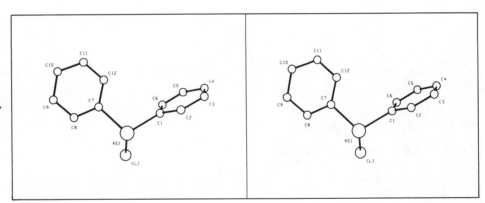

Bond Lengths

As1	Cl1	2.26	C5	C6	1.33
As1	C1	1.97	C7	C8	1.35
As1	C7	1.97	C7	C12	1.37
C1	C2	1.39	C8	C9	1.39
C1	C6	1.42	C9	C10	1.43
C2	C3	1.36	C10	C11	1.41
C3	C4	1.43	C11	C12	1.38
C4	C5	1.41			

Bond Angles

Cl1	As1	C1	94	C2	C3	C4	118	C7	C8	C9	117
Cl1	As1	C7	98	C3	C4	C5	123	C8	C9	C10	122
C1	As1	C7	105	C4	C5	C6	118	C9	C10	C11	117
As1	C1	C2	118	C1	C6	C5	120	C10	C11	C12	120
As1	C1	C6	120	As1	C7	C8	115	C7	C12	C11	120
C2	C1	C6	122	As1	C7	C12	122				
C1	C2	C3	119	C8	C7	C12	123				

Torsion Angles

C7	As1	C1	C6	−61

65.14 Iododiphenylarsine

$C_{12}H_{10}AsI$

J.Trotter, Canad. J. Chem., 41, 191, 1963

Atomic coordinates were not reported in the paper.
$P2_1/a$ $Z = 4$ No R factor was given.

IDPARS   LB 12-10-9

65.15   9 - Phenyl - 9 - arsafluorene (monoclinic form)

$C_{18}H_{13}As$

D.Sartain, M.R.Truter, J. Chem. Soc., 4414, 1963

No comparison of bond lengths is possible since they are not reported in the paper.
$P2_1$ Z = 4   R = 0.10

PHARFE   LB 18-13-2

Bond Lengths

As1	C1	1.99	As2	C19	1.98
As1	C7	1.97	As2	C30	2.06
As1	C18	1.91	As2	C31	2.06
C1	C2	1.59	C19	C20	1.49
C1	C6	1.38	C19	C24	1.41
C2	C3	1.41	C20	C21	1.31
C3	C4	1.38	C21	C22	1.62
C4	C5	1.35	C22	C23	1.32
C5	C6	1.57	C23	C24	1.37
C7	C8	1.47	C24	C25	1.54
C7	C12	1.46	C25	C26	1.51
C8	C9	1.35	C25	C30	1.50
C9	C10	1.44	C26	C27	1.35
C10	C11	1.50	C27	C28	1.55
C11	C12	1.52	C28	C29	1.23
C12	C13	1.41	C29	C30	1.39
C13	C14	1.49	C31	C32	1.39
C13	C18	1.44	C31	C36	1.37
C14	C15	1.40	C32	C33	1.51
C15	C16	1.44	C33	C34	1.52
C16	C17	1.44	C34	C35	1.32
C17	C18	1.51	C35	C36	1.37

Bond Angles

C1	As1	C7	96	C12	C13	C14	130	C19	C24	C23	120
C1	As1	C18	99	C12	C13	C18	110	C19	C24	C25	111
C7	As1	C18	88	C14	C13	C18	118	C23	C24	C25	129
As1	C1	C2	122	C13	C14	C15	127	C24	C25	C26	128
As1	C1	C6	122	C14	C15	C16	113	C24	C25	C30	119
C2	C1	C6	116	C15	C16	C17	122	C26	C25	C30	112
C1	C2	C3	114	C16	C17	C18	123	C25	C26	C27	124
C2	C3	C4	131	As1	C18	C13	114	C26	C27	C28	117
C3	C4	C5	116	As1	C18	C17	132	C27	C28	C29	119
C4	C5	C6	121	C13	C18	C17	114	C28	C29	C30	126
C1	C6	C5	122					As2	C30	C25	106
As1	C7	C8	129	C19	As2	C30	87	As2	C30	C29	133
As1	C7	C12	105	C19	As2	C31	96	C25	C30	C29	120
C8	C7	C12	124	C30	As2	C31	101	As2	C31	C32	117
C7	C8	C9	119	As2	C19	C20	123	As2	C31	C36	115
C8	C9	C10	122	As2	C19	C24	117	C32	C31	C36	127
C9	C10	C11	119	C20	C19	C24	121	C31	C32	C33	119
C10	C11	C12	118	C19	C20	C21	116	C32	C33	C34	111
C7	C12	C11	114	C20	C21	C22	124	C33	C34	C35	123
C7	C12	C13	121	C21	C22	C23	113	C34	C35	C36	126
C11	C12	C13	124	C22	C23	C24	127	C31	C36	C35	115

Torsion Angles

C18	As1	C7	C12	−6
C7	As1	C18	C13	−2
As1	C7	C12	C13	15
C7	C12	C13	C18	−18
C12	C13	C18	As1	10
C7	As1	C1	C2	−37
C30	As2	C19	C24	−1
C19	As2	C30	C25	−2
As2	C19	C24	C25	4
C19	C24	C25	C30	−6
C24	C25	C30	As2	5
C19	As2	C31	C36	−70

65.16   Tri - p - tolylarsine

$C_{21}H_{21}As$

J.Trotter, Canad. J. Chem., 41, 14, 1963

R-3   Z = 2 R_{hk0} = 0.15

TOLARS   LB 21-21-1

Bond Lengths

As1	C1	1.96
C1	C2	1.41
C1	C6	1.40
C2	C3	1.39
C3	C4	1.40
C4	C5	1.42
C4	C7	1.49
C5	C6	1.40

Bond Angles

C1	As1	C1A	102
As1	C1	C2	121
As1	C1	C6	119
C2	C1	C6	119
C1	C2	C3	122
C2	C3	C4	119
C3	C4	C5	120
C3	C4	C7	119
C5	C4	C7	121
C4	C5	C6	120
C1	C6	C5	120

Torsion Angles

C1B	As1	C1	C6	−1

65.17 bis(Diphenylarsenic) oxide

$C_{24}H_{20}As_2O$

W.R.Cullen, J.Trotter, Canad. J. Chem., 41, 2983, 1963

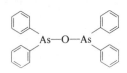

$P2_1/n$ Z = 4 R_{hk0} = 0.16,
R_{0kl} = 0.18

PHARSO   LB 24-20-7

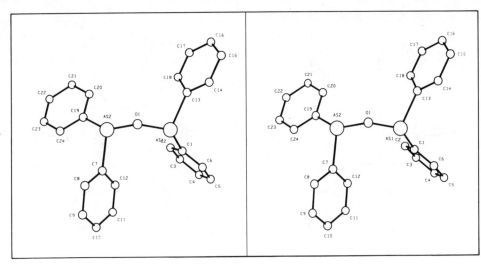

Bond Lengths

As1	O1	1.67	C9	C10	1.46
As1	C1	1.82	C10	C11	1.33
As1	C13	1.99	C11	C12	1.38
As2	O1	1.67	C13	C14	1.37
As2	C7	1.98	C13	C18	1.44
As2	C19	1.82	C14	C15	1.42
C1	C2	1.48	C15	C16	1.37
C1	C6	1.28	C16	C17	1.38
C2	C3	1.44	C17	C18	1.37
C3	C4	1.30	C19	C20	1.44
C4	C5	1.43	C19	C24	1.36
C5	C6	1.43	C20	C21	1.47
C7	C8	1.34	C21	C22	1.39
C7	C12	1.44	C22	C23	1.40
C8	C9	1.39	C23	C24	1.45

Bond Angles

O1	As1	C1	106	C4	C5	C6	126	C13	C14	C15	118
O1	As1	C13	103	C1	C6	C5	115	C14	C15	C16	122
C1	As1	C13	102	As2	C7	C8	115	C15	C16	C17	120
O1	As2	C7	101	As2	C7	C12	125	C16	C17	C18	119
O1	As2	C19	105	C8	C7	C12	120	C13	C18	C17	121
C7	As2	C19	98	C7	C8	C9	115	As2	C19	C20	122
As1	O1	As2	137	C8	C9	C10	125	As2	C19	C24	116
As1	C1	C2	121	C9	C10	C11	119	C20	C19	C24	121
As1	C1	C6	120	C10	C11	C12	115	C19	C20	C21	123
C2	C1	C6	119	C7	C12	C11	126	C20	C21	C22	113
C1	C2	C3	126	As1	C13	C14	118	C21	C22	C23	123
C2	C3	C4	113	As1	C13	C18	123	C22	C23	C24	124
C3	C4	C5	121	C14	C13	C18	119	C19	C24	C23	115

Torsion Angles

C1	As1	O1	As2	122
O1	As1	C1	C2	32
O1	As1	C13	C18	−40
O1	As2	C7	C12	−26
O1	As2	C19	C20	−36

65.18 Tri - p - xylylarsine

$C_{24}H_{27}As$

J.Trotter, Acta Cryst., 16, 1187, 1963

$P2_1/a$ Z = 4 R_{hk0} = 0.18,
R_{0kl} = 0.15

TXYLAS   LB 24-27-1

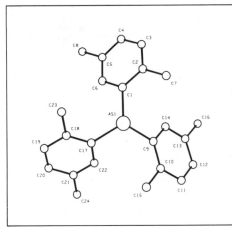
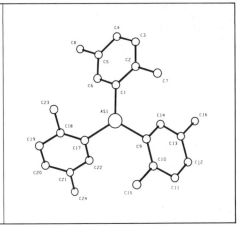

Bond Lengths

As1	C1	1.98	C10	C15	1.60
As1	C9	1.99	C11	C12	1.46
As1	C17	2.01	C12	C13	1.39
C1	C2	1.35	C13	C14	1.40
C1	C6	1.41	C13	C16	1.60
C2	C3	1.42	C17	C18	1.34
C2	C7	1.54	C17	C22	1.41
C3	C4	1.39	C18	C19	1.39
C4	C5	1.36	C18	C23	1.56
C5	C6	1.40	C19	C20	1.41
C5	C8	1.53	C20	C21	1.39
C9	C10	1.40	C21	C22	1.38
C9	C14	1.45	C21	C24	1.50
C10	C11	1.40			

Bond Angles

C1	As1	C9	100	C6	C5	C8	123	C9	C14	C13	120
C1	As1	C17	103	C1	C6	C5	122	As1	C17	C18	119
C9	As1	C17	102	As1	C9	C10	118	As1	C17	C22	123
As1	C1	C2	119	As1	C9	C14	120	C18	C17	C22	118
As1	C1	C6	122	C10	C9	C14	122	C17	C18	C19	122
C2	C1	C6	119	C9	C10	C11	118	C17	C18	C23	119
C1	C2	C3	119	C9	C10	C15	123	C19	C18	C23	120
C1	C2	C7	119	C11	C10	C15	119	C18	C19	C20	120
C3	C2	C7	123	C10	C11	C12	120	C19	C20	C21	120
C2	C3	C4	123	C11	C12	C13	122	C20	C21	C22	118
C3	C4	C5	118	C12	C13	C14	118	C20	C21	C24	120
C4	C5	C6	119	C12	C13	C16	121	C22	C21	C24	122
C4	C5	C8	118	C14	C13	C16	121	C17	C22	C21	122

Torsion Angles

C9	As1	C1	C2	−70
C1	As1	C9	C14	0
C1	As1	C17	C18	−75

65.19   Arsenobenzene

K.Hedberg, E.W.Hughes, J.Waser, Acta Cryst., 14, 369, 1961

C$_{36}$H$_{30}$As$_6$

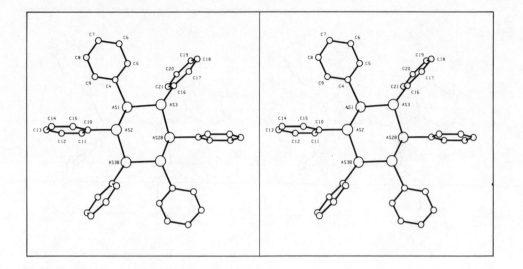

P2$_1$/c   Z = 12   R = 0.15

ASBENZ   LB 36-30-4

Bond Lengths

As1	As2	2.46
As1	As3	2.46
As1	C4	2.01
As2	As3B	2.46
As2	C10	1.92
As3	C16	1.97
C4	C5	1.40
C4	C9	1.40
C5	C6	1.39
C6	C7	1.40
C7	C8	1.40
C8	C9	1.39
C10	C11	1.40
C10	C15	1.41
C11	C12	1.41
C12	C13	1.41
C13	C14	1.40
C14	C15	1.41
C16	C17	1.39
C16	C21	1.39
C17	C18	1.40
C18	C19	1.39
C19	C20	1.39
C20	C21	1.40

Bond Angles

As2	As1	As3	89		As2	C10	C15	120
As2	As1	C4	100		C11	C10	C15	120
As3	As1	C4	101		C10	C11	C12	120
As1	As2	As3B	95		C11	C12	C13	120
As1	As2	C10	100		C12	C13	C14	120
As1	As3	As2B	90		C13	C14	C15	120
As1	As3	C16	102		C10	C15	C14	120
As1	C4	C5	119		As3	C16	C17	121
As1	C4	C9	121		As3	C16	C21	120
C5	C4	C9	120		C17	C16	C21	120
C4	C5	C6	120		C16	C17	C18	120
C5	C6	C7	120		C17	C18	C19	120
C6	C7	C8	120		C18	C19	C20	120
C7	C8	C9	120		C19	C20	C21	120
C4	C9	C8	120		C16	C21	C20	120
As2	C10	C11	120					

Torsion Angles

As3	As1	As2	As3B	−90		As1	C4	C5	C6	−179
As3	As1	As2	C10	169		C9	C4	C5	C6	0
C4	As1	As2	As3B	168		As1	C4	C9	C8	179
C4	As1	As2	C10	67		C5	C4	C9	C8	0
As2	As1	As3	As2B	85		C4	C5	C6	C7	0
As2	As1	As3	C16	−176		C5	C6	C7	C8	0
C4	As1	As3	As2B	−174		C6	C7	C8	C9	0
C4	As1	As3	C16	−76		C7	C8	C9	C4	0
As2	As1	C4	C5	105		As2	C10	C11	C12	−179
As2	As1	C4	C9	−74		C15	C10	C11	C12	0
As3	As1	C4	C5	14		As2	C10	C15	C14	179
As3	As1	C4	C9	−165		C11	C10	C15	C14	0
As1	As2	As3B	As1B	91		C10	C11	C12	C13	0
As1	As2	As3B	C16B	−167		C11	C12	C13	C14	0
C10	As2	As3B	As1B	−168		C12	C13	C14	C15	0
C10	As2	As3B	C16B	−67		C13	C14	C15	C10	0
As1	As2	C10	C11	46		As3	C16	C17	C18	180
As1	As2	C10	C15	−133		C21	C16	C17	C18	0
As3B	As2	C10	C11	−50		As3	C16	C21	C20	−180
As3B	As2	C10	C15	131		C17	C16	C21	C20	0
As1	As3	C16	C17	147		C16	C17	C18	C19	0
As1	As3	C16	C21	−33		C17	C18	C19	C20	0
As2B	As3	C16	C17	−121		C18	C19	C20	C21	0
As2B	As3	C16	C21	58		C19	C20	C21	C16	0

66.1 Trimethylphosphine oxide antimony(v) chloride

$C_3H_9Cl_5OPSb$

C.-I.Branden, I.Lindqvist, Acta Chem. Scand., 15, 167, 1961

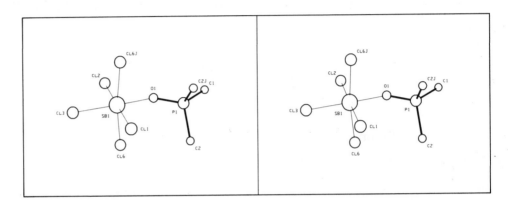

Pnma   Z = 4   R = 0.13

ACMEPO

Bond Lengths			Bond Angles								Torsion Angles			
Cl1	Sb1	2.32	O1	P1	C1	112	Cl2	Sb1	Cl3	92	C1	P1	O1	Sb1	−180
Cl2	Sb1	2.37	O1	P1	C2	111	Cl2	Sb1	Cl6	91				
Cl3	Sb1	2.32	C1	P1	C2	110	Cl2	Sb1	O1	87				
Cl6	Sb1	2.35	C2	P1	C2J	103	Cl3	Sb1	Cl6	94				
P1	O1	1.61	Cl1	Sb1	Cl2	179	Cl3	Sb1	O1	178				
P1	C1	1.83	Cl1	Sb1	Cl3	89	Cl6	Sb1	Cl6J	172				
P1	C2	1.89	Cl1	Sb1	Cl6	89	Cl6	Sb1	O1	86				
Sb1	O1	2.00	Cl1	Sb1	O1	93	P1	O1	Sb1	141				

66.2 Ammonium antimonyl DL - tartrate tetrahydrate

$C_8H_8O_{12}Sb_2^{2-}$, $2H_4N^+$, $4H_2O$

G.A.Kiosse, N.I.Golovastikov, N.V.Belov, Dokl. Akad. Nauk S. S. S. R., 155, 545, 1964

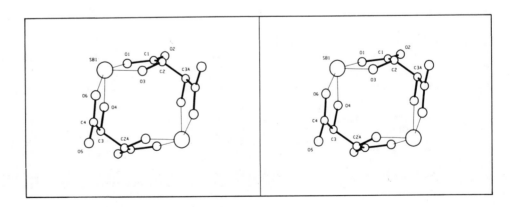

C2/c   Z = 8   R = 0.151

ASBTAR   LB 4-8-55

Bond Lengths						Bond Angles								Torsion Angles			
Sb1	O1	2.17	C3	O4	1.44	O1	Sb1	O3	79	Sb1	O4	C3	119	O4	C3	C4	108	O1	C1	C2	O3	9
Sb1	O3	2.03	C4	O5	1.29	O1	Sb1	O4	80	Sb1	O6	C4	115	O4	C3	C2A	110	O4	C3	C4	O6	−10
Sb1	O4	2.04	C4	O6	1.29	O1	Sb1	O6	149	O1	C1	O2	117	C4	C3	C2A	114
Sb1	O6	2.14	C1	C2	1.43	O3	Sb1	O4	99	O1	C1	C2	112	O5	C4	O6	123
C1	O1	1.42	C2	C3A	1.46	O3	Sb1	O6	82	O2	C1	C2	130	O5	C4	C3	117
C1	O2	1.17	C3	C4	1.57	O4	Sb1	O6	79	O3	C2	C1	118	O6	C4	C3	119
C2	O3	1.47				Sb1	O1	C1	115	O3	C2	C3A	111				
						Sb1	O3	C2	114	C1	C2	C3A	109				

66.3 Antimony(iii) xanthate $C_9H_{15}O_3S_6Sb$

G.Gottardi, Z. Kristallogr., 115, 451, 1961

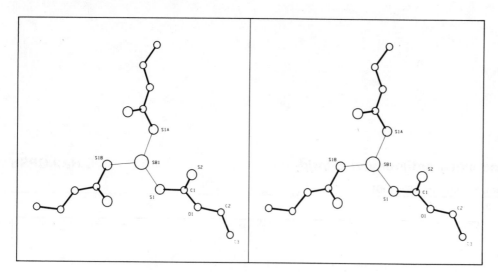

$$\left(H_5C_2 - O - C \begin{array}{c} S \\ \\ S \end{array} \right)_3 Sb$$

R-3   Z = 6   R = 0.119

SBXANT   LB 9-15-9

Bond Lengths

S1	Sb1	2.52
S1	C1	1.70
S2	C1	1.59
C1	O1	1.36
C2	O1	1.48
C2	C3	1.49

Bond Angles

Sb1	S1	C1	89
S1	Sb1	S1A	87
C1	O1	C2	120
S1	C1	S2	131
S1	C1	O1	108
S2	C1	O1	121
O1	C2	C3	110

Torsion Angles

C1	S1	Sb1	S1A	96
C1	S1	Sb1	S1B	−176
Sb1	S1	C1	S2	−8
Sb1	S1	C1	O1	169
C2	O1	C1	S1	180
C2	O1	C1	S2	−3
C1	O1	C2	C3	166

66.4 Pentaphenyl antimony $C_{30}H_{25}Sb$

P.J.Wheatley, J. Chem. Soc., 3718, 1964

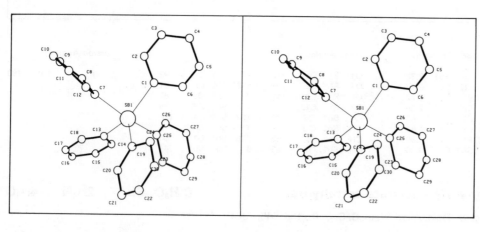

Comparison with the results of Beauchamp et al., J. Amer. Chem. Soc., 90, 6675, 1968 indicates that y(C29) should be 2.389A and not 1.389A.

P-1   Z = 2 R_{0kl} = 0.111, R_{h0l} = 0.123

PHENSB   LB 30-25-7

Bond Lengths

Sb1	C1	2.26	C7	C12	1.44	C19	C24	1.31
Sb1	C7	2.14	C8	C9	1.44	C20	C21	1.44
Sb1	C13	2.17	C9	C10	1.43	C21	C22	1.37
Sb1	C19	2.11	C10	C11	1.34	C22	C23	1.25
Sb1	C25	2.06	C11	C12	1.18	C23	C24	1.51
C1	C2	1.38	C13	C14	1.38	C25	C26	1.20
C1	C6	1.45	C13	C18	1.22	C25	C30	1.40
C2	C3	1.36	C14	C15	1.33	C26	C27	1.65
C3	C4	1.40	C15	C16	1.34	C27	C28	1.29
C4	C5	1.46	C16	C17	1.27	C28	C29	1.16
C5	C6	1.29	C17	C18	1.43	C29	C30	1.71
C7	C8	1.37	C19	C20	1.33			

Bond Angles

C1	Sb1	C7	88	C1	C6	C5	122	Sb1	C19	C20	120
C1	Sb1	C13	146	Sb1	C7	C8	125	Sb1	C19	C24	121
C1	Sb1	C19	104	Sb1	C7	C12	125	C20	C19	C24	119
C1	Sb1	C25	90	C7	C8	C12	108	C19	C20	C21	125
C7	Sb1	C13	87	C7	C8	C9	124	C20	C21	C22	114
C7	Sb1	C19	102	C8	C9	C10	117	C21	C22	C23	123
C7	Sb1	C25	162	C9	C10	C11	114	C22	C23	C24	121
C13	Sb1	C19	110	C10	C11	C12	126	C19	C24	C23	118
C13	Sb1	C25	84	C7	C12	C11	129	Sb1	C25	C26	121
C19	Sb1	C25	95	Sb1	C13	C14	126	Sb1	C25	C30	123
Sb1	C1	C2	122	Sb1	C13	C18	118	C26	C25	C30	114
Sb1	C1	C6	119	C14	C13	C18	115	C25	C26	C27	127
C2	C1	C6	118	C13	C14	C15	118	C26	C27	C28	114
C1	C2	C3	119	C14	C15	C16	129	C27	C28	C29	127
C2	C3	C4	124	C15	C16	C17	109	C28	C29	C30	117
C3	C4	C5	116	C16	C17	C18	124	C25	C30	C29	118
C4	C5	C6	121	C13	C18	C17	124				

Torsion Angles

C7	Sb1	C1	C2	−15
C1	Sb1	C7	C12	−75
C1	Sb1	C13	C14	64
C1	Sb1	C19	C24	−5
C1	Sb1	C25	C26	−56

66.5 tris - 3 - Sulfanilamido - 6 - methoxypyridazine - bismuth chloride $C_{33}H_{36}BiCl_3N_{12}O_9S_3$

L.Cavalca, M.Nardelli, G.Fava, G.Giraldi, Acta Cryst., 16, A69, 1963

Atomic coordinates were not reported in the paper.
R3   Z = 3   No R factor was given.

SMPBIC   LB 33-36-1

$$\left[H_3C-O-\underset{N}{\overset{N}{\bigcirc}}-NH-SO_2-\bigcirc-NH_2 \right]_3 BiCl_3$$

67.1   Ethyl lithium

$C_4H_{10}Li_2$

H.Dietrich, Acta Cryst., 16; 681, 1963

$C_2H_5—Li$

Pcan   Z = 16   R = 0.14

ETHYLI   LB 2-5-9

Bond Lengths   *Bond Angles*

Li1   Li1C   2.63   Li1 C2   C1   110
Li1   C2   2.25
C1   C2   1.54

Torsion Angles

C2   Li1   Li1C C2C   0
Li1C Li1   C2   C1   122

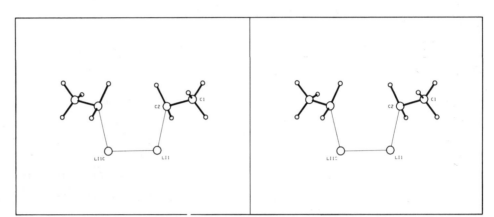

67.2   Sodium hydridodiethylberyllate dietherate

$C_8H_{22}Be_2{}^{2-}$, $2C_4H_{10}NaO^+$

G.W.Adamson, H.M.M.Shearer, Chem. Communic., 240, 1965

Atomic coordinates were not reported in the paper.
P2$_1$/c   Z = 2   R = 0.16

NHETBE   LB 16-42-1

$$\left[Na^+\!\leftarrow\!O\!\begin{array}{c}C_2H_5\\C_2H_5\end{array}\right]_2 \left[(C_2H_5)_2Be\begin{array}{c}H\\H\end{array}Be(C_2H_5)_2\right]^{2-}$$

67.3   Barium - 2 - dicyanomethylene - 1,1,3,3 - tetracyanopropane hexahydrate

$C_{10}N_6{}^{2-}$, Ba^{2+} , $6H_2O$

D.A.Bekoe, P.K.Gantzel, K.N.Trueblood, Acta Cryst., 16, A62, 1963

The structure is totally disordered.
P-3m1   Z = 2   No R factor was given.

BACMCP

$$Ba^{++}\quad \begin{array}{c}NC\\ \\NC\end{array}C=C\begin{array}{c}CN\\ \\ \\CN\end{array} \cdot 6\,H_2O$$

67.4   bis - Acetylacetone beryllium

$C_{10}H_{14}BeO_4$

V.Amirthalingam, V.M.Padmanabhan, J.Shankar, Acta Cryst., 13, 201, 1960

There is an error in this analysis. The structure has been redetermined by Stewart and Morosin, Amer. Cryst. Assoc., Abstr. Papers (Winter Meeting), 84, 1972.
P2$_1$ Z = 4   R$_{h0l}$ = 0.18, R$_{hk0}$ = 0.13

ACACBE   LB 10-14-2

67.5   Phenyl magnesium bromide dietherate

$C_{14}H_{25}BrMgO_2$

G.Stucky, R.E.Rundle, J. Amer. Chem. Soc., 86, 4825, 1964

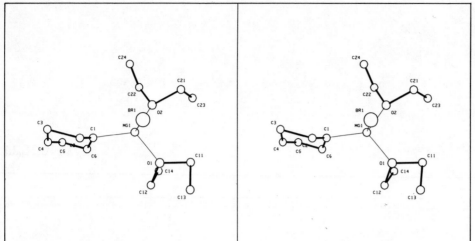

The author has provided us with improved coordinates for the ether carbon atoms.

$P2_12_12_1$ Z = 4   R = 0.178

PHMGBE   LB 6-5-4

Bond Lengths

Br1	Mg1	2.44	C21	O2	1.84	C4	C5	1.14
Mg1	O1	2.01	C22	O2	1.40	C5	C6	1.51
Mg1	O2	2.06	C1	C2	1.03	C11	C13	1.56
Mg1	C1	2.34	C1	C6	1.24	C12	C14	1.43
C11	O1	1.60	C2	C3	1.77	C21	C23	1.70
C12	O1	1.51	C3	C4	1.38	C22	C24	1.45

Bond Angles

Br1	Mg1	O1	103	C11	O1	C12	116	C2	C3	C4	93
Br1	Mg1	O2	110	Mg1	O2	C21	111	C3	C4	C5	132
Br1	Mg1	C1	120	Mg1	O2	C22	124	C4	C5	C6	107
O1	Mg1	O2	97	C21	O2	C22	111	C1	C6	C5	116
O1	Mg1	C1	117	Mg1	C1	C2	108	O1	C11	C13	93
O2	Mg1	C1	107	Mg1	C1	C6	129	O1	C12	C14	92
Mg1	O1	C11	124	C2	C1	C6	116	O2	C21	C23	82
Mg1	O1	C12	119	C1	C2	C3	122	O2	C22	C24	115

68.1   Methyl aluminium chloride dimer

$C_2H_6Al_2Cl_4$

G.Allegra, G.Perego, A.Immirzi, Makromol. Chem., 61, 69, 1963

$(CH_3AlCl_2)_2$

C2/c   Z = 4 R_{110} = 0.154,
R_{112} = 0.175

MALCLD   LB 2-6-2

Bond Lengths			Bond Angles			
Al1	Cl1	2.25	Cl1	Al1	Cl2	109
Al1	Cl2	2.06	Cl1	Al1	Cl1D	89
Al1	Cl1D	2.26	Cl1	Al1	C1	110
Al1	C1	1.93	Cl2	Al1	Cl1D	106
			Cl2	Al1	C1	124
			Al1	Cl1	Al1D	91

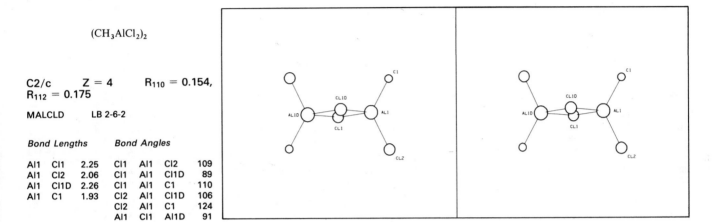

68.2   Trimethylamine gallane

$C_3H_{12}GaN$

D.F.Shriver, C.E.Nordman, Inorg. Chem., 2, 1298, 1963

$$H_3C \quad\quad H$$
$$H_3C—N→Ga—H$$
$$H_3C \quad\quad H$$

No comparison of bond lengths is possible since they are not reported in the paper. The published coordinates correspond to an ordered molecule but disorder of the $(CH_3)_3N$ group is possible.
R3m   Z = 1   R = 0.105

TMEGAL   LB 3-12-15

Bond Lengths			Bond Angles			
Ga1	N1	1.98	Ga1	N1	C1	113
C1	N1	1.47	C1	N1	C1A	106

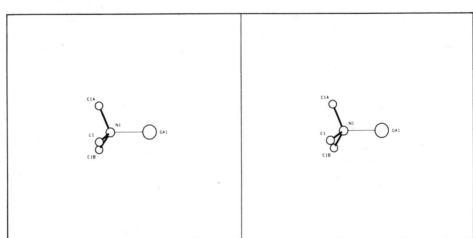

68.3   Cyclopentadienyl indium

$(C_5H_5In)_n$

E.Frasson, F.Menegus, C.Panattoni, Nature, 199, 1087, 1963

Atomic coordinates were not reported in the paper.
Cc   Z = 4 R_{hk0} = 0.08,
R_{0kl} = 0.07

CYPEIN

$$\left[\cdot\cdot In \cdot\cdot \bigcirc \cdot\cdot\cdot \right]_n$$

68.4 Aluminium hydride - N,N,N',N' - tetramethyl ethylenediamine adduct

$C_6H_{19}AIN_2$

G.J.Palenik, Acta Cryst., 17, 1573, 1964

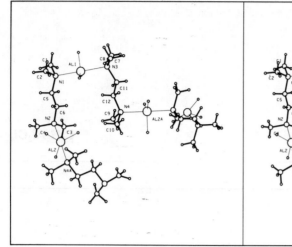

$P2_12_12_1$ Z = 8   R = 0.06

AHTMED   LB 6-19-1

Bond Lengths

Al1	N1	2.19	C6	N2	1.49
Al1	N3	2.24	C7	N3	1.46
Al2	N2	2.19	C8	N3	1.47
Al2	N4A	2.20	C11	N3	1.49
C1	N1	1.48	C9	N4	1.48
C2	N1	1.48	C10	N4	1.47
C5	N1	1.50	C12	N4	1.50
C3	N2	1.47	C5	C6	1.53
C4	N2	1.48	C11	C12	1.51

Bond Angles

N1	Al1	N3	178	Al2	N2	C4	108	C7	N3	C11	106
N2	Al2	N4A	176	Al2	N2	C6	108	C8	N3	C11	112
Al1	N1	C1	108	C3	N2	C4	110	C9	N4	C10	109
Al1	N1	C2	109	C3	N2	C6	112	C9	N4	C12	111
Al1	N1	C5	115	C4	N2	C6	112	C10	N4	C12	106
C1	N1	C2	109	Al1	N3	C7	107	N1	C5	C6	114
C1	N1	C5	105	Al1	N3	C8	109	N2	C6	C5	114
C2	N1	C5	110	Al1	N3	C11	113	N3	C11	C12	112
Al2	N2	C3	108	C7	N3	C8	109	N4	C12	C11	114

Torsion Angles

N3	Al1	N1	C5	66
N1	Al1	N3	C11	−69
N4A	Al2	N2	C6	166
N2	Al2	N4A	C9A	−173
N2	Al2	N4A	C10A	−55
N2	Al2	N4A	C12A	61
Al1	N1	C5	C6	59
Al2	N2	C6	C5	−178
Al1	N3	C11	C12	−63
Al2A	N4	C12	C11	60
N1	C5	C6	N2	−176
N3	C11	C12	N4	170

68.5 Aluminium hydride - trimethylamine complex

$C_6H_{21}AIN_2$

C.W.Heitsch, C.E.Nordman, R.W.Parry, Inorg. Chem., 2, 508, 1963

$2 N(CH_3)_3 \cdot AlH_3$

The methyl groups of the two $(CH_3)N$ ligands are disordered.
Cmca   Z = 4   R = 0.114

ALHTMA   LB 6-21-1

68.6 Lithium aluminium tetraethyl

$C_8H_{20}AlLi$

R.L.Gerteis, R.E.Dickerson, T.L.Brown, Inorg. Chem., 3, 872, 1964

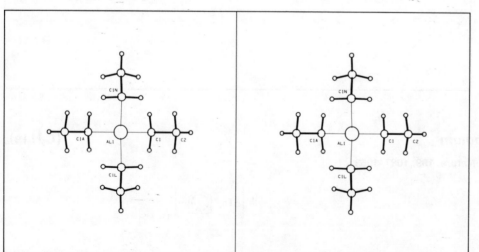

$Li^+ [Al(C_2H_5)_4]^-$

$P4_2/nmc$ Z = 2   R = 0.087

LIALET   LB 8-20-2

Bond Lengths   **Bond Angles**

Al1	C1	2.02	C1	Al1	C1A	112
C1	C2	1.52	C1	Al1	C1L	108
			Al1	C1	C2	109

Torsion Angles

C1A	Al1	C1	C2	−180

68.7 Hydrogen aquoethylenediamine tetra - acetato gallium(iii) $C_{10}H_{15}GaN_2O_9$

J.L.Hoard, C.H.L.Kennard, G.S.Smith, Inorg. Chem., 2, 1316, 1963

Atomic coordinates were not
reported in the paper.
$P2_1/c$ Z = 4   No R factor was
given.

EDTAGA   LB 10-15-13

$$\left[\left(\begin{array}{c}OOC-H_2C \\ OOC-H_2C\end{array}\right\rangle N-CH_2-CH_2-N\left\langle\begin{array}{c}CH_2-COO \\ CH_2-COOH\end{array}\right) Ga(OH_2)\right]$$

68.8 Aluminium triethyl - potassium fluoride $C_{12}H_{30}Al_2F^-$, K^+

G.Allegra, G.Perego, Acta Cryst., 16, 185, 1963

$$K^+ \left[\begin{array}{c}H_5C_2 \\ H_5C_2-Al\leftarrow F\rightarrow Al-C_2H_5 \\ H_5C_2\end{array}\begin{array}{c}C_2H_5 \\ C_2H_5 \\ C_2H_5\end{array}\right]^-$$

R-3   Z = 3 R_{100} = 0.126,
R_{2-21} = 0.116

ALETKF   LB 12-30-1

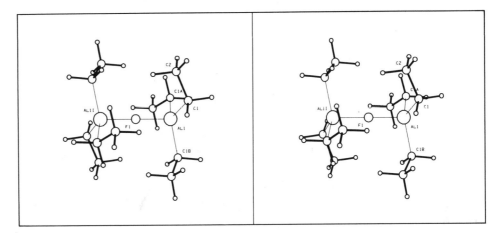

Bond Lengths			Bond Angles				Torsion Angles			
Al1	F1	1.83	F1	Al1	C1	102	C1	Al1	F1	Al1I	−90
Al1	C1	2.00	C1	Al1	C1A	116	C1A	Al1	F1	Al1I	−90
C1	C2	1.52	Al1	F1	Al1I	180	C1B	Al1	F1	Al1I	−90
			Al1	C1	C2	113	F1	Al1	C1	C2	−55
							C1A	Al1	C1	C2	56
							C1B	Al1	C1	C2	−165

68.9 Tetramethylstibonium tetrakis(trimethylsiloxy) aluminate $C_{12}H_{36}AlO_4Si_4$, $C_4H_{12}Sb^+$

P.J.Wheatley, J. Chem. Soc., 3200, 1963

$[(CH_3)_4Sb]^+ [Al(O-Si(CH_3)_3)_4]^-$

Pmmn   Z = 2 R_{hk0} = 0.075,
R_{h0l} = 0.095, R_{0kl} = 0.106

MESBOA   LB 16-48-1

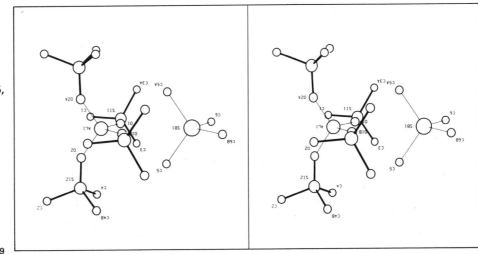

Bond Lengths			Bond Angles				Torsion Angles									
Sb1	C5	2.20	C5	Sb1	C6	109										
Sb1	C6	2.20	C5	Sb1	C5A	110										
			C6	Sb1	C6B	110										
Al1	O1	1.79														
Al1	O2	1.79	O1	Al1	O2	109										
Si1	O1	1.56	O1	Al1	O1B	110	O2	Si2	C2	113	O2	Al1	O1	Si1	60	C1	Si1	O1	Al1	0
Si1	C1	1.87	O2	Al1	O2A	110	O2	Si2	C4	112	O1B	Al1	O1	Si1	−180	C3	Si1	O1	Al1	−121
Si1	C3	1.87	O1	Si1	C1	112	C2	Si2	C4	106	O2A	Al1	O1	Si1	−60	C3A	Si1	O1	Al1	121
Si2	O2	1.56	O1	Si1	C3	112	C4	Si2	C4B	106	O1	Al1	O2	Si2	60	C2	Si2	O2	Al1	−180
Si2	C2	1.87	C1	Si1	C3	108	Al1	O1	Si1	147	O1B	Al1	O2	Si2	−60	C4	Si2	O2	Al1	−60
Si2	C4	1.87	C3	Si1	C3A	105	Al1	O2	Si2	147	O2A	Al1	O2	Si2	−180	C4B	Si2	O2	Al1	60

68.10 Diphenyl aluminium nitride tetramer

$C_{48}H_{40}Al_4N_4$

T.R.R.McDonald, W.S.McDonald, Proc. Chem. Soc., 382, 1963

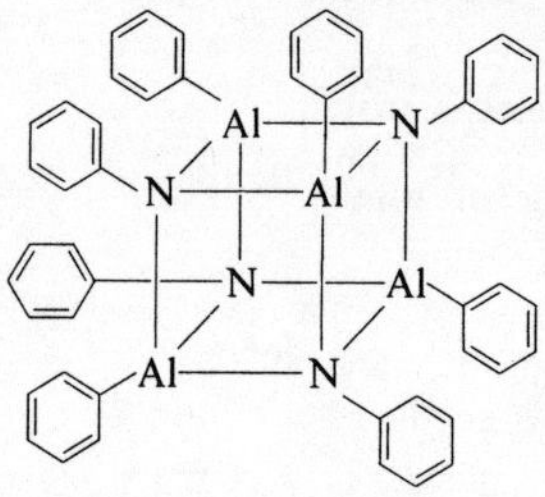

Atomic coordinates were not reported in the paper.
$I4_1/a$ Z = 4   R = 0.147

PHALNT   LB 48-40-1

69.1   Trimethyl tin fluoride

C$_3$H$_9$FSn

H.C.Clark, R.J.O'Brien, J.Trotter, J. Chem. Soc., 2332, 1964

Two of the methyl groups and the
fluorine atom are disordered.
Pmcn   Z = 4   R = 0.126

TIMSNF   LB 3-9-15

$$H_3C-\underset{\underset{CH_3}{|}}{\overset{\overset{CH_3}{|}}{Sn}}-F$$

69.2   Trimethyl tin hydroxide

C$_3$H$_{10}$OSn

N.Kasai, K.Yasuda, R.Okawara, J. Organometal. Chem., 3, 172, 1965

Atomic   coordinates   were   not
reported in the paper.
Pn   Z = 64   R = 0.12

TMESNH   LB 3-10-11

(CH$_3$)$_3$SnOH

69.3   Lead(ii) thiourea acetate

C$_5$H$_{10}$N$_2$O$_4$PbS

M.Nardelli, G.Fava, G.Branchi, Acta Cryst., 13, 898, 1960

(S=C(NH$_2$)$_2$ · Pb^{2+}(CH$_3$COO$^-$)$_2$)

P2$_1$/c   Z = 4   R = 0.068

PBTUAC   LB 5-10-15

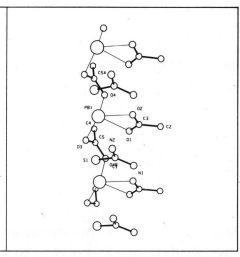

Bond Lengths

Pb1	O2	2.44		C2	C3	1.50
Pb1	O4	2.37		C4	C5	1.48
C3	O1	1.24				
C3	O2	1.27		S1	C1	1.68
C5	O3	1.24		C1	N1	1.38
C5	O4	1.34		C1	N2	1.35

Bond Angles

O2	Pb1	O4	93		O3	C5	C4	120
Pb1	O2	C3	95		O4	C5	C4	118
Pb1	O4	C5	109					
O1	C3	O2	126		S1	C1	N1	118
O1	C3	C2	118		S1	C1	N2	122
O2	C3	C2	116		N1	C1	N2	121
O3	C5	O4	122					

Torsion Angles

O4	Pb1	O2	C3	−69
O2	Pb1	O4	C5	−118
Pb1	O2	C3	O1	0
Pb1	O2	C3	C2	177
Pb1	O4	C5	O3	7
Pb1	O4	C5	C4	−169

69.4　Lead(iv) acetate

B.Kamenar, Acta Cryst., 16, A34, 1963

$C_8H_{12}O_8Pb$

Atomic coordinates were not reported in the paper.
$P2_1/c$　Z = 8　No R factor was given.

$Pb(OCOCH_3)_4$

PBACET

69.5　Chloro(trimethyl)pyridine tin

R.Hulme, J. Chem. Soc., 1524, 1963

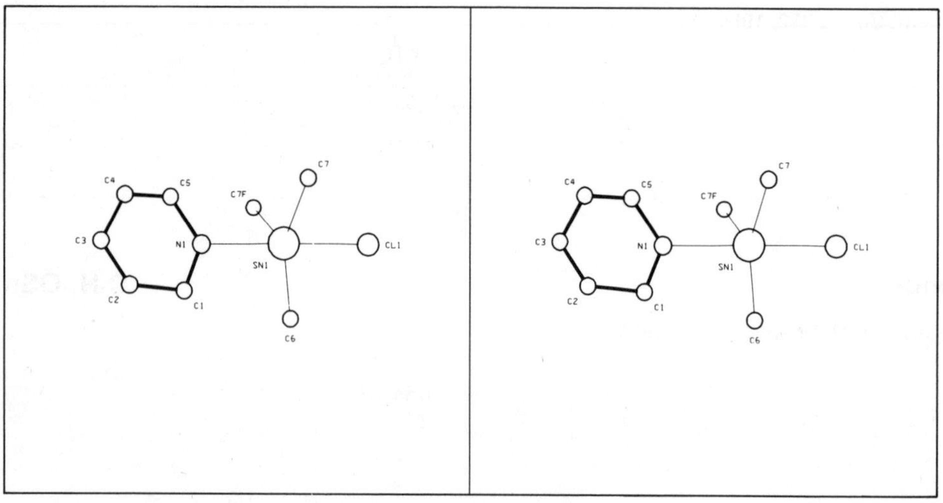

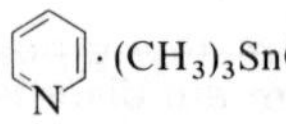

$C_8H_{14}ClNSn$

$\cdot (CH_3)_3SnCl$

Pnma　Z = 4　R = 0.186

CMEPSN　LB 8-14-11

Bond Lengths

Cl1	Sn1	2.43	C5	N1	1.38
Sn1	N1	2.26	C1	C2	1.43
Sn1	C6	1.85	C2	C3	1.24
Sn1	C7	2.15	C3	C4	1.30
C1	N1	1.24	C4	C5	1.20

Bond Angles

Cl1	Sn1	N1	179	C6	Sn1	C7	126	N1	C1	C2	109
Cl1	Sn1	C6	88	C7	Sn1	C7F	108	C1	C2	C3	129
Cl1	Sn1	C7	91	Sn1	N1·	C1	116	C2	C3	C4	116
N1	Sn1	C6	91	Sn1	N1	C5	123	C3	C4	C5	119
N1	Sn1	C7	90	C1	N1	C5	121	N1	C5	C4	126

Torsion Angles

C6	Sn1	N1	C1	0

69.6　Tin(iv) chloride tetrahydrothiophene complex

I.R.Beattie, R.Hulme, L.Rule, J. Chem. Soc., 1581, 1965

$C_8H_{16}Cl_4S_2Sn$

Atomic coordinates were not reported in the paper.
$P2_1/n$　Z = 2　No R factor given.

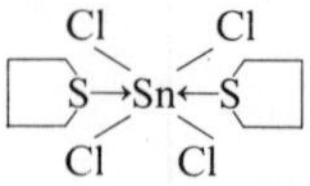

SNCTHT　LB 8-16-27

69.7　Diphenyl tin m - xylene solvate

D.H.Olson, R.E.Rundle, Inorg. Chem., 2, 1310, 1963

$C_{12}H_{10}Sn , 0.33C_8H_{10}$

Atomic coordinates were not given but bond lengths were reported.
$P112_1/b$　Z = 2　R = 0.07

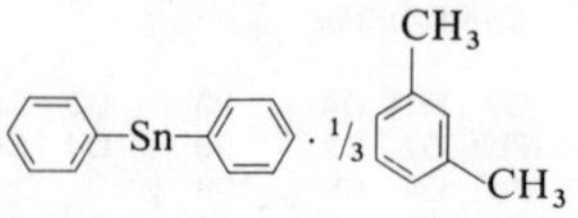

DPHSNX　LB 12-10-86

69.8   Tetrachloro - 1,4 - bis(triethylstannyloxy) - benzene $C_{18}H_{30}Cl_4O_2Sn_2$

P.J.Wheatley, J. Chem. Soc., 5027, 1961

$(C_2H_5)_3Sn{-}O{-}$ [benzene ring with Cl Cl on top and Cl Cl on bottom] $O{-}Sn(C_2H_5)_3$

$P2_1/n$ $Z = 2$ $R_{0kl} = 0.075$, $R_{h0l} = 0.070$

CLESOB   LB 18-30-19

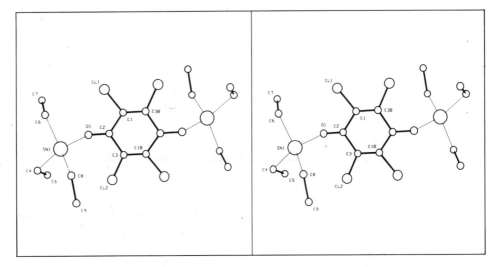

Bond Lengths

Cl1	C1	1.70	C1	C2	1.51	
Cl2	C3	1.71	C1	C3B	1.32	
Sn1	O1	2.08	C2	C3	1.51	
Sn1	C4	2.15	C4	C5	1.54	
Sn1	C6	2.17	C6	C7	1.55	
Sn1	C8	2.21	C8	C9	1.56	
C2	O1	1.30				

Bond Angles

O1	Sn1	C4	120	O1	C2	C1	131
O1	Sn1	C6	97	O1	C2	C3	118
O1	Sn1	C8	112	C1	C2	C3	111
C4	Sn1	C6	112	Cl2	C3	C2	119
C4	Sn1	C8	99	Cl2	C3	C1B	120
C6	Sn1	C8	119	C2	C3	C1B	121
Sn1	O1	C2	127	Sn1	C4	C5	109
Cl1	C1	C2	107	Sn1	C6	C7	110
Cl1	C1	C3B	125	Sn1	C8	C9	125
C2	C1	C3B	128				

Torsion Angles

C4	Sn1	O1	C2	−137	Sn1	O1	C2	C3	80
C6	Sn1	O1	C2	102	Cl1	C1	C2	O1	5
C8	Sn1	O1	C2	−22	Cl1	C1	C2	C3	−176
O1	Sn1	C4	C5	8	C3B	C1	C2	O1	−174
C6	Sn1	C4	C5	121	C3B	C1	C2	C3	5
C8	Sn1	C4	C5	−114	Cl1	C1	C3B	Cl2B	2
O1	Sn1	C6	C7	55	Cl1	C1	C3B	C2B	176
C4	Sn1	C6	C7	−71	C2	C1	C3B	Cl2B	−180
C8	Sn1	C6	C7	175	C2	C1	C3B	C2B	−6
O1	Sn1	C8	C9	−86	O1	C2	C3	Cl2	0
C4	Sn1	C8	C9	42	O1	C2	C3	C1B	174
C6	Sn1	C8	C9	163	C1	C2	C3	Cl2	−179
Sn1	O1	C2	C1	−102	C1	C2	C3	C1B	−5

69.9   Triphenylgermanium manganese pentacarbonyl $C_{23}H_{15}GeMnO_5$

B.T.Kilbourn, T.L.Blundell, H.M.Powell, Chem. Communic., 444, 1965

Atomic coordinates were not reported in the paper.
P-1   Z = 4   R = 0.12

TGEMCO   LB 23-15-2

[structural diagram: three phenyl groups attached to Ge→Mn with five CO groups]

69.10   Diphenyldichloro - lead $(C_{24}H_{20}Cl_4Pb_2)_n$

V.Busetti, M.Mammi, A.Del Pra, Acta Cryst., 16, A71, 1963

Atomic coordinates were not reported in the paper.
Pnnm   Z = 2   No R factor was given.

DPDCPB

[structural diagram: bridged lead chloride structure with phenyl groups]

70.1 Tellurium dimethanethiosulfonate thiourea complex

C₄H₁₄N₄O₄S₆Te — $C_4H_{14}N_4O_4S_6Te$

O.Foss, K.Maroy, S.Husebye, Acta Chem. Scand., 19, 2361, 1965

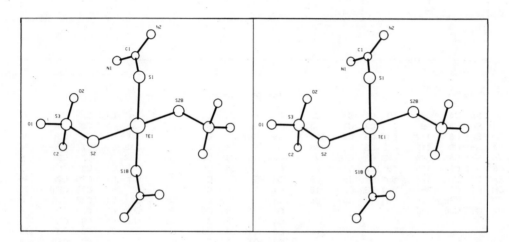

$P2_1/n$ Z = 1   R = 0.098

TEMEST   LB 4-14-11

Bond Lengths

S1	Te1	2.67		S3	O2	1.44
S1	C1	1.76		S3	C2	1.79
S2	S3	2.02		C1	N1	1.33
S2	Te1	2.68		C1	N2	1.33
S3	O1	1.47				

Bond Angles

Te1	S1	C1	101		S1	Te1	S2	91
S3	S2	Te1	101		S1	Te1	S1B	180
S2	S3	O1	107		S1	Te1	S2B	89
S2	S3	O2	113		S2	Te1	S1B	89
S2	S3	C2	107		S2	Te1	S2B	180
O1	S3	O2	112		S1	C1	N1	121
O1	S3	C2	107		S1	C1	N2	118
O2	S3	C2	111		N1	C1	N2	121

Torsion Angles

C1	S1	Te1	S2	−118		Te1	S2	S3	O2	−39
C1	S1	Te1	S1B	90		Te1	S2	S3	C2	83
C1	S1	Te1	S2B	62		S3	S2	Te1	S1	87
Te1	S1	C1	N1	48		S3	S2	Te1	S1B	−93
Te1	S1	C1	N2	−134		S3	S2	Te1	S2B	−90
Te1	S2	S3	O1	−163						

70.2 Tetrathiourea tellurium(ii) dichloride

C₄H₁₆N₈S₄Te²⁺ , 2Cl⁻ — $C_4H_{16}N_8S_4Te^{2+}$, $2Cl^-$

K.Fosheim, O.Foss, A.Scheie, S.Solheimsnes, Acta Chem. Scand., 19, 2336, 1965

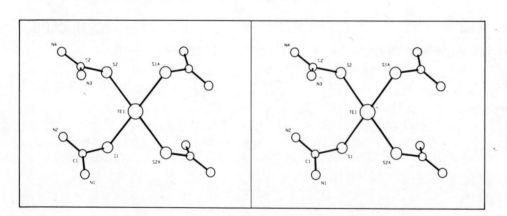

$Te[S=C(NH_2)_2]_4^{++} \cdot 2Cl^-$

P-1   Z = 1 R_{0kl} = 0.084, R_{h0l} = 0.096

THUTEC   LB 4-16-29

Bond Lengths

S1	Te1	2.69		C1	N1	1.35
S1	C1	1.76		C1	N2	1.31
S2	Te1	2.69		C2	N3	1.33
S2	C2	1.75		C2	N4	1.31

Bond Angles

Te1	S1	C1	99		S2	Te1	S1A	89		S2	C2	N3	120
Te1	S2	C2	105		S2	Te1	S2A	180		S2	C2	N4	120
S1	Te1	S2	91		S1	C1	N1	119		N3	C2	N4	119
S1	Te1	S1A	180		S1	C1	N2	120					
S1	Te1	S2A	89		N1	C1	N2	121					

Torsion Angles

S2	Te1	S1	C1	−88
S1	Te1	S2	C2	90
Te1	S1	C1	N1	−89
Te1	S2	C2	N3	18

70.3 Tetrathiourea tellurium(ii) dichloride dihydrate $C_4H_{16}N_8S_4Te^{2+}$, $2Cl^-$, $2H_2O$

K.Fosheim, O.Foss, A.Scheie, S.Solheimsnes, Acta Chem. Scand., 19, 2336, 1965

$Te[S=C(NH_2)_2]_4^{++} . 2Cl^- . 2H_2O$

Isomorphous with the di - iodide compound.
C2/c $\quad$ Z = 4 $\quad$ R_{h0l} = 0.102, R_{hhl} = 0.103

TEBETU $\quad$ LB 6-12-9

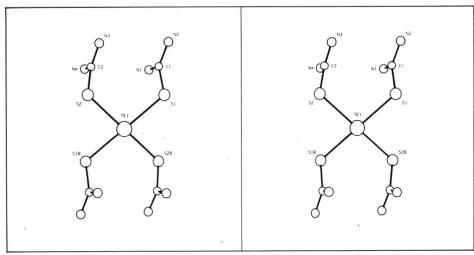

Bond Lengths			Bond Angles								Torsion Angles			
Br1	Te1	2.78	Te1	S1	C1	106	C1	N2	C3	114	C2	N1	C1	N2	2
S1	Te1	2.69	Br1	Te1	Br1F	180	S1	C1	N1	125	C1	N1	C2	C3	−7
S1	C1	1.76	Br1	Te1	S1	89	S1	C1	N2	124	C3	N2	C1	N1	5
C1	N1	1.31	Br1	Te1	S1F	91	N1	C1	N2	110	C1	N2	C3	C2	−8
C2	N1	1.47	S1	Te1	Br1F	91	N1	C2	C3	103	N1	C2	C3	N2	8
C1	N2	1.33	S1	Te1	S1F	180	N2	C3	C2	100	S1F	Te1	S1	C1	90
C3	N2	1.49	C1	N1	C2	112					Te1	S1	C1	N1	17
C2	C3	1.56													

70.4 Tellurium dibromide ethylenethiourea complex $C_6H_{12}Br_2N_4S_2Te$

O.Foss, H.M.Kjoge, K.Maroy, Acta Chem. Scand., 19, 2349, 1965

P2₁/c $\quad$ Z = 2 $\quad$ R_{0kl} = 0.096, R- $_{hkh}$ = 0.082

TUTECD $\quad$ LB 4-16-30

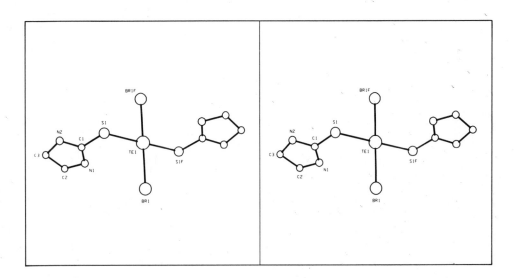

Bond Lengths			Bond Angles								Torsion Angles			
S1	Te1	2.69	Te1	S1	C1	105	S1	C1	N1	120	S2	Te1	S1	C1	−67
S1	C1	1.74	Te1	S2	C2	103	S1	C1	N2	119	S1	Te1	S2	C2	66
S2	Te1	2.68	S1	Te1	S2	90	N1	C1	N2	121	Te1	S1	C1	N1	−35
S2	C2	1.73	S1	Te1	S1B	180	S2	C2	N3	117	Te1	S2	C2	N3	−115
C1	N1	1.31	S1	Te1	S2B	90	S2	C2	N4	121					
C1	N2	1.34	S2	Te1	S1B	90	N3	C2	N4	122					
C2	N3	1.32	S2	Te1	S2B	180									
C2	N4	1.35													

70.5 Tellurium di - iodide ethylenethiourea complex

$C_6H_{12}I_2N_4S_2Te$

O.Foss, H.M.Kjoge, K.Maroy, Acta Chem. Scand., 19, 2349, 1965

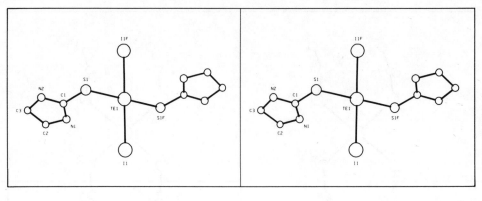

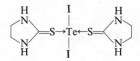

Isomorphous with the dibromide compound.

C2/c   Z = 4 R_{hol} = 0.099, R_{hhl} = 0.107

TEIETU   LB 6-12-28

Bond Lengths

I1	Te1	2.97
S1	Te1	2.69
S1	C1	1.75
C1	N1	1.32
C2	N1	1.47
C1	N2	1.32
C3	N2	1.48
C2	C3	1.55

Bond Angles

Te1	S1	C1	106	C1	N2	C3	112
I1	Te1	I1F	180	S1	C1	N1	125
I1	Te1	S1	89	S1	C1	N2	124
I1	Te1	S1F	91	N1	C1	N2	111
S1	Te1	I1F	91	N1	C2	C3	103
S1	Te1	S1F	180	N2	C3	C2	102
C1	N1	C2	112				

Torsion Angles

C2	N1	C1	N2	2
C1	N1	C2	C3	−3
C3	N2	C1	N1	0
C1	N2	C3	C2	−2
N1	C2	C3	N2	3
S1F	Te1	S1	C1	90
Te1	S1	C1	N1	16

70.6 Trithiourea tellurium(ii) hydrogen difluoride

$C_6H_{24}N_{12}S_6Te_2^{4+}$, $4HF_2^-$

O.Foss, S.Hauge, Acta Chem. Scand., 19, 2395, 1965

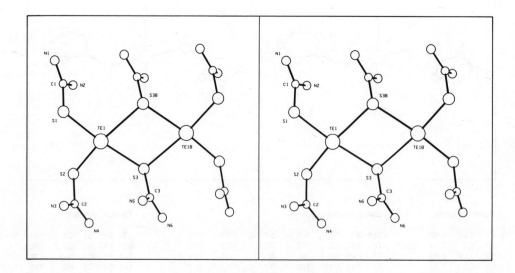

P2₁/c   Z = 2 R_{0kl} = 0.106, R_{hk0} = 0.094

TUTEHF   LB 3-14-1

Bond Lengths

S1	Te1	2.53
S1	C1	1.73
S2	Te1	2.47
S2	C2	1.77
S3	Te1	2.86
S3	Te1B	3.02
S3	C3	1.75
C1	N1	1.31
C1	N2	1.38
C2	N3	1.33
C2	N4	1.34
C3	N5	1.33
C3	N6	1.33

Bond Angles

Te1	S1	C1	107	S1	Te1	S3	175	S1	C1	N1	116	N3	C2	N4	123
Te1	S2	C2	104	S1	Te1	S3B	92	S1	C1	N2	122	S3	C3	N5	124
Te1	S3	Te1B	97	S2	Te1	S3	90	N1	C1	N2	122	S3	C3	N6	118
Te1	S3	C3	106	S2	Te1	S3B	173	S2	C2	N3	121	N5	C3	N6	118
S1	Te1	S2	95	S3	Te1	S3B	83	S2	C2	N4	115			

Torsion Angles

S2	Te1	S1	C1	−105
S1	Te1	S2	C2	−106
Te1	S1	C1	N2	25
Te1	S3	C3	N5	−23
Te1	S2	C2	N3	67

70.7 Di - p - chlorodiphenyl tellurium di - iodide

$C_{12}H_8Cl_2I_2Te$

G.Y.Chao, J.D.McCullough, Acta Cryst., 15, 887, 1962

P-1   Z = 2   R = 0.07

CLPTEI   LB 12-8-23

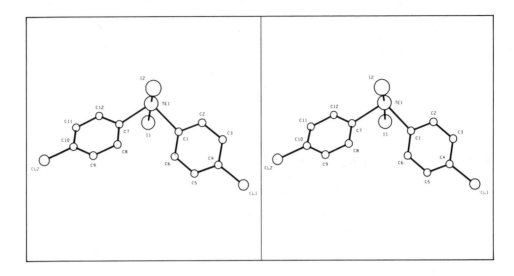

Bond Lengths

Cl1	C4	1.75	C3	C4	1.41
Cl2	C10	1.74	C4	C5	1.38
I1	Te1	2.95	C5	C6	1.41
I2	Te1	2.92	C7	C8	1.40
Te1	C1	2.13	C7	C12	1.41
Te1	C7	2.10	C8	C9	1.42
C1	C2	1.39	C9	C10	1.35
C1	C6	1.40	C10	C11	1.37
C2	C3	1.38	C11	C12	1.42

Bond Angles

I1	Te1	I2	174	C1	C2	C3	119	C8	C7	C12	122
I1	Te1	C1	87	C2	C3	C4	119˙	C7	C8	C9	114
I1	Te1	C7	88	Cl1	C4	C3	118	C8	C9	C10	124
I2	Te1	C1	89	Cl1	C4	C5	119	Cl2	C10	C9	119
I2	Te1	C7	87	C3	C4	C5	122	Cl2	C10	C11	118
C1	Te1	C7	101	C4	C5	C6	120	C9	C10	C11	122
Te1	C1	C2	116	C1	C6	C5	117	C10	C11	C12	117
Te1	C1	C6	121	Te1	C7	C8	123	C7	C12	C11	120
C2	C1	C6	123	Te1	C7	C12	115				

Torsion Angles

C7	Te1	C1	C6	40
C1	Te1	C7	C8	31

71.1   Methoxycarbonyl - chloro - mercury(ii)

$C_2H_3ClHgO_2$

T.C.W.Mak, J.Trotter, J. Chem. Soc., 3243, 1962

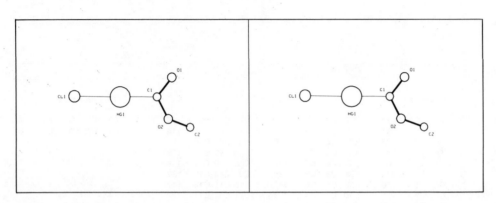

Pccn   Z = 8 R_{hk0} = 0.15,
R_{0kl} = 0.17

MXCOHC   LB 2-3-10

Bond Lengths			Bond Angles			
Hg1	Cl1	2.35	Cl1	Hg1	C1	179
Hg1	C1	1.96	C1	O2	C2	132
C1	O1	1.22	Hg1	C1	O1	128
C1	O2	1.24	Hg1	C1	O2	117
C2	O2	1.45	O1	C1	O2	114

71.2   Phenyl - bromo - mercury(ii)

C_6H_5BrHg

V.I.Pakhomov, Zh. Strukt. Khim., 4, 594, 1963

Atomic coordinates were not given but bond lengths were reported.
C2   Z = 8   No R factor was given.

PHHGBR   LB 6-5-3

71.3 α - Napthyl - iodo - mercury(ii)

$C_{10}H_7HgI$

V.I.Pakhomov, Kristallografija, 8, 789, 1963

Atomic coordinates were not reported in the paper.
$P2_1/m$ Z = 2   No R factor was given.

NPHHGI

71.4   Diphenyl mercury(ii)

$C_{12}H_{10}Hg$

B.Ziolkovska, R.M.Myasnikova, A.I.Kitaigorodskij, Zh. Strukt. Khim., 5, 737, 1964

$P2_1/a$ Z = 2   R = 0.22

DIPHHG   LB 12-10-41

Bond Lengths

Hg1	C1	2.12
C1	C2	1.35
C1	C6	1.36
C2	C3	1.32
C3	C4	1.43
C4	C5	1.28
C5	C6	1.35

Bond Angles

C1	Hg1	C1B	180
Hg1	C1	C2	125
Hg1	C1	C6	122
C2	C1	C6	112
C1	C2	C3	125
C2	C3	C4	119
C3	C4	C5	116
C4	C5	C6	122
C1	C6	C5	125

71.5   Deca(methylisonitrile) dicobalt(ii) perchlorate

$C_{20}H_{30}Co_2N_{10}^{4+}$, $4ClO_4^-$

F.A.Cotton, T.G.Dunne, J.S.Wood, Inorg. Chem., 3, 1495, 1964

No comparison of bond lengths is possible since they are not reported in the paper. Published value of y(Co1) = 0.3286. The correct value is 0.03286.

$P2_12_12$ Z = 2   R = 0.13

MISCPC   LB 20-30-4

$$[(H_3C-N\equiv C)_5Co-Co(C\equiv N-CH_3)_5]^{2+}(ClO_4^-)_4$$

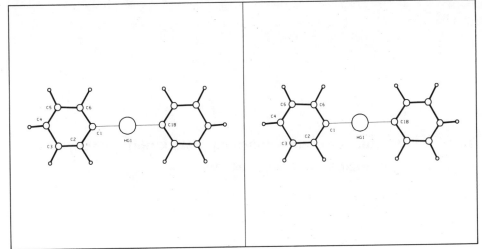

Bond Lengths

Co1	Co1C	2.74	C2	N2	1.15
Co1	C1	1.82	C7	N2	1.55
Co1	C2	1.92	C3	N3	1.17
Co1	C3	1.85	C8	N3	1.47
Co1	C4	1.89	C4	N4	1.20
Co1	C5	1.92	C9	N4	1.49
C1	N1	1.14	C5	N5	1.15
C6	N1	1.54	C10	N5	1.39

72.1   Potassium ethylene - tribromo platinum(ii) monohydrate

$C_2H_4Br_3Pt^-$, K^+ , H_2O

G.B.Bokii, G.A.Kukina, Zh. Strukt. Khim., 6, 706, 1965

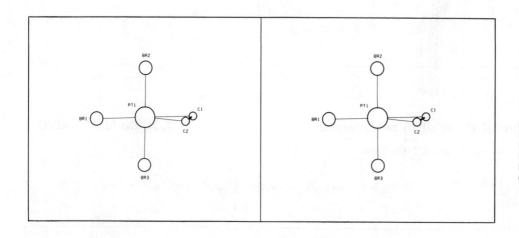

$K^+ [(C_2H_4) PtBr_3]^- \cdot H_2O$

$P2_1$ Z = 2   R = 0.15

KBREPT   LB 2-4-9

Bond Lengths			Bond Angles			
Pt1	Br1	2.49	Br1	Pt1	Br2	90
Pt1	Br2	2.48	Br1	Pt1	Br3	90
Pt1	Br3	2.47	Br1	Pt1	C1	179
Pt1	C1	2.50	Br1	Pt1	C2	155
Pt1	C2	2.14	Br2	Pt1	Br3	180
C1	C2	1.10	Br2	Pt1	C1	90
			Br2	Pt1	C2	90
			Br3	Pt1	C1	90
			Br3	Pt1	C2	90
			C1	Pt1	C2	26
			Pt1	C1	C2	58
			Pt1	C2	C1	96

72.2   cis - Ethylene ammine dibromo platinum(ii)

$C_2H_7Br_2NPt$

G.A.Kukina, G.B.Bokii, F.A.Brusentsev, Zh. Strukt. Khim., 5, 730, 1964

Using the published coordinates there is no connectivity between C1 and C2.
$I4_1/a$ Z = 16   No R factor was given.

PTETHA   LB 2-7-4

$$Br\underset{Br}{\overset{NH_3}{\underset{\displaystyle |}{\overset{\displaystyle \downarrow}{Pt}}}}\overset{CH_2}{\underset{CH_2}{\|}}$$

72.3   trans - Ethylenedimethylamine dichloro platinum(ii)

$C_4H_{11}Cl_2NPt$.

P.R.H.Alderman, P.G.Owston, J.M.Rowe, Acta Cryst., 13, 149, 1960

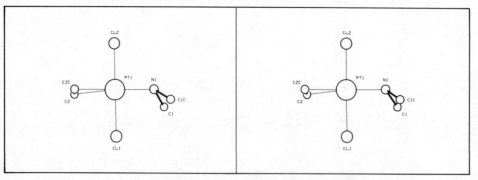

$$\overset{\displaystyle Cl}{\underset{\displaystyle Cl}{\underset{H_2C}{\overset{H_2C}{\|}}Pt\leftarrow HN(CH_3)_2}}$$

$P2_1/m$ Z = 2 $R_{h0l} = 0.14,$
$R_{hk0} = 0.08$

ETDMAX   LB 4-11-5

Bond Lengths

Pt1	Cl1	2.30	Pt1	C2	2.21
Pt1	Cl2	2.33	C1	N1	1.58
Pt1	N1	2.02	C2	C2C	1.47

Bond Angles

Cl1	Pt1	Cl2	179	Cl2	Pt1	C2	92	C1	N1	C1C	105
Cl1	Pt1	N1	90	N1	Pt1	C2	160	Pt1	C2	C2C	71
Cl1	Pt1	C2	89	C2	Pt1	C2C	39				
Cl2	Pt1	N1	89	Pt1	N1	C1	114				

72.4   Allyl chloro palladium(ii) dimer (three dimensional, at − 140 ° C) $C_6H_{10}Cl_2Pd_2$

Di - μ - chlorobis(π - allyl) dipalladium(ii)
A.E.Smith, Acta Cryst., 18, 331, 1965

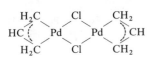

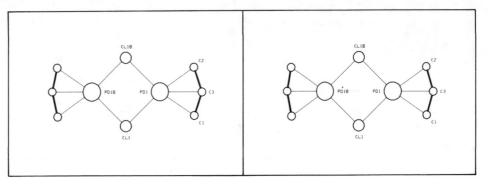

$P2_1/n$ Z = 2   R = 0.055

ALYLPC   LB 6-10-19

Bond Lengths		
Pd1	Cl1	2.41
Pd1	Cl1B	2.42
Pd1	C1	2.12
Pd1	C2	2.12
Pd1	C3	2.11
C1	C3	1.36
C2	C3	1.40

Bond Angles										
Cl1	Pd1	Cl1B	88	C1	Pd1	C2	68	Pd1	C1	C3	71
Cl1	Pd1	C1	102	C1	Pd1	C3	37	Pd1	C2	C3	70
Cl1	Pd1	C2	171	C2	Pd1	Cl1B	101	Pd1	C3	C1	72
Cl1	Pd1	C3	134	C2	Pd1	C3	39	Pd1	C3	C2	71
C1	Pd1	Cl1B	169	Pd1	Cl1	Pd1B	92	C1	C3	C2	120

72.5   Allyl chloro palladium(ii) dimer (three - dimensional study) $C_6H_{10}Cl_2Pd_2$

Di - μ - chlorobis(π - allyl) dipalladium(ii)
W.E.Oberhansli, L.F.Dahl, J. Organometal. Chem., 3, 43, 1965

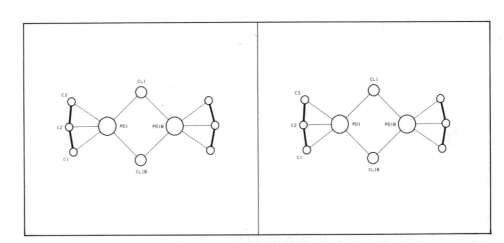

$P2_1/n$ Z = 2   R = 0.069

ALYLPC01   LB 6-10-19

Bond Lengths		
Pd1	Cl1	2.40
Pd1	Cl1B	2.40
Pd1	C1	2.14
Pd1	C2	2.02
Pd1	C3	2.18
C1	C2	1.35
C2	C3	1.37

Bond Angles										
Cl1	Pd1	Cl1B	88	C1	Pd1	C2	38	Pd1	C1	C2	66
Cl1	Pd1	C1	172	C1	Pd1	C3	69	Pd1	C2	C1	76
Cl1	Pd1	C2	136	C2	Pd1	Cl1B	133	Pd1	C2	C3	77
Cl1	Pd1	C3	103	C2	Pd1	C3	38	C1	C2	C3	129
C1	Pd1	Cl1B	100	Pd1	Cl1	Pd1B	92	Pd1	C3	C2	65

72.6   Allyl chloro palladium(ii) dimer (projections) $C_6H_{10}Cl_2Pd_2$

Di - μ - chlorobis(π - allyl) dipalladium(ii)
J.M.Rowe, Proc. Chem. Soc., 66, 1962

Atomic coordinates were not given
but bond lengths were reported.
$P2_1/c$ Z = 2 $R_{0kl} = 0.10$,
$R_{h0l} = 0.10$

ALYLPC02   LB 6-10-19

72.7 Allyl chloro palladium(ii) dimer (projections)

C₆H₁₀Cl₂Pd₂

Di - μ - chlorobis(π - allyl) dipalladium(ii)
V.F.Levdik, M.A.Porai-Koshits, Zh. Strukt. Khim., 3, 472, 1962

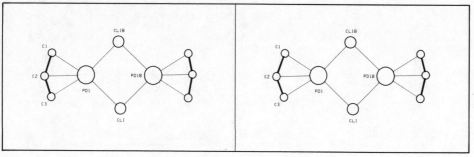

$P2_1/n$ Z = 4   No R factor was given.

ALYLPC03   LB 6-10-19

Bond Lengths

Pd1	Cl1	2.42	Pd1	C3	2.09
Pd1	Cl1B	2.34	C1	C2	1.43
Pd1	C1	2.09	C2	C3	1.23
Pd1	C2	2.17			

Bond Angles

Cl1	Pd1	Cl1B	87	C1	Pd1	C2	39	Pd1	C1	C2	73
Cl1	Pd1	C1	167	C1	Pd1	C3	63	Pd1	C2	C1	67
Cl1	Pd1	C2	134	C2	Pd1	Cl1B	133	Pd1	C2	C3	70
Cl1	Pd1	C3	106	C2	Pd1	C3	34	C1	C2	C3	110
C1	Pd1	Cl1B	104	Pd1	Cl1	Pd1B	93	Pd1	C3	C2	77

72.8 Tetracarbonyl acrylonitrile iron

C₇H₃FeNO₄

A.R.Luxmoore, M.R.Truter, Acta Cryst., 15, 1117, 1962

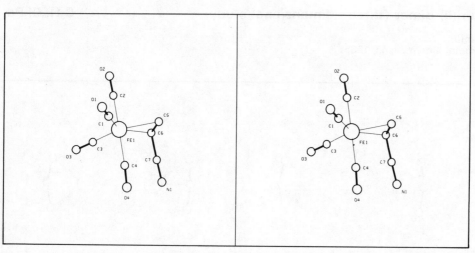

Published value of x(Fe1) = 0.2396.
The correct value is −0.2396.
$P2_1/a$ Z = 4   R = 0.09

COACFE   LB 7-3-4

Bond Lengths

Fe1	C1	1.74	C1	O1	1.11
Fe1	C2	1.98	C2	O2	1.16
Fe1	C3	1.77	C3	O3	1.13
Fe1	C4	2.00	C4	O4	1.14
Fe1	C5	2.10	C5	C6	1.40
Fe1	C6	2.10	C6	C7	1.45
C7	N1	1.20			

Bond Angles

C5	C6	C7	116
N1	C7	C6	178

72.9 Butadiene iron tricarbonyl (at −40 °C)

C₇H₆FeO₃

O.S.Mills, G.Robinson, Acta Cryst., 16, 758, 1963

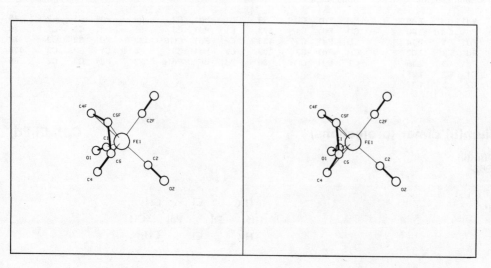

Pnma   Z = 4   R = 0.08

BUFECO   LB 7-6-13

Bond Lengths

Fe1	C1	1.74	C1	O1	1.18
Fe1	C2	1.77	C2	O2	1.13
Fe1	C4	2.14	C4	C5	1.45
Fe1	C5	2.06	C5	C5F	1.45

Bond Angles

C4	C5	C5F	118

72.10 Methallyl nickel(ii)

C₈H₁₄Ni

R.Uttech, H.Dietrich, Z. Kristallogr., 122, 60, 1965

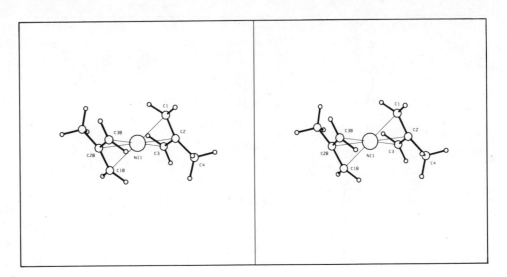

P2₁/c   Z = 2   R = 0.079

MEALNI   LB 8-14-22

Bond Lengths			Bond Angles			
Ni1	C1	2.01	C1	C2	C3	119
Ni1	C2	1.98	C1	C2	C4	120
Ni1	C3	2.03	C3	C2	C4	120
C1	C2	1.41				
C2	C3	1.42				
C2	C4	1.49				

72.11 Chloro rhodium(i) diethylene dimer

C₈H₁₆Cl₂Rh₂

K.A.Klanderman, Dissert. Abstr., 25, 6253, 1965

Atomic coordinates were not reported in the paper.
P4₁2₁2   Z = 8   R = 0.089

RHCETH   LB 8-16-23

72.12 Cyclopentadienyl rhodium diethylene complex

C₉H₁₃Rh

K.A.Klanderman, Dissert. Abstr., 25, 6253, 1965

Atomic coordinates were not reported in the paper.
Fd2d   Z = 8   R = 0.062

CPDRHE   LB 9-13-7

72.13 pentakis(Methylisonitrile) cobalt(i) perchlorate

C₁₀H₁₅CoN₅⁺ , ClO₄⁻

F.A.Cotton, T.G.Dunne, J.S.Wood, Inorg. Chem., 4, 318, 1965

[Co(CH₃—NC)₅]⁺ClO₄⁻

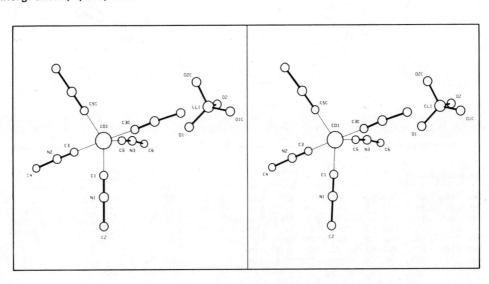

P3₁21   Z = 3   R = 0.091

MINCOP   LB 10-15-7

Bond Lengths			Bond Angles			
Co1	C1	1.89	C1	Co1	C3	89
Co1	C3	1.84	C1	Co1	C5	116
Co1	C5	1.87	C3	Co1	C5	89
C1	N1	1.14	C3	Co1	C3C	178
C2	N1	1.45	C3	Co1	C5C	91
C3	N2	1.14	C5	Co1	C5C	128
C4	N2	1.44	C1	N1	C2	180
C5	N3	1.15	C3	N2	C4	177
C6	N3	1.44	C5	N3	C6	174
			Co1	C1	N1	180
			Co1	C3	N2	178
			Co1	C5	N3	179

72.14   1,5 - Di(iron tricarbonyl) - 3 - methylene - penta - 1,4 - diene $C_{12}H_6Fe_2O_6$

P.Piret, J.Meunier-Piret, M.van Meerssche, G.S.D.King, Acta Cryst., 19, 78, 1965

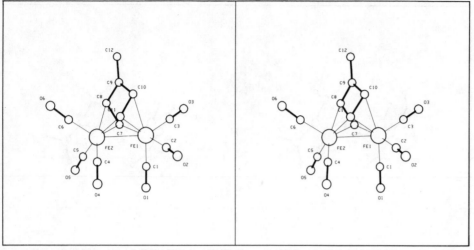

Orange - red chemical isomer. See
73.12 for the red isomer.
Cc   Z = 4   R = 0.123

FECMCP   LB 12-6-4

Bond Lengths

Fe1	Fe2	2.53	Fe2	C5	1.74	C4	O4	1.28
Fe1	C1	1.71	Fe2	C6	1.75	C5	O5	1.19
Fe1	C2	1.84	Fe2	C7	2.07	C6	O6	1.18
Fe1	C3	1.74	Fe2	C8	2.26	C7	C8	1.33
Fe1	C7	2.02	Fe2	C11	1.96	C8	C9	1.49
Fe1	C10	2.26	C1	O1	1.25	C9	C10	1.44
Fe1	C11	2.10	C2	O2	1.18	C9	C12	1.35
Fe2	C4	1.61	C3	O3	1.19	C10	C11	1.41

Bond Angles

Fe1	C1	O1	175	Fe1	C7	C8	117	C10 C9 C12	127
Fe1	C2	O2	172	Fe2	C7	C8	80	Fe1 C10 C9	106
Fe1	C3	O3	174	Fe2	C8	C7	65	Fe1 C10 C11	65
Fe2	C4	O4	176	Fe2	C8	C9	105	C9 C10 C11	116
Fe2	C5	O5	176	C7	C8	C9	115	Fe1 C11 Fe2	77
Fe2	C6	O6	174	C8	C9	C10	111	Fe1 C11 C10	77
Fe1	C7	Fe2	76	C8	C9	C12	122	Fe2 C11 C10	115

Torsion Angles

C11	C10	C9	C8		−39
C10	C9	C8	C7		−40

72.15   trans - Butadiene iron carbonyl complex $C_{12}H_6Fe_2O_8$

K.A.Klanderman, Dissert. Abstr., 25, 6253, 1965

$$[(H_2C\!=\!CH\!-\!CH\!=\!CH_2)Fe_2(CO)_8]$$

Atomic coordinates were not
reported in the paper.
P-1   Z = 1   R = 0.116

BUTDFE   LB 12-6-5

72.16   Iron carbonyl hydride - but - 2 - yne complex $C_{12}H_8Fe_2O_8$

A.A.Hock, O.S.Mills, Acta Cryst., 14, 139, 1961

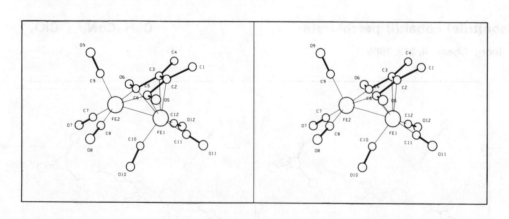

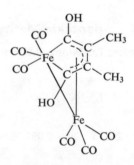

P2$_1$/c   Z = 4   R = 0.09

ICHBUT

Bond Lengths

Fe1	Fe2	2.49	Fe1	C12	1.78	C6	O6	1.36
Fe1	C2	2.15	Fe2	C5	1.95	C7	O7	1.17
Fe1	C3	2.14	Fe2	C6	1.94	C8	O8	1.13
Fe1	C5	2.11	Fe2	C7	1.80	C9	O9	1.13
Fe1	C6	2.12	Fe2	C8	1.81	C10	O10	1.17
Fe1	C10	1.74	Fe2	C9	1.74	C11	O11	1.13
Fe1	C11	1.78	C5	O5	1.38	C12	O12	1.12

C1	C2	1.51
C2	C3	1.43
C2	C5	1.42
C3	C4	1.50
C3	C6	1.41

Bond Angles

C1	C2	C3	125	C2	C3	C6	114
C1	C2	C5	124	C4	C3	C6	122
C3	C2	C5	111	O5	C5	C2	110
C2	C3	C4	124	O6	C6	C3	115

Torsion Angles

C5	C2	C3	C6	0
C2	C3	C6	Fe2	6
C3	C6	Fe2	C5	−7
C6	Fe2	C5	C2	7
Fe2	C5	C2	C3	−6

72.17   2,3 - Dimethylbuta - 1,3 - diene - osmium carbonyl complex

$C_{12}H_8O_6Os_2$

R.P.Dodge, O.S.Mills, V.Schomaker, Proc. Chem. Soc., 380, 1963

Atomic coordinates were not
reported in the paper.
P2$_1$/n   Z = 4   No R factor was
given.

MBOSCO   LB 12-8-69

72.18   trans - Dichloro cis - 2 - butene α - phenylethylamine platinum(ii)

$C_{12}H_{19}Cl_2NPt$

P.Ganis, C.Pedone, Ric. Sci., 2, A, 8, 1462, 1965

No comparison of bond lengths is
possible since they are not reported
in the paper.
P2$_1$2$_1$2$_1$ Z = 4   R = 0.125

BUPHPT   LB 12-19-4

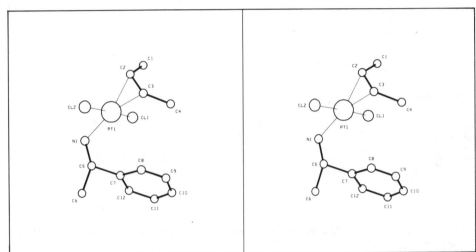

Bond Lengths

Pt1	Cl1	2.38	C1	C2	1.57	C7	C12	1.38
Pt1	Cl2	2.32	C2	C3	1.37	C8	C9	1.27
Pt1	N1	2.01	C3	C4	1.54	C9	C10	1.41
Pt1	C2	2.08	C5	C6	1.58	C10	C11	1.32
Pt1	C3	2.08	C5	C7	1.52	C11	C12	1.38
C5	N1	1.52	C7	C8	1.47			

Bond Angles

Pt1	C2	C1	114
Pt1	C2	C3	71
C1	C2	C3	119
Pt1	C3	C2	71
Pt1	C3	C4	115
C2	C3	C4	119

72.19   Tetracobalt decacarbonyl diethylacetylene

$C_{16}H_{10}Co_4O_{10}$

L.F.Dahl, D.L.Smith, J. Amer. Chem. Soc., 84, 2450, 1962

Atomic coordinates were not given
but bond lengths were reported.
C2/c   Z = 8   R = 0.07

TCOCAC   LB 16-10-6

$$[(H_5C_2-C\equiv C-C_2H_5)Co_4(CO)_{10}]$$

72.20 Styrene chloro palladium(ii) dimer

$C_{16}H_{16}Cl_4Pd_2$

N.C.Baenziger, J.R.Doyle, G.F.Richards, C.L.Carpenter,
Adv. Chem. Coord. Compounds, Proc. 6th Internat. Conf., Detroit, 131, 1961

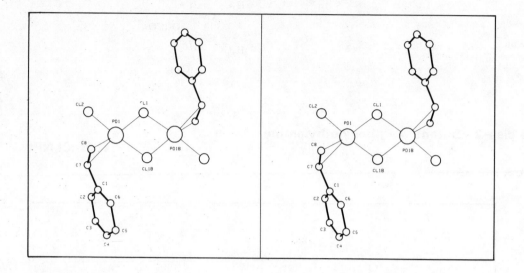

P2₁/n   Z = 2   R = 0.13

$P2_1/n$ Z = 2   R = 0.13

STYPDC

Bond Lengths

Pd1	Cl1	2.39	C1	C7	1.50
Pd1	Cl2	2.25	C2	C3	1.52
Pd1	Cl1B	2.32	C3	C4	1.42
Pd1	C7	2.32	C4	C5	1.33
Pd1	C8	2.09	C5	C6	1.55
C1	C2	1.38	C7	C8	1.45
C1	C6	1.29			

Bond Angles

Pd1	C7	C1	111
Pd1	C7	C8	62
C1	C7	C8	127
Pd1	C8	C7	80

Torsion Angles

C2	C1	C7	Pd1	−106
C2	C1	C7	C8	−177
C6	C1	C7	Pd1	77
C6	C1	C7	C8	7
C1	C7	C8	Pd1	97

72.21 (2,3 - bis - (Methoxycarbonyl) - 2 - π - 5 - norbornadien - 7 - yl) - (π - cyclopentadienyl) nickel (ii)

$C_{16}H_{16}NiO_4$

L.F.Dahl, C.H.Wei, Inorg. Chem., 2, 713, 1963

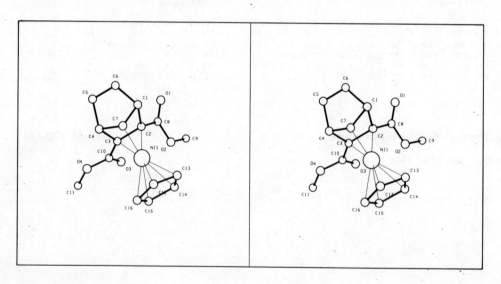

Cc   Z = 4   R = 0.07

CNIMAC   LB 16-16-27

Bond Lengths

Ni1	C2	1.97	C9	O2	1.52	C3	C10	1.45
Ni1	C3	1.97	C10	O3	1.23	C4	C5	1.53
Ni1	C7	1.97	C10	O4	1.31	C4	C7	1.55
Ni1	C12	2.10	C11	O4	1.48	C5	C6	1.33
Ni1	C13	2.09	C1	C2	1.57	C12	C13	1.43
Ni1	C14	2.19	C1	C6	1.52	C12	C16	1.38
Ni1	C15	2.15	C1	C7	1.52	C13	C14	1.43
Ni1	C16	2.12	C2	C3	1.45	C14	C15	1.47
C8	O1	1.19	C2	C8	1.44	C15	C16	1.39
C8	O2	1.35	C3	C4	1.55			

Bond Angles

C2	C1	C6	107	C4	C3	C10	126
C2	C1	C7	93	C3	C4	C5	109
C6	C1	C7	101	C3	C4	C7	93
C1	C2	C3	104	C5	C4	C7	104
C1	C2	C8	122	C4	C5	C6	105
C3	C2	C8	126	C1	C6	C5	111
C2	C3	C4	106	C1	C7	C4	95
C2	C3	C10	127				

72.22   Di(cobalt dicarbonyl) 1,6 - di(t - butyl) - 1,3,5 - hexatriene complex

C₁₈H₂₂Co₂O₄

O.S.Mills, G.Robinson, Proc. Chem. Soc., 187, 1964

Atomic coordinates were not reported in the paper.
I2/a   Z = 8   R = 0.09

COACBA   LB 18-22-5

72.23   Dichloro(2,7 - dimethyl - octa - 2,6 - diene - 1,8 - diyl) ruthenium(iv) dimer

C₂₀H₃₂Cl₄Ru₂

L.Porri, M.C.Gallazzi, A.Colombo, G.Allegra, Tetrahedron Letters, 4187, 1965

Atomic coordinates were not reported in the paper.
P-1   Z = 1   R = 0.10

DCOCRU   LB 20-32-15

72.24   Iron carbonyl - phenylacetylene complex Iron carbonyl phenylacetylene complex

C₃₀H₁₈Fe₂O₆

G.S.D.King, Acta Cryst., 15, 243, 1962

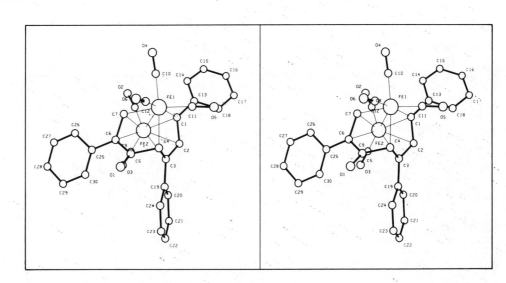

P2₁/n   Z = 4   R = 0.15

FCOPAC   LB 30-18-6

Bond Lengths

Fe1	Fe2	2.50	Fe2	C8	1.76	C3	C19	1.50	
Fe1	C1	2.09	Fe2	C9	1.76	C4	C5	1.49	
Fe1	C4	2.10	C5	O1	1.24	C5	C6	1.47	
Fe1	C7	2.01	C8	O2	1.16	C6	C7	1.42	
Fe1	C10	1.81	C9	O3	1.17	C6	C25	1.47	
Fe1	C11	1.80	C10	O4	1.14	C13	C14	1.41	
Fe1	C12	1.76	C11	O5	1.15	C13	C18	1.41	
Fe2	C1	1.97	C12	O6	1.14	C14	C15	1.37	
Fe2	C2	2.11	C1	C2	1.41	C15	C16	1.35	
Fe2	C3	2.20	C1	C13	1.48	C16	C17	1.37	
Fe2	C6	2.23	C2	C3	1.42	C17	C18	1.38	
Fe2	C7	1.96	C3	C4	1.50	C19	C20	1.40	

C19	C24	1.44
C20	C21	1.43
C21	C22	1.34
C22	C23	1.39
C23	C24	1.36
C25	C26	1.42
C25	C30	1.36
C26	C27	1.36
C27	C28	1.36
C28	C29	1.41
C29	C30	1.42

Bond Angles

C2	C1	C13	119
C1	C2	C3	116
C2	C3	C4	119
C2	C3	C19	118
C4	C3	C19	121
C3	C4	C5	107
O1	C5	C4	125
O1	C5	C6	122
C4	C5	C6	113
C5	C6	C7	110
C5	C6	C25	122
C7	C6	C25	125

72.25   Iron carbonyl - diphenylacetylene complex (black form)

C_{36}H_{20}Fe_3O_8

R.P.Dodge, V.Schomaker, J. Organometal. Chem., 3, 274, 1965

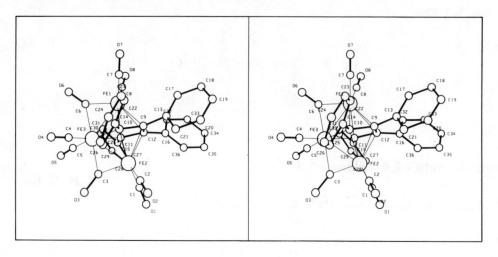
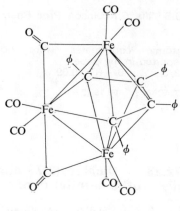

P2₁/c   Z = 4   R = 0.087

FECPAC   LB 36-20-2

Bond Lengths

Fe1	Fe3	2.43	Fe3	C3	1.99	C9	C13	1.50	C20 C21 1.45
Fe1	C6	1.84	Fe3	C4	1.70	C10	C14	1.53	C22 C23 1.38
Fe1	C7	1.75	Fe3	C5	1.77	C11	C12	1.46	C23 C24 1.37
Fe1	C8	1.73	Fe3	C6	1.99	C11	C15	1.50	C24 C25 1.36
Fe1	C9	2.16	Fe3	C10	2.03	C12	C16	1.50	C25 C26 1.44
Fe1	C10	2.13	Fe3	C11	2.06	C13	C17	1.38	C27 C28 1.39
Fe1	C11	2.09	C1	O1	1.19	C13	C21	1.42	C28 C29 1.37
Fe1	C12	2.20	C2	O2	1.17	C14	C22	1.41	C29 C30 1.40
Fe2	Fe3	2.43	C3	O3	1.24	C14	C26	1.43	C30 C31 1.40
Fe2	C1	1.72	C4	O4	1.18	C15	C27	1.43	C32 C33 1.42
Fe2	C2	1.73	C5	O5	1.16	C15	C31	1.41	C33 C34 1.37
Fe2	C3	1.77	C6	O6	1.19	C16	C32	1.39	C34 C35 1.37
Fe2	C9	2.19	C7	O7	1.14	C16	C36	1.39	C35 C36 1.42
Fe2	C10	2.09	C8	O8	1.17	C17	C18	1.45	
Fe2	C11	2.17	C9	C10	1.43	C18	C19	1.39	
Fe2	C12	2.17	C9	C12	1.46	C19	C20	1.37	

Bond Angles

Fe2	C3	Fe3	81	Fe1	C10	Fe2	106	Fe2 C11 C15	129
Fe2	C3	O3	148	Fe1	C10	Fe3	71	Fe3 C11 C12	118
Fe3	C3	O3	131	Fe1	C10	C9	72	Fe3 C11 C15	120
Fe1	C6	Fe3	79	Fe1	C10	C14	128	C12 C11 C15	122
Fe1	C6	O6	144	Fe2	C10	Fe3	72	Fe1 C12 Fe2	101
Fe3	C6	O6	138	Fe2	C10	C9	74	Fe1 C12 C9	69
Fe1	C9	Fe2	101	Fe2	C10	C14	126	Fe1 C12 C11	66
Fe1	C9	C10	69	Fe3	C10	C9	120	Fe1 C12 C16	133
Fe1	C9	C12	72	Fe3	C10	C14	122	Fe2 C12 C9	71
Fe1	C9	C13	125	C9	C10	C14	118	Fe2 C12 C11	70
Fe2	C9	C10	67	Fe1	C11	Fe2	104	Fe2 C12 C16	126
Fe2	C9	C12	70	Fe1	C11	Fe3	72	C9 C12 C11	112
Fe2	C9	C13	134	Fe1	C11	C12	74	C9 C12 C16	123
C10	C9	C12	112	Fe1	C11	C15	126	C11 C12 C16	125
C10	C9	C13	129	Fe2	C11	Fe3	70		
C12	C9	C13	119	Fe2	C11	C12	70		

72.26   Iron carbonyl - diphenylacetylene complex (violet form)

C_{36}H_{20}Fe_3O_8

R.P.Dodge, V.Schomaker, J. Organometal. Chem., 3, 274, 1965

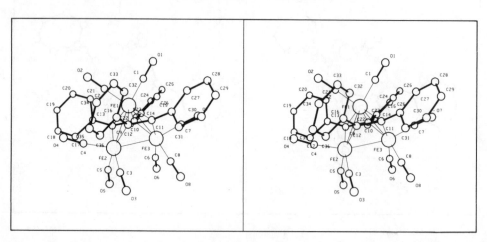
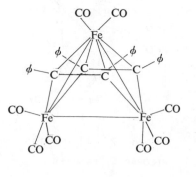

C2/c   Z = 8   R = 0.127

FECPAC01   LB 36-20-1

Bond Lengths

Fe1	Fe2	2.47	Fe2	C9	1.99	C6	O6	1.16	C14 C26 1.43	C25 C26 1.48
Fe1	Fe3	2.46	Fe2	C12	2.03	C7	O7	1.15	C15 C27 1.43	C27 C28 1.47
Fe1	C1	1.72	Fe3	C6	1.75	C8	O8	1.14	C15 C31 1.42	C28 C29 1.36
Fe1	C2	1.70	Fe3	C7	1.74	C9	C10	1.39	C16 C32 1.44	C29 C30 1.31
Fe1	C9	1.98	Fe3	C8	1.80	C9	C13	1.49	C16 C36 1.46	C30 C31 1.46
Fe1	C10	1.98	Fe3	C10	2.06	C10	C14	1.47	C17 C18 1.40	C32 C33 1.40
Fe1	C11	1.97	Fe3	C11	2.05	C11	C12	1.38	C18 C19 1.37	C33 C34 1.43
Fe1	C12	1.95	C1	O1	1.14	C11	C15	1.47	C19 C20 1.40	C34 C35 1.39
Fe2	Fe3	2.59	C2	O2	1.16	C12	C16	1.49	C20 C21 1.39	C35 C36 1.34
Fe2	C3	1.80	C3	O3	1.18	C13	C17	1.44	C22 C23 1.40	
Fe2	C4	1.78	C4	O4	1.18	C13	C21	1.42	C23 C24 1.42	
Fe2	C5	1.76	C5	O5	1.21	C14	C22	1.43	C24 C25 1.43	

Bond Angles

Fe1	C9	Fe2	77	Fe1 C11 Fe3	75
Fe1	C9	C10	69	Fe1 C11 C12	69
Fe1	C9	C13	130	Fe1 C11 C15	139
Fe2	C9	C10	108	Fe3 C11 C12	107
Fe2	C9	C13	128	Fe3 C11 C15	126
C10	C9	C13	122	C12 C11 C15	123
Fe1	C10	Fe3	75	Fe1 C12 Fe2	76
Fe1	C10	C9	69	Fe1 C12 C11	70
Fe3	C10	C9	106	Fe1 C12 C16	129
Fe3	C10	C14	122	Fe2 C12 C11	107
C9	C10	C14	128	Fe2 C12 C16	127
				C11 C12 C16	125

73.1 π - Cyclopentadienyl - π - (1)2,3 - dicarbollyl iron(iii)

$C_7H_{16}B_9Fe$

A.Zalkin, D.H.Templeton, T.E.Hopkins, J. Amer. Chem. Soc., 87, 3988, 1965

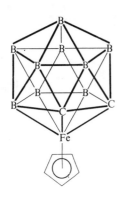

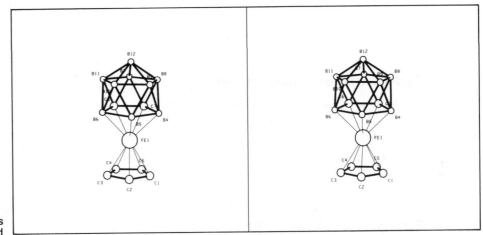

No comparison of bond lengths is possible since they are not reported in the paper.

P2₁/c   Z = 4   R = 0.074

CYPCFE   LB 7-16-2

Bond Lengths

Fe1	B4	2.09	Fe1	C6	2.03	B5	B10	1.76	B7	C7	1.68	B11	B12	1.74
Fe1	B5	2.10	Fe1	C7	2.05	B6	B10	1.75	B8	B9	1.75	B11	C6	1.68
Fe1	B6	2.09	B4	B5	1.77	B6	B11	1.75	B8	B12	1.75	C1	C2	1.35
Fe1	C1	2.05	B4	B8	1.77	B6	C6	1.66	B8	C7	1.69	C1	C5	1.33
Fe1	C2	2.04	B4	B9	1.76	B7	B8	1.72	B9	B10	1.74	C2	C3	1.37
Fe1	C3	2.07	B4	C7	1.70	B7	B11	1.72	B9	B12	1.76	C3	C4	1.38
Fe1	C4	2.10	B5	B6	1.76	B7	B12	1.74	B10	B11	1.74	C4	C5	1.36
Fe1	C5	2.10	B5	B9	1.76	B7	C6	1.70	B10	B12	1.74	C6	C7	1.57

73.2 Iodocarbonyl - π - cyclopentadienyl - pentafluoroethyl rhodium(iii)

$C_8H_5F_5IORh$

M.R.Churchill, Inorg. Chem., 4, 1734, 1965

P2₁/c   Z = 4   R = 0.07

ICPFRH10   LB 8-5-7

Bond Lengths

Rh1	I1	2.65	F3	C2	1.28
Rh1	C1	2.08	F4	C2	1.34
Rh1	C3	1.97	F5	C2	1.29
Rh1	C4	2.26	C3	O1	1.05
Rh1	C5	2.26	C1	C2	1.57
Rh1	C6	2.22	C4	C5	1.41
Rh1	C7	2.24	C4	C8	1.50
Rh1	C8	2.26	C5	C6	1.50
F1	C1	1.34	C6	C7	1.42
F2	C1	1.33	C7	C8	1.43

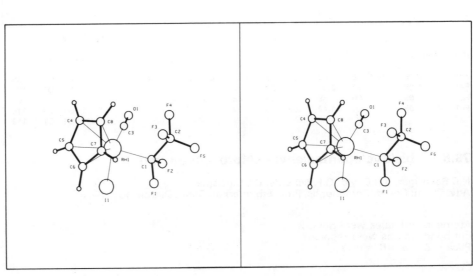

73.3   Cyclopentadienyl manganese tricarbonyl   C₈H₅MnO₃

A.F.Berndt, R.E.Marsh, Acta Cryst., 16, 118, 1963

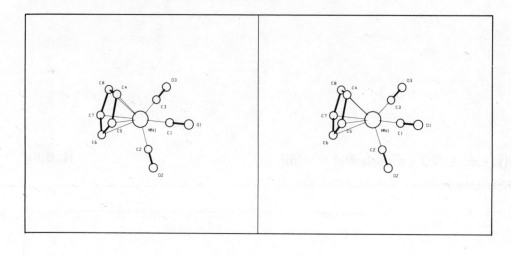

P2₁/a   Z = 4   R = 0.08

CPMNCO   LB 8-5-9

Bond Lengths

Mn1	C1	1.79	C1	O1	1.13
Mn1	C2	1.79	C2	O2	1.14
Mn1	C3	1.81	C3	O3	1.13
Mn1	C4	2.14	C4	C5	1.40
Mn1	C5	2.13	C4	C8	1.40
Mn1	C6	2.17	C5	C6	1.35
Mn1	C7	2.14	C6	C7	1.38
Mn1	C8	2.17	C7	C8	1.43

73.4   Cyclopentadienyl niobium carbonyl   C₉H₅NbO₄

W.Baird, L.F.Dahl, Amer. Chem. Soc., Abstr. Papers, 145, 27N, 1963

Atomic coordinates were not
reported in the paper.
Pnam   Z = 4   R = 0.074

CPNBCO

73.5   Ferrocene disulfonyl chloride   C₁₀H₈Cl₂FeO₄S₂

O.V.Starovskii, Yu.T.Struchkov, Zh. Strukt. Khim., 5, 257, 1964

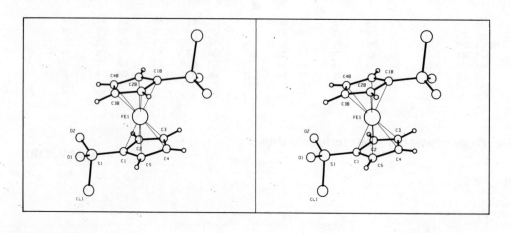

P2₁/c   Z = 2   R = 0.27

FERDSC   LB 10-8-6

Bond Lengths

Fe1	C1	2.06	Fe1	C5	2.03	S1	C1	1.70	C3	C4	1.44
Fe1	C2	2.09	Cl1	S1	2.08	C1	C2	1.44	C4	C5	1.40
Fe1	C3	2.09	S1	O1	1.39	C1	C5	1.48			
Fe1	C4	2.08	S1	O2	1.43	C2	C3	1.39			

Bond Angles

Cl1	S1	O1	109	O2	S1	C1	115	C2	C3	C4	111
Cl1	S1	O2	102	S1	C1	C2	127	C3	C4	C5	107
Cl1	S1	C1	101	S1	C1	C5	127	C1	C5	C4	109
O1	S1	O2	116	C2	C1	C5	106				
O1	S1	C1	112	C1	C2	C3	108				

73.6   bis(Cyclopentadienyl - chloro) platinum(iv)   C₁₀H₁₀Cl₂Pt

N.C.Baenziger, J.R.Doyle, G.F.Richards, C.L.Carpenter,
Adv. Chem. Coord. Compounds, Proc. 6th Internat. Conf., Detroit, 131, 1961

Atomic coordinates were not given
but bond lengths were reported.
Pbca   Z = 8   R = 0.13

CYPPTC

73.7 Cyclopentadienyl dichloro titanium(iv) - μ - oxo - cyclopentadienyl dichloro titanium(iv)

$C_{10}H_{10}Cl_4OTi_2$

P.Ganis, G.Allegra, Atti Accad. Nazion. Lincei, R. C., Cl. Sci. Fis. Mat. Nat., 33, 303, 1962

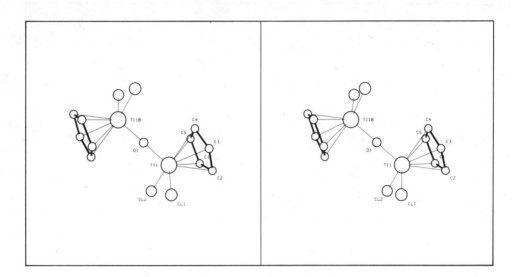

$P2_1/c$ Z = 2   R = 0.20

CYTIDC   LB 10-10-29

Bond Lengths

Ti1	Cl1	2.28	Ti1	C5	2.25
Ti1	Cl2	2.29	C1	C2	1.45
Ti1	O1	1.73	C1	C5	1.36
Ti1	C1	2.25	C2	C3	1.41
Ti1	C2	2.27	C3	C4	1.43
Ti1	C3	2.27	C4	C5	1.37
Ti1	C4	2.26			

Bond Angles

| Ti1 | O1 | Ti1B | 180 |

73.8 bis(Cyclopentadienyl) cobalt perchlorate

$C_{10}H_{10}Co^+$, ClO_4^-

E.Frasson, G.Bombieri, C.Panattoni, Acta Cryst., 16, A68, 1963

Atomic coordinates were not reported in the paper.
I4/mcm   Z = 16 R_{hk0} = 0.17,
R_{0kl} = 0.15

CPDCOP

73.9 Ferrocene (neutron study)

$C_{10}H_{10}Fe$

B.T.M.Willis, Acta Cryst., 13, 1088, 1960

Atomic coordinates were not reported in the paper.
See also Eiland & Pepinsky, J. Amer. Chem. Soc., 74, 4971, 1952; Dunitz et al., Acta Cryst., 9, 373, 1956.
$P2_1/a$ Z was not reported.   No R factor was given.

FEROCE02   LB 10-10-36

73.10 Tricarbonyl - π - cyclopentadienyl ethyl molybdenum

$C_{10}H_{10}MoO_3$

M.J.Bennett, R.Mason, Proc. Chem. Soc., 273, 1963

Atomic coordinates were not given but bond lengths were reported. The space group and Z were not reported.   R = 0.09

CPDEMO   LB 10-10-43

73.11   Dihydrido di - π - (cyclopentadienyl) molybdenum

C₁₀H₁₂Mo

M.Gerloch, R.Mason, J. Chem. Soc., 296, 1965

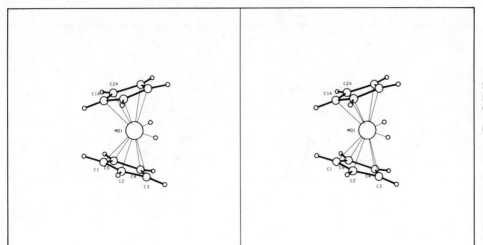

See also Abrahams & Ginsberg, Inorg. Chem., 5, 500, 1966.
C2/c   Z = 4   R = 0.09

HCYPMO   LB 10-12-23

Bond Lengths

Mo1	C1	2.22	C3	C4	1.42
Mo1	C2	2.25	C4	C5	1.48
Mo1	C3	2.37	Mo1	H6	1.17
Mo1	C4	2.33	C1	H1	1.08
Mo1	C5	2.28	C2	H2	1.14
C1	C2	1.34	C3	H3	1.06
C1	C5	1.38	C4	H4	1.08
C2	C3	1.50	C5	H5	1.09

73.12   Di - iron hexacarbonyl - methylenecyclopentadiene complex

C₁₂H₆Fe₂O₆

J.Meunier-Piret, P.Piret, M.van Meerssche, Acta Cryst., 19, 85, 1965

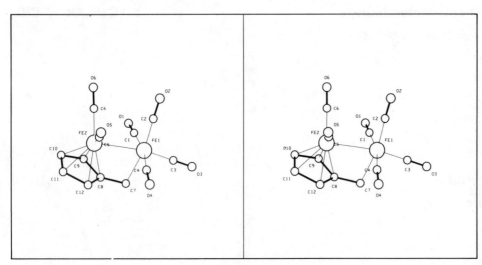

Red chemical isomer. See 72.14 for the orange - red isomer.
P2₁/c   Z = 4   R = 0.15

FCOMCP   LB 12-6-3

Bond Lengths

Fe1	Fe2	2.68	C1	O1	1.13
Fe1	C1	1.78	C2	O2	1.10
Fe1	C2	1.81	C3	O3	1.16
Fe1	C3	1.76	C4	O4	1.14
Fe1	C4	1.80	C5	O5	1.16
Fe1	C7	2.12	C6	O6	1.12
Fe2	C5	1.75	C7	C8	1.46
Fe2	C6	1.77	C8	C9	1.45
Fe2	C8	2.06	C8	C12	1.42
Fe2	C9	2.02	C9	C10	1.44
Fe2	C10	2.08	C10	C11	1.42
Fe2	C11	2.12	C11	C12	1.43
Fe2	C12	2.05			

73.13   α - Keto - 1,1' - trimethyleneferrocene

C₁₃H₁₂FeO

N.D.Jones, R.E.Marsh, J.H.Richards, Acta Cryst., 19, 330, 1965

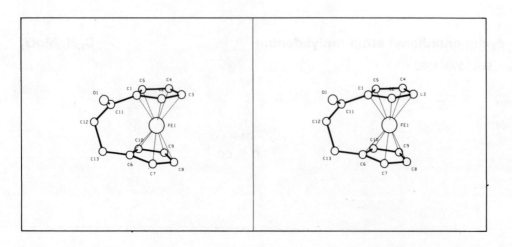

P2₁/a   Z = 4   R = 0.067

KMEFER   LB 13-12-3

Bond Lengths

Fe1	C1	2.01	C1	C11	1.49
Fe1	C2	2.04	C2	C3	1.41
Fe1	C3	2.07	C3	C4	1.43
Fe1	C4	2.07	C4	C5	1.43
Fe1	C5	2.02	C6	C7	1.45
Fe1	C6	2.03	C6	C10	1.42
Fe1	C7	2.04	C6	C13	1.53
Fe1	C8	2.05	C7	C8	1.41
Fe1	C9	2.04	C8	C9	1.43
Fe1	C10	2.04	C9	C10	1.41
C11	O1	1.21	C11	C12	1.51
C1	C2	1.42	C12	C13	1.53
C1	C5	1.43			

Bond Angles

C2	C1	C5	108	C6	C7	C8	109
C2	C1	C11	124	C7	C8	C9	108
C5	C1	C11	126	C8	C9	C10	108
C1	C2	C3	109	C6	C10	C9	109
C2	C3	C4	108	O1	C11	C1	121
C3	C4	C5	108	O1	C11	C12	121
C1	C5	C4	107	C1	C11	C12	118
C7	C6	C10	107	C11	C12	C13	110
C7	C6	C13	125	C6	C13	C12	112
C10	C6	C13	128				

Torsion Angles

Fe1	C1	C11	O1	125
Fe1	C1	C11	C12	−48
C2	C1	C11	O1	44
C2	C1	C11	C12	−129
C5	C1	C11	O1	−154
C5	C1	C11	C12	33
Fe1	C6	C13	C12	26
C7	C6	C13	C12	112
C10	C6	C13	C12	−62
C6	C13	C12	C11	−65
C13	C12	C11	C1	82

73.14 tetrakis(Trifluoromethyl) cyclopentadienone - π - cyclopentadiene cobalt

C$_{14}$H$_5$CoF$_{12}$O

M.Gerloch, R.Mason, Proc. R. Soc., A, 279, 170, 1964

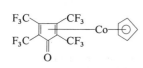

C2/c   Z = 8   R = 0.09

FMCPCO   LB 14-5-1

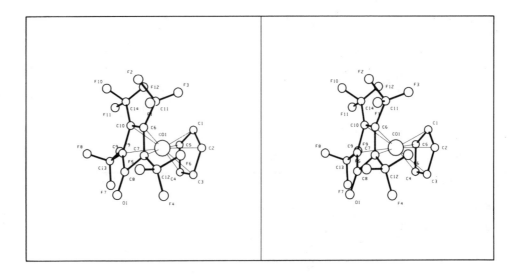

Bond Lengths

Co1	C1	2.09	Co1	C7	2.03	F4	C12	1.28	F10	C14	1.26	C2	C3	1.46	C7	C8	1.50
Co1	C2	2.04	Co1	C9	2.08	F5	C12	1.29	F11	C14	1.22	C3	C4	1.38	C7	C12	1.50
Co1	C3	2.11	Co1	C10	1.99	F6	C12	1.35	F12	C14	1.20	C4	C5	1.49	C8	C9	1.50
Co1	C4	2.09	F1	C11	1.34	F7	C13	1.28	C8	O1	1.18	C6	C7	1.40	C9	C10	1.50
Co1	C5	2.06	F2	C11	1.34	F8	C13	1.29	C1	C2	1.43	C6	C10	1.44	C9	C13	1.51
Co1	C6	1.98	F3	C11	1.21	F9	C13	1.28	C1	C5	1.43	C6	C11	1.54	C10	C14	1.50

73.15 Diacetyl ruthenocene

C$_{14}$H$_{14}$O$_2$Ru

J.Trotter, Acta Cryst., 16, 571, 1963

No comparison of bond lengths is possible since they are not reported in the paper.

P-1   Z = 2   R$_{0kl}$ = 0.14, R$_{h0l}$ = 0.15

DARUOC   LB 14-14-42

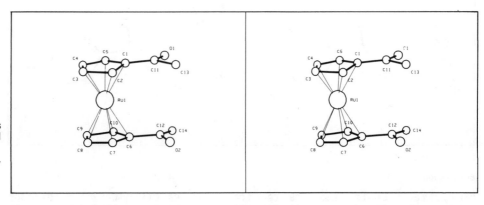

Bond Lengths

Ru1	C1	2.08	Ru1	C6	2.21	C11	O1	1.22	C2	C3	1.49	C6	C12	1.57
Ru1	C2	1.82	Ru1	C7	2.31	C12	O2	1.24	C3	C4	1.36	C7	C8	1.29
Ru1	C3	1.95	Ru1	C8	2.32	C1	C2	1.47	C4	C5	1.29	C8	C9	1.41
Ru1	C4	2.12	Ru1	C9	2.12	C1	C5	1.41	C6	C7	1.49	C9	C10	1.48
Ru1	C5	2.20	Ru1	C10	2.11	C1	C11	1.49	C6	C10	1.36	C11	C13	1.48
												C12	C14	1.37

73.16   Cyclopentadiene - tetramethylcyclopentadienone cobalt(0)

L.F.Dahl, D.L.Smith, J. Amer. Chem. Soc., 83, 752, 1961

Atomic coordinates were not given
but bond lengths were reported.
P2₁/n   Z = 4   R = 0.05

CPMECO   LB 14-17-1

C₁₄H₁₇CoO

73.17   π - Tri - cyclopentadienyl chloro uranium(iv)

C.H.Wong, T.-M.Yen, T.Lee, Acta Cryst., 18, 340, 1965

C₁₅H₁₅ClU

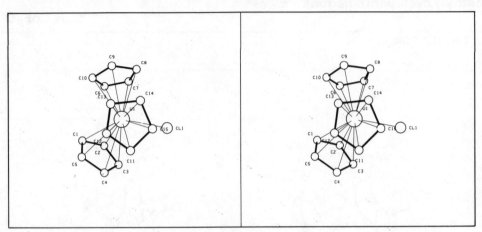

No comparison of bond lengths is
possible since they are not reported
in the paper.
P2₁/n   Z = 4   R = 0.12

CYPUCL   LB 15-15-9

Bond Lengths

U1	Cl1	2.56	U1	C8	2.69	C1	C2	1.44	C8 C9	1.46
U1	C1	2.73	U1	C9	2.69	C1	C5	1.40	C9 C10	1.46
U1	C2	2.73	U1	C10	2.70	C2	C3	1.42	C11 C12	1.41
U1	C3	2.72	U1	C11	2.78	C3	C4	1.44	C11 C15	1.47
U1	C4	2.82	U1	C12	2.75	C4	C5	1.41	C12 C13	1.38
U1	C5	2.81	U1	C13	2.78	C6	C7	1.33	C13 C14	1.44
U1	C6	2.73	U1	C14	2.73	C6	C10	1.36	C14 C15	1.45
U1	C7	2.73	U1	C15	2.73	C7	C8	1.45		

73.18   π - Cyclopentadienyl 1 - phenylcyclopentadiene cobalt

M.R.Churchill, R.Mason, Proc. R. Soc., A, 279, 191, 1964

C₁₆H₁₅Co

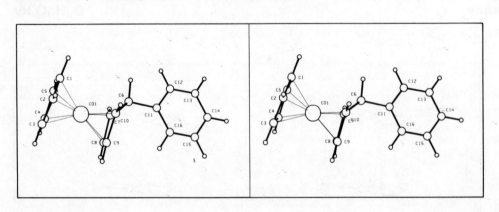

Pbca   Z = 8   R = 0.11

CPCPCO   LB 16-15-7

Bond Lengths

Co1 C1	2.09	C1 C2	1.44	C8 C9	1.36
Co1 C2	2.05	C1 C5	1.42	C9 C10	1.54
Co1 C3	2.15	C2 C3	1.48	C11 C12	1.37
Co1 C4	2.05	C3 C4	1.46	C11 C16	1.45
Co1 C5	2.06	C4 C5	1.50	C12 C13	1.41
Co1 C7	2.02	C6 C7	1.53	C13 C14	1.43
Co1 C8	2.03	C6 C10	1.51	C14 C15	1.42
Co1 C9	1.97	C6 C11	1.54	C15 C16	1.38
Co1 C10	1.98	C7 C8	1.49		

Bond Angles

C7 C6 C10	94	C8 C9 C9	106
C7 C6 C11	112	Co1 C9 C8	73
C10 C6 C11	122	Co1 C9 C10	67
Co1 C7 C6	91	C8 C9 C10	107
Co1 C7 C8	69	Co1 C10 C6	94
C6 C7 C8	109	Co1 C10 C9	67
Co1 C8 C7	68	C6 C10 C9	108
Co1 C8 C9	68		

73.19 μ - (Dimethylphosphido) hydrido di - π - cyclopentadienyl tetracarbonyl dimolybdenum

$C_{16}H_{17}Mo_2O_4P$

R.J.Doedens, L.F.Dahl, J. Amer. Chem. Soc., 87, 2576, 1965

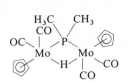

C-1   Z = 2   R = 0.105

PHCCMO   LB 16-17-3

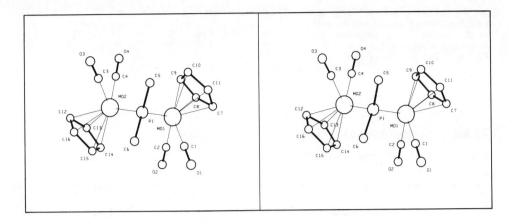

Bond Lengths

												Bond Angles		
Mo1	P1	2.43	Mo2	P1	2.42	P1	C5	1.83	C8	C9	1.32	Mo1 P1 Mo2		85
Mo1	C1	1.93	Mo2	C3	1.96	P1	C6	1.86	C9	C10	1.45	Mo1 P1 C5		116
Mo1	C2	1.92	Mo2	C4	1.92	C1	O1	1.14	C10	C11	1.37	Mo1 P1 C6		124
Mo1	C7	2.28	Mo2	C12	2.29	C2	O2	1.17	C12	C13	1.39	Mo2 P1 C5		123
Mo1	C8	2.36	Mo2	C13	2.34	C3	O3	1.13	C12	C16	1.41	Mo2 P1 C6		115
Mo1	C9	2.37	Mo2	C14	2.39	C4	O4	1.17	C13	C14	1.39	C5 P1 C6		97
Mo1	C10	2.37	Mo2	C15	2.36	C7	C8	1.40	C14	C15	1.42			
Mo1	C11	2.27	Mo2	C16	2.26	C7	C11	1.40	C15	C16	1.36			

73.20   1,1' - Tetramethylethyleneferrocene

$C_{16}H_{20}Fe$

M.B.Laing, K.N.Trueblood, Acta Cryst., 19, 373, 1965

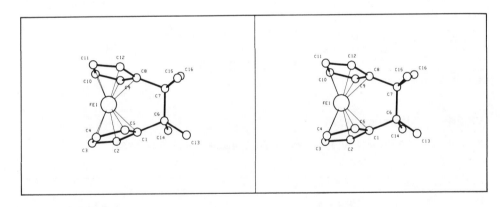

$P2_1/c$ Z = 4   R = 0.08

METFER   LB 16-20-10

Bond Lengths

									Torsion Angles				
Fe1	C1	1.98	Fe1	C12	2.02	C6	C14	1.57	C1	C6	C7	C8	−25
Fe1	C2	2.04	C1	C2	1.45	C7	C8	1.54	C1	C6	C7	C15	92
Fe1	C3	2.08	C1	C5	1.44	C7	C15	1.55	C1	C6	C7	C16	−147
Fe1	C4	2.09	C1	C6	1.55	C7	C16	1.55	C13	C6	C7	C8	−146
Fe1	C5	2.02	C2	C3	1.43	C8	C9	1.46	C13	C6	C7	C15	−28
Fe1	C8	1.97	C3	C4	1.40	C8	C12	1.43	C13	C6	C7	C16	93
Fe1	C9	2.07	C4	C5	1.45	C9	C10	1.42	C14	C6	C7	C8	96
Fe1	C10	2.04	C6	C7	1.58	C10	C11	1.43	C14	C6	C7	C15	−146
Fe1	C11	2.10	C6	C13	1.55	C11	C12	1.45	C14	C6	C7	C16	−26

73.21   π - Cyclopentadienyl - (1 - benzoyl - cyclopentadienyl) cobalt

$C_{17}H_{14}CoO$

M.R.Churchill, J. Organometal. Chem., 4, 258, 1965

Atomic coordinates were not reported in the paper.
$P2_1$ Z = 2   R = 0.085

CPBOCO   LB 17-15-6

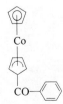

73.22   Tricyclopentadienyl trinickel dicarbonyl

$C_{17}H_{15}Ni_3O_2$

A.A.Hock, O.S.Mills, Adv. Chem. Coord. Compounds, Proc. 6th
Internat. Conf., Detroit, 640, 1961

No comparison of bond lengths is
possible since they are not reported
in the paper. The cyclopentadienyl
rings are disordered.
$P6_3/m$ Z = 2   R = 0.094

TCPDNI

Bond Lengths			Bond Angles		
Ni1	Ni1A	2.39	C1	Ni1	C1I	89
Ni1	C1	1.93	Ni1	C1	Ni1A	77
C1	O1	1.19	Ni1	C1	O1	134

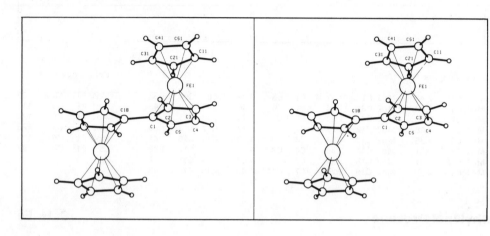

73.23   Biferrocenyl

$C_{20}H_{18}Fe_2$

A.C.Macdonald, J.Trotter, Acta Cryst., 17, 872, 1964

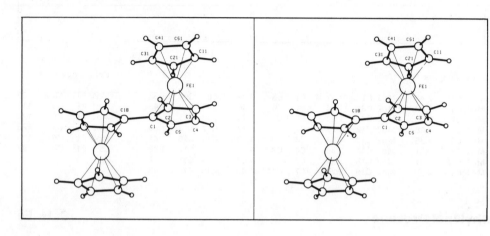

P2$_1$/c   Z = 2   R = 0.16

BIFERO   LB 20-18-6

Bond Lengths

Fe11	C1	2.06	Fe11	C8	2.07	C4	C5	1.35
Fe11	C2	2.07	Fe11	C9	2.03	C6	C7	1.38
Fe11	C3	2.04	Fe11	C10	1.97	C6	C10	1.34
Fe11	C4	2.04	C1	C2	1.46	C7	C8	1.45
Fe11	C5	2.02	C1	C5	1.42	C7	C7B	1.48
Fe11	C6	2.00	C2	C3	1.39	C8	C9	1.41
Fe11	C7	2.04	C3	C4	1.39	C9	C10	1.40

73.24   Biferrocenyl

$C_{20}H_{18}Fe_2$

Z.L.Kaluski, Yu.T.Struchkov, R.L.Avoyan, Zh. Strukt. Khim., 5, 743, 1964

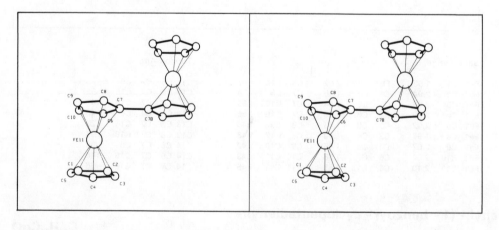

P2$_1$/c   Z = 2   R = 0.15

BIFERO11   LB 20-18-6

Bond Lengths

Fe1	C1	2.01	Fe1	C31	2.02	C3	C4	1.47
Fe1	C2	2.00	Fe1	C41	2.09	C4	C5	1.37
Fe1	C3	2.03	Fe1	C51	2.05	C11	C21	1.39
Fe1	C4	2.06	C1	C2	1.41	C11	C51	1.42
Fe1	C5	2.05	C1	C5	1.44	C21	C31	1.39
Fe1	C11	2.03	C1	C1B	1.48	C31	C41	1.43
Fe1	C21	2.00	C2	C3	1.43	C41	C51	1.41

73.25 Diethylbiferrocene

C₂₄H₂₆Fe₂ → $C_{24}H_{26}Fe_2$

Z.L.Kaluski, Yu.T.Struchkov, Zh. Strukt. Khim., 6, 104, 1965

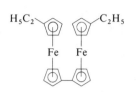

Published value of x(C7) = 0.472.
The correct value is 0.427.
See also Kaluski & Struchkov, Zh.
Strukt. Khim., 7, 283, 1966.
C2/c   Z = 4   R = 0.16

DETFER10   LB 24-26-1

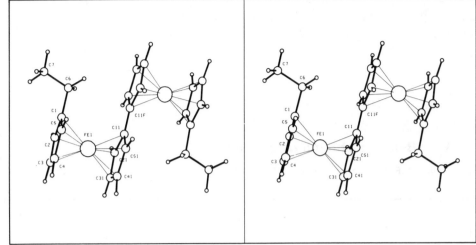

Bond Lengths

Fe1	C1	2.06	Fe1	C21	2.07	C1	C6	1.59	C11	C51	1.43
Fe1	C2	2.07	Fe1	C31	2.07	C2	C3	1.43	C11	C11F	1.37
Fe1	C3	2.07	Fe1	C41	2.06	C3	C4	1.45	C21	C31	1.44
Fe1	C4	2.07	Fe1	C51	2.06	C4	C5	1.42	C31	C41	1.45
Fe1	C5	2.07	C1	C2	1.45	C6	C7	1.50	C41	C51	1.44
Fe1	C11	2.08	C1	C5	1.45	C11	C21	1.46			

73.26 Di - π - cyclopentadienyl dicobalt tricyclopentadienyl

C₂₅H₂₄Co₂ → $C_{25}H_{24}Co_2$

O.V.Starovskii, Yu.T.Struchkov, Zh. Strukt. Khim., 6, 248, 1965

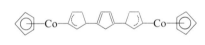

Published value of y(H25) = 0.055.
The correct value is −0.055.
Pbc2₁   Z = 4   R = 0.17

CPCOTC   LB 25-24-2

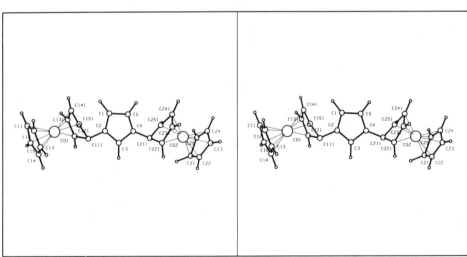

Bond Lengths

Co1	C11	2.08	Co2	C231	1.96	C21	C22	1.55
Co1	C12	2.03	Co2	C241	1.93	C21	C25	1.53
Co1	C13	2.04	Co2	C251	1.97	C22	C23	1.37
Co1	C14	2.01	C1	C2	1.39	C23	C24	1.36
Co1	C15	2.08	C1	C5	1.53	C24	C25	1.39
Co1	C121	2.09	C2	C3	1.37	C111	C121	1.58
Co1	C131	1.92	C2	C111	1.48	C111	C151	1.52
Co1	C141	1.97	C3	C4	1.53	C121	C131	1.34
Co1	C151	2.04	C4	C5	1.32	C131	C141	1.56
Co2	C21	2.08	C4	C211	1.45	C141	C151	1.34
Co2	C22	1.97	C11	C12	1.49	C211	C221	1.53
Co2	C23	2.17	C11	C15	1.41	C211	C251	1.41
Co2	C24	2.08	C12	C13	1.26	C221	C231	1.49
Co2	C25	2.07	C13	C14	1.35	C231	C241	1.40
Co2	C221	2.01	C14	C15	1.30	C241	C251	1.60

Bond Angles

C2	C111	C121	106	C4	C211	C221	113
C2	C111	C151	110	C4	C211	C251	115
C121	C111	C151	95	C221	C211	C251	94
Co1	C121	C111	89	Co2	C221	C211	91
Co1	C121	C131	64	Co2	C221	C231	66
C111	C121	C131	110	C211	C221	C231	113
Co1	C131	C121	78	Co2	C231	C221	70
Co1	C131	C141	68	Co2	C231	C241	68
C121	C131	C141	108	C221	C231	C241	106
Co1	C141	C131	64	Co2	C241	C231	70
Co1	C141	C151	73	Co2	C241	C251	67
C131	C141	C151	103	C231	C241	C251	102
Co1	C151	C111	92	Co2	C251	C211	96
Co1	C151	C141	68	Co2	C251	C241	64
C111	C151	C141	113	C211	C251	C241	113

Torsion Angles

C1	C2	C111	C121	63
C1	C2	C111	C151	−38
C3	C2	C111	C121	−112
C3	C2	C111	C151	146
C3	C4	C211	C221	−73
C3	C4	C211	C251	−179
C5	C4	C211	C221	104
C5	C4	C211	C251	−2

74.1 Benzene chromium tricarbonyl

$C_9H_6CrO_3$

M.F.Bailey, L.F.Dahl, Inorg. Chem., 4, 1314, 1965

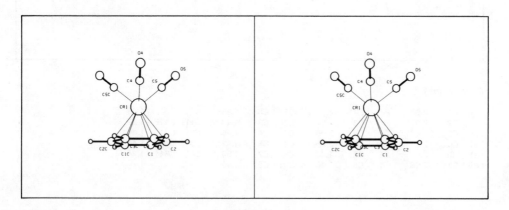

$\bigcirc \cdot Cr(CO)_3$

P2$_1$/m   Z = 2   R = 0.042

BZCRCO   LB 9-6-10

Bond Lengths

Cr1	C1	2.23	C5	O5	1.15
Cr1	C2	2.22	C1	C2	1.40
Cr1	C3	2.22	C1	C1C	1.37
Cr1	C4	1.84	C2	C3	1.40
Cr1	C5	1.84	C3	C3C	1.42
C4	O4	1.14			

74.2 Benzene chromium tricarbonyl

$C_9H_6CrO_3$

G.Allegra, G.Natta, Atti Accad. Nazion. Lincei, R. C., Cl. Sci. Fis. Mat. Nat., 31, 241, 1961

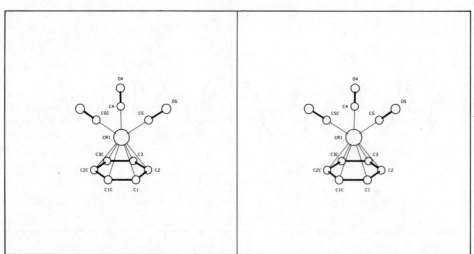

$\bigcirc \cdot Cr(CO)_3$

No comparison of bond lengths is possible since they are not reported in the paper.
P2$_1$/m   Z = 2   R = 0.033

BZCRCO01   LB 9-6-10

Bond Lengths

Cr1	C1	2.24	C5	O5	1.16
Cr1	C2	2.23	C1	C2	1.41
Cr1	C3	2.23	C1	C1C	1.41
Cr1	C4	1.87	C2	C3	1.41
Cr1	C5	1.90	C3	C3C	1.41
C4	O4	1.14			

74.3 Dibenzene chromium(0)

$C_{12}H_{12}Cr$

F.A.Cotton, W.A.Dollase, J.S.Wood, J. Amer. Chem. Soc., 85, 1543, 1963

Atomic coordinates were not given but bond lengths were reported. The benzene ring bond lengths were found to be equal within the standard error.
Pa3   Z = 4   R = 0.061

DBENCR01   LB 12-12-20

74.4 Dibenzene chromium(0) (refinement of data of Cotton et al., J.Amer.Chem.Soc., 85,1543,1963)

$C_{12}H_{12}Cr$

J.A.Ibers, J. Chem. Phys., 40, 3129, 1964

Atomic coordinates were not given but bond lengths were reported. The benzene ring bond lengths were found to be equal within the standard error.
Pa3   Z = 4   No R factor was given.

DBENCR02   LB 12-12-20

74.5 Dibenzene chromium(0)

$C_{12}H_{12}Cr$

F.Jellinek, J. Organometal. Chem., 1, 43, 1963

The benzene ring bond lengths were found not to be equal within the standard error. However in a later determination at 100°K by Keulen and Jellinek, J. Organometal. Chem., 5, 496, 1966. the benzene ring bonds were found to be equal.

Pa3   Z = 4   R = 0.053

DBENCR10   LB 12-12-20

Bond Lengths

Cr1	C1	2.13	C1	C2D	1.36
Cr1	C2	2.13	C1	C2H	1.44

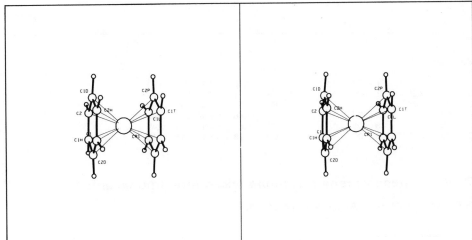

74.6 Ditoluene chromium iodide

$C_{14}H_{16}Cr^+$, I^-

O.V.Starovskii, Yu.T.Struchkov, Zh. Strukt. Khim., 2, 162, 1961

I2/m   Z = 2   R = 0.13

DTOLCR   LB 14-16-13

Bond Lengths

Cr1	C1	2.08	C1	C2	1.41
Cr1	C2	2.08	C1	C10	1.50
Cr1	C3	2.07	C2	C3	1.42
Cr1	C4	2.08	C3	C4	1.42

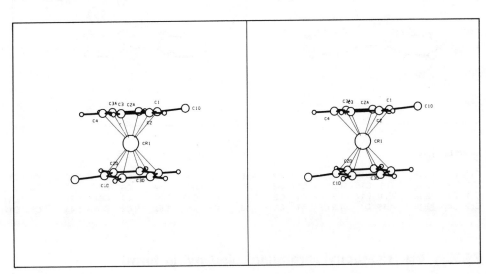

74.7 Hexamethylbenzene chromium tricarbonyl

$C_{15}H_{18}CrO_3$

M.F.Bailey, L.F.Dahl, Inorg. Chem., 4, 1298, 1965

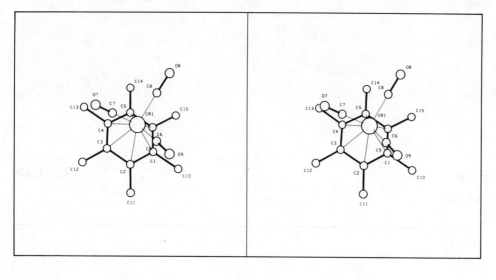

Pbca   Z = 8   R = 0.105

HBCRTC   LB 15-18-5

Bond Lengths

Cr1	C1	2.21	Cr1	C7	1.82	C1	C2	1.45	C3	C12	1.51
Cr1	C2	2.25	Cr1	C8	1.83	C1	C6	1.37	C4	C5	1.42
Cr1	C3	2.24	Cr1	C9	1.79	C1	C10	1.56	C4	C13	1.54
Cr1	C4	2.23	C7	O7	1.14	C2	C3	1.46	C5	C6	1.42
Cr1	C5	2.24	C8	O8	1.15	C2	C11	1.49	C5	C14	1.49
Cr1	C6	2.23	C9	O9	1.20	C3	C4	1.38	C6	C15	1.53

74.8 Phenanthrene chromium tricarbonyl (monoclinic form)

$C_{17}H_{10}CrO_3$

H.Deuschl, W.Hoppe, Acta Cryst., 17, 800, 1964

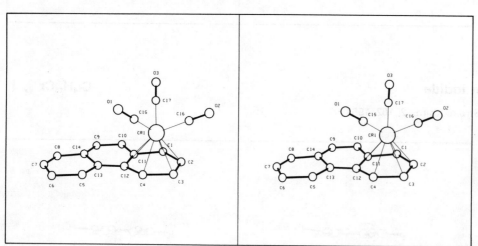

See also Muir et al., J. Chem. Soc. (B), 467, 1968.
P2₁/a   Z = 4 R_{h0l} = 0.13,
R_{0kl} = 0.13, R_{hk0} = 0.13

PANCRO   LB 17-10-3

Bond Lengths

Cr1	C1	2.15	Cr1	C15	1.80	C16	O2	1.15	C2	C3	1.40	C5	C13	1.46	C9	C10	1.39	C12	C13	1.37
Cr1	C2	2.16	Cr1	C16	1.91	C17	O3	1.09	C3	C4	1.54	C6	C7	1.37	C9	C14	1.45	C13	C14	1.45
Cr1	C3	2.16	Cr1	C17	1.88	C1	C2	1.37	C4	C12	1.36	C7	C8	1.24	C10	C11	1.40
Cr1	C4	2.16	C15	O1	1.21	C1	C11	1.56	C5	C6	1.52	C8	C14	1.43	C11	C12	1.37

74.9 bis(Tricarbonyl chromium) biphenyl (α form)

$C_{18}H_{10}Cr_2O_6$

P.Corradini, G.Allegra, J. Amer. Chem. Soc., 82, 2075, 1960

Atomic coordinates were not reported in the paper.
P2₁/c   Z = 2   R = 0.17

COCRDP   LB 18-10-4

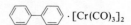

74.10   bis(Tricarbonyl chromium) biphenyl (β form) $C_{18}H_{10}Cr_2O_6$

G.Allegra, G.Natta, Atti Accad. Nazion. Lincei, R. C., Cl. Sci. Fis. Mat. Nat., 31, 399, 1961

· $[Cr(CO)_3]_2$

Published value of z(O2) = 0.095.
The correct value is −0.095.
P-1   Z = 1   R = 0.17

COCRDP01   LB 18-10-5

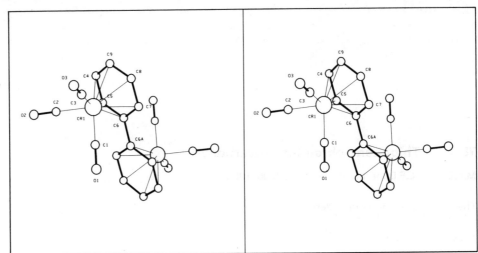

Bond Lengths

Cr1	C1	1.89		C3	O3	1.16
Cr1	C2	1.87		C4	C5	1.43
Cr1	C3	1.80		C4	C9	1.37
Cr1	C5	2.21		C5	C6	1.44
Cr1	C6	2.20		C6	C7	1.36
Cr1	C7	2.26		C6	C6A	1.48
C1	O1	1.18		C7	C8	1.44
C2	O2	1.16		C8	C9	1.43

75.1 Thiophene chromium tricarbonyl

C₇H₄CrO₃S

M.F.Bailey, L.F.Dahl, Inorg. Chem., 4, 1306, 1965

The thiophene ring is disordered.
P2₁/m   Z = 2   R = 0.132

THCRCO   LB 7-4-8

75.2 Norbornadiene dichloro palladium(ii)

C₇H₈Cl₂Pd

N.C.Baenziger, G.F.Richards, J.R.Doyle, Acta Cryst., 18, 924, 1965

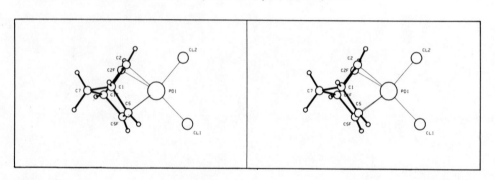

Pnma   Z = 4   R = 0.034

NBOPDC   LB 7-8-7

Bond Lengths

Pd1	Cl1	2.32	Pd1	C5	2.17	C1	C7	1.55
Pd1	Cl2	2.31	C1	C2	1.55	C2	C2F	1.37
Pd1	C2	2.16	C1	C5	1.55	C5	C5F	1.37

Bond Angles

C2	C1	C5	100	C1	C2	C2F	107
C2	C1	C7	100	C1	C5	C5F	107
C5	C1	C7	100	C1	C7	C1F	95

75.3 Norbornadiene dichloro palladium(ii) (liquid nitrogen temp.)

C₇H₈Cl₂Pd

N.C.Baenziger, J.R.Doyle, C.Carpenter, Acta Cryst., 14, 303, 1961

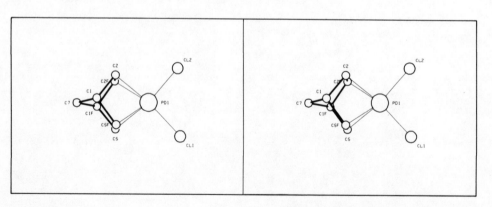

Pnma   Z = 4   R = 0.074

NBOPDC01   LB 7-8-7

Bond Lengths

Pd1	Cl1	2.31	Pd1	C5	2.21	C1	C5F	1.63
Pd1	Cl2	2.31	C1	C2	1.61	C2	C2F	1.53
Pd1	C2	2.22	C1	C7	1.60	C5	C5F	1.52

Bond Angles

C2	C1	C7	100	C1	C2	C2F	106
C2	C1	C5F	98	C1	C7	C1F	100
C7	C1	C5F	100				

75.4   Cyclo - octatetraene chloro copper(i)

C₈H₈ClCu

N.C.Baenziger, G.F.Richards, J.R.Doyle, Inorg. Chem., 3, 1529, 1964

Pbca   Z = 8   R = 0.12

OCTCUC   LB 8-8-13

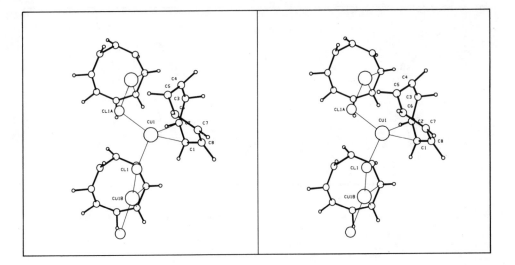

Bond Lengths

Cu1	Cl1	2.29	C2	C3	1.44
Cu1	Cl1G	2.28	C3	C4	1.38
Cu1	C1	2.07	C4	C5	1.50
Cu1	C2	2.10	C5	C6	1.32
C1	C2	1.39	C6	C7	1.49
C1	C8	1.46	C7	C8	1.37

Bond Angles

Cl1	Cu1	Cl1G	106	Cu1	C1	C2	71	C2	C3	C4	126
Cl1	Cu1	C1	104	Cu1	C1	C8	115	C3	C4	C5	123
Cl1	Cu1	C2	142	C2	C1	C8	124	C4	C5	C6	125
C1	Cu1	Cl1G	150	Cu1	C2	C1	70	C5	C6	C7	126
C1	Cu1	C2	39	Cu1	C2	C3	113	C6	C7	C8	125
Cu1	Cl1	Cu1G	109	C1	C2	C3	125	C1	C8	C7	124

75.5   Tropone iron tricarbonyl

C₁₀H₆FeO₄

R.P.Dodge, J. Amer. Chem. Soc., 86, 5429, 1964

P2₁/c   Z = 4   R = 0.12

TROICO   LB 10-6-14

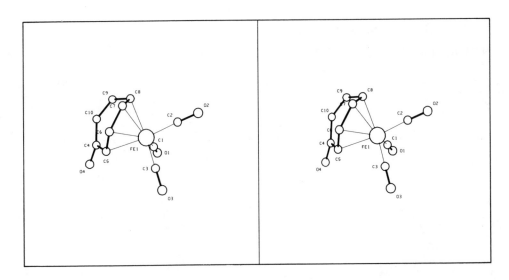

Bond Lengths

Fe1	C1	1.76	C3	O3	1.17
Fe1	C2	1.77	C4	O4	1.25
Fe1	C3	1.75	C4	C5	1.49
Fe1	C5	2.11	C4	C10	1.45
Fe1	C6	2.07	C5	C6	1.44
Fe1	C7	2.04	C6	C7	1.40
Fe1	C8	2.15	C7	C8	1.44
C1	O1	1.16	C8	C9	1.46
C2	O2	1.13	C9	C10	1.34

Bond Angles

O4	C4	C5	115
O4	C4	C10	121
C5	C4	C10	123
C4	C5	C6	127
C5	C6	C7	120
C6	C7	C8	121
C7	C8	C9	122
C8	C9	C10	127
C4	C10	C9	124

Torsion Angles

O4	C4	C5	C6	−162
C10	C4	C5	C6	23
O4	C4	C10	C9	−152
C5	C4	C10	C9	22
C4	C5	C6	C7	−49
C5	C6	C7	C8	4
C6	C7	C8	C9	53
C7	C8	C9	C10	−48
C8	C9	C10	C4	−7

75.6 Cycloheptatriene molybdenum tricarbonyl $C_{10}H_8MoO_3$

J.D.Dunitz, P.Pauling, Helv. Chim. Acta, 43, 2188, 1960

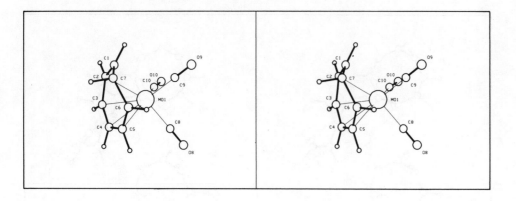

 · $Mo(CO)_3$

$P2_1/a$ $Z = 4$ $R = 0.06$

CHMOCO   LB 10-8-17

Bond Lengths

Mo1	C2	2.37	Mo1	C10	1.95	C2	C3	1.45
Mo1	C3	2.31	C8	O8	1.13	C3	C4	1.38
Mo1	C4	2.31	C9	O9	1.13	C4	C5	1.40
Mo1	C5	2.33	C10	O10	1.18	C5	C6	1.34
Mo1	C8	1.99	C1	C2	1.35	C6	C7	1.54
Mo1	C9	1.99	C1	C7	1.51			

Bond Angles

C2	C1	C7	126
C1	C2	C3	126
C2	C3	C4	129
C3	C4	C5	129
C4	C5	C6	127
C5	C6	C7	125
C1	C7	C6	111

Torsion Angles

C7	C1	C2	C3	−24
C2	C1	C7	C6	59
C1	C2	C3	C4	−6
C2	C3	C4	C5	−2
C3	C4	C5	C6	9
C4	C5	C6	C7	23
C5	C6	C7	C1	−59

75.7 Cycloheptatrienyl vanadium(0) tricarbonyl $C_{10}H_8O_3V$

G.Allegra, G.Perego, Ric. Sci., 2, A, 1, 362, 1961

Atomic coordinates were not reported in the paper.
$P2_12_12_1$ $Z = 4$ No R factor was given.

CYHPVC

75.8 Dipentene dichloro platinum(ii) $C_{10}H_{16}Cl_2Pt$

N.C.Baenziger, R.C.Medrud, J.R.Doyle, Acta Cryst., 18, 237, 1965

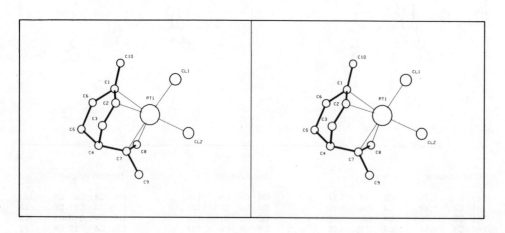

$P2_1cn$ $Z = 4$ $R = 0.071$

DIPTCL   LB 10-16-18

Bond Lengths

Pt1	Cl1	2.34	C1	C10	1.36
Pt1	Cl2	2.32	C2	C3	1.34
Pt1	C1	2.24	C3	C4	1.59
Pt1	C2	2.25	C4	C5	1.60
Pt1	C7	2.18	C4	C7	1.50
Pt1	C8	2.11	C5	C6	1.48
C1	C2	1.53	C7	C8	1.56
C1	C6	1.48	C7	C9	1.46

Bond Angles

C2	C1	C6	100
C2	C1	C10	129
C6	C1	C10	122
C1	C2	C3	133
C2	C3	C4	106
C3	C4	C5	108
C3	C4	C7	102
C5	C4	C7	119
C4	C5	C6	105
C1	C6	C5	133
C4	C7	C8	123
C4	C7	C9	114
C8	C7	C9	118

Torsion Angles

C6	C1	C2	C3	9	C3	C4	C5	C6	48
C10	C1	C2	C3	155	C7	C4	C5	C6	−66
C2	C1	C6	C5	−28	C3	C4	C7	C8	−123
C10	C1	C6	C5	−177	C3	C4	C7	C9	83
C1	C2	C3	C4	34	C5	C4	C7	C8	−5
C2	C3	C4	C5	−63	C5	C4	C7	C9	−159
C2	C3	C4	C7	63	C4	C5	C6	C1	−1

75.9   Cyclo - octatetraene iron tricarbonyl

$C_{11}H_8FeO_3$

B.Dickens, W.N.Lipscomb, J. Chem. Phys., 37, 2084, 1962

Pnam   Z = 4   R = 0.09

OCTFEC   LB 11-8-2

Bond Lengths		Bond Angles			
Fe1	C1	2.18	C2	C1	C3*	132
Fe1	C2	2.05	C1	C2	C2F	125
Fe1	C5	1.80	C1	C3	C4	134
Fe1	C6	1.80	C3	C4	C4F	131
C5	O5	1.12				
C6	O6	1.14				
C1	C2	1.42				
C1	C3	1.45				
C2	C2F	1.43				
C3	C4	1.34				
C4	C4F	1.50				

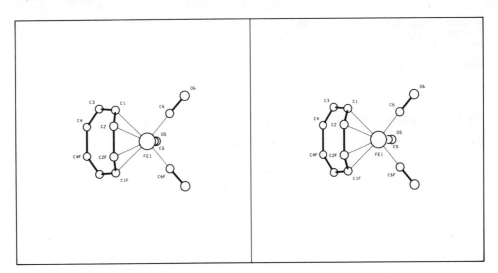

75.10   Bicyclo(3,2,1)octadienyl iron tricarbonyl tetrafluoroborate

$C_{11}H_9FeO_3^+$, BF_4^-

T.N.Margulis, L.Schiff, M.Rosenblum, J. Amer. Chem. Soc., 87, 3269, 1965

Atomic coordinates were not given
but bond lengths were reported.
P2₁/a   Z = 4   R = 0.12

OFECOB   LB 11-9-1

75.11   Tricarbonyl - cyclo - octa - 1,3,5 - trienyl chromium

$C_{11}H_{10}CrO_3$

V.S.Armstrong, C.K.Prout, J. Chem. Soc., 3770, 1962

No comparison of bond lengths is
possible since they are not reported
in the paper. The published bond
lengths are incorrect (private communication).
P2₁   Z = 2   R = 0.13

TCOCCR   LB 11-10-4

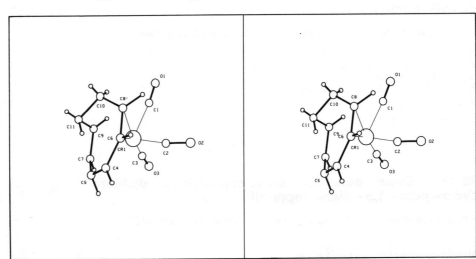

Bond Lengths

Cr1	C1	2.14	C4	C5	1.46
Cr1	C2	1.80	C4	C6	1.62
Cr1	C3	1.57	C5	C7	1.42
Cr1	C6	1.86	C6	C8	1.55
Cr1	C8	1.98	C7	C9	1.55
C1	O1	1.36	C8	C10	1.56
C2	O2	1.26	C9	C11	1.18
C3	O3	0.94	C10	C11	1.73

Bond Angles				Torsion Angles			
C5	C4	C6	128	C6	C8	C10	120
C4	C5	C7	125	C7	C9	C11	104
C4	C6	C8	142	C8	C10	C11	116
C5	C7	C9	128	C9	C11	C10	95

Torsion Angles					
C6	C4	C5	C7	9	
C5	C4	C6	C8	9	
C4	C5	C7	C9	−25	
C4	C6	C8	C10	25	
C5	C7	C9	C11	−54	
C6	C8	C10	C11	−16	
C7	C9	C11	C10	133	
C8	C10	C11	C9	−71	

75.12   π - Cyclopentadienyl - π - cycloheptatrienyl vanadium $C_{12}H_{12}V$

G.R.Engebretson, R.E.Rundle, J. Amer. Chem. Soc., 85, 481, 1963

Atomic coordinates were not reported in the paper.
Pnma   Z = 4   R = 0.19

CPLHLV   LB 12-12-38

75.13   Cyclo - octatetraene bis(tricarbonyl iron) $C_{14}H_8Fe_2O_6$

B.Dickens, W.N.Lipscomb, J. Chem. Phys., 37, 2084, 1962

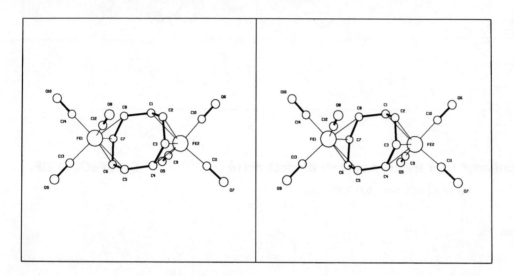

$(CO)_3Fe \cdots\cdots Fe(CO)_3$

$P2_1/n$ Z = 4   R = 0.10

OTFECO   LB 14-8-19

Bond Lengths

Fe1	C5	2.15	Fe2	C1	2.14	C9	O5	1.14	C1	C8	1.48
Fe1	C6	2.04	Fe2	C2	2.09	C10	O6	1.16	C2	C3	1.40
Fe1	C7	2.03	Fe2	C3	2.06	C11	O7	1.16	C3	C4	1.40
Fe1	C8	2.17	Fe2	C4	2.12	C12	O8	1.20	C4	C5	1.51
Fe1	C12	1.73	Fe2	C9	1.77	C13	O9	1.13	C5	C6	1.44
Fe1	C13	1.81	Fe2	C10	1.77	C14	O10	1.13	C6	C7	1.41
Fe1	C14	1.77	Fe2	C11	1.76	C1	C2	1.43	C7	C8	1.47

Bond Angles

C2	C1	C8	130	C4	C5	C6	133
C1	C2	C3	121	C5	C6	C7	118
C2	C3	C4	119	C6	C7	C8	123
C3	C4	C5	130	C1	C8	C7	127

75.14   trans - Dichloro(ethylenediamine)(cyclododeca - 1,5 - dienyl) rhodium(iii) $C_{14}H_{27}Cl_2N_2Rh$

G.Paiaro, A.Musco, G.Diana, J. Organometal. Chem., 4, 466, 1965

Atomic coordinates were not reported in the paper.
Pbc2₁   Z = 4   No R factor was given.

CECYRH   LB 14-27-4

75.15   Cyclo - octa - 1,5 - diene copper(i) - μ - dichloro - cyclo - octa - 1,5 - diene copper(i) $C_{16}H_{24}Cl_2Cu_2$

J.H.van den Hende, W.C.Baird, J. Amer. Chem. Soc., 85, 1009, 1963

Atomic coordinates were not given but bond lengths were reported.
P-1   Z = 2   R = 0.13

CUCLOC   LB 8-12-9

75.16 Cyclo - octa - 1,5 - diene rhodium(i) - μ - dichloro - cyclo - octa - 1,5 - diene rhodium(i)

$C_{16}H_{24}Cl_2Rh_2$

J.A.Ibers, R.G.Snyder, Acta Cryst., 15, 923, 1962

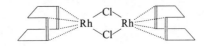

$P2_1/n$ $Z = 4$ $R = 0.10$

RHCOCT   LB 16-24-6

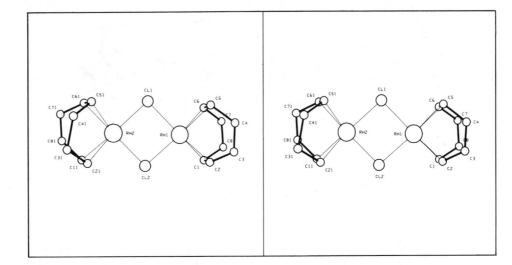

Bond Lengths

Rh1	Cl1	2.37	C2	C3	1.55
Rh1	Cl2	2.38	C3	C4	1.43
Rh1	C1	2.10	C4	C5	1.59
Rh1	C2	2.07	C5	C6	1.42
Rh1	C5	2.18	C6	C7	1.63
Rh1	C6	2.09	C7	C8	1.38
Rh2	Cl1	2.39	C11	C21	1.35
Rh2	Cl2	2.38	C11	C81	1.49
Rh2	C11	2.14	C21	C31	1.62
Rh2	C21	2.12	C31	C41	1.61
Rh2	C51	2.15	C41	C51	1.59
Rh2	C61	2.14	C51	C61	1.44
C1	C2	1.51	C61	C71	1.50
C1	C8	1.48	C71	C81	1.36

Bond Angles

C2	C1	C8	117	C4	C5	C6	118	C21	C11	C81	122	C41	C51	C61	123
C1	C2	C3	132	C5	C6	C7	125	C11	C21	C31	120	C51	C61	C71	131
C2	C3	C4	105	C6	C7	C8	111	C21	C31	C41	113	C61	C71	C81	106
C3	C4	C5	126	C1	C8	C7	118	C31	C41	C51	116	C11	C81	C71	134

75.17 1,2,3,4 - Tetramethyl cyclobutadiene nickel(ii) - μ - dichloro - 1,2,3,4 - tetramethyl - cyclobutadiene nickel(ii) benzene solvate

$C_{16}H_{24}Cl_4Ni_2$, C_6H_6

J.D.Dunitz, H.C.Mez, O.S.Mills, H.M.M.Shearer, Helv. Chim. Acta, 45, 647, 1962

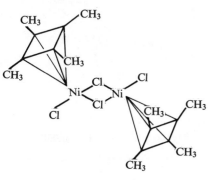

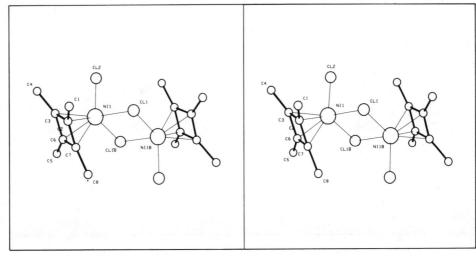

The benzene solvent of crystalliza-
tion is disordered.
$P2_1/c$ $Z = 2$ $R = 0.07$

NCBNIB   LB 8-12-18

Bond Lengths

Ni1	Cl1	2.34	Ni1	C6	2.01	C3	C4	1.52
Ni1	Cl2	2.26	Ni1	C7	2.00	C3	C6	1.45
Ni1	Cl1B	2.35	C1	C2	1.49	C5	C6	1.51
Ni1	C2	2.03	C2	C3	1.40	C6	C7	1.45
Ni1	C3	2.05	C2	C7	1.41	C7	C8	1.50

75.18 bis(Cyclo - octa - 1,5 - diene) nickel(0)

$C_{16}H_{24}Ni$

H.Dierks, H.Dietrich, Z. Kristallogr., 122, 1, 1965

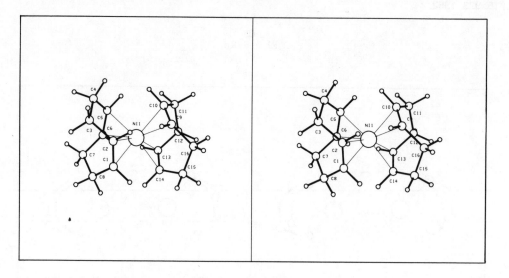

P-1   Z = 2   R = 0.102

OCDINI   LB 16-24-13

Bond Lengths

Ni1	C1	2.12	C4	C5	1.49
Ni1	C2	2.14	C5	C6	1.38
Ni1	C5	2.12	C6	C7	1.51
Ni1	C6	2.13	C7	C8	1.55
Ni1	C9	2.12	C9	C10	1.39
Ni1	C10	2.12	C9	C16	1.52
Ni1	C13	2.13	C10	C11	1.49
Ni1	C14	2.11	C11	C12	1.55
C1	C2	1.38	C12	C13	1.49
C1	C8	1.50	C13	C14	1.39
C2	C3	1.52	C14	C15	1.50
C3	C4	1.54	C15	C16	1.54

Bond Angles

C2	C1	C8	126	C10	C9	C16	125
C1	C2	C3	125	C9	C10	C11	126
C2	C3	C4	112	C10	C11	C12	113
C3	C4	C5	114	C11	C12	C13	112
C4	C5	C6	126	C12	C13	C14	125
C5	C6	C7	125	C13	C14	C15	124
C6	C7	C8	113	C14	C15	C16	114
C1	C8	C7	114	C9	C16	C15	113

Torsion Angles

C8	C1	C2	C3	3	C16	C9	C10	C11	4
C2	C1	C8	C7	44	C10	C9	C16	C15	−91
C1	C2	C3	C4	−93	C9	C10	C11	C12	41
C2	C3	C4	C5	33	C10	C11	C12	C13	36
C3	C4	C5	C6	44	C11	C12	C13	C14	−97
C4	C5	C6	C7	3	C12	C13	C14	C15	4
C5	C6	C7	C8	−92	C13	C14	C15	C16	45
C6	C7	C8	C1	32	C14	C15	C16	C9	31

75.19 π - Cyclopentadienyl - 1,2,3,4 - tetramethyl - 1 - exo - cyclopenta - 1′,3′ - dienecyclobutenyl nickel(ii)

$C_{18}H_{22}Ni$

W.Oberhansli, L.F.Dahl, Inorg. Chem., 4, 150, 1965

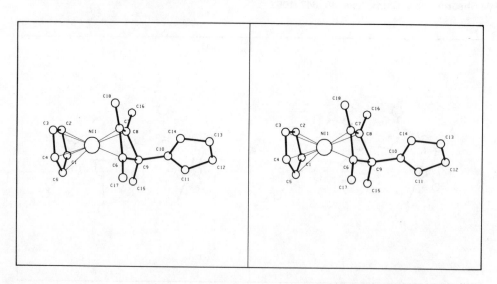

P2₁2₁2₁   Z = 4   R = 0.078

CTCDNI   LB 18-22-17

Bond Lengths

Ni1	C1	2.13	C1	C5	1.40	C8	C9	1.58
Ni1	C2	2.15	C2	C3	1.39	C8	C16	1.51
Ni1	C3	2.17	C3	C4	1.42	C9	C10	1.56
Ni1	C4	2.10	C4	C5	1.41	C9	C15	1.50
Ni1	C5	2.11	C6	C7	1.44	C10	C11	1.34
Ni1	C6	2.00	C6	C9	1.55	C10	C14	1.41
Ni1	C7	1.89	C6	C17	1.52	C11	C12	1.54
Ni1	C8	1.98	C7	C8	1.44	C12	C13	1.41
C1	C2	1.41	C7	C18	1.49	C13	C14	1.49

Bond Angles

C7	C6	C9	93	C9	C8	C16	128
C7	C6	C17	132	C6	C9	C8	80
C9	C6	C17	129	C6	C9	C10	111
C6	C7	C8	89	C6	C9	C15	120
C6	C7	C18	137	C8	C9	C10	108
C8	C7	C18	134	C8	C9	C15	120
C7	C8	C9	92	C10	C9	C15	113
C7	C8	C16	133				

75.20   Cyclo - octadiene duroquinone nickel(0) $C_{18}H_{24}NiO_2$

M.D.Glick, L.F.Dahl, J. Organometal. Chem., 3, 200, 1965

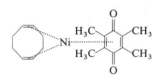

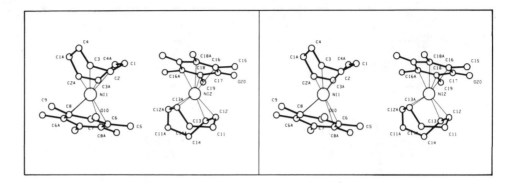

P2/n   Z = 4   R = 0.101

OCDUNI   LB 18-24-18

Bond Lengths

Ni1	C2	2.10	C6	C7	1.47	C11	C12	1.51
Ni1	C3	2.12	C6	C8A	1.41	C11	C14A	1.58
Ni1	C6	2.24	C7	C8	1.47	C12	C13	1.33
Ni1	C8	2.21	C8	C9	1.52	C13	C14	1.54
C7	O10	1.23				C15	C16	1.53
C1	C2	1.51	Ni2	C12	2.08	C16	C17	1.45
C1	C4A	1.56	Ni2	C13	2.12	C16	C18A	1.39
C2	C3	1.33	Ni2	C16	2.22	C17	C18	1.44
C3	C4	1.51	Ni2	C18	2.22	C18	C19	1.55
C5	C6	1.49	C17	O20	1.24			

Bond Angles

C2	C1	C4A	114	C6	C7	C8	118	C15	C16	C17	118
C1	C2	C3	129	C7	C8	C9	117	C15	C16	C18A	121
C2	C3	C4	123	C7	C8	C6A	122	C17	C16	C18A	121
C3	C4	C1A	116	C9	C8	C6A	121	O20	C17	C16	121
C5	C6	C7	118					O20	C17	C18	122
C5	C6	C8A	123	C12	C11	C14A	112	C16	C17	C18	117
C7	C6	C8A	119	C11	C12	C13	130	C17	C18	C19	116
O10	C7	C6	121	C12	C13	C14	119	C17	C18	C16A	122
O10	C7	C8	121	C13	C14	C11A	116	C19	C18	C16A	122

75.21   2,4,6 - Triphenyltropone iron tricarbonyl $C_{28}H_{18}FeO_4$

D.L.Smith, L.F.Dahl, J. Amer. Chem. Soc., 84, 1743, 1962

Atomic coordinates were not given
but bond lengths were reported.
$P2_12_12_1$ Z = 4   R = 0.09

TPTFEC   LB 28-18-2

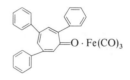

75.22   Norbornadiene chloro copper(i) tetramer $C_{28}H_{32}Cl_4Cu_4$

N.C.Baenziger, H.L.Haight, J.R.Doyle, Inorg. Chem., 3, 1535, 1964

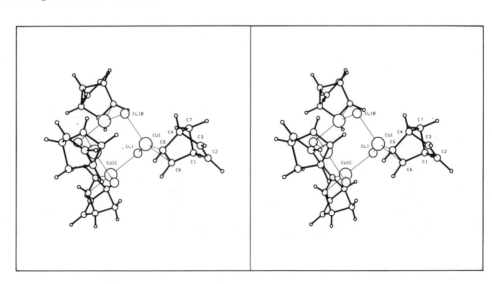

P-42₁c   Z = 2   R = 0.06

NOBCUC   LB 7-8-4

Bond Lengths

Cu1	Cl1	2.27	C1	C7	1.53
Cu1	Cl1B	2.30	C2	C3	1.32
Cu1	C5	2.05	C3	C4	1.58
Cu1	C6	2.11	C4	C5	1.52
C1	C2	1.54	C4	C7	1.53
C1	C6	1.52	C5	C6	1.34

Bond Angles

C2	C1	C6	103	C3	C4	C7	98
C2	C1	C7	99	C5	C4	C7	101
C6	C1	C7	100	C4	C5	C6	106
C1	C2	C3	108	C1	C6	C5	108
C2	C3	C4	105	C1	C7	C4	93
C3	C4	C5	104				

75.23   Tetraphenylcyclobutadiene iron tricarbonyl

R.P.Dodge, V.Schomaker, Acta Cryst., 18, 614, 1965

$C_{31}H_{20}FeO_3$

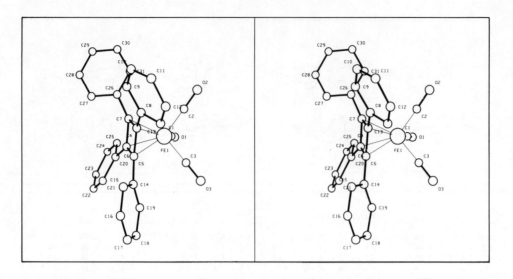

$P2_1/c$ Z = 4   R = 0.14

PCYFCO   LB 31-20-1

Bond Lengths

Fe1	C1	1.74	Fe1	C7	2.05	C4	C8	1.45	C8	C9	1.40
Fe1	C2	1.75	C1	O1	1.19	C5	C6	1.44	C8	C13	1.43
Fe1	C3	1.76	C2	O2	1.17	C5	C14	1.49	C9	C10	1.41
Fe1	C4	2.05	C3	O3	1.17	C6	C7	1.47	C10	C11	1.46
Fe1	C5	2.09	C4	C5	1.45	C6	C20	1.46	C11	C12	1.39
Fe1	C6	2.07	C4	C7	1.47	C7	C26	1.47	C12	C13	1.42

C14	C15	1.41	C20	C21	1.43
C14	C19	1.40	C20	C25	1.38
C15	C16	1.40	C21	C22	1.37
C16	C17	1.40	C22	C23	1.36
C17	C18	1.35	C23	C24	1.44
C18	C19	1.44	C24	C25	1.43

C26	C27	1.40
C26	C31	1.38
C27	C28	1.43
C28	C29	1.40
C29	C30	1.38
C30	C31	1.42

75.24   endo - 1 - Ethoxy - 1,2,3,4 - tetraphenylcyclobutenyl chloro palladium dimer

L.F.Dahl, W.E.Oberhansli, Inorg. Chem., 4, 629, 1965

$C_{60}H_{50}Cl_2O_2Pd_2$

$P2_1/c$ Z = 2   R = 0.112

NEPBPD   LB 60-50-1

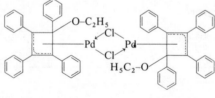

Bond Lengths

Pd1	Cl1	2.43	C9	C10	1.40
Pd1	Cl1B	2.42	C11	C12	1.38
Pd1	C2	2.18	C11	C16	1.46
Pd1	C3	2.09	C12	C13	1.43
Pd1	C4	2.11	C13	C14	1.40
C1	O1	1.39	C14	C15	1.36
C29	O1	1.41	C15	C16	1.26
C1	C2	1.58	C17	C18	1.41
C1	C4	1.54	C17	C22	1.43
C1	C5	1.51	C18	C19	1.36
C2	C3	1.44	C19	C20	1.44
C2	C11	1.47	C20	C21	1.38
C3	C4	1.46	C21	C22	1.40
C3	C17	1.47	C23	C24	1.39
C4	C23	1.46	C23	C28	1.36
C5	C6	1.34	C24	C25	1.42
C5	C10	1.42	C25	C26	1.30
C6	C7	1.58	C26	C27	1.27
C7	C8	1.26	C27	C28	1.37
C8	C9	1.26	C29	C30	1.50

Bond Angles

O1	C1	C2	119	C4	C1	C5	113	C2	C3	C17	135
O1	C1	C4	115	C1	C2	C3	91	C4	C3	C17	134
O1	C1	C5	110	C1	C2	C11	133	C1	C4	C3	92
C2	C1	C4	82	C3	C2	C11	133	C1	C4	C23	130
C2	C1	C5	116	C2	C3	C4	91	C3	C4	C23	134

Torsion Angles

C1	C2	C3	C4	− 16
C2	C3	C4	C1	17
C3	C4	C1	C2	−15
C4	C1	C2	C3	15

75.25   exo - 1 - Ethoxy - 1,2,3,4 - tetraphenylcyclobutenyl chloro palladium dimer

$C_{60}H_{50}Cl_2O_2Pd_2$

L.F.Dahl, W.E.Oberhansli, Inorg. Chem., 4, 629, 1965

Published values of y(C3) = 0.2845
and y(C27) = 0.2887 are incorrect.
The correct values are −0.2845 and
−0.2887 respectively.
$P2_1/n$ Z = 2   R = 0.127

XEPBPD   LB 60-50-2

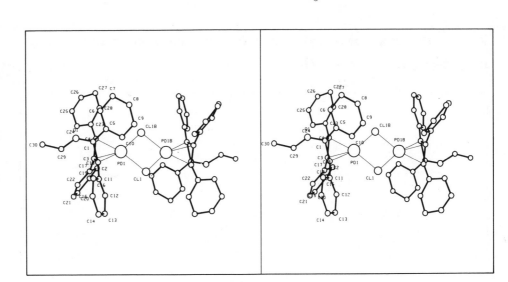

Bond Lengths

Pd1	Cl1	2.43	C9	C10	1.49
Pd1	Cl1B	2.41	C11	C12	1.36
Pd1	C2	2.18	C11	C16	1.36
Pd1	C3	2.14	C12	C13	1.45
Pd1	C4	2.12	C13	C14	1.37
C1	O1	1.38	C14	C15	1.42
C29	O1	1.48	C15	C16	1.42
C1	C2	1.56	C17	C18	1.35
C1	C4	1.56	C17	C22	1.39
C1	C5	1.55	C18	C19	1.54
C2	C3	1.47	C19	C20	1.54
C2	C11	1.44	C20	C21	1.20
C3	C4	1.48	C21	C22	1.39
C3	C17	1.47	C23	C24	1.37
C4	C23	1.45	C23	C28	1.37
C5	C6	1.33	C24	C25	1.50
C5	C10	1.39	C25	C26	1.25
C6	C7	1.53	C26	C27	1.42
C7	C8	1.41	C27	C28	1.46
C8	C9	1.35	C29	C30	1.56

Bond Angles

O1	C1	C2	117	C4	C1	C5	114	C2	C3	C17	130
O1	C1	C4	118	C1	C2	C3	90	C4	C3	C17	139
O1	C1	C5	103	C1	C2	C11	130	C1	C4	C3	89
C2	C1	C4	84	C3	C2	C11	137	C1	C4	C23	133
C2	C1	C5	121	C2	C3	C4	91	C3	C4	C23	128

Torsion Angles

C29	O1	C1	C2	−43	C2	C3	C4	C1	−19
C29	O1	C1	C4	55	C3	C4	C1	C2	18
C29	O1	C1	C5	−178	C4	C1	C2	C3	−18
C1	C2	C3	C4	19				

76.1 Diperoxoaquoethylenediamine chromium(iv) monohydrate $C_2H_{10}CrN_2O_5$, H_2O

R.Stomberg, Ark. Kemi, 24, 47, 1965

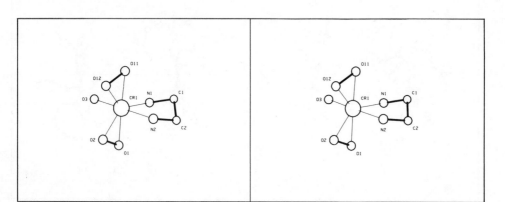

Pbc2$_1$ Z = 4   R = 0.115

OETDCR   LB 2-10-10

Bond Angles

N1	Cr1	N2	82	N2	Cr1	O12	92	O11 Cr1 O12	47
N1	Cr1	O1	88	O1	Cr1	O2	45	Cr1 N1 C1	108
N1	Cr1	O2	132	O1	Cr1	O3	88	Cr1 N2 C2	111
N1	Cr1	O3	92	O1	Cr1	O11	175	Cr1 O1 O2	65
N1	Cr1	O11	87	O1	Cr1	O12	137	Cr1 O2 O1	71
N1	Cr1	O12	134	O2	Cr1	O3	93	Cr1 O11 O12	65
N2	Cr1	O1	90	O2	Cr1	O11	140	Cr1 O12 O11	68
N2	Cr1	O2	90	O2	Cr1	O12	93	N1 C1 C2	108
N2	Cr1	O3	173	O3	Cr1	O11	91	N2 C2 C1	109
N2	Cr1	O11	91	O3	Cr1	O12	94		

Bond Lengths

Cr1	N1	2.08	Cr1	O12	1.84
Cr1	N2	2.05	O1	O2	1.46
Cr1	O1	1.95	O11	O12	1.48
Cr1	O2	1.87	C1	N1	1.45
Cr1	O3	2.03	C2	N2	1.44
Cr1	O11	1.87	C1	C2	1.53

Torsion Angles

N1	C1	C2	N2	−52

76.2 Trioxo(diethylenetriamine) molybdenum(vi) $C_4H_{13}MoN_3O_3$

F.A.Cotton, R.C.Elder, Inorg. Chem., 3, 397, 1964

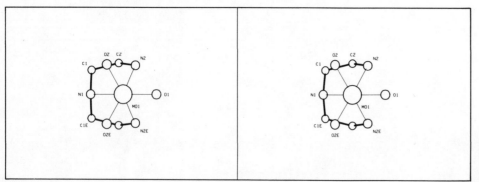

The published Mo1 - O2 bond length is incorrect.
Pbcm   Z = 4   R = 0.06

ODEAMO   LB 4-13-5

Bond Lengths

Mo1	N1	2.33	C1	N1	1.46
Mo1	N2	2.29	C2	N2	1.49
Mo1	O1	1.74	C1	C2	1.55
Mo1	O2	1.75			

Bond Angles

N1	Mo1	N2	73	N2	Mo1	O2	86	Mo1 N1 C1	111
N1	Mo1	O1	155	N2	Mo1	O2E	158	C1 N1 C1E	115
N1	Mo1	O2	88	O1	Mo1	O2	107	Mo1 N2 C2	119
N2	Mo1	N2E	78	O2	Mo1	N2E	158	N1 C1 C2	112
N2	Mo1	O1	88	O2	Mo1	O2E	105	N2 C2 C1	107

Torsion Angles

C1E	N1	C1	C2	−82
N1	C1	C2	N2	−45

76.3   bis(Ethylenediamine) chloro nickel(ii) chloride $C_4H_{16}ClN_4Ni^+$, Cl^-

A.S.Antsyshkina, M.A.Porai-Koshits, Dokl. Akad. Nauk S. S. S. R., 143, 105, 1962

Atomic coordinates were not
reported in the paper.
$P2_1/n$ Z = 4   No R factor was
given.

NIETDC

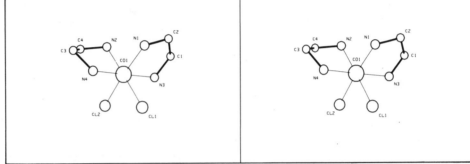

76.4   ($\pm$)cis - Dichloro - bis(ethylenediamine) cobalt(iii) chloride monohydrate $C_4H_{16}Cl_2CoN_4^+$, Cl^- , H_2O

A.Hullen, K.Plieth, G.Ruban, Naturwissenschaften, 52, 618, 1965

No comparison of bond lengths is
possible since they are not reported
in the paper.
See also Matsumoto et al., J. Chem.
Soc. Jap., Pure Chem. Sect., 89, 167,
1968.
$P2_1/c$ Z = 4 $R_{h0l} = 0.116$,
$R_{hk0} = 0.17$, $R_{hk1} = 0.215$

CLECOC   LB 4-16-48

Bond Lengths					Bond Angles										Torsion Angles				
Co1	Cl1	2.26	C2	N1	1.43	Cl1	Co1	Cl2	90	Cl2	Co1	N2	89	N2	Co1	N3	91	Co1	N4	C3	107	N3 C1 C2 N1	−4
Co1	Cl2	2.22	C4	N2	1.45	Cl1	Co1	N1	87	Cl2	Co1	N3	87	N2	Co1	N4	90	N3	C1	C2	130	N4 C3 C4 N2	−44
Co1	N1	2.03	C1	N3	1.45	Cl1	Co1	N2	178	Cl2	Co1	N4	94	N3	Co1	N4	178	N1	C2	C1	110		
Co1	N2	2.02	C3	N4	1.54	Cl1	Co1	N3	91	N1	Co1	N2	94	Co1	N1	C2	112	N4	C3	C4	108		
Co1	N3	2.14	C1	C2	1.52	Cl1	Co1	N4	88	N1	Co1	N3	90	Co1	N2	C4	100	N2	C4	C3	120		
Co1	N4	2.02	C3	C4	1.48	Cl2	Co1	N1	175	N1	Co1	N4	89	Co1	N3	C1	98						

76.5   trans - Dichloro - bis(ethylenediamine) cobalt(iii) nitrate $C_4H_{16}Cl_2CoN_4^+$, NO_3^-

S.Ooi, H.Kuroya, Bull. Chem. Soc. Jap., 36, 1083, 1963

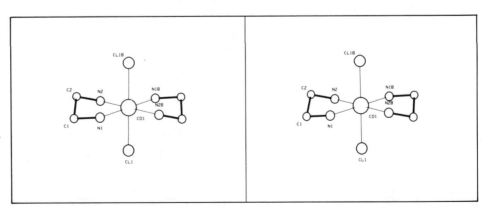

The nitrate ion is disordered.
$P2_1/c$ Z = 2 $R_{0kl} = 0.16$,
$R_{h0l} = 0.15$

CHECON   LB 4-16-31

Bond Lengths			Bond Angles											Torsion Angles	
Co1	Cl1	2.26	Cl1	Co1	Cl1B	180	N1	Co1	Cl1B	91	Co1	N1	C1	113	N1 C1 C2 N2	49
Co1	N1	1.97	Cl1	Co1	N1	89	N1	Co1	N2	86	Co1	N2	C2	107	
Co1	N2	2.00	CJ1	Co1	N2	88	N1	Co1	N1B	180	N1	C1	C2	105	
C1	N1	1.46	Cl1	Co1	N1B	91	N1	Co1	N2B	94	N2	C2	C1	110	
C2	N2	1.46	Cl1	Co1	N2B	92	N2	Co1	N2B	180					
C1	C2	1.59													

76.6 trans - Dichloro - bis(ethylenediamine) cobalt(iii) hexathionate monohydrate

$2C_4H_{16}Cl_2CoN_4^+$, $O_6S_6^{2-}$, H_2O

O.Foss, K.Maroy, Acta Chem. Scand., 19, 2219, 1965

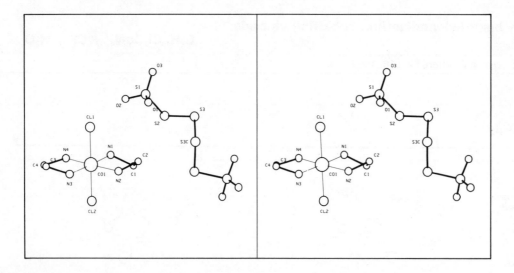

Pba2   Z = 2   R = 0.085

CETDCH   LB 8-32-3

Bond Lengths

S1	S2	2.12
S1	O1	1.44
S1	O2	1.43
S1	O3	1.43
S2	S3	2.03
S3	S3C	2.05
Co1	Cl1	2.22
Co1	Cl2	2.24
Co1	N1	1.95
Co1	N2	1.98
Co1	N3	1.98
Co1	N4	1.93
C1	N1	1.57
C2	N2	1.46
C3	N3	1.49
C4	N4	1.49
C1	C2	1.57
C3	C4	1.54

Bond Angles

S2	S1	O1	106	Cl1	Co1	Cl2	180	Cl2	Co1	N4	91
S2	S1	O2	98	Cl1	Co1	N1	89	N1	Co1	N2	86
S2	S1	O3	106	Cl1	Co1	N2	91	N1	Co1	N3	179
O1	S1	O2	116	Cl1	Co1	N3	90	N1	Co1	N4	93
O1	S1	O3	118	Cl1	Co1	N4	89	N2	Co1	N3	94
O2	S1	O3	110	Cl2	Co1	N1	92	N2	Co1	N4	178
S1	S2	S3	106	Cl2	Co1	N2	89	N3	Co1	N4	87
S2	S3	S3C	107	Cl2	Co1	N3	89	Co1	N1	C1	108

Co1	N2	C2	111
Co1	N3	C3	109
Co1	N4	C4	114
N1	C1	C2	102
N2	C2	C1	106
N3	C3	C4	112
N4	C4	C3	108

Torsion Angles

O1	S1	S2	S3	−51
O2	S1	S2	S3	−171
O3	S1	S2	S3	75
S1	S2	S3	S3C	85
S2	S3	S3C	S2C	73
N1	C1	C2	N2	54
N3	C3	C4	N4	−34

76.7 trans - Dichloro - bis(ethylenediamine) chromium(iii) chloride hydrochloride dihydrate

$C_4H_{16}Cl_2CrN_4^+$, $2Cl^-$, $H_5O_2^+$

S.Ooi, Y.Komiyama, H.Kuroya, Bull. Chem. Soc. Jap., 33, 354, 1960

$P2_1/c$ Z = 2 $R_{hk0} = 0.131$, $R_{h0l} = 0.121$

CEDCRC

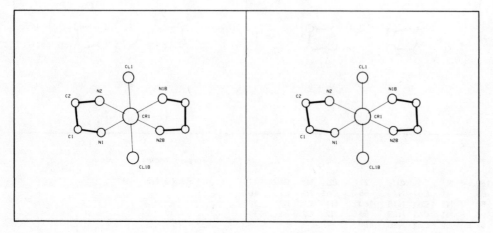

Bond Lengths			**Bond Angles**			
Cr1	Cl1	2.33	Cl1	Cr1	Cl1B	180
Cr1	N1	2.11	Cl1	Cr1	N1	91
Cr1	N2	2.13	Cl1	Cr1	N2	90
C1	N1	1.44	Cl1	Cr1	N1B	89
C2	N2	1.49	Cl1	Cr1	N2B	90
C1	C2	1.57	N1	Cr1	Cl1B	89
			N1	Cr1	N2	85
			N1	Cr1	N1B	180
			N1	Cr1	N2B	95
			N2	Cr1	Cl1B	90
			N2	Cr1	N1B	95
			N2	Cr1	N2B	180
			Cr1	N1	C1	106
			Cr1	N2	C2	108
			N1	C1	C2	117
			N2	C2	C1	107

Torsion Angles

N1	C1	C2	N2	−49

76.8   Copper(ii) bis(ethylenediamine) nitrate $C_4H_{16}CuN_4^{2+}$, $2NO_3^-$

Y.Komiyama, E.C.Lingafelter, Acta Cryst., 17, 1145, 1964

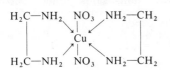

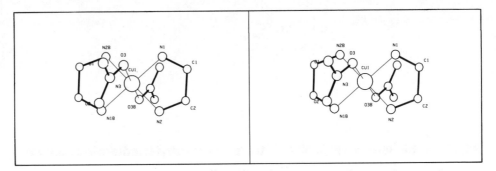

$P2_1/c$ Z = 2   R = 0.10

COPDEN   LB 4-16-63

Bond Lengths

Cu1	N1	2.04	N3	O3	1.26
Cu1	N2	2.01	C1	N1	1.49
Cu1	O3	2.59	C2	N2	1.48
N3	O1	1.25	C1	C2	1.54
N3	O2	1.27			

Bond Angles

N1	Cu1	N2	86	N2	Cu1	N2B	180	O1	N3	O2	120
N1	Cu1	N1B	180	N2	Cu1	O3	92	O1	N3	O3	119
N1	Cu1	N2B	94	N2	Cu1	O3B	88	O2	N3	O3	120
N1	Cu1	O3	88	O3	Cu1	O3B	180	Cu1	O3	N3	127
N1	Cu1	O3B	92	Cu1	N1	C1	109	N1	C1	C2	110
N2	Cu1	N1B	94	Cu1	N2	C2	109	N2	C2	C1	111

Torsion Angles

N1 C1 C2 N2   −45

76.9   bis(Ethylenediamine) copper(ii) thiocyanate $C_4H_{16}CuN_4^{2+}$, $2CNS^-$

B.W.Brown, E.C.Lingafelter, Acta Cryst., 17, 254, 1964

The sulphur atom of the thiocyanate group is 3.27A from the copper atom.
P-1   Z = 1   R = 0.08

EDCOPT   LB 6-16-19

$$\left[\begin{array}{c} H_2C-NH_2 \quad H_2N-CH_2 \\ Cu \\ H_2C-NH_2 \quad H_2N-CH_2 \end{array}\right]^{2+} (SCN^-)_2$$

Bond Lengths

Cu1	N2	2.01
Cu1	N3	1.99
C2	N2	1.49
C3	N3	1.45
C2	C3	1.56
S1	C1	1.62
C1	N1	1.16

Bond Angles

N2	Cu1	N3	85
N2	Cu1	N2A	180
N2	Cu1	N3A	95
N3	Cu1	N2A	95
N3	Cu1	N3A	180
Cu1	N2	C2	109
Cu1	N3	C3	111
N2	C2	C3	105
N3	C3	C2	110
S1	C1	N1	177

Torsion Angles

N2 C2 C3 N3   50

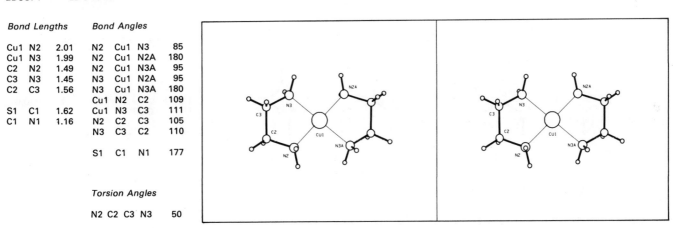

76.10   Nitrito - bis(ethylenediamine) nickel(ii) tetrafluoroborate $C_4H_{16}N_5NiO_2+$, BF_4^-

M.G.B.Drew, D.M.L.Goodgame, M.A.Hitchman, D.Rogers, Chem. Communic., 477, 1965

The nitrate and fluoroborate groups are disordered.
Pnma   Z = 4   R = 0.14

NIDENT   LB 4-16-4

$$\left[\begin{array}{c} CH_2-NH_2 \quad NO_2 \quad H_2N-CH_2 \\ Ni \\ CH_2-NH_2 \quad H_2N-CH_2 \end{array}\right]^+ [BF_4]^-$$

76.11   Nitrito bis (ethylene diamine) nickel (ii) perchlorate

$C_4H_{16}N_5NiO_2^+$, ClO_4^-

F.J.Llewellyn, J.M.Waters, J. Chem. Soc., 3845, 1962

$$\left[\begin{array}{c} CH_2-NH_2 \quad\quad NH_2-CH_2 \\ \quad\quad\quad Ni \\ CH_2-NH_2 \quad\quad NH_2-CH_2 \\ NO_2 \end{array}\right]^+ \cdot ClO_4^-$$

The structure was determined in two dimensions only. Atomic coordinates were not reported in the paper.

Pnma   Z = 4 $R_{h0l} = 0.17$,
$R_{hk0} = 0.22$

NETNIP   LB 4-16-24

76.12   bis(Nitrito) N,N,N',N', - tetramethyethylenediamine nickel(ii)

$C_6H_{16}N_4NiO_4$

M.G.B.Drew, D.Rogers, Chem. Communic., 476, 1965

$$\begin{array}{c} H_3C \quad\quad N \quad\quad CH_3 \\ O \quad\quad O \\ H_3C-N\rightarrow Ni\leftarrow N-CH_3 \\ O \quad\quad O \\ \quad\quad N \\ CH_2-CH_2 \end{array}$$

Atomic coordinates were not given but bond lengths were reported.

P2₁/n   Z = 4   R = 0.115

NITMNI   LB 6-16-27

76.13   trans - bis(Ethylenediamine) bis(isothiocyanato) nickel(ii)

$C_6H_{16}N_6NiS_2$

B.W.Brown, E.C.Lingafelter, Acta Cryst., 16, 753, 1963

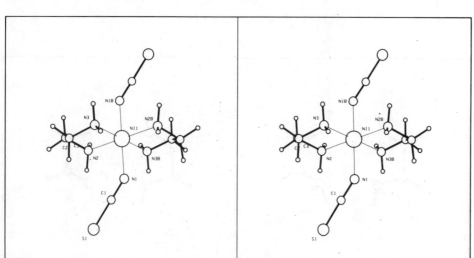

$$\begin{array}{c} H_2C-NH_2 \searrow \underset{NCS}{\downarrow} \swarrow H_2N-CH_2 \\ Ni \\ H_2C-NH_2 \nearrow \underset{NCS}{\uparrow} \nwarrow H_2N-CH_2 \end{array}$$

P2₁/a   Z = 2 $R_{0kl} = 0.07$,
$R_{hk0} = 0.07$

EDITCN   LB 6-16-28

Bond Lengths			Bond Angles												Torsion Angles			
Ni1	N1	2.15	N1	Ni1	N2	90	N2	Ni1	N1B	90	Ni1	N1	C1	140	N2	C2	C3	N3	53
Ni1	N2	2.09	N1	Ni1	N3	89	N2	Ni1	N2B	180	Ni1	N2	C2	110				
Ni1	N3	2.11	N1	Ni1	N1B	180	N2	Ni1	N3B	98	Ni1	N3	C3	107				
S1	C1	1.64	N1	Ni1	N2B	90	N3	Ni1	N1B	91	S1	C1	N1	178				
C1	N1	1.20	N1	Ni1	N3B	91	N3	Ni1	N2B	98	N2	C2	C3	106				
C2	N2	1.50	N2	Ni1	N3	82	N3	Ni1	N3B	180	N3	C3	C2	112				
C3	N3	1.46																
C2	C3	1.50																

76.14 trans - Dichloro - bis - l - propylenediamine cobalt(iii) chloride hydrochloride dihydrate

$C_6H_{20}Cl_2CoN_4^+$, $2Cl^-$, $H_5O_2^+$

Y.Saito, H.Iwasaki, Bull. Chem. Soc. Jap., 35, 1131, 1962

C2   Z = 4 R_{h0l} = 0.14,
R_{hk0} = 0.15

CPRCOC   LB 6-21-5

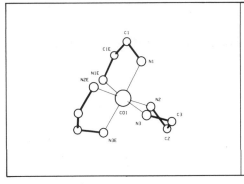
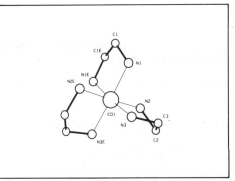

Bond Lengths

Co1	Cl3	2.28	C2	N2	1.45
Co1	Cl4	2.29	C4	N3	1.50
Co1	N1	1.99	C5	N4	1.45
Co1	N2	1.97	C1	C2	1.50
Co1	N3	2.02	C2	C3	1.54
Co1	N4	1.94	C4	C5	1.45
C1	N1	1.45	C5	C6	1.53

Bond Angles

Cl3	Co1	Cl4	179	N1	Co1	N2	88	Co1	N4	C5	102
Cl3	Co1	N1	91	N1	Co1	N3	178	N1	C1	C2	108
Cl3	Co1	N2	90	N1	Co1	N4	91	N2	C2	C1	113
Cl3	Co1	N3	91	N2	Co1	N3	92	N2	C2	C3	110
Cl3	Co1	N4	89	N2	Co1	N4	178	C1	C2	C3	109
Cl4	Co1	N1	89	N3	Co1	N4	89	N3	C4	C5	104
Cl4	Co1	N2	91	Co1	N1	C1	107	N4	C5	C4	112
Cl4	Co1	N3	89	Co1	N2	C2	106	N4	C5	C6	113
Cl4	Co1	N4	91	Co1	N3	C4	103	C4	C5	C6	112

Torsion Angles

N1	C1	C2	N2	−46
N1	C1	C2	C3	−170
N3	C4	C5	N4	−63
N3	C4	C5	C6	169

76.15 D - tris(Ethylenediamine) cobalt(iii) bromide monohydrate

$C_6H_{24}CoN_6^{3+}$, $3Br^-$, H_2O

K.Nakatsu, Bull. Chem. Soc. Jap., 35, 832, 1962

$P4_32_12$ Z = 4 R_{hk0} = 0.13,
R_{0kl} = 0.15

EDCOBR   LB 6-24-4

Bond Lengths

Co1	N1	2.03
Co1	N2	1.98
Co1	N3	2.00
C1	N1	1.44
C2	N2	1.50
C3	N3	1.49
C1	C1E	1.54
C2	C3	1.54

Bond Angles

N1	Co1	N2	87	N2	Co1	N1E	91	Co1	N1	C1	109
N1	Co1	N3	90	N2	Co1	N2E	177	Co1	N2	C2	109
N1	Co1	N1E	86	N2	Co1	N3E	94	Co1	N3	C3	105
N1	Co1	N2E	91	N3	Co1	N1E	176	N1	C1	C1E	111
N1	Co1	N3E	176	N3	Co1	N2E	94	N2	C2	C3	103
N2	Co1	N3	88	N3	Co1	N3E	94	N3	C3	C2	115

Torsion Angles

N1	C1	C1E	N1E	43
N2	C2	C3	N3	51

76.16   tris(Ethylenediamine) nickel(ii) nitrate

$C_6H_{24}N_6Ni^{2+}$, $2NO_3^-$

L.N.Swink, M.Atoji, Acta Cryst., 13, 639, 1960

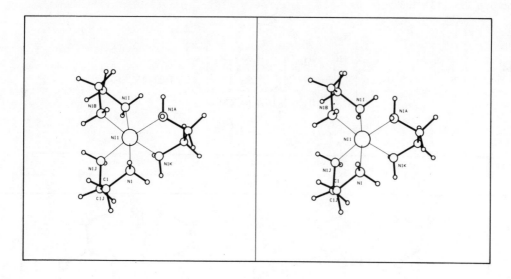

$$\left[\left(\begin{array}{c}H_2C-NH_2\\H_2C-NH_2\end{array}\right)_3 Ni\right]^{2+} \cdot 2NO_3^-$$

P6$_3$22   Z = 4   R = 0.08

TEANIN   LB 6-24-4

Bond Lengths

Ni1	N1	2.12		Ni1	N1K	2.12
Ni1	N1A	2.12		C1	N1	1.50
Ni1	N1B	2.12		C1	C1J	1.49
Ni1	N1J	2.12				

Bond Angles

N1	Ni1	N1A	93		N1	Ni1	N1K	91
N1	Ni1	N1B	93		Ni1	N1	C1	110
N1	Ni1	N1I	174		N1	C1	C1J	111
N1	Ni1	N1J	82				

Torsion Angles

N1	C1	C1J	N1J	−46

76.17   Dinitrito bis(N,N - dimethylethylenediamine) nickel(ii)

$C_8H_{24}N_6NiO_4$

M.G.B.Drew, D.M.L.Goodgame, M.A.Hitchman, D.Rogers, Proc. Chem. Soc., 363, 1964

Atomic coordinates were not given
but bond lengths were reported.
P2$_1$/c   Z = 2   R = 0.149

NMEDNI   LB 8-24-38

76.18   DL - tetrakis(Ethylenediamine) - μ - amido - μ - nitro dicobalt(iii) nitrate

$C_8H_{34}Co_2N_{10}O_2^{4+}$, $4NO_3^-$

C.E.Wilkes, Dissert. Abstr., 26, 2509, 1965

Atomic coordinates were not
reported in the paper.
The space group was not
reported.   Z = 2   R = 0.17

ETDMCO   LB 8-34-2

76.19 DL - tetrakis(Ethylenediamine) - μ - amido - μ - nitro dicobalt(iii) nitrate

$C_8H_{34}Co_2N_{10}O_2{}^{4+}$, $4NO_3{}^-$

P.Goldstein, Dissert. Abstr., 24, 2708, 1964

Atomic coordinates were not reported in the paper.
P2$_1$/n   Z = 4   R = 0.235

ETDMCO01   LB 8-34-2

$$\left[\left(\begin{array}{c} H_2C-NH_2 \\ | \\ H_2C-NH_2 \end{array} \right)_2 Co \underset{NH_2}{\overset{NO_2}{\diagup\diagdown}} Co \left(\begin{array}{c} H_2N-CH_2 \\ | \\ H_2N-CH_2 \end{array} \right)_2 \right]^{4+} (NO_3^-)_4$$

76.20 Lithium ethylenediaminetetra - acetato - aquo - ferrate(iii) dihydrate

$C_{10}H_{14}FeN_2O_9{}^-$, Li^+ , $2H_2O$

M.D.Lind, M.J.Hamor, T.A.Hamor, J.L.Hoard, Inorg. Chem., 3, 34, 1964

Pbca   Z = 8   R = 0.095

LIEDFE   LB 10-14-22

$$Li^+ \left[Fe^{3+}(OH_2) \left(\begin{array}{c} {}^-OOC-H_2C \\ {}^-OOC-H_2C \end{array} \diagdown N-CH_2-CH_2-N \diagup \begin{array}{c} CH_2-COO^- \\ CH_2-COO^- \end{array} \right) \right] 2H_2O$$

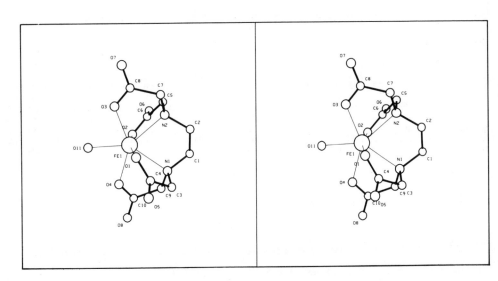

Bond Lengths

Fe1	N1	2.34	C4	O1	1.28
Fe1	N2	2.30	C6	O2	1.27
Fe1	O1	1.94	C8	O3	1.26
Fe1	O2	2.00	C10	O4	1.26
Fe1	O3	2.10	C4	O5	1.21
Fe1	O4	2.12	C6	O6	1.23
Fe1	O11	2.11	C8	O7	1.25
C1	N1	1.47	C10	O8	1.22
C3	N1	1.48	C1	C2	1.50
C9	N1	1.47	C3	C4	1.52
C2	N2	1.47	C5	C6	1.52
C5	N2	1.47	C7	C8	1.51
C7	N2	1.45	C9	C10	1.52

Bond Angles

N1	Fe1	N2	73	O1	Fe1	O11	101	Fe1	N2	C5	105	O5	C4	C3	118
N1	Fe1	O1	79	O2	Fe1	O3	96	Fe1	N2	C7	107	N2	C5	C6	115
N1	Fe1	O2	88	O2	Fe1	O4	90	C2	N2	C5	112	O2	C6	O6	123
N1	Fe1	O3	144	O2	Fe1	O11	94	C2	N2	C7	110	O2	C6	C5	117
N1	Fe1	O4	71	O3	Fe1	O4	145	C5	N2	C7	111	O6	C6	C5	120
N1	Fe1	O11	142	O3	Fe1	O11	74	Fe1	O1	C4	119	N2	C7	C8	109
N2	Fe1	O1	91	O4	Fe1	O11	71	Fe1	O2	C6	122	O3	C8	O7	124
N2	Fe1	O2	79	Fe1	N1	C1	112	Fe1	O3	C8	121	O3	C8	C7	116
N2	Fe1	O3	72	Fe1	N1	C3	103	Fe1	O4	C10	123	O7	C8	C7	120
N2	Fe1	O4	143	Fe1	N1	C9	107	N1	C1	C2	108	N1	C9	C10	109
N2	Fe1	O11	144	C1	N1	C3	112	N2	C2	C1	109	O4	C10	O8	126
O1	Fe1	O2	166	C1	N1	C9	111	N1	C3	C4	114	O4	C10	C9	116
O1	Fe1	O3	91	C3	N1	C9	111	O1	C4	O5	124	O8	C10	C9	119
O1	Fe1	O4	91	Fe1	N2	C2	112	O1	C4	C3	118				

Torsion Angles

C3	N1	C1	C2	−74	C5	N2	C7	C8	76
C9	N1	C1	C2	161	N1	C1	C2	N2	−57
C1	N1	C3	C4	119	N1	C3	C4	O1	−16
C9	N1	C3	C4	−116	N1	C3	C4	O5	167
C1	N1	C9	C10	−160	N2	C5	C6	O2	16
C3	N1	C9	C10	74	N2	C5	C6	O6	−165
C5	N2	C2	C1	−73	N2	C7	C8	O3	22
C7	N2	C2	C1	163	N2	C7	C8	O7	−159
C2	N2	C5	C6	102	N1	C9	C10	O4	20
C7	N2	C5	C6	−134	N1	C9	C10	O8	−158
C2	N2	C7	C8	−159				

76.21 Rubidium ethylenediaminetetra - acetato - aquo - ferrate(iii) monohydrate

M.D.Lind, J.L.Hoard, Inorg. Chem., 3, 34, 1964

$C_{10}H_{14}FeN_2O_9^-$, Rb^+ , H_2O

$$Rb^+\left[Fe^{3+}(OH_2)\left(\begin{array}{c}^-OOC-H_2C\\ ^-OOC-H_2C\end{array}N-CH_2-CH_2-N\begin{array}{c}CH_2-COO^-\\ CH_2-COO^-\end{array}\right)\right].H_2O$$

No comparison of bond lengths is possible since they are not reported in the paper.
P2/a   Z = 4   R = 0.126

RBEDFE10   LB 10-14-23

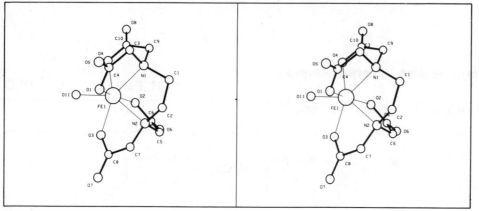

Bond Lengths

Fe1	N1	2.32	C4	O1	1.32
Fe1	N2	2.31	C6	O2	1.29
Fe1	O1	1.97	C8	O3	1.29
Fe1	O2	2.01	C10	O4	1.29
Fe1	O3	2.08	C4	O5	1.21
Fe1	O4	2.07	C6	O6	1.21
Fe1	O11	2.11	C8	O7	1.24
C1	N1	1.49	C10	O8	1.22
C3	N1	1.48	C1	C2	1.50
C9	N1	1.45	C3	C4	1.46
C2	N2	1.47	C5	C6	1.52
C5	N2	1.46	C7	C8	1.50
C7	N2	1.50	C9	C10	1.51

Bond Angles

N1	Fe1	N2	75	O1	Fe1	O11	90	Fe1	N2	C5	105	O5	C4	C3	123
N1	Fe1	O1	78	O2	Fe1	O3	87	Fe1	N2	C7	104	N2	C5	C6	118
N1	Fe1	O2	90	O2	Fe1	O4	83	C2	N2	C5	113	O2	C6	O6	123
N1	Fe1	O3	147	O2	Fe1	O11	107	C2	N2	C7	113	O2	C6	C5	114
N1	Fe1	O4	73	O3	Fe1	O4	139	C5	N2	C7	111	O6	C6	C5	122
N1	Fe1	O11	138	O3	Fe1	O11	74	Fe1	O1	C4	121	N2	C7	C8	109
N2	Fe1	O1	86	O4	Fe1	O11	72	Fe1	O2	C6	121	O3	C8	O7	123
N2	Fe1	O2	79	Fe1	N1	C1	111	Fe1	O3	C8	121	O3	C8	C7	115
N2	Fe1	O3	72	Fe1	N1	C3	102	Fe1	O4	C10	121	O7	C8	C7	122
N2	Fe1	O4	142	Fe1	N1	C9	106	N1	C1	C2	111	N1	C9	C10	112
N2	Fe1	O11	145	C1	N1	C3	113	N2	C2	C1	109	O4	C10	O8	124
O1	Fe1	O2	163	C1	N1	C9	111	N1	C3	C4	114	O4	C10	C9	115
O1	Fe1	O3	97	C3	N1	C9	112	O1	C4	O5	120	O8	C10	C9	122
O1	Fe1	O4	105	Fe1	N2	C2	111	O1	C4	C3	117				

Torsion Angles

C3	N1	C1	C2	79	C5	N2	C7	C8	-71
C9	N1	C1	C2	-154	N1	C1	C2	N2	54
C1	N1	C3	C4	-89	N1	C3	C4	O1	-24
C9	N1	C3	C4	144	N1	C3	C4	O5	160
C1	N1	C9	C10	153	N2	C5	C6	O2	8
C3	N1	C9	C10	-79	N2	C5	C6	O6	-172
C5	N2	C2	C1	71	N2	C7	C8	O3	-25
C7	N2	C2	C1	-162	N2	C7	C8	O7	.158
C2	N2	C5	C6	-117	N1	C9	C10	O4	-12
C7	N2	C5	C6	116	N1	C9	C10	O8	169
C2	N2	C7	C8	162					

76.22 Hydrogen aquoethylenediaminetetra - acetato chromate(iii)

J.L.Hoard, C.H.L.Kennard, G.S.Smith, Inorg. Chem., 2, 1316, 1963

$C_{10}H_{15}CrN_2O_9$

$$\left(\begin{array}{c}OOC-H_2C\\ OOC-H_2C\end{array}N-CH_2-CH_2-N\begin{array}{c}CH_2-COO\\ CH_2-COOH\end{array}\right)Cr(OH_2)$$

Atomic coordinates were not reported in the paper.
P2₁/c   Z = 4   No R factor was given.

EDTACR   LB 10-15-11

76.23 Hydrogen aquoethylenediaminetetra - acetato ferrate(iii)

J.L.Hoard, C.H.L.Kennard, G.S.Smith, Inorg. Chem., 2, 1316, 1963

$C_{10}H_{15}FeN_2O_9$

$$\left(\begin{array}{c}OOC-H_2C\\ OOC-H_2C\end{array}N-CH_2-CH_2-N\begin{array}{c}CH_2-COO\\ CH_2-COOH\end{array}\right)Fe(OH_2)$$

Atomic coordinates were not reported in the paper.
P2₁/c   Z = 4   No R factor was given.

EDTAFE   LB 10-15-12

76.24 Potassium triaquo lanthanum(iii) ethylenediamine tetra - acetate pentahydrate

J.L.Hoard, B.Lee, M.D.Lind, J. Amer. Chem. Soc., 87, 1612, 1965

$C_{10}H_{18}KLaN_2O_{11}$, $5H_2O$

$$K^+\left[\left(\begin{array}{c}OOC-CH_2\\ OOC-CH_2\end{array}N-CH_2-CH_2-N\begin{array}{c}CH_2-COO\\ CH_2-COO\end{array}\right)La(H_2O)_3\right]^-.5H_2O$$

Atomic coordinates were not reported in the paper.
Fdd2   Z = 16   R = 0.065

KLAEAA   LB 10-18-11

76.25 Tetra - aquo lanthanum(iii) hydrogen ethylenediamine tetra - acetate trihydrate

$C_{10}H_{21}LaN_2O_{12}$, $3H_2O$

M.D.Lind, B.Lee, J.L.Hoard, J. Amer. Chem. Soc., 87, 1611, 1965

Atomic coordinates were not reported in the paper.
P2$_1$/a Z = 4 R = 0.059

LAHEAA   LB 10-13-14

$$H^+ \left[\begin{pmatrix} OOC-CH_2 \\ OOC-CH_2 \end{pmatrix} N-CH_2-CH_2-N \begin{pmatrix} CH_2-COO \\ CH_2-COO \end{pmatrix} La(H_2O)_4 \right]^- \cdot 3H_2O$$

76.26 bis(Aquo manganese(ii) hydrogen ethylenediamine tetra - acetate) tetra - aquo manganese(ii) tetrahydrate

$C_{20}H_{30}Mn_2N_4O_{18}{}^{2-}$, $H_8MnO_4{}^{2+}$, $4H_2O$

S.Richards, B.Pedersen, J.V.Silverton, J.L.Hoard, Inorg. Chem., 3, 27, 1964

P2$_1$/n   Z = 2   R = 0.10

MHEDTA10   LB 12-10-48

$$\left[Mn^{2+}(OH_2) \begin{pmatrix} {}^-OOC-CH_2 \\ {}^-OOC-CH_2 \end{pmatrix} N-CH_2-CH_2-N \begin{pmatrix} CH_2-COOH \\ CH_2-COO^- \end{pmatrix} \right]_2 \left[Mn^{2+}(OH_2)_4 \right] \cdot 4H_2O$$

Bond Lengths

Mn1	O8	2.21	C10	N2	1.48
Mn1	O10	2.16	C5	O1	1.25
Mn1	O11	2.15	C6	O2	1.26
Mn2	N1	2.35	C7	O3	1.24
Mn2	N2	2.40	C8	O4	1.26
Mn2	O1	2.26	C5	O5	1.28
Mn2	O2	2.22	C6	O6	1.25
Mn2	O3	2.23	C7	O7	1.28
Mn2	O4	2.26	C8	O8	1.26
Mn2	O9	2.23	C1	C5	1.52
C1	N1	1.48	C2	C6	1.52
C4	N1	1.47	C3	C7	1.53
C9	N1	1.48	C4	C8	1.52
C2	N2	1.47	C9	C10	1.52
C3	N2	1.47			

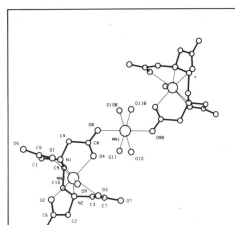
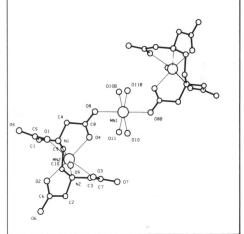

Bond Angles

O8	Mn1	O10	90							
O8	Mn1	O11	91							
O8	Mn1	O8B	180							
O8	Mn1	O10B	90							
O8	Mn1	O11B	89							
O10	Mn1	O11	89	O2	Mn2	O4	167	Mn2	O4	C8	119
O10	Mn1	O10B	180	O2	Mn2	O9	86	Mn1	O8	C8	130
O10	Mn1	O11B	91	O3	Mn2	O4	80	N1	C1	C5	109
O11	Mn1	O11B	180	O3	Mn2	O9	79	N2	C2	C6	112
N1	Mn2	N2	75	O4	Mn2	O9	107	N2	C3	C7	109
N1	Mn2	O1	70	Mn2	N1	C1	105	N1	C4	C8	112
N1	Mn2	O2	97	Mn2	N1	C4	107	O1	C5	O5	124
N1	Mn2	O3	131	Mn2	N1	C9	110	O1	C5	C1	120
N1	Mn2	O4	73	C1	N1	C4	111	O5	C5	C1	116
N1	Mn2	O9	148	C1	N1	C9	114	O2	C6	O6	126
N2	Mn2	O1	135	C4	N1	C9	109	O2	C6	C2	118
N2	Mn2	O2	71	Mn2	N2	C2	106	O6	C6	C2	117
N2	Mn2	O3	70	Mn2	N2	C3	106	O3	C7	O7	123
N2	Mn2	O4	99	Mn2	N2	C10	109	O3	C7	C3	120
N2	Mn2	O9	135	C2	N2	C3	112	O7	C7	C3	116
O1	Mn2	O2	85	C2	N2	C10	110	O4	C8	O8	126
O1	Mn2	O3	155	C3	N2	C10	114	O4	C8	C4	117
O1	Mn2	O4	98	Mn2	O1	C5	114	O8	C8	C4	117
O1	Mn2	O9	78	Mn2	O2	C6	119	N1	C9	C10	112
O2	Mn2	O3	103	Mn2	O3	C7	116	N2	C10	C9	112

Torsion Angles

C4	N1	C1	C5	−74	C3	N2	C10	C9	−77
C9	N1	C1	C5	163	N1	C1	C5	O1	−15
C1	N1	C4	C8	152	N1	C1	C5	O5	165
C9	N1	C4	C8	−81	N2	C2	C6	O2	−14
C1	N1	C9	C10	−80	N2	C2	C6	O6	168
C4	N1	C9	C10	156	N2	C3	C7	O3	−10
C3	N2	C2	C6	148	N2	C3	C7	O7	171
C10	N2	C2	C6	−84	N1	C4	C8	O4	−31
C2	N2	C3	C7	−78	N1	C4	C8	O8	152
C10	N2	C3	C7	156	N1	C9	C10	N2	−55
C2	N2	C10	C9	156					

77.1 Acetylacetonato diaquo copper(ii) picrate

$C_5H_{11}CuO_4^+$, $C_6H_2N_3O_7^-$

R.D.Gillard, D.Rogers, R.D.Diamand, D.J.Williams, Acta Cryst., 16, A67, 1963

Atomic coordinates were not given
but bond lengths were reported.
$P2_1/m$ $Z = 2$ $R = 0.16$

ACACUP

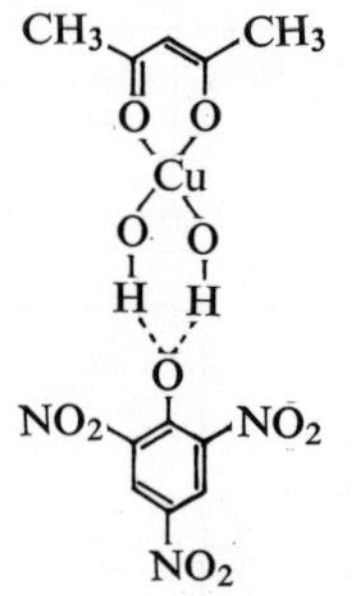

77.2 Vanadyl bisacetylacetonate

$C_{10}H_{14}O_5V$

R.P.Dodge, D.H.Templeton, A.Zalkin, J. Chem. Phys., 35, 55, 1961

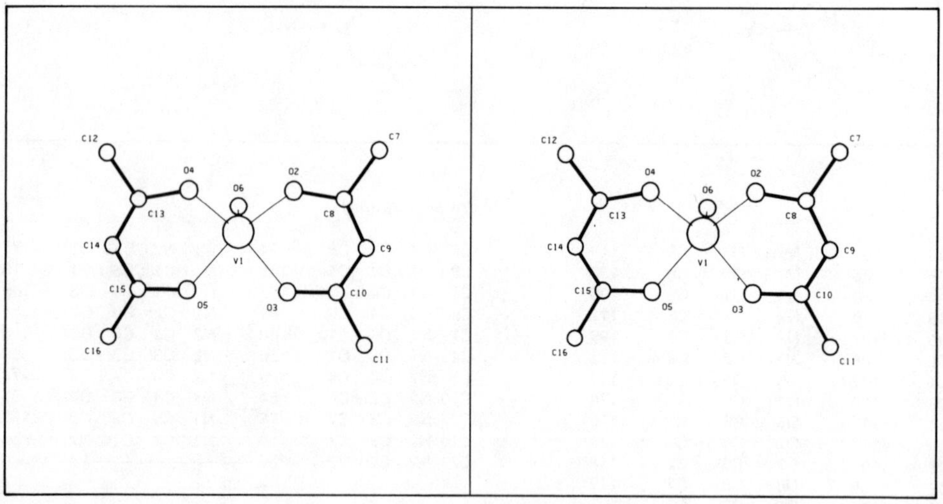

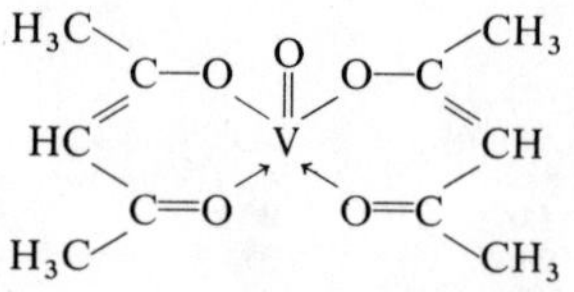

P-1 $Z = 2$ $R = 0.09$

ACACVO   LB 10-14-49

Bond Lengths

V1	O2	1.97
V1	O3	1.96
V1	O4	1.98
V1	O5	1.96
V1	O6	1.56
C8	O2	1.29
C10	O3	1.28
C13	O4	1.28
C15	O5	1.29

C7	C8	1.51
C8	C9	1.39
C9	C10	1.40
C10	C11	1.53
C12	C13	1.52
C13	C14	1.38
C14	C15	1.42
C15	C16	1.51

Bond Angles

O2	V1	O3	87
O2	V1	O4	84
O2	V1	O5	150
O2	V1	O6	105
O3	V1	O4	146
O3	V1	O5	83
O3	V1	O6	106
O4	V1	O5	88
O4	V1	O6	108
O5	V1	O6	106

V1	O2	C8	129
V1	O3	C10	129
V1	O4	C13	129
V1	O5	C15	130
O2	C8	C7	115
O2	C8	C9	124
C7	C8	C9	121
C8	C9	C10	123
O3	C10	C9	124
O3	C10	C11	117

C9	C10	C11	119
O4	C13	C12	115
O4	C13	C14	125
C12	C13	C14	120
C13	C14	C15	124
O5	C15	C14	123
O5	C15	C16	116
C14	C15	C16	122

Torsion Angles

O2	C8	C9	C10	−1
C7	C8	C9	C10	178
C8	C9	C10	O3	6
C8	C9	C10	C11	−171
O4	C13	C14	C15	3
C12	C13	C14	C15	−177
C13	C14	C15	O5	−1
C13	C14	C15	C16	177

77.3   Vanadyl bisacetylacetonate (refinement)

$C_{10}H_{14}O_5V$

P.Hon, R.L.Belford, C.E.Pfluger, J. Chem. Phys., 43, 3111, 1965

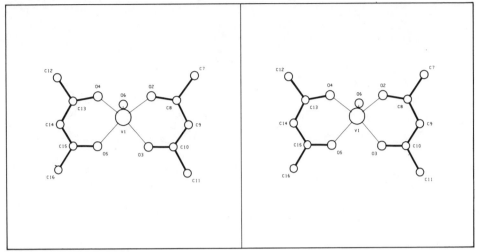

An alternative refinement using the data of Dodge et al. See 77.2.
P-1   Z = 2   R = 0.078

ACACVO01   LB 10-14-49

Bond Lengths

V1	O2	1.97	C7	C8	1.51
V1	O3	1.96	C8	C9	1.39
V1	O4	1.98	C9	C10	1.41
V1	O5	1.96	C10	C11	1.53
V1	O6	1.57	C12	C13	1.51
C8	O2	1.28	C13	C14	1.39
C10	O3	1.28	C14	C15	1.42
C13	O4	1.27	C15	C16	1.51
C15	O5	1.29			

Bond Angles

O2	V1	O3	87	V1	O2	C8	129	C9	C10	C11	119
O2	V1	O4	84	V1	O3	C10	130	O4	C13	C12	115
O2	V1	O5	150	V1	O4	C13	129	O4	C13	C14	124
O2	V1	O6	105	V1	O5	C15	129	C12	C13	C14	120
O3	V1	O4	145	O2	C8	C7	115	C13	C14	C15	124
O3	V1	O5	84	O2	C8	C9	124	O5	C15	C14	123
O3	V1	O6	106	C7	C8	C9	121	O5	C15	C16	116
O4	V1	O5	88	C8	C9	C10	123	C14	C15	C16	121
O4	V1	O6	108	O3	C10	C9	124				
O5	V1	O6	106	O3	C10	C11	117				

Torsion Angles

O2	C8	C9	C10	0
C7	C8	C9	C10	178
C8	C9	C10	O3	5
C8	C9	C10	C11	−171
O4	C13	C14	C15	4
C12	C13	C14	C15	−177
C13	C14	C15	O5	−1
C13	C14	C15	C16	177

77.4   bis(Acetylacetonato) aquo zinc(ii)

$C_{10}H_{16}O_5Zn$

H.Montgomery, E.C.Lingafelter, Acta Cryst., 16, 748, 1963

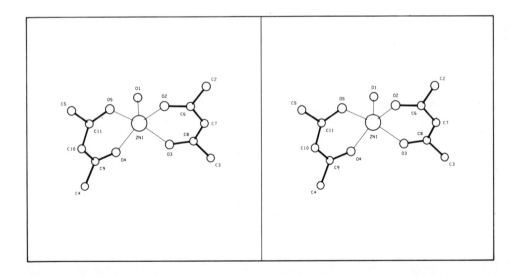

P2₁   Z = 2   R = 0.07

ACACZM   LB 10-14-48

Bond Lengths

Zn1	O1	2.00	C2	C6	1.49
Zn1	O2	2.03	C3	C8	1.49
Zn1	O3	2.04	C4	C9	1.51
Zn1	O4	2.01	C5	C11	1.56
Zn1	O5	2.01	C6	C7	1.40
C6	O2	1.30	C7	C8	1.37
C8	O3	1.29	C9	C10	1.40
C9	O4	1.27	C10	C11	1.40
C11	O5	1.30			

Bond Angles

O1	Zn1	O2	105	Zn1	O2	C6	127	C3	C8	C7	119
O1	Zn1	O3	98	Zn1	O3	C8	127	O4	C9	C4	119
O1	Zn1	O4	105	Zn1	O4	C9	130	O4	C9	C10	123
O1	Zn1	O5	100	Zn1	O5	C11	125	C4	C9	C10	119
O2	Zn1	O3	88	O2	C6	C2	117	C9	C10	C11	125
O2	Zn1	O4	150	O2	C6	C7	123	O5	C11	C5	115
O2	Zn1	O5	85	C2	C6	C7	120	O5	C11	C10	125
O3	Zn1	O4	89	C6	C7	C8	127	C5	C11	C10	119
O3	Zn1	O5	162	O3	C8	C3	116				
O4	Zn1	O5	88	O3	C8	C7	126				

Torsion Angles

O2	C6	C7	C8	0
C2	C6	C7	C8	179
C6	C7	C8	O3	4
C6	C7	C8	C3	−174
O4	C9	C10	C11	2
C4	C9	C10	C11	−180
C9	C10	C11	O5	2
C9	C10	C11	C5	−178

77.5   bis(Acetylacetonato) aquo zinc(ii)

$C_{10}H_{16}O_5Zn$

E.L.Lippert, M.R.Truter, J. Chem. Soc., 4996, 1960

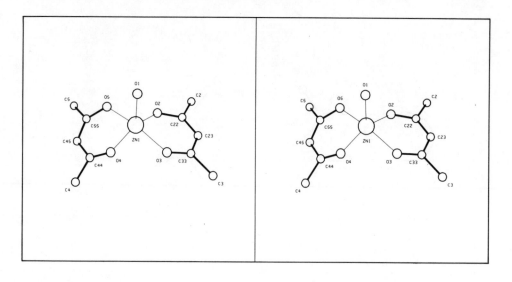

$P2_1$ $Z = 2$ $R = 0.09$

ACACZM01   LB 10-14-48

Bond Lengths

Zn1	O1	2.02	C2	C22	1.53
Zn1	O2	2.00	C3	C33	1.71
Zn1	O3	2.12	C4	C44	1.42
Zn1	O4	1.92	C5	C55	1.64
Zn1	O5	2.10	C22	C23	1.45
C22	O2	1.34	C23	C33	1.36
C33	O3	1.29	C44	C45	1.53
C44	O4	1.18	C45	C55	1.37
C55	O5	1.29			

Bond Angles

O1	Zn1	O2	108	Zn1	O2	C22	124	C3	C33	C23	125
O1	Zn1	O3	101	Zn1	O3	C33	129	O4	C44	C4	118
O1	Zn1	O4	104	Zn1	O4	C44	127	O4	C44	C45	125
O1	Zn1	O5	96	Zn1	O5	C55	122	C4	C44	C45	117
O2	Zn1	O3	90	O2	C22	C2	109	C44	C45	C55	128
O2	Zn1	O4	148	O2	C22	C23	126	O5	C55	C5	113
O2	Zn1	O5	82	C2	C22	C23	126	O5	C55	C45	121
O3	Zn1	O4	86	C22	C23	C33	129	C5	C55	C45	126
O3	Zn1	O5	162	O3	C33	C3	113				
O4	Zn1	O5	93	O3	C33	C23	121				

Torsion Angles

O2	C22	C23	C33	4
C2	C22	C23	C33	−174
C22	C23	C33	O3	−12
C22	C23	C33	C3	−178
O4	C44	C45	C55	0
C4	C44	C45	C55	180
C44	C45	C55	O5	−6
C44	C45	C55	C5	174

77.6   bis(Acetylacetonato) diaquo nickel(ii)

$C_{10}H_{18}NiO_6$

H.Montgomery, E.C.Lingafelter, Acta Cryst., 17, 1481, 1964

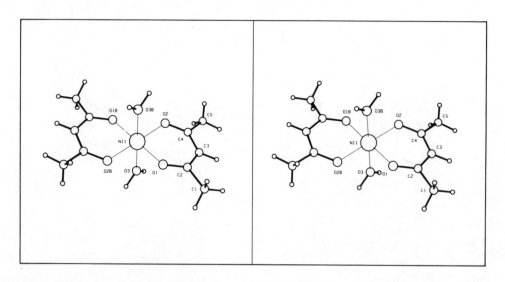

$P2_1/c$ $Z = 2$ $R = 0.07$

DACANI   LB 10-18-22

Bond Lengths

Ni1	O1	2.02
Ni1	O2	2.01
Ni1	O3	2.14
C2	O1	1.27
C4	O2	1.27
C1	C2	1.52
C2	C3	1.40
C3	C4	1.42
C4	C5	1.50

Bond Angles

O1	Ni1	O2	92	O2	Ni1	O2B	180	O1	C2	C1	115
O1	Ni1	O3	91	O2	Ni1	O3B	91	O1	C2	C3	126
O1	Ni1	O1B	180	O3	Ni1	O1B	89	C1	C2	C3	118
O1	Ni1	O2B	88	O3	Ni1	O2B	91	C2	C3	C4	127
O1	Ni1	O3B	89	O3	Ni1	O3B	180	O2	C4	C3	125
O2	Ni1	O3	89	Ni1	O1	C2	123	O2	C4	C5	117
O2	Ni1	O1B	88	Ni1	O2	C4	124	C3	C4	C5	119

Torsion Angles

O1	C2	C3	C4	5
C1	C2	C3	C4	−175
C2	C3	C4	O2	0
C2	C3	C4	C5	−179

77.7 Copper(ii) ethylacetoacetate

$C_{12}H_{18}CuO_6$

G.A.Barclay, A.Cooper, J. Chem. Soc., 3746, 1965

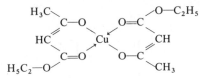

See also Hall et al., J. Chem. Soc.
(A), 615, 1966.
$P2_1/n$ Z = 2   R = 0.12

CUEACA   LB 12-18-31

Bond Lengths

Cu1	O1	1.89
Cu1	O2	1.92
C2	O1	1.32
C4	O2	1.28
C4	O3	1.31
C5	O3	1.45
C1	C2	1.51
C2	C3	1.31
C3	C4	1.39
C5	C6	1.46

Bond Angles

O1	Cu1	O2	90
O1	Cu1	O1B	180
O1	Cu1	O2B	90
O2	Cu1	O1B	90
O2	Cu1	O2B	180
Cu1	O1	C2	125
Cu1	O2	C4	127
C4	O3	C5	116

O1	C2	C1	111
O1	C2	C3	131
C1	C2	C3	118
C2	C3	C4	118

O2	C4	O3	121
O2	C4	C3	127
O3	C4	C3	112
O3	C5	C6	106

Torsion Angles

C5	O3	C4	O2	0
C5	O3	C4	C3	−177
C4	O3	C5	C6	−161
O1	C2	C3	C4	−2

C1	C2	C3	C4	176
C2	C3	C4	O2	5
C2	C3	C4	O3	−177

77.8 tris(Acetylacetonato) cobalt(iii)

$C_{15}H_{21}CoO_6$

L.M.Shkol'nikova, E.A.Shugam, Zh. Strukt. Khim., 2, 72, 1961

Atomic coordinates were not reported in the paper. The crystal
data were taken from Padmanabhan, Proc. Indian Acad. Sci., 47, 329, 1958.
The space group and Z were not reported.
No R factor was given.

COACAC   LB 15-21-6

77.9 tris(Acetylacetonato) chromium(iii)

$C_{15}H_{21}CrO_6$

B.Morosin, Acta Cryst., 19, 131, 1965

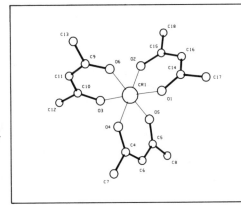
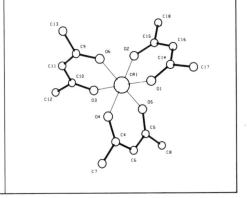

See also Trus & Marsh, Amer. Cryst.
Assoc., Abstr. Papers (Winter
Meeting), 30, 1969.
$P2_1/c$ Z = 4   R = 0.066

ACACCR   LB 15-21-7

Bond Lengths

Cr1	O1	1.95	C4	C6	1.37
Cr1	O2	1.95	C4	C7	1.51
Cr1	O3	1.95	C5	C6	1.40
Cr1	O4	1.96	C5	C8	1.51
Cr1	O5	1.96	C9	C11	1.39
Cr1	O6	1.96	C9	C13	1.52
C14	O1	1.25	C10	C11	1.39
C15	O2	1.26	C10	C12	1.52
C10	O3	1.27	C14	C16	1.40
C4	O4	1.28	C14	C17	1.53
C5	O5	1.27	C15	C16	1.40
C9	O6	1.25	C15	C18	1.54

Bond Angles

O1	Cr1	O2	92
O1	Cr1	O3	177
O1	Cr1	O4	89
O1	Cr1	O5	90
O1	Cr1	O6	90
O2	Cr1	O3	91
O2	Cr1	O4	179
O2	Cr1	O5	89
O2	Cr1	O6	90
O3	Cr1	O4	89
O3	Cr1	O5	89
O3	Cr1	O6	91
O4	Cr1	O5	91
O4	Cr1	O6	90

O5	Cr1	O6	179
Cr1	O1	C14	127
Cr1	O2	C15	127
Cr1	O3	C10	126
Cr1	O4	C4	126
Cr1	O5	C5	127
Cr1	O6	C9	128
O4	C4	C6	125
O4	C4	C7	115
C6	C4	C7	120
O5	C5	C6	124
O5	C5	C8	115
C6	C5	C8	121
C4	C6	C5	126

O6	C9	C11	124
O6	C9	C13	116
C11	C9	C13	120
O3	C10	C11	125
O3	C10	C12	116
C11	C10	C12	119
C9	C11	C10	126
O1	C14	C16	126
O1	C14	C17	114
C16	C14	C17	120
O2	C15	C16	125
O2	C15	C18	114
C16	C15	C18	121
C14	C16	C15	124

Torsion Angles

O4	C4	C6	C5	−2
C7	C4	C6	C5	179
O5	C5	C6	C4	3
C8	C5	C6	C4	−176
O6	C9	C11	C10	−5
C13	C9	C11	C10	174
O3	C10	C11	C9	2
C12	C10	C11	C9	−177
O1	C14	C16	C15	5
C17	C14	C16	C15	−178
O2	C15	C16	C14	−6
C18	C15	C16	C14	175

77.10 tris(Acetylacetonato) manganese(iii)

$C_{15}H_{21}MnO_6$

B.Morosin, J.R.Brathovde, Acta Cryst., 17, 705, 1964

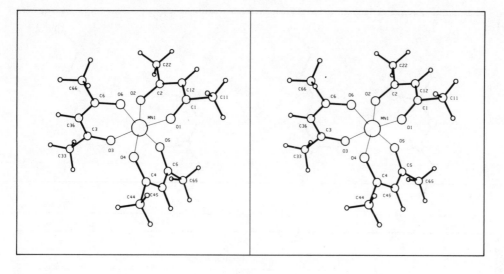

$P2_1/c$ $Z = 4$ $R = 0.09$

ACACMN   LB 15-21-15

Bond Lengths

Mn1	O1	1.86	C1	C11	1.52
Mn1	O2	1.86	C1	C12	1.40
Mn1	O3	1.89	C2	C12	1.40
Mn1	O4	1.88	C2	C22	1.54
Mn1	O5	1.88	C3	C33	1.50
Mn1	O6	1.87	C3	C36	1.40
C1	O1	1.26	C4	C44	1.49
C2	O2	1.30	C4	C45	1.38
C3	O3	1.28	C5	C45	1.34
C4	O4	1.31	C5	C65	1.50
C5	O5	1.30	C6	C36	1.37
C6	O6	1.28	C6	C66	1.55

Bond Angles

O1	Mn1	O2	98	O5	Mn1	O6	174	O3	C3	C36	125	
O1	Mn1	O3	174	Mn1	O1	C1	124	C33	C3	C36	121	
O1	Mn1	O4	88	Mn1	O2	C2	122	O4	C4	C44	115	
O1	Mn1	O5	89	Mn1	O3	C3	123	O4	C4	C45	124	
O1	Mn1	O6	88	Mn1	O4	C4	123	C44	C4	C45	122	
O2	Mn1	O3	87	Mn1	O5	C5	124	O5	C5	C45	125	
O2	Mn1	O4	173	Mn1	O6	C6	123	O5	C5	C65	112	
O2	Mn1	O5	87	O1	C1	C11	113	C45	C5	C65	123	
O2	Mn1	O6	88	O1	C1	C12	127	O6	C6	C36	127	
O3	Mn1	O4	88	C11	C1	C12	120	O6	C6	C66	114	
O3	Mn1	O5	87	O2	C2	C12	126	C36	C6	C66	119	
O3	Mn1	O6	97	O2	C2	C22	114	C1	C12	C2	123	
O4	Mn1	O5	97	C12	C2	C22	120	C3	C36	C6	124	
O4	Mn1	O6	88	O3	C3	C33	114	C4	C45	C5	128	

Torsion Angles

O1	C1	C12	C2	3
C11	C1	C12	C2	−179
O2	C2	C12	C1	−2
C22	C2	C12	C1	174
O3	C3	C36	C6	−2
C33	C3	C36	C6	−177
O4	C4	C45	C5	−1
C44	C4	C45	C5	179
O5	C5	C45	C4	0
C65	C5	C45	C4	−176
O6	C6	C36	C3	−2
C66	C6	C36	C3	177

77.11 Ethyl - (trimethyl platinum) aceto - acetate dimer

$C_{18}H_{36}O_6Pt_2$

A.C.Hazell, M.R.Truter, Proc. R. Soc., A, 254, 218, 1960

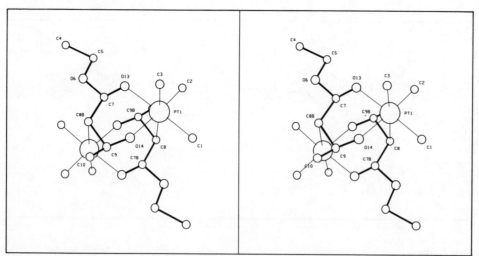

Published value of x(Pt1) = 0.1879.
The correct value is 0.1985 (private communication).
$P2_1/c$ $Z = 2$ $R = 0.09$

EMPTAA   LB 18-36-8

Bond Lengths

Pt1	O13	2.19	C7	O6	1.45
Pt1	O14	2.19	C7	O13	1.19
Pt1	C1	2.14	C9	O14	1.22
Pt1	C2	1.96	C4	C5	1.75
Pt1	C3	2.17	C7	C8B	1.74
Pt1	C8	2.55	C8	C9B	1.65
C5	O6	1.45	C9	C10	1.17

Bond Angles

O13	Pt1	O14	85	C1	Pt1	C2	94	O6	C5	C4	100
O13	Pt1	C1	174	C1	Pt1	C3	93	O6	C7	O13	114
O13	Pt1	C2	91	C1	Pt1	C8	89	O6	C7	C8B	102
O13	Pt1	C3	82	C2	Pt1	C3	95	O13	C7	C8B	127
O13	Pt1	C8	95	C2	Pt1	C8	86	Pt1	C8	C7B	85
O14	Pt1	C1	90	C3	Pt1	C8	177	Pt1	C8	C9B	89
O14	Pt1	C2	176	C5	O6	C7	108	O14	C9	C10	134
O14	Pt1	C3	84	Pt1	O13	C7	119	O14	C9	C8B	108
O14	Pt1	C8	95	Pt1	O14	C9	142	C10	C9	C8B	99

Torsion Angles

C7	O6	C5	C4	166
C5	O6	C7	O13	39
C5	O6	C7	C8B	180
O6	C7	C8B	Pt1B	103
O6	C7	C8B	C9	−171
O13	C7	C8B	Pt1B	−124
O13	C7	C8B	C9	−38
C7B	C8	C9B	O14B	−24
C7B	C8	C9B	C10B	−167

77.12 μ - Ethylenediamine - bis(trimethyl(acetylacetonato) platinum(iv)) $C_{18}H_{40}N_2O_4Pt_2$

A.Robson, M.R.Truter, J. Chem. Soc., 630, 1965

I2/a   Z = 4   R = 0.09

EMACPT   LB 18-40-3

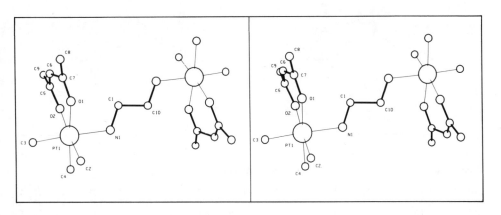

Bond Lengths

Pt1	N1	2.31
Pt1	O1	2.16
Pt1	O2	2.18
Pt1	C2	2.17
Pt1	C3	2.04
Pt1	C4	2.12
C1	N1	1.38
C7	O1	1.29
C5	O2	1.34
C1	C1D	1.72
C5	C6	1.18
C5	C9	1.55
C6	C7	1.56
C7	C8	1.41

Bond Angles

N1	Pt1	O1	91
N1	Pt1	O2	88
N1	Pt1	C2	91
N1	Pt1	C3	177
N1	Pt1	C4	87
O1	Pt1	O2	85
O1	Pt1	C2	88
O1	Pt1	C3	89
O1	Pt1	C4	173
O2	Pt1	C2	173
O2	Pt1	C3	95
O2	Pt1	C4	102
C2	Pt1	C3	86
C2	Pt1	C4	85
C3	Pt1	C4	92
Pt1	N1	C1	111
Pt1	O1	C7	128
Pt1	O2	C5	123
N1	C1	C1D	104
O2	C5	C6	128
O2	C5	C9	110
C6	C5	C9	121
C5	C6	C7	131
O1	C7	C6	119
O1	C7	C8	115
C6	C7	C8	124

Torsion Angles

N1	C1	C1D	N1D	180
O2	C5	C6	C7	4
C9	C5	C6	C7	−161
C5	C6	C7	O1	−16
C5	C6	C7	C8	−179

77.13   Vanadyl 1 - phenyl - 1,3 - butanedionate (further refinement) $C_{20}H_{18}O_5V$

P.Hon, R.L.Belford, C.E.Pfluger, J. Chem. Phys., 43, 3111, 1965

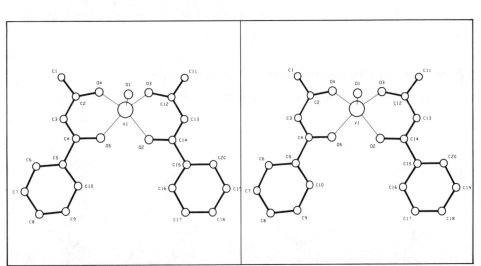

For full details of structure determination see Hon et al., J. Chem. Phys., 43, 1323, 1965.
P2₁/c   Z = 4   R = 0.068

VOPBUO10   LB 20-18-16

Bond Lengths

V1	O1	1.60	C2	C3	1.44	C12	C13	1.41
V1	O2	1.95	C3	C4	1.37	C13	C14	1.41
V1	O3	1.97	C4	C5	1.52	C14	C15	1.48
V1	O4	1.97	C5	C6	1.39	C15	C16	1.41
V1	O5	1.95	C5	C10	1.40	C15	C20	1.40
C14	O2	1.29	C6	C7	1.43	C16	C17	1.39
C12	O3	1.30	C7	C8	1.40	C17	C18	1.39
C2	O4	1.28	C8	C9	1.37	C18	C19	1.38
C4	O5	1.29	C9	C10	1.42	C19	C20	1.41
C1	C2	1.53	C11	C12	1.54			

Bond Angles

O1	V1	O2	107	V1	O2	C14	130	C3	C4	C5	121
O1	V1	O3	104	V1	O3	C12	128	O3	C12	C11	115
O1	V1	O4	106	V1	O4	C2	129	O3	C12	C13	124
O1	V1	O5	106	V1	O5	C4	131	C11	C12	C13	121
O2	V1	O3	88	O4	C2	C1	116	C12	C13	C14	123
O2	V1	O4	147	O4	C2	C3	124	O2	C14	C13	123
O2	V1	O5	82	C1	C2	C3	120	O2	C14	C15	115
O3	V1	O4	86	C2	C3	C4	122	C13	C14	C15	122
O3	V1	O5	150	O5	C4	C3	125				
O4	V1	O5	87	O5	C4	C5	114				

77.14   tetrakis(Acetylacetonato) cerium(iv) $C_{20}H_{28}CeO_8$

B.Matkovic, D.Grdenic, Acta Cryst., 16, 456, 1963

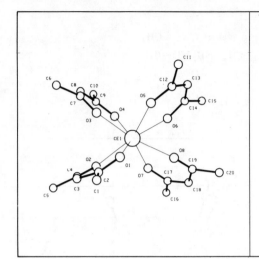 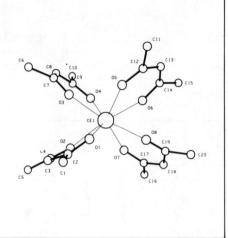

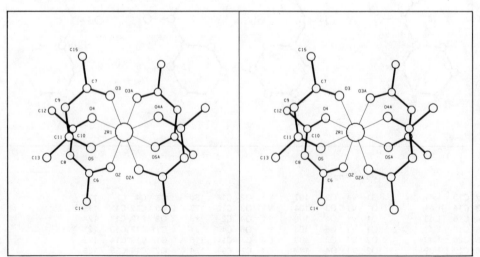

See also Titze, Acta Chem. Scand., 23, 399, 1969.
P2₁/c   Z = 4 R_{hol} = 0.16,
R_{0kl} = 0.17

ACACCE   LB 20-28-2

Bond Lengths

Ce1	O1	2.40	C1	C2	1.54
Ce1	O2	2.39	C2	C3	1.41
Ce1	O3	2.36	C3	C4	1.41
Ce1	O4	2.36	C4	C5	1.56
Ce1	O5	2.38	C6	C7	1.54
Ce1	O6	2.40	C7	C8	1.38
Ce1	O7	2.43	C8	C9	1.39
Ce1	O8	2.43	C9	C10	1.52
C2	O1	1.32	C11	C12	1.56
C4	O2	1.30	C12	C13	1.43
C7	O3	1.28	C13	C14	1.39
C9	O4	1.30	C14	C15	1.54
C12	O5	1.30	C16	C17	1.53
C14	O6	1.27	C17	C18	1.40
C17	O7	1.29	C18	C19	1.42
C19	O8	1.26	C19	C20	1.53

Bond Angles

O1	Ce1	O2	73	O5	Ce1	O6	71	O3	C7	C8	122
O1	Ce1	O3	72	O5	Ce1	O7	136	C6	C7	C8	119
O1	Ce1	O4	140	O5	Ce1	O8	76	C7	C8	C9	129
O1	Ce1	O5	80	O6	Ce1	O7	71	O4	C9	C8	122
O1	Ce1	O6	140	O6	Ce1	O8	69	O4	C9	C10	116
O1	Ce1	O7	118	O7	Ce1	O8	71	C8	C9	C10	121
O1	Ce1	O8	78	Ce1	O1	C2	135	O5	C12	C11	117
O2	Ce1	O3	76	Ce1	O2	C4	134	O5	C12	C13	126
O2	Ce1	O4	81	Ce1	O3	C7	138	C11	C12	C13	117
O2	Ce1	O5	144	Ce1	O4	C9	136	C12	C13	C14	126
O2	Ce1	O6	143	Ce1	O5	C12	135	O6	C14	C13	120
O2	Ce1	O7	78	Ce1	O6	C14	142	O6	C14	C15	114
O2	Ce1	O8	120	Ce1	O7	C17	140	C13	C14	C15	126
O3	Ce1	O4	73	Ce1	O8	C19	134	C7	C17	C16	115
O3	Ce1	O5	74	O1	C2	C1	117	O7	C17	C18	120
O3	Ce1	O6	123	O1	C2	C3	122	C16	C17	C18	125
O3	Ce1	O7	148	C1	C2	C3	121	C17	C18	C19	127
O3	Ce1	O8	140	C2	C3	C4	128	O8	C19	C18	125
O4	Ce1	O5	106	O2	C4	C3	124	O8	C19	C20	115
O4	Ce1	O6	76	O2	C4	C5	120	C18	C19	C20	119
O4	Ce1	O7	85	C3	C4	C5	116				
O4	Ce1	O8	142	O3	C7	C6	118				

Torsion Angles

O1	C2	C3	C4	16
C1	C2	C3	C4	−171
C2	C3	C4	O2	−7
C2	C3	C4	C5	172
O3	C7	C8	C9	0
C6	C7	C8	C9	−169
C7	C8	C9	O4	−6
C7	C8	C9	C10	−179
O5	C12	C13	C14	−6
C11	C12	C13	C14	−180
C12	C13	C14	O6	2
C12	C13	C14	C15	−173
O7	C17	C18	C19	−4
C16	C17	C18	C19	175
C17	C18	C19	O8	15
C17	C18	C19	C20	−177

77.15   tetrakis(Acetylacetonato) zirconium(iv) $C_{20}H_{28}O_8Zr$

J.V.Silverton, J.L.Hoard, Inorg. Chem., 2, 243, 1963

No comparison of bond lengths is possible since they are not reported in the paper.
I2/c   Z = 4   R = 0.13

ACACZR   LB 20-28-18

Bond Lengths

Zr1	O2	2.22	C6	C8	1.40
Zr1	O3	2.20	C6	C14	1.52
Zr1	O4	2.19	C7	C9	1.41
Zr1	O5	2.18	C7	C15	1.51
C6	O2	1.27	C8	C10	1.39
C7	O3	1.27	C9	C11	1.40
C10	O4	1.26	C10	C12	1.54
C11	O5	1.28	C11	C13	1.50

Bond Angles

O2	Zr1	O3	142	O3	Zr1	O5	75	O4	Zr1	O4A	141
O2	Zr1	O4	75	O3	Zr1	O2A	118	O4	Zr1	O5A	114
O2	Zr1	O5	76	O3	Zr1	O3A	75	O5	Zr1	O2A	72
O2	Zr1	O2A	75	O3	Zr1	O4A	73	O5	Zr1	O3A	143
O2	Zr1	O3A	118	O3	Zr1	O5A	143	O5	Zr1	O4A	114
O2	Zr1	O5A	142	O4	Zr1	O5	80	O5	Zr1	O5A	140
O2	Zr1	O5A	72	O4	Zr1	O2A	142	Zr1	O2	C6	132
O3	Zr1	O4	77	O4	Zr1	O3A	73	Zr1	O3	C7	133

Zr1	O4	C10	133	C6	C8	C10	123
Zr1	O5	C11	134	C7	C9	C11	122
O2	C6	C8	123	O4	C10	C8	124
O2	C6	C14	115	O4	C10	C12	116
C8	C6	C14	122	C8	C10	C12	120
O3	C7	C9	123	O5	C11	C9	123
O3	C7	C15	118	O5	C11	C13	116
C9	C7	C15	119	C9	C11	C13	120

Torsion Angles

O2	C6	C8	C10	5
C14	C6	C8	C10	−174
O3	C7	C9	C11	7
C15	C7	C9	C11	−171
C6	C8	C10	O4	−5
C6	C8	C10	C12	176
C7	C9	C11	O5	−8
C7	C9	C11	C13	169

77.16   bis(3 - Phenyl - 2,4 - pentanedionato) copper(ii) $C_{22}H_{22}CuO_4$

J.W.Carmichael, L.K.Steinrauf, R.L.Belford, J. Chem. Phys., 43, 3959, 1965

$P2_1/c$ Z = 2   R = 0.08

CUPHPO   LB 22-22-10

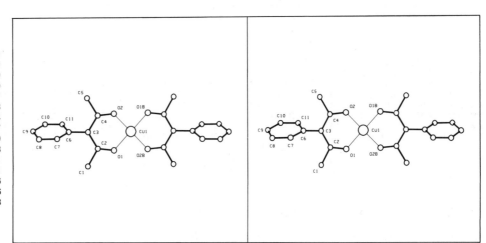

Bond Lengths

Cu1	O1	1.91
Cu1	O2	1.90
C2	O1	1.26
C4	O2	1.25
C1	C2	1.53
C2	C3	1.44
C3	C4	1.45
C3	C6	1.49
C4	C5	1.54
C6	C7	1.39
C6	C11	1.42
C7	C8	1.40
C8	C9	1.42
C9	C10	1.42
C10	C11	1.39

Bond Angles

O1	Cu1	O2	91
O1	Cu1	O1B	180
O1	Cu1	O2B	89
O2	Cu1	O1B	89
O2	Cu1	O2B	180
Cu1	O1	C2	127
Cu1	O2	C4	128
O1	C2	C1	114
O1	C2	C3	127
C1	C2	C3	119
C2	C3	C4	118
C2	C3	C6	121
C4	C3	C6	121
O2	C4	C3	126
O2	C4	C5	116
C3	C4	C5	118

77.17   bis(Dipivaloylmethanido) zinc(ii) $C_{22}H_{38}O_4Zn$

F.A.Cotton, J.S.Wood, Inorg. Chem., 3, 245, 1964

$I4_1/a$ Z = 4   R = 0.08

DPIMZN   LB 22-38-4

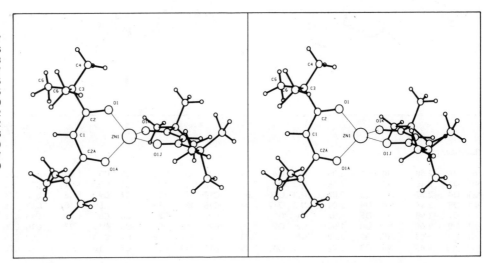

Bond Lengths

Zn1	O1	1.94
C2	O1	1.27
C1	C2	1.41
C2	C3	1.52
C3	C4	1.54
C3	C5	1.55
C3	C6	1.56

Bond Angles

O1	Zn1	O1A	97
O1	Zn1	O1J	116
Zn1	O1	C2	123
C2	C1	C2A	127
O1	C2	C1	125
O1	C2	C3	115
C1	C2	C3	120
C2	C3	C4	112
C2	C3	C5	112
C2	C3	C6	106
C4	C3	C5	110
C4	C3	C6	107
C5	C3	C6	110

77.18 Trimethyl 4,6 - dioxonyl platinum

$C_{24}H_{48}O_4Pt_2$

A.G.Swallow, M.R.Truter, Proc. R. Soc., A, 254, 205, 1960

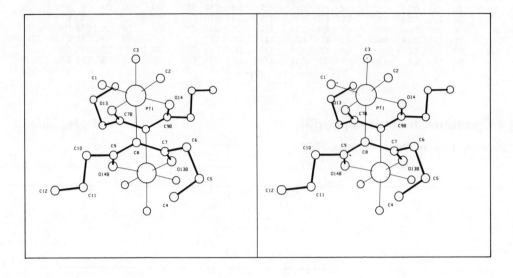

$P2_1/a$ Z = 2   R = 0.08

MEOXPT   LB 24-48-3

Bond Lengths

Pt1	O13	2.14
Pt1	O14	2.17
Pt1	C1	2.02
Pt1	C2	2.04
Pt1	C3	2.01
Pt1	C8	2.39
C7B	O13	1.22
C9B	O14	1.24
C4	C5	1.60
C5	C6	1.58
C6	C7	1.44
C7	C8	1.48
C8	C9	1.44
C9	C10	1.50
C10	C11	1.56
C11	C12	1.52

Bond Angles

O13	Pt1	O14	89
O13	Pt1	C1	91
O13	Pt1	C2	177
O13	Pt1	C3	89
O13	Pt1	C8	90
O14	Pt1	C1	177
O14	Pt1	C2	91
O14	Pt1	C3	86
O14	Pt1	C8	92
C1	Pt1	C2	89
C1	Pt1	C3	91
C1	Pt1	C8	91
C2	Pt1	C3	88
C2	Pt1	C8	93
C3	Pt1	C8	178
Pt1	O13	C7B	126
Pt1	O14	C9B	123
C4	C5	C6	109
C5	C6	C7	110
C6	C7	C8	117
Pt1	C8	C7	102
Pt1	C8	C9	103
C7	C8	C9	121
C8	C9	C10	117
C9	C10	C11	105
C10	C11	C12	110

Torsion Angles

C4	C5	C6	C7	−66
C5	C6	C7	O13B	−67
C5	C6	C7	C8	114
O13B	C7	C8	C9	27
C6	C7	C8	C9	−155
C7	C8	C9	O14B	−26
C7	C8	C9	C10	152
O14B	C9	C10	C11	78
C8	C9	C10	C11	−100
C9	C10	C11	C12	177

77.19 bis(Acetylacetonato) nickel(ii) trimer

$C_{30}H_{42}Ni_3O_{12}$

G.J.Bullen, R.Mason, P.Pauling, Inorg. Chem., 4, 456, 1965

The published Ni2 - O5 bond length is incorrect.
Pca2₁   Z = 4   R = 0.14

ACACNI   LB 10-14-36

Bond Lengths

Ni1	Ni2	2.88	Ni2	O1	2.08	Ni3	O6	2.15	C22	O5	1.23	C1	C3	1.60
Ni1	O1	2.15	Ni2	O2	2.18	Ni3	O9	2.08	C12	O6	1.55	C1	C5	1.57
Ni1	O4	2.27	Ni2	O3	2.05	Ni3	O10	1.89	C17	O7	1.50	C2	C4	1.53
Ni1	O5	2.14	Ni2	O4	2.04	Ni3	O12	2.00	C16	O8	1.33	C2	C5	1.48
Ni1	O7	1.98	Ni2	O5	1.97	C1	O1	1.37	C27	O9	1.21	C6	C8	1.94
Ni1	O8	2.06	Ni2	O6	1.96	C2	O2	1.06	C26	O10	1.22	C6	C10	1.23
Ni1	O11	2.03	Ni3	O2	2.40	C6	O3	1.63	C21	O11	1.25	C7	C9	1.72
Ni2	Ni3	2.90	Ni3	O3	2.07	C7	O4	1.38	C11	O12	1.24	C7	C10	1.53

C11	C13	1.63	C21	C23	1.17
C11	C15	1.90	C21	C25	1.54
C12	C14	1.40	C22	C24	1.55
C12	C15	1.59	C22	C25	1.63
C16	C18	1.85	C26	C28	1.30
C16	C20	1.40	C26	C30	1.67
C17	C19	1.33	C27	C29	1.38
C17	C20	1.64	C27	C30	1.44

77.20 bis(Acetylacetonato) cobalt(ii) tetramer

$C_{40}H_{56}Co_4O_{16}$

F.A.Cotton, R.C.Elder, Inorg. Chem., 4, 1145, 1965

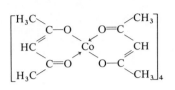

P-1   Z = 1   R = 0.154

ACACCO   LB 10-14-15

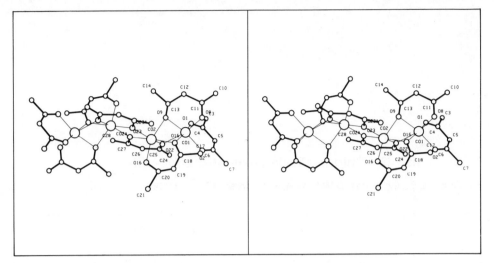

Bond Lengths

Co1	O1	1.97	Co2	O9	2.25	C4	O1	1.27	C25	O22	1.12	C10	C11	1.36	C19	C20	1.29
Co1	O2	2.07	Co2	O15	2.08	C6	O2	1.27	C27	O23	1.22	C11	C12	1.62	C20	C21	1.62
Co1	O8	1.95	Co2	O16	2.05	C11	O8	1.27	C3	C4	1.62	C12	C13	1.56	C24	C25	1.52
Co1	O9	2.11	Co2	O22	1.96	C13	O9	1.19	C4	C5	1.59	C13	C14	1.63	C25	C26	1.52
Co1	O15	2.15	Co2	O23	2.12	C18	O15	1.33	C5	C6	1.42	C17	C18	1.61	C26	C27	1.42
Co1	O22	2.28	Co2	O23A	2.15	C20	O16	1.49	C6	C7	1.61	C18	C19	1.27	C27	C28	1.51

77.21 Di(μ - diphenylphosphinatoacetylacetonato chromium(iii))

$C_{44}H_{48}Cr_2O_{12}P_2$

C.E.Wilkes, R.A.Jacobson, Inorg. Chem., 4, 99, 1965

Bond Lengths

Cr1	O1	1.97		C4	C20	1.40
Cr1	O2	1.97		C4	C24	1.42
Cr1	O3	1.94		C5	C6	1.43
Cr1	O4	1.97		C6	C7	1.35
Cr1	O5	1.95		C7	C8	1.36
Cr1	O6	1.95		C8	C9	1.41
Cr2	O7	1.95		C10	C11	1.41
Cr2	O8	1.96		C11	C12	1.38
Cr2	O9	1.94		C12	C13	1.42
Cr2	O10	1.96		C13	C14	1.40
Cr2	O11	1.96		C15	C16	1.41
Cr2	O12	1.94		C16	C17	1.38
P1	O1	1.52		C17	C18	1.37
P1	O7	1.49		C18	C19	1.41
P1	C1	1.81		C20	C21	1.40
P1	C2	1.81		C21	C22	1.40
P2	O2	1.49		C22	C23	1.36
P2	O12	1.51		C23	C24	1.43
P2	C3	1.80		C25	C26	1.52
P2	C4	1.78		C25	C27	1.37
C40	O3	1.25		C27	C28	1.39
C28	O4	1.25		C28	C29	1.55
C25	O5	1.27		C30	C31	1.47
C43	O6	1.27		C30	C32	1.38
C30	O8	1.28		C32	C33	1.44
C33	O9	1.29		C33	C34	1.52
C35	O10	1.27		C35	C36	1.49
C38	O11	1.27		C35	C37	1.38
C1	C15	1.37		C37	C38	1.39
C1	C19	1.37		C38	C39	1.53
C2	C10	1.38		C40	C41	1.54
C2	C14	1.38		C40	C42	1.40
C3	C5	1.38		C42	C43	1.41
C3	C9	1.39		C43	C44	1.53

P-1   Z = 2   R = 0.09

PHACCR   LB 44-48-1

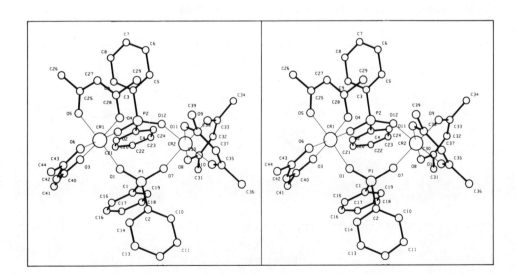

METAL COMPLEXES (SALICYLIC DERIVATIVES)

78.1   bis - (5 - Chlorosalicylaldoximato) copper(ii)

$C_{14}H_{10}Cl_2CuN_2O_4$

P.L.Orioli, E.C.Lingafelter, B.W.Brown, Acta Cryst., 17, 1113, 1964

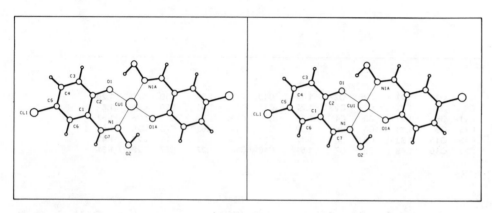

P-1   Z = 2   R = 0.07

CSALCU   LB 14-10-12

Bond Lengths

Cu1	N1	1.96
Cu1	O1	1.91
Cl1	C5	1.76
N1	O2	1.42
C7	N1	1.25
C2	O1	1.33
C1	C2	1.44
C1	C6	1.40
C1	C7	1.44
C2	C3	1.40
C3	C4	1.38
C4	C5	1.40
C5	C6	1.36

Bond Angles

N1	Cu1	N1A	180
N1	Cu1	O1	92
N1	Cu1	O1A	88
O1	Cu1	N1A	88
O1	Cu1	O1A	180
Cu1	N1	O2	117
Cu1	N1	C7	128
O2	N1	C7	115
Cu1	O1	C2	127
C2	C1	C6	118
C2	C1	C7	124
C6	C1	C7	118
O1	C2	C1	122
O1	C2	C3	119
C1	C2	C3	119
C2	C3	C4	121
C3	C4	C5	119
Cl1	C5	C4	119
Cl1	C5	C6	120
C4	C5	C6	121
C1	C6	C5	121
N1	C7	C1	124

78.2   Copper(ii) bis(salicylaldehyde) (form A)

$C_{14}H_{10}CuO_4$

A.J.McKinnon, T.N.Waters, D.Hall, J. Chem. Soc., 3290, 1964

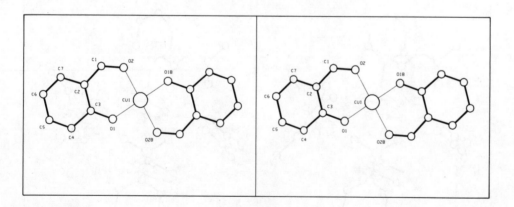

P2₁/n   Z = 2   R = 0.09

CUSALA   LB 14-10-22

Bond Lengths

Cu1	O1	1.86
Cu1	O2	1.98
C3	O1	1.32
C1	O2	1.26
C1	C2	1.39
C2	C3	1.45
C2	C7	1.39
C3	C4	1.43
C4	C5	1.31
C5	C6	1.43
C6	C7	1.35

Bond Angles

O1	Cu1	O2	95
O1	Cu1	O1B	180
O1	Cu1	O2B	85
O2	Cu1	O1B	85
O2	Cu1	O2B	180
Cu1	O1	C3	127
Cu1	O2	C1	122
O2	C1	C2	130
C1	C2	C3	122
C1	C2	C7	117
C3	C2	C7	121
O1	C3	C2	123
O1	C3	C4	121
C2	C3	C4	116
C3	C4	C5	121
C4	C5	C6	123
C5	C6	C7	118
C2	C7	C6	120

78.3 Copper(ii) bis(salicylaldehyde) (form B)

$C_{14}H_{10}CuO_4$

D.Hall, A.J.McKinnon, T.N.Waters, J. Chem. Soc., 425, 1965

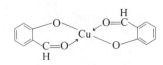

Published value of z(O2) = 0.1553.
The correct value is 0.1535.
P2₁/c   Z = 2   R = 0.14

CUSALA01   LB 14-10-23

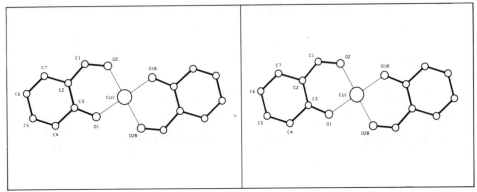

Bond Lengths

Cu1 O1	1.90	C2 C7	1.43
Cu1 O2	1.94	C3 C4	1.44
C3 O1	1.32	C4 C5	1.37
C1 O2	1.28	C5 C6	1.40
C1 C2	1.40	C6 C7	1.41
C2 C3	1.39		

Bond Angles

O1 Cu1 O2	95	Cu1 O2 C1	124	O1 C3 C4	117
O1 Cu1 O1B	180	O2 C1 C2	128	C2 C3 C4	118
O1 Cu1 O2B	85	C1 C2 C3	123	C3 C4 C5	121
O2 Cu1 O1B	85	C1 C2 C7	116	C4 C5 C6	122
O2 Cu1 O2B	180	C3 C2 C7	120	C5 C6 C7	118
Cu1 O1 C3	125	O1 C3 C2	125	C2 C7 C6	121

78.4 Copper(ii) bis(salicylaldehyde) (form A)

$C_{14}H_{10}CuO_4$

J.A.Bevan, D.P.Graddon, J.F.McConnell, Nature, 199, 373, 1963

Atomic coordinates were not reported in the paper.
P2₁/c   Z = 2   No R factor was given.

CUSALA02   LB 14-10-22

78.5 bis(Salicylaldoximato) copper(ii)

$C_{14}H_{12}CuN_2O_4$

M.A.Jarski, E.C.Lingafelter, Acta Cryst., 17, 1109, 1964

P2₁/c   Z = 2   R = 0.20

SALCOP   LB 14-12-12

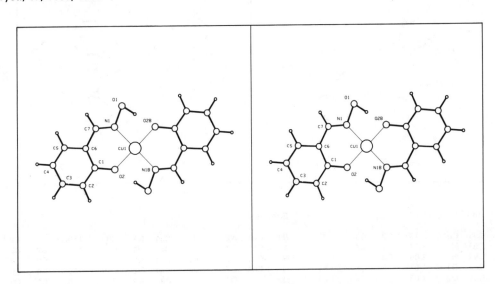

Bond Lengths

Cu1 N1	1.94	C1 C6	1.40
Cu1 O2	1.91	C2 C3	1.38
N1 O1	1.45	C3 C4	1.36
C7 N1	1.25	C4 C5	1.36
C1 O2	1.36	C5 C6	1.44
C1 C2	1.39	C6 C7	1.45

Bond Angles

N1 Cu1 N1B	180	Cu1 N1 O1	115	O2 C1 C6	121	C4 C5 C6	121
N1 Cu1 O2	91	Cu1 N1 C7	130	C2 C1 C6	119	C1 C6 C5	118
N1 Cu1 O2B	89	O1 N1 C7	115	C1 C2 C3	120	C1 C6 C7	127
O2 Cu1 N1B	89	Cu1 O2 C1	129	C2 C3 C4	123	C5 C6 C7	115
O2 Cu1 O2B	180	O2 C1 C2	120	C3 C4 C5	119	N1 C7 C6	122

78.6   bis(Salicylaldehydato) diaquo nickel(ii) (trans form) $C_{14}H_{14}NiO_6$

J.M.Stewart, E.C.Lingafelter, J.D.Breazeale, Acta Cryst., 14, 888, 1961

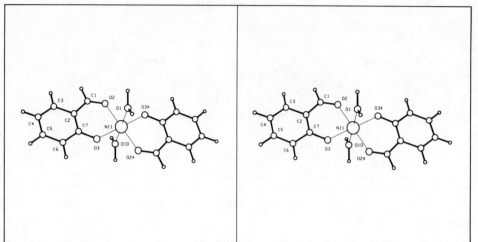

A2/m   Z = 2 R_{h0l} = 0.05,
R_{0kl} = 0.06

SALANI   LB 14-14-36

Bond Lengths

Ni1 O1	2.04
Ni1 O2	2.02
Ni1 O3	2.02
C1 O2	1.22
C7 O3	1.30
C1 C2	1.45
C2 C3	1.44
C2 C7	1.39
C3 C4	1.39
C4 C5	1.37
C5 C6	1.39
C6 C7	1.40

Bond Angles

O1 Ni1 O2	90
O1 Ni1 O3	90
O1 Ni1 O1D	180
O2 Ni1 O3	92
O2 Ni1 O2A	180
O2 Ni1 O3A	88
O3 Ni1 O2A	88
O3 Ni1 O3A	180
Ni1 O2 C1	125
Ni1 O3 C7	126
O2 C1 C2	126
C1 C2 C3	113
C1 C2 C7	128
C3 C2 C7	119
C2 C3 C4	120
C3 C4 C5	119
C4 C5 C6	122
C5 C6 C7	120
O3 C7 C2	122
O3 C7 C6	118
C2 C7 C6	120

78.7   N,N' - Disalicylidene ethylenediamine copper $C_{16}H_{14}CuN_2O_2$

D.Hall, T.N.Waters, J. Chem. Soc., 2644, 1960

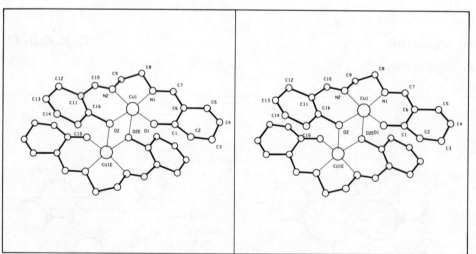

C2/c   Z = 8 R_{hk0} = 0.20,
R_{0kl} = 0.18

SEACOP   LB 16-14-13

Bond Lengths

Cu1 Cu1E	3.18
Cu1 N1	1.94
Cu1 N2	2.08
Cu1 O1	1.91
Cu1 O2	2.03
Cu1 O2E	2.41
C7 N1	1.31
C8 N1	1.55
C9 N2	1.55
C10 N2	1.25
C1 O1	1.28
C16 O2	1.48
C1 C2	1.31
C1 C6	1.43
C2 C3	1.32
C3 C4	1.47
C4 C5	1.32
C5 C6	1.54
C6 C7	1.50
C8 C9	1.56
C10 C11	1.47
C11 C12	1.56
C11 C16	1.45
C12 C13	1.42
C13 C14	1.30
C14 C15	1.43
C15 C16	1.30

Bond Angles

N1 Cu1 N2	82
N1 Cu1 O1	92
N1 Cu1 O2	169
N1 Cu1 O2E	102
N2 Cu1 O1	171
N2 Cu1 O2	96
N2 Cu1 O2E	93
O1 Cu1 O2	89
O1 Cu1 O2E	94
O2 Cu1 O2E	89
Cu1 N1 C7	128
Cu1 N1 C8	110
C7 N1 C8	121
Cu1 N2 C9	116
Cu1 N2 C10	116
C9 N2 C10	128
Cu1 O1 C1	134
Cu1 O2 Cu1E	91
Cu1 O2 C16	122
O1 C1 C2	136
O1 C1 C6	116
C2 C1 C6	108
C1 C2 C3	141
C2 C3 C4	110
C3 C4 C5	123
C4 C5 C6	116
C1 C6 C5	122
C1 C6 C7	130
C5 C6 C7	108
N1 C7 C6	119
N1 C8 C9	115
N2 C9 C8	93
N2 C10 C11	137
C10 C11 C12	126
C10 C11 C16	121
C12 C11 C16	111
C11 C12 C13	118
C12 C13 C14	115
C13 C14 C15	133
C14 C15 C16	110
O2 C16 C11	122
O2 C16 C15	107
C11 C16 C15	130

78.8 bis(N - Methylsalicylaldiminato) copper(ii) (α form)

$C_{16}H_{16}CuN_2O_2$

E.C.Lingafelter, G.L.Simmons, B.Morosin, C.Scheringer, C.Freiburg,
Acta Cryst., 14, 1222, 1961

See also Hall et al., J. Chem. Soc.
(A), 460, 1968.
Ibam $Z = 4$ $R_{hk0} = 0.08$,
$R_{hk1} = 0.08$

MSACOP   LB 16-16-9

Bond Lengths

Cu1	N1	1.99	C1	C6	1.42
Cu1	O1	1.90	C2	C3	1.39
C7	N1	1.31	C3	C4	1.40
C8	N1	1.52	C4	C5	1.37
C1	O1	1.32	C5	C6	1.39
C1	C2	1.40	C6	C7	1.44

Bond Angles

N1	Cu1	N1A	180	Cu1	N1	C7	126	O1	C1	C6	123	C4	C5	C6	121
N1	Cu1	O1	91	Cu1	N1	C8	119	C2	C1	C6	119	C1	C6	C5	119
N1	Cu1	O1A	89	C7	N1	C8	115	C1	C2	C3	120	C1	C6	C7	123
O1	Cu1	N1A	89	Cu1	O1	C1	131	C2	C3	C4	120	C5	C6	C7	118
O1	Cu1	O1A	180	O1	C1	C2	118	C3	C4	C5	120	N1	C7	C6	126

78.9 bis(N - Methylsalicylaldiminato) copper(ii) (α form)

$C_{16}H_{16}CuN_2O_2$

B.Meuthen, M.v. Stackelberg, Z. Anorg. Allg. Chem., 305, 279, 1960

The structure was determined in
two dimensions only. Atomic
coordinates were not reported in
the paper.
Ibam $Z = 4$ $R = 0.26$

MSACOP01   LB 16-16-9

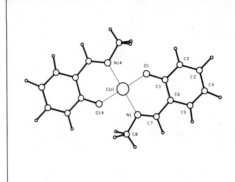

78.10 N,N' - Disalicylidene - propane - 1,2 - diamine copper monohydrate

$C_{17}H_{16}CuN_2O_2$, H_2O

F.J.Llewellyn, T.N.Waters, J. Chem. Soc., 2639, 1960

Published value of $y(C3) = 0.120$.
The correct value is -0.120.
$P2_12_12_1$ $Z = 4$ $R_{0kl} = 0.16$,
$R_{h0l} = 0.18$

SPACOM   LB 17-16-3

Bond Lengths

Cu1	N1	1.78	C11	O1	1.24	C8	C9	1.39
Cu1	N2	1.95	C10	O2	1.31	C9	C10	1.43
Cu1	O1	1.94	C1	C2	1.50	C11	C12	1.44
Cu1	O2	1.88	C2	C3	1.61	C11	C16	1.41
Cu1	O3	2.53	C4	C5	1.40	C12	C13	1.32
C2	N1	1.52	C5	C6	1.37	C13	C14	1.33
C17	N1	1.31	C5	C10	1.44	C14	C15	1.39
C3	N2	1.47	C6	C7	1.32	C15	C16	1.34
C4	N2	1.27	C7	C8	1.38	C16	C17	1.38

Bond Angles

N1	Cu1	N2	83	Cu1	N1	C17	129	N2	C4	C5	128	O1	C11	C12	121
N1	Cu1	O1	90	C2	N1	C17	110	C4	C5	C6	128	O1	C11	C16	122
N1	Cu1	O2	168	Cu1	N2	C3	115	C4	C5	C10	120	C12	C11	C16	117
N1	Cu1	O3	93	Cu1	N2	C4	125	C6	C5	C10	111	C11	C12	C13	121
N2	Cu1	O1	167	C3	N2	C4	119	C6	C7	C8	115	C12	C13	C14	124
N2	Cu1	O2	93	Cu1	O1	C11	127	C5	C6	C7	132	C13	C14	C15	112
N2	Cu1	O3	102	Cu1	O2	C10	129	C6	C7	C8	118	C14	C15	C16	131
O1	Cu1	O2	93	N1	C2	C1	111	C7	C8	C9	115	C11	C16	C15	114
O1	Cu1	O3	89	N1	C2	C3	104	O2	C10	C5	124	C11	C16	C17	124
O2	Cu1	O3	99	C1	C2	C3	109	O2	C10	C9	119	C15	C16	C17	122
Cu1	N1	C2	120	N2	C3	C2	102	C5	C10	C9	117	N1	C17	C16	122

78.11   bis - N - Ethylsalicylaldimine palladium $C_{18}H_{20}N_2O_2Pd$

E.Frasson, C.Panattoni, L.Sacconi, Acta Cryst., 17, 85, 1964

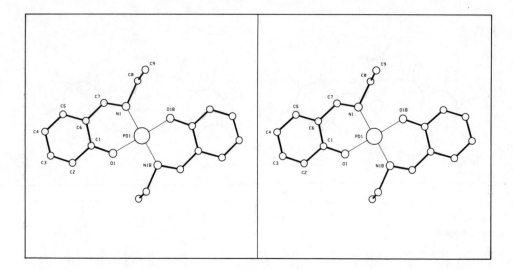

$P2_1/c$ $Z = 2$ $R_{0kl} = 0.10$,
$R_{h0l} = 0.09$

ESALPD   LB 18-20-20

Bond Lengths

Pd1	N1	1.85	C1	C6	1.44
Pd1	O1	1.94	C2	C3	1.33
C7	N1	1.32			(1.40)
C8	N1	1.61	C3	C4	1.40
C1	O1	1.33	C4	C5	1.42
C1	C2	1.45	C5	C6	1.38
		(1.40)	C6	C7	1.47
			C8	C9	1.48

Bond Angles

N1	Pd1	N1B	180	C7	N1	C8	103	C3 C4 C5	119
N1	Pd1	O1	92	Pd1	O1	C1	128	C4 C5 C6	121
N1	Pd1	O1B	88	O1	C1	C2	117	C1 C6 C5	118
O1	Pd1	N1B	88	O1	C1	C6	123	C1 C6 C7	121
O1	Pd1	O1B	180	C2	C1	C6	119	C5 C6 C7	121
Pd1	N1	C7	129	C1	C2	C3	119	N1 C7 C6	124
Pd1	N1	C8	125	C2	C3	C4	122	N1 C8 C9	105

78.12   bis(N - iso - Propylsalicylaldiminato) nickel(ii) $C_{20}H_{24}N_2NiO_2$

M.R.Fox, P.L.Orioli, E.C.Lingafelter, L.Sacconi, Acta Cryst., 17, 1159, 1964

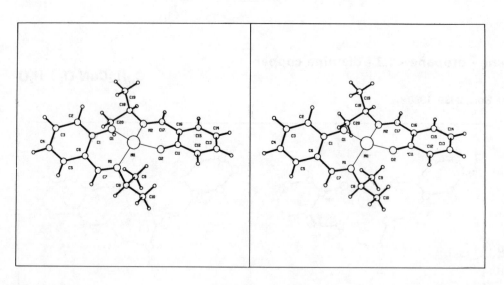

Pbca $Z = 8$ $R = 0.06$

ISALNI   LB 20-24-7

Bond Lengths

Ni1	N1	1.99	C4	C5	1.38
Ni1	N2	1.95	C5	C6	1.43
Ni1	O1	1.89	C6	C7	1.42
Ni1	O2	1.90	C8	C9	1.52
C7	N1	1.30	C8	C10	1.51
C8	N1	1.46	C11	C12	1.45
C17	N2	1.30	C11	C16	1.42
C18	N2	1.50	C12	C13	1.41
C1	O1	1.30	C13	C14	1.40
C11	O2	1.29	C14	C15	1.38
C1	C2	1.41	C15	C16	1.45
C1	C6	1.46	C16	C17	1.48
C2	C3	1.40	C18	C19	1.54
C3	C4	1.39	C18	C20	1.55

Bond Angles

N1	Ni1	N2	121	O1 C1 C2	120	O2 C11 C12	119
N1	Ni1	O1	94	O1 C1 C6	122	O2 C11 C16	126
N1	Ni1	O2	113	C2 C1 C6	118	C12 C11 C16	115
N2	Ni1	O1	112	C1 C2 C3	122	C11 C12 C13	122
N2	Ni1	O2	95	C2 C3 C4	120	C12 C13 C14	120
O1	Ni1	O2	125	C3 C4 C5	120	C13 C14 C15	122
Ni1	N1	C7	123	C4 C5 C6	122	C14 C15 C16	118
Ni1	N1	C8	121	C1 C6 C5	118	C11 C16 C15	123
C7	N1	C8	116	C1 C6 C7	124	C11 C16 C17	122
Ni1	N2	C17	125	C5 C6 C7	118	C15 C16 C17	115
Ni1	N2	C18	122	N1 C7 C6	127	N2 C17 C16	124
C17	N2	C18	113	N1 C8 C9	109	N2 C18 C19	108
Ni1	O1	C1	129	N1 C8 C10	112	N2 C18 C20	111
Ni1	O2	C11	127	C9 C8 C10	109	C19 C18 C20	111

78.13 bis(N - n - Butylsalicylaldiminato) palladium(ii)

$C_{22}H_{28}N_2O_2Pd$

E.Frasson, C.Panattoni, L.Sacconi, Acta Cryst., 17, 477, 1964

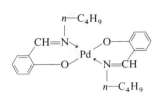

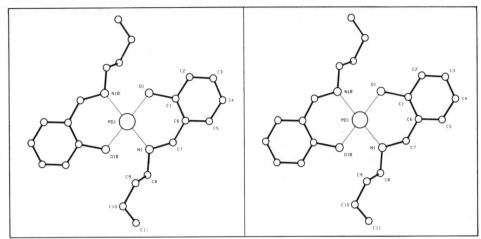

$P2_1/c$ Z = 2 R_{h0l} = 0.11,
R_{0kl} = 0.08

BSALPD   LB 22-28-21

Bond Lengths

Pd1	N1	2.02	C3	C4	1.37
Pd1	O1	2.00	C4	C5	1.39
C7	N1	1.42	C5	C6	1.38
C8	N1	1.40	C6	C7	1.41
C1	O1	1.58	C8	C9	1.38
C1	C2	1.39	C9	C10	1.48
C1	C6	1.39	C10	C11	1.47
C2	C3	1.37			

Bond Angles

N1	Pd1	N1B	180	Pd1	N1	C8	135	C1	C2	C3	118	C5	C6	C7	117
N1	Pd1	O1	103	C7	N1	C8	110	C2	C3	C4	121	N1	C7	C6	134
N1	Pd1	O1B	77	Pd1	O1	C1	115	C3	C4	C5	121	N1	C8	C9	107
O1	Pd1	N1B	77	O1	C1	C2	111	C4	C5	C6	120	C8	C9	C10	109
O1	Pd1	O1B	180	O1	C1	C6	127	C1	C6	C5	118	C9	C10	C11	117
Pd1	N1	C7	114	C2	C1	C6	122	C1	C6	C7	125				

78.14 bis(N - Methyl - 2 - hydroxy - 1 - naphthaldiminato) copper(ii)

$C_{24}H_{20}CuN_2O_2$

D.Hall, A.J.McKinnon, J.M.Waters, T.N.Waters, Nature, 201, 607, 1964

Atomic coordinates were not
reported in the paper.
$P2_1/n$ Z = 2   R = 0.16

MHNACU   LB 24-20-13

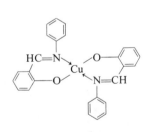

78.15 bis(N - Phenylsalicylaldiminato) copper(ii)

$C_{26}H_{20}CuN_2O_2$

L.Wei, R.M.Stogsdill, E.C.Lingafelter, Acta Cryst., 17, 1058, 1964

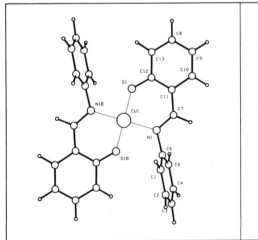

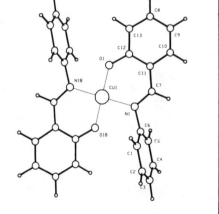

$P2_1/n$ Z = 2   R = 0.06

PSALCU   LB 26-20-7

Bond Lengths

Cu1	N1	1.99	C4	C5	1.43
Cu1	O1	1.88	C5	C6	1.34
C6	N1	1.44	C7	C11	1.44
C7	N1	1.30	C8	C9	1.37
C12	O1	1.31	C8	C13	1.40
C1	C2	1.41	C9	C10	1.37
C1	C6	1.39	C10	C11	1.42
C2	C3	1.32	C11	C12	1.40
C3	C4	1.35	C12	C13	1.42

Bond Angles

N1	Cu1	N1B	180	C6	N1	C7	117	N1	C6	C1	119	C7	C11	C10	118
N1	Cu1	O1	91	Cu1	O1	C12	128	N1	C6	C5	121	C7	C11	C12	123
N1	Cu1	O1B	89	C2	C1	C6	119	C1	C6	C5	120	C10	C11	C12	119
O1	Cu1	N1B	89	C1	C2	C3	121	N1	C7	C11	126	O1	C12	C11	124
O1	Cu1	O1B	180	C2	C3	C4	119	C9	C8	C13	122	O1	C12	C13	118
Cu1	N1	C6	120	C3	C4	C5	122	C8	C9	C10	118	C11	C12	C13	118
Cu1	N1	C7	123	C4	C5	C6	118	C9	C10	C11	122	C8	C13	C12	120

METAL COMPLEXES (THIOUREA)

79.1 bis(Thiourea) mercury(ii) chloride

$C_2H_8ClHgN_4S_2^+$, Cl^-

K.K.Cheung, R.S.McEwen, G.A.Sim, Nature, 205, 383, 1965

Atomic coordinates were not reported in the paper.
Pmnm Z = 2 R = 0.183

HGCSUR   LB 2-8-23

$$\left([(NH_2)_2C{=}S]_2\, HgCl\right)^+ Cl^-$$

79.2 Copper(i) tris(thiourea) chloride

$(C_3H_{12}CuN_6S_3^+)_n$, nCl^-

Y.Okaya, C.Knobler, Acta Cryst., 17, 928, 1964

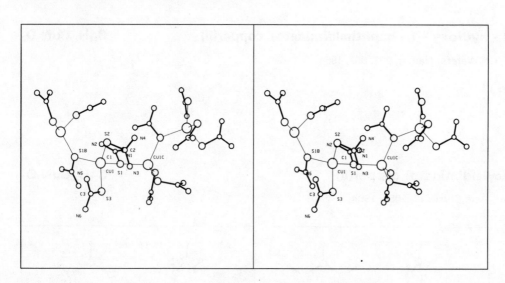

$$[(NH_2)_2C{=}S]_3\, Cu^+ Cl^-$$

$P4_12_12$ Z = 8   R = 0.10

CUTHIC   LB 3-12-11

Bond Lengths

Cu1	S1	2.43	C1	N1	1.31
Cu1	S2	2.28	C1	N2	1.31
Cu1	S3	2.35	C2	N3	1.29
Cu1	S1B	2.38	C2	N4	1.38
S1	C1	1.73	C3	N5	1.37
S2	C2	1.74	C3	N6	1.33
S3	C3	1.71			

Bond Angles

S1	Cu1	S2	111	Cu1	S1	C1	111	S2	C2	N4	116
S1	Cu1	S3	100	Cu1	S2	C2	105	N3	C2	N4	118
S1	Cu1	S1B	114	Cu1	S3	C3	108	S3	C3	N5	122
S2	Cu1	S3	116	S1	C1	N1	121	S3	C3	N6	122
S2	Cu1	S1B	107	S1	C1	N2	121	N5	C3	N6	116
S3	Cu1	S1B	109	N1	C1	N2	118				
Cu1	S1	Cu1C	134	S2	C2	N3	125				

79.3 bis(Thiourea) cadmium formate

$C_4H_{10}CdN_4O_4S_2$

M.Nardelli, G.F.Gasparri, P.Boldrini, Acta Cryst., 18, 618, 1965

$(S═C(NH_2)_2)_2 \cdot Cd^{2+}(HCOO^-)_2$

$P2_12_12$ Z = 2   R = 0.128

SURCDF   LB 4-10-12

Bond Lengths			Bond Angles			
Cd1	S1	2.71	S1	Cd1	S1A	88
Cd1	O1	2.28	S1	Cd1	O1	98
S1	C1	1.76	S1	Cd1	O1A	92
C1	N1	1.29	O1	Cd1	O1A	166
C1	N2	1.30	Cd1	S1	C1	102
C2	O1	1.28	Cd1	O1	C2	131
C2	O2	1.21	S1	C1	N1	120
			S1	C1	N2	120
			N1	C1	N2	120
			O1	C2	O2	126

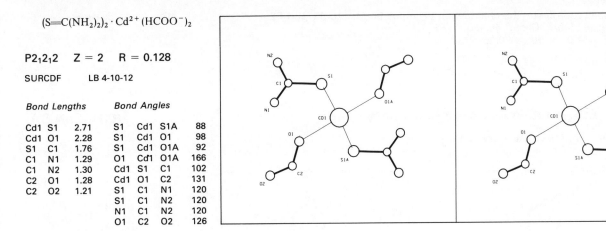

79.4 Dichloro tetrakisthiourea nickel

$C_4H_{16}Cl_2N_8NiS_4$

A.Lopez-Castro, M.R.Truter, J. Chem. Soc., 1309, 1963

$4\,S═C(NH_2)_2 \cdot NiCl_2$

No comparison of bond lengths is possible since they are not reported in the paper.
I4   Z = 2   R = 0.07

SURNIC   LB 4-16-43

Bond Lengths			Bond Angles			
Ni1	Cl1	2.39	Cl1	Ni1	Cl2	180
Ni1	Cl2	2.51	Cl1	Ni1	S1	97
Ni1	S1	2.47	Cl2	Ni1	S1	83
S1	C1	1.73	S1	Ni1	S1A	167
C1	N1	1.35	S1	Ni1	S1B	89
C1	N2	1.33	Ni1	S1	C1	114
			S1	C1	N1	117
			S1	C1	N2	122
			N1	C1	N2	120

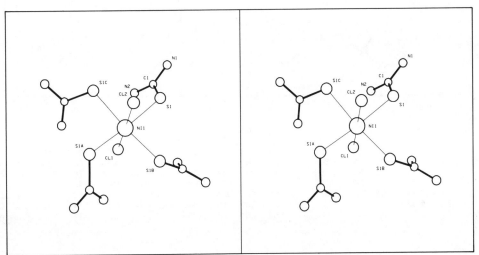

79.5 Mercury(ii) tetrathiourea cobalt(ii) tetrathiocyanate

$C_4H_{16}HgN_8S_4{}^{2+}$, $C_4CoN_4S_4{}^{2-}$

A.Korczynski, M.A.Porai-Koshits, Rocz. Chem., 39, 1567, 1965

$$\left[\left(S═C\begin{smallmatrix}NH_2\\NH_2\end{smallmatrix}\right)_4 Hg\right]^{2+} [Co(SCN)_4]^{2-}$$

I-4   Z = 2   R = 0.14

HGTCOT   LB 8-16-29

Bond Lengths			Bond Angles			
Hg1	S1	2.59	S1	Hg1	S1A	110
S1	C1	1.73	S1	Hg1	S1B	109
C1	N1	1.25	Hg1	S1	C1	107
C1	N3	1.40	S1	C1	N1	125
			S1	C1	N3	130
			N1	C1	N3	105
Co1	N2	2.01				
S2	C2	1.79				
C2	N2	1.09	N2	Co1	N2A	127
			N2	Co1	N2F	101
			Co1	N2	C2	174
			S2	C2	N2	170

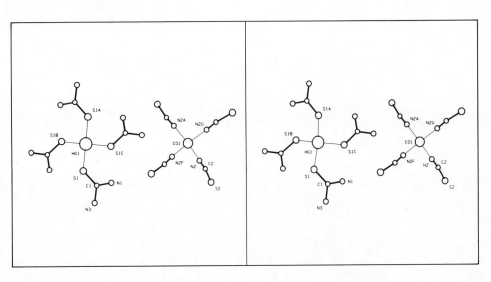

79.6   Tetrathiourea palladium(ii) chloride

S.Ooi, T.Kawase, K.Nakatsu, H.Kuroya, Bull. Chem. Soc. Jap., 33, 861, 1960

$$C_4H_{16}N_8PdS_4^{2+}, 2Cl^-$$

Using the published coordinates the chloride ion becomes bonded to S2 and C2.
See also Berta et al., Inorg. Chem., 9, 136, 1970.
C2/c   Z = 4 R_{h0l} = 0.18, R_{hk0} = 0.16

$$4(S=C(NH_2)_2) \cdot PdCl_2$$

THUPDC   LB 4-16-47

79.7   bis - Ethylenethiourea cadmium thiocyanate

L.Cavalca, M.Nardelli, G.Fava, Acta Cryst., 13, 125, 1960

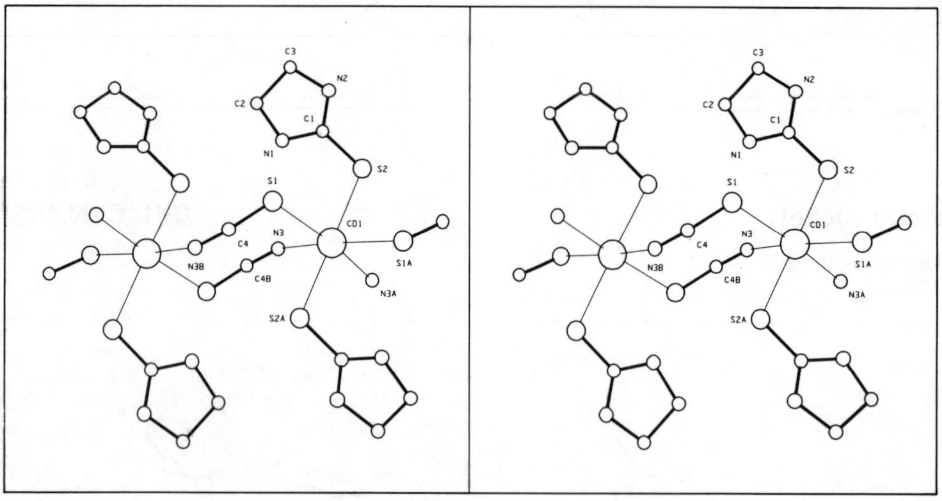

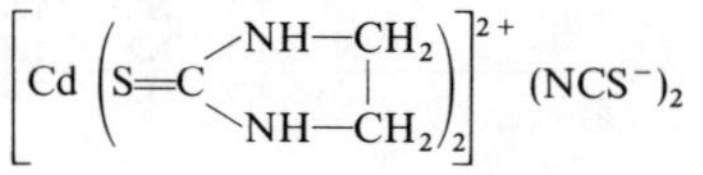

$$(C_8H_{12}CdN_6S_4)_n$$

$$\left[Cd \left(S=C \begin{matrix} NH-CH_2 \\ | \\ NH-CH_2 \end{matrix} \right)_2 \right]^{2+} (NCS^-)_2$$

C2/c   Z = 4 R_{h0l} = 0.16,
R_{hk0} = 0.23, R_{h1l} = 0.11, R_{hk1} = 0.15

ETCDTH   LB 8-12-8

Bond Lengths

Cd1	S1	2.73		C2	N1	1.47
Cd1	S2	2.60		C1	N2	1.30
Cd1	N3	2.53		C3	N2	1.48
S1	C4	1.55		C4D	N3	1.19
S2	C1	1.74		C2	C3	1.57
C1	N1	1.32				

Bond Angles

S1	Cd1	S2	93		S2	Cd1	N3	95		Cd1	N3	C4D	141
S1	Cd1	S1A	95		S2	Cd1	N3A	88		S2	C1	N1	126
S1	Cd1	S2A	84		N3	Cd1	N3A	78		S2	C1	N2	125
S1	Cd1	N3	93		Cd1	S1	C4	109		N1	C1	N2	109
S1	Cd1	N3A	172		Cd1	S2	C1	112		N1	C2	C3	101
S2	Cd1	S1A	84		C1	N1	C2	114		N2	C3	C2	101
S2	Cd1	S2A	175		C1	N2	C3	114		S1	C4	N3D	166

506

80.1   Gold dipropyldithiocarbamate

$(C_5H_{10}AuNS_2)_n$

R.Hesse, Acta Cryst., 13, 1025, 1960

$[(n—C_3H_7)_2NCS_2Au]_2$

Atomic coordinates were not reported in the paper.
The space group and Z were not reported.
No R factor was given.

AUDTHC

80.2   Nickel xanthate

$C_6H_{10}NiO_2S_4$

M.Franzini, Z. Kristallogr., 118, 393, 1963

$H_5C_2—O—C\overset{S}{\underset{S}{\diagdown}}\rightarrow Ni \overset{S}{\underset{S}{\diagup}}C—O—C_2H_5$

Pbca   Z = 4   R = 0.13

NIXANT   LB 6-10-32

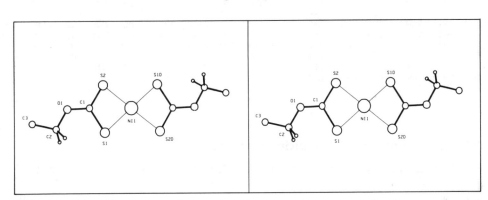

Bond Lengths			Bond Angles			
Ni1	S1	2.24	S1	Ni1	S2	80
Ni1	S2	2.23	S1	Ni1	S1D	180
S1	C1	1.73	S1	Ni1	S2D	100
S2	C1	1.65	S2	Ni1	S1D	100
C1	O1	1.38	S2	Ni1	S2D	180
C2	O1	1.38	Ni1	S1	C1	81
C2	C3	1.48	Ni1	S2	C1	83
			C1	O1	C2	123
			S1	C1	S2	116
			S1	C1	O1	119
			S2	C1	O1	125
			O1	C2	C3	109

80.3   Nitroso - (dimethyldithiocarbamato) cobalt

$C_6H_{12}CoN_3OS_4$

P.R.H.Alderman, P.G.Owston, J.M.Rowe, J. Chem. Soc., 668, 1962

$P2_1/c$ Z = 4 $R_{0kl} = 0.09,$
$R_{h0l} = 0.16$

NOMTCO   LB 6-12-18

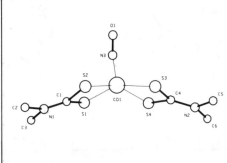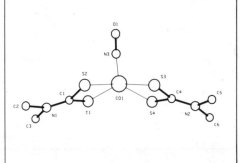

Bond Lengths

Co1	S1	2.19	S4	C4	1.71
Co1	S2	2.35	N3	O1	1.10
Co1	S3	2.42	C1	N1	1.21
Co1	S4	2.24	C2	N1	1.57
Co1	N3	1.70	C3	N1	1.46
S1	C1	1.59	C4	N2	1.26
S2	C1	1.91	C5	N2	1.42
S3	C4	1.77	C6	N2	1.42

Bond Angles

S1	Co1	S2	79	S3	Co1	S4	75	C1	N1	C2	124	S1	C1	S2	111
S1	Co1	S3	154	S3	Co1	N3	113	C1	N1	C3	124	S1	C1	N1	126
S1	Co1	S4	101	S4	Co1	N3	104	C2	N1	C3	112	S2	C1	N1	123
S1	Co1	N3	93	Co1	S1	C1	91	C4	N2	C5	120	S3	C4	S4	110
S2	Co1	S3	92	Co1	S2	C1	79	C4	N2	C6	129	S3	C4	N2	124
S2	Co1	S4	151	Co1	S3	C4	84	C5	N2	C6	111	S4	C4	N2	127
S2	Co1	N3	105	Co1	S4	C4	91	Co1	N3	O1	127				

80.4 Cadmium n - butyl xanthate $(C_{10}H_{18}CdO_2S_4)_n$

H.M.Rietveld, E.N.Maslen, Acta Cryst., 18, 429, 1965

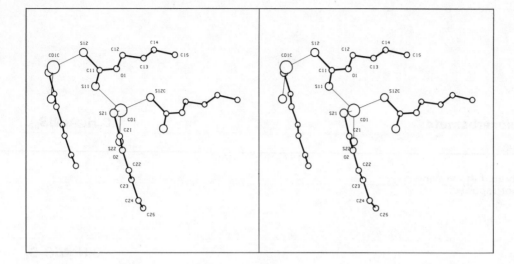

$P2_1/a$ $Z = 4$ $R = 0.122$

CADBUX   LB 10-18-7

Bond Lengths

Cd1	S11	2.63	C21	O2	1.39
Cd1	S21	2.57	C22	O2	1.48
Cd1	S22	2.54	C12	C13	1.48
Cd1	S12C	2.56	C13	C14	1.53
S11	C11	1.63	C14	C15	1.55
S12	C11	1.77	C22	C23	1.61
S21	C21	1.69	C23	C24	1.51
C11	O1	1.33	C24	C25	1.54
C12	O1	1.49			

Bond Angles

S11	Cd1	S21	95	Cd1	S21	C21	109	C12	C13	C14	115
S11	Cd1	S22	118	C11	O1	C12	123	C13	C14	C15	113
S11	Cd1	S12C	108	C21	O2	C22	118	S21	C21	O2	117
S21	Cd1	S22	113	S11	C11	S12	125	O2	C22	C23	103
S21	Cd1	S12C	122	S11	C11	O1	118	C22	C23	C24	107
S22	Cd1	S12C	101	S12	C11	O1	116	C23	C24	C25	109
Cd1	S11	C11	98	O1	C12	C13	103				

80.5 Copper(ii) diethyldithiocarbamate $C_{10}H_{20}CuN_2S_4$

M.Bonamico, G.Dessy, A.Mugnoli, A.Vaciago, L.Zambonelli, Acta Cryst., 19, 886, 1965

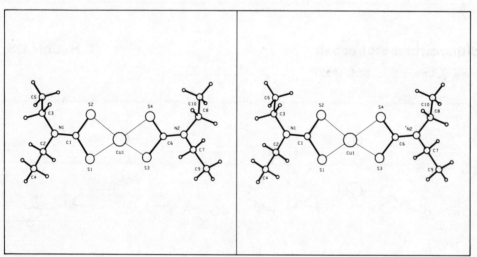

See also O'Connor & Maslen, Acta Cryst., 21, 828, 1966; Bally, These Doct. Sci. Phys. —Paris, 1966.

$P2_1/c$ $Z = 4$ $R = 0.081$

CETCAM   LB 10-20-9

Bond Lengths

Cu1	S1	2.32	C2	N1	1.47
Cu1	S2	2.30	C3	N1	1.47
Cu1	S3	2.30	C6	N2	1.33
Cu1	S4	2.34	C7	N2	1.46
S1	C1	1.71	C8	N2	1.48
S2	C1	1.71	C2	C4	1.52
S3	C6	1.71	C3	C5	1.52
S4	C6	1.74	C7	C9	1.53
C1	N1	1.35	C8	C10	1.51

Bond Angles

S1	Cu1	S2	77	Cu1	S4	C6	84	S2	C1	N1	123
S1	Cu1	S3	101	C1	N1	C2	121	N1	C2	C4	110
S1	Cu1	S4	172	C1	N1	C3	122	N1	C3	C5	112
S2	Cu1	S3	162	C2	N1	C3	117	S3	C6	S4	113
S2	Cu1	S4	102	C6	N2	C7	121	S3	C6	N2	124
S3	Cu1	S4	76	C6	N2	C8	122	S4	C6	N2	123
Cu1	S1	C1	84	C7	N2	C8	117	N2	C7	C9	112
Cu1	S2	C1	84	S1	C1	S2	115	N2	C8	C10	112
Cu1	S3	C6	86	S1	C1	N1	122				

80.6   Nickel(ii) diethyldithiocarbamate

$C_{10}H_{20}N_2NiS_4$

M.Bonamico, G.Dessy, C.Mariani, A.Vaciago, L.Zambonelli, Acta Cryst., 19, 619, 1965

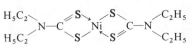

P2$_1$/c   Z = 2   R = 0.101

NIDCAR   LB 10-20-15

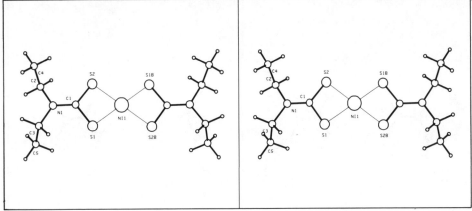

Bond Lengths

Ni1	S1	2.21	C2	N1	1.49
Ni1	S2	2.20	C3	N1	1.48
S1	C1	1.71	C2	C4	1.50
S2	C1	1.70	C3	C5	1.53
C1	N1	1.33			

Bond Angles

S1	Ni1	S2	79	Ni1	S1	C1	85	S1	C1	S2	111
S1	Ni1	S1B	180	Ni1	S2	C1	85	S1	C1	N1	124
S1	Ni1	S2B	101	C1	N1	C2	120	S2	C1	N1	126
S2	Ni1	S1B	101	C1	N1	C3	123	N1	C2	C4	111
S2	Ni1	S2B	180	C2	N1	C3	117	N1	C3	C5	111

80.7   bis(Ethyl xanthanato) oxo molybdenum(v) - μ - oxo - bis(ethyl xanthanato) oxo molybdenum(v)

$C_{12}H_{20}Mo_2O_7S_8$

A.B.Blake, F.A.Cotton, J.S.Wood, J. Amer. Chem. Soc., 86, 3024, 1964

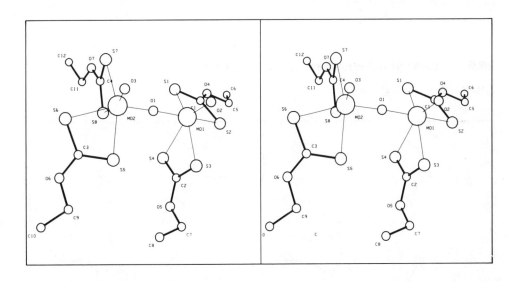

P2$_1$ Z = 2   R = 0.09

OMOETX   LB 12-20-7

Bond Lengths

Mo1	S1	2.46	S5	C3	1.65
Mo1	S2	2.53	S6	C3	1.72
Mo1	S3	2.51	S7	C4	1.72
Mo1	S4	2.69	S8	C4	1.56
Mo1	O1	1.85	C1	O4	1.39
Mo1	O2	1.64	C5	O4	1.44
Mo2	S5	2.47	C2	O5	1.39
Mo2	S6	2.54	C7	O5	1.48
Mo2	S7	2.51	C3	O6	1.37
Mo2	S8	2.72	C9	O6	1.46
Mo2	O1	1.87	C4	O7	1.40
Mo2	O3	1.65	C11	O7	1.46
S1	C1	1.65	C5	C6	1.46
S2	C1	1.72	C7	C8	1.51
S3	C2	1.71	C9	C10	1.53
S4	C2	1.56	C11	C12	1.50

Bond Angles

S1	Mo1	S2	70	S6	Mo2	S7	92	C2	O5	C7	122
S1	Mo1	S3	151	S6	Mo2	S8	81	C3	O6	C9	123
S1	Mo1	S4	86	S6	Mo2	O1	155	C4	O7	C11	123
S1	Mo1	O1	92	S6	Mo2	O3	99	S1	C1	S2	117
S1	Mo1	O2	115	S7	Mo2	S8	67	S1	C1	O4	124
S2	Mo1	S3	95	S7	Mo2	O1	99	S2	C1	O4	119
S2	Mo1	S4	81	S7	Mo2	O3	94	S3	C2	S4	123
S2	Mo1	O1	158	S8	Mo2	O1	83	S3	C2	O5	113
S2	Mo1	O2	93	S8	Mo2	O3	161	S4	C2	O5	123
S3	Mo1	S4	67	O1	Mo2	O3	102	S5	C3	S6	119
S3	Mo1	O1	96	Mo1	S1	C1	88	S5	C3	O6	122
S3	Mo1	O2	90	Mo1	S2	C1	84	S6	C3	O6	119
S4	Mo1	O1	86	Mo1	S3	C2	86	S7	C4	S8	124
S4	Mo1	O2	156	Mo1	S4	C2	83	S7	C4	O7	115
O1	Mo1	O2	105	Mo2	S5	C3	87	O4	C5	C6	105
S5	Mo2	S6	71	Mo2	S6	C3	83	O5	C7	C8	113
S5	Mo2	S7	152	Mo2	S7	C4	86	O6	C9	C10	106
S5	Mo2	S8	88	Mo2	S8	C4	82	O7	C11	C12	105
S5	Mo2	O1	90	Mo1	O1	Mo2	178				
S5	Mo2	O3	110	C1	O4	C5	121				

Torsion Angles

S1	Mo1	O1	Mo2	157
S2	Mo1	O1	Mo2	125
S3	Mo1	O1	Mo2	4
S4	Mo1	O1	Mo2	71
O2	Mo1	O1	Mo2	−87
S5	Mo2	O1	Mo1	−28
S6	Mo2	O1	Mo1	−65
S7	Mo2	O1	Mo1	180
S8	Mo2	O1	Mo1	−116
O3	Mo2	O1	Mo1	82

80.8 bis - (N,N - Di - n - propyldithiocarbamato) copper(ii) C₁₄H₂₈CuN₂S₄

A.Pignedoli, G.Peyronel, Gazz. Chim. Ital., 92, 745, 1962

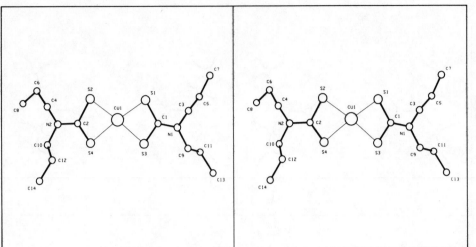

$P2_1/a$ $Z = 4$ $R_{hk0} = 0.12$, $R_{0kl} = 0.15$

PRSCCU   LB 14-28-5

Bond Lengths

Cu1	S1	2.32	C2	N2	1.33
Cu1	S2	2.33	C4	N2	1.46
Cu1	S3	2.32	C10	N2	1.45
Cu1	S4	2.32	C3	C5	1.54
S1	C1	1.67	C4	C6	1.55
S2	C2	1.73	C5	C7	1.55
S3	C1	1.70	C6	C8	1.57
S4	C2	1.67	C9	C11	1.53
C1	N1	1.33	C10	C12	1.54
C3	N1	1.47	C11	C13	1.56
C9	N1	1.47	C12	C14	1.53

Bond Angles

S1	Cu1	S2	101	C1	N1	C3	119	S2	C2	N2	119
S1	Cu1	S3	76	C1	N1	C9	127	S4	C2	N2	124
S1	Cu1	S4	159	C3	N1	C9	111	N1	C3	C5	104
S2	Cu1	S3	161	C2	N2	C4	121	N2	C4	C6	112
S2	Cu1	S4	76	C2	N2	C10	121	C3	C5	C7	112
S3	Cu1	S4	100	C4	N2	C10	112	C4	C6	C8	110
Cu1	S1	C1	84	S1	C1	S3	116	N1	C9	C11	111
Cu1	S2	C2	83	S1	C1	N1	125	N2	C10	C12	121
Cu1	S3	C1	83	S3	C1	N1	119	C9	C11	C13	116
Cu1	S4	C2	84	S2	C2	S4	115	C10	C12	C14	103

80.9 Diethyldithiocarbamato copper(i) tetramer C₂₀H₄₀Cu₄N₄S₈

R.Hesse, Ark. Kemi, 20, 481, 1963

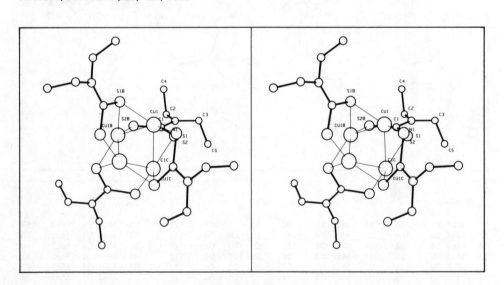

$P\text{-}42_1c$ $Z = 8$ $R = 0.11$

CUETSC   LB 5-10-5

Bond Lengths

Cu1	Cu1B	2.66	C1	N1	1.41
Cu1	S1	2.29	C2	N1	1.50
Cu1	S2	2.25	C3	N1	1.46
Cu1	S1B	2.26	C2	C4	1.53
S1	C1	1.72	C3	C5	1.54
S2	C1C	1.69			

Bond Angles

S1	Cu1	Cú1C	54	Cu1	S1	Cu1C	71	C2	N1	C3	115
S1	Cu1	S2	110	Cu1	S1	C1	113	S1	C1	S2B	125
S1	Cu1	S1B	121	Cu1	S2	C1C	102	S1	C1	N1	117
S2	Cu1	Cu1C	101	C1	N1	C2	123	N1	C2	C4	109
S2	Cu1	S1B	128	C1	N1	C3	122	N1	C3	C5	111

80.10 bis(Diethyldithiocarbamato) zinc(ii) dimer

$C_{20}H_{40}N_4S_8Zn_2$

M.Bonamico, G.Mazzone, A.Vaciago, L.Zambonelli, Acta Cryst., 19, 898, 1965

See also Zvonkova et al., Kristallografija, 12, 1065, 1967.
$P2_1/c$ $Z = 4$ $R = 0.106$

ZETCAM   LB 10-20-26

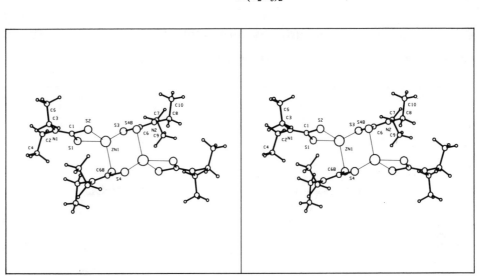

Bond Lengths

Zn1	S1	2.44
Zn1	S2	2.36
Zn1	S3	2.33
Zn1	S4	2.38
S1	C1	1.72
S2	C1	1.73
S3	C6	1.72
S4	C6B	1.74
C1	N1	1.34
C2	N1	1.44
C3	N1	1.49
C6	N2	1.31
C7	N2	1.48
C8	N2	1.48
C2	C4	1.52
C3	C5	1.48
C7	C9	1.51
C8	C10	1.53

Bond Angles

S1	Zn1	S2	76
S1	Zn1	S3	107
S1	Zn1	S4	105
S2	Zn1	S3	138
S2	Zn1	S4	112
S3	Zn1	S4	108
Zn1	S1	C1	82
Zn1	S2	C1	84
Zn1	S3	C6	94
Zn1	S4	C6B	102
C1	N1	C2	122
C1	N1	C3	122
C2	N1	C3	116
C6	N2	C7	123
C6	N2	C8	121
C7	N2	C8	115
S1	C1	S2	118
S1	C1	N1	121
S2	C1	N1	121
N1	C2	C4	111
N1	C3	C5	113
S3	C6	S4B	118
S3	C6	N2	120
N2	C7	C9	112
N2	C8	C10	111

80.11   Silver(i) diethyldithiocarbamate hexamer

$C_{30}H_{60}Ag_6N_6S_{12}$

R.Hesse, Acta Cryst., 13, 1025, 1960

$[(C_2H_5)_2 NCS_2Ag]_6$

Atomic coordinates were not
reported in the paper.
The space group and Z were not
reported.   No R factor was
given.

AGDTHC

81.1 Sodium ammonium oxy molybdenum oxalate dihydrate $C_2MoO_7^{2-}$, H_4N^+, Na^+, $2H_2O$

L.O.Atovmyan, G.B.Bokii, Zh. Strukt. Khim., 4, 576, 1963

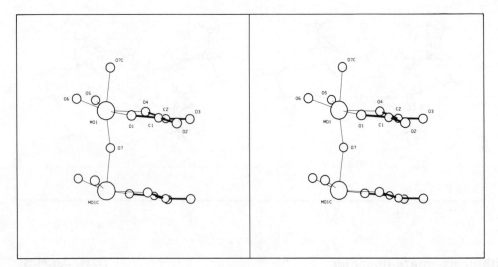

$$Na^+\ (NH_4)^+\left[\left(\begin{array}{c}COO\\|\\COO\end{array}\right)MoO_3\right]^{2-}\cdot 2\,H_2O$$

$P2_1/c$ $Z = 4$ $R = 0.15$

SAMOOX   LB 2-4-27

Bond Lengths

Mo1	O1	2.22	C1	O1	1.33
Mo1	O4	2.17	C1	O2	1.23
		(2.24)	C2	O3	1.29
Mo1	O5	1.82	C2	O4	1.41
Mo1	O6	1.85			(1.36)
Mo1	O7	1.86	C1	C2	1.49
Mo1	O7C	2.16			
		(2.23)			

Bond Angles

O1	Mo1	O4	73	O4	Mo1	O7C	89	Mo1	O4	C2	117
O1	Mo1	O5	161	O5	Mo1	O6	97	Mo1	O7	Mo1C	157
O1	Mo1	O6	93	O5	Mo1	O7	105	O1	C1	O2	127
O1	Mo1	O7	84	O5	Mo1	O7C	85	O1	C1	C2	113
O1	Mo1	O7C	83	O6	Mo1	O7	116	O2	C1	C2	119
O4	Mo1	O5	92	O6	Mo1	O7C	71	O3	C2	O4	122
O4	Mo1	O6	157	O7	Mo1	O7C	166	O3	C2	C1	121
O4	Mo1	O7	81	Mo1	O1	C1	120	O4	C2	C1	115

81.2 Diaquo copper(ii) formate $(C_2H_6CuO_6)_n$

M.Bukowska-Strzyzewska, Acta Cryst., 19, 357, 1965

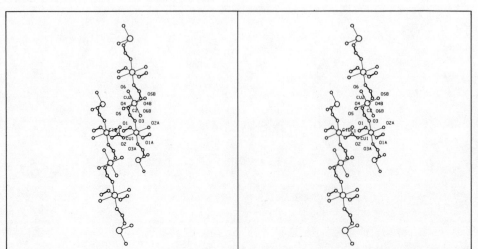

$$\left[\,Cu^{2+}\ (HCOO^-)_2\ (H_2O)_2\,\right]_n$$

See also Kay et al., Acta Cryst. (B), 24, 1312, 1968.
$P2_1/c$ $Z = 4$ $R_{hk0} = 0.08$,
$R_{h0l} = 0.09$, $R_{0kl} = 0.10$

CUFORD   LB 2-2-14

Bond Lengths

Cu1	O1	2.02	C2	O3	1.22
Cu1	O2	2.28	C2	O4	1.27
Cu1	O3	2.03			
C1	O1	1.19	Cu2	O5	1.96
C1A	O2	1.29	Cu2	O6	2.02

Bond Angles

O1	Cu1	O2	89	O2	Cu1	O3	91	Cu1	O2	C1A	128	O5 Cu2 O6 89
O1	Cu1	O3	93	O2	Cu1	O2B	180	Cu1	O3	C2	125	O5 Cu2 O5B 180
O1	Cu1	O1B	180	O2	Cu1	O3B	89	O1	C1	O2A	126	O5 Cu2 O6B 91
O1	Cu1	O2B	91	O3	Cu1	O3B	180	O3	C2	O4	123	O6 Cu2 O6B 180
O1	Cu1	O3B	87	Cu1	O1	C1	119					

81.3 Diaquo manganese(ii) formate $(C_2H_6MnO_6)_n$

K.Osaki, Y.Nakai, T.Watanabe, J. Phys. Soc. Jap., 19, 717, 1964

$$\left[Mn^{2+} (HCOO^-)_2 (H_2O)_2 \right]_n$$

See also Kay et al., Acta Cryst. (B), 24, 1312, 1968.
$P2_1/c$ $Z = 4$ $R_{0kl} = 0.11$, $R_{h0l} = 0.09$

MNFORD   LB 2-2-25

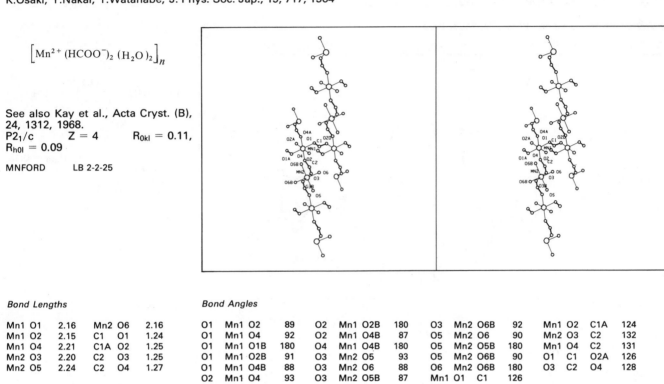

Bond Lengths

Mn1	O1	2.16	Mn2	O6	2.16
Mn1	O2	2.15	C1	O1	1.24
Mn1	O4	2.21	C1A	O2	1.25
Mn2	O3	2.20	C2	O3	1.25
Mn2	O5	2.24	C2	O4	1.27

Bond Angles

O1	Mn1	O2	89	O2	Mn1	O2B	180	O3	Mn2	O6B	92	Mn1	O2	C1A	124
O1	Mn1	O4	92	O2	Mn1	O4B	87	O5	Mn2	O6	90	Mn2	O3	C2	132
O1	Mn1	O1B	180	O4	Mn1	O4B	180	O5	Mn2	O5B	180	Mn1	O4	C2	131
O1	Mn1	O2B	91	O3	Mn2	O5	93	O5	Mn2	O6B	90	O1	C1	O2A	126
O1	Mn1	O4B	88	O3	Mn2	O6	88	O6	Mn2	O6B	180	O3	C2	O4	128
O2	Mn1	O4	93	O3	Mn2	O5B	87	Mn1	O1	C1	126				

81.4 Diaquo nickel(ii) formate $(C_2H_6NiO_6)_n$

K.Krogmann, R.Mattes, Z. Kristallogr., 118, 291, 1963

$$\left[Ni^{2+} (HCOO^-)_2 (H_2O)_2 \right]_n$$

$P2_1/c$ $Z = 4$ $R = 0.08$

NIFORM   LB 2-2-29

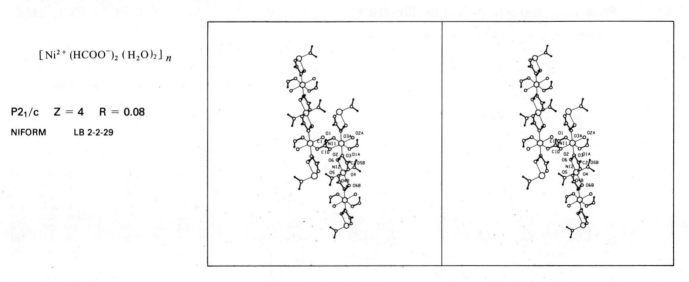

Bond Lengths

Ni1	O1	2.03	Ni2	O6	2.06
Ni1	O2	2.06	C1	O1	1.26
Ni1	O3	2.10	C1A	O2	1.22
Ni2	O4	2.09	C2	O3	1.28
Ni2	O5	2.04	C2	O4	1.25

Bond Angles

O1	Ni1	O2	90	O2	Ni1	O1B	90	O4	Ni2	O5B	90	Ni1	O1	C1	123
O1	Ni1	O3	87	O2	Ni1	O2B	180	O4	Ni2	O6B	91	Ni1	O2	C1A	126
O1	Ni1	O1B	180	O2	Ni1	O3B	93	O5	Ni2	O6	90	Ni1	O3	C2	126
O1	Ni1	O2B	90	O3	Ni1	O3B	180	O5	Ni2	O5B	180	Ni2	O4	C2	137
O1	Ni1	O3B	93	O4	Ni2	O5	90	O5	Ni2	O6B	90	O1	C1	O2A	126
O2	Ni1	O3	87	O4	Ni2	O6	89	O6	Ni2	O6B	180	O3	C2	O4	123

81.5   Cobalt(iii) penta - ammine acetate chloride perchlorate $C_2H_{18}CoN_5O_2{}^{2+}$, Cl^- , $ClO_4{}^-$

E.B.Fleischer, R.Frost, J. Amer. Chem. Soc., 87, 3998, 1965

Atomic coordinates were not given
but bond lengths were reported.
Pbca   Z = 8   R = 0.14

$[Co(NH_3)_5CH_3COO]^{2+} Cl^- (ClO_4)^-$

COAMAC   LB 2-18-2

81.6   Copper ammonium oxalate dihydrate $C_4CuO_8{}^{2-}$, $2H_4N^+$, $2H_2O$

M.A.Viswamitra, J. Chem. Phys., 37, 1408, 1962

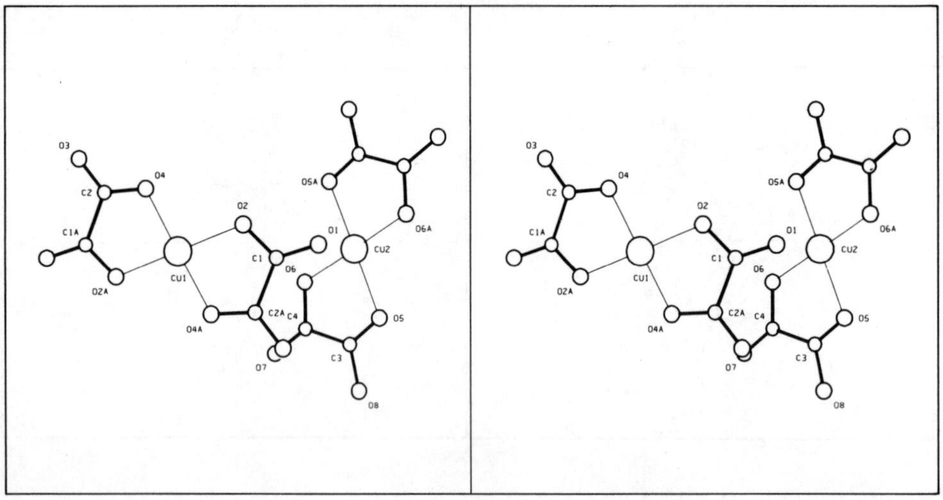

$$Cu^{2+}(NH_4^+)_2\left[\begin{pmatrix}COO\\ |\\ COO\end{pmatrix}^{2-}\right]_2 \cdot 2\,H_2O$$

P-1   Z = 2 R_{hk0} = 0.13,
R_{0kl} = 0.16

CUAMOX   LB 4-8-40

Bond Lengths

Cu2	O5	2.13	Cu1	O2	2.12
Cu2	O6	1.97	Cu1	O4	1.98
C3	O5	1.20	C1	O1	1.23
C4	O6	1.35	C1	O2	1.30
C4	O7	1.30	C2	O3	1.25
C3	O8	1.32	C2	O4	1.31
C3	C4	1.58	C1	C2A	1.61

Bond Angles

O5	Cu2	O6	85	O5	C3	O8	116	O2	Cu1	O4	99	O1 C1 O2 119
O5	Cu2	O5A	180	O5	C3	C4	126	O2	Cu1	O2A	180	O1 C1 C2A 129
O5	Cu2	O6A	95	O8	C3	C4	117	O2	Cu1	O4A	81	O2 C1 C2A 110
O6	Cu2	O6A	180	O6	C4	O7	119	O4	Cu1	O2A	81	O3 C2 O4 127
Cu2	O5	C3	105	O6	C4	C3	111	O4	Cu1	O4A	180	O3 C2 C1A 116
Cu2	O6	C4	113	O7	C4	C3	130	Cu1	O2	C1	116	O4 C2 C1A 117
								Cu1	O4	C2	116	

81.7   Potassium oxalato platinate dihydrate $C_4O_8Pt^{2-}$, $2K^+$, $2H_2O$

R.Mattes, K.Krogmann, Z. Anorg. Allg. Chem., 332, 247, 1964

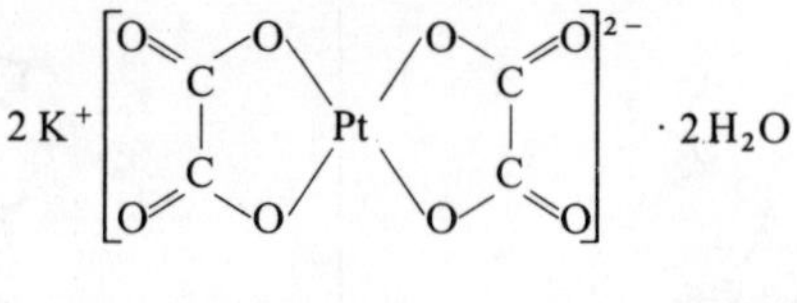

$$2\,K^+ \left[\begin{array}{c} \end{array}\right]^{2-} \cdot 2\,H_2O$$

P2$_1$/n   Z = 2   R = 0.08

KOXPTD   LB 4-0-21

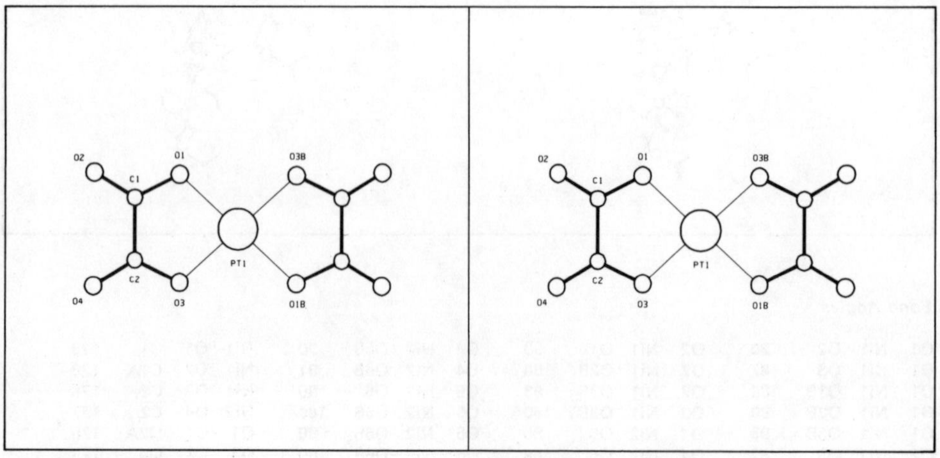

Bond Lengths

Pt1	O1	2.01
Pt1	O3	2.00
C1	O1	1.29
C1	O2	1.21
C2	O3	1.28
C2	O4	1.23
C1	C2	1.54

Bond Angles

O1	Pt1	O3	83
O1	Pt1	O1B	180
O1	Pt1	O3B	97
O3	Pt1	O3B	180
Pt1	O1	C1	113
Pt1	O3	C2	114
O1	C1	O2	124
O1	C1	C2	116
O2	C1	C2	121
O3	C2	O4	124
O3	C2	C1	115
O4	C2	C1	121

81.8   Copper(ii) formate

G.A.Barclay, C.H.L.Kennard, J. Chem. Soc., 3289, 1961

$(C_4H_4Cu_2O_8)_n$

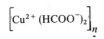

$$\left[Cu^{2+}(HCOO^-)_2 \right]_n \cdot$$

Pbca   Z = 8   R = 0.12

CUFORM   LB 2-2-13

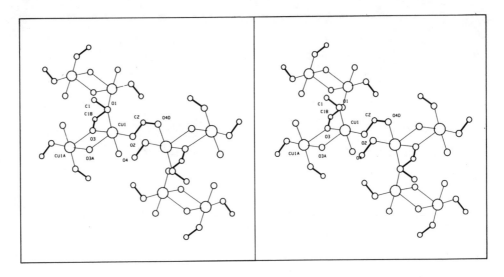

Bond Lengths

Cu1	O1	1.95	C1	O1	1.23
Cu1	O2	1.94	C2	O2	1.28
Cu1	O3	1.97	C1F	O3	1.29
Cu1	O4	1.93	C2C	O4	1.28

Bond Angles

O1	Cu1	O2	89	Cu1	O1	C1	130
O1	Cu1	O3	95	Cu1	O2	C2	119
O1	Cu1	O4	176	Cu1	O3	C1F	114
O2	Cu1	O3	176	Cu1	O4	C2C	125
O2	Cu1	O4	89	O1	C1	O3F	120
O3	Cu1	O4	88	O2	C2	O4C	122

81.9   Aquo barium(ii) oxalato - oxo - molybdenum(v) - μ - dioxo - oxalato - oxo - molybdenum(v) dihydrate

F.A.Cotton, S.M.Morehouse, Inorg. Chem., 4, 1377, 1965

$C_4H_4Mo_2O_{14}{}^{2-}$, H_2BaO^{2+} , $2H_2O$

$P3_121$ Z = 3   R = 0.102

BAOMOX   LB 4-0-3

$$Ba(H_2O)^{2+} \left[\cdots \right]^{2-} \cdot 3H_2O$$

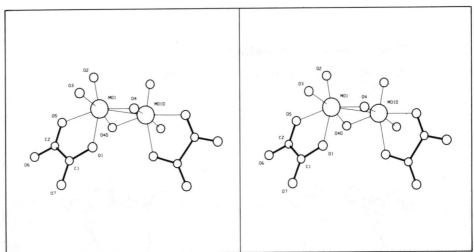

Bond Lengths

Mo1	Mo1D	2.54
Mo1	O1	2.11
Mo1	O2	1.70
Mo1	O3	2.21
Mo1	O4	1.93
Mo1	O5	2.14
Mo1	O4D	1.88
C1	O1	1.32
C2	O5	1.25
C2	O6	1.24
C1	O7	1.22
C1	C2	1.56

Bond Angles

O1	Mo1	O2	159	O2	Mo1	O4	108	O4	Mo1	O5	160	O1	C1	O7	132
O1	Mo1	O3	79	O2	Mo1	O5	91	O4	Mo1	O4D	93	O1	C1	C2	111
O1	Mo1	O4	86	O2	Mo1	O4D	104	O5	Mo1	O4D	86	O7	C1	C2	116
O1	Mo1	O5	75	O3	Mo1	O4	89	Mo1	O1	C1	119	O5	C2	O6	126
O1	Mo1	O4D	91	O3	Mo1	O5	89	Mo1	O4	Mo1D	84	O5	C2	C1	116
O2	Mo1	O3	85	O3	Mo1	O4D	169	Mo1	O5	C2	117	O6	C2	C1	117

81.10 Copper(ii) diammine acetate

M.Bukowska-Strzyzewska, Rocz. Chem., 37, 1335, 1963

$C_4H_{12}CuN_2O_4$

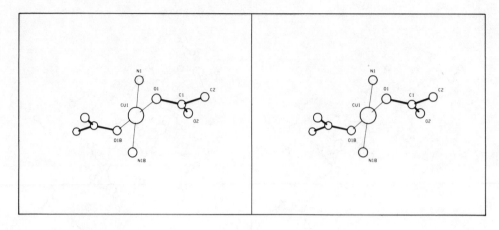

$(NH_3)_2 Cu^{2+} (HCOO^-)_2$

$P2_1/c$ $Z = 2$ $R = 0.12$

CUAMAC   LB 4-12-30

Bond Lengths			Bond Angles			
Cu1	N1	1.99	N1	Cu1	N1B	180
Cu1	O1	2.02	N1	Cu1	O1	88
C1	O1	1.27	N1	Cu1	O1B	92
C1	O2	1.24	O1	Cu1	N1B	92
C1	C2	1.47	O1	Cu1	O1B	180
			Cu1	O1	C1	108
			O1	C1	O2	119
			O1	C1	C2	123
			O2	C1	C2	117

81.11 Copper(ii) diammine acetate

Yu.A.Simonov, A.V.Ablov, T.I.Malinovskii, Kristallografija, 8, 270, 1963

$C_4H_{12}CuN_2O_4$

$(NH_3)_2 Cu^{2+} (HCOO^-)_2$

$P2_1/c$ $Z = 2$
No R factor was given.

CUAMAC01   LB 4-12-30

Bond Lengths			Bond Angles			
Cu1	N1	1.97	N1	Cu1	N1B	180
Cu1	O1	2.06	N1	Cu1	O1	94
C1	O1	1.21	N1	Cu1	O1B	86
C1	O2	1.17	O1	Cu1	N1B	86
C1	C2	1.60	O1	Cu1	O1B	180
			Cu1	O1	C1	106
			O1	C1	O2	131
			O1	C1	C2	116
			O2	C1	C2	114

81.12 Zinc dihydrazine diacetate

A.Ferrari, A.Braibanti, G.Bigliardi, A.M.Lanfredi, Acta Cryst., 19, 548, 1965

$(C_4H_{14}N_4O_4Zn)_n$

$([Zn(N_2H_4)_2]^{2+} (CH_3COO^-)_2)_n$

P-1 $Z = 1$ $R = 0.093$

ZHACET   LB 4-14-12

Bond Lengths			Bond Angles			
Zn1	N1	2.18	N1	Zn1	N2	90
Zn1	N2	2.21	N1	Zn1	N1A	180
Zn1	O1	2.15	N1	Zn1	N2A	90
C1	O1	1.26	N1	Zn1	O1	85
C1	O2	1.25	N1	Zn1	O1A	95
C1	C2	1.53	N2	Zn1	N1A	90
			N2	Zn1	N2A	180
			N2	Zn1	O1	86
			N2	Zn1	O1A	94
			O1	Zn1	N1A	95
			O1	Zn1	N2A	94
			O1	Zn1	O1A	180
			Zn1	O1	C1	130
			O1	C1	O2	126
			O1	C1	C2	116
			O2	C1	C2	118

81.13   Sodium tetrakisoxalato zirconate(iv) trihydrate

G.L.Glen, J.V.Silverton, J.L.Hoard, Inorg. Chem., 2, 250, 1963

$C_8O_{16}Zr^{4-}$, $4Na^+$, $3H_2O$

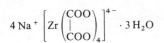

$$4\,Na^+ \left[Zr \binom{COO}{COO}_4 \right]^{4-} \cdot 3\,H_2O$$

B22$_1$2   Z = 4   R = 0.08

NAOXZR   LB 8-0-13

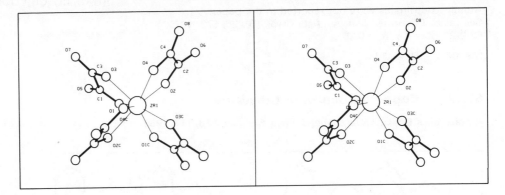

Bond Lengths

Zr1 O1	2.22	C4 O4	1.29
Zr1 O2	2.19	C1 O5	1.21
Zr1 O3	2.14	C2 O6	1.22
Zr1 O4	2.24	C3 O7	1.22
C1 O1	1.28	C4 O8	1.23
C2 O2	1.27	C1 C3	1.54
C3 O3	1.27	C2 C4	1.55

Bond Angles

O1 Zr1 O2	78	O2 Zr1 O2C	151
O1 Zr1 O3	71	O2 Zr1 O3C	88
O1 Zr1 O4	128	O2 Zr1 O4C	138
O1 Zr1 O1C	73	O3 Zr1 O4	75
O1 Zr1 O2C	78	O3 Zr1 O1C	144
O1 Zr1 O3C	144	O3 Zr1 O2C	88
O1 Zr1 O4C	136	O3 Zr1 O3C	145
O2 Zr1 O3	101	O3 Zr1 O4C	76
O2 Zr1 O4	71	O4 Zr1 O1C	136
O2 Zr1 O1C	78	O4 Zr1 O2C	138

O4 Zr1 O3C	76	O2 C2 C4	114
O4 Zr1 O4C	68	O6 C2 C4	118
Zr1 O1 C1	120	O3 C3 O7	127
Zr1 O2 C2	121	O3 C3 C1	114
Zr1 O3 C3	122	O7 C3 C1	120
Zr1 O4 C4	120	O4 C4 O8	125
O1 C1 O5	126	O4 C4 C2	113
O1 C1 C3	112	O8 C4 C2	122
O5 C1 C3	121	
O2 C2 O6	128	

81.14   Molybdenum (ii) acetate dimer

D.Lawton, R.Mason, J. Amer. Chem. Soc., 87, 921, 1965

$C_8H_{12}Mo_2O_8$

Atomic coordinates were not given
but bond lengths were reported.
P-1   Z = 1   R = 0.071

MOLACE   LB 4-6-44

$Mo^{2+}(CH_3COO^-)_2$

81.15   Uranium (iv) acetate

I.Jelenic, D.Grdenic, A.Bezjak, Acta Cryst., 17, 758, 1964

$(C_8H_{12}O_8U)_n$

$$\left[U^{4+}(H_3C\cdot COO^-)_4 \right]_n$$

No comparison of bond lengths is
possible since they are not reported
in the paper.
C2/c   Z = 4 R_{hk0} = 0.11,
R_{h0l} = 0.15

URACET   LB 8-12-49

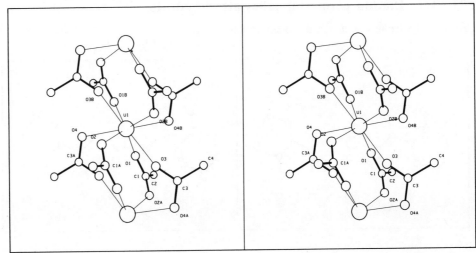

Bond Lengths

U1 O1	2.49	C3 O3	1.27
U1 O2	2.48	C3 O4	1.29
U1 O4	2.49	C1 C2	1.48
C1 O1	1.28	C3 C4	1.50
C1D O2	1.26		

Bond Angles

O1 U1 O2	126	O2 U1 O2A	72
O1 U1 O4	81	O2 U1 O4A	143
O1 U1 O1A	76	O4 U1 O4A	139
O1 U1 O2A	133	U1 O1 C1	143
O1 U1 O4A	67	U1 O2 C1D	134
O2 U1 O4	76	U1 O4 C3	103

O1 C1 O2D	120
O1 C1 C2	116
O3 C3 O4	116
O3 C3 C4	118
O4 C3 C4	126

81.16   Triaquo - hexa - acetato - μ_3 - oxo - trichromium (iii) chloride pentahydrate

B.N.Figgis, G.B.Robertson, Nature, 205, 694, 1965

$C_{12}H_{24}Cr_3O_{16}{}^+, Cl^-, 5H_2O$

$[(H_2O)_3 Cr_3 (CH_3COO)_6]^+ Cl^- . 5H_2O$

Atomic coordinates were not reported in the paper.
See also Chang & Jeffrey, Acta Cryst. (B), 26, 673, 1970.
$P2_12_12$ Z = 4   R = 0.16

CRACOP   LB 12-18-18

81.17   Copper(ii) benzoate trihydrate

$C_{14}H_{10}CuO_4 , 3H_2O$

H.Koizumi, K.Osaki, T.Watanabe, J. Phys. Soc. Jap., 18, 117, 1963

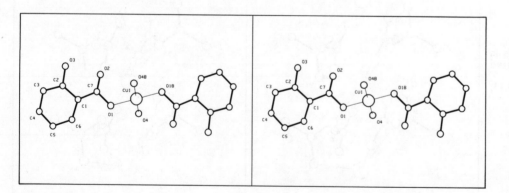

$Cu^{2+}\left(\begin{array}{c}COO^-\\ \\ \end{array}\right)_2 \cdot 3 H_2O$

I2/c   Z = 4 R_{hk0} = 0.09,
R_{0kl} = 0.12

CUBNZT   LB 14-10-26

Bond Lengths

Cu1	O1	1.91	C6	O2	1.25
Cu1	O3	1.97	C6	C7	1.50
C1	O1	1.24	C7	C8	1.41
C1	C2	1.47	C8	C9	1.40
C2	C3	1.40	C9	C10	1.36
C3	C4	1.42			
C4	C5	1.40			

Bond Angles

O1	Cu1	O3	91	O1	C1	C2	118	O2	C6	O2A	125
O1	Cu1	O1D	180	C1	C2	C3	122	O2	C6	C7	118
O1	Cu1	O3D	89	C3	C2	C3A	117	C6	C7	C8	120
O3	Cu1	O1D	89	C2	C3	C4	124	C8	C7	C8A	120
O3	Cu1	O3D	180	C3	C4	C5	116	C7	C8	C9	118
Cu1	O1	C1	131	C4	C5	C4A	124	C8	C9	C10	121
O1	C1	O1A	124					C9	C10	C9A	120

81.18   Diaquo copper(ii) salicylate dihydrate

$C_{14}H_{14}CuO_8 , 2H_2O$

F.Hanic, J.Michalov, Acta Cryst., 13, 299, 1960

$P2_1/c$ Z = 2   R = 0.24

CUSALC   LB 14-10-27

Bond Lengths

Cu1	O1	1.84	C1	C6	1.40
Cu1	O4	1.92	C1	C7	1.44
C7	O1	1.38	C2	C3	1.40
C7	O2	1.22	C3	C4	1.40
C2	O3	1.36	C4	C5	1.37
C1	C2	1.41	C5	C6	1.41

Bond Angles

O1	Cu1	O4	89	C2	C1	C7	118	C4	C5	C6	116
O1	Cu1	O1B	180	C6	C1	C7	128	C1	C6	C5	125
O1	Cu1	O4B	91	O3	C2	C1	122	O1	C7	O2	122
O4	Cu1	O1B	91	O3	C2	C3	112	O1	C7	C1	114
O4	Cu1	O4B	180	C1	C2	C3	126	O2	C7	C1	124
Cu1	O1	C7	122	C2	C3	C4	116				
C2	C1	C6	113	C3	C4	C5	124				

81.19 Pyridine copper(ii) acetate dimer (monoclinic form)

$C_{18}H_{22}Cu_2N_2O_8$

G.A.Barclay, C.H.L.Kennard, J. Chem. Soc., 5244, 1961

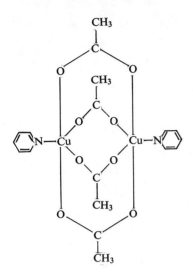

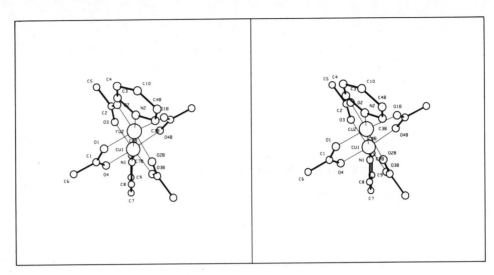

A2/a   Z = 8   R = 0.13

PYCUAC   LB 9-11-7

Bond Lengths

Cu1	Cu2	2.63	C2	O2	1.22
Cu1	N1	2.12	C2	O3	1.23
Cu1	O3	1.99	C1	O4	1.25
Cu1	O4	1.97	C1	C6	1.47
Cu2	N2	2.13	C2	C5	1.54
Cu2	O1	1.98	C3	C4	1.38
Cu2	O2	1.99	C4	C10	1.41
C8	N1	1.38	C7	C8	1.41
C3	N2	1.38	C7	C9	1.43
C1	O1	1.25			

Bond Angles

Cu2	Cu1	N1	180	N2	Cu2	O2	96	O1	C1	O4	123
Cu2	Cu1	O3	84	O1	Cu2	O2	88	O1	C1	C6	118
Cu2	Cu1	O4	84	O1	Cu2	O1B	166	O4	C1	C6	119
N1	Cu1	O3	96	O1	Cu2	O2B	90	O2	C2	O3	127
N1	Cu1	O4	96	O2	Cu2	O1B	90	O2	C2	C5	117
O3	Cu1	O4	89	O2	Cu2	O2B	167	O3	C2	C5	115
O3	Cu1	O3B	167	Cu1	N1	C8	121	N2	C3	C4	122
O3	Cu1	O4B	90	C8	N1	C8B	118	C3	C4	C10	121
O4	Cu1	O3B	90	Cu2	N2	C3	121	C8	C7	C9	114
O4	Cu1	O4B	168	C3	N2	C3B	118	N1	C8	C7	125
Cu1	Cu2	N2	180	Cu2	O1	C1	125	C7	C9	C7B	125
Cu1	Cu2	O1	83	Cu2	O2	C2	123	C4	C10	C4B	117
Cu1	Cu2	O2	84	Cu1	O3	C2	123				
N2	Cu2	O1	97	Cu1	O4	C1	124				

81.20 Pyridine copper(ii) acetate dimer (orthorhombic form)

$C_{18}H_{22}Cu_2N_2O_8$

F.Hanic, D.Stempelova, K.Hanicova, Acta Cryst., 17, 633, 1964

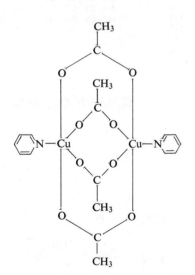

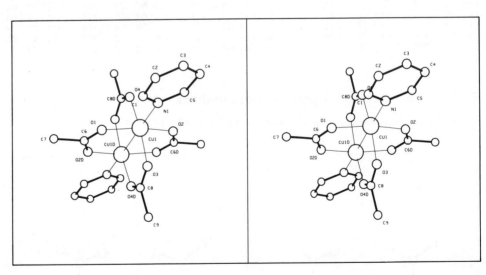

Pbca   Z = 4   R = 0.13

PYCUAC01   LB 9-11-7

Bond Lengths

Cu1	Cu1D	2.65	C6D	O2	1.24
Cu1	N1	2.19	C8	O3	1.25
Cu1	O1	1.98	C8D	O4	1.25
Cu1	O2	1.97	C1	C2	1.40
Cu1	O3	1.95	C2	C3	1.34
Cu1	O4	1.93	C4	C5	1.38
C1	N1	1.31	C4	C5	1.42
C5	N1	1.35	C6	C7	1.55
C6	O1	1.25	C8	C9	1.53

Bond Angles

N1	Cu1	O1	96	O3	Cu1	O4	167	C1	C2	C3	120
N1	Cu1	O2	96	Cu1	N1	C1	121	C2	C3	C4	122
N1	Cu1	O3	97	Cu1	N1	C5	120	C3	C4	C5	115
N1	Cu1	O4	96	C1	N1	C5	119	N1	C5	C4	123
O1	Cu1	O2	168	Cu1	O1	C6	120	O1	C6	O2D	128
O1	Cu1	O3	90	Cu1	O2	C6D	124	O1	C6	C7	116
O1	Cu1	O4	89	Cu1	O3	C8	123	O3	C8	O4D	123
O2	Cu1	O3	87	Cu1	O4	C8D	127	O3	C8	C9	117
O2	Cu1	O4	91	N1	C1	C2	121				

82.1   cis - Copper(ii) glycine monohydrate

K.Tomita, I.Nitta, Bull. Chem. Soc. Jap., 34, 286, 1961

$C_4H_8CuN_2O_4$, H_2O

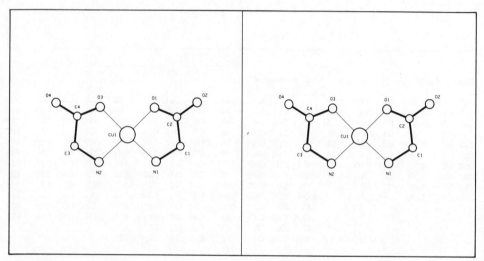

The structure was solved from two - dimensional projections.
$P2_12_12_1$ Z = 4 R_{h0l} = 0.16, R_{0kl} = 0.17, R_{hk0} = 0.17

CUGLYM   LB 4-8-37

Bond Lengths						Bond Angles									Torsion Angles				
Cu1	N1	1.99	C2	O1	1.23	N1	Cu1	N2	96	Cu1	N1	C1	106	O1	C2	C1	119	N1 C1 C2 O1	7
Cu1	N2	1.98	C2	O2	1.26	N1	Cu1	O1	85	Cu1	N2	C3	105	O2	C2	C1	118	N1 C1 C2 O2	−175
Cu1	O1	1.93	C4	O3	1.27	N1	Cu1	O3	177	Cu1	O1	C2	115	N2	C3	C4	117	N2 C3 C4 O3	5
Cu1	O3	1.95	C4	O4	1.29	N2	Cu1	O1	177	Cu1	O3	C4	114	O3	C4	O4	127	N2 C3 C4 O4	176
C1	N1	1.44	C1	C2	1.44	N2	Cu1	O3	87	N1	C1	C2	115	O3	C4	C3	116		
C3	N2	1.48	C3	C4	1.47	O1	Cu1	O3	92	O1	C2	O2	123	O4	C4	C3	116		

82.2   cis - Copper(ii) glycine monohydrate

H.C.Freeman, M.R.Snow, I.Nitta, K.Tomita, Acta Cryst., 17, 1463, 1964

$C_4H_8CuN_2O_4$, H_2O

Three - dimensional film data were used for the anisotropic refinement.

$P2_12_12_1$ Z = 4   R = 0.09

CUGLYM01   LB 4-8-37

Bond Lengths

Cu1	N1	1.98	C2	O1	1.28	
Cu1	N2	2.02	C2	O2	1.23	
Cu1	O1	1.96	C4	O3	1.29	
Cu1	O3	1.95	C4	O4	1.24	
Cu1	O5	2.40	C1	C2	1.50	
C1	N1	1.47	C3	C4	1.54	
C3	N2	1.48				

Bond Angles

N1	Cu1	N2	97	O1	Cu1	O5	92	O1	C2	C1	117
N1	Cu1	O1	85	O3	Cu1	O5	89	O2	C2	C1	118
N1	Cu1	O3	175	Cu1	N1	C1	109	N2	C3	C4	111
N1	Cu1	O5	96	Cu1	N2	C3	110	O3	C4	O4	123
N2	Cu1	O1	178	Cu1	O1	C2	115	O3	C4	C3	117
N2	Cu1	O3	85	Cu1	O3	C4	116	O4	C4	C3	120
N2	Cu1	O5	90	N1	C1	C2	113				
O1	Cu1	O3	93	O1	C2	O2	124				

Torsion Angles

N1	C1	C2	O1	5
N1	C1	C2	O2	−176
N2	C3	C4	O3	−8
N2	C3	C4	O4	174

82.3   Aquo copper(ii) glycylglycine dihydrate

$C_4H_8CuN_2O_4$, $2H_2O$

B.Strandberg, I.Lindqvist, R.Rosenstein, Z. Kristallogr., 116, 266, 1961

$P2_1/n$ Z = 8   R = 0.13

CGLGLT   LB 8-14-14

$Cu(H_2O)^{2+}(NH_2\text{—}CH_2\text{—}CO\text{—}NH\text{—}CH_2\text{—}COO^-)_2 . 2H_2O$

Bond Lengths

Cu1	N1	2.02	Cu2	N3	2.05	
Cu1	N2	1.87	Cu2	N4	1.88	
Cu1	O3	1.97	Cu2	O9	1.99	
Cu1	O4	1.97	Cu2	O10	1.99	
C1	N1	1.51	C5	N3	1.47	
C2	N2	1.28	C6	N4	1.27	
C3	N2	1.49	C7	N4	1.49	
C2	O1	1.26	C6	O7	1.28	
C4	O2	1.24	C8	O8	1.26	
C4	O3	1.25	C8	O9	1.27	
C1	C2	1.53	C5	C6	1.53	
C3	C4	1.54	C7	C8	1.51	

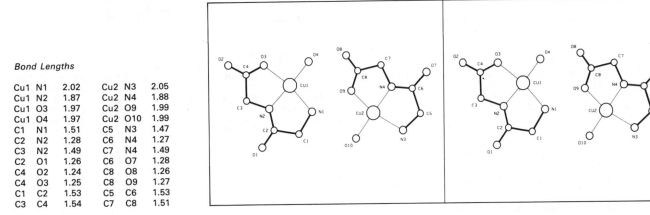

Bond Angles

N1	Cu1	N2	83	Cu1	O3	C4	116	N3	Cu2	N4	83	Cu2	O9	C8	114
N1	Cu1	O3	168	N1	C1	C2	113	N3	Cu2	O9	163	N3	C5	C6	112
N1	Cu1	O4	100	N2	C2	O1	131	N3	Cu2	O10	98	N4	C6	O7	128
N2	Cu1	O3	84	N2	C2	C1	111	N4	Cu2	O9	83	N4	C6	C5	114
N2	Cu1	O4	162	O1	C2	C1	118	N4	Cu2	O10	163	O7	C6	C5	118
O3	Cu1	O4	92	N2	C3	C4	107	O9	Cu2	O10	92	N4	C7	C8	106
Cu1	N1	C1	108	O2	C4	O3	126	Cu2	N3	C5	109	O8	C8	O9	121
Cu1	N2	C2	124	O2	C4	C3	116	Cu2	N4	C6	121	O8	C8	C7	118
Cu1	N2	C3	115	O3	C4	C3	117	Cu2	N4	C7	117	O9	C8	C7	120
C2	N2	C3	121					C6	N4	C7	122				

Torsion Angles

C3	N2	C2	O1	0	C7	N4	C6	O7	5	
C3	N2	C2	C1	−180	C7	N4	C6	C5	−178	
C2	N2	C3	C4	174	C6	N4	C7	C8	177	
N1	C1	C2	N2	−6	N3	C5	C6	N4	9	
N1	C1	C2	O1	173	N3	C5	C6	O7	−174	
N2	C3	C4	O2	−179	N4	C7	C8	O8	−176	
N2	C3	C4	O3	1	N4	C7	C8	O9	−2	

82.4   syn - Dichloro - bis - glycino - biaquo manganese(ii)

$C_4H_{14}Cl_2MnN_2O_6$

M.Lee, Y.Okaya, R.Pepinsky, Bull. Amer. Phys. Soc., 7, 177, 1962

Atomic   coordinates   were   not reported in the paper.
$P2_1$ Z = 2   R = 0.16

GLYCMN

$$H_2O\ \ \overset{\displaystyle Cl}{\underset{\displaystyle Cl}{\underset{|}{\overset{|}{Mn}}}}\ \ \overset{OOC\,CH_2\,NH_3^+}{\underset{OOC\,CH_2\,NH_3^+}{}}$$

82.5   Iron(ii) sulfate pentahydrate glycine

$C_4H_{18}FeN_2O_8{}^{2+}$, $H_{12}FeO_6{}^{2+}$, $2O_4S^{2-}$

I.Lindqvist, R.Rosenstein, Acta Chem. Scand., 14, 1228, 1960

The published values of x(O10) and x(O11) are incorrect (private communication). This destroys the connectivity of the molecule.
P-1   Z = 2 R_{hk0} = 0.14,
R_{0kl} = 0.18

GLYCFE   LB 4-10-25

$[(NH_2\text{—}CH_2\text{—}COOH)_2 . FeSO_4 . 5H_2O]_2$

82.6 Glycylglycylglycino aquo copper(ii) chloride sesquihydrate $(C_6H_{10}ClCuN_3O_4)_{2n}$, $3nH_2O$

H.C.Freeman, G.Robinson, J.C.Schoone, Acta Cryst., 17, 719, 1964

$$[(H_2N-CH_2-CO-NH-CH_2-CO-NH-CH_2-COO)Cu]^+Cl^-\cdot 1{,}5H_2O$$

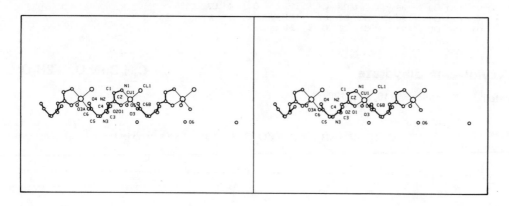

C2/c   Z = 8   R = 0.12

GGGCUC   LB 6-10-11

Bond Lengths

Cu1	Cl1	2.24	C5F	N3	1.47
Cu1	N1	1.99	C2	O1	1.23
Cu1	O1	1.99	C4	O2	1.19
Cu1	O3	1.93	C6	O3	1.31
Cu1	O5	2.31	C6	O4	1.21
C1	N1	1.44	C1	C2	1.54
C2	N2	1.30	C3	C4	1.54
C3	N2	1.45	C5	C6	1.51
C4	N3	1.31			

Bond Angles

Cl1	Cu1	N1	92	O1	Cu1	O3	90	Cu1	O3	C6	114	N3 C4 C3 113
Cl1	Cu1	O1	162	O1	Cu1	O5	94	N1	C1	C2	108	O2 C4 C3 122
Cl1	Cu1	O3	93	O3	Cu1	O5	91	N2	C2	O1	123	O3 C6 O4 122
Cl1	Cu1	O5	105	Cu1	N1	C1	111	N2	C2	C1	115	O3 C6 C5 113
N1	Cu1	O1	84	C2	N2	C3	121	O1	C2	C1	121	O4 C6 C5 125
N1	Cu1	O3	174	C4	N3	C5F	121	N2	C3	C4	111	
N1	Cu1	O5	91	Cu1	O1	C2	113	N3	C4	O2	125	

Torsion Angles

C3	N2	C2	O1	−4	N1	C1	C2	N2	167
C3	N2	C2	C1	172	N1	C1	C2	O1	−17
C2	N2	C3	C4	114	N2	C3	C4	N3	135
C5F	N3	C4	O2	6	N2	C3	C4	O2	−49
C5F	N3	C4	C3	−179	N3F	C5	C6	O3	−175
C4	N3	C5F	C6F	85	N3F	C5	C6	O4	7

82.7 Diaquo copper(ii) β - alanine tetrahydrate $C_6H_{16}CuN_2O_6$, $4H_2O$

K.Tomita, Bull. Chem. Soc. Jap., 34, 297, 1961

$P2_1/c$ Z = 2 $R_{0kl} = 0.19$, $R_{h0l} = 0.22$

CUBALN

Bond Lengths

Cu1	N1	2.09 (2.04)	C1	O1	1.17 (1.23)
Cu1	O1	2.09 (2.01)	C1	O2	1.20 (1.26)
Cu1	O3	2.49	C1	C2	1.60 (1.55)
C3	N1	1.58 (1.46)	C2	C3	1.48 (1.56)

Bond Angles

N1	Cu1	N1B	180	O1	Cu1	O3	88	O1	C1	O2	129
N1	Cu1	O1	90	O1	Cu1	O1B	180	O1	C1	C2	116
N1	Cu1	O3	90	O1	Cu1	O3B	92	O2	C1	C2	115
N1	Cu1	O1B	90	O3	Cu1	O3B	180	C1	C2	C3	117
N1	Cu1	O3B	90	Cu1	N1	C3	113	N1	C3	C2	117
O1	Cu1	N1B	90	Cu1	O1	C1	140				

Torsion Angles

O1	C1	C2	C3	−28
O2	C1	C2	C3	153
C1	C2	C3	N1	62

82.8 Diaquo nickel(ii) β - alanine $\qquad$ $C_6H_{16}N_2NiO_6$

P.Jose, L.M.Pant, A.B.Biswas, Acta Cryst., 17, 24, 1964

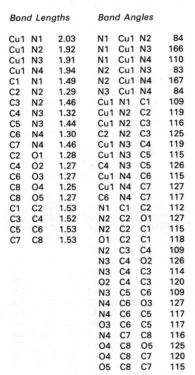

P-1 $\qquad$ Z = 1 $\qquad$ $R_{hk0} = 0.15$,
$R_{0kl} = 0.12$, $R_{h0l} = 0.15$

NICALA $\qquad$ LB 6-12-31

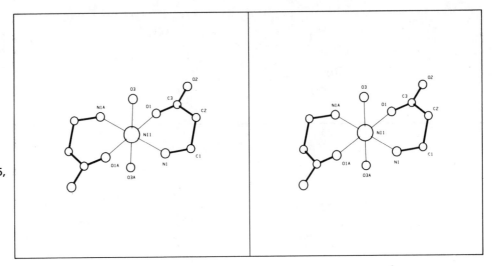

Bond Lengths

Ni1	N1	2.10		C3	O1	1.22
Ni1	O1	2.14		C3	O2	1.28
Ni1	O3	2.17		C1	C2	1.57
C1	N1	1.50		C2	C3	1.54

Bond Angles

N1	Ni1	N1A	180		O1	Ni1	O3	90		N1	C1	C2	110
N1	Ni1	O1	91		O1	Ni1	O1A	180		C1	C2	C3	113
N1	Ni1	O3	92		O1	Ni1	O3A	90		O1	C3	O2	123
N1	Ni1	O1A	89		O3	Ni1	O3A	180		O1	C3	C2	123
N1	Ni1	O3A	88		Ni1	N1	C1	115		O2	C3	C2	114
O1	Ni1	N1A	89		Ni1	O1	C3	123					

Torsion Angles

N1	C1	C2	C3	−74
C1	C2	C3	O1	27
C1	C2	C3	O2	−147

82.9 Disodium glycylglycylglycylglycino cuprate(ii) decahydrate $C_8H_{10}CuN_4O_5^{2-}$, $2Na^+$, $10H_2O$

H.C.Freeman, M.R.Taylor, Acta Cryst., 18, 939, 1965

P-1 $\quad$ Z = 2 $\quad$ R = 0.09

NGLYCU $\qquad$ LB 8-10-8

$$2\,Na^+ \left[\begin{array}{c} CH_2\!-\!NH \qquad COOH \\ \\ \end{array} \right]^{2-} \cdot 10\,H_2O$$

Bond Lengths

Cu1	N1	2.03
Cu1	N2	1.92
Cu1	N3	1.91
Cu1	N4	1.94
C1	N1	1.49
C2	N2	1.29
C3	N2	1.46
C4	N3	1.32
C5	N3	1.44
C6	N4	1.30
C7	N4	1.46
C2	O1	1.28
C4	O2	1.27
C6	O3	1.27
C8	O4	1.25
C8	O5	1.27
C1	C2	1.53
C3	C4	1.52
C5	C6	1.53
C7	C8	1.53

Bond Angles

N1	Cu1	N2	84
N1	Cu1	N3	166
N1	Cu1	N4	110
N2	Cu1	N3	83
N2	Cu1	N4	167
N3	Cu1	N4	84
Cu1	N1	C1	109
Cu1	N2	C2	119
Cu1	N2	C3	116
C2	N2	C3	125
Cu1	N3	C4	119
Cu1	N3	C5	115
C4	N3	C5	126
Cu1	N4	C6	115
Cu1	N4	C7	127
C6	N4	C7	117
N1	C1	C2	112
N2	C2	O1	127
N2	C2	C1	115
O1	C2	C1	118
N2	C3	C4	109
N3	C4	O2	126
N3	C4	C3	114
O2	C4	C3	120
N3	C5	C6	109
N4	C6	O3	127
N4	C6	C5	117
O3	C6	C5	117
N4	C7	C8	116
O4	C8	O5	125
O4	C8	C7	120
O5	C8	C7	115

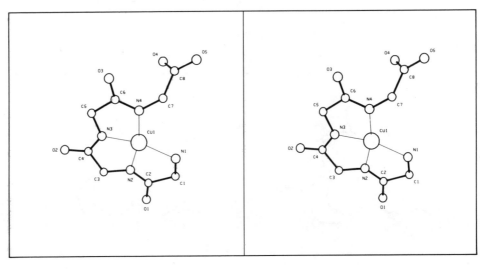

Torsion Angles

C3	N2	C2	O1	−1		C7	N4	C6	O3	1		N2	C3	C4	O2	180
C3	N2	C2	C1	178		C7	N4	C6	C5	−178		N3	C5	C6	N4	3
C2	N2	C3	C4	−175		C6	N4	C7	C8	−81		N3	C5	C6	O3	−176
C5	N3	C4	O2	−1		N1	C1	C2	N2	10		N4	C7	C8	O4	0
C5	N3	C4	C3	180		N1	C1	C2	O1	−171		N4	C7	C8	O5	180
C4	N3	C5	C6	180		N2	C3	C4	N3	−1						

82.10 Diaquo nickel(ii) di - α - amino isobutyrate dihydrate $C_8H_{20}N_2NiO_6$, $2H_2O$

T.Neguchi, Bull. Chem. Soc. Jap., 35, 99, 1962

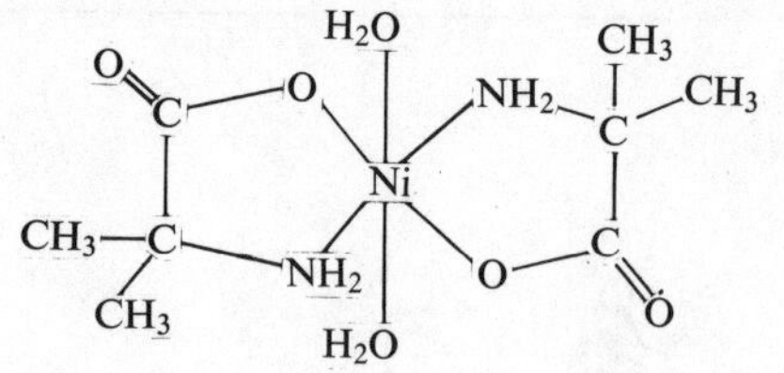

P2₁/a Z = 4 R_{0kl} = 0.168, R_{h0l} = 0.157, R_{hk0} = 0.181

NDAMIB

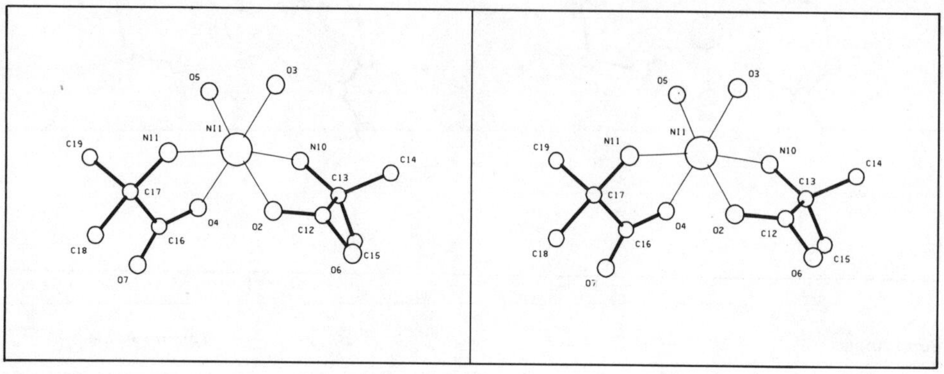

Bond Lengths

Ni1	N10	2.11	C16	O4	1.29
Ni1	N11	2.10	C12	O6	1.29
Ni1	O2	2.10	C16	O7	1.22
Ni1	O3	2.14	C12	C13	1.48
Ni1	O4	2.17	C13	C14	1.49
		(2.24)	C13	C15	1.56
Ni1	O5	2.00	C16	C17	1.59
C13	N10	1.47	C17	C18	1.56
C17	N11	1.49	C17	C19	1.60
C12	O2	1.32			

Bond Angles

N10	Ni1	N11	170	O2	Ni1	O4	92	O2	C12	C13	122	O7	C16	C17	118
N10	Ni1	O2	83	O2	Ni1	O5	175	O6	C12	C13	119	N11	C17	C16	112
N10	Ni1	O3	91	O3	Ni1	O4	177	N10	C13	C12	113	N11	C17	C18	122
N10	Ni1	O4	89	O3	Ni1	O5	86	N10	C13	C14	119	N11	C17	C19	108
N10	Ni1	O5	94	O4	Ni1	O5	92	N10	C13	C15	114	C16	C17	C18	105
N11	Ni1	O2	90	Ni1	N10	C13	109	C12	C13	C14	98	C16	C17	C19	104
N11	Ni1	O3	96	Ni1	N11	C17	109	C12	C13	C15	111	C18	C17	C19	104
N11	Ni1	O4	85	Ni1	O2	C12	109	C14	C13	C15	100				
N11	Ni1	O5	94	Ni1	O4	C16	107	O4	C16	O7	119				
O2	Ni1	O3	91	O2	C12	O6	115	O4	C16	C17	121				

Torsion Angles

O2	C12	C13	N10	14	O4	C16	C17	N11	−28
O2	C12	C13	C14	140	O4	C16	C17	C18	−162
O2	C12	C13	C15	−116	O4	C16	C17	C19	89
O6	C12	C13	N10	174	O7	C16	C17	N11	165
O6	C12	C13	C14	−61	O7	C16	C17	C18	31
O6	C12	C13	C15	43	O7	C16	C17	C19	−78

82.11 Sodium glycylglycylglycino cuprate(ii) dihydrate $C_{12}H_{16}Cu_2N_6O_8^{2-}$, $2Na^+$, $2H_2O$

H.C.Freeman, J.C.Schoone, J.G.Sime, Acta Cryst., 18, 381, 1965

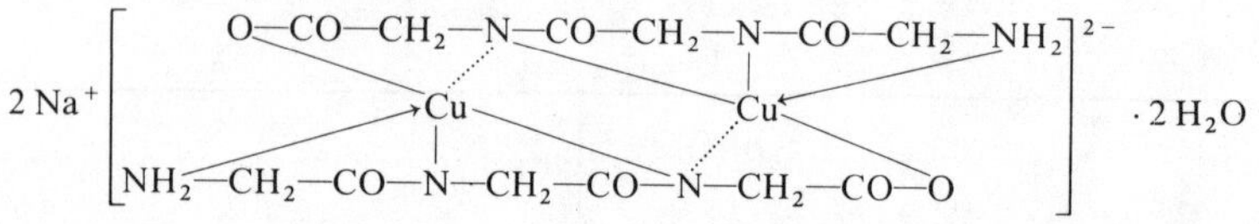

I2/c Z = 8 R = 0.132

NGGGCU LB 6-8-32

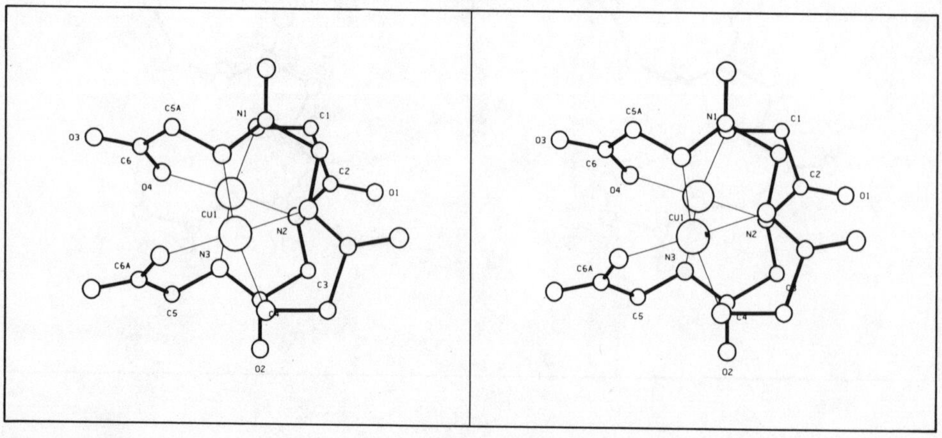

Bond Lengths

Cu1	N1	2.04
Cu1	N2	1.89
Cu1	N3	2.00
Cu1	O4	1.93
C1	N1	1.49
C2	N2	1.29
C3	N2	1.44
C4	N3	1.36
C5	N3	1.43
C2	O1	1.23
C4	O2	1.24
C6	O3	1.23
C6	O4	1.28
C1	C2	1.57
C3	C4	1.53
C5	C6A	1.53

Bond Angles

N1	Cu1	N2	83
N1	Cu1	N3	166
N1	Cu1	O4	97
N2	Cu1	N3	84
N2	Cu1	O4	173
N3	Cu1	O4	95
Cu1	N1	C1	110
Cu1	N2	C2	121
Cu1	N2	C3	117
C2	N2	C3	121
Cu1	N3	C4	113
Cu1	N3	C5	127
C4	N3	C5	117
Cu1	O4	C6	125
N1	C1	C2	110
N2	C2	O1	128
N2	C2	C1	113
O1	C2	C1	118
N2	C3	C4	109
N3	C4	O2	126
N3	C4	C3	115
O2	C4	C3	119
N3	C5	C6A	116
O3	C6	O4	121
O3	C6	C5A	119
O4	C6	C5A	120

Torsion Angles

C3	N2	C2	O1	1	C5	N3	C4	C3	173	N2	C3	C4	N3	−12
C3	N2	C2	C1	−180	C4	N3	C5	C6A	131	N2	C3	C4	O2	169
C2	N2	C3	C4	179	N1	C1	C2	N2	−6	N3	C5	C6A	O3A	161
C5	N3	C4	O2	−8	N1	C1	C2	O1	173	N3	C5	C6A	O4A	−17

82.12 Di - (L - histidino) - zinc(ii) dihydrate

$C_{12}H_{16}N_6O_4Zn$, $2H_2O$

R.H.Kretsinger, F.A.Cotton, R.F.Bryan, Acta Cryst., 16, 651, 1963

$P4_12_12$ Z = 4 R = 0.15

HISZND   LB 12-16-21

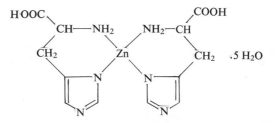

Bond Lengths

Zn1	N1	2.06
Zn1	N2	2.04
C2	N1	1.49
C4	N2	1.40
C5	N2	1.28
C5	N3	1.29
C6	N3	1.37
C1	O1	1.19
C1	O2	1.23
C1	C2	1.54
C2	C3	1.56
C3	C4	1.40
C4	C6	1.33

Bond Angles

N1	Zn1	N2	96
N1	Zn1	N1E	120
N1	Zn1	N2E	116
N2	Zn1	N1E	116
N2	Zn1	N2E	112
Zn1	N1	C2	112
Zn1	N2	C4	120
Zn1	N2	C5	130
C4	N2	C5	107
C5	N3	C6	107
O1	C1	O2	125
O1	C1	C2	119
O2	C1	C2	117
N1	C2	C1	109
N1	C2	C3	112
C1	C2	C3	110
C2	C3	C4	114
N2	C4	C3	127
N2	C4	C6	106
C3	C4	C6	127
N2	C5	N3	112
N3	C6	C4	108

Torsion Angles

C5	N2	C4	C3	178	O1	C1	C2	N1	12	C1	C2	C3	C4	50
C5	N2	C4	C6	−2	O1	C1	C2	C3	−111	C2	C3	C4	N2	45
C4	N2	C5	N3	5	O2	C1	C2	N1	−171	C2	C3	C4	C6	−134
C6	N3	C5	N2	−5	O2	C1	C2	C3	66	N2	C4	C6	N3	−1
C5	N3	C6	C4	3	N1	C2	C3	C4	−71	C3	C4	C6	N3	179

82.13 Di - (histidino) zinc pentahydrate

$C_{12}H_{16}N_6O_4Zn$, $5H_2O$

M.M.Harding, S.J.Cole, Acta Cryst., 16, 643, 1963

C2/c Z = 4 R = 0.11

HISZNP   LB 12-16-22

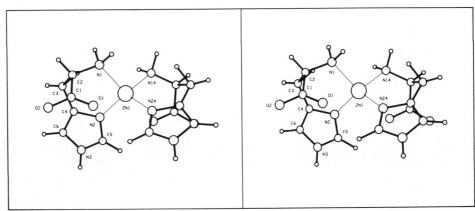

Bond Lengths

Zn1	N1	2.05
Zn1	N2	2.00
C2	N1	1.47
C4	N2	1.42
C5	N2	1.33
C5	N3	1.32
C6	N3	1.37
C1	O1	1.24
C1	O2	1.26
C1	C2	1.52
C2	C3	1.54
C3	C4	1.49
C4	C6	1.37

Bond Angles

N1	Zn1	N2	96
N1	Zn1	N1A	104
N1	Zn1	N2A	123
N2	Zn1	N1A	123
N2	Zn1	N2A	117
Zn1	N1	C2	115
Zn1	N2	C4	123
Zn1	N2	C5	130
C4	N2	C5	107
C5	N3	C6	109
O1	C1	O2	123
O1	C1	C2	119
O2	C1	C2	117
N1	C2	C1	111
N1	C2	C3	110
C1	C2	C3	110
C2	C3	C4	113
N2	C4	C3	124
N2	C4	C6	107
C3	C4	C6	129
N2	C5	N3	110
N3	C6	C4	107

Torsion Angles

C5	N2	C4	C3	179	O1	C1	C2	N1	−4	C1	C2	C3	C4	−49
C5	N2	C4	C6	−2	O1	C1	C2	C3	118	C2	C3	C4	N2	−42
C4	N2	C5	N3	2	O2	C1	C2	N1	176	C2	C3	C4	C6	140
C6	N3	C5	N2	−1	O2	C1	C2	C3	−62	N2	C4	C6	N3	2
C5	N3	C6	C4	−1	N1	C2	C3	C4	73	C3	C4	C6	N3	180

82.14   Manganese(ii) bis(pyridoxylidene valine) tetrahydrate $C_{26}H_{32}MnN_4O_8$, $4H_2O$

E.Willstadter, T.A.Hamor, J.L.Hoard, J. Amer. Chem. Soc., 85, 1205, 1963

Atomic coordinates were not given
but bond lengths were reported.
Pcan   Z = 4   R = 0.10

MNPOXV   LB 26-34-1

83.1   Dichloro copper(ii) 1,2,4 - triazole

$C_2H_3Cl_2CuN_3$

J.A.J.Jarvis, Acta Cryst., 15, 964, 1962

I2/c   Z = 4   R = 0.13

CUCTAZ   LB 2-3-12

Bond Lengths

Cu1	Cl1	2.34
Cu1	N1	1.99
N1	N1E	1.38
C1	N1	1.29
C1	N2	1.31

Bond Angles

Cl1	Cu1	Cl1D	180
Cl1	Cu1	N1	89
Cl1	Cu1	N1D	91
N1	Cu1	N1D	180
Cu1	N1	N1E	121
Cu1	N1	C1	134
C1	N2	C1E	105
N1	C1	N2	112

83.2   Chloro copper(i) azomethane complex

$(C_2H_6Cl_2Cu_2N_2)_n$

I.D.Brown, J.D.Dunitz, Acta Cryst., 13, 28, 1960

P-1   Z = 1   R = 0.11

CUCLAZ   LB 2-6-18

Bond Lengths

Cu1	Cl1	2.32
Cu1	Cl1A	2.55
Cu1	N1	1.99
N1	N1A	1.26
C1	N1	1.46

Bond Angles

Cl1	Cu1	Cl1A	96
Cl1	Cu1	N1	132
Cu1	Cl1	Cu1A	84
Cu1	N1	N1A	126
Cu1	N1	C1	116

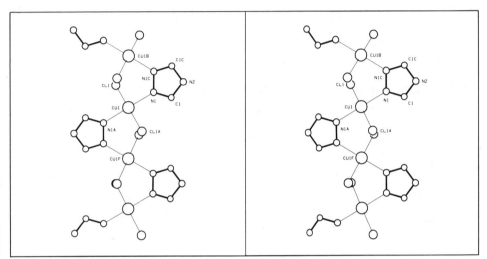

83.3   Copper(ii) chloride bis(semicarbazide) complex

$C_2H_{10}CuN_6O_2^{2+}$, $2Cl^-$

M.Nardelli, G.F.Gasparri, P.Boldrini, G.G.Battistini, Acta Cryst., 19, 491, 1965

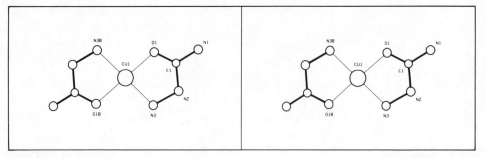

$$\left[\left(NH_2-\overset{\overset{O}{\|}}{C}-NH-NH_2\right)_2 Cu\right]^{2+} 2Cl^-$$

P2$_1$/c   Z = 2   R = 0.132

SCACUC   LB 2-10-6

Bond Lengths

Cu1	N3	1.99	C1	N1	1.31	
Cu1	O1	1.97	C1	N2	1.37	
N2	N3	1.47	C1	O1	1.23	

Bond Angles

N3	Cu1	N3B	180	Cu1	N3	N2	106
N3	Cu1	O1	83	Cu1	O1	C1	112
N3	Cu1	O1B	97	N1	C1	N2	115
O1	Cu1	O1B	180	N1	C1	O1	123
N3	N2	C1	113	N2	C1	O1	122

Torsion Angles

N3	N2	C1	N1	−176
N3	N2	C1	O1	6

83.4   Zinc chloride bis(semicarbazide) complex

$C_2H_{10}N_6O_2Zn^{2+}$, $2Cl^-$

M.Nardelli, G.F.Gasparri, P.Boldrini, G.G.Battistini, Acta Cryst., 19, 491, 1965

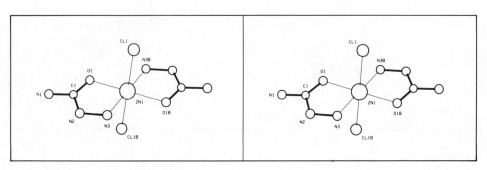

$$\left[\left(NH_2-\overset{\overset{O}{\|}}{C}-NH-NH_2\right)_2 Zn\right]^{2+} 2Cl^-$$

P2$_1$/c   Z = 2   R = 0.152

SCAZNC   LB 2-10-8

Bond Lengths

Zn1	Cl1	2.59	C1	N1	1.33	
Zn1	N3	2.07	C1	N2	1.35	
Zn1	O1	2.06	C1	O1	1.23	
N2	N3	1.41				

Bond Angles

Cl1	Zn1	Cl1B	180	N3	Zn1	N3B	180	Zn1	N3	N2	107
Cl1	Zn1	N3	91	N3	Zn1	O1	80	Zn1	O1	C1	112
Cl1	Zn1	N3B	89	N3	Zn1	O1B	100	N1	C1	N2	116
Cl1	Zn1	O1	92	O1	Zn1	O1B	180	N1	C1	O1	123
Cl1	Zn1	O1B	88	N3	N2	C1	118	N2	C1	O1	121

Torsion Angles

N3	N2	C1	N1	179
N3	N2	C1	O1	0

83.5   Zinc hydrazinecarboxylate hydrazine complex

$C_2H_{14}N_8O_4Zn$

A.Ferrari, A.Braibanti, G.Bigliardi, A.M.Lanfredi, Z. Kristallogr., 122, 259, 1965

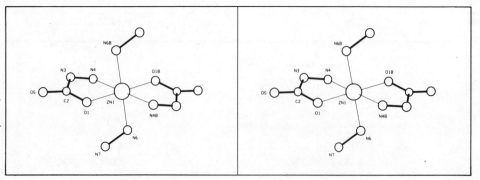

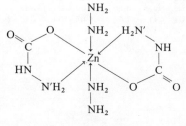

P2$_1$/c   Z = 2   R = 0.17

ZNHCHY   LB 2-14-4

Bond Lengths

Zn1	N4	2.25	N6	N7	1.46	
Zn1	N6	2.17	C2	N3	1.39	
Zn1	O1	2.04	C2	O1	1.30	
N3	N4	1.39	C2	O5	1.25	

Bond Angles

N4	Zn1	N6	94	N6	Zn1	N6B	180	Zn1	N6	N7	117
N4	Zn1	N4B	180	N6	Zn1	O1	94	Zn1	O1	C2	116
N4	Zn1	N6B	86	N6	Zn1	O1B	86	N3	C2	O1	117
N4	Zn1	O1	78	O1	Zn1	O1B	180	N3	C2	O5	117
N4	Zn1	O1B	102	N4	N3	C2	120	O1	C2	O5	126
N6	Zn1	N4B	86	Zn1	N4	N3	104				

Torsion Angles

N4	N3	C2	O1	11
N4	N3	C2	O5	−170

83.6 Dichloro zinc(ii) diacetonitrile

$C_4H_6Cl_2N_2Zn$

I.V.Isakov, E.V.Evonkova, Dokl. Akad. Nauk S. S. S. R., 145, 801, 1962

$ZnCl_2 \cdot 2\,CH_3CN$

No comparison of bond lengths is possible since they are not reported in the paper.
Pnma   Z = 4 R_{hk0} = 0.19

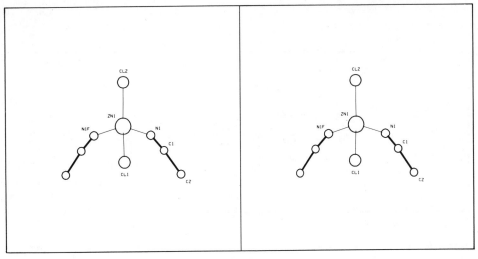

Bond Lengths

Zn1	Cl1	2.19
Zn1	Cl2	2.18
Zn1	N1	1.95
C1	N1	1.12
C1	C2	1.51

Bond Angles

Cl1	Zn1	Cl2	131
Cl1	Zn1	N1	100
Cl2	Zn1	N1	110
N1	Zn1	N1F	101
Zn1	N1	C1	110
N1	C1	C2	171

Torsion Angles

Cl1	Zn1	N1	C1	−19
Cl2	Zn1	N1	C1	122
N1F	Zn1	N1	C1	−122
Zn1	N1	C1	C2	110

83.7 Chloro copper(ii) acetonitrile - μ - dichloro - chloro copper(ii) acetonitrile

$C_4H_6Cl_4Cu_2N_2$

R.D.Willett, R.E.Rundle, J. Chem. Phys., 40, 838, 1964

H₃C—CN, Cl, Cl
Cu Cu
Cl, Cl, NC—CH₃

P2₁/c   Z = 2 R_{h0l} = 0.13,
R_{0kl} = 0.12

DCUCAN   LB 4-6-28

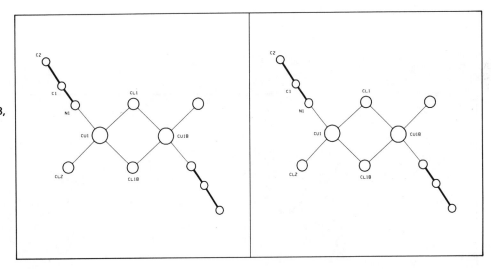

Bond Lengths

Cu1	Cl1	2.31
Cu1	Cl2	2.26
Cu1	Cl1B	2.30
Cu1	N1	1.95
C1	N1	1.18
C1	C2	1.44

Bond Angles

Cl1	Cu1	Cl2	172
Cl1	Cu1	Cl1B	85
Cl1	Cu1	N1	88
Cl2	Cu1	Cl1B	92
Cl2	Cu1	N1	94
Cu1	Cl1	Cu1B	95
Cu1	N1	C1	169
N1	C1	C2	170

Torsion Angles

Cl2	Cu1	Cl1	Cu1B	−72
Cl1B	Cu1	Cl1	Cu1B	0
N1	Cu1	Cl1	Cu1B	−176
Cl1	Cu1	Cl1B	Cu1B	0
Cl2	Cu1	Cl1B	Cu1B	173
N1	Cu1	Cl1B	Cu1B	28
Cl1	Cu1	N1	C1	−73
Cl2	Cu1	N1	C1	115
Cl1B	Cu1	N1	C1	−101
Cu1	N1	C1	C2	144

83.8   Tri(dichloro copper(ii)) acetonitrile complex

R.D.Willett, R.E.Rundle, J. Chem. Phys., 40, 838, 1964

$C_4H_6Cl_6Cu_3N_2$

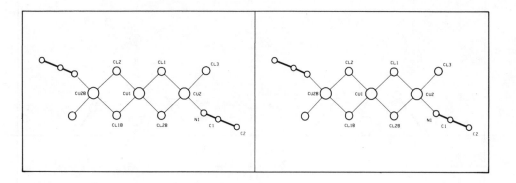

P2$_1$/c   Z = 2   R = 0.13

TCUCAN   LB 4-6-29

Bond Lengths

Cu1	Cl1	2.26
Cu1	Cl2	2.29
Cu2	Cl1	2.30
Cu2	Cl3	2.25
Cu2	Cl2B	2.30
Cu2	N1	1.97
C1	N1	1.14
C1	C2	1.48

Bond Angles

Cl1	Cu1	Cl2	93		Cl1	Cu2	N1	170
Cl1	Cu1	Cl1B	180		Cl3	Cu2	Cl2B	174
Cl1	Cu1	Cl2B	87		Cl3	Cu2	N1	89
Cl2	Cu1	Cl1B	87		Cu1	Cl1	Cu2	94
Cl2	Cu1	Cl2B	180		Cu1	Cl2	Cu2B	94
Cl1	Cu2	Cl3	91		Cu2	N1	C1	159
Cl1	Cu2	Cl2B	85		N1	C1	C2	178

Torsion Angles

Cl2	Cu1	Cl1	Cu2	−179	N1	Cu2	Cl1	Cu1	−83
Cl1B	Cu1	Cl1	Cu2	−90	Cl1	Cu2	Cl2B	Cu1	1
Cl2B	Cu1	Cl1	Cu2	1	Cl3	Cu2	Cl2B	Cu1	58
Cl1	Cu1	Cl2	Cu2B	−179	N1	Cu2	Cl2B	Cu1	171
Cl1B	Cu1	Cl2	Cu2B	1	Cl1	Cu2	N1	C1	−106
Cl2B	Cu1	Cl2	Cu2B	−90	Cl3	Cu2	N1	C1	−14
Cl3	Cu2	Cl1	Cu1	−175	Cl2B	Cu2	N1	C1	172
Cl2B	Cu2	Cl1	Cu1	−1	Cu2	N1	C1	C2	−25

83.9   Potassium bis - biureto cuprate(ii) tetrahydrate

H.C.Freeman, J.E.W.L.Smith, J.C.Taylor, Acta Cryst., 14, 407, 1961

$C_4H_6CuN_6O_4{}^{2-}$, $2K^+$, $4H_2O$

$$2K^+ \begin{bmatrix} OC-NH & HN-CO \\ HN & \underset{Cu}{\nearrow} & NH \\ OC-NH & HN-CO \end{bmatrix}^{2-} 4H_2O$$

P2$_1$/n   Z = 2   R = 0.08

KBURCU   LB 4-6-32

Bond Lengths

Cu1	N1	1.93
Cu1	N3	1.93
C1	N1	1.34
C1	N2	1.38
C2	N2	1.41
C2	N3	1.34
C1	O1	1.25
C2	O2	1.27

Bond Angles

N1	Cu1	N3	90		Cu1	N3	C2	131
N1	Cu1	N1B	180		N1	C1	N2	118
N1	Cu1	N3B	90		N1	C1	O1	126
N3	Cu1	N1B	90		N2	C1	O1	116
N3	Cu1	N3B	180		N2	C2	N3	117
Cu1	N1	C1	131		N2	C2	O2	115
C1	N2	C2	132		N3	C2	O2	127

Torsion Angles

C2	N2	C1	N1	5
C2	N2	C1	O1	−174
C1	N2	C2	N3	−6
C1	N2	C2	O2	174

83.10 Diammine bis(acetamidine) platinum(ii) chloride monohydrate

$C_4H_{18}N_6Pt^{2+}$, $2Cl^-$, H_2O

N.C.Stephenson, J. Inorg. Nucl. Chem., 24, 801, 1962

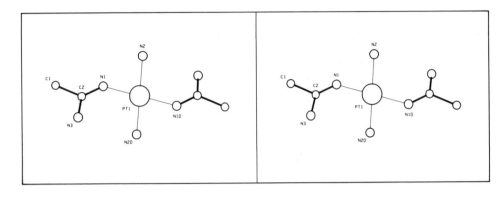

A2/a   Z = 4   R = 0.13

ACMPTC   LB 4-18-5

Bond Lengths

Pt1	N1	1.96
Pt1	N2	2.04
C2	N1	1.27
C2	N3	1.32
C1	C2	1.53

Bond Angles

N1	Pt1	N2	84
N1	Pt1	N1D	180
N1	Pt1	N2D	96
N2	Pt1	N1D	96
N2	Pt1	N2D	180
Pt1	N1	C2	130
N1	C2	N3	127
N1	C2	C1	123
N3	C2	C1	110

Torsion Angles

N2	Pt1	N1	C2	−121
N1D	Pt1	N1	C2	−90
N2D	Pt1	N1	C2	59
Pt1	N1	C2	N3	2
Pt1	N1	C2	C1	178

83.11 Pyridinium diperoxo chromate

$C_5H_5CrNO_5$

R.Stomberg, Ark. Kemi, 22, 29, 1964

$CrO(O_2)_2 \cdot$

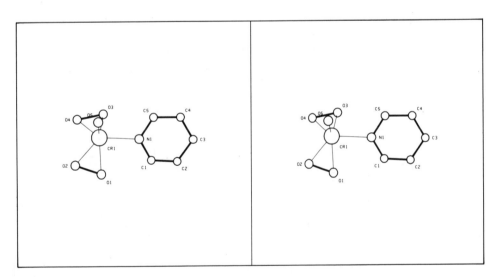

P2₁/n   Z = 4   R = 0.10

PYROCR   LB 5-5-11

Bond Lengths

Cr1	N1	2.05		O3	O4	1.40		
Cr1	O1	1.79		C1	N1	1.32		
Cr1	O2	1.83		C5	N1	1.34		
Cr1	O3	1.80		C1	C2	1.38		
Cr1	O4	1.84		C2	C3	1.39		
Cr1	O5	1.58		C3	C4	1.39		
O1	O2	1.41		C4	C5	1.39		

Bond Angles

N1	Cr1	O1	85		O2	Cr1	O3	125		Cr1	O1	O2	68
N1	Cr1	O2	130		O2	Cr1	O4	88		Cr1	O2	O1	66
N1	Cr1	O3	83		O2	Cr1	O5	109		Cr1	O3	O4	69
N1	Cr1	O4	128		O3	Cr1	O4	45		Cr1	O4	O3	66
N1	Cr1	O5	95		O3	Cr1	O5	110		N1	C1	C2	123
O1	Cr1	O2	46		O4	Cr1	O5	106		C1	C2	C3	120
O1	Cr1	O3	137		Cr1	N1	C1	122		C2	C3	C4	116
O1	Cr1	O4	127		Cr1	N1	C5	119		C3	C4	C5	121
O1	Cr1	O5	112		C1	N1	C5	119		N1	C5	C4	121

Torsion Angles

O1	Cr1	N1	C1	29
O1	Cr1	N1	C5	−152
O2	Cr1	N1	C1	21
O2	Cr1	N1	C5	−160
O3	Cr1	N1	C1	−110
O3	Cr1	N1	C5	69
O4	Cr1	N1	C1	−105
O4	Cr1	N1	C5	74
O5	Cr1	N1	C1	140
O5	Cr1	N1	C5	−41

83.12   Dibromo - 2,5 - dimethylpyrazine nickel(ii) $(C_6H_8Br_2N_2Ni)_n$

F.D.Ayres, P.Pauling, G.B.Robertson, Inorg. Chem., 3, 1303, 1964

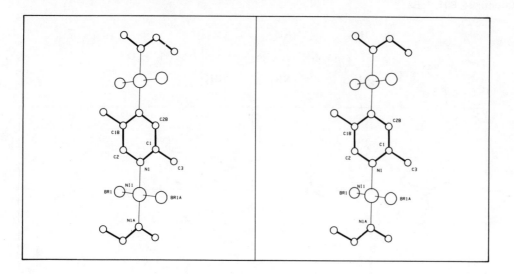

C2/m   Z = 4   R = 0.08

BRMPYN   LB 6-8-11

Bond Lengths

Ni1	Br1	2.31
Ni1	N1	1.85
C1	N1	1.32
C2	N1	1.38
C1	C3	1.53
C1	C2D	1.40

Bond Angles

Br1	Ni1	Br1A	180	C1	N1	C2	117
Br1	Ni1	N1	90	N1	C1	C3	119
N1	Ni1	N1D	180	N1	C1	C2D	122
Ni1	N1	C1	125	C3	C1	C2D	119
Ni1	N1	C2	119	N1	C2	C1D	121

83.13   Dipotassium bis(trimethylenedinitramine) nickelate(ii) tetrahydrate $C_6H_{12}N_8NiO_8{}^{2-}$, $2K^+$, $4H_2O$

D.M.Liebig, J.H.Robertson, J. Chem. Soc., 5801, 1965

$$2\,K^+ \left[\begin{array}{c} O_2N\!-\!N \quad\overset{(CH_2)_3}{\quad} \quad N\!-\!NO_2 \\ Ni \\ O_2N\!-\!N \quad\underset{(CH_2)_3}{\quad} \quad N\!-\!NO_2 \end{array} \right]^{2-} \cdot 4\,H_2O$$

Pbam   Z = 2   R = 0.125

KMENIT   LB 6-12-29

Bond Lengths

Ni1	N1	1.90
N1	N2	1.29
N2	O1	1.31
N2	O2	1.26
C2	N1	1.50
C1	C2	1.51

Bond Angles

N1	Ni1	N1A	94	N1	N2	O1	117
N1	Ni1	N1D	180	N1	N2	O2	122
N1	Ni1	N1E	86	O1	N2	O2	120
Ni1	N1	N2	124	C2	C1	C2E	115
Ni1	N1	C2	120	N1	C2	C1	109
N2	N1	C2	117				

Torsion Angles

N1A	Ni1	N1	N2	−51	Ni1	N1	N2	O2	174
N1A	Ni1	N1	C2	124	C2	N1	N2	O1	175
N1D	Ni1	N1	N2	0	C2	N1	N2	O2	−1
N1D	Ni1	N1	C2	180	Ni1	N1	C2	C1	10
N1E	Ni1	N1	N2	129	N2	N1	C2	C1	−175
N1E	Ni1	N1	C2	−56	C2E	C1	C2	N1	60
Ni1	N1	N2	O1	−10					

83.14   Cobalt(iii) bis(dimethylglyoximino) diamine nitrate $C_8H_{20}CoN_6O_4{}^+$, $NO_3{}^-$

K.S.Viswanathan, N.R.Kunchur, Acta Cryst., 14, 675, 1961

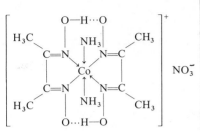

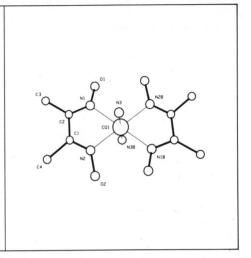

$P2_1/c$ $Z = 2$ $R_{h0l} = 0.11$, $R_{hk0} = 0.11$

CDMGDN   LB 8-20-21

Bond Lengths

Co1	N1	1.97	C2	N1	1.24
Co1	N2	1.93	C1	N2	1.21
Co1	N3	1.95	C1	C2	1.53
N1	O1	1.34	C1	C4	1.49
N2	O2	1.37	C2	C3	1.52

Bond Angles

N1	Co1	N2	76	N2	Co1	N3B	92	Co1	N2	C1	118
N1	Co1	N3	91	N3	Co1	N1B	89	O2	N2	C1	123
N1	Co1	N1B	180	N3	Co1	N2B	92	N2	C1	C2	115
N1	Co1	N2B	104	N3	Co1	N3B	180	N2	C1	C4	115
N1	Co1	N3B	89	Co1	N1	O1	117	C2	C1	C4	126
N2	Co1	N3	88	Co1	N1	C2	123	N1	C2	C1	104
N2	Co1	N1B	104	O1	N1	C2	115	N1	C2	C3	128
N2	Co1	N2B	180	Co1	N2	O2	118	C1	C2	C3	127

Torsion Angles

O1	N1	C2	C1	169
O1	N1	C2	C3	−22
O2	N2	C1	C2	−175
O2	N2	C1	C4	−15
N2	C1	C2	N1	−23
N2	C1	C2	C3	168
C4	C1	C2	N1	179
C4	C1	C2	C3	10

83.15   bis - (β - Aminobutyrate) - diaquo copper(ii) $C_8H_{20}CuN_2O_6$

R.F.Bryan, R.J.Poljak, K.Tomita, Acta Cryst., 14, 1125, 1961

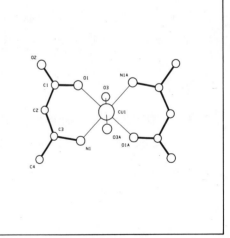

$P-1$ $Z = 2$ $R = 0.11$

ABCOPD   LB 8-16-33

Bond Lengths

Cu1	N1	1.99	C1	O2	1.23
Cu1	O1	2.00	C1	C2	1.49
Cu1	O3	2.45	C2	C3	1.49
C3	N1	1.44	C3	C4	1.49
C1	O1	1.30			

Bond Angles

N1	Cu1	N1A	180	O1	Cu1	O1A	180	O1	C1	O2	123
N1	Cu1	O1	92	O1	Cu1	O3A	87	O1	C1	C2	121
N1	Cu1	O3	93	O3	Cu1	N1A	87	O2	C1	C2	117
N1	Cu1	O1A	88	O3	Cu1	O1A	87	C1	C2	C3	115
N1	Cu1	O3A	87	O3	Cu1	O3A	180	N1	C3	C2	114
O1	Cu1	N1A	88	Cu1	N1	C3	119	N1	C3	C4	109
O1	Cu1	O3	93	Cu1	O1	C1	126	C2	C3	C4	111

Torsion Angles

O1	C1	C2	C3	28
O2	C1	C2	C3	−150
C1	C2	C3	N1	−67
C1	C2	C3	C4	170

83.16 Dichlorotetraethylamine platinum(iv) tetraethyl amine platinum(ii) tetrachloride tetrahydrate

$C_8H_{28}N_4Pt^{2+}$, $C_8H_{28}Cl_2N_4Pt^{2+}$, $4Cl^-$, $4H_2O$

Wolfram's red salt
B.M.Craven, D.Hall, Acta Cryst., 14, 475, 1961

$[Pt(C_2H_5NH_2)_4Cl_2]^{2+} [Pt(C_2H_5NH_2)_4]^{2+}(Cl^-)_4 \cdot 4H_2O$

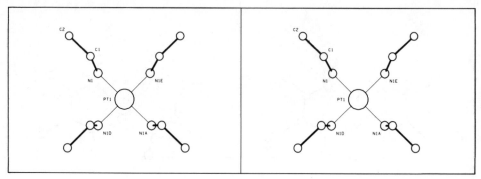

The chlorine atoms are disordered.

I4mm   Z = 1   R = 0.09

WOLRED   LB 16-56-2

Bond Lengths			Bond Angles				
Pt1	N1	1.97	N1	Pt1	N1A	180
C1	N1	1.41	N1	Pt1	N1D	90
C1	C2	1.57	Pt1	N1	C1	113
			N1	C1	C2	113

83.17 Dibromo copper(ii) dipyridine

$C_{10}H_{10}Br_2CuN_2$

V.Kupcik, S.Durovic, Czechosl. J. Phys., 10, 182, 1960

P2₁/n   Z = 2   R = 0.141

CUPYBR

Bond Lengths			Bond Angles									Torsion Angles				
Cu1	Br1	2.46	Br1	Cu1	Br1B	180	C1	N1	C5	115		Br1	Cu1	N1	C1	49
Cu1	N1	1.98	Br1	Cu1	N1	90	N1	C1	C2	124		Br1	Cu1	N1	C5	−124
C1	N1	1.40	Br1	Cu1	N1B	90	C1	C2	C3	113		Br1B	Cu1	N1	C1	−131
C5	N1	1.45	N1	Cu1	Br1B	90	C2	C3	C4	117		Br1B	Cu1	N1	C5	56
C1	C2	1.50	N1	Cu1	N1B	180	C3	C4	C5	136		N1B	Cu1	N1	C1	−90
C2	C3	1.32	Cu1	N1	C1	125	N1	C5	C4	113		N1B	Cu1	N1	C5	90
C3	C4	1.36	Cu1	N1	C5	119										
C4	C5	1.25														

83.18 Dichloro cadmium(ii) dipyridine

$C_{10}H_{10}CdCl_2N_2$

R.Zannetti, Gazz. Chim. Ital., 90, 1428, 1960

2 (pyridine) · CdCl₂

See also Paulus, Z. Anorg. Allg. Chem., 369, 38, 1969.
P2₁/n   Z = 2   R = 0.105

CDPYCL   LB 10-10-10

Bond Lengths						Bond Angles									Torsion Angles				
Cd1	Cl1	2.33	C1	C2	1.39	Cl1	Cd1	Cl1B	180	N1	Cd1	N1B	180	N1	C1	C2	123	Cl1	Cd1	N1	C1	57
Cd1	N1	2.46	C2	C3	1.38	Cl1	Cd1	N1	90	Cd1	N1	C1	114	C1	C2	C3	117	Cl1	Cd1	N1	C5	−116
C1	N1	1.36	C3	C4	1.40	Cl1	Cd1	N1B	90	Cd1	N1	C5	125	C2	C3	C4	114	Cl1B	Cd1	N1	C1	−123
C5	N1	1.29	C4	C5	1.35	N1	Cd1	Cl1B	90	C1	N1	C5	121	C3	C4	C5	128	Cl1B	Cd1	N1	C5	64
														N1	C5	C4	116	N1B	Cd1	N1	C1	−90
																		N1B	Cd1	N1	C5	−90

83.19 Diaquo copper(ii) dipyridine sulphate

$C_{10}H_{14}CuN_2O_2^{2+}$, O_4S^{2-}

E.Cannilo, G.Giuseppetti,
Atti Accad. Nazion. Lincei, R. C., Cl. Sci. Fis. Mat. Nat., 36, 878, 1964

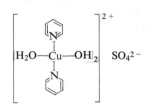

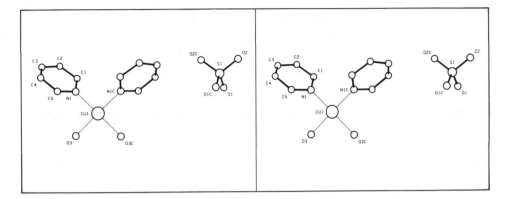

Pbcn   Z = 4   R = 0.163

CUPYRD   LB 10-10-33

Bond Lengths

Cu1	N1	2.00	C3	C4	1.30	
Cu1	O3	2.04	C4	C5	1.36	
C1	N1	1.35				
C5	N1	1.36	S1	O1	1.45	
C1	C2	1.43	S1	O2	1.50	
C2	C3	1.41				

Bond Angles

N1	Cu1	N1C	95	C1	N1	C5	118
N1	Cu1	O3	86	N1	C1	C2	118
N1	Cu1	O3C	179	C1	C2	C3	119
O3	Cu1	N1C	179	C2	C3	C4	122
O3	Cu1	O3C	93	C3	C4	C5	115
Cu1	N1	C1	122	N1	C5	C4	127
Cu1	N1	C5	120				

Torsion Angles

N1C	Cu1	N1	C1	66
N1C	Cu1	N1	C5	−120
O3	Cu1	N1	C1	−114
O3	Cu1	N1	C5	60
O3C	Cu1	N1	C1	−106
O3C	Cu1	N1	C5	68

83.20   Copper methylethylglyoxime

$C_{10}H_{18}CuN_4O_4$

E.Frasson, C.Panattoni, Acta Cryst., 13, 1028, 1960

Atomic coordinates were not reported in the paper.
$P2_1/n$ Z was not reported.   No R factor was given.

CUMEGL   LB 10-18-10

83.21   Nickel methylethylglyoxime

$C_{10}H_{18}N_4NiO_4$

E.Frasson, C.Panattoni, Acta Cryst., 13, 893, 1960

$P2_1/c$ Z = 2   R = 0.11

NIMEGL   LB 10-18-18

Bond Lengths

Ni1	N1	1.87
Ni1	N2	1.68
		(1.83)
N1	O1	1.44
N2	O2	1.50
		(1.36)
C1	N1	1.24
C2	N2	1.36
		(1.29)
C1	C2	1.52
C1	C3	1.57
C2	C4	1.34
		(1.40)
C4	C5	1.60

Bond Angles

N1	Ni1	N2	80	Ni1	N1	C1	117	N1	C1	C3	122
N1	Ni1	N1B	180	O1	N1	C1	121	C2	C1	C3	125
N1	Ni1	N2B	100	Ni1	N2	O2	122	N2	C2	C1	101
N2	Ni1	N1B	100	Ni1	N2	C2	126	N2	C2	C4	133
N2	Ni1	N2B	180	O2	N2	C2	107	C1	C2	C4	123
Ni1	N1	O1	121	N1	C1	C2	113	C2	C4	C5	113

Torsion Angles

O1	N1	C1	C2	180
O1	N1	C1	C3	1
O2	N2	C2	C1	172
O2	N2	C2	C4	−27
N1	C1	C2	N2	−7
N1	C1	C2	C4	−171
C3	C1	C2	N2	172
C3	C1	C2	C4	8
N2	C2	C4	C5	−77
C1	C2	C4	C5	81

83.22 1,4,8,11 - Tetra - azacyclotetradecane chloro nickel(ii) chloride

$C_{10}H_{24}ClN_4Ni^+$, Cl^-

B.Bosnich, R.Mason, P.J.Pauling, G.B.Robertson, M.L.Tobe, Chem. Communic., 97, 1965

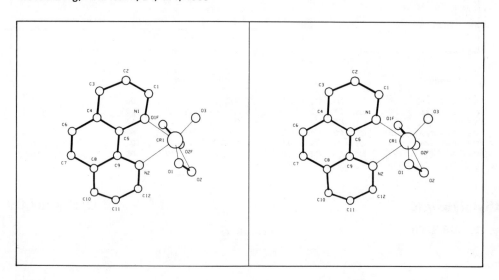

Atomic coordinates were not given but bond lengths were reported.
$P2_1/a$ Z = 2   R = 0.047

TAZDNC   LB 10-24-5

83.23 Oxodiperoxo chromium(vi) 1,10 - phenanthroline complex

$C_{12}H_8CrN_2O_5$

R.Stomberg, Ark. Kemi, 24, 111, 1965

Pnma   Z = 4   R = 0.134

OCRPOL   LB 12-8-30

Bond Lengths

Cr1	N1	2.11		C2	C3	1.37
Cr1	N2	2.26		C3	C4	1.41
Cr1	O1	1.87		C4	C5	1.41
Cr1	O2	1.80		C4	C6	1.43
Cr1	O3	1.57		C5	C9	1.40
O1	O2	1.40		C6	C7	1.36
C1	N1	1.36		C7	C8	1.45
C5	N1	1.42		C8	C9	1.39
C9	N2	1.35		C8	C10	1.44
C12	N2	1.43		C10	C11	1.30
C1	C2	1.38		C11	C12	1.33

Bond Angles

N1	Cr1	N2	75	O2	Cr1	O3	103	N1	C1	C2	118	C7 C8 C9	116
N1	Cr1	O1	87	O2	Cr1	O1F	134	C1	C2	C3	126	C7 C8 C10	127
N1	Cr1	O2	131	O2	Cr1	O2F	91	C2	C3	C4	115	C9 C8 C10	117
N1	Cr1	O3	91	Cr1	N1	C1	123	C3	C4	C5	121	N2 C9 C5	116
N2	Cr1	O1	81	Cr1	N1	C5	116	C3	C4	C6	123	N2 C9 C8	123
N2	Cr1	O2	86	C1	N1	C5	121	C5	C4	C6	116	C5 C9 C8	121
N2	Cr1	O3	166	Cr1	N2	C9	115	N1	C5	C4	119	C8 C10 C11	118
O1	Cr1	O2	45	Cr1	N2	C12	127	N1	C5	C9	118	C10 C11 C12	127
O1	Cr1	O3	98	C9	N2	C12	119	C4	C5	C9	123	N2 C12 C11	117
O1	Cr1	O1F	163	Cr1	O1	O2	65	C4	C6	C7	121		
O1	Cr1	O2F	134	Cr1	O2	O1	70	C6	C7	C8	123		

Torsion Angles

N2	Cr1	N1	C1	−180	N1	Cr1	N2 C9	0
N2	Cr1	N1	C5	0	N1	Cr1	N2 C12	−180
O1	Cr1	N1	C1	98	O1	Cr1	N2 C9	90
O1	Cr1	N1	C5	−82	O1	Cr1	N2 C12	−90
O2	Cr1	N1	C1	109	O2	Cr1	N2 C9	135
O2	Cr1	N1	C5	−71	O2	Cr1	N2 C12	−45
O3	Cr1	N1	C1	0	O3	Cr1	N2 C9	0
O3	Cr1	N1	C5	−180	O3	Cr1	N2 C12	−180
O1F	Cr1	N1	C1	−98	O1F	Cr1	N2 C9	−90
O1F	Cr1	N1	C5	82	O1F	Cr1	N2 C12	90
O2F	Cr1	N1	C1	−109	O2F	Cr1	N2 C9	−135
O2F	Cr1	N1	C5	71	O2F	Cr1	N2 C12	45

83.24 Cobalt(ii) dithiocyanate dipyridine

$C_{12}H_{10}CoN_4S_2$

M.A.Porai-Koshits, G.N.Tishchenko, Kristallografija, 4, 239, 1960

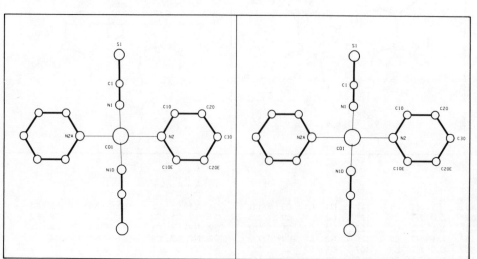

C2/m   Z = 2   No R factor was given.

COSCPY   LB 12-10-35

Bond Lengths

Co1	N1	2.09
Co1	N2	2.12
S1	C1	1.65
C1	N1	1.18
C10	N2	1.41
C10	C20	1.45
C20	C30	1.42

Bond Angles

N1	Co1	N2	90
N1	Co1	N1D	180
N2	Co1	N2A	180
Co1	N1	C1	158
Co1	N2	C10	121
C10	N2	C10E	118
S1	C1	N1	179
N2	C10	C20	121
C10	C20	C30	122
C20	C30	C20E	117

83.25   Copper(ii) imidazole

$(C_{12}H_{12}Cu_2N_8)_n$

J.A.J.Jarvis, A.F.Wells, Acta Cryst., 13, 1027, 1960

Atomic coordinates were not
reported in the paper.
I2/a   Z = 8   R = 0.115

CUIMDZ

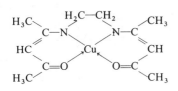

83.26   N,N′ - Ethylene bis(acetylacetoneiminato) copper(ii)

$C_{12}H_{18}CuN_2O_2$

D.Hall, A.D.Rae, T.N.Waters, J. Chem. Soc., 5897, 1963

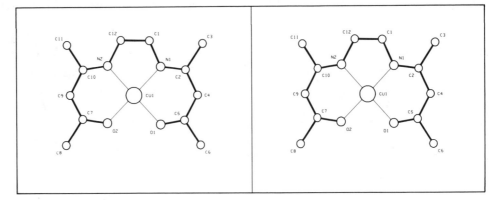

P2₁/c   Z = 4   R = 0.12

EACIMC   LB 12-18-26

Bond Lengths

Cu1	N1	1.95	C1	C12	1.55
Cu1	N2	1.99	C2	C3	1.54
Cu1	O1	1.96	C2	C4	1.41
Cu1	O2	1.92	C4	C5	1.42
C1	N1	1.43	C5	C6	1.49
C2	N1	1.30	C7	C8	1.53
C10	N2	1.28	C7	C9	1.35
C12	N2	1.43	C9	C10	1.43
C5	O1	1.26	C10	C11	1.51
C7	O2	1.28			

Bond Angles

N1	Cu1	N2	86	Cu1	N2	C12	110	O1	C5	C6	115
N1	Cu1	O1	93	C10	N2	C12	126	C4	C5	C6	117
N1	Cu1	O2	176	Cu1	O1	C5	123	O2	C7	C8	113
N2	Cu1	O1	179	Cu1	O2	C7	126	O2	C7	C9	127
N2	Cu1	O2	93	N1	C1	C12	108	C8	C7	C9	118
O1	Cu1	O2	88	N1	C2	C3	116	C7	C9	C10	123
Cu1	N1	C1	112	N1	C2	C4	124	N2	C10	C9	126
Cu1	N1	C2	126	C3	C2	C4	120	N2	C10	C11	116
C1	N1	C2	122	C2	C4	C5	123	C9	C10	C11	118
Cu1	N2	C10	124	O1	C5	C4	128	N2	C12	C1	112

Torsion Angles

Cu1	N1	C1	C12	−34
C2	N1	C1	C12	150
Cu1	N2	C12	C1	−25
C10	N2	C12	C1	159
N1	C1	C12	N2	39

83.27   bis - 1 - Aminocyclopentane carboxylato copper(ii)

$C_{12}H_{20}CuN_2O_4$

G.A.Barclay, F.S.Stephens, J. Chem. Soc., 2027, 1963

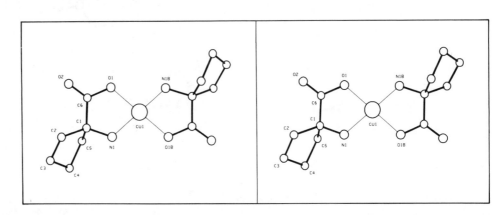

P2₁/a   Z = 2   R = 0.13

AMCYPC   LB 12-20-5

Bond Lengths

Cu1	N1	1.98
Cu1	O1	1.91
C1	N1	1.49
C6	O1	1.33
C6	O2	1.21
C1	C2	1.55
C1	C5	1.50
C1	C6	1.49
C2	C3	1.47
C3	C4	1.53
C4	C5	1.53

Bond Angles

N1	Cu1	N1B	180	C2	C1	C5	102
N1	Cu1	O1	84	C2	C1	C6	112
N1	Cu1	O1B	96	C5	C1	C6	110
O1	Cu1	N1B	96	C1	C2	C3	107
O1	Cu1	O1B	180	C2	C3	C4	109
Cu1	N1	C1	107	C3	C4	C5	100
Cu1	O1	C6	115	C1	C5	C4	106
N1	C1	C2	113	O1	C6	O2	119
N1	C1	C5	112	O1	C6	C1	116
N1	C1	C6	108	O2	C6	C1	125

C2	C1	C6	O1	151
C2	C1	C6	O2	−36
C5	C1	C6	O1	−96
C5	C1	C6	O2	76
C1	C2	C3	C4	9
C2	C3	C4	C5	−30
C3	C4	C5	C1	41

Torsion Angles

N1	C1	C2	C3	−104
C5	C1	C2	C3	17
C6	C1	C2	C3	134
N1	C1	C5	C4	85
C2	C1	C5	C4	−36
C6	C1	C5	C4	−155
N1	C1	C6	O1	26
N1	C1	C6	O2	−162

83.28 Copper(ii) bis(2 - imino - 4 - amino - 4 - methylpentane) nitrate $C_{12}H_{28}CuN_4^{2+}$, $2NO_3^-$

F.Hanic, M.Serator, Chem. Zvesti, 18, 572, 1964

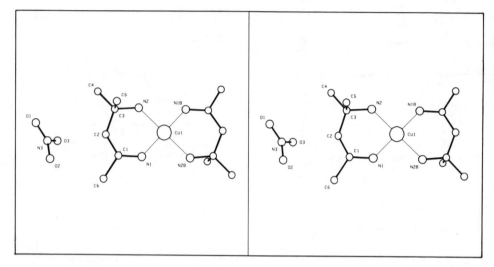

$P2_1/c$ $Z = 2$ $R = 0.161$

CUNMPN   LB 12-28-9

Bond Lengths			Bond Angles			
Cu1	N1	1.98	N1	Cu1	N2	92
Cu1	N2	2.01	N1	Cu1	N1B	180
C1	N1	1.30	N1	Cu1	N2B	88
C3	N2	1.51	N2	Cu1	N1B	88
C1	C2	1.47	N2	Cu1	N2B	180
C1	C6	1.57	Cu1	N1	C1	127
C2	C3	1.49	Cu1	N2	C3	123
C3	C4	1.55	N1	C1	C2	123
C3	C5	1.51	N1	C1	C6	117
			C2	C1	C6	119
N3	O1	1.24	C1	C2	C3	118
N3	O2	1.24	N2	C3	C2	107
N3	O3	1.23	N2	C3	C4	111
			N2	C3	C5	107
			C2	C3	C4	108
			C2	C3	C5	115
			C4	C3	C5	109
			O1	N3	O2	122
			O1	N3	O3	119
			O2	N3	O3	119

Torsion Angles

N1	C1	C2	C3	−41
C6	C1	C2	C3	141
C1	C2	C3	N2	64
C1	C2	C3	C4	−176
C1	C2	C3	C5	−55

83.29 Copper(ii) bis(8 - hydroxyquinolinate) (β form)

G.J.Palenik, Acta Cryst., 17, 687, 1964

$C_{18}H_{12}CuN_2O_2$

See also Hoy & Morriss, Acta Cryst., 22, 476, 1967.

$P2_1/c$ $Z = 4$ $R = 0.07$

CUQUIN   LB 18-12-16

Bond Lengths

Cu1	N1	1.97	C4	C9	1.42
Cu1	N2	1.97	C5	C6	1.36
Cu1	O1	1.94	C6	C7	1.42
Cu1	O2	1.93	C7	C8	1.38
C1	N1	1.32	C8	C9	1.42
C9	N1	1.35	C10	C11	1.41
C10	N2	1.33	C11	C12	1.35
C18	N2	1.36	C12	C13	1.42
C8	O1	1.32	C13	C14	1.40
C17	O2	1.32	C13	C18	1.42
C1	C2	1.40	C14	C15	1.36
C2	C3	1.36	C15	C16	1.45
C3	C4	1.41	C16	C17	1.37
C4	C5	1.40	C17	C18	1.43

Bond Angles

N1	Cu1	N2	173	C10	N2	C18	120	C6	C7	C8	121	C12	C13	C18	115
N1	Cu1	O1	84	Cu1	O1	C8	110	O1	C8	C7	124	C14	C13	C18	118
N1	Cu1	O2	96	Cu1	O2	C17	111	O1	C8	C9	118	C13	C14	C15	121
N2	Cu1	O1	95	N1	C1	C2	123	C7	C8	C9	117	C14	C15	C16	121
N2	Cu1	O2	85	C1	C2	C3	119	N1	C9	C4	123	C15	C16	C17	121
O1	Cu1	O2	179	C2	C3	C4	121	N1	C9	C8	115	O2	C17	C16	124
Cu1	N1	C1	131	C3	C4	C5	126	C4	C9	C8	122	O2	C17	C18	118
Cu1	N1	C9	110	C3	C4	C9	116	N2	C10	C11	121	C16	C17	C18	118
C1	N1	C9	119	C4	C5	C6	121	C10	C11	C12	120	N2	C18	C13	123
Cu1	N2	C10	130	C5	C6	C7	121	C11	C12	C13	122	N2	C18	C17	115
Cu1	N2	C18	110					C12	C13	C14	127	C13	C18	C17	122

83.30   Copper(ii) bis(8 - hydroxyquinolinate) (β form)

$C_{18}H_{12}CuN_2O_2$

F.Kanamaru, K.Ogawa, I.Nitta, Bull. Chem. Soc. Jap., 36, 422, 1963

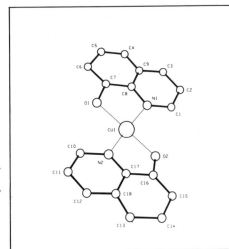 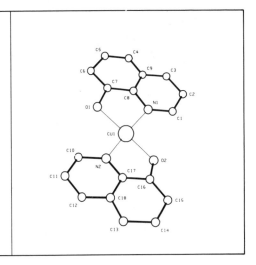

See also Hoy & Morriss, Acta Cryst., 22, 476, 1967.
$B2_1/a$ $Z = 8$ $R_{h0l} = 0.18$,
$R_{hk0} = 0.195$

CUQUIN01   LB 18-12-16

Bond Lengths

Cu1	N1	1.92	C4	C9	1.35
Cu1	N2	1.89	C5	C6	1.38
Cu1	O1	2.07	C6	C7	1.48
Cu1	O2	2.01	C7	C8	1.41
C1	N1	1.33	C8	C9	1.35
C8	N1	1.39	C10	C11	1.37
C10	N2	1.42	C11	C12	1.44
C17	N2	1.36	C12	C18	1.39
C7	O1	1.37	C13	C14	1.52
C16	O2	1.27	C13	C18	1.33
C1	C2	1.43	C14	C15	1.45
C2	C3	1.44	C15	C16	1.43
C3	C9	1.36	C16	C17	1.38
C4	C5	1.34	C17	C18	1.38

Bond Angles

N1	Cu1	N2	173	C10	N2	C17	124	C6	C7	C8	128	C13	C14	C15	118
N1	Cu1	O1	84	Cu1	O1	C7	112	N1	C8	C7	124	C14	C15	C16	118
N1	Cu1	O2	97	Cu1	O2	C16	122	N1	C8	C9	124	O2	C16	C15	134
N2	Cu1	O1	101	N1	C1	C2	119	C7	C8	C9	112	O2	C16	C17	104
N2	Cu1	O2	77	C1	C2	C3	116	C3	C9	C4	120	C15	C16	C17	122
O1	Cu1	O2	178	C2	C3	C9	124	C3	C9	C8	116	N2	C17	C16	123
Cu1	N1	C1	130	C5	C4	C9	121	C4	C9	C8	124	N2	C17	C18	118
Cu1	N1	C8	109	C4	C5	C6	126	N2	C10	C11	120	C16	C17	C18	119
C1	N1	C8	121	C5	C6	C7	108	C10	C11	C12	115	C12	C18	C13	115
Cu1	N2	C10	124	O1	C7	C6	120	C11	C12	C18	124	C12	C18	C17	119
Cu1	N2	C17	112	O1	C7	C8	111	C14	C13	C18	116	C13	C18	C17	126

83.31   Copper(ii) bis(8 - hydroxyquinolinate) (β form)

$C_{18}H_{12}CuN_2O_2$

J.A.Bevan, D.P.Graddon, J.F.McConnell, Nature, 199, 373, 1963

Atomic coordinates were not reported in the paper.
See also Hoy & Morriss, Acta Cryst., 22, 476, 1967.
$P2_1/c$ $Z = 4$ No R factor was given.

CUQUIN02   LB 18-12-16

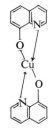

83.32 Zinc(ii) bis(8 - hydroxyquinolinate) dihydrate

$C_{18}H_{12}N_2O_2Zn$, $2H_2O$

G.J.Palenik, Acta Cryst., 17, 696, 1964

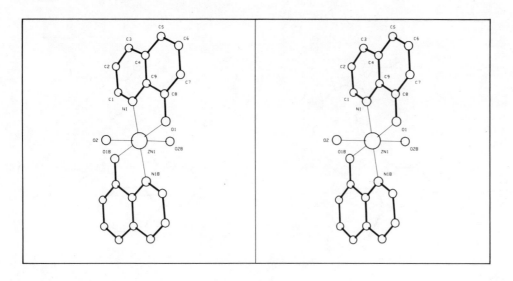

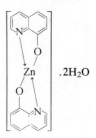

$P2_1/c$ $Z = 2$ $R = 0.13$

ZNQUIN   LB 18-12-23

Bond Lengths

Zn1	N1	2.10	C3	C4	1.42
Zn1	O1	2.07	C4	C5	1.41
Zn1	O2	2.26	C4	C9	1.42
C1	N1	1.33	C5	C6	1.36
C9	N1	1.34	C6	C7	1.39
C8	O1	1.32	C7	C8	1.39
C1	C2	1.39	C8	C9	1.45
C2	C3	1.36			

Bond Angles

N1	Zn1	N1B	180	O2	Zn1	O2B	180	C4	C5	C6	121
N1	Zn1	O1	82	Zn1	N1	C1	131	C5	C6	C7	122
N1	Zn1	O2	93	Zn1	N1	C9	110	C6	C7	C8	121
N1	Zn1	O1B	98	C1	N1	C9	119	O1	C8	C7	123
N1	Zn1	O2B	87	Zn1	O1	C8	111	O1	C8	C9	119
O1	Zn1	N1B	98	N1	C1	C2	123	C7	C8	C9	118
O1	Zn1	O2	91	C1	C2	C3	119	N1	C9	C4	122
O1	Zn1	O1B	180	C2	C3	C4	120	N1	C9	C8	118
O1	Zn1	O2B	89	C3	C4	C5	125	C4	C9	C8	120
O2	Zn1	N1B	87	C3	C4	C9	116				
O2	Zn1	O1B	89	C5	C4	C9	119				

83.33 Trimethyl(acetylacetonyl) - 2,2' - bipyridyl platinum

$C_{18}H_{24}N_2O_2Pt$

A.G.Swallow, M.R.Truter, Proc. R. Soc., A, 266, 527, 1962

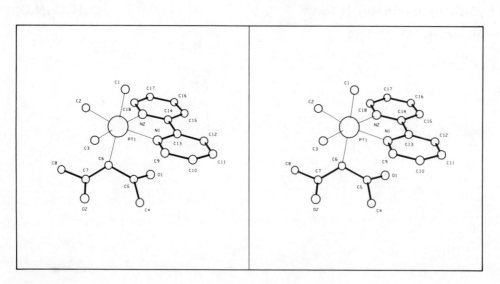

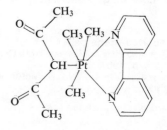

$P2_1/c$ $Z = 4$ $R = 0.08$

MACPPT   LB 18-24-14

Bond Lengths

Pt1	N1	2.16	C18	N2	1.35	C11	C12	1.40
Pt1	N2	2.14	C5	O1	1.22	C12	C13	1.38
Pt1	C1	2.05	C7	O2	1.22	C13	C14	1.52
Pt1	C2	2.03	C4	C5	1.56	C14	C15	1.39
Pt1	C3	2.06	C5	C6	1.50	C15	C16	1.40
Pt1	C6	2.35	C6	C7	1.45	C16	C17	1.37
C9	N1	1.37	C7	C8	1.52	C17	C18	1.41
C13	N1	1.35	C9	C10	1.36			
C14	N2	1.34	C10	C11	1.38			

Bond Angles

N1	Pt1	N2	77	C1	Pt1	C6	177	O1	C5	C6	124	C11	C12	C13	118
N1	Pt1	C1	87	C2	Pt1	C3	90	C4	C5	C6	119	N1	C13	C12	123
N1	Pt1	C2	170	C2	Pt1	C6	90	Pt1	C6	C5	100	N1	C13	C14	115
N1	Pt1	C3	98	C3	Pt1	C6	92	Pt1	C6	C7	111	C12	C13	C14	122
N1	Pt1	C6	96	Pt1	N1	C9	126	C5	C6	C7	119	N2	C14	C13	116
N2	Pt1	C1	92	Pt1	N1	C13	116	O2	C7	C6	126	N2	C14	C15	123
N2	Pt1	C2	95	C9	N1	C13	118	O2	C7	C8	119	C13	C14	C15	121
N2	Pt1	C3	176	Pt1	N2	C14	116	C6	C7	C8	115	C14	C15	C16	116
N2	Pt1	C6	88	Pt1	N2	C18	125	N1	C9	C10	120	C15	C16	C17	122
C1	Pt1	C2	87	C14	N2	C18	119	C9	C10	C11	122	C16	C17	C18	116
C1	Pt1	C3	87	O1	C5	C4	117	C10	C11	C12	118	N2	C18	C17	123

83.34 Di(cyclohexane - 1,2 - dioximato(1)) di - imidazole iron(ii) dihydrate

$C_{18}H_{26}FeN_8O_4$, $2H_2O$

C.K.Prout, T.J.Wiseman, J. Chem. Soc., 497, 1964

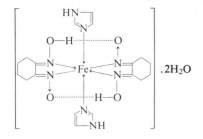

.2H₂O

P-1   Z = 2   R = 0.13

DICHIF   LB 18-26-5

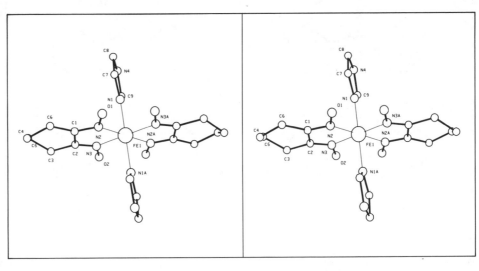

Bond Lengths

Fe1	N1	2.05
Fe1	N2	1.96
Fe1	N3	1.91
N2	O1	1.37
N3	O2	1.39
C7	N1	1.42
C9	N1	1.30
C1	N2	1.33
C2	N3	1.28
C8	N4	1.38
C9	N4	1.44
C1	C2	1.50
C1	C6	1.49
C2	C3	1.50
C3	C4	1.56
C4	C5	1.44
C5	C6	1.49
C7	C8	1.36

Bond Angles

N1	Fe1	N2	86	Fe1	N2	O1	125	
N1	Fe1	N3	91	Fe1	N2	C1	119	
N1	Fe1	N1A	180	O1	N2	C1	116	
N1	Fe1	N2A	94	Fe1	N3	O2	120	
N1	Fe1	N3A	89	Fe1	N3	C2	120	
N2	Fe1	N3	79	O2	N3	C2	120	
N2	Fe1	N1A	94	C8	N4	C9	111	
N2	Fe1	N2A	180	N2	C1	C2	109	
N2	Fe1	N3A	101	N2	C1	C6	128	
N3	Fe1	N1A	89	C2	C1	C6	123	
N3	Fe1	N2A	101	N3	C2	C1	114	
N3	Fe1	N3A	180	N3	C2	C3	131	
Fe1	N1	C7	136	C1	C2	C3	115	
Fe1	N1	C9	119	C2	C3	C4	117	
C7	N1	C9	105	C3	C4	C5	111	
				C4	C5	C6	114	
				C1	C6	C5	116	
				N1	C7	C8	114	
				N4	C8	C7	102	
				N1	C9	N4	108	

Torsion Angles

C9	N1	C7	C8	-2	C6	C1	C2	N3	177
C7	N1	C9	N4	1	C6	C1	C2	C3	0
O1	N2	C1	C2	180	N2	C1	C6	C5	-169
O1	N2	C1	C6	-3	C2	C1	C6	C5	8
O2	N3	C2	C1	180	N3	C2	C3	C4	-158
O2	N3	C2	C3	-4	C1	C2	C3	C4	19
C9	N4	C8	C7	-1	C2	C3	C4	C5	-47
C8	N4	C9	N1	0	C3	C4	C5	C6	56
N2	C1	C2	N3	-5	C4	C5	C6	C1	-38
N2	C1	C2	C3	178	N1	C7	C8	N4	2

83.35 Iodo bis - (2,2′ - bipyridyl) copper(ii) iodide

$C_{20}H_{16}CuIN_4^+$, I^-

G.A.Barclay, B.F.Hoskins, C.H.L.Kennard, J. Chem. Soc., 5691, 1963

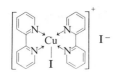

Published value of z(C8) = 0.7061. The correct value is 0.7601 (private communication).

P-1   Z = 2   R = 0.09

IBIPCI   LB 20-16-8

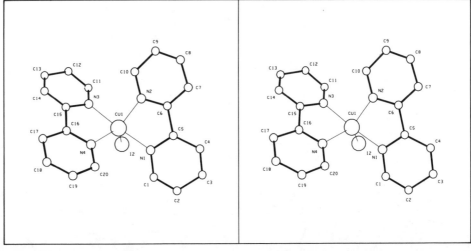

Bond Lengths

Cu1	I2	2.70		C4	C5	1.44
Cu1	N1	1.99		C5	C6	1.48
Cu1	N2	1.96		C6	C7	1.41
Cu1	N3	2.02		C7	C8	1.37
Cu1	N4	2.11		C8	C9	1.31
C1	N1	1.33		C9	C10	1.50
C5	N1	1.40		C11	C12	1.38
C6	N2	1.39		C12	C13	1.50
C10	N2	1.35		C13	C14	1.24
C11	N3	1.29		C14	C15	1.38
C15	N3	1.41		C15	C16	1.55
C16	N4	1.38		C16	C17	1.49
C20	N4	1.31		C17	C18	1.42
C1	C2	1.35		C18	C19	1.37
C2	C3	1.48		C19	C20	1.41
C3	C4	1.29				

Bond Angles

I2	Cu1	N1	89	Cu1	N1	C1	130	Cu1	N4	C20	127	N2	C6	C7	125	N3	C15	C14	122
I2	Cu1	N2	122	Cu1	N1	C5	117	C16	N4	C20	120	C5	C6	C7	120	N3	C15	C16	115
I2	Cu1	N3	92	C1	N1	C5	114	N1	C1	C2	126	C6	C7	C8	114	C14	C15	C16	123
I2	Cu1	N4	124	Cu1	N2	C6	116	C1	C2	C3	119	C7	C8	C9	125	N4	C16	C15	115
N1	Cu1	N2	81	Cu1	N2	C10	126	C2	C3	C4	117	C8	C9	C10	120	N4	C16	C17	121
N1	Cu1	N3	176	C6	N2	C10	118	C3	C4	C5	121	N2	C10	C9	117	C15	C16	C17	124
N1	Cu1	N4	100	Cu1	N3	C11	127	N1	C5	C4	122	N3	C11	C12	121	C16	C17	C18	117
N2	Cu1	N3	95	Cu1	N3	C15	114	N1	C5	C6	111	C11	C12	C13	118	C17	C18	C19	119
N2	Cu1	N4	114	C11	N3	C15	119	C4	C5	C6	127	C12	C13	C14	119	C18	C19	C20	123
N3	Cu1	N4	83	Cu1	N4	C16	113	N2	C6	C5	115	C13	C14	C15	121	N4	C20	C19	120

83.36   bis(2,2' - Dipyridyliminato) palladium(ii) $C_{20}H_{16}N_6Pd$

H.C.Freeman, M.R.Snow, Acta Cryst., 18, 843, 1965

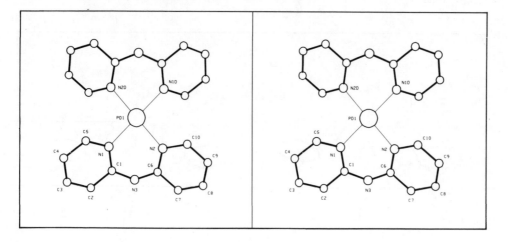

C2/c   Z = 4   R = 0.085

PYIMPD   LB 20-16-16

Bond Lengths

Pd1	N1	2.02	C1	C2	1.40
Pd1	N2	2.02	C2	C3	1.41
C1	N1	1.36	C3	C4	1.40
C5	N1	1.36	C4	C5	1.38
C6	N2	1.38	C6	C7	1.41
C10	N2	1.36	C7	C8	1.40
C1	N3	1.37	C8	C9	1.42
C6	N3	1.33	C9	C10	1.37

Bond Angles

N1	Pd1	N2	86	Pd1	N2	C10	120	N1	C5	C4	123
N1	Pd1	N1D	180	C6	N2	C10	120	N2	C6	N3	125
N1	Pd1	N2D	94	C1	N3	C6	123	N2	C6	C7	119
N2	Pd1	N1D	94	N1	C1	N3	124	N3	C6	C7	116
N2	Pd1	N2D	180	N1	C1	C2	119	C6	C7	C8	120
Pd1	N1	C1	120	N3	C1	C2	117	C7	C8	C9	119
Pd1	N1	C5	120	C1	C2	C3	119	C8	C9	C10	119
C1	N1	C5	120	C2	C3	C4	121	N2	C10	C9	122
Pd1	N2	C6	119	C3	C4	C5	117				

83.37   Tribenzo(b,f,j,)(1.5.9)triazacycloduodecine diaquo nickel(ii) nitrate $C_{21}H_{19}N_4NiO_5{}^+$, $NO_3{}^-$

E.B.Fleischer, E.Klem, Inorg. Chem., 4, 637, 1965

$P2_1/a$ Z = 4   R = 0.088

TBANIN   LB 21-15-5

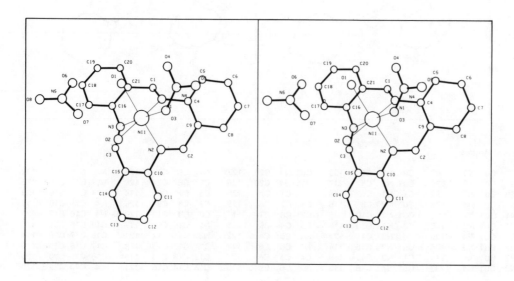

Bond Lengths

Ni1	N1	2.03	C16	N3	1.44
Ni1	N2	2.03	C1	C21	1.45
Ni1	N3	2.03	C2	C9	1.48
Ni1	O1	2.11	C3	C15	1.50
Ni1	O2	2.09	C4	C5	1.40
Ni1	O3	2.08	C4	C9	1.40
N4	O3	1.29	C5	C6	1.43
N4	O4	1.23	C6	C7	1.37
N4	O5	1.22	C7	C8	1.40
C1	N1	1.28	C8	C9	1.41
C4	N1	1.46	C10	C11	1.40
C2	N2	1.27	C10	C15	1.41
C10	N2	1.42	C11	C12	1.42
C3	N3	1.25	C12	C13	1.37
			C13	C14	1.44
			C14	C15	1.42
			C16	C17	1.43
			C16	C21	1.40
			C17	C18	1.39
			C18	C19	1.35
			C19	C20	1.41
			C20	C21	1.42
			N5	O6	1.26
			N5	O7	1.21
			N5	O8	1.15

Bond Angles

N1	Ni1	N2	86	C1	N1	C4	119	C4	C5	C6	117	N3	C16	C17	120
N1	Ni1	N3	85	Ni1	N2	C2	124	C5	C6	C7	120	N3	C16	C21	118
N1	Ni1	O1	91	Ni1	N2	C10	118	C6	C7	C8	122	C17	C16	C21	121
N1	Ni1	O2	178	C2	N2	C10	118	C7	C8	C9	119	C16	C17	C18	119
N1	Ni1	O3	96	Ni1	N3	C3	126	C2	C9	C4	124	C17	C18	C19	120
N2	Ni1	N3	85	Ni1	N3	C16	115	C2	C9	C8	117	C18	C19	C20	123
N2	Ni1	O1	177	C3	N3	C16	120	C4	C9	C8	118	C19	C20	C21	118
N2	Ni1	O2	94	O3	N4	O4	119	N2	C10	C11	121	C1	C21	C16	124
N2	Ni1	O3	93	O3	N4	O5	120	N2	C10	C15	118	C1	C21	C20	117
N3	Ni1	O1	94	O4	N4	O5	121	C11	C10	C15	120	C16	C21	C20	118
N3	Ni1	O2	93	Ni1	O3	N4	127	C10	C11	C12	119				
N3	Ni1	O3	177	N1	C1	C21	122	C11	C12	C13	122	O6	N5	O7	114
O1	Ni1	O2	89	N2	C2	C9	123	C12	C13	C14	120	O6	N5	O8	124
O1	Ni1	O3	88	N3	C3	C15	123	C13	C14	C15	118	O7	N5	O8	122
O2	Ni1	O3	86	N1	C4	C5	120	C3	C15	C10	123				
Ni1	N1	C1	125	N1	C4	C9	118	C3	C15	C14	116				
Ni1	N1	C4	116	C5	C4	C9	123	C10	C15	C14	121				

83.38 Acetylacetone - mono - (o - hydroxyanil) copper(ii) dimer

$C_{22}H_{22}Cu_2N_2O_4$

G.A.Barclay, B.F.Hoskins, J. Chem. Soc., 1979, 1965

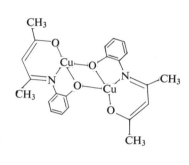

P-1   Z = 4   R = 0.15

ACHANC   LB 11-11-2

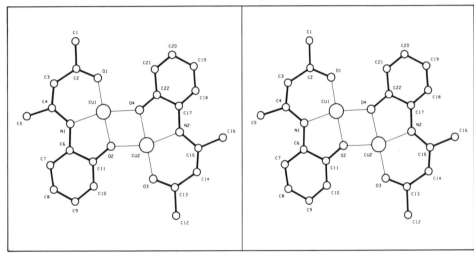

Bond Lengths

Cu1	N1	1.97	C3	C4	1.33
Cu1	O1	1.88	C4	C5	1.48
Cu1	O2	1.90	C6	C7	1.40
Cu1	O4	2.03	C6	C11	1.45
Cu2	N2	2.00	C7	C8	1.36
Cu2	O2	1.98	C8	C9	1.38
Cu2	O3	1.90	C9	C10	1.37
Cu2	O4	1.96	C10	C11	1.35
C4	N1	1.34	C12	C13	1.51
C6	N1	1.43	C13	C14	1.47
C15	N2	1.33	C14	C15	1.30
C17	N2	1.41	C15	C16	1.51
C2	O1	1.31	C17	C18	1.39
C11	O2	1.32	C17	C22	1.43
C13	O3	1.29	C18	C19	1.33
C22	O4	1.36	C19	C20	1.43
C1	C2	1.50	C20	C21	1.36
C2	C3	1.50	C21	C22	1.37

Bond Angles

N1	Cu1	O1	99	Cu2	N2	C15	120	N1	C4	C3	125	C12	C13	C14	121
N1	Cu1	O2	84	Cu2	N2	C17	109	N1	C4	C5	123	C13	C14	C15	128
N1	Cu1	O4	161	C15	N2	C17	131	C3	C4	C5	112	N2	C15	C14	125
O1	Cu1	O2	176	Cu1	O1	C2	121	N1	C6	C7	127	N2	C15	C16	119
O1	Cu1	O4	99	Cu1	O2	Cu2	101	N1	C6	C11	112	C14	C15	C16	115
O2	Cu1	O4	78	Cu1	O2	C11	114	C7	C6	C11	120	N2	C17	C18	128
N2	Cu2	O2	161	Cu2	O2	C11	140	C6	C7	C8	118	N2	C17	C22	115
N2	Cu2	O3	97	Cu2	O3	C13	120	C7	C8	C9	124	C18	C17	C22	116
N2	Cu2	O4	84	Cu1	O4	Cu2	97	C8	C9	C10	116	C17	C18	C19	123
O2	Cu1	O3	101	Cu1	O4	C22	131	C9	C10	C11	126	C18	C19	C20	119
O2	Cu2	O4	78	Cu2	O4	C22	112	O2	C11	C6	117	C19	C20	C21	119
O3	Cu2	O4	177	O1	C2	C1	115	O2	C11	C10	127	C20	C21	C22	121
Cu1	N1	C4	121	O1	C2	C3	125	C6	C11	C10	116	O4	C22	C17	117
Cu1	N1	C6	110	C1	C2	C3	120	O3	C13	C12	113	O4	C22	C21	123
C4	N1	C6	128	C2	C3	C4	127	O3	C13	C14	126	C17	C22	C21	120

83.39 Chromium(iii) pyridinium O,O' - dihydroxy - trans - azobenzene complex

$C_{24}H_{16}CrN_4O_4^-$, $C_5H_6N^+$

R.Grieb, A.Niggli, Helv. Chim. Acta, 48, 317, 1965

Atomic coordinates were not reported in the paper.
P2₁/n   Z = 4   R = 0.177

CRPAZB   LB 29-22-1

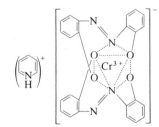

83.40   Diazoaminobenzene copper(i) dimer

$C_{24}H_{20}Cu_2N_6$

I.D.Brown, J.D.Dunitz, Acta Cryst., 14, 480, 1961

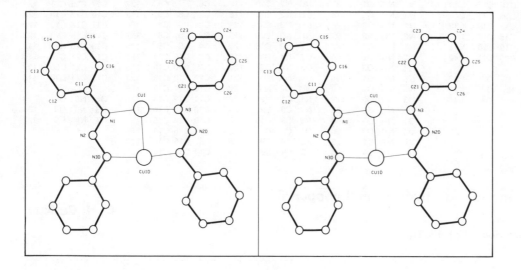

C2/c   Z = 8   R = 0.09

DAABCU

Bond Lengths

Cu1	Cu1D	2.45	C13	C14	1.39
Cu1	N1	1.90	C14	C15	1.40
Cu1	N3	1.94	C15	C16	1.44
N1	N2	1.27	C21	C22	1.39
N2	N3D	1.32	C21	C26	1.40
C11	N1	1.48	C22	C23	1.42
C21	N3	1.39	C23	C24	1.39
C11	C12	1.39	C24	C25	1.39
C11	C16	1.40	C25	C26	1.43
C12	C13	1.42			

Bond Angles

N1	Cu1	N3	172	N1	C11	C16	115	N3	C21	C26	124
Cu1	N1	N2	128	C12	C11	C16	123	C22	C21	C26	118
Cu1	N1	C11	122	C11	C12	C13	120	C21	C22	C23	123
N2	N1	C11	110	C12	C13	C14	120	C22	C23	C24	117
N1	N2	N3D	116	C13	C14	C15	120	C23	C24	C25	121
Cu1	N3	N2D	124	C14	C15	C16	122	C24	C25	C26	121
Cu1	N3	C21	122	C11	C16	C15	116	C21	C26	C25	119
N1	C11	C12	122	N3	C21	C22	118				

83.41   bis - (3 - Hydroxyl - 1,3 - diphenyltriazene) palladium

$C_{24}H_{20}N_6O_2Pd$

E.F.Meyer Junior, S.H.Simonsen, Acta Cryst., 16, A67, 1963

Atomic coordinates were not reported in the paper.
P2/c   Z = 2   R = 0.06

HPTRPD   LB 24-20-18

83.42   Trimethyl - (8 - quinolinolato) platinum(iv) dimer

$C_{24}H_{30}N_2O_2Pt_2$

J.E.Lydon, M.R.Truter, J. Chem. Soc., 6899, 1965

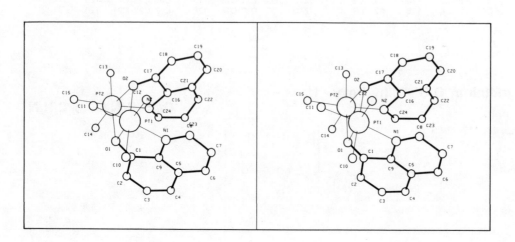

P2₁2₁2₁   Z = 8   R = 0.10

TMEQPT   LB 12-15-4

Bond Lengths

Pt1	N1	2.19	C1	C2	1.51
Pt1	O1	2.22	C1	C9	1.50
Pt1	O2	2.29	C2	C3	1.45
Pt1	C10	2.03	C3	C4	1.37
Pt1	C11	2.00	C4	C5	1.48
Pt1	C12	2.07	C5	C6	1.43
Pt2	N2	2.08	C5	C9	1.43
Pt2	O1	2.23	C6	C7	1.25
Pt2	O2	2.23	C7	C8	1.58
Pt2	C13	2.02	C16	C17	1.53
Pt2	C14	2.16	C16	C21	1.39
Pt2	C15	2.12	C17	C18	1.36
C8	N1	1.25	C18	C19	1.43
C9	N1	1.33	C19	C20	1.30
C16	N2	1.41	C20	C21	1.44
C24	N2	1.37	C21	C22	1.33
C1	O1	1.22	C22	C23	1.41
C17	O2	1.26	C23	C24	1.55

Bond Angles

N1	Pt1	O1	76	N2	Pt2	C14	101	Pt1	O1	Pt2	99	N1	C9	C1	117
N1	Pt1	O2	90	N2	Pt2	C15	175	Pt1	O1	C1	113	N1	C9	C5	119
N1	Pt1	C10	89	O1	Pt2	O2	81	Pt2	O1	C1	112	C1	C9	C5	124
N1	Pt1	C11	174	O1	Pt2	C13	174	Pt1	O2	Pt2	97	N2	C16	C17	109
N1	Pt1	C12	102	O1	Pt2	C14	92	Pt1	O2	C17	119	N2	C16	C21	132
O1	Pt1	O2	80	O1	Pt2	C15	91	Pt2	O2	C17	113	C17	C16	C21	120
O1	Pt1	C10	96	O2	Pt2	C13	93	O1	C1	C2	127	O2	C17	C16	119
O1	Pt1	C11	98	O2	Pt2	C14	172	O1	C1	C9	120	O2	C17	C18	122
O1	Pt1	C12	177	O2	Pt2	C15	101	C2	C1	C9	113	C16	C17	C18	117
O2	Pt1	C10	176	C13	Pt2	C14	94	C1	C2	C3	121	C17	C18	C19	120
O2	Pt1	C11	91	C13	Pt2	C15	90	C2	C3	C4	124	C18	C19	C20	121
O2	Pt1	C12	98	C14	Pt2	C15	83	C3	C4	C5	119	C19	C20	C21	123
C10	Pt1	C11	90	Pt1	N1	C8	124	C4	C5	C6	119	C16	C21	C20	117
C10	Pt1	C12	85	Pt1	N1	C9	111	C4	C5	C9	119	C16	C21	C22	114
C11	Pt1	C12	84	C8	N1	C9	125	C6	C5	C9	122	C20	C21	C22	130
N2	Pt2	O1	90	Pt2	N2	C16	119	C5	C6	C7	114	C21	C22	C23	128
N2	Pt2	O2	75	Pt2	N2	C24	129	C6	C7	C8	124	C22	C23	C24	109
N2	Pt2	C13	88	C16	N2	C24	108	N1	C8	C7	115	N2	C24	C23	127

83.43   2,2′ - Diphenyl bis - (2 - iminomethylenephenolato) copper(ii) $C_{26}H_{22}CuN_2O_2$

T.P.Cheeseman, D.Hall, T.N.Waters, Proc. Chem. Soc., 379, 1963

Atomic coordinates were not given
but bond lengths were reported.
Pc   Z = 2   R = 0.13

DPIPCU   LB 26-22-2

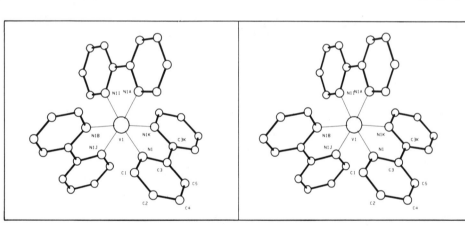

83.44   tris - 2,2′ - Dipyridyl vanadium(0) $C_{30}H_{24}N_6V$

G.Albrecht, Z. Chem., 3, 182, 1963

No comparison of bond lengths is
possible since they are not reported
in the paper.
P-3c1   Z = 6   R = 0.06

DPYRDV   LB 30-24-7

Bond Lengths

V1	N1	2.10
C1	N1	1.40
C3	N1	1.41
C1	C2	1.43
C2	C4	1.40
C3	C5	1.39
C3	C3K	1.47
C4	C5	1.41

Bond Angles

N1	V1	N1A	96	N1	C1	C2	120
N1	V1	N1I	174	C1	C2	C4	122
N1	V1	N1J	89	N1	C3	C5	120
N1	V1	N1K	80	N1	C3	C3K	116
V1	N1	C1	127	C5	C3	C3K	124
V1	N1	C3	114	C2	C4	C5	116
C1	N1	C3	118	C3	C5	C4	123

83.45   Pyridinium bis(2 - hydroxy - naphthalene - 1 - azo) - (2′ - hydroxy - 4′ - nitrobenzene) chromium(iii) pyridine solvate $C_{32}H_{18}CrN_6O_8^{-}$, $C_5H_6N^{+}$, $0.5C_5H_5N$

R.Grieb, A.Niggli, Helv. Chim. Acta, 48, 317, 1965

Atomic coordinates were not
reported in the paper.
P-1 Z = 2   R = 0.21

PACRPS   LB 37-24-1

83.46 Copper(ii) bis - (benzeneazo - β - naphthol)

$C_{32}H_{22}CuN_4O_2$

J.A.J.Jarvis, Acta Cryst., 14, 961, 1961

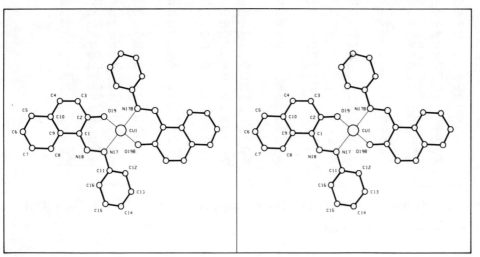

$P2_1/n$ Z = 4   R = 0.16

CBANAP   LB 32-22-1

Bond Lengths

Cu1	N17	2.01
Cu1	O19	1.93
N17	N18	1.31
C11	N17	1.41
C1	N18	1.34
C2	O19	1.30
C1	C2	1.42
C1	C9	1.45
C2	C3	1.44
C3	C4	1.37
C4	C10	1.40
C5	C6	1.37
C5	C10	1.42
C6	C7	1.38
C7	C8	1.40
C8	C9	1.39
C9	C10	1.41
C11	C12	1.38
C11	C16	1.38
C12	C13	1.42
C13	C14	1.39
C14	C15	1.35
C15	C16	1.41

Bond Angles

N17	Cu1	N17B	180
N17	Cu1	O19	87
N17	Cu1	O19B	93
O19	Cu1	N17B	93
O19	Cu1	O19B	180
Cu1	N17	N18	123
Cu1	N17	C11	124
N17	N18	C11	112
N17	N18	C1	121
Cu1	O19	C2	118
N18	C1	C2	126
N18	C1	C9	116
C2	C1	C9	118
O19	C2	C1	123
O19	C2	C3	117
C1	C2	C3	119
C2	C3	C4	120
C3	C4	C10	123
C6	C5	C10	118
C5	C6	C7	122
C6	C7	C8	120
C7	C8	C9	121
C1	C9	C8	121
C1	C9	C10	121
C8	C9	C10	118
C4	C10	C9	118
C5	C10	C9	122
C4	C10	C5	121
N17	C11	C12	115
N17	C11	C16	122
C12	C11	C16	123
C11	C12	C13	118
C12	C13	C14	119
C13	C14	C15	123
C14	C15	C16	119
C11	C16	C15	119

84.1 bis(Biuret) dichloro cadmium(ii)

C₄H₁₀CdCl₂N₆O₄

L.Cavalca, M.Nardelli, G.Fava, Acta Cryst., 13, 594, 1960

$$CdCl_2 \cdot (H_2N-CO-NH-CO-NH_2)_2$$

P2₁/c   Z = 2   R = 0.10

BICDCL   LB 4-10-11

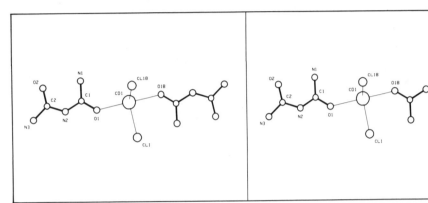

Bond Lengths			Bond Angles			
Cd1	Cl1	2.62	Cl1	Cd1	Cl1B	89
Cd1	Cl1B	2.55	Cl1	Cd1	O1	87
Cd1	O1	2.34	Cl1	Cd1	O1B	93
C1	N1	1.35	O1	Cd1	Cl1B	92
C1	N2	1.34	O1	Cd1	O1B	180
C2	N2	1.35	C1	N2	C2	132
C2	N3	1.34	Cd1	O1	C1	137
C1	O1	1.23	N1	C1	N2	119
C2	O2	1.27	N1	C1	O1	122
			N2	C1	O1	119
			N2	C2	N3	118
			N2	C2	O2	120
			N3	C2	O2	121

Torsion Angles

Cl1	Cd1	O1	C1	168	C2	N2	C1	N1	3	C1	N2	C2	O2	2
Cl1B	Cd1	O1	C1	80	C2	N2	C1	O1	−179	Cd1	O1	C1	N1	−16
O1B	Cd1	O1	C1	−90	C1	N2	C2	N3	−176	Cd1	O1	C1	N2	166

84.2 bis(Biuret) dichloro zinc(ii)

C₄H₁₀Cl₂N₆O₄Zn

M.Nardelli, G.Fava, G.Giraldi, Acta Cryst., 16, 343, 1963

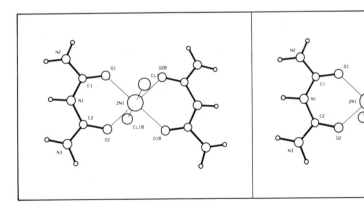

P2₁/c   Z = 2   R = 0.12

BIUZNC   LB 4-10-20

Bond Lengths			Bond Angles			
Zn1	Cl1	2.53	Cl1	Zn1	Cl1B	180
Zn1	O1	2.05	Cl1	Zn1	O1	91
Zn1	O2	2.03	Cl1	Zn1	O2	90
C1	N1	1.35	Cl1	Zn1	O1B	89
C2	N1	1.37	Cl1	Zn1	O2B	90
C1	N2	1.33	O1	Zn1	Cl1B	89
C2	N3	1.32	O1	Zn1	O2	87
C1	O1	1.23				
C2	O2	1.24				

O1	Zn1	O1B	180	Zn1	O2	C2	128
O1	Zn1	O2B	93	N1	C1	N2	114
O2	Zn1	Cl1B	90	N1	C1	O1	126
O2	Zn1	O1B	93	N2	C1	O1	120
O2	Zn1	O2B	180	N1	C2	N3	116
C1	N1	C2	127	N1	C2	O2	124
Zn1	O1	C1	127	N3	C2	O2	120

Torsion Angles

Cl1	Zn1	O1	C1	−87	O2B	Zn1	O2	C2	−90
Cl1B	Zn1	O1	C1	93	C2	N1	C1	N2	177
O2	Zn1	O1	C1	3	C2	N1	C1	O1	−3
O1B	Zn1	O1	C1	−90	C1	N1	C2	N3	177
O2B	Zn1	O1	C1	−177	C1	N1	C2	O2	−3
Cl1	Zn1	O2	C2	83	Zn1	O1	C1	N1	1
Cl1B	Zn1	O2	C2	−97	Zn1	O1	C1	N2	−179
O1	Zn1	O2	C2	−8	Zn1	O2	C2	N1	9
O1B	Zn1	O2	C2	172	Zn1	O2	C2	N3	−170

84.3 bis(2 - Hydroxyethylamine) tetra - aquo copper(ii) sulfate

$C_4H_{22}CuN_2O_6^{2+}$, O_4S^{2-}

G.K.Abdullaev, Kh.S.Mamedov, Zh. Strukt. Khim., 6, 171, 1965

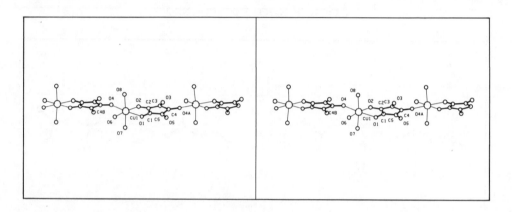

Atomic coordinates were not given but bond lengths were reported.
Pccn   Z = 4 R_{hol} = 0.19,
R_{0kl} = 0.25

CUETNM   LB 4-22-4

84.4   Croconato triaquo copper(ii)

$(C_5H_6CuO_8)_n$

M.D.Glick, G.L.Downs, L.F.Dahl, Inorg. Chem., 3, 1712, 1964

Pbca   Z = 8   R = 0.09

CUCROC   LB 5-0-1

Bond Lengths

Cu1	O1	2.32	C3	O3	1.24
Cu1	O2	1.98	C4	O4	1.24
Cu1	O4	2.35	C5	O5	1.22
Cu1	O6	1.94	C1	C2	1.45
Cu1	O7	2.00	C1	C5	1.46
Cu1	O8	2.05	C2	C3	1.43
C1	O1	1.24	C3	C4F	1.49
C2	O2	1.28	C4	C5F	1.46

Bond Angles

O1	Cu1	O2	81	O2	Cu1	O8	93	Cu1	O2	C2	112	O3	C3	C2	129
O1	Cu1	O4	172	O4	Cu1	O6	94	Cu1	O4	C4	143	O3	C3	C4F	125
O1	Cu1	O6	94	O4	Cu1	O7	88	O1	C1	C2	123	C2	C3	C4F	106
O1	Cu1	O7	93	O4	Cu1	O8	85	O1	C1	C5	129	O4	C4	C3F	127
O1	Cu1	O8	95	O6	Cu1	O7	89	C2	C1	C5	108	O4	C4	C5F	124
O2	Cu1	O4	91	O6	Cu1	O8	91	O2	C2	C1	122	O5	C5	C1	127
O2	Cu1	O6	175	O7	Cu1	O8	172	O2	C2	C3	127	O5	C5	C4F	126
O2	Cu1	O7	89	Cu1	O1	C1	102	C1	C2	C3	110	C1	C5	C4F	107

84.5   Croconato triaquo zinc(ii)

$(C_5H_6O_8Zn)_n$

M.D.Glick, G.L.Downs, L.F.Dahl, Inorg. Chem., 3, 1712, 1964

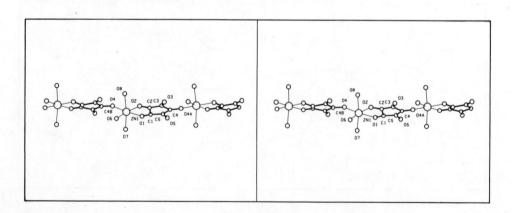

Pbca   Z = 8   R = 0.09

ZNCROC   LB 5-0-3

Bond Lengths

Zn1	O1	2.16	C3	O3	1.22
Zn1	O2	2.11	C4	O4	1.27
Zn1	O4	2.10	C5	O5	1.19
Zn1	O6	2.03	C1	C2	1.43
Zn1	O7	2.12	C1	C5	1.49
Zn1	O8	2.16	C2	C3	1.48
C1	O1	1.25	C3	C4F	1.50
C2	O2	1.26	C4	C5F	1.48

Bond Angles

O1	Zn1	O2	81	O2	Zn1	O8	91	Zn1	O2	C2	108	O3	C3	C2	129
O1	Zn1	O4	171	O4	Zn1	O6	100	Zn1	O4	C4	142	O3	C3	C4F	128
O1	Zn1	O6	89	O4	Zn1	O7	87	O1	C1	C2	122	C2	C3	C4F	103
O1	Zn1	O7	94	O4	Zn1	O8	84	O1	C1	C5	126	O4	C4	C3F	126
O1	Zn1	O8	95	O6	Zn1	O7	91	C2	C1	C5	109	O4	C4	C5F	123
O2	Zn1	O4	90	O6	Zn1	O8	91	O2	C2	C1	122	O5	C5	C1	130
O2	Zn1	O6	170	O7	Zn1	O8	171	O2	C2	C3	127	O5	C5	C4F	125
O2	Zn1	O7	89	Zn1	O1	C1	107	C1	C2	C3	110	C1	C5	C4F	104

84.6 Penta(dichloro copper(ii)) di - n - propanol complex

C₆H₁₆Cl₁₀Cu₅O₂

C$_6$H$_{16}$Cl$_{10}$Cu$_5$O$_2$

R.D.Willett, R.E.Rundle, J. Chem. Phys., 40, 838, 1964

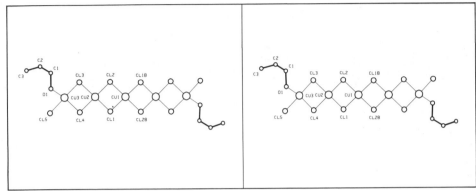

No comparison of bond lengths is possible since they are not reported in the paper.
See also Ugro, Dissert. Abstr. (B), 28, 1891, 1967.
P2₁/n   Z = 2   R = 0.16

PCUCPR   LB 6-16-18

Bond Lengths

Cu1	Cl1	2.23	Cu3	Cl4	2.27
Cu1	Cl2	2.29	Cu3	Cl5	2.29
Cu2	Cl1	2.26	Cu3	O1	1.77
Cu2	Cl2	2.27	C1	O1	1.72
Cu2	Cl3	2.27	C1	C2	1.48
Cu2	Cl4	2.31	C2	C3	1.62
Cu3	Cl3	2.29			

Bond Angles

Cl1	Cu1	Cl2	86	Cl2	Cu2	Cl3	93	Cl5	Cu3	O1	78
Cl1	Cu1	Cl1B	180	Cl2	Cu2	Cl4	171	Cu1	Cl1	Cu2	94
Cl1	Cu1	Cl2B	94	Cl3	Cu2	Cl4	87	Cu1	Cl2	Cu2	92
Cl2	Cu1	Cl1B	94	Cl3	Cu3	Cl4	88	Cu2	Cl3	Cu3	93
Cl2	Cu1	Cl2B	180	Cl3	Cu3	Cl5	170	Cu2	Cl4	Cu3	92
Cl1	Cu2	Cl2	86	Cl3	Cu3	O1	103	Cu3	O1	C1	119
Cl1	Cu2	Cl3	172	Cl4	Cu3	Cl5	91	O1	C1	C2	111
Cl1	Cu2	Cl4	92	Cl4	Cu3	O1	169	C1	C2	C3	118

84.7 bis(Trimethylphosphine oxide) cobalt(ii) dinitrate

C₆H₁₈CoO₂P₂²⁺ ; 2NO₃⁻

C$_6$H$_{18}$CoO$_2$P$_2^{2+}$; 2NO$_3^-$

F.A.Cotton, R.H.Soderberg, J. Amer. Chem. Soc., 85, 2402, 1963

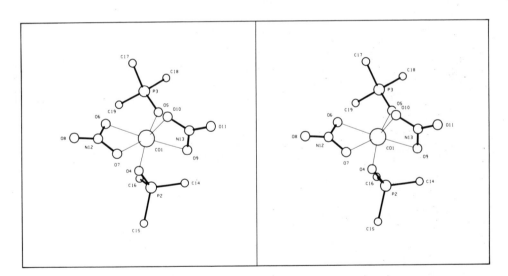

$$\left[\left(\begin{array}{c} H_3C \\ H_3C-P\rightarrow O \\ H_3C \end{array} \right)_2 Co \right]^{2+} (NO_3^-)_2$$

P2₁/c   Z = 4   R = 0.11

MPOCON   LB 6-18-18

Bond Lengths

Co1	O4	1.93	P3	O5	1.55
Co1	O5	1.95	P3	C17	1.82
Co1	O6	2.14	P3	C18	1.81
Co1	O7	2.23	P3	C19	1.79
Co1	O9	2.17	N12	O6	1.24
Co1	O10	2.15	N12	O7	1.25
P2	O4	1.53	N12	O8	1.21
P2	C14	1.80	N13	O9	1.23
P2	C15	1.87	N13	O10	1.22
P2	C16	1.82	N13	O11	1.21

Bond Angles

O4	Co1	O5	106	O7	Co1	O10	84	C18	P3	C19	110
O4	Co1	O6	97	O9	Co1	O10	57	O6	N12	O7	115
O4	Co1	O7	89	O4	P2	C14	114	O6	N12	O8	122
O4	Co1	O9	98	O4	P2	C15	108	O7	N12	O8	123
O4	Co1	O10	150	O4	P2	C16	113	O9	N13	O10	115
O5	Co1	O6	97	C14	P2	C15	109	O9	N13	O11	123
O5	Co1	O7	152	C14	P2	C16	104	O10	N13	O11	121
O5	Co1	O9	95	C15	P2	C16	108	Co1	O4	P2	140
O5	Co1	O10	93	O5	P3	C17	111	Co1	O5	P3	133
O6	Co1	O7	57	O5	P3	C18	109	Co1	O6	N12	96
O6	Co1	O9	158	O5	P3	C19	113	Co1	O7	N12	91
O6	Co1	O10	104	C17	P3	C18	106	Co1	O9	N13	93
O7	Co1	O9	107	C17	P3	C19	109	Co1	O10	N13	94

84.8   Manganese(ii) dichlorophosphate di - ethylacetate

J.Danielsen, S.E.Rasmussen, Acta Chem. Scand., 17, 1971, 1963

$C_8H_{16}Cl_4MnO_8P_2$

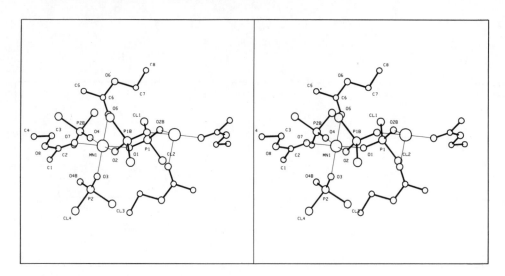

$[(CH_3COOC_2H_5)_2Mn]^{2+} 2(PO_2Cl_2)^-$

$P2_1/a$ Z = 4   R = 0.15

MCOPEC   LB 8-16-25

Bond Lengths

Mn1	O1	2.12	P2	O3	1.45
Mn1	O2	2.14	P2	O4B	1.47
Mn1	O3	2.15	C6	O5	1.20
Mn1	O4	2.11	C6	O6	1.35
Mn1	O5	2.17	C7	O6	1.53
Mn1	O7	2.24	C2	O7	1.18
Cl1	P1	2.01	C2	O8	1.38
Cl2	P1	2.02	C3	O8	1.42
Cl3	P2	2.00	C1	C2	1.48
Cl4	P2	2.01	C3	C4	1.49
P1	O1	1.46	C5	C6	1.43
P1	O2B	1.47	C7	C8	1.45

Bond Angles

O1	Mn1	O2	92	O3	Mn1	O4	92	Cl2	P1	O1	108	Mn1	O1	P1	151	O7	C2	C1	128
O1	Mn1	O3	93	O3	Mn1	O5	179	Cl2	P1	O2B	109	Mn1	O2	P1B	141	O8	C2	C1	112
O1	Mn1	O4	93	O3	Mn1	O7	90	O1	P1	O2B	122	Mn1	O3	P2	143	O8	C3	C4	105
O1	Mn1	O5	88	O4	Mn1	O7	88	Cl3	P2	Cl4	102	Mn1	O4	P2B	173	O5	C6	O6	125
O1	Mn1	O7	177	O4	Mn1	O7	90	Cl3	P2	O3	107	Mn1	O5	C6	151	O5	C6	C5	126
O2	Mn1	O3	93	O5	Mn1	O7	89	Cl3	P2	O4B	109	C6	O6	C7	112	O6	C6	C5	110
O2	Mn1	O4	173	Cl1	P1	Cl2	102	Cl4	P2	O3	107	Mn1	O7	C2	141	O6	C7	C8	104
O2	Mn1	O5	86	Cl1	P1	O1	108	Cl4	P2	O4B	108	C2	O8	C3	117				
O2	Mn1	O7	86	Cl1	P1	O2B	106	O3	P2	O4B	121	O7	C2	O8	120				

84.9   Dichloro copper(ii) di - μ - oxopyridine - dichloro copper(ii)

H.L.Schafer, J.C.Morrow, H.M.Smith, J. Chem. Phys., 42, 504, 1965

$C_{10}H_{10}Cl_4Cu_2N_2O_2$

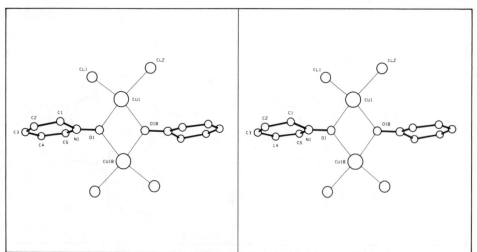

See also Sager et al., Inorg. Chem., 8, 694, 1969; Sager et al., Inorg. Chem., 6, 951, 1967.
$P112_1/b$ Z = 4 $R_{h0l} = 0.17$,
$R_{0kl} = 0.15$

CUCPYO   LB 10-10-25

Bond Lengths

Cu1	Cl1	2.21
Cu1	Cl2	2.24
Cu1	O1	1.99
Cu1	O1B	2.10
N1	O1	1.23
C1	N1	1.39
C5	N1	1.30
C1	C2	1.44
C2	C3	1.22
C3	C4	1.32
C4	C5	1.38

Bond Angles

Cl1	Cu1	Cl2	99	C1	N1	C5	113
Cl1	Cu1	O1	93	Cu1	O1	Cu1B	104
Cl1	Cu1	O1B	144	Cu1	O1	N1	124
Cl2	Cu1	O1	166	N1	C1	C2	116
Cl2	Cu1	O1B	98	C1	C2	C3	127
O1	Cu1	O1B	76	C2	C3	C4	115
O1	N1	C1	126	C3	C4	C5	122
O1	N1	C5	121	N1	C5	C4	124

84.10   bis(Nitrosophenylhydroxylamino) copper(ii)

C₁₂H₁₀CuN₄O₄

L.M.Shkol'nikova, E.A.Shugam, Zh. Strukt. Khim., 4, 380, 1963

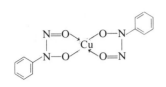

P2₁/c   Z = 2   R_h0l = 0.22,
R_h1l = 0.23, R_0kl = 0.19

CUNPHA   LB 12-10-36

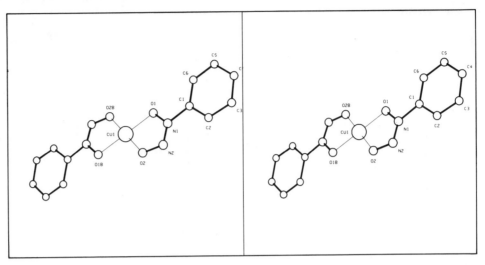

Bond Lengths		
Cu1	O1	1.87
Cu1	O2	1.89
N1	N2	1.27
N1	O1	1.37
N2	O2	1.27
C1	N1	1.42
C1	C2	1.41
C1	C6	1.40
C2	C3	1.39
C3	C4	1.39
C4	C5	1.41
C5	C6	1.38

Bond Angles								
O1	Cu1	O2	78		Cu1	O2	N2	125
O1	Cu1	O1B	180		N1	C1	C2	113
O1	Cu1	O2B	102		N1	C1	C6	130
O2	Cu1	O1B	102		C2	C1	C6	117
O2	Cu1	O2B	180		C1	C2	C3	122
N2	N1	O1	126		C2	C3	C4	118
N2	N1	C1	124		C3	C4	C5	122
O1	N1	C1	110		C4	C5	C6	117
N1	N2	O2	103		C1	C6	C5	124
Cu1	O1	N1	109					

84.11   Dinitrato uranyl triethyl phosphate

C₁₂H₃₀N₂O₁₆P₂U

J.E.Fleming, H.Lynton, Chem. and Industry, 1415, 1960

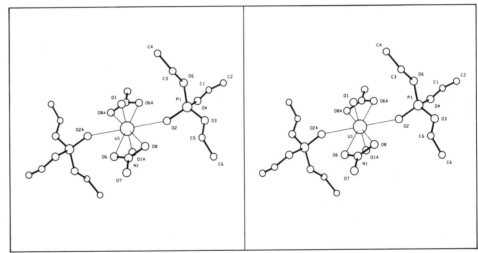

The space group is P -1 and not P1
as published. The length reported
for U - O1 is incorrect (private
communication).
P-1   Z = 1   R_hk0 = 0.23,
R_h0l = 0.24, R_0kl = 0.30

UNOEPO

Bond Lengths					
U1	O1	1.64	N1	O7	1.29
U1	O2	2.44	N1	O8	1.15
U1	O6	2.47	C5	O3	1.20
U1	O8	2.62	C1	O4	1.15
P1	O2	1.49	C3	O5	1.53
P1	O3	1.48	C1	C2	1.05
P1	O4	1.56	C3	C4	1.33
P1	O5	1.53	C5	C6	1.26
N1	O6	1.05			

Bond Angles															
O1	U1	O2	89	O2	U1	O1A	91	O2	P1	O4	103	P1	O3	C5	127
O1	U1	O6	98	O2	U1	O2A	180	O2	P1	O5	119	P1	O4	C1	149
O1	U1	O8	90	O2	U1	O6A	71	O3	P1	O4	107	P1	O5	C3	140
O1	U1	O1A	180	O2	U1	O8A	114	O3	P1	O5	107	U1	O6	N1	104
O1	U1	O2A	91	O6	U1	O8	44	O4	P1	O5	104	U1	O8	N1	93
O1	U1	O6A	82	O6	U1	O6A	180	O6	N1	O7	119	O4	C1	C2	122
O1	U1	O8A	90	O6	U1	O8A	136	O6	N1	O8	119	O5	C3	C4	119
O2	U1	O6	109	O8	U1	O8A	180	O7	N1	O8	122	O3	C5	C6	136
O2	U1	O8	66	O2	P1	O3	115	U1	O2	P1	153				

84.12 Copper(ii) tropolone

$C_{14}H_{10}CuO_4$

W.M.Macintyre, J.M.Robertson, R.F.Zahrobsky, Proc. R. Soc., A, 289, 161, 1965

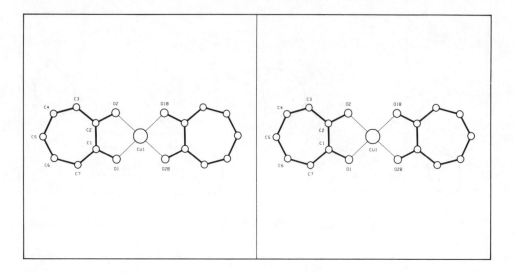

P2$_1$/c Z = 2 R = 0.10

CUTROP LB 14-10-25

Bond Lengths

Cu1 O1	1.89	
Cu1 O2	1.93	
C1 O1	1.31	
C2 O2	1.28	
C1 C2	1.44	
C1 C7	1.38	
C2 C3	1.43	
C3 C4	1.37	
C4 C5	1.43	
C5 C6	1.37	
C6 C7	1.43	

Bond Angles

O1 Cu1 O2	85	Cu1 O2 C2	112	C1 C2 C3	128
O1 Cu1 O1B	180	O1 C1 C2	116	C2 C3 C4	128
O1 Cu1 O2B	95	O1 C1 C7	115	C3 C4 C5	129
O2 Cu1 O1B	95	C2 C1 C7	129	C4 C5 C6	126
O2 Cu1 O2B	180	O2 C2 C1	116	C5 C6 C7	133
Cu1 O1 C1	112	O2 C2 C3	116	C1 C7 C6	126

84.13 tris(N - Nitrosophenylhydroxylamino) iron(iii)

$C_{18}H_{15}FeN_6O_6$

Iron cupferron
D.van der Helm, L.L.Merritt, R.Degeilh, Acta Cryst., 18, 355, 1965

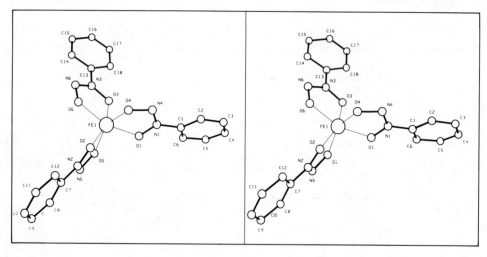

P2$_1$/a Z = 4 R = 0.15

ICUFER LB 18-15-16

Bond Lengths

Fe1 O1	1.99	N4 O4	1.32	C7 C8	1.37
Fe1 O2	2.00	N5 O5	1.32	C7 C12	1.39
Fe1 O3	1.99	N6 O6	1.30	C8 C9	1.40
Fe1 O4	2.01	C1 N1	1.42	C9 C10	1.37
Fe1 O5	2.01	C7 N2	1.43	C10 C11	1.33
Fe1 O6	2.00	C13 N3	1.45	C11 C12	1.42
N1 N4	1.30	C1 C2	1.39	C13 C14	1.41
N2 N5	1.31	C1 C6	1.38	C13 C18	1.37
N3 N6	1.30	C2 C3	1.38	C14 C15	1.41
N1 O1	1.33	C3 C4	1.39	C15 C16	1.42
N2 O2	1.31	C4 C5	1.35	C16 C17	1.35
N3 O3	1.31	C5 C6	1.44	C17 C18	1.42

Bond Angles

O1 Fe1 O2	113	O3 Fe1 O4	104	N5 N2 O2	121	Fe1 O1 N1	113
O1 Fe1 O3	88	O3 Fe1 O5	99	N5 N2 C7	118	Fe1 O2 N2	113
O1 Fe1 O4	76	O3 Fe1 O6	75	O2 N2 C7	121	Fe1 O3 N3	114
O1 Fe1 O5	88	O4 Fe1 O5	151	N6 N3 O3	121	Fe1 O4 N4	118
O1 Fe1 O6	160	O4 Fe1 O6	98	N6 N3 C13	118	Fe1 O5 N5	118
O2 Fe1 O3	158	O5 Fe1 O6	105	O3 N3 C13	121	Fe1 O6 N6	119
O2 Fe1 O4	89	N4 N1 O1	121	N1 N4 O4	111		
O2 Fe1 O5	76	N4 N1 C1	119	N2 N5 O5	111		
O2 Fe1 O6	86	O1 N1 C1	120	N3 N6 O6	111		

84.14 Ammonium uranyl cupferrate

$C_{18}H_{15}N_6O_8U^-$, H_4N^+

W.S.Arrington, Dissert. Abstr., 26, 3411, 1965

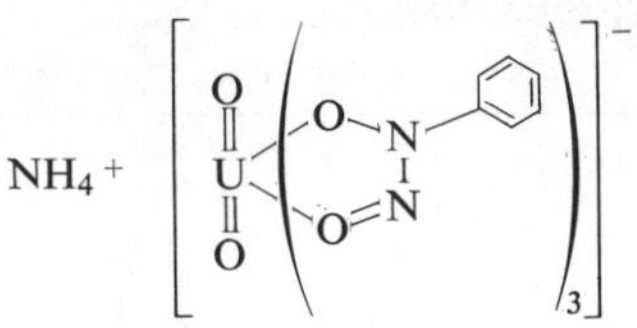

Atomic coordinates were not reported in the paper.
P2$_1$3   Z = 4   R = 0.08

AUCUPF

$$NH_4^+ \left[\begin{array}{c} O \\ U \\ O \end{array} \left(\begin{array}{c} O-N \\ O-N \end{array} \right) \right]_3^-$$

84.15 Copper(ii) bis - 1 - ephedrine - benzene

$C_{20}H_{28}CuN_2O_2$, $0.67C_6H_6$

Y.Amano, K.Osaki, T.Watanabe, Bull. Chem. Soc. Jap., 37, 1363, 1964

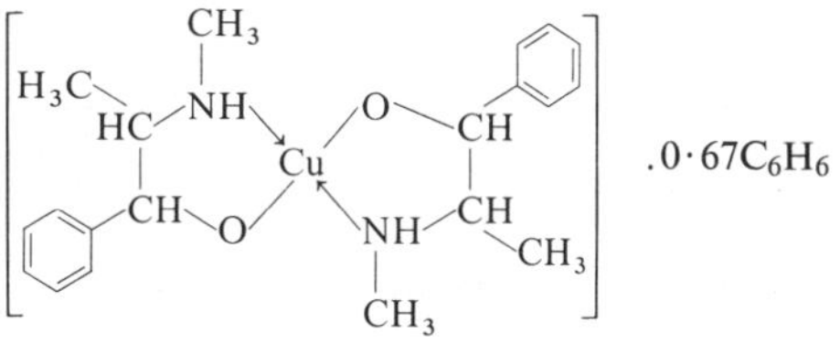

The benzene molecule is disordered.
P321   Z = 3   R = 0.16

CEPHBE   LB 20-28-4

$$\left[\begin{array}{c} CH_3 \\ \end{array} \right] .0 \cdot 67 C_6 H_6$$

Bond Lengths		Bond Angles			
Cu1	N1	2.05	N1	Cu1 N1E	166
Cu1	O1	1.88	N1	Cu1 O1	85
C8	N1	1.48	N1	Cu1 O1E	97
C10	N1	1.48	O1	Cu1 N1E	97
C7	O1	1.42	O1	Cu1 O1E	167
C1	C2	1.43	Cu1	N1 C8	105
C1	C6	1.51	Cu1	N1 C10	116
C2	C3	1.44	C8	N1 C10	114
C3	C4	1.37	Cu1	O1 C7	112
C4	C5	1.43	O1	C7 C6	107
C5	C6	1.38	O1	C7 C8	106
C6	C7	1.50	C6	C7 C8	103
C7	C8	1.60	N1	C8 C7	99
C8	C9	1.54	N1	C8 C9	110
			C7	C8 C9	116

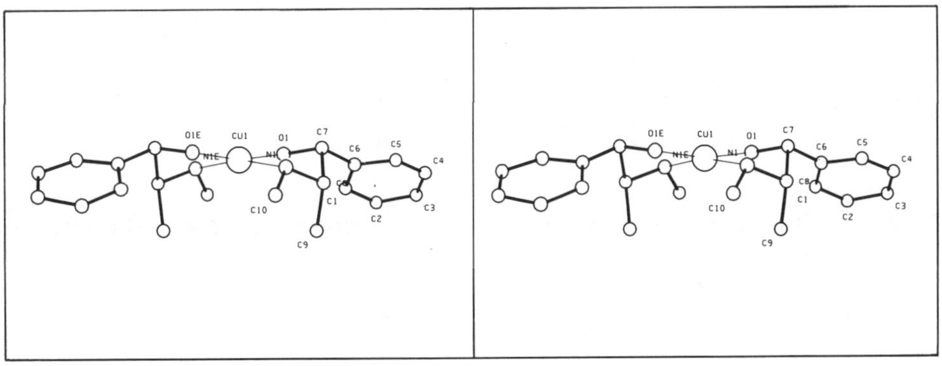

84.16 Palladium(ii) 2 - (o - hydroxyphenyl)benzoxazole

$C_{26}H_{16}N_2O_4Pd$

C.E.Urdy, Dissert. Abstr., 24, 4015, 1964

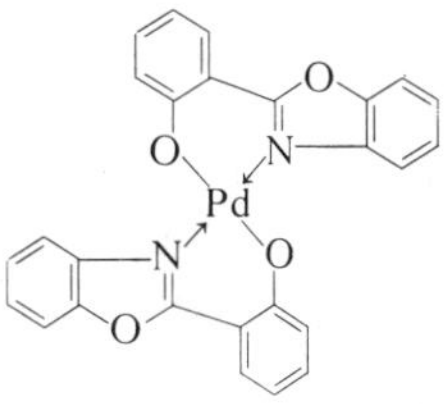

Atomic coordinates were not reported in the paper.
P2$_1$/c   Z = 2   R = 0.09

PDHPBX   LB 26-16-6

84.17 Methyltriethyl titanate tetramer

$C_{28}H_{72}O_{16}Ti_4$

R.D.Witters, C.N.Caughlan, Nature, 205, 1312, 1965

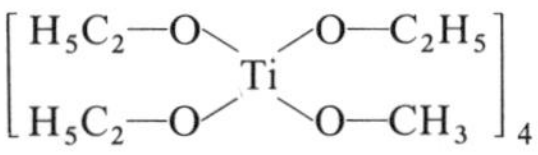

The structure is totally disordered.
P-1   Z = 8   R = 0.14

METTIT   LB 7-18-5

$$\left[\begin{array}{c} H_5C_2-O \quad O-C_2H_5 \\ Ti \\ H_5C_2-O \quad O-CH_3 \end{array} \right]_4$$

84.18 Titanium (iv) ethoxide tetramer

$C_{32}H_{80}O_{16}Ti_4$

J.A.Ibers, Nature, 197, 686, 1963

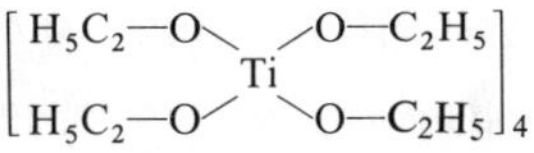

Atomic coordinates were not reported in the paper.
C2/c   Z = 16   R = 0.12

TIETOX   LB 8-10-28

$$\left[\begin{array}{c} H_5C_2-O \quad O-C_2H_5 \\ Ti \\ H_5C_2-O \quad O-C_2H_5 \end{array} \right]_4$$

84.19 bis(Triphenylarsine - oxo) dichloro mercury(ii) $C_{36}H_{30}As_2Cl_2HgO_2$

C.-I.Branden, Acta Chem. Scand., 17, 1363, 1963

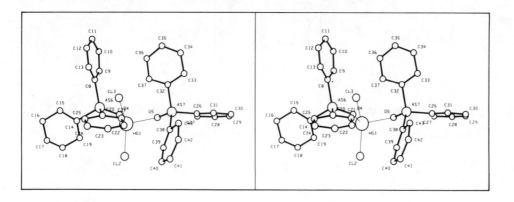

$P2_1/c$ Z = 4   R = 0.09

HGPARO   LB 36-30-1

Bond Lengths

Hg1	Cl2	2.33	As7	C32	1.98	C15	C16	1.49	C26	C27	1.40
Hg1	Cl3	2.32	As7	C38	1.89	C16	C17	1.47	C26	C31	1.40
Hg1	O4	2.32	C8	C9	1.43	C17	C18	1.25	C27	C28	1.44
Hg1	O5	2.37	C8	C13	1.43	C18	C19	1.46	C28	C29	1.29
As6	O4	1.69	C9	C10	1.36	C20	C21	1.37	C29	C30	1.40
As6	C8	1.90	C10	C11	1.37	C20	C25	1.42	C30	C31	1.42
As6	C14	1.95	C11	C12	1.43	C21	C22	1.52	C32	C33	1.44
As6	C20	1.89	C12	C13	1.29	C22	C23	1.27	C32	C37	1.39
As7	O5	1.69	C14	C15	1.37	C23	C24	1.43	C33	C34	1.44
As7	C26	1.92	C14	C19	1.36	C24	C25	1.43	C34	C35	1.40

C35	C36	1.42									
C36	C37	1.44									
C38	C39	1.31									
C38	C43	1.46									
C39	C40	1.34									
C40	C41	1.44									
C41	C42	1.38									
C42	C43	1.45									

Bond Angles

Cl2	Hg1	Cl3	147	C8	As6	C20	110
Cl2	Hg1	O4	100	C14	As6	C20	106
Cl2	Hg1	O5	103	O5	As7	C26	109
Cl3	Hg1	O4	104	O5	As7	C32	110
Cl3	Hg1	O5	99	O5	As7	C38	113
O4	Hg1	O5	93	C26	As7	C32	107
O4	As6	C8	114	C26	As7	C38	107
O4	As6	C14	114	C32	As7	C38	111
O4	As6	C20	107	Hg1	O4	As6	137
C8	As6	C14	106	Hg1	O5	As7	134

84.20 Dichloro mercury(ii) - di - μ - triphenylarsineoxo - dichloro mercury(ii) $C_{36}H_{30}As_2Cl_4Hg_2O_2$

C.-I.Branden, Ark. Kemi, 22, 485, 1964

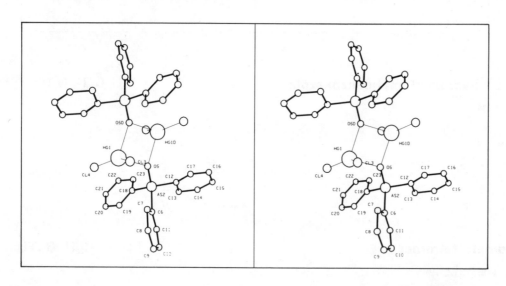

Pbca   Z = 8   R = 0.085

HGCPAO   LB 36-30-2

Bond Lengths

Hg1	Cl3	2.32	As2	C18	1.91	C12	C13	1.41	C18	C23	1.36
Hg1	Cl4	2.32	C6	C7	1.45	C12	C17	1.32	C19	C20	1.39
Hg1	O5	2.48	C6	C11	1.37	C13	C14	1.44	C20	C21	1.30
Hg1	O5D	2.46	C7	C8	1.49	C14	C15	1.30	C21	C22	1.35
As2	O5	1.66	C8	C9	1.37	C15	C16	1.38	C22	C23	1.41
As2	C6	1.91	C9	C10	1.36	C16	C17	1.47			
As2	C12	1.93	C10	C11	1.43	C18	C19	1.36			

Bond Angles

Cl3	Hg1	Cl4	145	O5	As2	C12	105
Cl3	Hg1	O5	106	O5	As2	C18	113
Cl3	Hg1	O5D	105	C6	As2	C12	110
Cl4	Hg1	O5	98	C6	As2	C18	104
Cl4	Hg1	O5D	105	C12	As2	C18	112
O5	Hg1	O5D	79	Hg1	O5	Hg1D	101
O5	As2	C6	112	Hg1	O5	As2	129

84.21 tetrakis(Diphenylmethylarsine - oxo) cobalt(ii) perchlorate $C_{52}H_{52}As_4ClCoO_8^+$, ClO_4^-

P.Pauling, G.B.Robertson, G.A.Rodley, Nature, 207, 73, 1965

The perchlorate ion is disordered.

P4/n   Z = 2   R = 0.12

COPMAS   LB 52-52-1

85.1   Thiosemicarbazido dichloro zinc(ii) $CH_5Cl_2N_3SZn$

L.Cavalca, M.Nardelli, G.Branchi, Acta Cryst., 13, 688, 1960

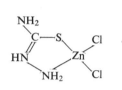

Pnma   Z = 8 R_{hol} = 0.13,
R_{0kl} = 0.14

TCAZNC   LB 1-5-9

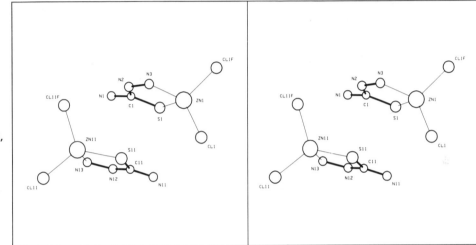

Bond Lengths

Zn1	Cl1	2.24	Zn11	Cl11	2.25
Zn1	S1	2.29	Zn11	S11	2.30
Zn1	N3	2.10	Zn11	N13	2.08
S1	C1	1.72	S11	C11	1.72
N2	N3	1.45	N12	N13	1.39
C1	N1	1.30	C11	N11	1.26
C1	N2	1.28	C11	N12	1.27

Bond Angles

Cl1	Zn1	Cl1F	106	S1	C1	N1	123	S11	Zn11	N13	90
Cl1	Zn1	S1	120	S1	C1	N2	119	Zn11	S11	C11	94
Cl1	Zn1	N3	110	N1	C1	N2	118	N13	N12	C11	135
S1	Zn1	N3	89					Zn11	N13	N12	103
Zn1	S1	C1	96	Cl11	Zn11	Cl11F	111	S11	C11	N11	121
N3	N2	C1	130	Cl11	Zn11	S11	118	S11	C11	N12	118
Zn1	N3	N2	105	Cl11	Zn11	N13	108	N11	C11	N12	122

85.2   Mercury methylmercaptide $C_2H_6HgS_2$

D.C.Bradley, N.R.Kunchur, J. Chem. Phys., 40, 2258, 1964

$Hg(SCH_3)_2$

Pbca   Z = 8   R = 0.16

MERMES   LB 2-6-25

Bond Lengths   *Bond Angles*

Hg2	S7	2.36	S7	Hg2	S8	180
Hg2	S8	2.36	Hg2	S7	C7	111
S7	C7	1.73	Hg2	S8	C8	111
S8	C8	1.73				

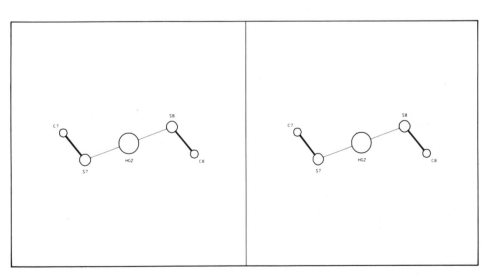

85.3   bis(Thiosemicarbazido) nickel(ii) (red form)

$C_2H_8N_6NiS_2$

L.Cavalca, M.Nardelli, G.Fava, Acta Cryst., 15, 1139, 1962

$P2_1/c$ Z = 2   R = 0.13

TCARNI   LB 2-8-42

Bond Lengths			Bond Angles			
Ni1	S1	2.16	S1	Ni1	S1B	180
Ni1	N3	1.91	S1	Ni1	N3	82
S1	C1	1.75	S1	Ni1	N3B	98
N2	N3	1.54	N3	Ni1	N3B	180
C1	N1	1.44	Ni1	S1	C1	103
C1	N2	1.25	N3	N2	C1	110
			Ni1	N3	N2	124
			S1	C1	N1	122
			S1	C1	N2	121
			N1	C1	N2	116

Torsion Angles

N3	N2	C1	S1	3
N3	N2	C1	N1	176

85.4   bis(Thiosemicarbazido) nickel(ii) sulfate trihydrate (α form) $C_2H_{10}N_6NiS_2^{2+}$, O_4S^{2-}, $3H_2O$

R.Gronbaek, S.E.Rasmussen, Acta Chem. Scand., 16, 2325, 1962

$SO_4^{2-}.3H_2O$

$P2_1/m$ Z = 2 R_{hk0} = 0.11, R_{0kl} = 0.10

NSEMSU   LB 2-10-16

Bond Lengths			Bond Angles			
Ni1	S1	2.16	S1	Ni1	S1B	180
Ni1	N1	1.90	S1	Ni1	N1	90
S1	C1	1.75	S1	Ni1	N1B	90
N1	N2	1.44	N1	Ni1	S1B	90
C1	N2	1.33	N1	Ni1	N1B	180
C1	N3	1.29	Ni1	S1	C1	97
			Ni1	N1	N2	115
			N1	N2	C1	119
			S1	C1	N2	118
			S1	C1	N3	121
			N2	C1	N3	121

Torsion Angles

N1	N2	C1	S1	−8
N1	N2	C1	N3	177

85.5   Tetrahydrothiophene dichloro mercury(ii)

$C_4H_8Cl_2HgS$

C.-I.Branden, Ark. Kemi, 22, 495, 1964

$\cdot$ HgCl$_2$

P-1   Z = 2   R = 0.13

HGCTHS   LB 4-8-24

Bond Lengths			Bond Angles			
Hg1	Cl2	2.62	Cl2	Hg1	Cl3	110
Hg1	Cl3	2.30	Cl2	Hg1	S4	105
Hg1	S4	2.40	Cl3	Hg1	S4	143
S4	C5	1.86	Hg1	S4	C5	100
S4	C8	2.00	Hg1	S4	C8	103
C5	C6	1.48	C5	S4	C8	87
C6	C7	1.31	S4	C5	C6	112
C7	C8	1.53	C5	C6	C7	102
			C6	C7	C8	126
			S4	C8	C7	98

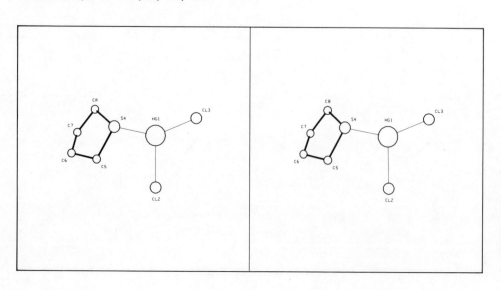

85.6 Diethylmercapto chloro mercury(ii) dichloro mercury(ii) chloride complex

$C_4H_{10}ClHgS^+$, Cl^- , Cl_2Hg

C.-I.Branden, Ark. Kemi, 22, 83, 1964

$2\,HgCl_2 \cdot (C_2H_5)_2S$

P-1   Z = 2   R = 0.10

HGCETS   LB 4-10-22

Bond Lengths			Bond Angles			
Hg1	Cl3	2.34	Cl3	Hg1	Cl6	106
Hg1	Cl6	2.70	Cl3	Hg1	S7	158
Hg1	S7	2.41	Cl6	Hg1	S7	93
S7	C8	1.86	Hg1	S7	C8	106
S7	C10	1.77	Hg1	S7	C10	100
C8	C9	1.45	C8	S7	C10	104
C10	C11	1.53	S7	C8	C9	116
			S7	C10	C11	113
Hg2	Cl4	2.32				
Hg2	Cl5	2.29	Cl4	Hg2	Cl5	172

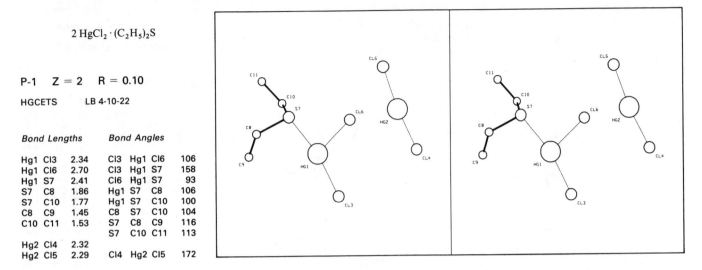

85.7 Mercury ethylmercaptide

$C_4H_{10}HgS_2$

D.C.Bradley, N.R.Kunchur, Canad. J. Chem., 43, 2786, 1965

$H_5C_2-S-Hg-S-C_2H_5$

Cc   Z = 4 $R_{h0l} = 0.133,$
$R\text{-}_{h0l} = 0.164,$ $R_{hk0} = 0.133,$
$R_{0kl} = 0.156$

MERSET   LB

Bond Lengths			Bond Angles			
Hg1	S1	2.45	S1	Hg1	S2	179
Hg1	S2	2.48	Hg1	S1	C1	107
S1	C1	1.65	Hg1	S2	C3	106
S2	C3	1.61	S1	C1	C2	118
C1	C2	1.52	S2	C3	C4	123
C3	C4	1.84				

85.8 Molybdenum tris(dithioglyoxal)

$C_6H_6MoS_6$

A.E.Smith, G.N.Schrauzer, V.P.Mayweg, W.Heinrich, J. Amer. Chem. Soc., 87, 5798, 1965

Atomic coordinates were not given
but bond lengths were reported.
P6₃/m   Z = 2   R = 0.11

MOLSGL   LB 6-6-40

$$Mo\left(\begin{array}{c}S-CH \\ \| \\ S-CH\end{array}\right)_3$$

85.9 Di(tetra - n - butylammonium) cobalt(ii) bis(maleonitrile dithiolate)

$C_8CoN_4S_4^{2-}$, $2C_{16}H_{36}N^+$

J.D.Forrester, A.Zalkin, D.H.Templeton, Inorg. Chem., 3, 1500, 1964

$$[(C_4H_9)_4N^+]_2 \left[\begin{array}{c} NC-C-S \\ NC-C-S \end{array} Co \begin{array}{c} S-C-CN \\ S-C-CN \end{array} \right]^{2-}$$

P-1   Z = 2   R = 0.09

BAMCOM   LB 40-72-1

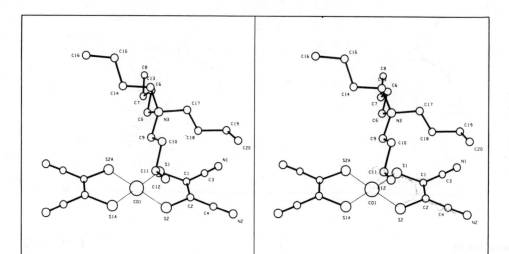

Bond Lengths

Co1	S1	2.16	C5	N3	1.53
Co1	S2	2.16	C9	N3	1.52
S1	C1	1.71	C13	N3	1.51
S2	C2	1.73	C17	N3	1.53
C3	N1	1.15	C5	C6	1.49
C4	N2	1.16	C6	C7	1.53
C1	C2	1.34	C7	C8	1.53
C1	C3	1.40	C9	C10	1.53
C2	C4	1.40	C10	C11	1.51
			C11	C12	1.53
			C13	C14	1.48
			C14	C15	1.52
			C15	C16	1.48
			C17	C18	1.52
			C18	C19	1.54
			C19	C20	1.50

Bond Angles

S1	Co1	S2	91	Co1	S1	C1	104	S2	C2	C1	120	C5	N3	C9	106	N3	C5	C6	116	N3	C13	C14	116
S1	Co1	S1A	180	Co1	S2	C2	104	S2	C2	C4	117	C5	N3	C13	112	C5	C6	C7	109	C13	C14	C15	112
S1	Co1	S2A	89	S1	C1	C2	121	C1	C2	C4	123	C5	N3	C17	109	C6	C7	C8	113	C14	C15	C16	114
S2	Co1	S1A	89	S1	C1	C3	118	N1	C3	C1	178	C9	N3	C13	113	N3	C9	C10	114	N3	C17	C18	115
S2	Co1	S2A	180	C2	C1	C3	121	N2	C4	C2	179	C9	N3	C17	110	C9	C10	C11	110	C17	C18	C19	111
												C13	N3	C17	106	C10	C11	C12	114	C18	C19	C20	113

85.10 Tetra - n - butylammonium copper(ii) bis(maleonitrile dithiolate)

$C_8CuN_4S_4^-$, $C_{16}H_{36}N^+$

J.D.Forrester, A.Zalkin, D.H.Templeton, Inorg. Chem., 3, 1507, 1964

$$[(C_4H_9)_4N]^+ \left[\begin{array}{c} NC-C-S \\ NC-C-S \end{array} Cu \begin{array}{c} S-C-CN \\ S-C-CN \end{array} \right]^-$$

I2/c   Z = 8   R = 0.10

BUACUM   LB 24-36-4

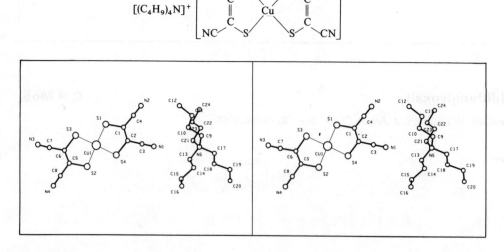

Bond Lengths

Cu1	S1	2.17	C9	N5	1.51
Cu1	S2	2.17	C13	N5	1.52
Cu1	S3	2.18	C17	N5	1.54
Cu1	S4	2.16	C21	N5	1.52
S1	C1	1.73	C9	C10	1.51
S2	C5	1.74	C10	C11	1.54
S3	C6	1.71	C11	C12	1.47
S4	C2	1.70	C13	C14	1.49
C3	N1	1.17	C14	C15	1.56
C4	N2	1.12	C15	C16	1.47
C7	N3	1.14	C17	C18	1.53
C8	N4	1.14	C18	C19	1.62
C1	C2	1.32	C19	C20	1.49
C1	C4	1.43	C21	C22	1.51
C2	C3	1.42	C22	C23	1.53
C5	C6	1.31	C23	C24	1.54
C5	C8	1.44			
C6	C7	1.44			

Bond Angles

S1	Cu1	S2	178	Cu1	S3	C6	102	N1	C3	C2	180	N3	C7	C6	176	C17	N5	C21	112	C17	C18	C19	107
S1	Cu1	S3	88	Cu1	S4	C2	102	N2	C4	C1	177	N4	C8	C5	179	N5	C9	C10	115	C18	C19	C20	110
S1	Cu1	S4	92	S1	C1	C2	119	S2	C5	C6	122					C9	C10	C11	110	N5	C21	C22	115
S2	Cu1	S3	93	S1	C1	C4	118	S2	C5	C8	115	C9	N5	C13	111	C10	C11	C12	112	C21	C22	C23	109
S2	Cu1	S4	87	C2	C1	C4	123	C6	C5	C8	123	C9	N5	C17	105	N5	C13	C14	117	C22	C23	C24	111
S3	Cu1	S4	179	S4	C2	C1	124	S3	C6	C5	122	C9	N5	C21	112	C13	C14	C15	105				
Cu1	S1	C1	103	S4	C2	C3	116	S3	C6	C7	116	C13	N5	C17	110	C14	C15	C16	110				
Cu1	S2	C5	101	C1	C2	C3	120	C5	C6	C7	121	C13	N5	C21	107	N5	C17	C18	112				

85.11 Tetramethylammonium bis(maleonitriledithiolato) nickel(ii) $C_8N_4NiS_4{}^{2-}$, $2C_4H_{12}N^+$

R.Eisenberg, J.A.Ibers, Inorg. Chem., 4, 605, 1965

C-1   Z = 2   R = 0.10

TMASNI   LB 16-24-12

$$[N(CH_3)_4{}^+]_2 \left[\begin{array}{c} NC-C-S \\ \\ NC-C-S \end{array} Ni \begin{array}{c} S-C-CN \\ \\ S-C-CN \end{array} \right]^{2-}$$

Bond Lengths			Bond Angles			
Ni1	S1	2.17	S1	Ni1	S2	92
Ni1	S2	2.16	S1	Ni1	S1B	180
S1	C1	1.74	S1	Ni1	S2B	88
S2	C3	1.76	S2	Ni1	S1B	88
C2	N1	1.13	S2	Ni1	S2B	180
C4	N2	1.12	Ni1	S1	C1	103
C1	C2	1.44	Ni1	S2	C3	104
C1	C3	1.33	S1	C1	C2	117
C3	C4	1.39	S1	C1	C3	122
			C2	C1	C3	122
C5	N3	1.53	N1	C2	C1	179
C6	N3	1.49	S2	C3	C1	119
C7	N3	1.46	S2	C3	C4	118
C8	N3	1.55	C1	C3	C4	123
			N2	C4	C3	177
			C5	N3	C6	113
			C5	N3	C7	111
			C5	N3	C8	110
			C6	N3	C7	105
			C6	N3	C8	110
			C7	N3	C8	109

85.12 bis(Dichloro mercury(ii)) - 1,6 - dithiacyclodeca - cis,cis - 3,8 - diene complex $(C_8H_{12}Cl_4Hg_2S_2)_n$

K.K.Cheung, G.A.Sim, J. Chem. Soc., 5988, 1965

P2$_1$/m   Z = 2   R = 0.136

HGCSCD10   LB 8-12-19

$$\left[\begin{array}{c} Cl \\ Hg-S \\ Cl \end{array} \begin{array}{c} CH_2-HC=CH-CH_2 \\ \\ CH_2-HC=CH-CH_2 \end{array} \begin{array}{c} Cl \\ S-Hg \\ Cl \end{array} \right]_n$$

Bond Lengths			Bond Angles									Torsion Angles									
Hg1	Cl1	2.30	Cl1	Hg1	Cl1C	168	Hg2	S1	C4	107		Cl2	Hg2	S1	C1	−128	C4	S1	C1	C2	63
							C1	S1	C4	103		Cl2	Hg2	S1	C4	−20	Hg2	S1	C4	C3B	52
Hg2	Cl2	2.50	Cl2	Hg2	Cl3	99	S1	C1	C2	110		Cl3	Hg2	S1	C1	−18	C1	S1	C4	C3B	55
Hg2	Cl3	2.51	Cl2	Hg2	S1	114	C1	C2	C3	128		Cl3	Hg2	S1	C4	90	S1	C1	C2	C3	−128
Hg2	S1	2.53	Cl3	Hg2	S1	111	C2	C3	C4B	123		S1C	Hg2	S1	C1	104	C1	C2	C3	C4B	−4
S1	C1	1.84	S1	Hg2	S1C	109	S1	C4	C3B	106		S1C	Hg2	S1	C4	−148	C2	C3	C4B	S1B	121
S1	C4	1.87	Hg2	S1	C1	101						Hg2	S1	C1	C2	174					
C1	C2	1.52																			
C2	C3	1.30																			
C3	C4B	1.60																			

85.13 Biacetyl bis(mercaptoethylimine) nickel(ii)

$C_8H_{14}N_2NiS_2$

Q.Fernando, P.J.Wheatley, Inorg. Chem., 4, 1726, 1965

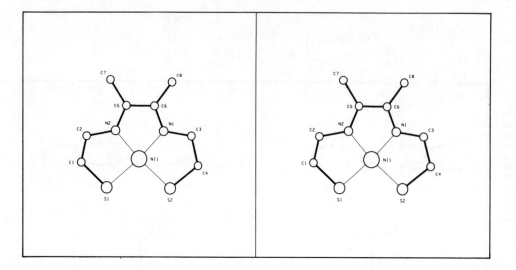

Pna2$_1$ Z = 4   R = 0.179

BAEINI   LB 8-14-18

Bond Lengths

Ni1	S1	2.17	C2	N2	1.51
Ni1	S2	2.15	C5	N2	1.34
Ni1	N1	1.86	C1	C2	1.35
Ni1	N2	1.85	C3	C4	1.52
S1	C1	1.83	C5	C6	1.44
S2	C4	1.82	C5	C7	1.51
C3	N1	1.44	C6	C8	1.47
C6	N1	1.32			

Bond Angles

S1	Ni1	S2	97	Ni1	N1	C3	123	N1	C3	C4	112
S1	Ni1	N1	173	Ni1	N1	C6	117	S2	C4	C3	113
S1	Ni1	N2	90	C3	N1	C6	120	N2	C5	C6	113
S2	Ni1	N1	90	Ni1	N2	C2	119	N2	C5	C7	123
S2	Ni1	N2	173	Ni1	N2	C5	115	C6	C5	C7	123
N1	Ni1	N2	83	C2	N2	C5	125	N1	C6	C5	111
Ni1	S1	C1	96	S1	C1	C2	118	N1	C6	C8	122
Ni1	S2	C4	100	N2	C2	C1	113	C5	C6	C8	126

Torsion Angles

S1	C1	C2	N2	−18
N2	C5	C6	N1	0
N2	C5	C6	C8	−174
C7	C5	C6	N1	173
C7	C5	C6	C8	−1

85.14 Mercury(ii) bis(t - butyl mercaptide)

$C_8H_{18}HgS_2$

N.R.Kunchur, Nature, 204, 468, 1964

Atomic coordinates were not given
but bond lengths were reported.
C222   Z = 4   R = 0.12

HGBUTS   LB 8-18-11

85.15 tetrakis(Thioacetamido) chloro copper(i)

$C_8H_{20}ClCuN_4S_4$

M.R.Truter, K.W.Rutherford, J. Chem. Soc., 1748, 1962

No comparison of bond lengths is
possible since they are not reported
in the paper.
I-4   Z = 2   R = 0.09

TAMCUC   LB 8-20-17

Bond Lengths

Cu1	S1	2.35
S1	C1	1.70
C1	N1	1.29
C1	C2	1.49

Bond Angles

S1	Cu1	S1A	104
S1	Cu1	S1B	112
Cu1	S1	C1	110
S1	C1	N1	121
S1	C1	C2	122
N1	C1	C2	117

85.16 Cobalt(ii) bis(2,5 - dithiahexane)perchlorate

$C_8H_{20}CoS_4^{2+}$, $2ClO_4^-$

F.A.Cotton, D.L.Weaver, J. Amer. Chem. Soc., 87, 4189, 1965

Atomic coordinates were not given
but bond lengths were reported.
P2$_1$/c   Z = 2   R = 0.135

COSHXP   LB 8-20-18

85.17 Nickel(ii) O,O' - diethyldithiophosphate

$C_8H_{20}NiO_4P_2S_4$

E.A.Glinskaya, M.A.Porai-Koshits, Kristallografija, 4, 241, 1960

The structure was determined in
two dimensions only. Atomic
coordinates were not reported in
the paper.
See also McConnell & Kastalsky,
Acta Cryst., 22, 853, 1967; Fernando
& Green, J. Inorg. Nucl. Chem., 29,
647, 1967.
A2/a   Z = 2   No R factor was
given.

NIETHP02   LB 8-20-31

85.18 Ethylthio iron tricarbonyl dimer

$C_{10}H_{10}Fe_2O_6S_2$

L.F.Dahl, C.H.Wei, Inorg. Chem., 2, 328, 1963

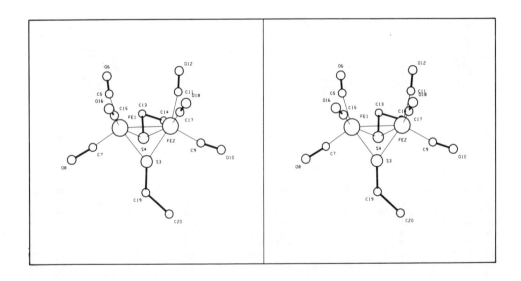

P2$_1$/c   Z = 4   R = 0.12

ETSICO   LB 10-10-38

Bond Lengths

Fe1	Fe2	2.54		S3	C19	1.79
Fe1	S3	2.27		S4	C13	1.83
Fe1	S4	2.22		C5	O6	1.04
Fe1	C5	1.88		C7	O8	1.26
Fe1	C7	1.71		C9	O10	1.18
Fe1	C15	1.84		C11	O12	1.17
Fe2	S3	2.28		C15	O16	1.10
Fe2	S4	2.26		C17	O18	1.16
Fe2	C9	1.81		C13	C14	1.58
Fe2	C11	1.83		C19	C20	1.55
Fe2	C17	1.81				

Bond Angles

Fe2	Fe1	S3	56	S4	Fe1	C15	154	S3	Fe2	C11	159	Fe1	S4	Fe2	69
Fe2	Fe1	S4	56	C5	Fe1	C7	100	S3	Fe2	C17	88	Fe1	S4	C13	114
Fe2	Fe1	C5	105	C5	Fe1	C15	91	S4	Fe2	C9	102	Fe2	S4	C13	113
Fe2	Fe1	C7	146	C7	Fe1	C15	104	S4	Fe2	C11	98	Fe1	C5	O6	168
Fe2	Fe1	C15	98	Fe1	Fe2	S3	56	S4	Fe2	C17	156	Fe1	C7	O8	175
S3	Fe1	S4	82	Fe1	Fe2	S4	55	C9	Fe2	C11	99	Fe2	C9	O10	169
S3	Fe1	C5	160	Fe1	Fe2	C9	148	C9	Fe2	C17	101	Fe2	C11	O12	170
S3	Fe1	C7	100	Fe1	Fe2	C11	106	C11	Fe2	C17	86	S4	C13	C14	105
S3	Fe1	C15	84	Fe1	Fe2	C17	101	Fe1	S3	Fe2	68	Fe1	C15	O16	175
S4	Fe1	C5	95	S3	Fe2	S4	80	Fe1	S3	C19	112	Fe2	C17	O18	178
S4	Fe1	C7	99	S3	Fe2	C9	103	Fe2	S3	C19	115	S3	C19	C20	119

85.19 Silver thiocyanate - tri - n - propyl phosphine complex

$C_{10}H_{21}AgNPS$

C.Panattoni, E.Frasson, Gazz. Chim. Ital., 93, 601, 1963

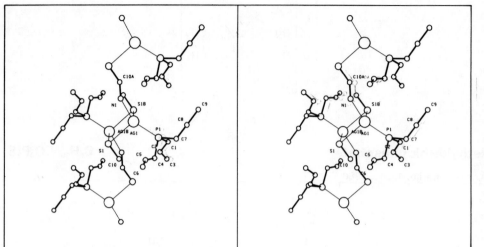

$$P(C_3H_7)_3 \cdot AgSCN$$

$P2_1/c$	Z = 4	$R_{0kl} = 0.10$,	
$R_{hol} = 0.11$			

SCNPRP   LB 10-21-1

Bond Lengths

Ag1	P1	2.47		C1	C2	1.60
Ag1	N1	2.27		C2	C3	1.55
		(2.10)		C4	C5	1.31
P1	C1	1.73				(1.54)
P1	C4	1.84		C5	C6	1.23
P1	C7	1.57				(1.50)
		(1.73)		C7	C8	1.46
S1	C10	1.61		C8	C9	1.51
		(1.81)				
C10	N1	1.29				
		(1.42)				

85.20 bis - (cis - 1,2 - bis(Trifluoromethyl)ethylene - 1,2 - dithiolato) cobalt(ii) dimer

$C_{16}F_{24}Co_2S_8$

J.H.Enemark, W.N.Lipscomb, Inorg. Chem., 4, 1729, 1965

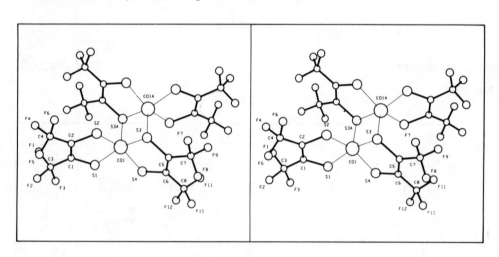

P-1   Z = 1   R = 0.08

TFMECO   LB 16-0-1

Bond Lengths

Co1	S1	2.14		F10	C8	1.28
Co1	S2	2.17		F11	C8	1.28
Co1	S3	2.16		F12	C8	1.32
Co1	S4	2.18		S1	C1	1.69
Co1	S3A	2.38		S2	C2	1.68
F1	C3	1.27		S3	C5	1.72
F2	C3	1.31		S4	C6	1.69
F3	C3	1.30		C1	C2	1.38
F4	C4	1.31		C1	C3	1.52
F5	C4	1.31		C2	C4	1.50
F6	C4	1.31		C5	C6	1.41
F7	C7	1.29		C5	C7	1.49
F8	C7	1.27		C6	C8	1.51
F9	C7	1.30				

Bond Angles

S1	Co1	S2	90		Co1	S3	C5	106		F3	C3	C1	111		F7	C7	F8	106
S1	Co1	S3	161		Co1	S4	C6	105		F4	C4	F5	108		F7	C7	F9	107
S1	Co1	S4	87		S1	C1	C2	120		F4	C4	F6	104		F7	C7	C5	110
S1	Co1	S3A	94		S1	C1	C3	115		F4	C4	C2	113		F8	C7	F9	106
S2	Co1	S3	86		C2	C1	C3	124		F5	C4	F6	104		F8	C7	C5	114
S2	Co1	S4	157		S2	C2	C1	119		F5	C4	C2	113		F9	C7	C5	113
S2	Co1	S3A	106		S2	C2	C4	116		F6	C4	C2	113		F10	C8	F11	107
S3	Co1	S4	90		C1	C2	C4	125		S3	C5	C6	118		F10	C8	F12	107
S3	Co1	S3A	105		F1	C3	F2	105		S3	C5	C7	117		F10	C8	C6	114
S4	Co1	S3A	97		F1	C3	F3	109		C6	C5	C7	125		F11	C8	F12	105
Co1	S1	C1	105		F1	C3	C1	113		S4	C6	C5	120		F11	C8	C6	113
Co1	S2	C2	106		F2	C3	F3	107		S4	C6	C8	116		F12	C8	C6	111
Co1	S3	Co1A	75		F2	C3	C1	111		C5	C6	C8	123					

85.21 Nickel(ii) ethylmercaptide hexamer

$C_{24}H_{60}Ni_6O_{12}S_{12}$

P.Woodward, L.F.Dahl, E.W.Abel, B.C.Crosse, J. Amer. Chem. Soc., 87, 5251, 1965

Atomic coordinates were not reported in the paper.

$P2_1/n$ Z = 12   R = 0.08

$$[Ni(S-CH_2-CH_2-OH)_2]_6$$

NIEMER   LB 4-10-36

86.1 Methyl bis(3 - propyldimethylarsine)arsine nickel dibromide

$C_{11}H_{27}As_3Ni^{2+}$, $2Br^-$

G.A.Mair, H.M.Powell, D.E.Henn, Proc. Chem. Soc., 415, 1960

Atomic coordinates were not reported in the paper.
Pbca   Z = 8   R = 0.15

MPASNB   LB 11-27-1

$[H_3C—As(CH_2—CH_2—CH_2—As(CH_3)_2)_2 Ni]^{2+} (Br^-)_2$

86.2   bis - Triethylphosphine hydrobromo platinum

$C_{12}H_{31}BrP_2Pt$

P.G.Owston, J.M.Partridge, J.M.Rowe, Acta Cryst., 13, 246, 1960

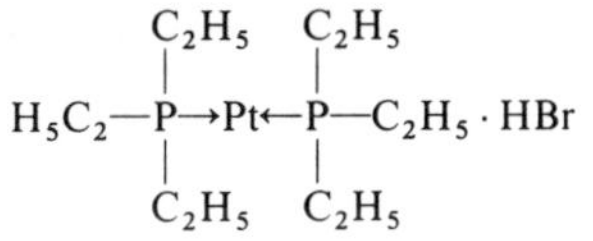

$$H_5C_2—\overset{\overset{\displaystyle C_2H_5}{|}}{\underset{\underset{\displaystyle C_2H_5}{|}}{P}}→Pt←\overset{\overset{\displaystyle C_2H_5}{|}}{\underset{\underset{\displaystyle C_2H_5}{|}}{P}}—C_2H_5 \cdot HBr$$

Pn2₁a   Z = 4 R_{hol} = 0.13,
R_{0kl} = 0.11

TEPHBP   LB 12-31-1

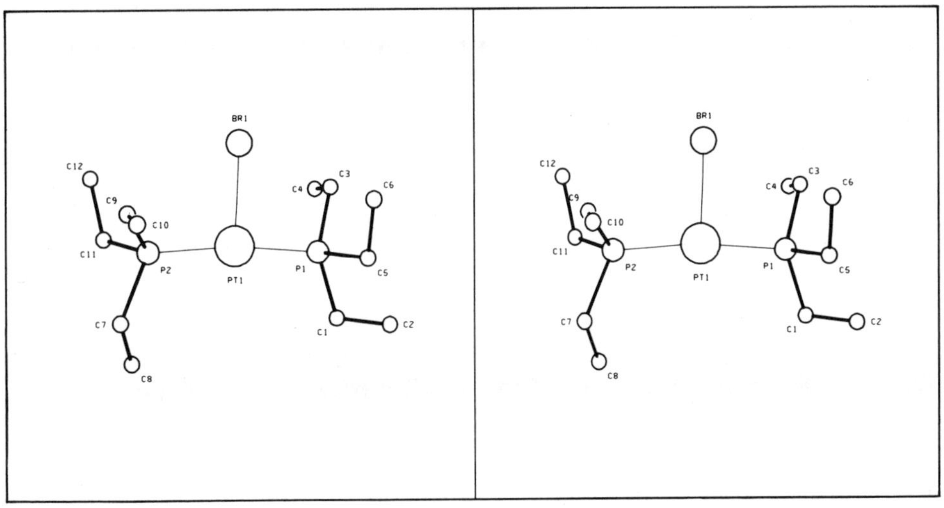

Bond Lengths

Pt1	Br1	2.56	P2	C11	1.87
Pt1	P1	2.26	C1	C2	1.47
Pt1	P2	2.26	C3	C4	1.37
P1	C1	1.89	C5	C6	1.63
P1	C3	1.91	C7	C8	1.61
P1	C5	1.94	C9	C10	1.34
P2	C7	1.97	C11	C12	1.59
P2	C9	1.84			

Bond Angles

Br1	Pt1	P1	94	C1	P1	C5	93	C9	P2	C11	111
Br1	Pt1	P2	94	C3	P1	C5	108	P1	C1	C2	102
P1	Pt1	P2	172	Pt1	P2	C7	118	P1	C3	C4	113
Pt1	P1	C1	115	Pt1	P2	C9	112	P1	C5	C6	114
Pt1	P1	C3	104	Pt1	P2	C11	119	P2	C7	C8	104
Pt1	P1	C5	111	C7	P2	C9	92	P2	C9	C10	130
C1	P1	C3	125	C7	P2	C11	101	P2	C11	C12	110

86.3 trans - Oxotrichloro bis(diethylphenylphosphine) rhenium(v)

$C_{20}H_{30}Cl_3OP_2Re$

H.W.W.Ehrlich, P.G.Owston, J. Chem. Soc., 4368, 1963

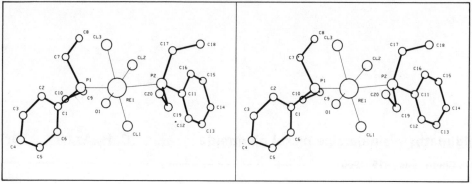

$P2_1/c$ Z = 4 $R_{hol} = 0.08$,
$R_{0kl} = 0.10$

OCEPRE   LB 20-30-5

Bond Lengths

Re1	Cl1	2.41	P1	C7	1.92	C2	C3	1.48	C11	C16	1.51
Re1	Cl2	2.47	P1	C9	1.82	C3	C4	1.29	C12	C13	1.35
Re1	Cl3	2.43	P2	C11	1.80	C4	C5	1.49	C13	C14	1.33
Re1	P1	2.45	P2	C17	1.84	C5	C6	1.34	C14	C15	1.52
Re1	P2	2.48	P2	C19	1.81	C7	C8	1.44	C15	C16	1.33
Re1	O1	1.61	C1	C2	1.36	C9	C10	1.43	C17	C18	1.52
P1	C1	1.76	C1	C6	1.40	C11	C12	1.38	C19	C20	1.58

Bond Angles

Cl1	Re1	Cl2	89	Cl3	Re1	P1	91	C1	P1	C7	103
Cl1	Re1	Cl3	175	Cl3	Re1	P2	92	C1	P1	C9	113
Cl1	Re1	P1	87	Cl3	Re1	O1	94	C7	P1	C9	88
Cl1	Re1	P2	88	P1	Re1	P2	162	Re1	P2	C11	114
Cl1	Re1	O1	92	P1	Re1	O1	98	Re1	P2	C17	116
Cl2	Re1	Cl3	86	P2	Re1	O1	100	Re1	P2	C19	106
Cl2	Re1	P1	82	Re1	P1	C1	110	C11	P2	C17	108
Cl2	Re1	P2	81	Re1	P1	C7	119	C11	P2	C19	105
Cl2	Re1	O1	179	Re1	P1	C9	121	C17	P2	C19	106

86.4 Dichloro di(o - phenylene bisdimethylarsine) platinum(ii)

$C_{20}H_{32}As_4Cl_2Pt$

N.C.Stephenson, Acta Cryst., 17, 1517, 1964

The published coordinates of C7 are incorrect. This atom is too close to C8, C9 and does not connect to C6 and C10, as it should.
Pcan   Z = 4   R = 0.12

DCARPT   LB 20-32-8

86.5 Di - iodo di(o - phenylene bisdimethylarsine) nickel(ii)

$C_{20}H_{32}As_4I_2Ni$

N.C.Stephenson, Acta Cryst., 17, 592, 1964

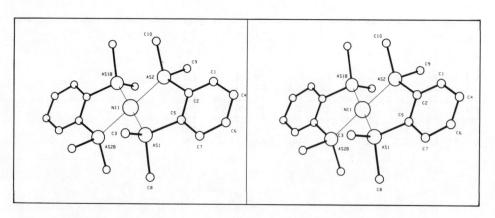

$P2_1/c$ Z = 2   R = 0.11

DIARNI   LB 20-32-10

Bond Lengths

Ni1	As1	2.28	As2	C10	1.87	
Ni1	As2	2.30	C1	C2	1.33	
Ni1	I1	3.22	C1	C4	1.36	
As1	C3	1.92	C2	C5	1.40	
As1	C5	1.95	C4	C6	1.38	
As1	C8	2.01	C5	C7	1.41	
As2	C2	1.95	C6	C7	1.35	
As2	C9	1.93				

Bond Angles

As1	Ni1	As2	87	As2	Ni1	I1B	86	C3	As1	C8	102
As1	Ni1	As1B	180	I1	Ni1	As1B	85	C5	As1	C8	106
As1	Ni1	As2B	93	I1	Ni1	As2B	86	Ni1	As2	C2	108
As1	Ni1	I1	95	I1	Ni1	I1B	180	Ni1	As2	C9	119
As1	Ni1	I1B	85	Ni1	As1	C3	117	Ni1	As2	C10	120
As2	Ni1	As1B	93	Ni1	As1	C5	109	C2	As2	C9	103
As2	Ni1	As2B	180	Ni1	As1	C8	121	C2	As2	C10	102
As2	Ni1	I1	94	C3	As1	C5	97	C9	As2	C10	102

86.6 Di - iodo - di - (o - phenylene bis(dimethylarsine)) palladium(ii)

$C_{20}H_{32}As_4I_2Pd$

N.C.Stephenson, J. Inorg. Nucl. Chem., 24, 797, 1962

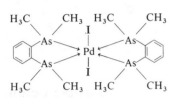

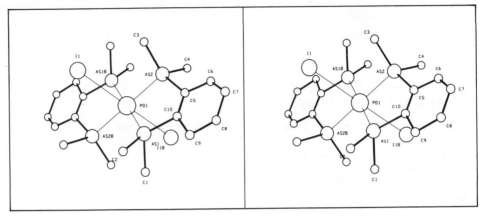

P2₁/c   Z = 2   R = 0.14

IPASPD   LB 20-32-11

Bond Lengths

Pd1	As1	2.39	As2	C5	1.97	
Pd1	As2	2.40	C5	C6	1.42	
Pd1	I1	3.40	C5	C10	1.27	
As1	C1	1.78	C6	C7	1.35	
As1	C2	1.79	C7	C8	1.37	
As1	C10	1.90	C8	C9	1.38	
As2	C3	1.92	C9	C10	1.54	
As2	C4	2.03				

Bond Angles

As1	Pd1	As2	85	As2	Pd1	I1B	85	C1	As1	C10	114
As1	Pd1	As1B	180	I1	Pd1	As1B	85	C2	As1	C10	112
As1	Pd1	As2B	95	I1	Pd1	As2B	85	Pd1	As2	C3	102
As1	Pd1	I1	95	I1	Pd1	I1B	180	Pd1	As2	C4	116
As1	Pd1	I1B	85	Pd1	As1	C1	123	Pd1	As2	C5	104
As2	Pd1	As1B	95	Pd1	As1	C2	126	C3	As2	C4	118
As2	Pd1	As2B	180	Pd1	As1	C10	109	C3	As2	C5	110
As2	Pd1	I1	95	C1	As1	C2	68	C4	As2	C5	106

86.7 Di - iodo - di - (o - phenylene bis(dimethylarsine)) platinum(ii)

$C_{20}H_{32}As_4I_2Pt$

N.C.Stephenson, J. Inorg. Nucl. Chem., 24, 791, 1962

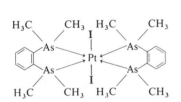

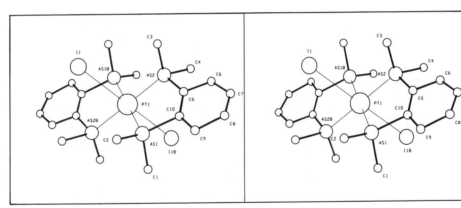

P2₁/c   Z = 2   R = 0.10

IPASPT   LB 20-32-12

Bond Lengths

Pt1	As1	2.38	As2	C5	1.63	
Pt1	As2	2.38			(1.79)	
Pt1	I1	3.50	C5	C6	1.41	
As1	C1	1.81	C5	C10	1.31	
As1	C2	1.84	C6	C7	1.38	
As1	C10	1.99	C7	C8	1.36	
As2	C3	1.81	C8	C9	1.52	
As2	C4	1.94	C9	C10	1.42	

Bond Angles

As1	Pt1	As2	86	As2	Pt1	I1B	84	C1	As1	C10	109
As1	Pt1	As1B	180	I1	Pt1	As1B	85	C2	As1	C10	117
As1	Pt1	As2B	94	I1	Pt1	As2B	84	Pt1	As2	C3	116
As1	Pt1	I1	95	I1	Pt1	I1B	180	Pt1	As2	C4	122
As1	Pt1	I1B	85	Pt1	As1	C1	111	Pt1	As2	C5	106
As2	Pt1	As1B	94	Pt1	As1	C2	116	C3	As2	C4	113
As2	Pt1	As2B	180	Pt1	As1	C10	101	C3	As2	C5	97
As2	Pt1	I1	96	C1	As1	C2	103	C4	As2	C5	97

86.8 Palladium(ii) bis(tri - n - propyl phosphine) thiocyanate

$C_{20}H_{42}N_2P_2PdS_2$

E.Frasson, C.Panattoni, A.Turco, Nature, 199, 803, 1963

Atomic coordinates were not reported in the paper.
P-1   Z = 2   No R factor was given.

$(NCS)_2Pd[P—(nC_3H_7)_3]_2$

PDPRPT

86.9 Triphenylphosphine gold cobalt tetracarbonyl

$C_{22}H_{15}AuCoO_4P$

B.T.Kilbourn, T.L.Blundell, H.M.Powell, Chem. Communic., 444, 1965

Atomic coordinates were not reported in the paper.
P-1   Z = 2   R = 0.124

TPAUCO   LB 22-15-1

86.10 bis(o - Dimethylarsinophenyl)methylarsine copper manganese pentacarbonyl

$C_{22}H_{23}As_3CuMnO_5$

B.T.Kilbourn, T.L.Blundell, H.M.Powell, Chem. Communic., 444, 1965

Atomic coordinates were not reported in the paper.
P2$_1$/c   Z = 4   R = 0.107

MACMCO   LB 22-23-1

86.11 Dichloro bis(diphenylphosphino)ethylamine palladium(ii)

$C_{26}H_{25}Cl_2NP_2Pd$

D.S.Payne, J.A.A.Mokuolu, J.C.Speakman, Chem. Communic., 599, 1965

Atomic coordinates were not reported in the paper.
Pbca   Z = 8   R = 0.109

DCPEPD   LB 26-25-1

86.12 Chloro platinum(ii) hydride bis(diphenylethyl phosphine)

$C_{28}H_{31}ClP_2Pt$

R.Eisenberg, J.A.Ibers, Inorg. Chem., 4, 773, 1965

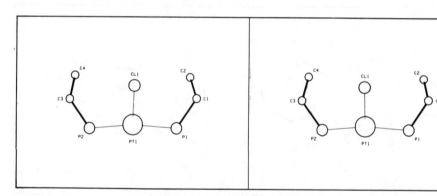

Coordinates of carbon atoms of phenyl rings were not reported.
P2$_1$/c   Z = 4   R = 0.076

PTCLPE   LB 28-31-3

Bond Lengths

Pt1	Cl1	2.42	P2	C13	1.84	C12	C62	1.40	C23	C33	1.39	C42	C52	1.40

Pt1	Cl1	2.42	
Pt1	P1	2.27	
Pt1	P2	2.27	
P1	C1	1.86	
P1	C11	1.83	
P1	C12	1.82	
P2	C3	1.84	
P2	C13	1.84
P2	C14	1.81
C1	C2	1.59
C3	C4	1.52
C11	C21	1.40
C11	C61	1.38
C12	C22	1.39
C12	C62	1.40
C13	C23	1.40
C13	C63	1.39
C14	C24	1.40
C14	C64	1.40
C21	C31	1.38
C22	C32	1.38
C23	C33	1.39
C24	C34	1.38
C31	C41	1.40
C32	C42	1.39
C33	C43	1.40
C34	C44	1.39
C41	C51	1.40
C42	C52	1.40
C43	C53	1.40
C44	C54	1.39
C51	C61	1.38
C52	C62	1.40
C53	C63	1.40
C54	C64	1.39

Bond Angles

Cl1	Pt1	P1	93
Cl1	Pt1	P2	95
P1	Pt1	P2	171
Pt1	P1	C1	118
Pt1	P1	C11	115
Pt1	P1	C12	112
C1	P1	C11	103
C1	P1	C12	102
C11	P1	C12	104
Pt1	P2	C3	118
Pt1	P2	C13	118
Pt1	P2	C14	112
C3	P2	C13	101
C3	P2	C14	103
C13	P2	C14	101

86.13 bis(Diphenylphosphino)ethylamine molybdenum tetracarbonyl

$C_{30}H_{25}MoNO_4P_2$

D.S.Payne, J.A.A.Mokuolu, J.C.Speakman, Chem. Communic., 599, 1965

Atomic coordinates were not reported in the paper.
Pbcn   Z = 4   R = 0.09

DPEMOC   LB 30-25-4

86.14 tris(Phenyldiethylphosphine) nonachloro trirhenium

$C_{30}H_{45}Cl_9P_3Re_3$

F.A.Cotton, J.T.Mague, Inorg. Chem., 3, 1094, 1964

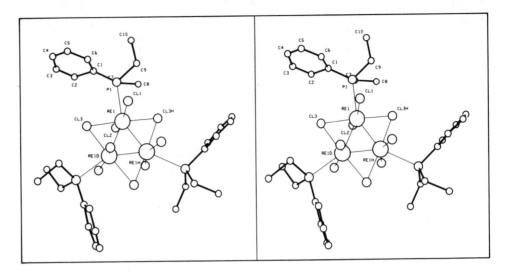

Pa3   Z = 8   R = 0.13

EPCLRE   LB 30-45-3

Bond Lengths

Re1	Re1D	2.49	C1	C2	1.70
Re1	Cl1	2.30	C1	C6	1.40
Re1	Cl2	2.32	C2	C3	1.37
Re1	Cl3	2.40	C3	C4	1.42
Re1	Cl3H	2.37	C4	C5	1.25
Re1	P1	2.70	C5	C6	1.38
P1	C1	1.77	C7	C8	1.59
P1	C7	1.84	C9	C10	1.68
P1	C9	1.88			

Bond Angles

Cl1	Re1	Re1H	99	Cl3	Re1	Cl3H	177
Cl1	Re1	Cl2	159	Cl3	Re1	P1	93
Cl1	Re1	Cl3	90	Re1	Cl3	Re1D	63
Cl1	Re1	Cl3H	90	Re1	P1	C1	112
Cl1	Re1	P1	79	Re1	P1	C7	111
Cl2	Re1	Re1H	99	Re1	P1	C9	110
Cl2	Re1	Cl3	91	C1	P1	C7	109
Cl2	Re1	Cl3H	90	C1	P1	C9	104
Cl2	Re1	P1	80	C7	P1	C9	112
Cl3	Re1	Re1H	118				

86.15 Dichloro bis(triphenylphosphine) nickel(ii)

$C_{36}H_{30}Cl_2NiP_2$

G.Garton, D.E.Henn, H.M.Powell, L.M.Venanzi, J. Chem. Soc., 3625, 1963

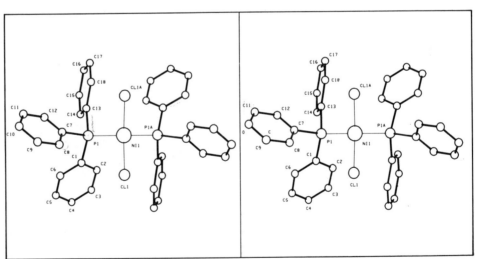

Published values of z(C16) = 0.007 and z(C17) = 0.015 are incorrect. The correct values are 0.507 and 0.515 respectively.
P2/c   Z = 2 R_{h0l} = 0.22

CLTPNI   LB 36-30-8

Bond Lengths

Ni1	Cl1	2.27	C7	C12	1.29
Ni1	P1	2.28	C8	C9	1.44
P1	C1	1.84	C9	C10	1.28
P1	C7	1.90	C10	C11	1.40
P1	C13	1.85	C11	C12	1.42
C1	C2	1.39	C13	C14	1.40
C1	C6	1.47	C13	C18	1.53
C2	C3	1.43	C14	C15	1.41
C3	C4	1.38	C15	C16	1.54
C4	C5	1.40	C16	C17	1.40
C5	C6	1.58	C17	C18	1.39
C7	C8	1.40			

Bond Angles

Cl1	Ni1	Cl1A	123
Cl1	Ni1	P1	104
Cl1	Ni1	P1A	105
P1	Ni1	Cl1A	105
P1	Ni1	P1A	117
Ni1	P1	C1	118
Ni1	P1	C7	106
Ni1	P1	C13	110
C1	P1	C7	106
C1	P1	C13	110
C7	P1	C13	105

86.16   bis(Tricyclohexylphosphine) dichloro nickel

$C_{36}H_{66}Cl_2NiP_2$

P.L.Bellon, V.Albano, V.D.Bianco, F.Pompa, V.Scatturin, Ric. Sci., 33, 1213, 1963

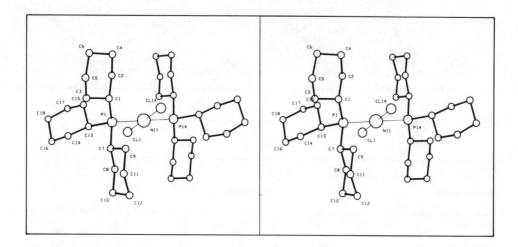

P-1   Z = 1   R = 0.165

TCHNIC

Bond Lengths

Ni1	Cl1	2.19	C7	C9	1.54
Ni1	P1	2.28	C8	C10	1.59
P1	C1	1.84	C9	C11	1.53
P1	C7	1.80	C10	C12	1.54
P1	C13	1.88	C11	C12	1.54
C1	C2	1.49	C13	C14	1.49
C1	C3	1.49	C13	C15	1.58
C2	C4	1.60	C14	C16	1.54
C3	C5	1.58	C15	C17	1.57
C4	C6	1.46	C16	C18	1.58
C5	C6	1.58	C17	C18	1.55
C7	C8	1.58			

Bond Angles

Cl1	Ni1	Cl1A	180	P1	C1	C3	113
Cl1	Ni1	P1	91	C2	C1	C3	107
Cl1	Ni1	P1A	89	C1	C2	C4	109
P1	Ni1	Cl1A	89	C1	C3	C5	110
P1	Ni1	P1A	180	C2	C4	C6	107
Ni1	P1	C1	112	C3	C5	C6	106
Ni1	P1	C7	110	C4	C6	C5	106
Ni1	P1	C13	113	P1	C13	C15	109
C1	P1	C7	103	C8	C7	C9	113
C1	P1	C13	117	C7	C8	C10	107
C7	P1	C13	101	C7	C9	C11	111
P1	C1	C2	112				

C8	C10	C12	114
C9	C11	C12	115
C10	C12	C11	105
P1	C13	C14	118
P1	C13	C15	110
C14	C13	C15	108
C13	C14	C16	114
C13	C15	C17	113
C14	C16	C18	105
C15	C17	C18	106
C16	C18	C17	115

Torsion Angles

C7	P1	C1	C2	175
C7	P1	C1	C3	−65
C13	P1	C1	C2	−76
C13	P1	C1	C3	44
C1	P1	C7	C8	−175
C1	P1	C7	C9	−46
C13	P1	C7	C8	64
C13	P1	C7	C9	−167
C1	P1	C13	C14	−68
C1	P1	C13	C15	56
C7	P1	C13	C14	42
C7	P1	C13	C15	167
P1	C1	C2	C4	−173
C3	C1	C2	C4	63
P1	C1	C3	C5	173
C2	C1	C3	C5	−64
C1	C2	C4	C6	−66
C1	C3	C5	C6	64

C2	C4	C6	C5	65
C3	C5	C6	C4	−65
P1	C7	C8	C10	−178
C9	C7	C8	C10	52
P1	C7	C9	C11	−179
C8	C7	C9	C11	−52
C7	C8	C10	C12	−58
C7	C9	C11	C12	56
C8	C10	C12	C11	60
C9	C11	C12	C10	−59
P1	C13	C14	C16	−173
C15	C13	C14	C16	61
P1	C13	C15	C17	172
C14	C13	C15	C17	−58
C13	C14	C16	C18	−59
C13	C15	C17	C18	55
C14	C16	C18	C17	57
C15	C17	C18	C16	−56

86.17 Chlorocarbonyl bis(triphenylphosphine) iridium - oxygen complex $C_{37}H_{30}ClIrO_3P_2$

S.J.La Placa, J.A.Ibers, J. Amer. Chem. Soc., 87, 2581, 1965

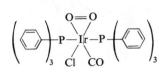

The chlorine atom and the CO group are disordered.

P-1   Z = 2   R = 0.071

CPHIRO   LB 37-30-2

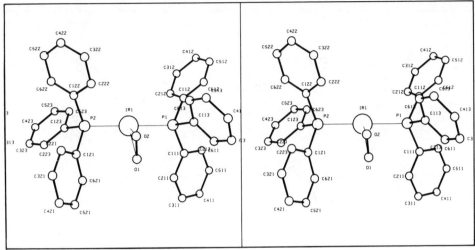

Bond Lengths

Ir1	P1	2.38
Ir1	P2	2.36
Ir1	O1	2.10
Ir1	O2	2.05
P1	C111	1.84
P1	C112	1.81
P1	C113	1.82
P2	C121	1.78
P2	C122	1.79
P2	C123	1.81
O1	O2	1.31
C111	C211	1.39

C111	C611	1.40
C112	C212	1.38
C112	C612	1.39
C113	C213	1.39
C113	C613	1.39
C121	C221	1.40
C121	C621	1.39
C122	C222	1.39
C122	C622	1.39
C123	C223	1.40
C123	C623	1.39
C211	C311	1.40

C212	C312	1.40
C213	C313	1.39
C221	C321	1.40
C222	C322	1.40
C223	C323	1.38
C311	C411	1.39
C312	C412	1.39
C313	C413	1.39
C321	C421	1.39
C322	C422	1.39
C323	C423	1.39
C411	C511	1.38

C412	C512	1.39
C413	C513	1.39
C421	C521	1.40
C422	C522	1.40
C423	C523	1.39
C511	C611	1.38
C512	C612	1.38
C513	C613	1.39
C521	C621	1.40
C522	C622	1.39
C523	C623	1.39

Bond Angles

P1	Ir1	P2	173
P1	Ir1	O1	85
P1	Ir1	O2	89
P2	Ir1	O1	91
P2	Ir1	O2	84
O1	Ir1	O2	37

Ir1	P1	C111	115
Ir1	P1	C112	116
Ir1	P1	C113	111
C111	P1	C112	104
C111	P1	C113	108
C112	P1	C113	102

86.18   trans - Dimesityl bis(diethylphenylphosphine) cobalt(ii) $C_{38}H_{52}CoP_2$

P.G.Owston, J.M.Rowe, J. Chem. Soc., 3411, 1963

P2₁/c   Z = 2   R = 0.16

DMDECO   LB 38-52-1

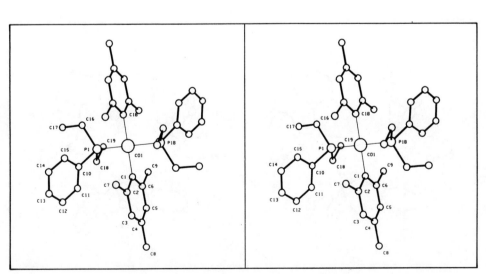

Bond Lengths

Co1	P1	2.23
Co1	C1	1.96
P1	C10	1.83
P1	C16	1.82
P1	C18	1.88
C1	C2	1.46
C1	C6	1.39
C2	C3	1.45
C2	C7	1.54
C3	C4	1.41
C4	C5	1.38
C4	C8	1.57
C5	C6	1.42
C6	C9	1.55
C10	C11	1.40
C10	C15	1.40
C11	C12	1.42
C12	C13	1.35
C13	C14	1.37
C14	C15	1.44
C16	C17	1.52
C18	C19	1.56

Bond Angles

P1	Co1	P1B	180
P1	Co1	C1	89
P1	Co1	C1B	91
C1	Co1	C1B	180
Co1	P1	C10	114
Co1	P1	C16	118
Co1	P1	C18	118
C10	P1	C16	102
C10	P1	C18	99
C16	P1	C18	104

86.19 tris - (o - Diphenylarsinophenyl)arsine dibromo ruthenium(ii)

C₅₄H₄₂As₄Br₂Ru

R.H.B.Mais, H.M.Powell, J. Chem. Soc., 7471, 1965

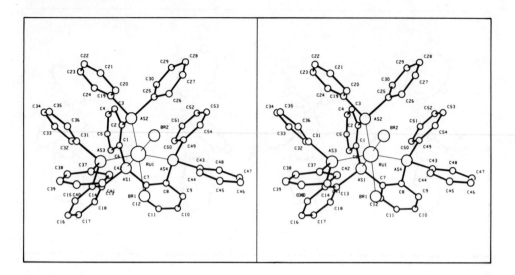

Pna2₁   Z = 4   R = 0.087

PASRUB   LB 54-42-2

Bond Lengths

Ru1	As1	2.31	C7	C8	1.44	C31	C32	1.39
Ru1	As2	2.40	C7	C12	1.41	C31	C36	1.39
Ru1	As3	2.47	C8	C9	1.44	C32	C33	1.49
Ru1	As4	2.47	C9	C10	1.53	C33	C34	1.42
Ru1	Br1	2.61	C10	C11	1.37	C34	C35	1.39
Ru1	Br2	2.61	C11	C12	1.37	C35	C36	1.45
As1	C1	1.94	C13	C14	1.40	C37	C38	1.41
As1	C7	1.96	C13	C18	1.46	C37	C42	1.44
As1	C13	1.95	C14	C15	1.42	C38	C39	1.50
As2	C2	1.91	C15	C16	1.42	C39	C40	1.32
As2	C19	2.05	C16	C17	1.46	C40	C41	1.45
As2	C25	1.97	C17	C18	1.37	C41	C42	1.47
As3	C14	1.97	C19	C20	1.37	C43	C44	1.35
As3	C31	1.94	C19	C24	1.42	C43	C48	1.40
As3	C37	1.91	C20	C21	1.47	C44	C45	1.38
As4	C8	1.95	C21	C22	1.40	C45	C46	1.36
As4	C43	1.94	C22	C23	1.30	C46	C47	1.45
As4	C49	1.99	C23	C24	1.46	C47	C48	1.42
C1	C2	1.40	C25	C26	1.43	C49	C50	1.33
C1	C6	1.45	C25	C30	1.44	C49	C54	1.44
C2	C3	1.44	C26	C27	1.41	C50	C51	1.48
C3	C4	1.49	C27	C28	1.39	C51	C52	1.32
C4	C5	1.36	C28	C29	1.33	C52	C53	1.45
C5	C6	1.42	C29	C30	1.44	C53	C54	1.38

Bond Angles

As1	Ru1	As2	87	C1	As1	C7	104
As1	Ru1	As3	83	C1	As1	C13	109
As1	Ru1	As4	83	C7	As1	C13	107
As1	Ru1	Br1	88	Ru1	As2	C2	106
As1	Ru1	Br2	179	Ru1	As2	C19	120
As2	Ru1	As3	97	Ru1	As2	C25	121
As2	Ru1	As4	97	C2	As2	C19	109
As2	Ru1	Br1	175	C2	As2	C25	106
As2	Ru1	Br2	93	C19	As2	C25	94
As3	Ru1	As4	159	Ru1	As3	C14	103
As3	Ru1	Br1	82	Ru1	As3	C31	124
As3	Ru1	Br2	98	Ru1	As3	C37	124
As4	Ru1	Br1	83	C14	As3	C31	97
As4	Ru1	Br2	96	C14	As3	C37	105
Br1	Ru1	Br2	92	C31	As3	C37	99
Ru1	As1	C1	110	Ru1	As4	C8	103
Ru1	As1	C7	114	Ru1	As4	C43	124
Ru1	As1	C13	112	Ru1	As4	C49	122
				C8	As4	C43	107
				C8	As4	C49	97
				C43	As4	C49	100

Torsion Angles

As1	C1	C2	As2	0
As1	C1	C2	C3	−171
C6	C1	C2	As2	173
C6	C1	C2	C3	2
As1	C7	C8	As4	−17
As1	C7	C8	C9	172
C12	C7	C8	As4	166
C12	C7	C8	C9	−5
As1	C13	C14	As3	14
As1	C13	C14	C15	−174
C18	C13	C14	As3	−172
C18	C13	C14	C15	0

86.20 Dichloro - tris(triphenylphosphine) ruthenium(ii)

C₅₄H₄₅Cl₂P₃Ru

S.J.LaPlaca, J.A.Ibers, Inorg. Chem., 4, 778, 1965

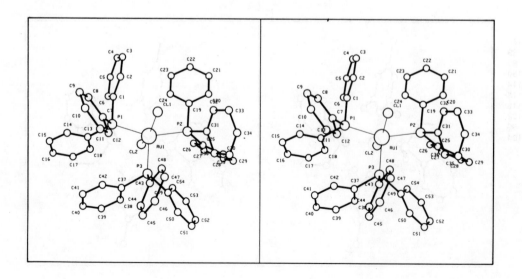

P2₁/c   Z = 4   R = 0.063

RUCLTP   LB 54-45-1

Bond Lengths

Ru1	Cl1	2.39	P3	C43	1.84	C10	C11	1.39	C22	C23	1.39	C34	C35	1.39
Ru1	Cl2	2.39	P3	C49	1.86	C11	C12	1.39	C23	C24	1.39	C35	C36	1.39
Ru1	P1	2.37	C1	C2	1.39	C13	C14	1.39	C25	C26	1.39	C37	C38	1.39
Ru1	P2	2.41	C1	C6	1.39	C13	C18	1.39	C25	C30	1.39	C37	C42	1.39
Ru1	P3	2.23	C2	C3	1.39	C14	C15	1.39	C26	C27	1.39	C38	C39	1.39
P1	C1	1.86	C3	C4	1.39	C15	C16	1.39	C27	C28	1.39	C39	C40	1.39
P1	C7	1.83	C4	C5	1.39	C16	C17	1.39	C28	C29	1.39	C40	C41	1.39
P1	C13	1.86	C5	C6	1.39	C17	C18	1.39	C29	C30	1.39	C41	C42	1.39
P2	C19	1.85	C7	C8	1.39	C19	C20	1.39	C31	C32	1.39	C43	C44	1.39
P2	C25	1.87	C7	C12	1.39	C19	C24	1.39	C31	C36	1.39	C43	C48	1.39
P2	C31	1.82	C8	C9	1.39	C20	C21	1.39	C32	C33	1.39	C44	C45	1.39
P3	C37	1.86	C9	C10	1.39	C21	C22	1.39	C33	C34	1.39	C45	C46	1.39

C46	C47	1.39
C47	C48	1.39
C49	C50	1.39
C49	C54	1.39
C50	C51	1.39
C51	C52	1.39
C52	C53	1.39
C53	C54	1.39

Bond Angles

Cl1	Ru1	Cl2	157
Cl1	Ru1	P1	84
Cl1	Ru1	P2	82
Cl1	Ru1	P3	110
Cl2	Ru1	P1	92
Cl2	Ru1	P2	93
Cl2	Ru1	P3	93
P1	Ru1	P2	156
P1	Ru1	P3	101
P2	Ru1	P3	101

86.21 Hydridobromocarbonyl osmium(ii) tris(triphenylphosphine)

$C_{55} H_{46} Br O Os P_3$

P. L. Orioli, L. Vaska, Proc. Chem. Soc., 333, 1962

Atomic coordinates were not reported in the paper.
Pbca Z = 8 R_{hol} = 0.29

HBRPOS

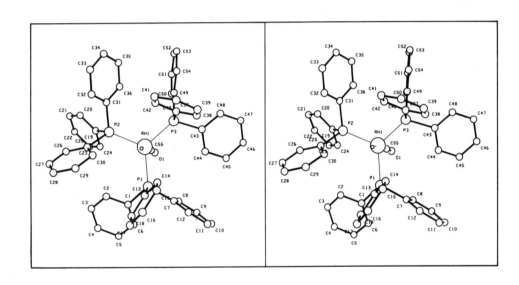

86.22 Rhodium carbonyl hydride tris(triphenylphosphine)

$C_{55}H_{46} OP_3 Rh$

S. J. La Placa, J. A. Ibers, Acta Cryst., 18, 511, 1965

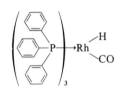

P2₁/n Z = 4 R = 0.078

RCOHPH   LB 55-46-1

Bond Lengths

Rh1	P1	2.34	P3	C49	1.85	C10	C11	1.39	C22	C23	1.39	C34	C35	1.39
Rh1	P2	2.32	C55	O1	1.17	C11	C12	1.39	C23	C24	1.39	C35	C36	1.39
Rh1	P3	2.32	C1	C2	1.39	C13	C14	1.39	C25	C26	1.39	C37	C38	1.39
Rh1	C55	1.83	C1	C6	1.39	C13	C18	1.39	C25	C30	1.39	C37	C42	1.39
P1	C1	1.83	C2	C3	1.39	C14	C15	1.39	C26	C27	1.39	C38	C39	1.39
P1	C7	1.82	C3	C4	1.39	C15	C16	1.39	C27	C28	1.39	C39	C40	1.39
P1	C13	1.82	C4	C5	1.39	C16	C17	1.39	C28	C29	1.39	C40	C41	1.39
P2	C19	1.82	C5	C6	1.39	C17	C18	1.39	C29	C30	1.39	C41	C42	1.39
P2	C25	1.87	C7	C8	1.39	C19	C20	1.39	C31	C32	1.39	C43	C44	1.39
P2	C31	1.79	C7	C12	1.39	C19	C24	1.39	C31	C36	1.39	C43	C48	1.39
P3	C37	1.83	C8	C9	1.39	C20	C21	1.39	C32	C33	1.39	C44	C45	1.39
P3	C43	1.83	C9	C10	1.39	C21	C22	1.39	C33	C34	1.39	C45	C46	1.39

C46	C47	1.39
C47	C48	1.39
C49	C50	1.39
C49	C54	1.39
C50	C51	1.39
C51	C52	1.39
C52	C53	1.39
C53	C54	1.39

Bond Angles

P1	Rh1	P2	116
P1	Rh1	P3	121
P1	Rh1	C55	95
P2	Rh1	P3	117
P2	Rh1	C55	104
P3	Rh1	C55	98

Summary Tables

In these tables the interatomic distances presented in the main body of this volume have been brought together for each bonded element-pair. The exceptions are:

(i) Carbon-carbon, carbon-nitrogen and carbon-oxygen distances are not listed individually. We present instead the table assembled by Olga Kennard and previously published in the *International Tables for X-Ray Crystallography, Vol. 3* (Birmingham: Kynoch Press, 1962).

(ii) Individual distances for other element-pairs are excluded if our recalculated values differ from those given in the original publications by more than 0.05Å.

The resulting tables contain 3002 distances spread over 170 element-pairs. The tables are arranged as follows:

(i) Element-pairs are listed in alphabetical order, and the list is non-redundant, i.e. Br-C occurs but not C-Br.

(ii) For each element-pair the distances are given to two decimal places (in Å) and are listed in increasing order.

(iii) Distances marked with an asterisk were obtained from a structure with a three-dimensional R-factor ≤ 0.120.

(iv) To facilitate reference to the main text, entry numbers are listed in increasing order within each distance-interval of 0.01Å.

(v) If there are two or more equal distances in an entry in the main text for a given element-pair, this is indicated in parentheses after the entry number.

An example of the rules (iii) and (v) above would be

$$B - B$$
$$1\cdot77^* \quad 62\cdot12 \ (7)$$

This indicates that there are seven B-B distances of 1.77Å in entry number 62.12 in the main text and that this structure was determined using three-dimensional data with R ≤ 0.120.

Use of the Summary Tables

The tables provide an element-pair index to the main text and will, we hope, be useful as a quick reference and for comparison of bond-lengths found in different structures. We would, however, stress the importance of referring back to the main text to examine the nature of the chemical structure in which the particular distance was observed. We would also recommend, particularly for the scientist who is not a specialist crystallographer, that the following factors be borne in mind when assessing the accuracy of a bond length in relation to a given R-factor:

(i) Many structures determined in the period 1960–65 were not fully refined and in such structures the R-factor is not a reliable indication of the accuracy of bond lengths, particularly when comparing structures with and without 'heavy' atoms. As an example, the accuracy of a C-C bond length in a hydrocarbon refined to an R-factor of 0.15 may be as good as or better than the accuracy of the corresponding bond length observed in the structure of the brominated hydrocarbon refined to R = 0.12.

(ii) In structures containing both heavy and light atoms the heavy-atom positions are determined with greater accuracy, consequently the bond lengths between heavy atoms will be more accurate than those between heavy and light atoms or between two light atoms.

(iii) In the period 1960–1965 a number of structures were solved only in two-dimensional projections. The accuracy of such determinations is generally less than the accuracy of determinations based on three-dimensional data and refined to the same R-factor.

Bond Distances Between Carbon and Selected Elements

Carbon-Carbon Bond Distances (in Å)

Single Bond

Paraffinic	1·541	± 3
In diamond	1·54452	± 14

Partial Double Bond

1 Single bond shortened in presence of carbon-carbon double bond, e.g. $(CH_3)_2C:CH_2$; or of aromatic ring, e.g. $C_6H_5.CH_3$	1·53	± 1
2 Shortened in presence of a carbon-oxygen double bond, e.g. $CH_3.CHO$	1·516	± 5
3 Shortened in presence of two carbon-oxygen double bonds, e.g. $(CO_2H)_2$	1·49	± 1
4 Shortened in presence of one carbon-carbon triple bond, e.g. $CH_3.C:CH$	1·460	± 3
5 In compounds with tendency to dipole formation, e.g. $C:C.C:N$	1·44	± 1
6 In graphite (at 15°C)	1·4210	± 1
7 In aromatic compounds	1·395	± 3
8 In presence of two carbon-carbon triple bonds, e.g. $HC:C.C:CH$	1·373	± 4

Double Bond

1 Simple	1·337	± 6
2 Partial triple bond, e.g. $CH_2:C:CH_2$	1·309	± 5

Triple Bond

1 Simple, e.g. C_2H_2	1·204	± 2
2 Conjugated, e.g. $CH_3.(C:C)_2.H$	1·206	± 4

Carbon-Nitrogen Bond Distances (in Å)

Single Bond

1 Paraffinic:		
(a) 4 covalent nitrogen	1·479	± 5
(b) 3 covalent nitrogen	1·472	± 5
2 In $C-N=$, e.g. CH_3NO_2	1·475	± 10
3 Aromatic in $C_6H_5.NH.CO.CH_3$	1·426	± 12
4 Shortened (partial double bond) in heterocyclic systems, e.g. C_5H_5N	1·352	± 5
5 Shortened (partial double bond) in $N-C=O$, e.g. $HCO.NH_2$	1·322	± 3

Triple Bond

1 In $R.C:N$	1·158	± 2

Carbon-Oxygen Bond Distances (in Å)

Single Bond

1 Paraffinic	1·43	± 1
2 Strained, e.g. epoxides	1·47	± 1
3 Shortened (partial double bond), as in carboxylic acids or through influence of aromatic ring, e.g. salicylic acid	1·36	± 1

Double Bond

1 In aldehydes, ketones, carboxylic acids, esters	1·23	± 1
2 In zwitterion forms, e.g. DL-serine	1·26	± 1
3 Shortened (partial triple bond), as in conjugated systems	1·207	± 6
4 Partial triple bond, as in acyl halides or isocyanates	1·17	± 1

Ag–P

2.47	85.19

Al–Br

1.93	60.32
2.36	60.32
2.38	60.32
2.50	60.32

Al–C

1.93	68.1
2.00	68.8
2.02*	68.6

Al–Cl

2.05	68.1
2.25	68.1
2.26	68.1

Al–F

1.83	68.8

Al–N

2.19*	68.4 (2)
2.20*	68.4
2.24*	68.4

Al–O

1.76	3.2
1.79	68.9 (2)
1.80	3.2
1.86	3.2
1.90	3.2 (2)
1.96	3.2

As–As

2.46	65.19 (3)

As–Br

2.40	65.12

As–C

1.78	86.6
1.79	86.6
1.81*	86.7 (2)
1.82	65.17 (2)
1.84*	86.7
1.85	65.4 (3)
1.87*	86.5
1.89	65.2
1.89*	84.19 (2)
1.90	65.4
1.90*	84.19
1.90	86.6
1.91	65.7
1.91	65.9
1.91*	65.11
1.91*	65.15
1.91	84.20 (2)
1.91	86.6
1.91*	86.19 (2)
1.92*	65.11
1.92	65.19
1.92*	84.19
1.92*	84.20
1.92*	86.5
1.93	65.3 (2)
1.93*	86.5
1.94*	65.2
1.94*	86.7
1.94*	86.19 (3)
1.95*	65.5
1.95*	84.19
1.95*	86.5 (2)
1.95*	86.19 (2)
1.96*	65.5
1.96	65.12
1.96	65.16
1.96*	86.19
1.97*	65.5
1.97	65.8
1.97	65.13 (2)
1.97*	65.15
1.97	65.17
1.97	65.19
1.97	86.6
1.97*	86.19 (2)
1.98*	65.15
1.98	65.18
1.98*	84.19
1.99*	65.15
1.99	65.17
1.99	65.18
1.99*	86.7
1.99*	86.19
2.00	65.6
2.00	65.19
2.01	65.3
2.01*	65.5
2.01	65.18
2.01*	86.5
2.03	65.12
2.03	86.6
2.05*	86.19
2.06*	65.15 (2)
2.07	65.1

As–Cl

2.21	65.6
2.26	65.13
2.30*	65.11

As–I

2.54	65.1 (2)

As–Ni

2.28*	86.5
2.30*	86.5

As–O

1.61	65.2
1.62	65.2
1.62	65.7
1.65	65.8
1.66*	84.20
1.67	65.17 (2)
1.69	65.6
1.69*	84.19 (2)
1.72	65.7
1.73	65.7
1.73	65.9
1.74	65.8
1.75	65.8
1.78	65.9 (2)

As–Pd

2.39	86.6
2.40	86.6

As–Pt

2.38*	86.7 (2)

As–Ru

2.31*	86.19
2.40*	86.19
2.46*	86.19
2.47*	86.19

As–S

2.07*	65.5
2.21*	65.5
2.28*	65.5
2.28	65.10

B–B

1.68	62.10
1.69*	3.11
1.69	62.10
1.70*	62.1
1.70*	62.6
1.70*	62.9
1.70	62.14
1.71*	62.4
1.71	62.10
1.71	62.13
1.72	62.5
1.72*	62.6
1.72	62.10
1.72*	73.1 (2)
1.73	62.10 (3)
1.73	62.13
1.73	62.14
1.74*	62.1 (3)
1.74	62.5
1.74*	62.6
1.74	62.13
1.74	62.14 (2)
1.74*	73.1 (5)
1.75*	62.1 (2)
1.75	62.5
1.75	62.10
1.75	62.14 (2)
1.75*	73.1 (4)
1.76*	62.1
1.76*	62.4
1.76	62.5 (2)
1.76*	62.6 (3)
1.76*	62.10 (3)
1.76*	62.12 (3)
1.76	62.14 (2)
1.76*	73.1 (5)
1.77*	62.1 (3)
1.77*	62.6 (3)
1.77*	62.9
1.77	62.10 (3)
1.77	62.12 (7)
1.77	62.13
1.77	62.14 (4)
1.77*	73.1 (2)
1.78*	62.4 (2)
1.78	62.5
1.78*	62.6 (4)
1.78*	62.9
1.78*	62.12 (8)
1.79*	62.1 (2)
1.79*	62.6 (5)
1.79	62.10
1.79	62.13 (2)
1.79	62.14 (2)
1.80*	62.1 (2)
1.80*	62.4
1.80*	62.6
1.80	62.10
1.81*	62.1 (2)
1.81	62.10 (2)
1.81	62.13 (3)
1.81	62.14
1.82*	62.1 (2)
1.82	62.10
1.83*	62.1
1.83	62.5
1.83	62.13
1.84	62.10
1.84	62.13
1.84	62.14
1.85*	62.1
1.85	62.5
1.85	62.10
1.86	62.14 (2)
1.87*	62.1
1.87	62.5 (2)
1.88	62.14
1.89	62.14
1.90	62.13
1.92	62.13 (2)
1.92	62.14
1.96*	62.6
1.99*	62.6
1.99	62.13

B–C

1.49*	62.4
1.51*	62.4
1.51	62.18
1.52*	62.9
1.59*	62.6
1.66*	62.1
1.66*	73.1
1.68*	62.1
1.68	62.10
1.68*	73.1 (2)
1.69	62.10
1.69*	73.1
1.70*	62.1
1.70	62.10
1.70*	73.1 (2)
1.71*	62.1 (2)
1.71	62.10
1.71*	62.12
1.72	62.10
1.72*	62.12
1.73*	62.12
1.75*	62.1 (2)
1.75*	62.4 (2)
1.75	62.10
1.76*	62.9
1.77*	62.1
1.77	62.10 (2)

B–Cl

1.72*	62.1
1.74*	62.1
1.77*	62.1 (3)
1.78*	62.1 (2)
1.79*	62.1
1.83	62.8 (2)

B–F

1.41	19.17
1.43	19.17
1.44	19.17
1.45	19.17

B–Fe

2.08*	73.1
2.09*	73.1
2.10*	73.1

B–N

1.50	62.5
1.56	62.15
1.57	62.13 (2)
1.57	62.15
1.58	62.13
1.59	62.8
1.62	62.15

B–S

1.92	62.14
1.93	62.14

Br–Br

2.25	60.8
2.32	60.8
2.54	9.6

Br–C

1.78	13.16
1.79	17.14
1.79	35.3
1.80	60.27
1.81	50.1
1.82	59.16
1.83	19.12
1.83	54.4
1.84	1.1
1.84	19.2
1.84*	20.11
1.84	33.24
1.84	60.24
1.85	13.4
1.85	19.4 (2)
1.85	52.1
1.85	59.10
1.85	60.27
1.86*	1.23
1.86	9.12
1.86	18.1
1.86	19.4
1.86*	20.11
1.87*	20.11
1.87	25.2
1.87	31.15
1.87	45.20
1.87	58.8
1.87*	59.20
1.88*	1.24
1.88	7.14
1.88	15.3
1.88	18.1
1.88	21.10
1.88	22.3
1.88*	38.13
1.88	47.8
1.88	59.20
1.88	60.27
1.89	7.12
1.89	9.12
1.89	13.2
1.89	13.4
1.89	19.3
1.89	26.10
1.89	28.5
1.89	31.8
1.89*	36.2
1.89*	40.2
1.89	43.17
1.89	45.21
1.89	52.1
1.89	54.4
1.89	59.16
1.89	60.1
1.90	9.13
1.90	13.3
1.90*	19.20
1.90*	31.9
1.90	43.17
1.90	47.9
1.90	59.11
1.90	59.14
1.90*	59.20
1.90	60.27
1.91	9.13
1.91	13.3
1.91	19.3
1.91	45.18
1.91	50.6
1.91	53.3
1.92	19.2
1.92	23.3
1.92*	24.11
1.92*	51.1
1.92	53.5
1.93	35.3
1.93*	36.2
1.93	51.2
1.93	58.8
1.93	60.1
1.93	60.27
1.94	45.19
1.94	53.6
1.94	56.5
1.94	62.10
1.95	1.22
1.95	16.18
1.95	52.3
1.95	56.6
1.95	64.20
1.96*	21.9 (2)
1.96	22.2
1.96*	28.1
1.96	45.20
1.96*	52.2
1.96	60.11
1.97*	45.16
1.97	53.7
1.97	62.10
1.98*	19.18
1.98	26.4
1.98*	31.3
1.98	38.2
1.98*	45.24
1.98	52.3
1.98	53.3
1.98	53.4
1.98	53.13
1.98	58.11
1.99*	28.1
1.99	53.11
1.99*	59.3
1.99	59.14
2.00	58.11
2.01	26.1
2.01*	51.4
2.02	1.26
2.03	26.4
2.04*	51.4
2.06	38.2
2.06	54.3

Br–Cu

2.46	83.17

Br–Hg

2.48*	3.7 (2)
2.51*	3.7
2.54*	3.7
2.55*	3.7
2.57*	3.7

Br–Mg

2.43	67.5

Br–Ni

2.31*	83.12

Br–Pt

2.41	3.20
2.42	3.20
2.45	3.20 (2)
2.47	72.1
2.48	72.1
2.49	72.1
2.56	86.2

Br–Ru

2.61*	86.19 (2)

Br–Te

2.78	70.4

C–Cl

1.67	17.1
1.67*	60.29
1.68	16.14 (2)
1.68	17.1
1.68	20.6
1.69	20.6 (2)
1.69	24.1
1.69	50.6
1.70	1.2
1.70	17.1
1.70	18.2
1.70*	20.2
1.70	20.6
1.70	24.1
1.70*	25.1
1.70	60.28
1.70	69.8
1.71	17.1
1.71	18.2
1.71	19.1 (2)
1.71	19.5 (3)
1.71	24.1
1.71*	25.1
1.71*	25.4
1.71*	36.4
1.71	69.8
1.72	5.1
1.72	16.12
1.72	17.2
1.72	19.1
1.72	19.7
1.72*	20.2
1.72	24.1 (3)
1.72*	25.3
1.72	40.1
1.72*	60.29
1.73*	10.9
1.73	11.5
1.73	16.2 (2)
1.73	17.1
1.73	24.3
1.73	24.4
1.73*	32.8
1.73*	36.4
1.73*	36.5 (2)
1.73*	46.7
1.73	60.12
1.74*	2.24
1.74	11.5
1.74*	11.13
1.74*	11.14
1.74*	13.5
1.74*	14.1
1.74*	16.15
1.74	17.2
1.74	18.3
1.74	24.1
1.74*	28.7
1.74*	70.7
1.75*	8.7
1.75*	13.1
1.75*	16.16
1.75	18.3
1.75	18.8
1.75*	20.2
1.75	24.1
1.75	24.3
1.75	52.1
1.75*	70.7
1.76*	16.1
1.76*	16.17
1.76	18.9
1.76*	20.2 (2)
1.76	20.7
1.76	24.4
1.76*	25.1
1.76	58.8
1.76	64.16
1.76*	78.1
1.77*	10.11
1.77	11.5
1.77	18.7
1.77*	20.2
1.78	10.10
1.78	20.7
1.78*	25.1
1.78	38.3
1.78	38.14
1.79	11.5
1.79	15.4
1.79	24.5
1.79	53.10 (2)
1.80	10.8
1.80	29.20
1.80	39.3
1.81	11.5
1.81	39.3
1.81	44.26
1.81	52.1
1.82	11.5
1.82*	31.4
1.82	38.3
1.82	53.9
1.83	38.7
1.83	60.28
1.84*	38.6
1.84	38.7
1.85	38.5
1.85	40.4
1.86	5.1
1.86	38.4
1.86	38.14
1.86	53.8
1.87	5.1
1.89	60.24 (2)
1.94	28.5
1.95	38.14

C–Co

1.82	71.5
1.84*	72.13
1.85	71.5
1.87*	72.13
1.89	71.5
1.89*	72.13
1.92	49.13
1.92	71.5 (2)
1.92	73.26
1.93	73.26
1.96	73.26
1.96	86.18
1.97*	73.18
1.97	73.26 (3)
1.98*	73.14
1.98*	73.18
1.99*	73.14
2.01	73.26 (2)
2.02*	73.18
2.03*	73.14
2.03*	73.18
2.03	73.26
2.04*	73.14
2.04	73.26 (2)
2.05*	73.18 (2)
2.06*	73.14
2.06*	73.18
2.07	73.26
2.08*	73.14 (2)
2.08	73.26 (4)
2.09*	73.14
2.09*	73.18
2.09	73.26
2.11*	73.14
2.14*	73.18
2.17	73.26

C–Cr

1.57	75.11
1.79*	74.7
1.80	74.8
1.80	74.10
1.80	75.11
1.82*	74.7
1.83*	74.7
1.84*	74.1 (2)
1.86	75.11
1.87*	74.2
1.87	74.10
1.88	74.8
1.89	74.10
1.90*	74.2
1.91	74.8
1.98	75.11
2.07	74.6
2.08	74.6 (3)
2.13*	74.5 (2)
2.14	75.11
2.15	74.8
2.16	74.8 (3)
2.20	74.10
2.21*	74.7
2.21	74.10
2.22*	74.1 (2)
2.23*	74.1
2.23*	74.2 (2)
2.23*	74.7 (3)
2.24*	74.2
2.24*	74.7
2.25*	74.7
2.26	74.10

C–Cu

2.05*	75.22
2.07*	75.4
2.10*	75.4
2.11*	75.22

C–F

1.20*	73.14
1.21*	73.14
1.22*	73.14
1.26*	73.14
1.27*	85.20 (2)
1.28	64.4
1.28*	73.2
1.28*	73.14 (3)
1.28*	85.20 (2)
1.29*	73.2
1.29*	73.14 (2)
1.29*	85.20
1.30	2.4
1.30	64.4
1.30*	85.20 (2)
1.31*	2.5
1.31*	64.3
1.31	64.4
1.31*	85.20 (4)
1.32*	64.3
1.32	64.4
1.32*	85.20
1.33*	60.52 (2)
1.33	64.4 (2)
1.33*	73.2
1.34*	2.3
1.34*	2.4
1.34*	2.5
1.34	64.4 (2)
1.34*	73.2 (2)
1.34*	73.14 (2)
1.35*	2.3 (2)
1.35*	2.4
1.35*	2.5
1.35	44.5
1.35*	47.1
1.35	64.4
1.35*	73.14
1.36	13.8
1.37	64.4 (4)
1.39*	1.3
1.39	64.4
1.40	64.4

C–Fe

1.61	72.14
1.70*	72.25
1.70	72.26
1.71	72.14
1.71*	85.18
1.72*	72.25
1.72	72.26
1.73*	72.16
1.73*	72.25 (2)
1.73*	75.13
1.74*	72.8
1.74	72.9
1.74*	72.14 (2)
1.74*	72.16
1.74	72.26
1.74	75.23
1.75	72.14
1.75*	72.24
1.75*	72.25
1.75	72.26
1.75*	73.12
1.75*	75.5
1.75	75.23
1.76	72.24 (2)
1.76	72.26
1.76	73.12
1.76*	75.5
1.76*	75.13 (2)
1.76	75.23
1.77*	72.8
1.77	72.9
1.77*	72.25 (2)
1.77	73.12
1.77*	75.5
1.77*	75.13 (2)
1.78*	72.16 (2)
1.78	72.26
1.78	73.12
1.79*	75.9
1.80*	72.16
1.80	72.24 (2)
1.80	72.26 (2)
1.80	73.12
1.80*	75.9
1.81*	72.16
1.81	73.12
1.81*	75.13
1.81*	85.18 (2)
1.83*	85.18
1.84	72.14
1.84*	72.25
1.84*	85.18
1.88*	85.18
1.94*	72.16
1.95*	72.16
1.95	72.26
1.96	72.14
1.96	72.24
1.96	73.20
1.97	72.24
1.97	72.26
1.97	73.23
1.98*	72.8
1.98	72.26 (2)
1.98*	73.20
1.99*	72.25 (2)
1.99	72.26
2.00*	72.8
2.00	73.23
2.00	73.24 (2)
2.01	72.24
2.01*	73.13
2.01	73.24
2.02	72.14
2.02	73.12
2.02*	73.13
2.02*	73.20 (2)
2.02	73.23
2.02	73.24
2.03*	72.25
2.03	72.26
2.03*	73.1
2.03	73.5
2.03*	73.13
2.03	73.23
2.03*	73.24 (2)
2.03*	75.13
2.04*	73.1 (2)
2.04*	73.13 (4)
2.04*	73.20 (2)
2.04*	73.23 (3)
2.04*	75.5
2.04*	75.13
2.05*	72.26 (2)
2.05*	73.1
2.05	73.12
2.05*	73.13
2.05	73.24 (2)
2.05*	75.9
2.05	75.23 (2)
2.06*	72.9
2.06*	72.25
2.06	73.5
2.06	73.12
2.06	73.23
2.06	73.24
2.06	73.25 (4)
2.06*	75.13
2.07	72.14
2.07*	73.1
2.07*	73.13 (2)
2.07	73.20 (2)
2.07	73.23 (2)
2.07	73.25 (5)
2.07*	75.5
2.07	75.23
2.08	73.5
2.08	73.12
2.08	73.24
2.08	73.25
2.09	72.24
2.09*	72.25 (2)
2.09	73.5 (2)
2.09*	73.20
2.09*	75.13
2.09	75.23
2.10*	72.8 (2)
2.10	72.14
2.10	72.24
2.10*	73.1 (2)
2.10*	73.20
2.11*	72.16
2.11	72.24
2.11*	75.5
2.12*	72.16
2.12	73.12 (2)
2.12*	75.13
2.13*	72.25
2.14*	72.9
2.14*	72.16
2.14*	75.13
2.15*	72.16
2.15*	75.5
2.15*	75.13
2.16*	72.25 (2)
2.17*	72.25
2.17*	75.13
2.18*	75.9
2.19*	72.25
2.20	72.24
2.20*	72.25
2.23	72.24
2.26	72.14 (2)

C–Hg

1.96	71.1
2.12	71.4

C–I

1.79	7.4
1.82	51.6
1.89	60.20
1.95	51.5
1.98*	60.34
2.01	26.2
2.02	19.17
2.03	56.2
2.03	60.21
2.05	19.17
2.05*	35.13
2.05*	47.2
2.05	56.1
2.05	60.4
2.06*	7.10
2.06*	56.9
2.08	20.12
2.09	50.13
2.09*	60.2
2.12*	60.3
2.13	60.4
2.15	33.25
2.15	60.38
2.16	42.1
2.19	64.17
2.20	60.21
2.21	56.2
2.25	60.4

C–Li

2.25	67.1

C–Mg

2.34	67.5

C–Mn

1.79*	73.3 (2)
1.81*	73.3
2.13*	73.3
2.14*	73.3 (2)
2.17*	73.3 (2)

C–Mo

1.92*	73.19 (2)
1.93*	73.19
1.95*	75.6
1.96*	73.19
1.99*	75.6 (2)
2.22*	73.11
2.25*	73.11
2.26*	73.19
2.27*	73.19
2.28*	73.11
2.28*	73.19
2.29*	73.19
2.31*	75.6 (2)
2.33*	73.11
2.33*	75.6
2.34*	73.19
2.35*	73.19
2.36*	73.11
2.36*	73.19
2.37*	73.19 (2)
2.37*	75.6
2.39*	73.19

C–Ni

1.89*	75.19
1.93*	73.22 (3)
1.97*	72.21 (3)
1.98*	72.10
1.98*	75.19
2.00*	75.17
2.00*	75.19
2.01*	72.10
2.01*	75.17
2.03*	72.10
2.03*	75.17
2.05*	75.17
2.08*	75.20
2.09*	72.21
2.10*	72.21
2.10*	75.19
2.10*	75.20
2.11*	75.18 (3)
2.11*	75.19
2.11*	75.20 (2)
2.12*	72.21
2.12*	75.18 (2)
2.13*	75.18 (3)
2.13*	75.19
2.15*	72.21
2.15*	75.19
2.17*	75.19
2.19*	72.21
2.21*	75.20
2.22*	75.20 (2)
2.24*	75.20

C–P

1.70	64.20
1.71	64.17
1.71	64.18
1.73	85.19
1.74	64.16
1.75	64.14
1.76	64.14
1.76	86.3
1.77*	64.7
1.77	64.17 (2)
1.77	86.14
1.77*	86.17
1.78*	64.10
1.78	64.18
1.78*	77.21
1.78*	84.7
1.79	64.7
1.79*	64.10
1.79*	86.17
1.79*	86.22
1.80	64.9
1.80	64.16 (2)
1.80*	77.21
1.80*	84.7
1.80	86.3
1.80	86.16
1.81*	64.7 (2)
1.81	64.9
1.81	64.14
1.81	64.18
1.81	64.20
1.81	64.22
1.81*	77.21 (2)
1.81*	84.7
1.81	86.3
1.81*	86.12
1.81*	86.17 (2)
1.81*	86.22
1.82	64.8
1.82	64.14
1.82	64.15
1.82	64.16
1.82	64.17
1.82	64.20
1.82*	84.7 (2)
1.82	86.3
1.82*	86.12
1.82*	86.17
1.82	86.18
1.82*	86.20
1.82*	86.22 (2)

1.83*	64.2				
1.83*	64.15 (2)				
1.83	64.18				
1.83*	64.21				
1.83	66.1				
1.83*	73.19				
1.83*	86.12				
1.83	86.18				
1.83*	86.20				
1.83*	86.22 (3)				
1.84	64.8				
1.84*	64.22				
1.84*	64.23				
1.84	85.19				
1.84	86.2				
1.84	86.3				
1.84*	86.12 (2)				
1.84	86.14				
1.84	86.15				
1.84	86.16				
1.84*	86.17				
1.84*	86.20				
1.85*	64.21				
1.85*	64.22				
1.85	86.15				
1.85*	86.20 (2)				
1.85*	86.22				
1.86*	64.22				
1.86*	73.19				
1.86*	86.12				
1.86*	86.20 (4)				
1.87*	64.3				
1.87	64.4				
1.87	64.20				
1.87*	64.21				
1.87*	64.22				
1.87*	84.7				
1.87	86.2				
1.87*	86.22				
1.88	86.14				
1.88	86.16				
1.88	86.18				
1.89	64.4				
1.89	66.1				
1.89	86.2				
1.90	86.15				
1.91	86.2				
1.92	64.4 (3)				
1.92	86.3				
1.94	86.2				
1.97	86.2				
1.99*	64.21 (2)				

C–Pd

2.02*	72.5
2.08	72.20
2.09	72.7 (2)
2.09*	75.24
2.11*	72.4
2.11*	75.24
2.12*	72.4 (2)
2.12	75.25
2.14*	72.5
2.14	75.25
2.16*	75.2
2.17*	72.5
2.17	72.7
2.17*	75.2
2.17	75.25
2.18*	75.24

C–S

1.65*	41.1
1.65*	41.2
1.65	41.11
1.65*	41.16
1.65*	80.7 (2)
1.65	83.24
1.65	85.7
1.66*	4.1
1.66*	8.10
1.66	11.7
1.66	65.10
1.67	11.7
1.67*	39.20
1.67*	41.13
1.67	65.10
1.67	80.8 (2)
1.68*	64.7
1.68	64.18
1.68*	69.3
1.68*	85.20
1.69*	4.2 (2)
1.69	11.2
1.69	11.7
1.69*	39.10
1.69	41.9

1.69*	64.7
1.69	80.4
1.69*	80.9
1.69*	85.20 (2)
1.70	11.2 (2)
1.70	39.9
1.70	39.10
1.70*	66.3
1.70	73.5
1.70*	80.6
1.70	80.8
1.70*	85.10
1.70*	85.15
1.71	11.2 (4)
1.71	11.7
1.71	39.9
1.71*	39.20
1.71	41.9
1.71	41.11
1.71*	79.2
1.71	80.3
1.71*	80.5 (3)
1.71*	80.6
1.71*	80.7
1.71*	85.9
1.71*	85.10
1.72*	8.11
1.72	31.15
1.72*	35.13
1.72*	41.3
1.72*	41.13
1.72	60.30
1.72*	80.7 (3)
1.72*	80.9
1.72*	80.10 (2)
1.72	85.1 (2)
1.72*	85.20
1.73*	1.27
1.73*	8.7
1.73	11.2
1.73*	11.9
1.73	11.10
1.73	41.7
1.73	41.9
1.73	41.15
1.73	70.3 (2)
1.73	70.6
1.73*	79.2
1.73*	79.4
1.73	79.5
1.73	80.2
1.73	80.8
1.73	80.10
1.73	85.2 (2)
1.73*	85.9
1.73*	85.10
1.74*	4.4 (2)
1.74	8.8
1.74	16.7
1.74	16.9
1.74*	41.3
1.74	41.4
1.74	41.9
1.74	41.10
1.74*	48.7
1.74	59.14
1.74*	79.2
1.74	79.7
1.74*	80.5
1.74*	80.10
1.74*	85.10
1.74*	85.11
1.75	1.35
1.75	11.2
1.75*	11.8
1.75*	11.9
1.75	16.8
1.75*	39.17 (2)
1.75*	41.2
1.75	41.9
1.75	41.10
1.75	45.20
1.75	60.21
1.75	70.2
1.75	70.5
1.75	70.6
1.75	85.3
1.75	85.4
1.76*	11.1
1.76	11.2
1.76*	11.8 (2)
1.76	11.11
1.76*	11.13
1.76*	11.14
1.76	31.9
1.76*	39.17 (2)
1.76*	41.1
1.76*	41.2
1.76	41.10
1.76	41.14
1.76*	48.8
1.76*	70.1
1.76	70.2
1.76	70.4
1.76	79.3

1.76*	85.11
1.77	1.35
1.77*	4.4 (2)
1.77	11.2 (2)
1.77	11.3
1.77	11.5
1.77	16.5
1.77	39.8
1.77*	41.1
1.77	41.6
1.77	41.7
1.77	41.11
1.77	41.12 (2)
1.77*	41.16
1.77	45.17
1.77*	60.26
1.77	60.30
1.77	64.18
1.77	70.6
1.77	80.3
1.77	80.4
1.77*	85.6
1.78	11.6
1.78	16.18
1.78	39.3
1.78	41.6
1.78	41.7
1.78*	41.8
1.78	41.11
1.78	45.24
1.78	48.25
1.79	11.12
1.79*	39.6
1.79	39.8
1.79	41.11
1.79	60.30
1.79*	70.1
1.79	79.5
1.79*	85.18
1.80	8.8
1.80	16.4
1.80	39.3
1.80	41.10
1.80	60.21
1.80	60.30
1.81*	8.7
1.81*	11.5
1.81*	41.8
1.81	41.9
1.81	45.20
1.81*	48.4
1.81*	48.8
1.81	48.11
1.81	50.5
1.81	62.14
1.82	1.35
1.82	11.4
1.82	11.12 (2)
1.82	41.4
1.82	41.7
1.82	50.4
1.82	50.5
1.82	60.51
1.82	62.14
1.82	85.13
1.83*	1.35
1.83*	11.10
1.83	11.11
1.83*	39.6
1.83	48.11
1.83	62.14
1.83	85.13
1.83*	85.18
1.84*	1.27
1.84	39.3 (2)
1.84*	41.16
1.84*	48.7
1.84	62.14
1.84	85.12
1.85	39.13
1.85	59.14
1.85*	85.6
1.86*	4.5
1.86	48.18
1.86	85.5
1.87	50.4
1.87	85.12
1.88	48.17
1.90	50.5
1.90	58.8
1.91	58.8
1.91	80.3
1.92	50.5
2.00	85.5
2.09	41.15

C–Sb

2.06	66.4
2.11	66.4
2.14	66.4

2.17	66.4
2.20	68.9 (2)
2.25	66.4

C–Se

1.82*	8.13
1.85*	39.12
1.87*	39.12
1.89	60.4
1.94	60.4
1.95*	39.7
1.97	39.14
1.98*	39.7

C–Si

1.81	63.9
1.85	63.2 (2)
1.85*	63.4
1.86	63.5 (2)
1.87	63.3
1.87*	63.4 (4)
1.87	68.9 (4)
1.88*	63.4
1.88	63.5 (2)
1.88	63.9
1.89	63.2
1.90*	63.4
1.90	63.5
1.91	63.9
1.92	63.2
1.92	63.3
1.92*	63.4
1.95	63.9

C–Sn

1.85	69.5
2.15	69.5
2.15	69.8
2.17	69.8
2.21	69.8

C–Te

2.10*	70.7
2.13*	70.7

C–Ti

2.25	73.7 (2)
2.26	73.7
2.27	73.7 (2)

C–U

2.69*	73.17 (2)
2.70*	73.17
2.72*	73.17
2.73*	73.17 (6)
2.75*	73.17
2.78*	73.17 (2)
2.81*	73.17
2.82*	73.17

Ca–O

2.44	45.2
2.45	45.2
2.47	45.2
2.52	45.2

Cd–Cl

2.33*	83.18
2.55*	84.1
2.62*	84.1

Cd–N

2.46*	83.18
2.53	79.7

Cd–O

2.28	79.3
2.34*	84.1

Cd–S

2.54	80.4
2.56	80.4
2.57	80.4
2.60	79.7
2.63	80.4
2.71	79.3
2.73	79.7

Ce–O

2.36	77.14 (2)
2.38	77.14
2.39	77.14 (2)
2.40	77.14
2.42	77.14
2.43	77.14

Cl–Co

2.22	76.4
2.22*	76.6
2.23*	76.6
2.26	76.4
2.26	76.5
2.28	76.14
2.29	76.14

Cl–Cr

2.33	76.7

Cl–Cu

2.21	84.9
2.23	84.6
2.24*	82.6
2.24	84.9
2.25	83.8
2.26	83.7
2.26	83.8
2.26	84.6
2.27*	75.22
2.27	84.6 (3)
2.28*	75.4
2.28	83.8
2.29*	75.4
2.29	84.6 (3)
2.30*	75.22
2.30	83.7
2.30	83.8 (2)
2.31	83.7
2.31	84.6
2.32*	83.2
2.34	83.1
2.55*	83.2

Cl–Fe

2.09	59.13
2.11	59.13
2.13	59.13

2.16	9.10
2.17	59.13
2.18	9.10
2.19	59.13 (3)
2.22*	49.5
2.23	9.10
2.25	59.13

Cl–Hg

2.29*	85.6
2.30	60.33
2.30	85.5
2.30	85.12
2.32*	84.19
2.32*	84.20 (2)
2.32*	85.6
2.33*	84.19
2.34*	85.6
2.35	71.1
2.50	85.12
2.51	85.12
2.62	85.5
2.70*	85.6

Cl–I

2.52*	3.5
2.55*	3.9

Cl–N

1.69	1.12

Cl–Ni

2.19	86.16
2.25*	75.17
2.27	86.15
2.34*	75.17
2.35*	75.17
2.39*	79.4
2.51*	79.4

Cl–O

1.34	11.12
1.37*	12.1
1.39	71.5
1.40*	72.13
1.41*	11.9
1.41	71.5 (2)
1.42	71.5 (2)
1.43	48.13 (2)
1.43	71.5
1.44	71.5
1.44*	72.13
1.45	11.12
1.46	48.13
1.46	71.5
1.47	11.12
1.48	48.13
1.54	11.12

Cl–P

1.99*	64.10 (2)
2.00*	64.10
2.00	84.8 (2)
2.01*	64.10
2.01	84.8
2.02	84.8

Cl–Pd

2.25	72.20
2.31*	75.2

2.31* 75.3 (2)
2.32 72.20
2.32* 75.2
2.34 72.7
2.39 72.20
2.40* 72.5 (2)
2.41* 72.4
2.41 75.25
2.42* 72.4
2.42 72.7
2.42* 75.24
2.43* 75.24
2.43 75.25

Cl–Pt

2.30 72.3
2.32 72.18
2.32* 75.8
2.33 72.3
2.34* 75.8
2.38 72.18
2.42* 86.12

Cl–Re

2.30 86.14
2.32 86.14
2.37 86.14
2.40 86.14
2.41 86.3
2.42 33.10
2.43 33.10
2.43 86.3
2.47 86.3

Cl–Rh

2.37* 75.16
2.38* 75.16 (2)
2.39* 75.16

Cl–Ru

2.39* 86.20 (2)

Cl–S

2.08 73.5

Cl–Sb

2.32 66.1 (2)
2.35 66.1
2.37 66.1

Cl–Sn

2.43 69.5

Cl–Ti

2.28 73.7
2.29 73.7

Cl–U

2.56* 73.17

Cl–Zn

2.18 83.6
2.19 83.6
2.24 85.1
2.25 85.1
2.53* 84.2
2.59 83.4

—

Co–Co

2.74 71.5

Co–N

1.70 80.3
1.80 49.13
1.86 49.13
1.87 49.13
1.92 49.13
1.93* 76.6
1.93 83.14
1.94 76.14
1.95* 76.6
1.95 83.14
1.97 49.13
1.97 76.5
1.97 76.14
1.97 83.14
1.98* 76.6 (2)
1.98 76.15
1.99 76.14
2.00 76.5
2.00 76.15
2.01 79.5
2.02 76.4 (2)
2.02 76.14
2.03 76.4
2.03 76.15
2.09 83.24
2.12 83.24
2.14 76.4

Co–O

1.93* 84.7
1.95 77.20
1.95* 84.7
1.96 77.20
1.97 77.20
2.05 77.20
2.07 77.20
2.08 77.20
2.11 77.20
2.12 77.20
2.14* 84.7
2.15 77.20 (2)
2.15* 84.7
2.17* 84.7
2.23* 84.7
2.25 77.20
2.28 77.20

Co–P

2.23 86.18

Co–S

2.14* 85.20
2.15* 85.20
2.16* 85.9 (2)
2.17* 85.20
2.18* 85.20
2.19 80.3
2.24 80.3
2.35 80.3
2.38* 85.20
2.41 80.3

Cr–N

2.05* 76.1
2.05* 83.11

2.08* 76.1
2.11 76.7
2.11 83.23
2.13 76.7
2.26 83.23

Cr–O

1.56 83.23
1.57 83.11
1.79* 83.11
1.79 83.23
1.80* 83.11
1.83* 83.11
1.84* 76.1
1.84* 83.11
1.87* 76.1 (2)
1.87 83.23
1.94* 77.21 (3)
1.95* 76.1
1.95* 77.9 (3)
1.95* 77.21 (3)
1.96* 77.9 (3)
1.96* 77.21 (3)
1.97* 77.21 (3)
2.03* 76.1

Cu–Cu

2.45* 83.40
2.63 81.19
2.65 81.20
2.66* 80.9
3.18 78.7

Cu–I

2.70* 83.35

Cu–N

1.78 78.10
1.87 82.3
1.88 82.3
1.89 82.11
1.89 83.30
1.90* 83.40
1.91* 82.9
1.92* 82.9
1.92 83.30
1.93* 83.9 (2)
1.94 78.5
1.94 78.7
1.94* 82.9
1.94* 83.40
1.95 78.10
1.95 83.7
1.95* 83.26
1.96 60.31
1.96* 78.1
1.96* 83.35
1.97 81.11
1.97 83.8
1.97* 83.29 (2)
1.97 83.38
1.98* 49.8
1.98 82.1
1.98* 82.2
1.98 83.17
1.98 83.27
1.98 83.28
1.99* 76.9
1.99 78.8
1.99* 78.15
1.99* 81.10
1.99 82.1
1.99* 82.6
1.99 83.1
1.99* 83.2
1.99 83.3
1.99* 83.15
1.99* 83.26
1.99* 83.35
2.00 82.11
2.00 83.19
2.00 83.38

2.00 83.46
2.01* 76.8
2.01* 76.9
2.01 83.28
2.02* 82.2
2.02 82.3
2.02* 83.35
2.03* 82.9
2.04* 76.8
2.04 82.3
2.04 82.11
2.05 84.15
2.08 78.7
2.11* 83.35
2.12 81.19
2.13 81.19
2.18 81.20

Cu–O

1.77 84.6
1.83 81.18
1.86* 78.2
1.87 84.10
1.88 78.10
1.88* 78.15
1.88 83.38
1.88 84.15
1.89 77.7
1.89 84.10
1.89* 84.12
1.90 78.3
1.90 78.8
1.90 83.38 (2)
1.91* 77.16
1.91* 78.1
1.91 78.5
1.91 78.7
1.91 81.17
1.91 81.18
1.91 83.27
1.92* 77.7
1.92* 83.26
1.92* 83.29
1.93* 81.8
1.93 81.20
1.93 82.1
1.93 82.6
1.93 82.11
1.93* 83.29
1.93 83.46
1.93* 84.12
1.94 78.3
1.94 78.10
1.94* 81.8 (2)
1.94* 84.4
1.95 60.31
1.95 81.20
1.95 82.1
1.95* 82.2
1.95 83.38
1.96 81.2
1.96 81.20
1.96* 82.2
1.96 82.3
1.96* 83.26
1.97 81.6
1.97* 81.8
1.97 81.17
1.97 81.19
1.97 82.3
1.97 83.3
1.97* 84.4
1.98* 78.2
1.98 81.6
1.98 81.19
1.98 81.20
1.98 83.38
1.98 84.9
1.99 81.19 (2)
1.99 82.3 (2)
1.99* 82.6
2.00* 83.15
2.00* 84.4
2.01 83.30
2.02 81.2 (2)
2.02* 81.10
2.03 78.7
2.03 81.2
2.03 83.38
2.04 83.19
2.05* 84.4
2.06 81.11
2.07 83.30
2.10 84.9
2.12 81.6
2.13 81.6
2.28 81.2
2.30* 82.6

2.32* 84.4
2.34* 84.4
2.40* 82.2
2.41 78.7
2.45* 83.15
2.48 82.7
2.53 78.10
2.59* 76.8

Cu–S

2.16* 85.10
2.17* 85.10 (2)
2.18* 85.10
2.25* 80.9
2.26* 80.9
2.28* 79.2
2.29* 80.9
2.30* 80.5 (2)
2.32* 80.5
2.32 80.8 (3)
2.33 80.8
2.34* 80.5
2.35* 79.2
2.35* 85.15
2.38* 79.2
2.43* 79.2

Fe–Fe

2.43* 72.25 (2)
2.46 72.26
2.47* 72.26
2.49* 72.16
2.50 72.24
2.53 72.14
2.54* 85.18
2.59 72.26
2.68 73.12

Fe–N

1.91 83.34
1.96 83.34
2.03 49.12
2.05* 49.5
2.05 83.34
2.06* 49.5
2.07* 49.5
2.07* 49.7 (2)
2.08* 49.5
2.30* 76.20
2.31 76.21
2.32 76.21
2.34* 76.20

Fe–O

1.84* 49.7
1.94* 76.20
1.97 76.21
1.99 84.13 (2)
2.00* 76.20
2.00 84.13 (2)
2.01 76.21
2.01 84.13 (2)
2.07 76.21
2.08 76.21
2.10* 76.20 (2)
2.11 76.21
2.12* 76.20
2.18 49.12

Fe–S

2.22* 85.18
2.26* 85.18
2.27* 85.18
2.28* 85.18

Ga–N

1.98* 68.2

Hg–O

2.32* 84.19
2.37* 84.19
2.46* 84.20
2.48* 84.20

Hg–S

2.36 85.2 (2)
2.40 85.5
2.40* 85.6
2.45 85.7
2.48 85.7
2.53 85.12
2.59 79.5

I–I

2.74 60.45
2.79* 39.6
2.82 33.14
2.82 60.51
2.87* 39.7
2.91 60.38
2.93 60.45
2.95 60.17

I–N

2.16 60.45
2.30* 3.5
2.32 33.14

I–Ni

3.21* 86.5

I–O

2.00 42.1
2.30 42.1

I–Pd

3.40 86.6

I–Pt

3.50* 86.7

I–Rh

2.65* 73.2

I–S

2.87* 39.6

I–Se

2.83* 39.7

I–Te

2.92*	70.7
2.95*	70.7
2.97	70.5

Ir–O

2.05*	86.17
2.10*	86.17

Ir–P

2.36*	86.17
2.38*	86.17

Li–Li

2.63	67.1

Mg–O

2.01	67.5
2.05	2.1
2.06	67.5
2.07	2.1
2.08	2.1 (2)
2.10	2.1
2.13	2.1

Mn–N

2.35*	76.26
2.40*	76.26

Mn–O

1.86*	77.10 (2)
1.87*	77.10 (2)
1.88*	77.10
1.89*	77.10
2.11	84.8
2.12	84.8
2.14	84.8 (2)
2.15*	76.26
2.15	81.3
2.16*	76.26
2.16	81.3 (2)
2.17	84.8
2.20	81.3
2.21*	76.26
2.21	81.3
2.22*	76.26
2.23*	76.26 (2)
2.24	81.3
2.24	84.8
2.26*	76.26 (2)

Mo–Mo

2.54*	81.9

Mo–N

2.29*	76.2
2.33*	76.2

Mo–O

1.64*	80.7
1.65*	80.7
1.70*	81.9
1.74*	76.2
1.75*	76.2
1.82	81.1
1.85*	80.7
1.85	81.1
1.86	81.1
1.87*	80.7
1.88*	81.9
1.93*	81.9
2.11*	81.9
2.14*	81.9
2.21*	81.9
2.22	81.1

Mo–P

2.42*	73.19
2.43*	73.19

Mo–S

2.46*	80.7
2.47*	80.7
2.51*	80.7 (2)
2.53*	80.7
2.54*	80.7
2.69*	80.7
2.71*	80.7

N–N

1.10*	9.8
1.10	9.10
1.11	9.6
1.12	60.31
1.13*	9.5
1.19	41.14
1.23	9.12
1.24	9.3
1.24	60.31
1.25*	9.1
1.25	9.13
1.26	9.12
1.26*	83.2
1.27*	9.5
1.27	10.12
1.27*	83.40
1.27	84.10
1.29	83.13
1.29	84.13
1.30*	32.8
1.30	84.13
1.31	10.3
1.31*	32.1
1.31*	35.1
1.31	83.46
1.31	84.13
1.32*	83.40
1.34*	40.2
1.35*	32.1
1.35	32.2
1.35*	33.4
1.35*	34.1
1.35	35.8
1.36	32.3 (2)
1.36	35.3
1.37*	34.1
1.37	34.2
1.37*	35.1
1.38	41.9
1.38	45.18
1.38	83.1
1.39*	32.8
1.39	83.5
1.39	85.1
1.40*	9.4
1.40	35.3
1.41	9.2
1.41	33.17
1.41	34.2
1.41	35.3
1.41	83.4
1.42*	9.11
1.42*	41.16
1.42	45.19
1.43	9.9
1.43	45.21
1.43	59.16
1.44	9.13
1.44	33.16
1.44	85.4
1.45	85.1
1.46	83.5
1.47*	32.4
1.47	83.3
1.48*	32.6
1.50	59.16
1.54	85.3

N–Ni

1.85*	83.12
1.85	85.13 (2)
1.87*	83.21
1.90	83.13
1.90	85.4
1.91	85.3
1.95*	49.6 (2)
1.95*	78.12
1.96*	49.4
1.96*	49.6
1.98*	49.6
1.99*	78.12
2.03*	83.37 (3)
2.09	76.13
2.10	82.8
2.10	82.10
2.11	76.13
2.11	82.10
2.12*	76.16 (5)
2.15	76.13

N–O

1.05	84.11
1.07	51.5
1.10	51.6
1.10	80.3
1.11	40.1
1.12	45.20
1.13	15.11
1.14	60.30
1.14	60.48
1.15	14.2
1.15	45.20
1.15*	83.37
1.15	84.11
1.16	52.1
1.16	60.31
1.17	15.11
1.17	28.8
1.17	60.48
1.18*	6.3
1.18	45.20
1.18	60.31
1.19*	14.3 (2)
1.19	15.6
1.19	24.6
1.19	28.8
1.19	40.4
1.19	45.20
1.19	60.31
1.19	60.49
1.20	15.6
1.20*	16.13
1.20	28.1
1.20	28.8
1.20	45.1
1.20	52.2
1.20	60.40
1.21	13.1
1.21*	13.6
1.21	15.3
1.21*	33.7
1.21*	34.1
1.21	51.6
1.21	52.1
1.21*	52.2
1.21	60.31 (2)
1.21	60.40 (2)
1.21*	76.16 (3)
1.21*	83.37
1.21*	84.7 (2)
1.22*	13.1
1.22*	14.3
1.22	15.4
1.22*	33.7
1.22*	34.1
1.22	34.2 (3)
1.22*	43.7
1.22	43.8
1.22	45.1
1.22	60.31
1.22	60.40 (2)
1.22	60.49 (2)
1.22*	83.37
1.22*	84.7
1.23*	9.5
1.23*	14.3
1.23	15.3
1.23*	15.8 (2)
1.23*	15.9 (2)
1.23*	16.1 (2)
1.23*	16.3 (2)
1.23	16.12
1.23*	17.4
1.23	24.6
1.23	24.7
1.23	28.8
1.23	34.2
1.23	40.1
1.23	43.8
1.23	60.30
1.23	60.40
1.23	83.28
1.23*	83.37
1.23*	84.7
1.23	84.9
1.24	13.6
1.24	14.2
1.24*	15.7 (4)
1.24	15.11
1.24*	17.3 (2)
1.24*	17.4
1.24	24.7 (3)
1.24*	28.1 (2)
1.24*	34.1 (2)
1.24	40.4
1.24	50.1
1.24	83.28 (2)
1.24*	84.7
1.25*	6.3
1.25*	9.5
1.25	15.4
1.25*	15.7
1.25	15.11
1.25*	28.1
1.25*	32.8
1.25*	76.8
1.25*	84.7
1.26*	15.7
1.26*	16.13
1.26*	33.7
1.26	36.8
1.26*	43.2
1.26*	43.7
1.26	43.8
1.26*	60.30
1.26*	76.8
1.26	83.13
1.26*	83.37
1.27	60.48
1.27*	76.8
1.27	84.10
1.28*	10.11
1.29	43.3
1.29	43.8
1.29*	83.37
1.29	84.11
1.30	10.3
1.30	10.12
1.30	84.13
1.31*	9.1
1.31	83.13
1.31	84.13 (2)
1.32	10.3
1.32	10.7
1.32	18.7
1.32	51.5
1.32	84.13 (2)
1.33	36.7
1.33*	43.5
1.33*	43.6
1.33	83.14
1.33	84.13
1.34	58.20
1.34	60.30
1.34	83.13
1.34	84.13 (2)
1.36*	18.12
1.36*	40.2
1.37	60.30
1.37	83.14
1.37	83.34
1.37	84.10
1.38	10.10
1.38	33.11
1.39*	10.4
1.39	18.8
1.39	60.30
1.39	83.34
1.40	18.9
1.40	40.1
1.40	45.1
1.41*	10.1
1.41*	10.9
1.41	28.8 (2)
1.41*	40.6
1.42	10.2
1.42	10.5
1.42	10.6
1.42*	78.1
1.44	10.8
1.44*	83.21
1.45	78.5
1.49	60.30
1.50	45.20
1.52	60.30
1.54	60.30
1.56	45.20

N–P

1.55*	64.10 (2)
1.58*	64.10 (2)
1.58*	64.13 (2)
1.59*	64.9
1.60*	64.9
1.61*	64.10
1.62*	64.10
1.67*	64.13
1.69*	64.13

N–Pd

1.85	78.11
1.98*	60.29
2.01*	49.9
2.02	78.13
2.02*	83.36 (2)

N–Pt

1.96	83.10
1.96*	83.16
2.01	72.18
2.02	72.3
2.04	83.10
2.07*	83.42
2.14*	83.33
2.16*	83.33
2.19*	83.42
2.31*	77.12

N–S

1.60	48.25
1.61*	4.3
1.61	16.7
1.63	16.8
1.64	16.18
1.66*	35.13
1.67*	16.9

N–Si

1.69*	63.4
1.71*	63.4
1.71	63.5
1.72	63.5 (2)
1.73*	63.4 (3)
1.74*	63.4 (2)
1.75*	63.4

N–Sn

2.26	69.5

N–V

2.10*	83.44

N–Zn

1.95	83.6
2.00*	82.13
2.04	49.11
2.04	82.12
2.05*	82.13
2.06	82.12
2.07	83.4
2.08	85.1
2.10	83.32
2.10	85.1
2.17	83.5
2.18*	81.12
2.21*	81.12
2.25	83.5

Ni–Ni

2.39*	73.22
2.88	77.19
2.90	77.19

Ni–O

1.89	77.19
1.89*	78.12
1.90*	78.12
1.96	77.19
1.97	77.19
1.98	77.19
2.00	77.19
2.00	82.10
2.01*	77.6
2.02*	77.6
2.02	78.6 (2)
2.02*	81.4
2.03	77.19
2.04	77.19
2.04	78.6
2.04*	81.4
2.05	77.19
2.06	77.19
2.06*	81.4 (2)
2.07	77.19
2.08	77.19 (2)
2.08*	83.37
2.09*	81.4
2.09*	83.37
2.10*	81.4
2.10	82.10
2.11*	83.37
2.14*	77.6
2.14	77.19
2.14	82.8
2.14	82.10
2.15	77.19 (2)
2.17	82.8
2.18	77.19
2.27	77.19
2.40	77.19

Ni–P

2.28	86.15
2.28	86.16

Ni–S

2.15	85.3
2.15	85.13
2.16	85.4
2.16*	85.11
2.17*	85.11
2.17	85.13
2.19*	80.6
2.21*	80.6
2.23	80.2
2.24	80.2
2.47*	79.4

O–O

1.31*	86.17
1.40*	83.11

1.40 83.23
1.41* 83.11
1.45 1.21
1.46* 76.1
1.47* 2.10
1.48* 13.6
1.48* 76.1

O–P

1.43* 46.9
1.44* 46.3
1.44 46.8
1.45 84.8 (2)
1.47* 46.6 (2)
1.47 47.6
1.47 84.8 (2)
1.48 45.10
1.48 46.2
1.48* 47.5
1.48* 77.21
1.48 84.11
1.49* 46.1
1.49 46.2
1.49* 46.6
1.49 47.6
1.49 47.10
1.49* 77.21
1.49 84.11
1.50* 46.1
1.50* 46.6
1.50* 46.7
1.50* 47.3
1.50* 47.5
1.51 45.4 (2)
1.51 47.6
1.51* 47.10
1.51* 77.21 (2)
1.52 45.4
1.52 45.10
1.52* 47.3
1.52 59.4 (2)
1.53 45.10
1.53* 46.6
1.53 49.13
1.53 59.4
1.53* 84.7
1.53 84.11
1.55* 46.9
1.55* 47.3
1.55* 47.5
1.55 49.13
1.55* 84.7
1.56* 46.1
1.56 46.2
1.56* 46.9
1.56 64.5
1.56 84.11
1.57* 46.3 (3)
1.57* 46.6
1.57* 47.10
1.58* 46.7
1.59 45.10
1.59* 46.1
1.59* 46.6 (2)
1.59 47.6
1.59 59.4
1.59 64.5
1.60 46.2
1.60* 46.9
1.60 49.13
1.60 64.5
1.61 46.8 (2)
1.61* 47.5
1.61* 47.10
1.61 66.1

1.64* 47.3
1.64 64.1
1.65 46.8
1.65 49.13
1.67 45.4

O–Pb

2.37* 69.3
2.44* 69.3

O–Pd

1.94 78.11
1.98* 60.29
2.00 78.13

O–Pt

2.00* 81.7
2.01* 81.7
2.13* 77.18
2.16* 77.12
2.17* 77.18
2.18* 77.12
2.19* 77.11 (2)
2.22* 83.42
2.23* 83.42 (2)
2.29* 83.42

O–Re

1.60 86.3

O–S

1.22 45.20
1.34 48.25
1.37* 35.13
1.37 45.20
1.38* 45.24
1.39 48.25
1.39 73.5
1.40 39.8
1.40 45.20
1.41* 4.3
1.41 16.7
1.41 45.20
1.41 60.19
1.42* 11.9
1.42 16.5
1.42 16.18
1.42 31.15
1.42* 45.24
1.42 85.4
1.43* 4.4 (2)
1.43* 11.10

1.43* 11.13
1.43* 11.14
1.43 39.8
1.43 73.5
1.43* 76.6 (2)
1.44 3.2
1.44* 4.3
1.44* 4.4 (2)
1.44* 11.8
1.44* 11.10
1.44 16.4 (2)
1.44 16.5
1.44 16.8 (2)
1.44 16.9
1.44* 31.9 (2)
1.44 45.17
1.44 60.19
1.44 64.18
1.44* 70.1
1.44* 76.6
1.44 83.19
1.45 3.2
1.45* 11.1 (2)
1.45 11.3
1.45 11.6
1.45 11.11
1.45* 16.9
1.45* 31.15
1.45* 48.4
1.45 85.4
1.46 3.2 (2)
1.46 8.8
1.46* 11.1
1.46 16.5
1.46 16.7
1.46 35.11
1.46* 48.4
1.46 85.4
1.47 8.8
1.47 11.11
1.47 16.18
1.47* 35.13
1.47 45.17 (2)
1.47 64.18
1.47* 70.1
1.48 3.2 (2)
1.48 3.4
1.48 35.11 (2)
1.48* 48.4
1.49 3.2
1.49 3.4
1.49* 8.3
1.49 48.11
1.50 83.19
1.51 3.2
1.51 11.4 (2)
1.51 35.11
1.51 60.19
1.52 60.19
1.55* 31.9
1.55* 45.24
1.56 45.20
1.57 31.15
1.60 45.20

O–Si

1.56 68.9 (2)
1.60 63.3 (2)
1.61 63.2 (2)
1.61 63.3
1.62 63.3

O–Sn

2.07 69.8

O–Ti

1.73 73.7

O–U

1.64 84.11
2.44 84.11
2.47 84.11
2.48 81.15
2.49 81.15 (2)
2.62 84.11

O–V

1.56* 77.2
1.57* 77.3
1.60* 77.13
1.94* 77.13
1.95* 77.3
1.95* 77.13
1.96*. 77.2 (2)
1.96* 77.3
1.97* 77.2
1.97* 77.3
1.97* 77.13 (2)
1.98* 77.2
1.98* 77.3

O–Zn

1.92* 77.5
1.94* 77.17
2.00* 77.4 (2)
2.00* 77.5
2.01* 77.4
2.02* 77.5
2.03* 77.4
2.03* 84.2
2.03* 84.5
2.04* 77.4
2.04 83.5
2.05* 84.2
2.06 83.4
2.07 83.32
2.09* 77.5
2.10* 84.5

O–Sb

2.00 66.1
2.03 66.2
2.04 66.2
2.14 66.2
2.17 66.2

2.11* 84.5
2.12* 77.5
2.12* 84.5
2.15* 81.12
2.16* 84.5 (2)
2.26 83.32
2.45 49.11

O–Zr

2.14* 81.13
2.18 77.15
2.19 77.15
2.19* 81.13
2.20 77.15
2.21* 81.13
2.22 77.15
2.24* 81.13

P–P

2.18* 64.22
2.19* 64.22
2.20 64.4
2.21* 64.3
2.21 64.4
2.21 64.8
2.21* 64.22
2.22 64.4
2.22* 64.22 (2)
2.23 64.4
2.24* 64.23
2.25 64.4

P–Pt

2.26 86.2 (2)
2.27* 86.12 (2)

P–Re

2.45 86.3
2.48 86.3
2.70 86.14

P–Rh

2.31* 86.22
2.32* 86.22
2.34* 86.22

P–Ru

2.23* 86.20
2.37* 86.20
2.41* 86.20

P–S

1.90 64.5
1.94* 64.2
1.94 64.8
1.96 64.1
2.14* 64.2

Re–Re

2.22 33.10
2.49 86.14

S–S

1.98 11.3
1.99* 60.2
2.00* 4.5
2.00* 39.20
2.01 48.17
2.02 48.18
2.02* 60.2
2.02* 70.1
2.03 11.5
2.03* 76.6
2.04 11.5
2.04* 60.2
2.05* 41.1
2.05* 76.6
2.06* 41.2
2.07 39.13
2.08* 41.3
2.09 58.8
2.11* 60.2
2.12* 76.6

S–Sb

2.52* 66.3

S–Te

2.47 70.6
2.53 70.6
2.67* 70.1
2.68* 70.1
2.68 70.3
2.69 70.2 (2)
2.69 70.3
2.69 70.4
2.69 70.5
2.86 70.6
3.02 70.6

S–Zn

2.29 85.1
2.30 85.1

Molecular Formula Index

The molecular formula is expressed in terms of residues, each residue being an independent set of covalently bonded atoms, e.g. sodium formate has two residues: CHO_2 and Na^+.

The formula of each residue follows the common convention:
$C_x H_y A_a B_b$ ... i.e. carbon and hydrogen atoms (if any) are recorded first with the remaining elements in alphabetic order.

In the index, compounds are grouped under the number of carbon atoms. Within each group, compounds are ordered by the number of hydrogen atoms (including $H =$ zero) and then alphabetically by element symbols.

Residues are listed in order of precedence as follows:
organic > inorganic ions > water (or organic solvent).

When more than one organic residue is present (excluding solvents of crystallisation), the compound is indexed under each residue.

Thus the carbon tetrabromide: p-xylene complex can be located by searching either in group C_1 where it will appear as CBr_4, $C_8 H_{10}$ or in group C_8 where it will appear as $C_8 H_{10}$, CBr_4.

The entry number m.n refers to the main entry where m is the class number and n is the sequence number within the class. Multiple entries are indicated by a $+$ sign after the entry number.

C_1

CBr_4, C_8H_{10}	60.1
$CHBrCl_2$, $C_4H_{10}O$	60.24
CHI_3, $3S_8$	60.2
CHI_3, $C_4H_8S_2$	60.21
CHI_3, $3C_9H_7N$	60.3
$2CHI_3$, $C_4H_8Se_2$	60.4
CHN_4, Na^+, H_2O	32.1
$2CHO_2^-$, Mg^{2+}, $2H_2O$	2.1
$2CHO_2^-$, Sr^{2+}, $2H_2O$	2.2
$CH_2O_6S_2^{2-}$, $2K^+$	11.1
CH_2S_3	11.2
CH_3AsI_2	65.1
$CH_3N_2O^-$, K^+	9.1
$CH_3O_2S_2^-$, Na^+, H_2O	11.3
$CH_3O_3S^-$, Na^+, $2H_2O$	11.4
CH_4N_2O	8.1+
CH_4N_2O	10.1
CH_4N_2O, Na^+, Cl^-, H_2O	60.5
CH_4N_2O, H_4N^+, Br^-	60.6
CH_4N_2O, H_4N^+, Cl^-	60.7
CH_4N_2O, C_7H_9N	60.36
$CH_4N_2O_2$, $C_5H_{12}NOS^+$, Cl^-	60.26
$CH_4N_2O_2S$	8.3
$2CH_4O$, Br_2	60.8
$3CH_4O$, Na^+, I^-	60.9
$CH_5Cl_2N_3SZn$	85.1
$CH_5N_2O^+$, $CdCl_3^-$	8.4
CH_6N^+, Br^-	3.1
CH_6N^+, $H_{12}AlO_6^{3+}$, $2O_4S^{2-}$, $6H_2O$	3.2
CH_6N^+, $C_2H_7BNO^-$	62.3
CH_6NO^+, Cl^-	10.2
$CH_6N_3^+$, Cl^-	8.5
$3CH_6N_3^+$, C_4H_9NO, $3Cl^-$	60.10
$CH_6N_3O^+$, Cl^-	9.2

C_2

$C_2Br_2O_2$	
$C_2Br_2O_2$, $C_4H_8O_2$	60.11
$C_2Cl_2O_2$	1.2
$C_2Cl_2O_2$, $C_4H_8O_2$	60.12
$C_2Cl_6S_3$	11.5
$C_2F_3O_2^-$, H_4N^+	2.3
$C_2F_3O_2^-$, $C_2HF_3O_2$, Cs^+	2.4
$C_2F_3O_2^-$, $C_2HF_3O_2$, K^+	2.5
C_2I_2, $C_4H_8O_2$	60.20
C_2I_2, $C_6H_8O_2$	60.34
C_2I_4, $C_4H_8Se_2$	60.22
$C_2MoO_7^{2-}$, H_4N^+, Na^+, $2H_2O$	81.1
C_2N_2	7.1
$C_2O_4^{2-}$, Ca^{2+}, H_2O	2.6
$C_2O_4^{2-}$, Ca^{2+}, $2H_2O$	2.7
$C_2O_4^{2-}$, $2K^+$, H_2O	2.8
$C_2O_4^{2-}$, $2Li^+$	2.9
$C_2O_4^{2-}$, $2Na^+$, H_2O_2	2.10
$C_2O_4^{2-}$, $2Rb^+$, H_2O	2.11
$C_2O_4^{2-}$, Sr^{2+}, $2.17H_2O$	2.12
$C_2O_4^{2-}$, $2H_4N^+$, H_2O	2.13+
$C_2HF_3O_2$, $C_2F_3O_2^-$, Cs^+	2.4
$C_2HF_3O_2$, $C_2F_3O_2^-$, K^+	2.5
$C_2HO_4^-$, $C_2H_2O_4$, K^+, $2H_2O$	2.15
$C_2H_2NO_3^-$, H_4N^+	2.16
$C_2H_2N_2S_3$	41.1+
$C_2H_2O_4$, $C_2HO_4^-$, K^+, $2H_2O$	2.15
$C_2H_3ClHgO_2$	71.1
$C_2H_3Cl_2CuN_3$	83.1
$C_2H_3Cl_3O_2$	5.1
$C_2H_3N_3$	32.2
$C_2H_3O_2^-$, Li^+, $2H_2O$	2.17
$C_2H_3O_2^-$, $C_2H_4O_2$, Na^+	2.18
$C_2H_3O_3^-$, Li^+, H_2O	2.19
$C_2H_3O_3^-$, $C_2H_4O_3$, Rb^+	2.20
$C_2H_2DO_3^-$, Li^+	2.21
$C_2H_4B_{10}Cl_8$	62.1
$C_2H_4Br_3Pt^-$, K^+, H_2O	72.1
C_2H_4FNO	1.3

$C_2H_4N_2S_2$	4.1
$C_2H_4N_3S_2^+$, Br^-	41.3
$C_2H_4N_4$	7.2+
$C_2H_4N_4O_2$	9.3
C_2H_4O, $7.2H_2O$	61.1
$C_2H_4O_2$, $C_2H_3O_2^-$, Na^+	2.18
$C_2H_4O_3$, $C_2H_3O_3^-$, Rb^+	2.20
C_2H_5NO	1.4
$C_2H_5NO_2$	48.1+
$C_2H_5NO_2$, $C_2H_6NO_2^+$, Cl^-	48.3
C_2H_5NS	4.2
$C_2H_5N_3O_2$, $0.6H_2O$	8.6
$C_2H_6Al_2Cl_4$	68.1
$C_2H_6BF_3OS$	62.2
$(C_2H_6Cl_2Cu_2N_2)_n$	83.2
$(C_2H_6CuO_6)_n$	81.2
$C_2H_6HgS_2$	85.2
$(C_2H_6MnO_6)_n$	81.3
$C_2H_6NO_2^+$, $C_2H_5NO_2$, Cl^-	48.3
$C_2H_6N_2O_2$	10.3
$C_2H_6N_2S^+$, $C_7H_5ClO_2^-$	8.7
$(C_2H_6NiO_6)_n$	81.4
$C_2H_6O_2PS_2^-$, K^+	64.1
$C_2H_6O_2S$	11.6
$C_2H_6P_2S_4$	64.2
$C_2H_7AsO_2$	65.2
$C_2H_7BNO^-$, CH_6N^+	62.3
$C_2H_7Br_2NPt$	72.2
$C_2H_7NO_3S$	48.4
$2C_2H_7N_2S^+$, O_4S^{2-}	8.8
$C_2H_8B_4$	62.4
$C_2H_8ClHgN_4S_2^+$, Cl^-	79.1
$C_2H_8NO_4P$	46.1+
$C_2H_8N_6NiS_2$	85.3
$C_2H_{10}CrN_2O_5$, H_2O	76.1
$C_2H_{10}CuN_6O_2^{2+}$, $2Cl^-$	83.3
$C_2H_{10}N_2^{2+}$, $2Cl^-$	3.3
$C_2H_{10}N_2^{2+}$, O_4S^{2-}	3.4
$C_2H_{10}N_6NiS_2^{2+}$, O_4S^{2-}, $3H_2O$	85.4
$C_2H_{10}N_6O_2Zn^{2+}$, $2Cl^-$	83.4
$C_2H_{14}N_8O_4Zn$	83.5
$C_2H_{16}B_9N$	62.5
$C_2H_{18}B_{10}$	62.6
$C_2H_{18}CoN_5O_2^{2+}$, Cl^-, ClO_4^-	81.5

C_3

C_3Cl_6	20.1
C_3IN	7.4
$C_3H_3BrO_2$	5.2
$C_3H_3NOS_2$	41.4
$C_3H_3O_3^-$, Li^+	2.22
$C_3H_3O_3^-$, Na^+	2.23
$C_3H_4N_2$	32.3
$C_3H_4O_2$	1.5+
$C_3H_4O_2S$	39.1
$C_3H_4O_5$	1.7
$C_3H_5N_2S_2^+$, I^-	39.2
$C_3H_5OS_2^-$, K^+	11.7
C_3H_6AsN	65.3
$C_3H_6N_4O_3$	8.9
$3C_3H_6O$, Na^+, I^-	60.13
$C_3H_6O_2$	1.8+
$C_3H_6O_3$	38.1
C_3H_7NO	1.10
$2C_3H_7NO$, Na^+, ClO_4^-	60.14
$3C_3H_7NO$, Na^+, I^-	60.15
$4C_3H_7NO$, Li^+, Cl^-	60.16
$6C_3H_7NO$, $2K^+$, I^-, I_3^-	60.17
$C_3H_7NO_2$	48.5
$C_3H_7N_2^+$, Cl^-	32.4
$C_3H_7O_4P$	46.3
C_3H_9ClIN	3.5
$C_3H_9Cl_5OPSb$	66.1
C_3H_9FSn	69.1
C_3H_9NO	10.4
$C_3H_9OS^+$, BF_4^-	11.8
$C_3H_9OS^+$, ClO_4^-	11.9
$C_3H_{10}NO^+$, Cl^-	10.5+
$C_3H_{10}OSn$	69.2

$(C_3H_{12}CuN_6S_3^+)_n$, nCl^-	79.2
$C_3H_{12}GaN$	68.2
$C_3H_{16}B_3N$	62.7

C_4

C_4Cl_8	20.2
$C_4CuO_8^{2-}$, $2H_4N^+$, $2H_2O$	81.6
$C_4F_{12}P_4$	64.3
$C_4N_3^-$, K^+	7.5
$C_4N_3^-$, H_4N^+	7.6
$2C_4N_3^-$, Cu^{2+}	7.7
$C_4O_4^{2-}$, $2K^+$, H_2O	6.1
$C_4O_8Pt^{2-}$, $2K^+$, $2H_2O$	81.7
$C_4H_2ClO_4^-$, K^+	2.24
$C_4H_2N_2O_4$	43.1
$C_4H_2N_3O_4^-$, K^+, $2H_2O$	43.2
$C_4H_2N_3O_4^-$, Rb^+	43.3
$C_4H_2O_3$	1.11
$C_4H_3BrN_2O_2$	50.1
$C_4H_3N_2O_3^-$, H_4N^+	43.4
$C_4D_3N_3O_4$, D_2O	43.5+
$C_4H_3N_3O_5$	43.7
$C_4H_3N_3O_5$, $3H_2O$	43.8
$C_4H_3O_4^-$, K^+	2.25+
$C_4H_4ClNO_2$	1.12
$(C_4H_4Cu_2O_8)_n$	81.8
$C_4H_4Mo_2O_{14}^{2-}$, H_2BaO^{2+}, $2H_2O$	81.9
$C_4H_4N_2$	44.1
$C_4H_4N_2O_3$	43.9
$C_4H_4N_2O_3$, $2H_2O$	43.10
$C_4H_4N_2O_4$, H_2O	43.11
$C_4H_4N_2O_5$	43.12
$C_4H_4N_2O_5$, $3H_2O$	43.13
$C_4H_4N_4$	7.8
$C_4H_4N_6O$, H_2O	35.1
$C_4H_4O_3$	1.13+
$C_4H_4O_6^{2-}$, K^+, Na^+, $4H_2O$	2.27
$C_4H_4O_6^{2-}$, $2K^+$, $2H_2O$	2.28
$C_4H_4O_6^{2-}$, $2Rb^+$, $2H_2O$	2.29
$C_4H_5NO_2$	1.15
$C_4H_5N_3O$	44.2
$C_4H_5N_3O$	44.3
$C_4H_5N_3O$, H_2O	44.4
$C_4H_5O_3^-$, Na^+	2.30
$C_4H_6Br_2O_2$	38.2
$C_4H_6Cl_2N_2Zn$	83.6
$C_4H_6Cl_2O_2$	38.3
$C_4H_6Cl_2O_2$	38.7
$C_4H_6Cl_2O_2$	38.4+
$C_4H_6Cl_2S_2$	39.3
$C_4H_6Cl_4Cu_2N_2$	83.7
$C_4H_6Cl_6Cu_3N_2$	83.8
$C_4H_6CuN_6O_4^{2-}$, $2K^+$, $4H_2O$	83.9
$C_4H_6N_2O_2$	33.1
$C_4H_6N_2O_2$, $C_7H_9N_5$	44.21
$C_4H_6N_4O_3$	32.5
$C_4H_7NO_3$	48.6
$C_4H_8Cl_2HgS$	85.5
$C_4H_8Cl_4Se_2$	39.4
$C_4H_8Cl_8Si_4$	63.1
$C_4H_8CuN_2O_4$, H_2O	82.1+
$C_4H_8CuN_2O_4$, $2H_2O$	82.3
$C_4H_8I_2Se$	39.5
$C_4H_8I_4S_2$	39.6
$C_4H_8I_4Se_2$	39.7
$C_4H_8NOS^+$, Cl^-	48.7+
$C_4H_8NO_4^+$, Cl^-	48.9
$C_4H_8N_2O_2$	9.4
$C_4H_8N_2O_2$	10.7
$C_4H_8N_2O_3$, H_2O	48.10
$C_4H_8N_2S$	8.10
$C_4H_8N_2S$	8.11
$C_4H_8N_3O^+$, $C_{10}H_{13}N_2O^+$, O_4S^{2-}, H_2O	35.11
$C_4H_8N_8O_8$	34.1+
$8C_4H_8O$, $7.33H_2S$, $136H_2O$	61.2
$C_4H_8O_2$	1.16
$C_4H_8O_2$, N_2O_4	60.18

$C_4H_8O_2$, H_2O_4S	60.19
$C_4H_8O_2$, $C_2Br_2O_2$	60.11
$C_4H_8O_2$, $C_2Cl_2O_2$	60.12
$C_4H_8O_2$, C_2I_2	60.20
$C_4H_8O_2S_2$	39.8
$C_4H_8O_5$	38.8
$C_4H_8S_2$, CHI_3	60.21
$C_4H_8Se_2$, $2CHI_3$	60.4
$C_4H_8Se_2$, C_2I_4	60.22
C_4H_9NO, $3CH_6N_3^+$, $3Cl^-$	60.10
C_4H_9NO, C_8H_5I	60.23
$C_4H_9NO_3S$	48.11
$C_4H_{10}CdCl_2N_6O_4$	84.1
$C_4H_{10}CdN_4O_4S_2$	79.3
$C_4H_{10}ClHgS^+$, Cl^-, Cl_2Hg	85.6
$C_4H_{10}Cl_2N_6O_4Zn$	84.2
$C_4H_{10}HgS_2$	85.7
$C_4H_{10}Li_2$	67.1
$C_4H_{10}O$, $CHBrCl_2$	60.24
$4C_4H_{10}O$, Br_6Mg_4O	60.25
$C_4H_{10}O_6S_3$	11.10
$C_4H_{11}Cl_2NPt$	72.3
$C_4H_{12}As^+$, Br^-	65.4
$C_4H_{12}As_2S_2$	65.5
$C_4H_{12}B_2Cl_4N_2$	62.8
$C_4H_{12}B_4$	62.9
$C_4H_{12}CuN_2O_4$	81.10 +
$C_4H_{12}N^+$, $Ag_2I_3^-$	3.6
$C_4H_{12}N^+$, Br_3Hg^-	3.7
$C_4H_{12}N^+$, ClO_4^-	3.8
$C_4H_{12}N^+$, Cl_2I^-	3.9
$2C_4H_{12}N^+$, Cl_4Cu^{2-}	3.10
$2C_4H_{12}N^+$, $H_6B_6^{2-}$	3.11
$2C_4H_{12}N^+$, $C_8N_4NiS_4^{2-}$	85.11
$C_4H_{12}N_2^{2+}$, $2Cl^-$, H_2O	33.2
$C_4H_{12}N_2O_2S$	4.3
$C_4H_{12}Sb^+$, $C_{12}H_{36}AlO_4Si_4^-$	68.9
$C_4H_{13}MoN_3O_3$	76.2
$C_4H_{14}B_{10}Br_2$	62.10
$C_4H_{14}Cl_2MnN_2O_6$	82.4
$C_4H_{14}N_2^{2+}$, $2Cl^-$	3.12
$C_4H_{14}N_4O_4S_6Te$	70.1
$(C_4H_{14}N_4O_4Zn)_n$	81.12
$C_4H_{16}B_2N_2$	62.11
$C_4H_{16}ClN_4Ni^+$, Cl^-	76.3
$C_4H_{16}Cl_2CoN_4^+$, Cl^-, H_2O	76.4
$C_4H_{16}Cl_2CoN_4^+$, NO_3^-	76.5
$2C_4H_{16}Cl_2CoN_4^+$, O_6Se^{2-}, H_2O	76.6
$C_4H_{16}Cl_2CrN_4^+$, $2Cl^-$, $H_5O_2^+$	76.7
$C_4H_{16}Cl_2N_8NiS_4$	79.4
$C_4H_{16}CuN_4^{2+}$, $2NO_3^-$	76.8
$C_4H_{16}CuN_4^{2+}$, $2CNS^-$	76.9
$C_4H_{16}HgN_8S_4^{2+}$, $C_4CoN_4S_4^{2-}$	79.5
$C_4H_{16}N_5NiO_2^+$, BF_4^-	76.10
$C_4H_{16}N_5NiO_2^+$, ClO_4^-	76.11
$C_4H_{16}N_8PdS_4^{2+}$, $2Cl^-$	79.6
$C_4H_{16}N_8S_4Te^{2+}$, $2Cl^-$	70.2
$C_4H_{16}N_8S_4Te^{2+}$, $2Cl^-$, $2H_2O$	70.3
$C_4H_{18}FeN_2O_8^{2+}$, $H_{12}FeO_6^{2+}$, $2O_4S^{2-}$	82.5
$C_4H_{18}N_6Pt^{2+}$, $2Cl^-$, H_2O	83.10
$C_4H_{22}B_{20}$	62.12
$C_4H_{22}CuN_2O_6^{2+}$, O_4S^{2-}	84.3
$C_4H_{24}B_8N_2$	62.13
$C_4H_{24}B_{10}S_2$	62.14

C_5

$C_5F_{15}P_5$	64.4
$C_5O_5^{2-}$, $2H_4N^+$	6.2
$C_5H_2FN_2O_4^-$, Rb^+, H_2O	44.5
$C_5H_4N_4$	44.6 +
$C_5H_4O_2S$	39.9
$C_5H_4O_2S$	39.10 +
$C_5H_4O_2Se$	39.12
$C_5H_4O_3$	38.9
$C_5H_5CrNO_5$	83.11
$(C_5H_5In)_n$	68.3
$C_5H_5N_3O$	33.3

$C_5H_5N_3O_2$	33.4
C_5H_6	20.3
$C_5H_6BrN_3O$, $C_7H_9N_5O$	44.22
$(C_5H_6CuO_8)_n$	84.4
$C_5H_6N^+$, AsF_4O^-	33.5
$C_5H_6N^+$, Cl^-	33.6
$C_5H_6N^+$, NO_3^-	33.7
$C_5H_6N^+$, HBr_4Re^-	33.8 +
$C_5H_6N^+$, $C_{24}H_{16}CrN_4O_4^-$	83.39
$C_5H_6N^+$, $C_{32}H_{18}CrN_6O_8^-$, $0.5C_5H_5N$	83.45
$2C_5H_6N^+$, $2H^+$, $Cl_8Re_2^{4-}$	33.10
$C_5H_6NO^+$, Cl^-	33.11
$C_5H_6N_2O_2$	44.8
$C_5H_6N_2O_2$, H_2O	44.9
$C_5H_6N_5O^+$, Cl^-, $2H_2O$	44.10
$C_5H_6O_3$	38.10
$(C_5H_6O_8Zn)_n$	84.5
$C_5H_7N_2O_2^+$, Br^-	44.11
$C_5H_7N_3O$	44.12
$C_5H_8N_3O^+$, Br^-	44.13
$C_5H_8N_4O_{12}$	45.1
$C_5H_9NO_2$	48.12
$2C_5H_9O_6^-$, Ca^{2+}, $5H_2O$	45.2
$2C_5H_9O_6^-$, Sr^{2+}, $5H_2O$	45.3
$C_5H_9O_8P^{2-}$, Ba^{2+}, $5H_2O$	45.4
$(C_5H_{10}AuNS_2)_n$	80.1
$C_5H_{10}N_2OS$	41.5
$C_5H_{10}N_2O_4PbS$	69.3
$C_5H_{10}O_2$	1.17
$C_5H_{10}O_4$	45.5
$C_5H_{10}O_5$	45.6
$C_5H_{11}CuO_4^+$, $C_6H_2N_3O_7^-$	77.1
$C_5H_{11}N_2O_2^+$, ClO_4^-	48.13
$C_5H_{11}N_3^{2+}$, $2Cl^-$	59.1
$C_5H_{12}N^+$, Cl^-	33.12
$C_5H_{12}NOS^+$, $CH_4N_2O_2$, Cl^-	60.26
$C_5H_{12}NO_2^+$, Br^-	48.14
$C_5H_{12}NO_2^+$, Cl^-	48.15
$C_5H_{14}NO^+$, Cl^-	59.2

C_6

$C_6Br_4O_2$	18.1
C_6Br_6, $C_6H_2Br_4$	60.27
$C_6Cl_4O_2$	18.2 +
$C_6Cl_4O_2$, $C_{12}H_{18}$	60.28
$C_6Cl_4O_2$, $C_{18}H_{12}N_2O_2Pd$	60.29
C_6Cl_6	19.1
$C_6F_4O_2$, $C_{20}H_{12}$	60.52
C_6N_4	7.9
$C_6N_6O_6$, $C_{12}H_{12}S_2$	60.30
C_6HCl_5O	17.1
$C_6H_2Br_4$	19.2 +
$C_6H_2Br_4$, C_6Br_6	60.27
$C_6H_2Cl_4O_2$	17.2
$C_6H_2N_3O_7^-$, $C_5H_{11}CuO_4^+$	77.1
$C_6H_2N_4O_4^{2-}$, $2Rb^+$, $2H_2O$	35.2
$2C_6H_2N_6O_6$, $C_{18}H_{12}CuN_2O_2$	60.31
$C_6H_2O_8^{2-}$, $2K^+$	2.31
$C_6H_3BrN_2O_4$	15.1
$C_6H_3Br_3$	19.4
$C_6H_3ClN_2O_2$	40.1
$C_6H_3ClN_2O_4$	15.2
$C_6H_3Cl_3$	19.5 +
$C_6H_3N_3O_6$, C_8H_7N	60.37
$C_6H_3N_3O_6$, C_9H_9N	60.40
$C_6H_3N_3O_6$, $C_{10}H_8$	60.43 +
$C_6H_3N_3O_6$, $C_{14}H_{10}$	60.48 +
$C_6H_4As_2Cl_2O$	65.6
$C_6H_4BrNO_2$	15.3
$C_6H_4ClNO_2$	15.4
$C_6H_4ClNO_2$	15.5
$C_6H_4Cl_2$	19.7
$C_6H_4NO_3^-$, K^+, $0.5H_2O$	6.3
$C_6H_4N_2O_4$	15.6
$C_6H_4N_4O_2$	9.5
$C_6H_4O_2$	18.4 +
$C_6H_4O_5$	38.11
$C_6H_4O_6$, $2H_2O$	18.6

C_6H_5BrHg	71.2
$C_6H_5ClN_2O_2$	16.1
$C_6H_5Cl_2N$	16.2
$C_6H_5NO_3$	17.3 +
$C_6H_5N_2^+$, Br_3^-	9.6
$C_6H_5N_2^+$, $Br_3Cu_2^-$	9.7
$C_6H_5N_2^+$, Cl^-	9.8
$C_6H_5O_4P^{2-}$, Ba^{2+}, $1.5H_2O$	46.4
$C_6H_5O_6^-$, K^+	2.32
$2C_6H_5O_7^{3-}$, $3Mg^{2+}$, $10H_2O$	2.33
C_6H_6	19.8 +
C_6H_6, Al_2Br_6	60.32
$C_6H_6Br_2N_4$	35.3
$C_6H_6MoS_6$	85.8
$C_6H_6NO_2^+$, Cl^-	33.13
$C_6H_6N_2O_2$	16.3
$C_6H_6N_6O_6$	15.7
C_6H_6O	17.5
C_6H_6O, $0.5H_2O$	17.6
$C_6H_6O_2$	17.7
$C_6H_6O_3$	17.8
$C_6H_7AsO_3$	65.7 +
$C_6H_7I_2N$	33.14
$C_6H_7NO_3S$	16.4
$C_6H_7NO_3S$, H_2O	16.5
$C_6H_7N_3O_3$	44.14
$C_6H_7N_5$	44.15
$C_6H_7N_5$, $C_6H_8N_2O_2$	44.17
$C_6H_7O_7^-$, Li^+	2.34
$C_6H_7O_7^-$, Na^+	2.35
$C_6H_7O_7^-$, Rb^+	2.36
$C_6H_8AsNO_3$	65.9
$(C_6H_8Br_2N_2Ni)_n$	83.12
$C_6H_8N^+$, Br^-	16.6
$C_6H_8NO^+$, Cl^-	17.9
$C_6H_8NO^+$, Cl^-	33.15
$C_6H_8NO_2^+$, Cl^-	17.10
$C_6H_8N_2O_2$	44.16
$C_6H_8N_2O_2$, $C_6H_7N_5$	44.17
$C_6H_8N_2O_2S$	16.7 +
$C_6H_8N_5O^+$, Br^-	44.18
$C_6H_8O_2$	21.1 +
$C_6H_8O_2$, C_2I_2	60.34
$(C_6H_8O_2)_n$, $(Cl_2Hg)_n$	60.33
$C_6H_8O_4S_2$	39.13
$C_6H_8O_4Se_2$	39.14
$C_6H_9N_2^+$, Cl^-	9.9
$C_6H_9N_3O^{2+}$, $2Cl^-$	33.16 +
$C_6H_9N_5^{2+}$, $2Br^-$	44.19
$C_6H_9O_3PS$	64.5
$C_6H_9O_7^-$, K^+, $2H_2O$	45.7
$C_6H_9O_7^-$, Rb^+, $2H_2O$	45.8
$2C_6H_9O_7^-$, Ca^{2+}, $2H_2O$	45.9
$(C_6H_{10}ClCuN_3O_4)_{2n}$, $3nH_2O$	82.6
$C_6H_{10}Cl_2$	21.3
$C_6H_{10}Cl_2Pd_2$	72.4 +
$C_6H_{10}N_2^{2+}$, $2Cl^-$	33.18
$C_6H_{10}N_3O_2^+$, Cl^-, H_2O	48.16
$C_6H_{10}NiO_2S_4$	80.2
$C_6H_{10}O_4$	1.18
$C_6H_{11}NO_4S_2$	4.4
$C_6H_{11}O_9P^{2-}$, $2K^+$, $2H_2O$	45.10
$C_6H_{12}Br_2N_4S_2Te$	70.4
$C_6H_{12}CoN_3OS_4$	80.3
$C_6H_{12}I_2N_4S_2Te$	70.5
$C_6H_{12}N_2$	37.1 +
$C_6H_{12}N_2S_4$	4.5
$C_6H_{12}N_4$	37.4 +
$C_6H_{12}N_4$, $6H_2O$	61.3
$C_6H_{12}N_8NiO_8^{2-}$, $2K^+$, $4H_2O$	83.13
$C_6H_{12}O_6$	21.4
$C_6H_{12}O_6$	45.11
$C_6H_{12}O_6$	45.12
$C_6H_{12}O_6$, H_2O	45.13
$C_6H_{12}O_6$, $2H_2O$	21.5
C_6H_{14}	5.3
$C_6H_{14}NO_4^+$, Cl^-	45.14
$C_6H_{14}NO_5^+$, Br^-	45.15
$C_6H_{14}N_2O_4S_2^{2+}$, $2Br^-$	48.17 +
$C_6H_{14}N_4O_2$, $2H_2O$	48.19
$C_6H_{15}N_2O_2^+$, Cl^-, $2H_2O$	48.20
$C_6H_{15}PSe$	64.6

$C_6H_{16}Cl_{10}Cu_5O_2$	84.6
$C_6H_{16}CuN_2O_6$, $4H_2O$	82.7
$C_6H_{16}N^+$, Cl^-	3.13
$C_6H_{16}N^+$, $C_{11}HFe_3O_{11}^-$	3.14
$C_6H_{16}N_2NiO_6$	82.8
$C_6H_{16}N_4NiO_4$	76.12
$C_6H_{16}N_6NiS_2$	76.13
$C_6H_{18}CoO_2P_2^{2+}$, $2NO_3^-$	84.7
$C_6H_{18}N_2^{2+}$, $2I^-$	3.15
$C_6H_{19}AlN_2$	68.4
$C_6H_{20}Cl_2CoN_4^+$, $2Cl^-$, $H_5O_2^+$	76.14
$C_6H_{21}AlN_2$	68.5
$C_6H_{21}N_4^{3+}$, $3Cl^-$	3.16
$C_6H_{24}B_3N_3$	62.15
$C_6H_{24}CoN_6^{3+}$, $3Br^-$, H_2O	76.15
$C_6H_{24}N_6Ni^{2+}$, $2NO_3^-$	76.16
$C_6H_{24}N_{12}S_6Te_2^{4+}$, $4HF_2^-$	70.6

C₇

$C_7H_3FeNO_4$	72.8
$C_7H_4ClNO_4$	13.1
$C_7H_4ClO_2^-$, $C_7H_5ClO_2$, K^+	14.1
$C_7H_4CrO_3S$	75.1
C_7H_4IN	7.10
$C_7H_4NO_4^-$, $C_7H_5NO_4$, Rb^+	14.2
$C_7H_4O_4^-$, $C_7H_5NO_4$, K^+	14.3
$C_7H_5BrO_2$	13.2
$C_7H_5Br_2NO_2$	13.3+
$C_7H_5ClO_2$	13.5
$C_7H_5ClO_2$, $C_7H_4ClO_2^-$, K^+	14.1
$C_7H_5ClO_2^-$, $C_2H_6N_2S^+$	8.7
$C_7H_5IO_3$	42.1
$C_7H_5NO_3$	15.8+
$C_7H_5NO_4$, $C_7H_4NO_4^-$, Rb^+	14.2
$C_7H_5NO_4$, $C_7H_4O_4^-$, K^+	14.3
$C_7H_5NO_5$	13.6
$C_7H_5O_2^-$, Na^+	22.1
$C_7H_5O_2^-$, $C_{16}H_{36}N^+$, $39.5H_2O$	61.7
C_7H_6ClNO	10.8
C_7H_6ClNO	10.9
$C_7H_6ClNO_2$	10.10
$C_7H_6ClNO_2$	18.7
C_7H_6FNO	13.7
C_7H_6FNO	13.8
$C_7H_6FeO_3$	72.9
$C_7H_6N_2S$	16.10
$C_7H_6O_3$	13.9
$2C_7H_7NO$, HI_3	60.35
$C_7H_7NO_2$	13.10
$C_7H_7NO_3S$	15.10
$C_7H_7N_2O^+$, Cl_4Fe^-	9.10
$C_7H_8Cl_2Pd$	75.2+
$C_7H_8N_2O_3$	44.20
$C_7H_8OS_2$	39.15
$C_7H_8O_2S$	11.11
$C_7H_8S_3$	39.16
C_7H_9N	16.11
C_7H_9N , CH_4N_2O	60.36
$C_7H_9N_5$, $C_4H_6N_2O_2$	44.21
$C_7H_9N_5O$, $C_5H_6BrN_3O$	44.22
$C_7H_9O_2^+$, Br^- , H_2O	38.12
$C_7H_{13}BrO_5$	45.16
$C_7H_{13}N_2O_2^+$, Br^-	32.6
$C_7H_{14}N_2O_2$	1.19
$C_7H_{15}PS_2$	64.7
C_7H_{16}	5.4
$C_7H_{18}B_9Fe$	73.1
$C_7H_{16}N^+$, Br^-	34.3
$C_7H_{16}O$, $0.5H_2O$	5.5
$C_7H_{18}N^+$, Cl^-	3.17

C₈

$C_8CoN_4S_4^{2-}$, $2C_{16}H_{36}N^+$	85.9
$C_8CuN_4S_4^-$, $C_{16}H_{36}N^+$	85.10
C_8F_{12}	31.1
$C_8N_4NiS_4^{2-}$, $2C_4H_{12}N^+$	85.11

$C_8N_4S_2$	39.17
$C_8O_{16}Zr^{4-}$, $4Na^+$, $3H_2O$	81.13
$C_8HBrN_4O_5S$	39.18
$C_8H_5BrN_2O_2$	40.2
$C_8H_5F_5IORh$	73.2
C_8H_5I , C_4H_9NO	60.23
$C_8H_5MnO_3$	73.3
$C_8H_5N_3$	33.19
$C_8H_5O_4^-$, K^+	14.4
$C_8H_6Br_2N_2O_5$	28.1
$C_8H_6Br_4$	19.10
$C_8H_6ClNO_3$	18.8
$C_8H_6ClNO_3$	18.9
$C_8H_6N_2$, $2H_2O$	35.4
$C_8H_6N_4O_4^{2-}$, $2Rb^+$, $2H_2O$	35.5
$C_8H_6N_4O_8$, $2H_2O$	43.14
$C_8H_7BrO_2$	22.2
$C_8H_7BrO_2$	22.3
C_8H_7N , $C_6H_3N_3O_6$	60.37
$C_8H_7NS_2$	41.6
$C_8H_7NS_2$	41.7
$C_8H_7O_2^-$, $C_8H_8O_2$, K^+	2.37+
C_8H_8	31.2
C_8H_8ClCu	75.4
C_8H_8ClNO	10.11
$C_8H_8ClNO_3$	18.10
$C_8H_8Cl_2N_2O_2$	16.12
$C_8H_8O_2$	18.11
$C_8H_8O_2$, $C_8H_7O_2^-$, K^+	2.37+
$C_8H_8O_{12}Sb_2^{2-}$, $2H_4N^+$, $4H_2O$	66.2
$C_8H_8S_2$	39.19
C_8H_9NO	13.11
$C_8H_9NO_2$	13.12+
C_8H_{10}	20.4
C_8H_{10} , CBr_4	60.1
$C_8H_{10}CuN_4O_5^{2-}$, $2Na^+$, $10H_2O$	82.9
$C_8H_{10}N_2O_2$	16.13
$C_8H_{10}O$	17.11
$2C_8H_{11}IN^+$, Cl^- , I_3^-	60.38+
$C_8H_{11}N_2O_3^-$, K^+	43.15
$C_8H_{11}N_2O_3^-$, Na^+	43.16
$C_8H_{11}S^+$, ClO_4^-	11.12
$(C_8H_{12}CdN_6S_4)_n$	79.7
$(C_8H_{12}Cl_4Hg_2S_2)_n$	85.12
$C_8H_{12}Mo_2O_8$	81.14
$C_8H_{12}N^+$, Cl^-	3.18
$C_8H_{12}O_8Pb$	69.4
$(C_8H_{12}O_8U)_n$	81.15
$C_8H_{13}N_2O_2^+$, Br^- , H_2O	20.5
$C_8H_{13}O_3^-$, Na^+	2.39
$C_8H_{14}ClNSn$	69.5
$C_8H_{14}NO^+$, Cl^-	40.3
$C_8H_{14}N_2NiS_2$	85.13
$C_8H_{14}Ni$	72.10
$C_8H_{14}O_4$	1.20
$2C_8H_{15}O_2^-$, Sr^{2+} , xH_2O	2.40
$C_8H_{16}Cl_2Rh_2$	72.11
$C_8H_{16}Cl_4MnO_8P_2$	84.8
$C_8H_{16}Cl_4S_2Sn$	69.6
$C_8H_{16}N^+$, Br^-	37.10
$C_8H_{16}NO_2^+$, Br^-	21.6
$C_8H_{16}N_2O^{2+}$, $2Cl^-$	58.1
$C_8H_{16}N_2O_2$	32.7
$C_8H_{18}HgS_2$	85.14
$C_8H_{18}N_2O_2$	10.12
$C_8H_{20}AlLi$	68.6
$C_8H_{20}ClCuN_4S_4$	85.15
$C_8H_{20}CoN_6O_4^+$, NO_3^-	83.14
$C_8H_{20}CoS_4^{2+}$, $2ClO_4^-$	85.16
$C_8H_{20}CuN_2O_6$	83.15
$C_8H_{20}N^+$, $H_2Br_4O_2Re^-$	3.19
$2C_8H_{20}N^+$, $Br_6Pt_2^{2-}$	3.20
$C_8H_{20}NO_6P$, $CdCl_2$, $3H_2O$	46.5
$C_8H_{20}N_2NiO_6$, $2H_2O$	82.10
$C_8H_{20}NiO_4P_2S_4$	85.17
$C_8H_{20}P_2S_2$	64.8
$C_8H_{22}Be_2^{2-}$, $2C_4H_{10}NaO^+$	67.2
$C_8H_{24}N_4P_4$	64.9
$C_8H_{24}N_6NiO_4$	76.17
$C_8H_{24}O_2Si_4$	63.2
$C_8H_{24}O_{12}Si_8$	63.3

$C_8H_{28}Cl_2N_4Pt^{2+}$, $C_8H_{28}N_4Pt^{2+}$, $4Cl^-$, $4H_2O$	83.16
$C_8H_{28}N_4Pt^{2+}$, $C_8H_{28}Cl_2N_4Pt^{2+}$, $4Cl^-$, $4H_2O$	83.16
$C_8H_{28}N_4Si_4$	63.4
$C_8H_{32}B_4P_4$	62.16
$C_8H_{34}Co_2N_{10}O_2^{4+}$, $4NO_3^-$	76.18+

C₉

$C_9H_4O_3$	27.1
C_9H_5BrO	19.11
$C_9H_5BrO_3$, H_2O	38.13
$C_9H_5NbO_4$	73.4
$C_9H_6CrO_3$	74.1+
$C_9H_6NO_2S^-$, Na^+	41.8
$3C_9H_7N$, CHI_3	60.3
$C_9H_7O_2^-$, $C_9H_8O_2$, H_4N^+	2.41
$C_9H_7S_2^+$, I^-	39.20
$C_9H_8N^+$, Cl^-	35.6
$C_9H_8N^+$, Cl^- , H_2O	35.7
$C_9H_8O_2$	22.4
$C_9H_8O_2$, $C_9H_7O_2^-$, H_4N^+	2.41
$C_9H_8O_4$	13.14
$C_9H_9Cl_3O_3$	38.14
C_9H_9N , $C_6H_3N_3O_6$	60.40
$C_9H_{11}BrN_2O_6$, $C_{10}H_{13}N_5O_4$, H_2O	47.8
$C_9H_{11}FN_2O_5$	47.1
$C_9H_{11}IN_2O_5$	47.2
$C_9H_{11}NO_3$	18.12
$C_9H_{11}NS$	4.6
$C_9H_{11}N_2O_9P^{2-}$, Ba^{2+} , $8.9H_2O$	47.3
$C_9H_{11}N_3OS_4$	41.9
C_9H_{12}	23.1
$C_9H_{12}BrN_3O_4$, $C_{10}H_{13}N_5O_4$	47.9
$C_9H_{12}NO_2^+$, Cl^-	48.21+
$C_9H_{12}N_2OS_3$	41.10
$C_9H_{12}N_4O$	44.23
$C_9H_{12}N_4O_3$	44.24+
$C_9H_{12}N_4O_3$, $C_{16}H_{10}$	60.41
$2C_9H_{12}N_4O_3$, $C_{24}H_{12}$	60.42
$C_9H_{12}O_4S_3$	39.21
$C_9H_{13}BrO$	31.3
$C_9H_{13}ClO$	31.4
$C_9H_{13}N_3O_5$	47.4
$C_9H_{13}Rh$	72.12
$C_9H_{14}N_2O$	33.20
$C_9H_{14}N_3O_8P$	47.5
$C_9H_{14}N_5^+$, Cl^-	35.8
$C_9H_{15}AsO_3S_6$	65.10
$C_9H_{15}O_3S_6Sb$	66.3
$C_9H_{17}O_{10}S^-$, Rb^+	45.17
$C_9H_{18}N^+$, I^-	35.9
$C_9H_{18}O_3$	1.21
$C_9H_{20}N^+$, Br^-	23.2
$C_9H_{20}N_2O$	9.11
$C_9H_{21}N_4^{3+}$, $3Cl^-$, $0.5H_2O$	36.1

C₁₀

$C_{10}Cl_8$	20.6
$C_{10}Cl_8$	24.1
$C_{10}N_6^{2-}$, Ba^{2+} , $6H_2O$	67.3
$C_{10}H_2O_6$, $C_{14}H_{10}$	60.50
$C_{10}H_2O_6$, $C_{20}H_{12}$	60.53
$C_{10}H_4Br_2Cl_2$	24.2
$C_{10}H_4Cl_2O_2$	25.1
$C_{10}H_4Cl_4$	24.3+
$C_{10}H_5BrO_2$	25.2
$C_{10}H_5Br_2N$	36.2
$C_{10}H_5ClO_3$	25.3
$C_{10}H_6ClNO_2$	25.4
$C_{10}H_6Cl_2$	24.5
$C_{10}H_6Cl_2O$	20.7
$C_{10}H_6FeO_4$	75.5
$C_{10}H_6N_2O_4$	24.6
$C_{10}H_6N_2O_4$	24.7

$C_{10}H_6O_2$ 20.8
$C_{10}H_6O_2$ 25.5
$C_{10}H_6O_4$ 25.6 +
$C_{10}H_6O_4^{2-}$, Ca^{2+} , $2H_2O$ 22.5
$C_{10}H_7HgI$ 71.3
$C_{10}H_8$ 27.2 +
$C_{10}H_8$, $C_6H_3N_3O_6$ 60.43 +
$C_{10}H_8BrNO_2$ 1.22
$C_{10}H_8Cl_2FeO_4S_2$ 73.5
$C_{10}H_8MoO_3$ 75.6
$C_{10}H_8O$ 24.8
$C_{10}H_8O_3V$ 75.7
$2C_{10}H_8O_4P^-$, Ca^{2+} , $3H_2O$ 46.6
$C_{10}H_9BrO_2$ 1.23
$C_{10}H_9BrO_2$ 1.24
$C_{10}H_9NO_2$ 35.10
$C_{10}H_{10}Br_2CuN_2$ 83.17
$C_{10}H_{10}CdCl_2N_2$ 83.18
$C_{10}H_{10}Cl_2Pt$ 73.6
$C_{10}H_{10}Cl_4Cu_2N_2O_2$ 84.9
$C_{10}H_{10}Cl_4OTi_2$ 73.7
$C_{10}H_{10}Co^+$, ClO_4^- 73.8
$C_{10}H_{10}Fe$ 73.9
$C_{10}H_{10}Fe_2O_6S_2$ 85.18
$C_{10}H_{10}IN_2^+$, I_3^- , $2I_2$ 60.45
$C_{10}H_{10}MoO_3$ 73.10
$C_{10}H_{10}N_2^{2+}$, $2Br^-$ 33.21
$C_{10}H_{10}O_2$ 20.9
$C_{10}H_{12}ClN_5O$, H_2O 32.8
$C_{10}H_{12}Mo$ 73.11
$C_{10}H_{12}N_2OS_3$ 41.11
$2C_{10}H_{12}O$, $HClO_4$ 60.46
$C_{10}H_{12}O_2$ 20.10
$C_{10}H_{12}O_2$ 28.2
$C_{10}H_{12}O_6$ 21.7 +
$C_{10}H_{13}Br$ 19.12 +
$C_{10}H_{13}BrO_4$ 59.3
$C_{10}H_{13}ClN_5^+$, I^- 44.26
$C_{10}H_{13}N_2O^+$, $C_4H_8N_3O^+$, O_4S^{2-} , H_2O 35.11
$C_{10}H_{13}N_2O_8P^{2-}$, Ca^{2+} , $6H_2O$ 47.6
$C_{10}H_{13}N_5O_3$, H_2O 47.7
$C_{10}H_{13}N_5O_4$, $C_9H_{11}BrN_2O_6$, H_2O 47.8
$C_{10}H_{13}N_5O_4$, $C_9H_{12}BrN_3O_4$ 47.9
$C_{10}H_{14}BeO_4$ 67.4
$C_{10}H_{14}CuN_2O_2^{2+}$, O_4S^{2-} 83.19
$C_{10}H_{14}FeN_2O_9^-$, Li^+ , $2H_2O$ 76.20
$C_{10}H_{14}FeN_2O_9^-$, Rb^+ , H_2O 76.21
$C_{10}H_{14}N_5O_7P$, H_2O 47.10
$C_{10}H_{14}O_5V$ 77.2 +
$C_{10}H_{15}BrClNO$ 52.1
$C_{10}H_{15}CoN_5^+$, ClO_4^- 72.13
$C_{10}H_{15}CrN_2O_9$ 76.22
$C_{10}H_{15}FeN_2O_9$ 76.23
$C_{10}H_{15}GaN_2O_9$ 68.7
$C_{10}H_{16}$ 31.5 +
$C_{10}H_{16}BrNO_2$ 52.2
$C_{10}H_{16}Br_2O_2$ 21.9
$C_{10}H_{16}Br_2O$ 52.3
$C_{10}H_{16}Cl_2Pt$ 75.8
$C_{10}H_{16}N_2$, $C_{12}H_4N_4$ 60.47
$C_{10}H_{16}N_2^{2+}$, $2I^-$ 58.2
$C_{10}H_{16}N_2O_8$ 1.25
$C_{10}H_{16}O_2$ 52.4
$C_{10}H_{16}O_2$ 52.5
$C_{10}H_{16}O_5Zn$ 77.4 +
$C_{10}H_{17}BrO$ 21.10
$C_{10}H_{18}Br_2$ 23.3
$(C_{10}H_{18}CdO_2S_4)_n$ 80.4
$C_{10}H_{18}CuN_4O_4$ 83.20
$C_{10}H_{18}KLaN_2O_{11}$, $5H_2O$ 76.24
$C_{10}H_{18}N_4NiO_4$ 83.21
$C_{10}H_{18}NiO_6$ 77.6
$C_{10}H_{20}CuN_2S_4$ 80.5
$C_{10}H_{20}N^+$, I^- 35.12
$C_{10}H_{20}N_2NiS_4$ 80.6
$C_{10}H_{21}AgNPS$ 85.19
$C_{10}H_{21}LaN_2O_{12}$, $3H_2O$ 76.25
$C_{10}H_{22}N^+$, Cl^- , $1.5H_2O$ 23.4
$C_{10}H_{24}ClN_4Ni^+$, Cl^- 83.22

$C_{10}H_{24}N_2^{2+}$, $2Cl^-$ 23.5
$C_{10}H_{24}N_2^{2+}$, $2Cl^-$, $2H_2O$ 23.6
$C_{10}H_{30}N_2Si_4$ 63.5
$C_{10}H_{30}N_4^{4+}$, $2HO_4P^{2-}$, $6H_2O$ 59.4

C_{11}

$C_{11}H_7ClO_2$ 25.10
$C_{11}H_7NO$ 36.3
$C_{11}H_8FeO_3$ 75.9
$C_{11}H_8O_2$ 24.9
$C_{11}H_8O_2$ 24.10
$C_{11}H_8O_2$ 28.3
$C_{11}H_8O_3$ 25.11
$C_{11}H_9ClN_2O_3$ 40.4
$C_{11}H_9FeO_3^+$, BF_4^- 75.10
$C_{11}H_{10}CrO_3$ 75.11
$C_{11}H_{10}N_2O_2S$ 41.12
$C_{11}H_{10}N_2O_3$ 40.5
$C_{11}H_{15}BrN_2O_4$ 45.18
$C_{11}H_{15}BrN_2O_4$ 45.19
$C_{11}H_{15}BrN_3O_7^+$, Br^- 58.3
$C_{11}H_{21}BrO_2$ 1.26
$C_{11}H_{22}O_2S$ 1.27
$C_{11}H_{24}N^+$, Cl^- 34.4
$C_{11}H_{27}As_3Ni^{2+}$, $2Br^-$ 86.1
$C_{11}H_{28}N_2^{2+}$, $2I^-$, $0.25H_2O$ 3.21

C_{12}

$C_{12}H_4Cl_4N_2$ 36.4
$C_{12}H_4Cl_4N_2$ 36.5
$C_{12}H_4N_4$ 7.11
$C_{12}H_4N_4$, $C_{10}H_{16}N_2$ 60.47
$C_{12}H_6Fe_2O_6$ 72.14
$C_{12}H_6Fe_2O_6$ 73.12
$C_{12}H_6Fe_2O_8$ 72.15
$C_{12}H_6O_2$ 28.4
$C_{12}H_6O_{12}$ 13.15
$C_{12}H_8BrCl$ 28.5
$C_{12}H_8Br_2$ 28.6
$C_{12}H_8Cl_2$ 28.7
$C_{12}H_8Cl_2I_2Te$ 70.7
$C_{12}H_8Cl_2O_2S$ 11.13 +
$C_{12}H_8CrN_2O_5$ 83.23
$C_{12}H_8Fe_2O_8$ 72.16
$C_{12}H_8N_2O$ 36.6
$C_{12}H_8N_2O_2$ 33.22
$C_{12}H_8N_2O_2$ 36.7 +
$C_{12}H_8N_2O_4$ 15.11
$C_{12}H_8N_2O_6$ 28.8
$C_{12}H_8N_4$ 36.9
$C_{12}H_8O_6Os_2$ 72.17
$C_{12}H_9AsClN$ 65.11
$C_{12}H_9Br_2N_3$ 9.12
$C_{12}H_9Br_2N_3$ 9.13
$C_{12}H_9Cl_2N$ 16.14
$C_{12}H_9Cl_2O_4P$ 46.7
$C_{12}H_{10}$ 19.14 +
$C_{12}H_{10}AsBr$ 65.12
$C_{12}H_{10}AsCl$ 65.13
$C_{12}H_{10}AsI$ 65.14
$C_{12}H_{10}Cl_4N_3P_3$ 64.10
$C_{12}H_{10}CoN_4S_2$ 83.24
$C_{12}H_{10}CuN_4O_4$ 84.10
$C_{12}H_{10}Hg$ 71.4
$C_{12}H_{10}I^+$, BF_4^- 19.17
$C_{12}H_{10}N_2O_2$ 33.23
$C_{12}H_{10}O_2$ 28.9
$C_{12}H_{10}O_2$ 31.7
$C_{12}H_{10}O_4$ 17.12
$C_{12}H_{10}Sn$, $0.33C_8H_{10}$ 69.7
$C_{12}H_{11}Br$ 24.11
$C_{12}H_{12}$ 24.12
$C_{12}H_{12}BrNO_8S$ 45.20
$C_{12}H_{12}Br_6$ 19.18
$C_{12}H_{12}Cr$ 74.3 +
$(C_{12}H_{12}Cu_2N_8)_n$ 83.25

$C_{12}H_{12}S_2$, $C_6N_6O_6$ 60.30
$C_{12}H_{12}V$ 75.12
$C_{12}H_{14}INO_2S$ 35.13
$C_{12}H_{14}N_2O_2$ 37.11
$C_{12}H_{16}Cu_2N_6O_8^{2-}$, $2Na^+$, $2H_2O$ 82.11
$C_{12}H_{16}N_6O_4Zn$, $2H_2O$ 82.12
$C_{12}H_{16}N_6O_4Zn$, $5H_2O$ 82.13
$C_{12}H_{17}BrN_2O_5$ 45.21
$C_{12}H_{18}$, $C_6Cl_4O_2$ 60.28
$C_{12}H_{18}CuN_2O_2$ 83.26
$C_{12}H_{18}CuO_6$ 77.7
$C_{12}H_{18}N_4OS^{2+}$, $2Cl^-$, H_2O 41.13
$C_{12}H_{18}N_6O_6$, $0.5H_2O$ 48.23
$C_{12}H_{19}Cl_2NPt$ 72.18
$C_{12}H_{20}$ 21.11
$C_{12}H_{20}CuN_2O_4$ 83.27
$C_{12}H_{20}Mo_2O_7S_8$ 80.7
$C_{12}H_{22}O_{11}$ 45.22
$C_{12}H_{22}O_{11}$ 45.23
$C_{12}H_{23}N_3O_5^{2+}$, $2Cl^-$ 58.4
$C_{12}H_{24}$ 23.7
$C_{12}H_{24}Cr_3O_{16}^+$, Cl^- , $5H_2O$ 81.16
$C_{12}H_{24}N_2O_2$ 1.28 +
$C_{12}H_{24}O_2$ 1.30
$C_{12}H_{27}S^+$, F^- , $20H_2O$ 61.4
$C_{12}H_{27}S^+$, F^- , $23H_2O$ 61.5
$C_{12}H_{28}CuN_4^{2+}$, $2NO_3^-$ 83.28
$C_{12}H_{28}N_2^{2+}$, $2Br^-$ 34.5
$C_{12}H_{30}AlF^-$, K^+ 68.8
$C_{12}H_{30}B_3N_3$ 62.17
$C_{12}H_{30}N_2^{2+}$, $2Br^-$, $2H_2O$ 3.22
$C_{12}H_{30}N_2O_{16}P_2U$ 84.11
$C_{12}H_{31}BrP_2Pt$ 86.2
$C_{12}H_{36}AlO_4Si_4^-$, $C_4H_{12}Sb^+$ 68.9

C_{13}

$C_{13}H_9Br_3O$ 20.11
$C_{13}H_9N$ 36.10
$C_{13}H_{10}ClNO$ 16.15
$C_{13}H_{10}ClNO$ 16.16 +
$C_{13}H_{10}O_2S$, H_2O 17.13
$C_{13}H_{11}O_2P$ 64.11
$C_{13}H_{12}BrNO_2$ 33.24
$C_{13}H_{12}FeO$ 73.13
$C_{13}H_{14}INO_2$ 33.25
$C_{13}H_{14}N_2O$ 33.26
$C_{13}H_{16}NO_2^+$, Br^- , $2H_2O$ 58.5
$C_{13}H_{17}N_3O_4$, $0.5H_2O$ 48.24
$C_{13}H_{20}N_2OS_2$ 8.12
$C_{13}H_{28}N^+$, I^- 52.6

C_{14}

$C_{14}H_5CoF_{12}O$ 73.14
$C_{14}H_6Br_2O_2$ 26.1
$C_{14}H_6I_2O_2$ 26.2
$C_{14}H_8BrCl$ 26.3
$C_{14}H_8Br_2O$ 26.4
$C_{14}H_8Br_2O_3$ 13.16
$C_{14}H_8Fe_2O_6$ 75.13
$C_{14}H_8O_2$ 26.5
$C_{14}H_8O_4$ 26.6
$C_{14}H_9NO_2$ 40.6
$C_{14}H_{10}$ 26.7 +
$C_{14}H_{10}$ 28.10 +
$C_{14}H_{10}$, $C_6H_3N_3O_6$ 60.48 +
$C_{14}H_{10}$, $C_{10}H_2O_6$ 60.50
$C_{14}H_{10}Cl_2CuN_2O_4$ 78.1
$C_{14}H_{10}CuO_4$ 78.2 +
$C_{14}H_{10}CuO_4$ 84.12
$C_{14}H_{10}CuO_4$, $3H_2O$ 81.17
$C_{14}H_{10}N_2S$ 41.14
$C_{14}H_{10}O$ 26.9
$C_{14}H_{10}O_2$ 19.19
$C_{14}H_{12}$ 29.1
$C_{14}H_{12}CuN_2O_4$ 78.5

C_{22}

$C_{22}H_{10}$	5.8
$C_{22}H_{14}$	30.4
$C_{22}H_{15}AuCoO_4P$	86.9
$C_{22}H_{16}$	30.5
$C_{22}H_{20}O_4$	29.18 +
$C_{22}H_{22}CuO_4$	77.16
$C_{22}H_{22}Cu_2N_2O_4$	83.38
$C_{22}H_{23}As_3CuMnO_5$	86.10
$C_{22}H_{24}ClN_2O_8^+$, Cl^-	50.10
$C_{22}H_{25}N_2O_9^+$, Cl^-	50.11
$C_{22}H_{25}O_6^+$, Cl_4Fe^-	59.13
$C_{22}H_{27}N_2O_3^+$, I^-	58.23
$C_{22}H_{27}N_2O_3^+$, I^-, H_2O	58.24
$C_{22}H_{27}N_2O_4^+$, Br^-, H_2O	58.25
$C_{22}H_{28}N_2O_2Pd$	78.13
$C_{22}H_{28}N_4^{2+}$, $2Br^-$	58.26
$C_{22}H_{28}N_4^{2+}$, $2Br^-$, $2H_2O$	58.27
$C_{22}H_{29}N_2O_4^+$, I^-	58.28
$C_{22}H_{29}N_2O_4^+$, CH_4O, Br^-	58.29
$C_{22}H_{31}N_2O^+$, I^-	58.30
$C_{22}H_{33}BrO_6S$	53.14
$C_{22}H_{34}NO_5^+$, Br^-, H_2O	58.31
$C_{22}H_{36}NO_2^+$, Br^-, H_2O	58.32
$C_{22}H_{38}O_4Zn$	77.17

C_{23}

$C_{23}H_{15}GeMnO_5$	69.9
$C_{23}H_{22}N_2OS_2$	41.16
$C_{23}H_{24}Br_2N_4O_3S$	59.14
$C_{23}H_{31}N_2O_4^+$, I^-	58.33
$C_{23}H_{33}N_2O_2^+$, I^-	58.34

C_{24}

$C_{24}H_{12}$	30.6
$C_{24}H_{12}$, $2C_9H_{12}N_4O_3$	60.42
$C_{24}H_{16}CrN_4O_4^-$, $C_5H_6N^+$	83.39
$C_{24}H_{16}N_2O_2$	40.7
$C_{24}H_{20}As_2O$	65.17
$C_{24}H_{20}B^-$, Rb^+	62.18
$(C_{24}H_{20}Cl_4Pb_2)_n$	69.10
$C_{24}H_{20}CuN_2O_2$	78.14
$C_{24}H_{20}Cu_2N_6$	83.40
$C_{24}H_{20}N_6O_2Pd$	83.41
$C_{24}H_{26}Fe_2$	73.25
$C_{24}H_{27}As$	65.18
$C_{24}H_{30}N_2O_2Pt_2$	83.42
$C_{24}H_{31}N_2O_5^+$, I^-	58.35
$C_{24}H_{33}BrO_8$	54.3
$C_{24}H_{36}NO_8^+$, I^-, $3H_2O$	58.36
$C_{24}H_{40}NO_6^+$, I^-, H_2O	58.37
$C_{24}H_{48}O_4Pt_2$	77.18
$C_{24}H_{60}Ni_6O_{12}S_{12}$	85.21

C_{25}

$C_{25}H_{23}IO_8$	59.15
$C_{25}H_{24}Co_2$	73.26

$C_{25}H_{30}N_5Ni^+$, Cl^-, xH_2O, yCH_4O	49.2
$C_{25}H_{48}O_5S_2$	1.35

C_{26}

$C_{26}H_{16}N_2O_4Pd$	84.16
$C_{26}H_{16}O_2$	38.17 +
$C_{26}H_{20}ClOP$	64.16
$C_{26}H_{20}CuN_2O_2$	78.15
$C_{26}H_{20}IOP$	64.17
$C_{26}H_{22}CuN_2O_2$	83.43
$C_{26}H_{23}O_2PS$	64.18
$C_{26}H_{25}Cl_2NP_2Pd$	86.11
$C_{26}H_{32}MnN_4O_8$, $4H_2O$	82.14

C_{27}

$C_{27}H_{18}N_2$	36.13
$C_{27}H_{32}NO_5^+$, CH_4O, Br^-	58.38
$C_{27}H_{44}NO_8^+$, I^-, $2H_2O$	58.39
$C_{27}H_{44}O_6$	51.3

C_{28}

$C_{28}H_{18}FeO_4$	75.21
$C_{28}H_{18}O_4$	26.11
$C_{28}H_{20}Cl^+$, Cl_5Sn^-	12.3
$C_{28}H_{22}$	5.9
$C_{28}H_{24}$	20.13
$C_{28}H_{30}NP_2^+$, I^-	64.19
$C_{28}H_{31}ClP_2Pt$	86.12
$C_{28}H_{31}IO_6$	56.1
$C_{28}H_{32}Cl_4Cu_4$	75.22
$C_{28}H_{33}IO_9$	56.2
$C_{28}H_{72}O_{16}Ti_4$	84.17

C_{30-34}

$C_{30}H_{18}Cl_2$	29.20
$C_{30}H_{18}Fe_2O_6$	72.24
$C_{30}H_{24}N_6V$	83.44
$C_{30}H_{25}BrNO_4P$	64.20
$C_{30}H_{25}MoNO_4P_2$	86.13
$C_{30}H_{25}P$	64.21
$C_{30}H_{25}P_5$	64.22
$C_{30}H_{25}Sb$	66.4
$C_{30}H_{30}Br_2N_4O_4$	59.16
$C_{30}H_{36}O_4$	59.17
$C_{30}H_{38}ClIO_8$	59.18
$C_{30}H_{39}IO_8$	56.3
$C_{30}H_{41}CoN_7O^+$, Br^-, $xC_4H_8O_2$, yCH_4O	49.3
$C_{30}H_{42}Ni_3O_{12}$	77.19
$C_{30}H_{44}Br_2O_2$	51.4
$C_{30}H_{45}Cl_9P_3Re_3$	86.14
$C_{30}H_{50}CrO_4$	53.15
$C_{30}H_{60}Ag_6N_6S_{12}$	80.11
$C_{31}H_{20}FeO_3$	75.23
$C_{31}H_{43}IO_5$	56.4

C_{32}

$C_{32}H_{16}$	30.7
$C_{32}H_{18}CrN_6O_8^-$, $C_5H_6N^+$, $0.5C_5H_5N$	83.45
$C_{32}H_{22}CuN_4O_2$	83.46
$C_{32}H_{32}Si_2$	63.9
$C_{32}H_{36}N_4Ni$	49.4
$C_{32}H_{39}BrO_{11}$	56.5
$C_{32}H_{80}O_{16}Ti_4$	84.18
$C_{33}H_{36}BiCl_3N_{12}O_9S_3$	66.5
$C_{33}H_{51}BrO_4$	56.6
$C_{33}H_{51}NO_6$	56.7
$C_{34}H_{16}O_2$	30.8
$C_{34}H_{16}O_2$	30.9
$C_{34}H_{30}Br_2O_8$	54.4
$C_{34}H_{32}ClFeN_4O_4$	49.5
$C_{34}H_{38}INO_{12}$, C_3H_6O	56.8
$C_{34}H_{51}IO_6$	56.9

C_{35-39}

$C_{35}H_{46}INO_4$	51.5
$C_{35}H_{46}INO_4$	51.6
$C_{36}H_{20}Fe_3O_8$	72.25 +
$C_{36}H_{30}As_2Cl_2HgO_2$	84.19
$C_{36}H_{30}As_2Cl_4Hg_2O_2$	84.20
$C_{36}H_{30}As_6$	65.19
$C_{36}H_{30}Cl_2NiP_2$	86.15
$C_{36}H_{30}P_6$	64.23
$C_{36}H_{36}N_4NiO_6$, $0.5C_6H_6$	49.6
$C_{36}H_{65}Br_3O_6$	1.36
$C_{36}H_{66}Cl_2NiP_2$	86.16
$C_{37}H_{30}ClIrO_3P_2$	86.17
$C_{37}H_{43}FeN_4O_5$	49.7
$C_{37}H_{68}NO_{13}^+$, I^-, $2H_2O$	50.12
$C_{38}H_{52}CoP_2$	86.18
$C_{39}H_{39}BrO_9S$	59.19
$C_{39}H_{74}O_6$	1.37

C_{40-49}

$C_{40}H_{20}$	30.10
$C_{40}H_{44}N_4O_2^{2+}$, $2I^-$	58.40
$C_{40}H_{48}N_4O_2^{2+}$, $2I^-$, xH_2O	58.41
$C_{40}H_{54}$	57.3
$C_{40}H_{56}$	57.4
$C_{40}H_{56}Co_4O_{16}$	77.20
$C_{40}H_{58}$	57.5
$C_{41}H_{48}N_4O_4$, CH_4O	58.42
$C_{42}H_{18}$	30.11
$C_{42}H_{47}Br_3O_8$	59.20
$C_{44}H_{28}CuN_4$	49.8
$C_{44}H_{28}N_4Pd$	49.9
$C_{44}H_{30}N_4$	49.10
$C_{44}H_{30}N_4OZn$	49.11
$C_{44}H_{31}FeN_4O_2$	49.12
$C_{44}H_{48}Cr_2O_{12}P_2$	77.21
$C_{45}H_{53}IN_2O_{13}$, C_3H_6O, $5H_2O$	50.13
$C_{48}H_{40}Al_4N_4$	68.10

C_{50-99}

$C_{52}H_{52}As_4ClCoO_8^+$, ClO_4^-	84.21
$C_{54}H_{42}As_4Br_2Ru$	86.19

Author index

Compound Name Index

Instead of a single alphabetic name index, a multiple name index is presented with each compound appearing at a number of entry points. These entry points were selected by utilising the chemical 'structure' expressed in the chemical nomenclature but excluding trivial terms such as acid, exo, sesqui, etc.

The sorted index entries are displayed using a KWIC type of layout with the indexing points aligned in the centre of the page. The context of the indexing point in the compound name is shown to the left and right on the same line.

COMPOUND NAME INDEX

rate]

entahydrate]